Life Science: Teacher's Edition

Contents in Brief

Teacher's Edition

Student Edition

See Program Component List on page ii

Prentice Hall Science Explorer

Series Tables of Contents

Teacher's Edition

Science Explorer

PRENTICE HALL

Life Science

PEARSON
Prentice Hall

Boston, Massachusetts
Upper Saddle River, New Jersey

ISBN 0-13-201245-6

3 4 5 6 7 8 9 10   11 10 09 08 07

Pacing Options

SCIENCE EXPLORER offers many aids to help you plan your instruction time whether regular class periods or block scheduling. Section-by-section lesson plans for each chapter include suggested times for Student Edition activities. TeacherEXPRESS™ and the Lab zone™ Easy Planner CD-ROM will help you manage your time electronically.

Pacing Chart

	PERIODS	BLOCKS		PERIODS	BLOCKS
Careers in Science: A Steely Athletic Trainer	1	$^1/_2$	**Chapter 5 Modern Genetics**		
Chapter 1 Introduction to Life Sciences			Chapter 5 Project *Teach Others About a Trait*	Ongoing	Ongoing
Chapter 1 Project *Is It Really True?*	Ongoing	Ongoing	**1** Human Inheritance	2	1
1 What Is Science?	1	$^1/_2$	**2** Human Genetic Disorders	2	1
2 Scientific Inquiry	1	$^1/_2$	**3** Tech & Design: Advances in Genetics	2	1
3 Tech & Design: Understanding Technology	1	$^1/_2$	Chapter 5 Review and Assessment	1	$^1/_2$
4 Safety in the Science Laboratory	1	$^1/_2$	**Chapter 6 Changes Over Time**		
Chapter 1 Review and Assessment	1	$^1/_2$	Chapter 6 Project *Life's Long Calendar*	Ongoing	Ongoing
Chapter 2 Living Things			**1** Darwin's *Theory*	2	1
Chapter 2 Project *Mystery Object*	Ongoing	Ongoing	**2** Evidence of Evolution	2	1
1 What Is Life?	2	1	**3** Integrating Earth Science: The Fossil Record	2	1
2 Classifying Organisms	1	$^1/_2$	Chapter 6 Review and Assessment	1	$^1/_2$
3 Tech & Design: Discovering Cells	2	1	Interdisciplinary Exploration: Dogs—Loyal Companions	1	$^1/_2$
4 Looking Inside Cells	2	1	**Chapter 7 Viruses, Bacteria, Protists, and Fungi**		
Chapter 2 Review and Assessment	1	$^1/_2$	Chapter 7 Project *A Mushroom Farm*	Ongoing	Ongoing
Chapter 3 Cell Processes and Energy			**1** Integrating Health: Viruses	2	1
Chapter 3 Project *Shine On!*	Ongoing	Ongoing	**2** Bacteria	2	1
1 Integrating Chemistry: Chemical Compounds in Cells	2	1	**3** Protists	2	1
2 The Cell in its Environment	1	$^1/_2$	**4** Fungi	2	1
3 Photosynthesis	1	$^1/_2$	Chapter 7 Review and Assessment	1	$^1/_2$
4 Respiration	1	$^1/_2$	**Chapter 8 Plants**		
5 Cell Division	3	$1^1/_2$	Chapter 8 Project *Design and Build an Interactive Exhibit*	Ongoing	Ongoing
Chapter 3 Review and Assessment	1	$^1/_2$	**1** The Plant Kingdom	2	1
Chapter 4 Genetics: The Science of Heredity			**2** Plants Without Seeds	2	1
Chapter 4 Project *All in the Family*	Ongoing	Ongoing	**3** The Characteristics of Seed Plants	2	1
1 Mendel's Work	2	1	**4** Gymnosperms and Angiosperms	3	$1^1/_2$
2 Integrating Mathematics: Probability and Heredity	2	1	**5** Integrating Chemistry: Plant Responses and Growth	1	$^1/_2$
3 The Cell and Inheritance	1	$^1/_2$	Chapter 8 Review and Assessment	1	$^1/_2$
4 The DNA Connection	2	1			
Chapter 4 Review and Assessment	1	$^1/_2$			

Pacing Chart

	PERIODS	BLOCKS
Chapter 9 Sponges, Cnidarians, and Worms		
Chapter 9 Project *Design and Build an Animal Habitat*	Ongoing	Ongoing
1 What Is an Animal?	1	$1/2$
2 Integrating Mathematics: Animal Symmetry	2	1
3 Sponges and Cnidarians	2	1
4 Worms	2	1
Chapter 9 Review and Assessment	1	$1/2$
Chapter 10 Mollusks, Arthropods, and Echinoderms		
Chapter 10 Project *Going Through Changes*	Ongoing	Ongoing
1 Mollusks	2	1
2 Arthropods	2	1
3 Insects	2	1
4 Integrating Environmental Science: Insect Ecology	1	$1/2$
5 Echinoderms	1	$1/2$
Chapter 10 Review and Assessment	1	$1/2$
Chapter 11 Fishes, Amphibians, and Reptiles		
Chapter 11 Project *Animal Adaptations*	Ongoing	Ongoing
1 What Is a Vertebrate?	2	1
2 Fishes	3	$1 1/2$
3 Amphibians	1	$1/2$
4 Reptiles	2	1
5 Integrating Earth Science: Vertebrate History in Rocks	1	$1/2$
Chapter 11 Review and Assessment	1	$1/2$
Chapter 12 Birds and Mammals		
Chapter 12 Project *Bird Watch*	Ongoing	Ongoing
1 Birds	2	1
2 Integrating Physics: The Physics of Bird Flight	1	$1/2$
3 Mammals	3	$1 1/2$
Chapter 12 Review and Assessment	1	$1/2$
Chapter 13 Animal Behavior		
Chapter 13 Project *Learning New Tricks*	Ongoing	Ongoing
1 What Is Behavior?	2	1
2 Patterns of Behavior	2	1
3 Tech & Design: Tracking Migrations	1	$1/2$
Chapter 13 Review and Assessment	1	$1/2$

	PERIODS	BLOCKS
Chapter 14 Bones, Muscles, and Skin		
Chapter 14 Project *Design and Build a Hand Prosthesis*	Ongoing	Ongoing
1 Integrating Health: Body Organization and Homeostasis	1	$1/2$
2 The Skeletal System	2	1
3 The Muscular System	1	$1/2$
4 The Skin	2	1
Chapter 14 Review and Assessment	1	$1/2$
Chapter 15 Food and Digestion		
Chapter 15 Project *What's for Lunch?*	Ongoing	Ongoing
1 Integrating Health: Food and Energy	3	$1 1/2$
2 The Digestive Process Begins	2	1
3 Final Digestion and Absorption	1	$1/2$
Chapter 15 Review and Assessment	1	$1/2$
Chapter 16 Circulation		
Chapter 16 Project *Travels of a Red Blood Cell*	Ongoing	Ongoing
1 The Body's Transport System	3	$1 1/2$
2 Blood and Lymph	1	$1/2$
3 Integrating Health: Cardiovascular Health	2	1
Chapter 16 Review and Assessment	1	$1/2$
Chapter 17 Respiration and Excretion		
Chapter 17 Project *Get the Message Out*	Ongoing	Ongoing
1 The Respiratory System	3	$1 1/2$
2 Integrating Health: Smoking and Your Health	1	$1/2$
3 The Excretory System	2	1
Chapter 17 Review and Assessment	1	$1/2$
Chapter 18 Fighting Disease		
Chapter 18 Project *Stop the Invasion!*	Ongoing	Ongoing
1 Infectious Disease	1	$1/2$
2 The Body's Defenses	3	$1 1/2$
3 Integrating Health: Preventing Infectious Disease	1	$1/2$
4 Noninfectious Disease	2	1
Chapter 18 Review and Assessment	1	$1/2$

Pacing Options

Pacing Chart

Chapter 19 The Nervous System	PERIODS	BLOCKS
Chapter 19 Project *Tricks and Illusions*	Ongoing	Ongoing
1 How the Nervous System Works	2	1
2 Divisions of the Nervous System	1	$1/2$
3 The Senses	2	1
4 Integrating Health: Alcohol and Other Drugs	2	1
Chapter 19 Review and Assessment	1	$1/2$

Chapter 20 The Endocrine System and Reproduction	PERIODS	BLOCKS
Chapter 20 Project *A Precious Bundle*	Ongoing	Ongoing
1 The Endocrine System	2	1
2 The Male and Female Reproductive Systems	2	1
3 Integrating Health: The Human Life Cycle	2	1
Chapter 20 Review and Assessment	1	$1/2$
Interdisciplinary Exploration: African Rain Forests	1	$1/2$

Chapter 21 Populations and Communities	PERIODS	BLOCKS
Chapter 21 Project *What's a Crowd?*	Ongoing	Ongoing
1 Living Things and the Environment	2	1
2 Integrating Mathematics: Studying Populations	2	1
3 Interactions Among Living Things	1	$1/2$
4 Changes in Communities	1	$1/2$
Chapter 21 Review and Assessment	1	$1/2$

Chapter 22 Ecosystems and Biomes	PERIODS	BLOCKS
Chapter 22 Project *Breaking It Down*	Ongoing	Ongoing
1 Energy Flow in Ecosystems	1	$1/2$
2 Integrating Chemistry: Cycles of Matter	1	$1/2$
3 Biogeography	2	1
4 Biomes and Aquatic Ecosystems	3	$1 1/2$
Chapter 22 Review and Assessment	1	$1/2$

Chapter 23 Living Resources	PERIODS	BLOCKS
Chapter 23 Project *Variety Show*	Ongoing	Ongoing
1 Integrating Environmental Science: Environmental Issues	2	1
2 Forests and Fisheries	2	1
3 Biodiversity	2	1
Chapter 23 Review and Assessment	1	$1/2$

Research-Based and Proven to Work

As the originator of the small book concept in middle school science, and as the nation's number one science publisher, Prentice Hall takes pride in the fact that we've always listened closely to teachers. In doing so, we've developed programs that effectively meet the needs of your classroom.

As we continue to listen, we realize that raising the achievement level of all students is the number one challenge facing teachers today. To assist you in meeting this latest challenge, Prentice Hall has combined the very best author team with solid research to create a program that meets your high standards and will ensure that no child is left behind.

With Prentice Hall, you can be confident that your students will not only be motivated, inspired, and excited to learn science, but that they will also achieve the success needed in today's environment of the No Child Left Behind (NCLB) legislation and testing reform.

On the following pages, you will read about the key elements found throughout *Science Explorer* that truly set this program apart and ensure success for you and your students.

> As we continue to listen, we realize that raising the achievement level of all students is the number one challenge facing teachers today.

A Science Program Backed by Research

In developing Prentice Hall *Science Explorer*, we used research studies as a central, guiding element. Research on *Science Explorer* indicated key elements of a textbook program that ensure students' success: support for reading and mathematics in science, consistent opportunities for inquiry, and an ongoing assessment strand. This research was conducted in phases and continues today.

1. Exploratory: Needs Assessment

Along with periodic surveys concerning state and national standards as well as curriculum issues and challenges, we conducted specific product development research, which included discussions with teachers and advisory panels, focus groups, and quantitative surveys. We explored the specific needs of teachers, students, and other educators regarding each book we developed in Prentice Hall *Science Explorer*.

2. Formative: Prototype Development and Field-Testing

During this phase of research, we worked to develop prototype materials. Then we tested the materials by field-testing with students and teachers and by performing qualitative and quantitative surveys. In our early prototype testing, we received feedback about our lesson structure. Results were channeled back into the program development for improvement.

3. Summative: Validation Research

Finally, we conducted and continue to conduct long-term research based on scientific, experimental designs under actual classroom conditions. This research identifies what works and what can be improved in the next revision of Prentice Hall *Science Explorer*. We also continue to monitor the program in the market. We talk to our users about what works, and then we begin the cycle over again. The next section contains highlights of this research.

A Science Program With Proven Results

In a year-long study in 2000–2001, students in six states using Prentice Hall *Science Explorer* outscored students using other science programs on a nationally normed standardized test.

The study investigated the effects of science textbook programs at the eighth-grade level. Twelve eighth-grade science classes with a total of 223 students participated in the study. The selected classes were of similar student ability levels.

Each class was tested at the beginning of the school year using the TerraNova CTBS Basic Battery Plus, and then retested at the end of the school year. The final results, shown in the graph, show a significant improvement in test scores from the pre-test to the post-test evaluation.

• All tests were scored by CTB/McGraw-Hill, the publisher of the TerraNova exam. Statistical analyses and conclusions were performed by an independent firm, Pulse Analytics, Inc.

In Japan, Lesson Study Research has been employed for a number of years as a tool for teachers to improve their curriculum. In April 2003, Prentice Hall adapted this methodology to focus on a lesson from this edition. Our goal was to test the effectiveness of lesson pedagogy and improve it while in the program development stage. In all three classrooms tested, student learning increased an average of 10 points from the pre- to the post-assessment.

• Detailed results of these studies can be obtained at **www.PHSchool.com/research.**

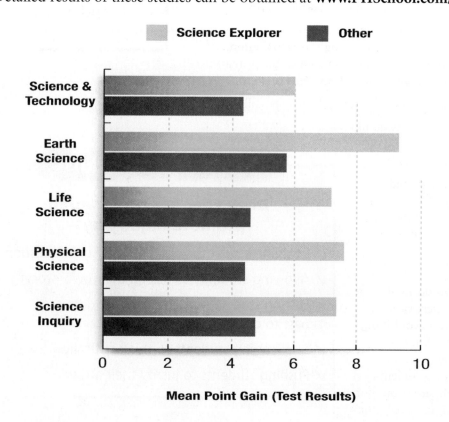

Mean Point Gain (Test Results)

Foundational Research: Inquiry in the Science Classroom

"How do I know if my students are inquiring?" "If students are busy doing lots of hands-on activities, are they using inquiry?" "What is inquiry, anyway?" If you're confused, you are not alone. Inquiry is the heart and soul of science education, with most of us in continuous pursuit of achieving it with our students!

Defining Science Inquiry

What is it? Simply put, inquiry is the intellectual side of science. It is thinking like a scientist—being inquisitive, asking why, and searching for answers. The National Science Education Content Standards define inquiry as the process in which students begin with a question, design an investigation, gather evidence, formulate an answer to the original question, and communicate the investigative process and results. Since it is often difficult to accomplish all this in one class period, the standards also acknowledge that at times students need to practice only one or two inquiry components.

Understanding Inquiry

The National Research Council in Inquiry and the National Science Education Standards (2000) identified several "essential features" of classroom inquiry. We have modified these essential features into questions to guide you in your quest for enhanced and more thoughtful student inquiry.

1. *Who asks the question?* In most curricula, these focusing questions are an element given in the materials. As a teacher you can look for labs that, at least on a periodic basis, allow students to pursue their own questions.

2. *Who designs the procedures?* To gain experience with the logic underlying experimentation, students need continuous practice with designing procedures. Some labs in which the primary target is content acquisition designate procedures. But others should ask students to do so.

3. *Who decides what data to collect?* Students need practice in determining the data to collect.

4. *Who formulates explanations based upon the data?* Students should be challenged to think—to analyze and draw conclusions based on their data, not just copy answers from the text materials.

5. *Who communicates and justifies the results?* Activities should push students not only to communicate but also to justify their answers. Activities also should be thoughtfully designed and interesting so that students want to share their results and argue about conclusions.

Making Time for Inquiry

One last question—Must each and every activity have students do all of this? The answer is an obvious and emphatic "No." You will find a great variety of activities in *Science Explorer*. Some activities focus on content acquisition, and thus they specify the question and most of the procedures. But many others stress in-depth inquiry from start to finish. Because inquiry is an intellectual pursuit, it cannot merely be characterized by keeping students busy and active. Too many students have a knack for being physically but not intellectually engaged in science. It is our job to help them engage intellectually.

Michael J. Padilla, Ph.D.
Program Author of *Science Explorer*
Professor of Science Education
University of Georgia
Athens, Georgia

"Because inquiry is an intellectual pursuit, it cannot merely be characterized by keeping students busy and active."

Evaluator's Checklist

Does your science program promote inquiry by—

✔ Enabling students to pursue their own questions

✔ Allowing students to design their own procedures

✔ Letting students determine what data are best to collect

✔ Challenging students to think critically

✔ Pushing students to justify their answers

Inquiry in *Science Explorer*

Science Explorer offers the most opportunities to get students to think like a scientist. By providing inquiry opportunities throughout the program, *Science Explorer* enables students to enhance their understanding by participating in the discovery.

Student Edition Inquiry

Six lab and activity options are included in every chapter, structured from directed to open-ended—providing you the flexibility to address all types of learners and accommodate your class time and equipment requirements. As Michael Padilla notes, some activities focus on content acquisition, and thus the question and most of the procedures are specified. But many others stress in-depth inquiry from start to finish. The graph below shows how, in general, inquiry levels are addressed in the Student Edition.

Science Explorer encourages students to develop inquiry skills across the spectrum from teacher-guided to open-ended. Even more opportunities for real-life applications of inquiry are included in Science & Society, Technology & Society, Careers in Science, and Interdisciplinary Exploration features.

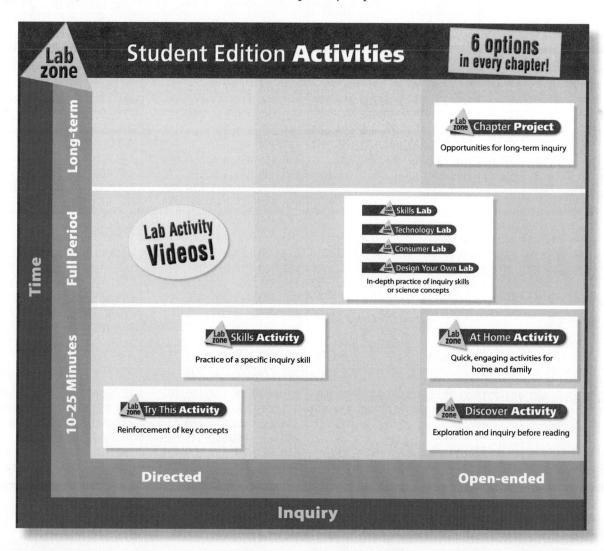

Lab zone — **Student Edition Activities** — 6 options in every chapter!

Time

Long-term

Lab zone Chapter **Project**
Opportunities for long-term inquiry

Full Period

Lab Activity Videos!

Lab zone Skills **Lab**
Lab zone Technology **Lab**
Lab zone Consumer **Lab**
Lab zone Design Your Own **Lab**
In-depth practice of inquiry skills or science concepts

10-25 Minutes

Lab zone Skills **Activity**
Practice of a specific inquiry skill

Lab zone At Home **Activity**
Quick, engaging activities for home and family

Lab zone Try This **Activity**
Reinforcement of key concepts

Lab zone Discover **Activity**
Exploration and inquiry before reading

Directed — **Open-ended**

Inquiry

Inquiry Skills Chart

SCIENCE EXPLORER provides comprehensive teaching, practice, and assessment of science skills, with an emphasis on the process skills necessary for inquiry. This chart lists the skills covered in the program and cites the page numbers where each skill is covered.

Basic Process SKILLS

	Student Text: Projects and Labs	Student Text: Activities	Student Text: Caption and Review Questions	Teacher's Edition: Extensions
Observing	33, 41, 59, 73, 79, 103, 109, 116, 181, 249, 261, 283, 293, 306, 321, 327, 349, 381, 405, 415, 435, 453, 467, 487, 495, 501, 573, 585, 605, 617, 625, 659, 665, 673, 710, 739, 757, 771, 783, 789	6, 40, 50, 55, 66, 91, 157, 210, 219, 226, 264, 236, 303, 314, 374, 379, 395, 406, 411, 451, 474, 525, 545, 579, 611, 642, 674, 682, 729, 755, 761	24, 315, 354, 518, 547, 723, 747	6, 33, 40, 41, 50, 55, 56, 56, 59, 65, 66, 73, 76, 79, 82, 89, 91, 103, 109,112,114, 116,121, 157, 177, 181,184, 210, 219, 226, 228, 234, 236, 239, 249, 252, 254, 261, 264, 267, 269, 283, 293, 303, 304, 305, 306, 314, 317, 319, 321, 327, 330, 337, 339, 349, 374, 379, 381, 391, 393, 395, 405, 406,411, 411, 415, 435, 446, 451, 453, 467, 470, 474, 477, 479, 484, 487, 495, 501, 518, 525, 537, 541, 545, 573, 579, 582, 585, 598, 605, 611, 617, 625, 642, 644, 653, 659, 665, 673, 674, 682, 706, 710, 724,726, 729, 739, 743, 755, 757, 761, 771, 783, 789
Inferring	33, 41, 79, 125, 163, 242, 261, 283, 349, 372, 381, 453, 487, 523, 544, 557, 563, 605, 673, 710, 757, 771, 783, 789, 777	60, 77, 83, 86, 89, 111, 144, 151, 175, 190, 210, 231, 250, 259, 274, 284, 328, 343, 350, 368, 382, 387, 420, 422, 454, 484, 488, 534, 564, 597, 626, 632, 644, 651, 666, 704, 746, 748, 764, 784, 792, 795	8, 30, 38, 63, 67, 70, 78, 94, 102, 106, 114, 137, 140, 155, 168, 187, 200, 215, 230, 237, 241, 246, 311, 335, 345, 361, 371, 394, 399, 402, 421, 442, 446, 450, 455, 456, 460, 468, 460, 498, 521, 530, 556, 578, 588, 595, 610, 615, 626, 639, 650, 657, 662, 694, 708, 718, 726, 754, 769, 774, 798	33, 36, 41, 60,63, 77, 79, 83, 86, 89, 111, 113, 125, 144, 151, 163, 175, 190, 210, 231, 242, 250, 259, 261, 274, 283, 284, 296, 328, 343, 349, 350, 368, 372, 381, 382, 387, 389, 420, 422, 439, 453, 454, 484, 487, 488, 523, 534, 544, 557, 563, 564, 597, 605, 626, 632, 644, 651, 666, 673, 704, 710, 746, 748, 757, 764, 768, 771, 777, 783, 784, 789, 792, 795
Predicting	625, 125, 156, 181, 216, 306, 334, 372, 495, 691, 710, 719, 783	20, 22, 114, 118, 152, 210, 232, 256, 358, 416, 436, 438, 482, 505, 516, 524, 553, 568, 574, 722, 752	9, 30, 70, 82, 94, 106, 123, 140, 187, 200, 224, 241, 246, 331, 333, 355, 361, 369, 432, 437, 440, 442, 448, 451, 460, 473, 481, 486, 498, 521, 525,530, 543, 551, 560, 556, 560, 572, 583, 588, 603, 615, 630, 647, 662, 671, 681, 708, 745, 751, 755, 774, 788, 800, 804	20, 22, 114, 118, 125, 152, 156, 181, 210, 211, 216, 232, 256, 306, 334, 358, 372, 416, 436, 438, 482, 495, 505, 516, 524, 553,554, 568, 574, 625, 691, 710, 719, 722, 749, 752, 783
Classifying	33, 405, 283, 349, 487, 757, 771, 777	13, 35, 42, 47, 49, 262, 272, 300, 307, 331, 340, 477, 580, 728, 740	13, 49, 70, 78, 123, 130, 197, 215, 235, 240, 297, 299, 320, 324, 333, 364, 377, 380, 424, 460, 481, 483, 530, 535, 543, 560, 567, 607, 637, 708, 729, 733, 736, 741, 745, 774, 782	10, 13, 33, 35, 42, 46, 47, 49, 52, 219, 253, 262, 272, 283, 300, 307, 331, 340, 349, 405, 427, 477, 487, 506, 512, 580, 628, 636, 728, 740, 757, 771, 777

The *Science Explorer* program provides additional teaching, reinforcement, and assessment of skills in the *Inquiry Skills Activities Book* and the *Integrated Science Laboratory Manual*.

	Student Text: Projects and Labs	Student Text: Activities	Student Text: Caption and Review Questions	Teacher's Edition: Extensions
Making Models	143, 125, 171, 181, 216, 249, 367, 381, 467, 533, 573, 605, 665, 673, 710, 739, 757	62, 96, 126, 177, 238, 297, 385, 418, 468, 519, 548, 600, 668, 685, 717, 742		62, 77, 96, 98, 99,101, 125, 126, 129, 133, 135, 143, 148, 161, 171, 177, 181, 191,193, 216, 230, 232, 238, 249, 265, 277, 297, 297, 308, 332, 367, 381, 385, 385, 409, 418, 456, 467, 468, 485, 519, 533, 547, 548, 567, 573, 577, 581, 600, 605, 609, 612, 635, 644, 647, 648, 665, 668, 673, 685, 685, 710, 717, 739, 742, 750, 757, 761, 763, 786
Communicating	5, 27, 41, 58, 59, 79, 103, 125, 156, 181, 209, 216, 249, 261, 283, 293, 306, 321, 334, 349, 367, 373, 381, 415, 429, 435, 443, 453, 487, 495, 515, 523, 533, 544, 557, 563, 573, 585, 591, 605, 617, 625, 659, 665, 691, 693, 703, 710, 739, 719, 757, 771, 783, 789, 777	18, 22, 26, 29, 53, 57, 67, 69, 78, 90, 102, 105, 115, 130, 137, 139, 150, 155, 161, 162, 167, 179, 187, 197, 199, 215, 223, 225, 235, 241, 245, 255, 260, 271, 287, 289, 299, 302, 320, 323, 333, 342, 347, 353, 361, 363, 371, 380, 386, 394, 397, 399, 401, 413, 419, 428, 431, 442, 457, 459, 473, 481, 486, 493, 497, 521, 529, 527, 551, 555, 556, 551, 555, 556, 559, 578, 583, 587, 596, 603, 609, 610, 615, 621, 639, 650, 653, 657, 661, 671, 681, 690, 708, 733, 735, 745, 751, 769, 773, 781, 782, 788, 801, 803	736	5, 18, 22, 26, 27, 29, 37, 41, 53, 57, 58, 59, 67, 69, 78, 79, 90, 102, 103, 105, 115, 125, 130, 137, 139, 150, 155, 156, 161, 162, 167, 179, 181, 187, 197, 199, 209, 213, 215, 216, 223, 225, 235, 241, 245, 249, 255, 260, 261, 271, 283, 287, 289, 293, 299, 302, 306, 320, 321, 323, 333, 334, 342, 347, 349, 353, 361, 363, 367, 371, 373, 380, 381, 386, 394, 397, 399, 401, 413, 415, 419, 428, 429, 431, 435, 442, 443, 453, 457, 459, 472, 473, 481, 486, 487, 493, 495, 497, 515, 521, 523, 527, 529, 533, 544, 551, 555, 556, 557, 559, 563, 573, 578, 583, 585, 587, 591, 596, 601, 603, 605, 609, 610, 615, 617, 621, 625, 639, 650, 653, 656, 657, 659, 661, 665, 669, 671, 676, 681, 686, 690, 691, 693, 703, 708, 710, 719, 733, 735, 739, 745, 751, 757, 766, 769, 771, 773, 777, 781, 782, 783, 788, 789, 801, 803
Measuring	109, 242, 261, 283, 501, 515, 703, 739	491	694	92, 109, 242, 261, 283, 491, 501, 515, 703, 739
Calculating	103, 171, 181, 216, 415, 443, 515, 691, 789	217, 268, 449, 576, 592, 679, 713, 787	56, 120, 168, 200, 324, 513, 530, 588, 694, 716, 718, 744	97, 103, 171, 181, 216, 217, 268, 396, 415, 443, 449, 505, 513, 515, 571, 576, 592, 679, 691, 713, 715, 787, 789
Creating Data Tables	327, 625	538		327, 538, 625
Graphing	27, 73, 109, 334, 429, 501, 544, 617, 625, 719	344	106, 364, 432, 694, 736, 804	27, 73, 109, 334, 344, 429, 501, 544, 617, 625, 719, 780

Inquiry Skills Chart

Advanced Process SKILLS

	Student Text: Projects and Labs	Student Text: Activities	Student Text: Caption and Review Questions	Teacher's Edition: Extensions
Posing Questions	443, 591	14, 502, 595, 730		14, 443, 502, 591, 595, 730
Developing Hypotheses	5, 27, 117, 209, 349, 703, 771	80, 95, 447, 747, 758	15, 18, 30, 70, 179, 442, 451, 578, 729, 736, 751, 788, 801, 804	5, 27, 80, 95, 117, 209, 349, 447, 703, 747, 758, 771
Designing Experiments	5, 27, 49, 73, 79, 109, 117, 181, 209, 243, 306, 321, 327, 334, 349, 381, 415, 429, 453, 515, 523, 544, 605, 625, 659, 691, 710, 739, 757, 771, 783, 789	38, 147, 606, 649	30, 70	5, 27, 38, 49, 73, 79, 109, 117, 147, 178, 181, 209, 221, 243, 306, 321, 327, 334, 349, 381, 415, 429, 440, 453, 515, 523, 544, 605, 606, 625, 649, 659, 691, 710, 739, 757, 771, 783, 789
Controlling Variables	41, 515, 523, 605, 659, 703	16, 634	16, 30, 36, 70, 324, 402, 662	16, 41, 515, 523, 605, 634, 659, 703
Forming Operational Definitions		19, 34, 74, 131, 294, 444, 552, 711, 778		19, 34, 74, 131, 294, 444, 552, 711, 778
Interpreting Data	5, 79, 117, 125, 156, 188, 321, 334, 372, 405, 429, 495, 515, 523, 544, 557, 585, 617, 625, 659, 719, 739, 789	120, 339, 403, 637	106, 121, 168, 246, 402, 432, 498, 530, 588, 622, 662, 694, 736, 804	5, 79, 117, 120, 125, 156, 188, 238, 274, 321, 334, 339, 372, 403, 405, 429, 495, 509, 515, 523, 544, 557, 585, 617, 625, 637, 659, 719, 739, 789
Drawing Conclusions	5, 27, 73, 109, 163, 188, 209, 242, 293, 306, 327, 373, 415, 435, 495, 523, 544, 557, 563, 573, 585, 617, 625, 659	133, 184, 478, 612, 689, 707, 747, 758	30, 140, 150, 187, 200, 246, 299, 324, 332, 364, 402, 432, 460, 560, 588, 622, 718	5, 17, 27, 48, 73, 109, 133, 163, 184, 188, 209, 222, 224, 242, 293, 306, 327, 373, 376, 410, 415, 435, 478, 495, 523, 544, 557, 563, 573, 585, 612, 617, 625, 659, 689, 707, 747, 758

Critical Thinking SKILLS

	Student Text: Projects and Labs	Student Text: Activities	Student Text: Caption and Review Questions	Teacher's Edition: Extensions
Comparing and Contrasting	367, 501		12, 13, 22, 49, 57, 64, 67, 78, 85, 90, 93, 94, 98, 106, 115, 130, 136, 150, 174, 175, 179, 183, 187, 197, 200, 215, 227, 235, 241, 246, 302, 311, 316, 320, 324, 333, 342, 355, 361, 364, 371, 380, 386, 392, 413, 419, 451, 457, 473, 475, 476, 481, 486, 521, 530, 542, 543, 572, 577, 588, 593, 596, 622, 630, 639, 644, 650, 657, 681, 724, 729, 733, 745, 751, 763, 769, 774, 788, 804	278, 367, 423, 501, 677, 795
Applying Concepts	143, 563, 591		13, 20, 26, 30, 49, 51, 57, 66, 67, 70, 75, 85, 90, 97, 106, 115, 123, 127, 140, 149, 150, 155, 158, 162, 178, 179, 187, 197, 200, 225, 238, 300, 302, 336, 342, 347, 355, 364, 380, 383, 402, 408, 410, 418, 419, 432, 445, 457, 460, 472, 473, 481, 486, 493, 504, 514, 527, 530, 537, 556, 572, 582, 588, 596, 610, 615, 622,	55, 143, 147, 158, 185, 195, 240, 398, 408, 563, 568, 591, 595, 713, 717

Critical Thinking SKILLS (continued)

	Student Text: Projects and Labs	Student Text: Activities	Student Text: Caption and Review Questions	Teacher's Edition: Extensions
			639, 650, 657, 662, 667, 671, 675, 680, 687, 688, 706, 718, 729, 731, 755, 769, 788, 801	
Interpreting Diagrams, Graphs, Photographs, Tables and Maps	109, 501, 625		11, 46, 55, 61, 84, 88, 92, 102, 111, 113, 122, 128, 130, 132, 134, 140, 145, 147, 153, 154, 160, 168, 169, 172, 184, 186, 193, 197, 232, 233, 295, 298, 299, 304, 309, 319, 337, 338, 347, 355, 358, 360, 364, 365, 375, 379, 384, 398, 399, 402, 407, 409, 428, 469, 471, 478, 485, 490, 506, 509, 510, 517, 539, 549, 560, 601, 627, 629, 643, 652, 655, 662, 676, 684, 715, 743, 749, 753, 759, 767, 774, 785	11, 12, 25, 64, 66, 92, 98, 109, 113, 134, 146, 153, 175, 178, 194, 214, 229, 233, 264, 270, 275, 279, 298, 309, 337, 426, 447, 449, 491, 501, 509, 510, 526, 547, 600, 625, 629, 635, 638, 645, 655, 687, 707, 708, 727
Relating Cause and Effect			21, 22, 26, 57, 78, 85, 87, 94, 106, 115, 123, 137, 140, 150, 162, 177, 179, 196, 197, 200, 215, 324, 371, 402, 413, 417, 428, 432, 439, 442, 473, 481, 489, 498, 521, 526, 527, 530, 540, 548, 551, 553, 556, 560, 572, 575, 578, 583, 588, 596, 598, 602, 603, 610, 613, 615, 639, 648, 650, 657, 662, 671, 678, 690, 694, 708, 736, 745, 750, 755, 765, 769, 782, 793, 801, 804	754
Making Generalizations	665		48, 76, 90, 235, 302, 347, 371, 391, 432, 498, 560, 736, 751, 761, 779, 794, 804	447, 665
Making Judgments			18, 30, 200, 235, 246, 311, 324, 364, 457, 460, 493, 530, 588, 622, 662, 690, 782, 801, 804	
Problem Solving	467, 665		18, 30, 168, 246, 460, 596, 736, 801	467, 665

Math and Technology SKILLS

	Student Text: Projects and Labs	Student Text: Activities	Student Text: Caption and Review Questions	Teacher's Edition: Extensions
Math		81, 100, 119, 122, 159, 192, 221, 253, 288, 305, 318, 341, 351, 425, 441, 492, 507, 520, 541, 550, 565, 570, 614, 646, 680, 714, 725, 766, 799	9, 85, 140, 281, 311, 355, 393, 514, 530, 543, 560, 572, 718, 736,	81, 100, 119, 122, 159, 192, 221, 253, 288, 305, 318, 341, 351, 425, 441, 492, 507, 520, 541, 550, 565, 570, 614, 646, 680, 714, 725, 766, 799
Technology Design and Evaluation	59, 249, 293, 467, 673			58, 59, 164, 165, 249, 293, 312, 356, 467, 619, 641, 673, 721, 791

A National Look at Science Education

Project 2061 was established by the American Association for the Advancement of Science (AAAS) as a long-term project to improve science education nationwide. A primary goal of Project 2061 is to define a "common core of learning"—the knowledge and skills we want all students to achieve. Project 2061 published *Science for All Americans* in 1989 and followed this with *Benchmarks for Science Literacy* in 1993. *Benchmarks* recommends what students should know and be able to do by the end of grades 2, 5, 8, and 12. Project 2061 clearly states that *Benchmarks* is not a curriculum but a tool for designing successful curricula.

The National Research Council (NRC) used *Science for All Americans* and *Benchmarks* to develop the National Science Education Standards (NSES), which were published in 1996. The NSES are organized into six categories (Content, Teaching, Assessment, Professional Development, Program, and System) to help schools establish the conditions necessary to achieve scientific literacy for all students.

Michael Padilla, the program author of *Science Explorer,* guided one of six teams of teachers whose work led to the publication of *Benchmarks.* He also was a contributing writer of the National Science Education Standards. Under his guidance, *Science Explorer* has implemented these standards through its inquiry approach, a focus on student learning of important concepts and skills, and teacher support aligned with the NSES teaching standards.

Neither *Benchmarks* nor the NSES requires a single, uniform national curriculum, and in fact there is a great diversity nationwide in science curricula. The correlations that follow are designed to help you use the *Science Explorer* program to meet your particular curriculum needs.

Meeting the National Science Education Standards

INTRODUCTION TO LIFE SCIENCE?

Science as Inquiry (Content Standard A)

● **Identify questions that can be answered through scientific investigations** Students distinguish between scientific questions and those that cannot be answered by scientific inquiry. *(Scientific Inquiry)*

● **Design and conduct a scientific investigation** Students design and conduct a scientific experiment to test whether or not a common belief is true. Students design an experiment to investigate how cut flowers can stay fresher longer. *(Chapter Project; Design Your Own Lab)*

● **Understandings about scientific inquiry** Scientists use skills of observing, inferring, predicting, classifying, and making models to learn more about the world. Scientific inquiry refers to the diverse ways in which scientists study the natural world and propose explanations based on the evidence they gather. *(What Is Science?, Scientific Inquiry)*

Science and Technology (Content Standard E)

● **Understandings about science and technology** Science is the study of the natural world to understand how it functions while technology modifies the natural world to meet human needs or solve problems. Technology does not provide perfect solutions and can have negative consequences in addition to positive effects. *(Understanding Technology)*

History and Nature of Science (Content Standard G)

● **Science as a human endeavor** Life science is the study of living things. Life scientists work in diverse places and study different things. Science relies on habits of mind including curiosity, honesty, open-mindedness, skepticism, and creativity. *(What Is Science?, Scientific Inquiry)*

LIVING THINGS

Science as Inquiry (Content Standard A)

● **Identify questions that can be answered through scientific investigations** Students develop a list of characteristics shared by living things. *(Chapter Project)*

● **Design and conduct a scientific investigation** Students devise a system for determining if an object is alive. *(Chapter Project)*

● **Communicate scientific procedures and explanations** Students report on the results of the investigation of the mystery object. *(Chapter Project)*

Life Science (Content Standard C)

● **Structure and function in living systems** All living things are composed of cells. Each of the various structures in a cell has a different function. *(Discovering Cells, Looking Inside Cells)*

● **Reproduction and heredity** Reproduction is a fundamental characteristic of living things. *(What Is Life?)*

History and Nature of Science (Content Standard G)

● **History of science** Redi and Pasteur established that life comes from life. *(What Is Life?)*

Science and Technology (Content Standard E)

● **Understandings about science and technology** The invention of the microscope enabled people to discover and learn about cells. *(Discovering Cells, Tech & Design in History)*

CELL PROCESSES AND ENERGY

Science as Inquiry (Content Standard A)

● **Design and conduct a scientific investigation** Students investigate how different light conditions affect plants. *(Chapter Project)*

● **Use appropriate tools and techniques to gather, analyze, and interpret data** Students investigate how long the stages of the cell cycle take. *(Skills Lab—Multiplying by Dividing)*

Life Science (Content Standard C)

● **Structure and function in living systems** Important organic compounds found in living things are carbohydrates, lipids, proteins, and nucleic acids. Photosynthesis occurs inside chloroplasts in the cells of plants and some other organisms. During respiration, cells break down food molecules and release the energy they contain. The regular sequence of growth and division that cells undergo is called the cell cycle. *(Chapter Project, Chemical Compounds in Cells, Photosynthesis, Respiration, Cell Division, Skills Lab—Multiplying by Dividing)*

● **Regulation and behavior** Substances can move into and out of a cell by diffusion, osmosis, or active transport. *(The Cell in its Environment)*

● **Populations and ecosystems** Nearly all living things obtain energy either directly or indirectly from the energy of sunlight captured during photosynthesis. Photosynthesis and respiration form a cycle that keeps the levels of oxygen and carbon dioxide fairly constant in the atmosphere. *(Photosynthesis, Respiration)*

GENETICS: THE SCIENCE OF HEREDITY

Science as Inquiry (Content Standard A)

● **Use appropriate tools and techniques to gather, analyze, and interpret data** Students investigate genetic traits among classmates and have the option of sharing their data online. *(Skills Lab—Take a Class Survey)*

● **Develop descriptions, explanations, predictions, and models using evidence** Students model and predict the possible results of genetic crosses. *(Chapter Project, Skills Labs)*

● **Use mathematics in all aspects of scientific inquiry** Geneticists use Punnett squares to determine the probability of a particular outcome. *(Chapter Project, Mendel's Work, Skills Labs)*

Life Science (Content Standard C)

● **Structure and function in living systems** Meiosis is the process by which the number of chromosomes is reduced by half to form sex cells. During protein synthesis, the cell uses information from genes to produce proteins. *(The Cell and Inheritance, The DNA Connection)*

● **Reproduction and heredity** The passing of traits from parents to offspring is called heredity. Genes are carried from parents to offspring on chromosomes. Mutations can be a source of genetic variety. *(Chapter Project, Mendel's Work, The Cell and Inheritance, The DNA Connection, Skills Labs)*

History and Nature of Science (Content Standard G)

● **History of science** The genetic principles that Mendel discovered still stand to this day. *(Mendel's Work, Probability and Genetics)*

MODERN GENETICS

Science as Inquiry (Content Standard A)

● **Develop descriptions, explanations, predictions, and models using evidence** Students create a pedigree for an imaginary family, investigate inheritance patterns in families, and model DNA fingerprinting. *(Skills Labs)*

Life Science (Content Standard C)

● **Reproduction and heredity** Human traits can be controlled by single genes, multiple alleles, or many genes. A pedigree is used to trace the inheritance of traits. Genetic disorders are caused by mutations. People have used selective breeding, cloning, and genetic engineering to develop organisms with desirable traits. *(Human Inheritance, Human Genetic Disorders, Skills Labs)*

A National Look at Science Education *(continued)*

Science and Technology (Content Standard E)
- **Understandings about science and technology** Doctors use tools such as karyotypes to help detect genetic disorders. In genetic engineering, genes from one organism are transferred into the DNA of another organism. DNA can be used to identify individuals. (*Human Genetic Disorders, Advances in Genetics, Skills Labs*)

Science in Personal and Social Perspectives (Content Standard F)
- **Science and technology in society** Students examine the use of DNA fingerprinting. (*Technology and Society*)

CHANGES OVER TIME

Science as Inquiry (Content Standard A)
- **Develop descriptions, explanations, predictions, and models using evidence** Students create timelines of Earth's history. Students model how natural selection leads to changes in a species over time. Students model how natural selection leads to changes in a species over time. Students compare the structure of a protein in several animals to determine their evolutionary relationships. (*Chapter Project, Skills Labs*)

Life Science (Content Standard C)
- **Diversity and adaptations of organisms** Over a long period of time, natural selection can lead to evolution. A species is extinct if no members of that species are still alive. Scientists compare fossils, body structures, early development, DNA sequences, and protein structure to determine evolutionary relationships. (*Darwin's Theory, The Fossil Record, Evidence of Evolution, Skills Labs*)

Earth and Space Science (Content Standard D)
- **Earth's history** The fossil record provides clues about how and when new groups of organisms evolved. (*Chapter Project, The Fossil Record*)

History and Nature of Science (Content Standard G)
- **History of Science** Charles Darwin theorized that evolution occurs by means of natural selection. (*Darwin's Theory*)

VIRUSES, BACTERIA, PROTISTS, AND FUNGI

Science as Inquiry (Content Standard A)
- **Identify questions that can be answered through scientific investigations** How does the presence of salt or sugar affect the activity of yeast? (*Skills Lab—What's for Lunch?*)
- **Design and conduct a scientific investigation** Students design and conduct an investigation about how light and moisture affect the growth of mushrooms. (*Chapter Project*)
- **Use mathematics in all aspects of scientific inquiry** Students calculate the number of viruses that could fit on the head of a pin. (*Skills Lab—How Many Viruses Fit on a Pin?*)

Life Science (Content Standard C)
- **Structure and function in living systems** Students learn that the cells of bacteria are different from those of other organisms. Students learn the main characteristics of protists and the differences among the protist groups. Students learn the characteristics of fungi, how they obtain food, and their role in nature. (*Chapter Project, Bacteria, Protists, Fungi*)
- **Populations and ecosystems** Students learn that bacteria and fungi function as decomposers of dead organic matter. (*Bacteria, Fungi*)
- **Diversity and adaptations of organisms** Students learn the main characteristics of viruses and their dependence on organisms. Students learn about the diversity among protists and fungi. (*Viruses, Protists, Fungi*)

PLANTS

Science as Inquiry (Content Standard A)
- **Communicate scientific procedures and explanations** Students create an interactive exhibit that teaches young children how a plant becomes a useful product. (*Chapter Project*)

Life Science (Content Standard C)
- **Structure and function in living systems** Plants are multicellular and have a variety of structures that carry out life functions. Seed plants have specialized tissues that carry out specific functions. Gymnosperms and angiosperms have different structures involved in reproduction. (*Chapter Project, The Plant Kingdom, Plants Without Seeds, The Characteristics of Seed Plants, Gymnosperms and Angiosperms, Skills Labs*)
- **Reproduction and heredity** Mosses and ferns have life cycles that include gametophyte and sporophyte stages. Seeds are specialized structures for reproduction. Most gymnosperms sexually reproduce using cones. Angiosperms sexually reproduce using flowers and fruit. (*Plants Without Seeds, The Characteristics of Seed Plants, Gymnosperms and Angiosperms, Skills Lab—A Close Look at Flowers*)
- **Diversity and adaptations of organisms** Plants are diverse. Mosses and ferns evolved adaptations that allowed them to survive on land. (*The Plant Kingdom, Plants Without Seeds, The Characteristics of Seed Plants, Skills Lab—Masses of Mosses*)

SPONGES, CNIDARIANS, AND WORMS

Science as Inquiry (Content Standard A)
- **Identify questions that can be answered through scientific investigations** Do earthworms prefer dry or moist environments? Do they prefer dark light or dark conditions? (*Skills Lab—Earthworm Responses*)
- **Design and conduct a scientific investigation** Students design a plan to investigate whether earthworms prefer smooth or rough surfaces. (*Skills Lab—Earthworm Responses*)

Life Science (Content Standard C)

● **Structure and function in living systems** The bodies of complex animals all have either radial or bilateral symmetry. (*Animal Symmetry*)

● **Populations and ecosystems** Students learn about effects humans can have on coral reefs. (*Sponges and Cnidarians*)

● **Diversity and adaptations of organisms** Students learn the main characteristics and adaptations of animals. Students learn the characteristics and adaptations of sponges and cnidarians. Students learn the characteristics and adaptations of the three main groups of worms. (*What Is an Animal?, Sponges and Cnidarians, Worms*)

MOLLUSKS, ARTHROPODS, AND ECHINODERMS

Science as Inquiry (Content Standard A)

● **Identify questions that can be answered through scientific investigations** How do changes in environmental temperature affect the activity level of a snail? How do different conditions affect mealworm development? (*Skills Lab—A Snail's Pace, Chapter Project*)

● **Design and conduct a scientific investigation** Students design a plan to investigate mealworm development. (*Chapter Project*)

Life Science (Content Standard C)

● **Populations and ecosystems** Insects play a key role in food chains because of the ways in which they obtain food and then become food for other animals. Students examine the animal life of a specific soil environment. (*Skills Lab—What's Living in the Soil?*)

● **Diversity and adaptations of organisms** Students learn the characteristics and adaptations of mollusks, arthropods, insects, and echinoderms. (*Mollusks, Arthropods, Insects, Insect Ecology, Echinoderms*)

FISHES, AMPHIBIANS, AND REPTILES

Science as Inquiry (Content Standard A)

● **Design and conduct a scientific investigation** Students create an artificial environment for two organisms and monitor the organisms' behavior. They also design an extension to the activity allowing more organisms to be added. (*Skills Lab—Home Sweet Home*)

Life Science (Content Standard C)

● **Structure and function in living systems** Vertebrates have similar structures to perform similar functions. Different vertebrate groups have specialized structures, such as a two-loop circulatory system and three-chambered heart. (*What Is a Vertebrate?, Fishes, Amphibians, Reptiles*)

● **Diversity and adaptations of organisms** The specialized characteristics of vertebrates reveal great diversity of form. Adaptations allow vertebrates to occupy many different habitats. (*What Is a Vertebrate?, Fishes, Amphibians, Reptiles*)

Earth and Space Science (Content Standard D)

● **Earth's history** The fossils found in sedimentary rocks reveal the history of vertebrate evolution through time. (*Vertebrate History in Rocks*)

BIRDS AND MAMMALS

Science as Inquiry (Content Standard A)

● **Recognize and analyze alternative explanations and predictions** Students may suggest explanations for observed animal behavior. (*Chapter Project*)

● **Design and conduct a scientific investigation** Students implement a plan to investigate the effectiveness of wool as an insulator. Additionally, they will design their own experiment to test the insulation properties of wool to model fur as an adaptation to varying climates. (*Consumer Lab*)

Physical Science (Content Standard B)

● **Motions and forces** The flight of birds depends on lift and can be described using principles from physics. (*The Physics of Bird Flight*)

Life Science (Content Standard C)

● **Structure and function in living systems** The structural features of both birds and mammals are related to their life-supporting functions. The physical adaptations of different animals enable them to behave in complex ways. (*Birds, The Physics of Bird Flight, Mammals*)

● **Diversity and adaptations of organisms** Many characteristics of birds and mammals are adaptations that allow the animals to live in different environments. This is reflected in differences in physical and behavioral traits. (*Birds, The Physics of Bird Flight, Mammals*)

ANIMAL BEHAVIOR

Science as Inquiry (Content Standard A)

● **Identify questions that can be answered through scientific investigations** Students pose questions about teaching an animal and design a procedure to investigate their questions. (*Chapter Project*)

● **Think critically and logically to make the relationships between evidence and explanations** Ants' social and group behavior provides a starting point from which scientific investigation and discussion can proceed. Evidence may be contrary to students' previous opinions and will be the source of lively scientific inquiry. (*Skills Lab—One for All*)

Life Science (Content Standard C)

● **Regulation and behavior** Behavior is a response to a stimulus. Behavior has an adaptive function, and it enables animals to meet basic needs such as finding food. Some animal behaviors, such as migration and hibernation, are related to seasonal and other environmental changes. (*What Is Behavior?, Patterns of Behavior, Tracking Migrations*)

A National Look at Science Education (continued)

● **Diversity and adaptations of organisms** Most behaviors serve adaptive functions, such as reproduction or finding food. Different kinds of animals may exhibit similar behavior patterns, such as establishing a territory or living in groups. (*Patterns of Behavior, Tracking Migrations*)

BONES, MUSCLES, AND SKIN

Science as Inquiry (Content Standard A)
● **Ask questions that can be answered by scientific investigations** Students observe the structure and function of muscles in a chicken wing, and draw conclusions about how the muscles work together. (*Skills Lab—A Look Beneath the Skin*)

Life Science (Content Standard C)
● **Structure and function in living systems** The human body is organized into cells, tissues, organs, and organs systems. The skeleton has five major functions: shape and support, movement, protection, production of blood cells, and storage of minerals and other materials. The human body has three types of muscles and muscles work in pairs to move the bones of the body. The skin functions in protection, maintaining temperature, eliminating wastes, gathering information, and producing Vitamin D. (*Body Organization and Homeostasis, The Skeletal System, The Muscular System, The Skin*)

FOOD AND DIGESTION

Life Science (Content Standard C)
● **Structure and function in living systems** The digestive system breaks down food into molecules that the body can use. These molecules are absorbed into the blood carried throughout the body. Wastes are eliminated from the body. Most of the chemical digestion takes place in the small intestine. Most of the absorption of water takes place in the large intestine. (*The Digestive Process Begins, Final Digestion and Absorption*)

Science in Personal and Social Perspectives (Content Standard F)
● **Personal Health** Food provides energy and nutrients for growth and development. The six kinds of nutrients are carbohydrates, fats, proteins, vitamins, minerals, and water. Nutritional requirements vary. The Food Guide Pyramid and food nutritional labels can help a person plan a healthy diet. (*Food and Energy*)

CIRCULATION

Science as Inquiry (Content Standard A)
● **Ask questions that can be answered by scientific investigations** Students investigate how physical activity affects pulse rate. Students draw conclusions on which blood types can safely receive transfusions of type A and type O blood. (*Skills Labs*)

Life Science (Content Standard C)
● **Structure and function in living systems** The cardiovascular system consists of heart, blood vessels, and blood and functions as the transport system of the body. Arteries, capillaries, and veins transport blood to organs of the body. (*The Body's Transport System, Blood and Lymph*)

Science in Personal and Social Perspectives (Content Standard F)
● **Personal Health** Personal behaviors can help maintain cardiovascular health. (*Cardiovascular Health*)

History and Nature of Science (Content Standard G)
● **History of Science** Many people have contributed to cardiovascular advances in history. (*Science and History*)

RESPIRATION AND EXCRETION

Science as Inquiry (Content Standard A)
● **Ask questions that can be answered by scientific investigations** Students conduct an investigation to determine how air gets into the lungs. (*Skills Lab—A Breath of Fresh Air*)

Life Science (Content Standard C)
● **Structure and funtion in living systems** The respiratory and excretory systems work together to transport substances to and from the blood. (*The Respiratory System, The Excretory System*)

Science in Personal and Social Perspectives (Content Standard F)
● **Personal Health** Smoking can damage the respiratory system. The body can repair some of the damage when the smoker quits. (*Smoking and Your Health*)

FIGHTING DISEASE

Science as Inquiry (Content Standard A)
● **Develop descriptions, explanations, predictions, and models using evidence** Students develop a model to show how the skin acts as a barrier against infectious diseases. (*Skills Lab—The Skin as a Barrier*)

Life Science (Content Standard C)
● **Structures and funtion in living systems** The human organism has systems for protection from disease that interact with other systems. (*The Body's Defenses*)

THE NERVOUS SYSTEM

Science as Inquiry (Content Standard A)
● **Design and conduct a scientific investigation** Students design a test on people's responses to optical illusions. Students investigate how time of day affects reaction time. (*Chapter Project, Design Your Own Lab*)

● **Think critically and logically to make the relationships between evidence and explanations** Students draw conclusions about the effect of stimulants on water fleas. *(Consumer Lab)*

Life Science (Content Standard C)

● **Structure and function in living systems** The nervous system has specialized cells that allow it to receive information, respond to information, and maintain homeostasis. *(How the Nervous System Works)*

● **Regulation and Behavior** The nervous system maintains stable body conditions. The nervous system uses senses to receive information about the environment. The brain processes this information to help humans survive. *(Chapter Project, How the Nervous System Works, Divisions of the Nervous System, The Senses)*

Science in Personal and Social Perspectives (Content Standard F)

● **Personal Health** Abusing drugs and alcohol can cause both short-term and long-term damage to a person's health. *(Alcohol and Other Drugs, Consumer Lab)*

● **Risks and Benefits** Students debate whether bicycle helmet laws should be enacted to protect people from injury. *(Science and Society)*

THE ENDOCRINE SYSTEM AND REPRODUCTION

Life Science (Content Standard C)

● **Reproduction and heredity** The female body produces eggs and the male body produces sperm. The egg and sperm unite to form a new individual. *(The Male and Female Reproductive Systems)*

● **Regulation and Behavior** The endocrine system controls many of the body's daily activities as well as regulating developmental change. During the menstrual cycle, the body prepares itself to reproduce by releasing an egg and by thickening the uterine wall. *(The Endocrine System, The Male and Female Reproductive Systems)*

POPULATIONS AND COMMUNITIES

Science as Inquiry (Content Standard A)

● **Design and conduct a scientific investigation** Students design an experiment to determine the effect of crowding on plant growth. *(Chapter Project)*

● **Use appropriate tools and techniques to gather, analyze, and interpret data** Students model using the mark-and-recapture method to estimate the size of a population. *(Skills Lab)*

● **Develop descriptions, explanations, predictions, and models using evidence** Students study the interactions between biotic and abiotic factors in a model ecosystem. *(Skills Lab)*

● **Communicate scientific procedures and explanations** Students present a report and graph of results of their project on the effect of crowding on plant growth. *(Chapter Project)*

Life Science (Content Standard C)

● **Populations and ecosystems** The levels of organization in the environment include organisms, population, community, and ecosystem. *(Living Things and the Environment)*

Science in Personal and Social Perspectives (Content Standard F)

● **Science and technology in society** Students analyze the issue of animal overpopulation. *(Science and Society)*

ECOSYSTEMS AND BIOMES

Science as Inquiry (Content Standard A)

● **Design and conduct a scientific investigation** Students investigate the effects of variables on decomposition. *(Chapter Project)*

● **Develop descriptions, explanations, predictions, and models using evidence** Students investigate how abiotic factors create different biomes. Students observe how a community changes over time. *(Skills Lab)*

Life Science (Content Standard C)

● **Populations and ecosystems** Students observe the role of soil organisms on decomposition. An organism's energy role in an ecosystem may be that of producer, consumer, or decomposer. Biogeography is the study of where organisms live. Students observe how climate affects biomes. Students observe succession in a pond community. *(Energy Flow in Ecosystems, Biogeography, Biomes and Aquatic Ecosystems, Skills Lab)*

Earth and Space Science (Content Standard D)

● **Structure of the Earth system** The water cycle is the continuous process by which water moves from Earth's surface to the atmosphere and back. *(Cycles of Matter)*

LIVING RESOURCES

Science as Inquiry (Content Standard A)

● **Design and conduct a scientific investigation** Students observe a diversity of organisms. *(Chapter Project)*

● **Develop descriptions, explanations, predictions, and models using evidence** Students model paper recycling. Students observe a tree cross-section to draw conclusions about how the tree grew. *(Skills Lab)*

Life Science (Content Standard C)

● **Diversity and adaptations of organisms** The number of different species in an area is called biodiversity. Extinction is the disappearance of all members of a species from Earth. *(Biodiversity)*

Science in Personal and Social Perspectives (Content Standard F)

● **Populations, resources, and environments** Human activities can threaten biodiversity. *(Biodiversity)*

● **Science and technology in society** Environmental issues include resource management, population growth, and pollution. *(Environmental Issues)*

Reading Comprehension in the Science Classroom

Q&A

Q: Why are science texts often difficult for students to read and comprehend?

A: In general, science texts make complex literacy and knowledge demands on learners. They have a more technical vocabulary and a more demanding syntax, and place a greater emphasis on inferential reasoning.

Q: What does research say about facilitating comprehension?

A: Studies comparing novices and experts show that the conceptual organization of experts' knowledge is very different from that of novices. For example, experts emphasize core concepts when organizing knowledge, while novices focus on superficial details. To facilitate comprehension, effective teaching strategies should support and scaffold students as they build an understanding of the key concepts and concept relationships within a text unit.

Q: What strategies can teachers use to facilitate comprehension?

A: Three complementary strategies are very important in facilitating student comprehension of science texts. First, guide student interaction with the text using the built-in strategies. Second, organize the curriculum in terms of core concepts (e.g., the **Key Concepts** in each section). Third, develop visual representations of the relationships among the key concepts and vocabulary that can be referred to during instruction.

Nancy Romance, Ph.D.
Professor of Science Education
Florida Atlantic University
Fort Lauderdale, Florida

"Effective teaching strategies should support and scaffold students as they build an understanding of the key concepts and concept relationships within a text unit."

Reading Support in *Science Explorer*

The latest research emphasizes the importance of activating learners' prior knowledge and teaching them to distinguish core concepts from less important information. These skills are now more important than ever, because success in science requires students to read, understand, and connect complex terms and concepts.

Before students read—
Reading Preview introduces students to the key concepts and key terms they'll find in each section. The **Target Reading Skill** is identified and applied with a graphic organizer.

During the section—
Boldface Sentences identify each key concept and encourage students to focus on the big ideas of science.

Reading Checkpoints reinforce students' understanding by slowing them down to review after every concept is discussed.

Caption Questions draw students into the art and photos, helping them connect the content to the images.

After students read—
Section Assessment revisits the **Target Reading Skill** and encourages students to use the graphic organizer.

Each review question is scaffolded and models the way students think, by first easing them into a review and then challenging them with increasingly more difficult questions.

Evaluator's Checklist

Does your science program promote reading comprehension with—

✔ Text structured in an outline format and key concepts highlighted in boldface type

✔ Real-world applications to activate prior knowledge

✔ Key concepts, critical vocabulary, and a reading skill for every section

✔ Sample graphic organizers for each section

✔ Relevant photos and carefully constructed graphics with questions

✔ Reading checkpoints that appear in each section

✔ Scaffolded questions in section assessments

Math in the Science Classroom

Why should students concern themselves with mathematics in your science class?

Good science requires good data from which to draw conclusions. Technology enhances the ability to measure in a variety of ways. Often the scientist must measure large amounts of data, and thus an aim of analysis is to reduce the data to a summary that makes sense and is consistent with established norms of communication—i.e., mathematics.

Calculating measures of central tendency (e.g., mean, median, or mode), variability (e.g., range), and shape (graphic representations) can effectively reduce 500 data points to 3 without losing the essential characteristics of the data. Scientists understand that a trade-off exists between precision and richness as data are folded into categories, and so margins of error can be quantified in mathematical terms and factored into all scientific findings.

Mathematics is the language used by scientists to model change in the world. Understanding change is a vital part of the inquiry process. Mathematics serves as a common language to communicate across the sciences. Fields of scientific research that originated as separate disciplines are now integrated, such as happened with bioengineering. What do the sciences have in common? Each uses the language of mathematics to communicate about data and the process of data analysis. Recognizing this need, *Science Explorer* integrates mathematics practice throughout the program and gives students ample opportunity to hone their math skills.

Clearly, mathematics plays an important role in your science classroom!

William Tate, Ph.D.
Professor of Education and
Applied Statistics and
Computation
Washington University
St. Louis, Missouri

> "Mathematics is the language used by scientists to model change in the world."

Integrated Math Support

In the Student Edition

The math instruction is based on principles derived from Prentice Hall's research-based mathematics program.

Sample Problems, Math Practice, Analyzing Data, and a Math Skills Handbook all help to provide practice at point of use, encouraging students to Read and Understand, Plan and Solve, and then Look Back and Check.

Color-coded variables aid student navigation and help reinforce their comprehension.

In the Teacher's Edition

Math teaching notes enable the science teacher to support math instruction and math objectives on high-stakes tests.

In the Guided Reading and Study Workbook

These unique worksheets help students master reading and enhance their study and math skills. Students can create a record of their work for study and review.

Evaluator's Checklist

Does your science program promote math skills by—

✔ Giving students opportunities to collect data

✔ Providing students opportunities to analyze data

✔ Enabling students to practice math skills

✔ Helping students solve equations by using color-coded variables

✔ Using sample problems to apply science concepts

Technology and Design

Technology and Design in the Science Classroom

Much of the world we live in is designed and made by humans. The buildings in which we live, the cars we drive, the medicines we take, and often the food we eat are products of technology. The knowledge and skills needed to understand the processes used to create these products should be a component of every student's basic literacy.

Some schools offer hands-on instruction on how technology development works through industrial arts curricula. Even then, there is a disconnect among science (understanding how nature works), mathematics (understanding data-driven models), and technology (understanding the human-made world). The link among these fields of study is the engineering design process—that process by which one identifies a human need and uses science knowledge and human ingenuity to create a technology to satisfy the need. Engineering gives students the problem-solving and design skills they will need to succeed in our sophisticated, three-dimensional, technological world.

As a complement to "science as inquiry," the National Science Education Standards (NRC, 1996) call for students at all age levels to develop the abilities related to "technology as design," including the ability to identify and frame a problem and then to design, implement, and evaluate a solution. At the 5–8 grade level, the standards call for students to be engaged in complex problem-solving and to learn more about how science and technology complement each other. It's also important for students to understand that there are often constraints involved in design as well as trade-offs and unintended consequences of technological solutions to problems.

As the *Standards for Technological Literacy* (ITEA, 2000) state, "Science and technology are like conjoined twins. While they have separate identities they must remain inextricably connected." Both sets of standards emphasize how progress in science leads to new developments in technology, while technological innovation in turn drives advances in science.

Ioannis Miaoulis, Ph.D.
President
Museum of Science
Boston, Massachusetts

"Engineering gives students the problem-solving and design skills they will need to succeed in our sophisticated, three-dimensional, technological world."

Evaluator's Checklist

Does your science program promote technology and design by—

✔ Incorporating technology and design concepts and skills into the science curriculum

✔ Giving students opportunities to identify and solve technological design problems

✔ Providing students opportunities to analyze the impact of technology on society

✔ Enabling students to practice technology and design skills

Technology and Design in *Science Explorer*

How often do you hear your students ask: "Why do I need to learn this?" Connecting them to the world of technology and design in their everyday life is one way to help answer this question. It is also why so many state science curricula are now emphasizing technology and design concepts and skills.

Science Explorer makes a special effort to include a technology and design strand that encourages students to not only identify a need but to take what they learned in science and apply it to design a possible solution, build a prototype, test and evaluate the design, and/or troubleshoot the design. This strand also provides definitions of technology and engineering and discusses the similarities and differences between these endeavors and science. Students will learn to analyze the risks and benefits of a new technology and to consider the tradeoffs, such as safety, costs, efficiency, and appearance.

In the Student Edition

Integrated Technology & Design Sections

Sections throughout *Science Explorer* specifically integrate technology and design with the content of the text. For example, students not only learn how seismographs work but also learn what role seismographs play in society and how people use the data that are gathered.

Technology Labs

These labs help students gain experience in designing and building a device or product that meets a particular need or solves a problem. Students follow a design process of Research and Investigate, Design and Build, and Evaluate and Redesign.

Chapter Projects

Chapter Projects work hand-in-hand with the chapter content. Students design, build, and test based on real-world situations. They have the opportunity to apply the knowledge and skills learned to building a product.

Special Features

This technology and design strand is also reflected in Technology & Society and Science & Society features as well as Science & History timelines and Tech & Design in History timelines. These highly visual features introduce a technology and its impact on society. For example, students learn how a hybrid car differs from a traditional car.

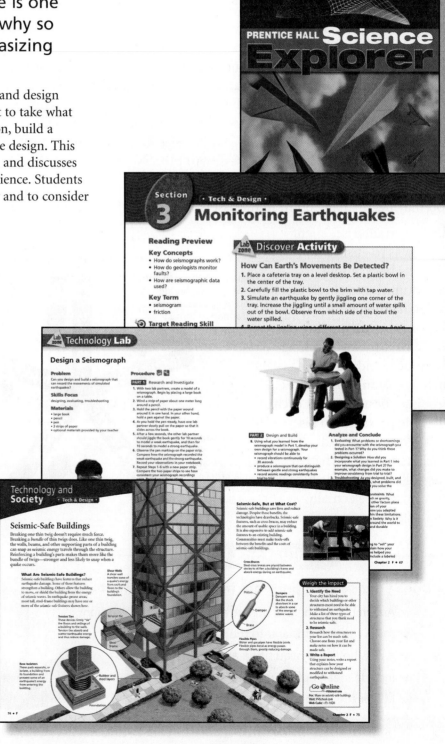

Assessment

Assessment in the Science Curriculum

No Child Left Behind clearly challenges school districts across the nation to raise expectations for all students with testing of student achievement in science beginning in 2007–2008.

A primary goal of NCLB is to provide classroom teachers with better data from scientifically valid assessments in order to inform instructional planning and to identify students who are at risk and require intervention. It has been a common practice to teach a science lesson, administer a test, grade it, and move on. This practice is a thing of the past. With the spotlight now on improving student performance, it is essential to use assessment results as a way to identify student strengths and challenges. Providing student feedback and obtaining student input is a valuable, essential part of the assessment process.

Assessment is a never-ending cycle, as is shown in the following diagram. Although you may begin at any point in the assessment cycle, the basic process is the same.

An important assessment strategy is to ensure that students have ample opportunities to check their understanding of skills and concepts before moving on to the next topic. Checking for understanding also includes asking appropriate, probing questions with each example presented. This enables students and teachers to know whether the skills or concepts being introduced are actually understood.

Eileen Depka
Supervisor of Standards and Assessment
Waukesha, Wisconsin

"Meeting the NCLB challenge will necessitate an integrated approach to assessment with a variety of assessment tools."

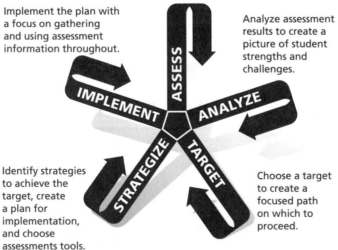

Use a variety of assessment tools to gain information and strengthen student understanding.

Implement the plan with a focus on gathering and using assessment information throughout.

Analyze assessment results to create a picture of student strengths and challenges.

Identify strategies to achieve the target, create a plan for implementation, and choose assessments tools.

Choose a target to create a focused path on which to proceed.

Evaluator's Checklist

Does your science program include assessments that—

✔ Are embedded before, during, and after lesson instruction
✔ Align to standards and to the instructional program
✔ Assess both skill acquisition and understanding
✔ Include meaningful rubrics to guide students
✔ Mirror the various formats of standardized tests

Assessment in *Science Explorer*

Science Explorer's remarkable range of strategies for checking progress will help teachers find the right opportunity for reaching all their students.

The assessment strategies in *Science Explorer* will help both students and teachers alike ensure student success in content mastery as well as high-stakes test performance. A wealth of opportunities built into the Student Edition help students monitor their own progress. Teachers are supported with ongoing assessment opportunities in the Teacher's Edition and an easy-to-use, editable test generator linked to content objectives. These integrated, ongoing assessment tools assure success.

Especially to support state and national testing objectives, Prentice Hall has developed test preparation materials that model the NCLB approach.

- **Diagnostic Assessment** tools provide in-depth analysis of strengths and weaknesses, areas of difficulty, and probable underlying causes that can help teachers make instructional decisions and plan intervention strategies.

- **Progress Monitoring** tools aligned with content objectives and state tests provide ongoing, longitudinal records of student achievement detailing individual student progress toward meeting end-of-year and end-of-schooling grade level, district, or state standards.

- **Outcomes** tools that mimic state and national tests show whether individual students have met the expected standards and can help a school system judge whether it has made adequate progress in improving its performance year by year.

Caption Questions enhance critical thinking skills

Reading Checkpoints reinforce students' understanding

Scaffolded Section Assessment Questions model the way students think

Comprehensive Chapter Reviews and Assessment provide opportunities for students to check their own understanding and practice valuable high-stakes test-taking skills

ExamView®, **Computer Test Bank CD-ROM** provides teachers access to thousands of modifiable test questions in English and Spanish

Test Preparation Blackline Masters and Student Workbook include diagnostic and prescription tools, progress-monitoring aids, and practice tests that help teachers focus on improving test scores.

Section 3 Assessment

Target Reading Skill Sequencing Refer to your flowchart about seismographs as you answer Question 1.

Reviewing Key Concepts

1. a. **Defining** What is a seismogram?
   b. **Explaining** How can geologists tell apart the different types of seismic waves on a seismogram?
   c. **Comparing and Contrasting** Two identical seismographs are located 1,000 km and 1,200 km from an earthquake's epicenter. How would the two seismograms for the earthquake compare?

2. a. **Reviewing** What changes are measured by the instruments used to monitor faults?
   b. **Describing** How are satellites used to measure movements along a fault?
   c. **Inferring** A satellite that monitors a fault detects an increasing tilt in the land surface along the fault. What could this change in the land surface indicate?

3. a. **Listing** What are three ways in which geologists use seismographic data?
   b. **Explaining** How do geologists use seismographic data to make maps of faults?
   c. **Making Generalizations** Why is it difficult to predict earthquakes?

Writing in Science

Dialogue Geologists in Alaska have just detected an earthquake and located the earthquake's epicenter. Write a dialogue in which the geologists notify a disaster response team that will help people in the earthquake area.

Chapter 2 F ◆ 65

Standardized Test Prep

Test-Taking Tip
When answering questions about diagrams, read all parts of the diagram carefully, including title, captions, and labels. Make sure that you understand the meaning of arrows and other symbols. Determine exactly what the question asks. Then eliminate those answer choices that are not supported by the diagram.

Practice answering this question.
The diagram shows how stress affects a mass of rock in a process called
A compression.
B tension.
C squeezing.
D shearing.
The correct answer is D because the arrows show rock being pulled in opposite directions.

Choose the letter that best answers the question or completes the statement.

1. In a strike-slip fault, rock masses along the fault move
   A in the same direction.
   B down only.
   C together.
   D sideways past each other.

2. Stress will build until an earthquake occurs if friction along a fault is
   F decreasing.   G high.
   H low.   J changed to heat.

Use the information below and your knowledge of science to answer Questions 3 and 4.

Seismic waves

3. When an earthquake occurs, seismic waves travel
   A from P in all directions.
   B from R to S.
   C from S in all directions.
   D from Q to P.

4. At point R, seismic waves from an earthquake would be
   F weaker than at P.
   G likely to cause little damage.
   H weaker than at Q.
   J likely to cause the most damage.

5. To estimate the total energy released by an earthquake, a geologist should use the
   A Mercalli scale.   B Richter scale.
   C epicenter scale.   D moment magnitude scale.

Constructed Response

6. A geologist discovers a large fault beneath a major city. Why would this information be helpful in determining earthquake risk in the area? What three safety steps should the geologist recommend?

Chapter 2 F ◆ 79

Master Materials List

SCIENCE EXPLORER offers an abundance of activity options in the Student Edition so you can pick and choose those that suit your needs. Prentice Hall has worked with Neo/SCI Corporation to develop Consumable Kits and Nonconsumable Kits that precisely match the needs of the SCIENCE EXPLORER labs. Use this Master Materials List or the Materials Ordering CD-ROM to help order your supplies. For more information on materials kits for this program, contact your local Prentice Hall sales representative or Neo/SCI Corporation at 1-800-526-6689 or **www.neosci.com**.

Consumable Materials

Item	Textbook Section(s)	Quantity per class	Item	Textbook Section(s)	Quantity per class
Activated carbon, 1 lb	21-1(Lab)	1	*Bread crumbs	13-2(Lab)	5
Adding machine tape, roll	22-4(DIS)	1	*Bread, moldy, bag	7-4(DIS)	1
Adrenaline chloride, 0.01%, 8 mL	19-4(Lab)	1	*Bread, without preservatives, bag	2-1(Lab)	1
*Air freshener	3-2(DIS)	1	Brine shrimp eggs, 6 drams	21-1(TT)	1
Aluminum foil roll, 12″ × 25′	7-3(SA)	1	Bromothymol blue, 0.01%, 100 mL	17-1(TT), 22-2(TT)	1
Ants, pkg/100	13-2(Lab)	1	*Cactus, live	22-4(TT)	1
*Apple	18-2(Lab)	20	*Can, aluminum	9-1(TT)	5
*Apple, peeled	19-3(SA)	5	*Candy, bag	19-4(DIS)	1
*Apple, rotting	18-2(Lab)	5	Cardboard, 32 × 32 cm	14-4(TT)	5
*Aquarium filter	11-2(Lab)	1	Cards, index, 3 × 5 blank, pkg/100	5-2(Lab), 21-2(Lab), 22-3(Lab)	1
*Aquarium gravel, 5 lbs	11-2(Lab)	1	*Carton, milk	22-3(Lab)	5
Bag, paper, 10 × 20 × 7.5 cm	4-2(Lab), 19-3(DIS)	20	Chalk pkg/12	3-1(DIS)	1
Bag, zipper 6 × 8″	2-1(Lab), 7-4(DIS), 14-4(Lab), 18-2(Lab)	40	Cheesecloth, sq yd	10-3(Lab), 16-2(TT)	3
Baking soda, 454 g	3-1(DIS), 15-3(TT)	1	*Chicken wing, uncooked, treated with bleach	14-3(Lab)	5
Balloon, large, 15″, pkg/10	7-4(Lab), 7-4(TT), 17-1(DIS), 17-1(Lab)	4	Chlorella	7-3(TT)	1
Balloon, large, 9″, pkg/10	17-1(Lab), 20-1(Lab)	1	Cloth, flannel, white, 12 × 36″	14-4(Lab)	1
*Bar codes, set	5-3(Lab)	5	Cloth, muslin 12 × 36″	14-4(Lab)	1
*Beverage with caffeine, variety	19-4(Lab)	10	Cloth, polyester, 9 × 12″ navy	14-4(Lab), 22-3(DIS)	2
*Beverage without caffeine, variety	19-4(Lab)	10	Coffee filter	3-3(SA)	5
Biuret reagent, 30 mL	17-3(Lab)	1	*Compost materials	21-4(CP)	5
Black Ramshorn snail, pkg/15	10-1(Lab), 11-2(Lab)	1	*Cornflakes	10-1(CP)	1
Blackworms, pkg/30	19-4(Lab)	1	Cotton balls, pkg/100	7-3(TT), 7-4(TT), 14-4(TT)	1
*Bone, chicken	14-2(TT)	10	Cotton swab	18-2(Lab)	26
*Bottle, plastic, 1-L	17-1(Lab), 20-1(Lab)	5	Coverslips, 1 oz	2-3(SA), 3-5(DIS), 7-2(TT), 7-3(DIS), 8-4(Lab), 22-4(Lab), 23-1(Lab)	1
*Bottle, plastic, 2-L with cap	10-3(Lab), 20-1(Lab), 21-1(Lab), 21-4(CP)	25	*Cracker	12-3(DIS)	5
*Bottle, plastic, narrow-necked, small	7-4(Lab)	25	*Crickets	9-1(DIS)	5
			Cup, paper, 7-oz, pkg/50	6-1(TT), 7-2(DIS), 16-3(Lab)	1

KEY: * = School Supplied; **CP:** Chapter Project; **DIS:** Discover; **SA:** Skills Activity; **TT:** Try This; **Lab:** Skills, Consumer, Design Your Own, or Technology   **Quantities based on five groups of six students per class.**

Master Materials List

Consumable Materials

Item	Textbook Section(s)	Quantity per class	Item	Textbook Section(s)	Quantity per class
Cup, clear plastic, 2-oz	16-1(DIS)	5	*Fruit, fresh, assortment	6-3(TT)	50
Cup, plastic, 9-oz, with lid, pkg/50	1-2(SA), 3-1(DIS), 3-2(TT), 3-3(SA), 6-3(TT), 6-4(Lab), 11-3(DIS), 12-3(Lab), 16-2(TT), 17-3(DIS), 22-2(TT), 23-3(DIS)	2	*Fruit, moldy	7-4(DIS)	5
			Gelatin, 3 oz	2-4(TT)	5
			*Gloves, plastic, pkg/100	11-2(SA), 12-3(TT), 14-2(TT), 14-3(Lab), 14-4(DIS), 14-4(TT)	2
*Dips, fat-containing, variety (with nutritional labels)	3-1(Lab)	5	Glucose 30 g	17-3(DIS), 17-3(Lab)	1
			Glucose test strips, pkg/50	17-3(DIS), 17-3(Lab)	1
*Drawing materials	9-1(TT)	5	*Glue stick	4-1(CP), 12-2(TT), 21-1(DIS)	5
Dropper, plastic, pkg/10	2-1(Lab), 2-3(SA), 3-2(TT), 3-5(DIS), 7-2(TT), 7-3(DIS), 7-3(TT), 8-2(Lab), 8-2(TT), 8-4(Lab), 9-4(DIS), 9-4(Lab), 10-5(DIS), 15-1(SA), 16-3(Lab), 17-3(Lab), 19-4(Lab), 22-4(Lab)	15	*Goldfish, live	11-2(DIS)	5
			*Grapefruit	11-4(DIS), 12-4(DIS)	10
			*Graph paper, sheet	5-1(DIS), 10-1(Lab), 12-3(Lab), 13-3(DIS), 16-1(Lab), 21-2(Lab)	80
			*Grass clipping	21-4(CP)	2
Duct tape, 10 yd	2-1(Lab), 20-1(Lab)	1	Gravel, 2.75-lb bag	21-1(Lab)	2
Dye solution, blue 30 mL	16-3(Lab)	1	*Guppies, live	11-2(Lab)	5
Dye solution, green 30 mL	16-3(Lab)	1	Hair pins	6-1(TT), 14-3(TT)	10
Dye solution, red 30 mL	3-2(TT), 16-3(Lab)	1	Hydra, brown	9-3(TT)	1
Dye solution, yellow 30 mL	16-3(Lab)	1	Hydrochloric acid, 1%, 30 mL	15-2(Lab)	1
Earthworms, pkg/10	9-4(Lab)	1	Ink pad	5-3(DIS)	5
*Egg	12-1(TT)	5	*Insect collection	10-3(DIS)	1
*Egg white, cubed	15-2(Lab)	20	Isopropyl alcohol, 500 mL	3-3(SA), 18-2(Lab)	1
*Eggshells	21-4(CP)	5	Knife, plastic, pkg/20	14-4(Lab), 16-3(TT)	1
Elodea, pkg/20	22-2(TT)	1	Label, 2 × 1″ white	3-1(DIS)	1
Euglena gracilis	7-3(SA)	1	*Leaf, average rainfall	8-1(DIS)	5
*Fat-testing strips, pkg/75	3-1(Lab)	1	*Leaf, desert	8-1(DIS)	5
*Fern	8-2(TT), 9-1(DIS)	1	*Leaves, variety	3-3(SA), 8-4(DIS)	20
Filter paper, 15 cm, pkg/99	17-3(DIS)	1	*Leg bone, chicken	14-2(DIS)	5
*Flour, bag	20-1(CP)	30	*Lemon, slice	2-1(TT)	5
*Flower, large	8-4(Lab)	5	Lens paper, 4 × 6″	8-4(Lab)	5
*Flowers, cut, fresh	6-4(Lab), 10-4(DIS)	10	Lugol's iodine, 30 mL	15-1(SA)	1
*Foam, plastic, piece	21-4(CP)	1	*Magazine picture	21-1(DIS)	5
*Food, appropriate for chosen small vertebrate	13-1(DIS)	1	Marker, permanent black	3-1(Lab), 4-2(Lab), 5-2(Lab), 6-1(Lab), 7-4(Lab), 16-3(Lab), 18-2(Lab)	5
*Food, assortment	8-3(DIS), 15-1(SA), 16-3(DIS)	30			
*Food, guppy	11-2(Lab)	1	*Markers, colored	4-1(CP)	5

KEY: * = School Supplied; **CP:** Chapter Project; **DIS:** Discover; **SA:** Skills Activity; **TT:** Try This; **Lab:** Skills, Consumer, Design Your Own, or Technology

Quantities based on five groups of six students per class.

Master Materials List

Consumable Materials

Item	Textbook Section(s)	Quantity per class	Item	Textbook Section(s)	Quantity per class
*Materials that resemble cell organelles, set	2-4(TT)	5	*Paramecium caudatum*	7-3(TT)	1
Mealworms, live (30)	1-2(DIS), 10-1(CP)	1	*Paste	13-2(TT), 16-3(TT)	1
Methylene blue biostain, 30 mL	3-5(DIS), 7-2(TT)	1	*Peanuts, shelled, bag	8-3(TT)	1
Microscope slides, pkg/72	2-3(SA), 3-5(DIS), 7-2(TT), 7-3(DIS), 7-3(TT), 8-4(Lab), 22-4(Lab), 23-1(Lab)	1	*Pear, peeled	19-3(SA)	5
			Peat moss, bag	8-2(DIS)	1
*Minnows	9-1(DIS)	5	*Pen	21-1(DIS)	5
Modeling clay, white, 1 lb	7-4(TT), 9-1(TT), 11-5(DIS), 12-5(DIS), 18-2(TT)	1	*Pen, variety	6-2(DIS)	25
Moss clump	8-2(Lab)	1	*Pencil	7-1(Lab), 8-5(DIS), 10-4(DIS), 11-1(Lab), 13-1(Lab), 14-4(Lab)	30
*Moss, woodland	21-1(Lab)	1	*Pencil, colored, pkg/4	3-5(Lab), 16-2(DIS), 18-4(Lab), 21-1(DIS), 23-2(Lab)	5
*Mouthwash	18-3(DIS)	1			
*Mushroom growing kit	7-1(CP)	1	Pepsin powder, 2 g, 1:3,000	15-2(Lab), 17-3(Lab)	2
*Newspaper	16-1(DIS), 23-1(Lab)	2	Petri plate, plastic, pkg/20	1-2(DIS), 7-3(SA), 9-3(TT), 9-4(DIS), 10-1(Lab), 16-3(Lab)	3
*Notebook	8-1(DIS)	5			
*Orange peel	21-4(CP)	1	*Photograph, black and white	2-3(DIS)	5
Owl pellet, small	12-1(Lab)	5	Pine cone	8-4(TT)	5
*Paper towel, roll	3-1(Lab), 8-4(Lab), 9-3(Lab), 9-4(Lab), 10-2(TT), 14-3(Lab), 17-3(Lab), 18-2(Lab)	1	Pipe cleaners, asst, 6″ pkg/100	3-5(TT), 9-1(TT)	1
			Planaria	9-4(DIS)	1
			*Plant, potted	9-1(DIS)	3
*Paper, assorted kinds, pkg	12-2(TT)	1	*Plants, sensitive	8-5(DIS)	5
Paper, construction, black	2-3(Lab), 9-1(TT), 13-2(Lab)	30	*Plants, variety	3-1(CP), 8-5(DIS)	5
Paper, construction, blue	4-1(CP), 6-1(Lab)	50	*Plant, vascular, variety	21-1(Lab)	15
Paper, construction, green	11-3(DIS)	5	*Plant, water	11-2(Lab)	1
Paper, construction, white	14-4(Lab)	5	Plastic wrap, roll	21-1(Lab), 22-2(TT), 22-3(Lab), 23-1(Lab)	1
Paper, construction, yellow, sheet	3-5(TT), 4-1(CP), 6-1(Lab)	55			
			Plate, paper, 9″, pkg/15	2-1(Lab), 6-1(TT), 23-3(DIS)	3
*Paper, tracing, tablet	9-2(DIS)	1	Pond culture mix	2-3(SA), 7-3(DIS)	2
*Paper, white, ream	4-3(DIS), 6-1(SA), 7-1(DIS), 7-1(Lab), 8-4(TT), 9-2(DIS), 11-1(Lab), 11-5(DIS), 12-2(DIS), 12-2(TT), 12-5(DIS), 13-1(Lab), 13-2(TT), 16-3(Lab), 18-1(DIS), 18-2(DIS), 19-1(DIS), 21-1(DIS), 21-1(TT), 21-3(DIS), 22-1(DIS), 23-1(DIS)	1	*Potato, raw, peeled	19-3(SA)	5
			*Potato, slice	2-1(SA)	5
			Potting soil, 8 qt	3-1(CP), 13-2(Lab), 21-1(CP), 21-1(Lab), 22-3(Lab)	3
			*Raisin bran cereal, box, var.	15-1(Lab)	4
			*Raisins, box	6-1(TT)	5
			Rubberband, size 33	10-3(Lab), 13-2(Lab)	10
Paperclips, jumbo, pkg/100	12-2(TT), 16-2(TT)	1	Rubberbands/assorted, 1.5 oz.	11-4(DIS), 12-2(TT), 12-4(DIS), 16-2(TT), 21-1(Lab)	1

KEY: * = School Supplied; **CP:** Chapter Project; **DIS:** Discover; **SA:** Skills Activity; **TT:** Try This; **Lab:** Skills, Consumer, Design Your Own, or Technology

Quantities based on five groups of six students per class.

Master Materials List

Consumable Materials

Item	Textbook Section(s)	Quantity per class	Item	Textbook Section(s)	Quantity per class
Salt, non-iodized, 737 g	1-2(SA), 3-1(DIS), 7-4(Lab), 21-1(TT)	1	*Substrate, lacking nutrients	7-1(CP)	5
Sand, fine white, 3 lb	8-2(DIS), 13-2(Lab), 17-3(DIS)	2	Sugar cubes, box	15-2(DIS)	1
Scalpel, steel, 140 mm	8-4(Lab)	5	*Sugar, granulated	1-2(SA), 3-4(DIS), 6-4(Lab), 7-4(Lab), 13-2(Lab)	1
Screen, aluminum, 12 × 36"	23-1(Lab)	1	*Sunblock	3-1(DIS)	5
Seed, grass, 30 g	22-3(Lab)	1	Sunprint paper, 8 × 12", pkg/15	14-4(Lab)	1
Seeds, Alaska smooth pea, 1 oz	8-3(TT)	1	*Sunscreen, SPF 30	14-4(Lab)	1
Seeds, black bean, 1 lb	7-2(DIS)	1	*Sunscreen, SPF 4	14-4(Lab)	1
Seeds, corn 30 g	8-3(TT), 22-3(DIS)	2	Swabs, sterile, 6"	3-1(Lab), 10-4(DIS)	10
Seeds, green split pea, 1 lb	11-3(DIS)	1	Tape, masking, roll	2-3(Lab), 4-2(TT), 7-1(Lab), 7-4(TT), 8-4(Lab), 10-2(DIS), 12-2(TT), 13-2(Lab), 13-2(TT), 18-2(TT), 21-2(TT), 21-3(DIS), 22-3(DIS), 22-3(Lab)	1
Seeds, impatiens, 105 mg	22-3(Lab)	1
Seeds, lima bean, 1 oz	8-3(TT), 21-2(DIS), 22-3(Lab)	2
Seeds, radish, pkg	21-1(CP)	1	Timothy hay, 2 oz	22-4(Lab)	1
Seeds, sunflower, 30 g	6-1(DIS), 6-1(TT)	2	Toothpicks, round pkg/250	8-2(Lab), 9-3(TT), 16-3(Lab), 16-3(TT), 18-2(Lab)	1
Seeds, white bean, 4 oz	21-1(Lab)	1
Seeds, yellow split pea, 1 lb	11-3(DIS)	1	UV changing beads, pkg/240	15-2(TT)	1
*Shortening, solid	12-3(TT)	1	Vegetable oil, 16 oz	15-3(TT)	1
*Small vertebrate	13-1(DIS)	1	Vinegar, 500 mL	14-2(TT)	1
*Soap, disinfectant	18-3(DIS)	1	*Water, pond, 1 L	22-4(Lab)	1
*Soda cracker, unsalted, package	3-1(TT)	1	*Water, spring, noncarbonated, gallon	9-4(DIS), 10-1(Lab), 19-4(Lab)	1
*Soil and leaf litter	10-3(Lab)	5	*Water, tap, gallon	2-1(Lab), 6-3(TT), 7-4(Lab), 8-2(DIS), 8-2(Lab), 8-2(TT), 12-3(Lab), 14-2(TT), 14-3(Lab), 14-4(TT), 16-1(DIS), 16-2(TT), 16-3(TT), 17-1(TT), 20-1(Lab), 23-1(Lab)	1
*Soil, garden, 1 lb	21-4(CP)	5
Soup mix, 1 lb	23-3(DIS)	1
Sow bugs, pkg/10	10-2(TT)	1
Spoon, plastic, pkg/25	6-4(Lab), 10-1(CP), 15-3(TT), 21-1(Lab)	2
*Spring water, 1 gallon	21-1(TT)	3	Wax pencil	13-2(Lab), 15-2(Lab), 17-1(TT), 17-3(Lab), 22-4(Lab)	5
*Staples, box	12-2(TT)	1
Steel wool, coarse, roll, pkg/5	10-3(Lab)	1	Yarn, skein	22-1(TT)	1
Stick, craft, pkg/25	4-3(DIS), 7-4(TT)	1	Yeast, dry baking, 25 g	3-4(DIS), 3-5(DIS), 7-4(Lab)	3
Stirrer, plastic, pkg/40	14-3(TT), 15-2(Lab)	2	*Yogurt, plain, container, small	7-2(TT)	5
Straw, plastic, pkg/50	3-4(DIS), 7-4(Lab), 15-2(TT), 17-1(TT), 18-4(DIS), 22-3(DIS)	2
String, ball	7-4(Lab), 12-2(TT), 14-1(CP), 15-3(DIS), 20-1(Lab)	1

KEY: * = School Supplied; **CP:** Chapter Project; **DIS:** Discover; **SA:** Skills Activity; **TT:** Try This; **Lab:** Skills, Consumer, Design Your Own, or Technology

Quantities based on five groups of six students per class.

T29

Master Materials List

Nonconsumable Materials

Item	Textbook Section(s)	Quantity per class	Item	Textbook Section(s)	Quantity per class
Aluminum pan, 9 × 7 × 2″	2-4(TT), 9-4(Lab)	5	Flashlight, size D-cell	9-4(Lab)	5
*Apron, safety, pkg/100	7-2(TT), 14-3(Lab), 15-1(SA), 21-1(Lab)	1	Flower pots, small	3-1(CP), 21-1(CP)	10
*Aquarium heater	11-2(Lab)	1	Forceps, plastic	6-1(TT), 12-1(Lab), 13-2(Lab)	5
*Aquarium tank, 15-L, with cover	11-2(DIS), 11-2(Lab)	1	Funnel, 3″ H	16-3(TT), 17-3(DIS)	5
*Aquarium thermometer	11-2(Lab)	1	*Glass, drinking	9-2(DIS)	5
*Balance, triple beam	2-1(SA), 9-3(Lab), 15-1(Lab), 20-3(TT)	5	*Goggles, safety	3-4(DIS), 11-2(SA), 14-3(Lab), 15-2(TT), 17-1(TT)	30
*Beaker, 1-L	12-3(Lab)	5	Graduated cylinder, plastic, 100-mL	7-4(Lab), 8-2(DIS), 9-3(Lab), 16-3(TT), 17-1(TT)	15
Beaker, glass, 400-mL	7-4(Lab)	5	Graduated cylinder, plastic, 10-mL	15-2(Lab)	5
Beaker, glass, 600-mL	21-1(TT)	4	*Hair clips	6-1(TT)	5
Beaker, polypropylene, 250-mL	9-3(Lab), 15-1(Lab), 21-2(DIS)	5	*Hairdryer	2-1(SA)	5
Bird feeder	12-1(CP)	1	Half-meter stick	5-1(DIS), 7-1(Lab), 19-1(Lab), 21-2(TT), 22-4(DIS)	5
*Book	2-3(Lab), 12-2(DIS), 14-1(DIS), 14-2(SA), 23-1(Lab)	10	Hand lens, pkg/5	1-2(DIS), 2-3(DIS), 2-3(Lab), 5-3(Lab), 6-1(DIS), 7-4(DIS), 8-1(DIS), 8-2(Lab), 8-2(TT), 8-3(TT), 8-4(DIS), 8-4(Lab), 8-4(TT), 9-3(DIS), 9-3(TT), 10-3(Lab), 12-1(DIS), 12-1(Lab), 12-1(TT), 13-2(Lab), 14-2(DIS), 14-4(DIS), 22-4(TT), 23-2(Lab)	2
Bowl, opaque, 2-L	9-3(Lab), 12-1(TT), 23-1(Lab)	5			
Brush, small	9-4(DIS)	5			
*Bucket	12-3(TT)	5			
Buttons, black	6-1(SA)	75			
Buttons, white	6-1(SA)	75			
*Calculator	3-3(DIS), 3-5(Lab), 7-1(Lab), 18-4(Lab), 21-2(Lab)	5	*Items, from junk drawer	2-2(DIS)	5
Cardboard, 32 × 32 cm	9-4(Lab), 10-2(DIS)	10	*Jar, baby food	22-4(Lab)	5
*Cassette player and tape of soft music	18-4(Lab)	5	Jar, plastic, 16-oz, with lid	14-2(TT), 15-2(DIS), 15-3(TT), 16-3(TT)	10
Choice chamber	10-1(CP), 10-2(TT)	5	Jar, plastic, 8-oz	10-3(Lab)	5
Clothespins, pkg/10	6-1(TT), 14-3(DIS)	1	Jar, wide-mouth, polystyrene, 12-oz	10-3(Lab), 13-2(Lab), 21-2(DIS)	10
*Coin	4-2(DIS), 4-2(TT), 16-2(TT)	20	*Key	7-1(DIS)	5
*Container, plastic, with lid	9-3(Lab), 10-1(CP), 10-1(Lab), 11-2(Lab)	5	*Lamp, gooseneck	10-3(Lab), 22-3(Lab)	5
*Dime	3-3(SA)	5	Litmus paper, blue, pkg/100	15-2(Lab)	1
Dip net, nylon, 3″	11-2(Lab)	5	*Microscope, compound	2-3(DIS), 2-4(TT), 3-5(DIS), 3-5(Lab), 8-4(Lab), 16-2(DIS), 20-2(DIS), 22-4(Lab), 23-1(Lab)	5
Drawing compass with pencil	18-4(Lab)	5			
*Eggbeater	23-1(Lab)	5	Mirror, plastic, 7.5 × 12.5 cm	2-1(TT), 4-1(Lab), 12-3(DIS), 22-2(DIS)	5
Feather, white, 12–20 cm	12-1(DIS)	5			

KEY: * = School Supplied; **CP:** Chapter Project; **DIS:** Discover; **SA:** Skills Activity; **TT:** Try This; **Lab:** Skills, Consumer, Design Your Own, or Technology

Quantities based on five groups of six students per class.

Master Materials List

Nonconsumable Materials

Item	Textbook Section(s)	Quantity per class	Item	Textbook Section(s)	Quantity per class
*Objects to make imprints	11-5(DIS), 12-5(DIS)	15	Sponge, natural, 2 × 3″	9-1(DIS), 9-3(DIS), 9-3(Lab)	5
*Objects, assortment	19-3(DIS)	5	Spray bottle w/trigger, 16-oz	7-1(CP), 21-1(Lab)	5
Pan, aluminum, 12 × 11 × 2″	16-1(DIS), 22-3(DIS), 23-1(Lab)	10	*Staple remover	14-4(Lab)	5
Pan, aluminum, round, 9″	2-4(TT), 13-2(Lab)	5	*Stapler	12-2(TT), 13-2(TT), 14-4(Lab), 22-3(Lab)	5
*Penny	19-1(DIS)	5	Starfish shell, 4–6″	9-1(DIS)	5
*Perch, preserved	11-2(SA)	5	*Stereomicroscope	19-4(Lab)	5
Pony bead, red	4-2(Lab)	15	*Stopwatch	6-1(SA), 6-1(TT), 8-2(DIS), 9-4(Lab), 10-1(Lab), 12-3(Lab), 16-3(TT), 19-4(Lab)	5
Pony bead, white	4-2(Lab)	15			
Protractor	18-4(Lab)	1			
*Rock	14-2(DIS)	5	Straight pins, steel, pkg/100	7-1(Lab), 7-4(TT)	1
Rubber stopper, size 0, solid	3-4(DIS)	20	Styrofoam ball, 1″	18-2(TT)	5
Rubber stopper, size 4, solid	20-1(Lab)	5	Styrofoam ball, 2″	18-2(TT)	5
Ruler, 12″	2-3(Lab), 2-4(DIS), 6-1(DIS), 7-4(Lab), 8-2(Lab), 8-4(DIS), 8-4(Lab), 10-1(Lab), 11-2(Lab), 12-1(Lab), 12-2(DIS), 14-4(Lab), 15-3(DIS), 18-4(Lab), 21-2(DIS), 23-2(Lab)	5	Tape measure	17-1(DIS)	5
			Teasing needle	12-1(Lab)	5
			*Terrarium	13-1(DIS)	1
			Test tube rack, holds 6	3-4(DIS), 15-2(Lab), 17-3(Lab)	5
*Scissors	3-3(SA), 5-2(Lab), 6-1(Lab), 7-1(Lab), 9-2(DIS), 9-3(DIS), 10-3(Lab), 12-2(DIS), 12-3(Lab), 13-2(TT), 14-3(Lab), 14-4(Lab), 17-1(Lab), 20-1(Lab), 21-3(DIS), 22-3(Lab), 22-4(TT)	5	Test tube, 18 × 150-mm, pkg/20	3-4(DIS), 15-2(Lab), 17-1(TT), 17-3(Lab)	2
			Thermometer, 12″ alcohol	7-1(CP), 10-1(Lab), 12-3(Lab), 14-4(TT)	15
			*Timer	21-2(DIS)	5
Screen, fiberglass, 12 × 36″	13-2(Lab)	5	Toy, wind-up	2-1(DIS)	5
Shells, bag	9-1(DIS), 10-1(DIS)	1	*Tray	9-4(Lab)	5
Slide, animal cell mitosis	2-4(TT)	5	Tray, dissecting	14-3(Lab)	5
Slide, cork, section	2-3(SA)	5	*Tray, foam	22-3(DIS)	15
Slide, human blood smear	16-2(DIS)	5	Tree cross-section, 3.5–4.5″	23-2(Lab)	5
Slide, human ovary	20-2(DIS)	5	*Trowel	10-3(Lab), 21-1(CP)	5
Slide, human sperm smear	20-2(DIS)	5	*Umbrella	11-1(DIS)	5
Slide, mammal ovary	20-2(DIS)	5	*Watch or clock with second hand	16-1(Lab)	5
Slide, plant cell mitosis	2-4(TT), 3-5(Lab)	5			
Slide, rat sperm smear	20-2(DIS)	5	*Watering can	21-1(CP)	5
*Socks, ribbed	11-4(DIS), 12-4(DIS)	10	Wax, 500 g	19-4(Lab)	1
*Socks, wool, pair	11-4(DIS), 12-3(Lab), 12-4(DIS)	5			
Sponge, cellulose	9-3(DIS), 9-3(Lab), 13-2(Lab)	5			
Sponge, artificial	9-3(Lab)	1			

KEY: * = School Supplied; CP: Chapter Project; DIS: Discover; SA: Skills Activity; TT: Try This; Lab: Skills, Consumer, Design Your Own, or Technology

Quantities based on five groups of six students per class

Life Science

Program Resources

Student Edition
Student Express™ with Interactive Textbook
Teacher's Edition
All-in-One Teaching Resources
Color Transparencies
Guided Reading and Study Workbook
Laboratory Manual
Consumable and Nonconsumable Materials Kits
Computer Microscope Lab Manual
Inquiry Skills Activity Books
Progress Monitoring Assessments
Test Preparation Workbook
Test-Taking Tips With Transparencies
Teacher's ELL Handbook
Reading Strategies for Science Content

Program Technology Resources

TeacherExpress™ CD-ROM
Interactive Textbooks Online
PresentationExpress™ CD-ROM
Student Edition on Audio CD
ExamView® Computer Test Bank CD-ROM
Lab zone™ Easy Planner CD-ROM
Probeware Lab Manual With CD-ROM
Computer Microscope and Lab Manual
Materials Ordering CD-ROM
Discovery Channel School® Video and DVD Library
Lab Activity Video and DVD Library
Web Site at PHSchool.com

Spanish Resources for Modular Series

Spanish Student Edition
Spanish Guided Reading and Study Workbook
Spanish Teaching Guide With Tests

Acknowledgments appear on pages 872–874, which constitute an extension of this copyright page.

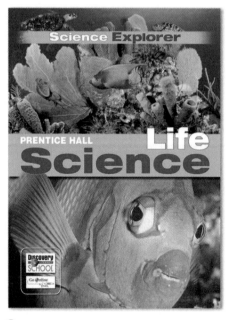

Cover
A rich variety of underwater life thrives among the reefs of the Cayman Islands (top). One striking reef resident is the queen angelfish (bottom), characterized by its brilliant blue and yellow coloring.

PEARSON
Prentice Hall

ISBN 0-13-201243-X

5 6 7 8 9 10   11 10 09 08 07

Program Authors

Michael J. Padilla, Ph.D.
Professor of Science Education
University of Georgia
Athens, Georgia

Michael Padilla is a leader in middle school science education. He has served as an author and elected officer for the National Science Teachers Association and as a writer of the National Science Education Standards. As lead author of Science Explorer, Mike has inspired the team in developing a program that meets the needs of middle grades students, promotes science inquiry, and is aligned with the National Science Education Standards.

Ioannis Miaoulis, Ph.D.
President
Museum of Science
Boston, Massachusetts

Originally trained as a mechanical engineer, Ioannis Miaoulis is in the forefront of the national movement to increase technological literacy. As dean of the Tufts University School of Engineering, Dr. Miaoulis spearheaded the introduction of engineering into the Massachusetts curriculum. Currently he is working with school systems across the country to engage students in engineering activities and to foster discussions on the impact of science and technology on society.

Martha Cyr, Ph.D.
Director of K–12 Outreach
Worcester Polytechnic Institute
Worcester, Massachusetts

Martha Cyr is a noted expert in engineering outreach. She has over nine years of experience with programs and activities that emphasize the use of engineering principles, through hands-on projects, to excite and motivate students and teachers of mathematics and science in grades K–12. Her goal is to stimulate a continued interest in science and mathematics through engineering.

Book Authors

Elizabeth Coolidge-Stolz, M.D.
Medical Writer
North Reading, Massachusetts

Donald Cronkite, Ph.D.
Professor of Biology
Hope College
Holland, Michigan

Jan Jenner, Ph.D.
Science Writer
Talladega, Alabama

Linda Cronin Jones, Ph.D.
Associate Professor of Science and
   Environmental Education
University of Florida
Gainesville, Florida

Marylin Lisowski, Ph.D
Professor of Science and
   Environmental Education
Eastern Illinois University
Charleston, Illinois

Contributing Writers

Douglas E. Bowman
Health/Physical Education Teacher
Welches Middle School
Welches, Oregon

Jorie Hunken
Science Consultant
Woodstock, Connecticut

Evan P. Silberstein
Science Instructor
The Frisch School
Paramus, New Jersey

Patricia M. Doran
Science Instructional Assistant
State University of New York at Ulster
Stone Ridge, New York

James Robert Kaczynski, Jr.
Science Instructor
Jamestown School
Jamestown, Rhode Island

Joseph Stukey, Ph.D.
Department of Biology
Hope College
Holland, Michigan

Fred Holtzclaw
Science Instructor
Oak Ridge High School
Oak Ridge, Tennessee

Andrew C. Kemp, Ph.D.
Assistant Professor of Education
University of Louisville
Louisville , Kentucky

Thomas R. Wellnitz
Science Instructor
The Paideia School
Atlanta, Georgia

Theresa K. Holtzclaw
Former Science Instructor
Clinton, Tennessee

Beth Miaoulis
Technology Writer
Sherborn, Massachusetts

Consultants

Reading Consultant

Nancy Romance, Ph.D.
Professor of Science
　Education
Florida Atlantic University
Fort Lauderdale, Florida

Mathematics Consultant

William Tate, Ph.D.
Professor of Education and
　Applied Statistics and
　Computation
Washington University
St. Louis, Missouri

Reviewers

Tufts University Content Reviewers

Faculty from Tufts University in Medford, Massachusetts, developed *Science Explorer* chapter projects and reviewed the student books.

Teacher Reviewers

Contents

Life Science

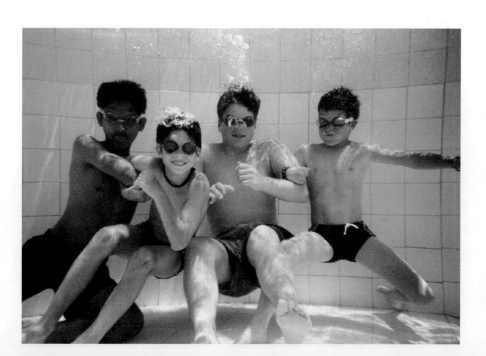

Unit 4   Ecology

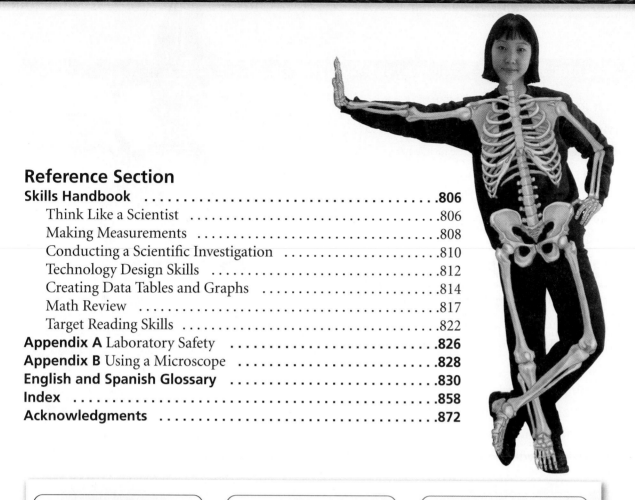

Reference Section

Enhance understanding through dynamic video.

Preview Get motivated with this introduction to the chapter content.

Field Trip Explore a real-world story related to the chapter content.

Assessment Review content and take an assessment.

Get connected to exciting Web resources in every lesson.

SCi*LINKS.* Find Web links on topics relating to every section.

Active Art Interact with selected visuals from every chapter online.

Planet Diary® Explore news and natural phenomena through weekly reports.

Science News® Keep up to date with the latest science discoveries.

Experience the complete text-book online and on CD-ROM.

Activities Practice skills and learn content.

Videos Explore content and learn important lab skills.

Audio Support Hear key terms spoken and defined.

Self-Assessment Use instant feedback to help you track your progress.

Activities

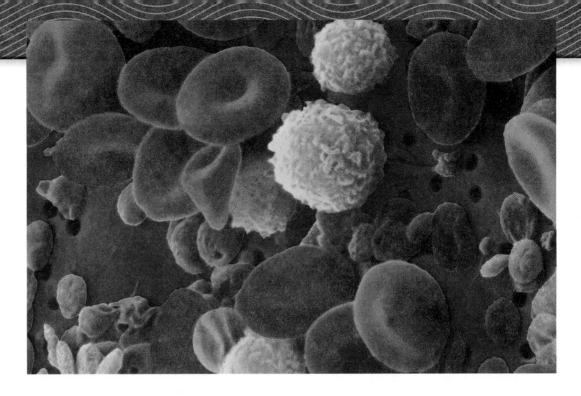

Lab zone Try This **Activity**　Reinforcement of key concepts

• Tech & Design • | Design, build, test, and communicate

active art — Illustrations come alive online

A Steely Athletic Trainer

Inquiry and Athletic Training

Ariko Iso works as an athletic trainer for the Pittsburgh Steelers, a National Football League (NFL) team . By reading about her work, students will gain insights about how science is important in everyday life. They will read about how Ariko applies her knowledge of the human body and its physiology to help athletes avoid or recover from injury. The skills that Ariko uses every day are the same inquiry skills that students need to become successful young scientists.

Build Background Knowledge

Knowledge about Muscles and Bones Have students recall what they know about the muscular and skeletal systems of the human body. Ask: **What is the function of the muscular system?** *(To produce body movements)* Explain that there are three types of muscle tissues—skeletal, smooth, and cardiac. **Which muscle tissues are used during physical activity?** *(Skeletal and cardiac)* **What is the function of the skeletal system?** *(To provide support and framework for the body, to provide a place for muscles to attach, to produce blood cells, to protect organs)*

Introduce the Career

Before students read the feature, have them think about why it is important to keep muscles and bones healthy. Ask: **What types of injuries can occur in the muscular and skeletal systems?** *(Bruises, tears, sprains, strains, breaks, dislocations)* **Why is it important to avoid injuring muscles, bones, and joints?** *(Some injuries can be serious and require surgery. Injuries may take a long time to heal. Even after healing, some injuries may lead to reduced performance.)* **How can injuries to muscles and bones during physical activity be avoided?** *(Wear proper equipment, stay well hydrated, warm-up and stretch properly, train properly)*

A Steely Athletic Trainer

"When I was young in Japan, I wanted to be a professional athlete," says National Football League athletic trainer Ariko Iso. "I was hoping to play sports forever." But all of that changed in one fateful moment on the basketball court. "I was playing junior high basketball, when I tore the anterior cruciate ligament (ACL) in my knee. I was 14."

Ariko gives fluids to a Pittsburgh Steeler at time out (above). A Steelers player hurdles an opponent (right).

"I was in the hospital for about seven weeks for recovery and rehabilitation. It was nearly a year before I played basketball again. I did play, but I was never the same as before. I was never as fast or as quick."

The experience changed Ariko's career plans. "I decided if I couldn't play sports, I would choose a profession where I could help athletes." Today, Ariko is the assistant athletic trainer for the Pittsburgh Steelers. Ariko is neither big nor tall, but she plays a vital role on the team. It's her job to help 200–300-pound athletes stay in the best condition possible. For Ariko, it's a dream job.

Background

Facts and Figures Certified athletic trainers have a minimum of a bachelor's degree. The degree may be in health, physical education, athletic training, or exercise science. Courses in human anatomy and physiology, exercise physiology, biomechanics, and nutrition are also part of the academic background of an athletic trainer. To become certified, an athletic trainer must pass an exam that includes both multiple choice and essay questions. An athletic trainer may help high school, college, or professional athletes train for their sport. An athletic trainer may also work in a sports medicine clinic, a hospital emergency room, a rehabilitation clinic, or a fitness center. The National Athletic Trainer's Association (NATA) is located in Dallas, Texas.

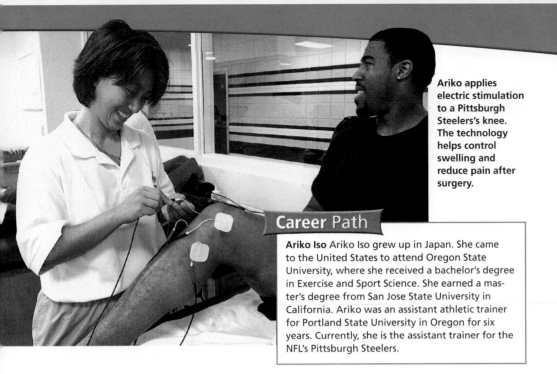

Ariko applies electric stimulation to a Pittsburgh Steelers's knee. The technology helps control swelling and reduce pain after surgery.

Talking With Ariko Iso

? What brought you to the United States?

Twenty years ago in Japan, athletic training was fairly new. There was no four-year college degree in athletic training. Furthermore, the techniques are from the West. I wanted to learn the science. Also, I had always wanted to go to a new country and learn a new language. My parents told me they would support my going overseas. So I ended up at Oregon State University.

? What science courses should a trainer take?

First, you have to learn about the human body. Anatomy and physiology are key courses to our education. In anatomy class, I learned all the bones and muscles in the body. I also learned the other parts of the body. But to an athletic trainer, the bone and muscle structures are the most important.

I studied physiology to learn how the different parts of the body function. Later, I studied kinesiology, or body movement. Kinesiology involves physics as well as anatomy and physiology.

? Why is kinesiology important?

When you throw a ball, for instance, you want to know the most efficient way to do it. That means you need to know the best angle of the shoulder and which muscles move the shoulder in a throwing motion. You also need to know and understand the internal rotation of the shoulder. It's helpful to analyze each joint, its motion, and the muscles that make a movement happen. Then you know which muscles to train in order to improve that motion.

◆ 1

Explore the Career

Choose from among the teaching strategies on these pages as you help your students explore the practical application of inquiry skills.

Use Models Use models to review the major muscles and bones of the human body. Ask: **Why is it important for an athletic trainer to study human anatomy and physiology?** *(The human body is complex and it is important to understand how the different body systems work together to allow peak athletic performances.)* **How could an injury to the knee affect an athlete's ability to perform?** *(An injury to the knee may result in an athlete's not being able to walk, run, jump, or change directions quickly—all essential movements in most sports.)*

Class Discussion Begin the discussion by telling students that before they use any kind of treatment for an injury, they should first consult a doctor. Then review with students the RICE treatment, the treatment used on muscle and joint injuries. Each letter represents a step in the treatment: Rest, Ice, Compression, and Elevation. Ask: **Why is it a good idea to rest an injured area of the body, such as a strained muscle?** *(Resting allows time for the body to heal.)* **What is the purpose of applying ice to an injury such as a sprain?** *(To help reduce pain and swelling)* **What is compression? How can this help an injury?** *(Compression involves applying light pressure, such as using an elastic wrap or bandage, to the injury. This can help reduce swelling.)* **How does elevating an injured area help an injury?** *(Elevating an injured area above the level of the heart helps reduce pain and swelling.)*

Discuss Ask: **Why do you think it is important to warm up before working out intensely?** *(Warming up gradually increases heart rate and increases blood flow to muscles, which prepares them for exercise. Warming up properly helps prevent injury to muscles.)* **What are some examples of things you can do to warm up before exercising?** *(Walking, jogging slowly, or stretching for 5-10 minutes)* **Why is it important to cool down after exercise?** *(Cooling down allows the heart rate and blood pressure to return to normal. It prevents blood from pooling in muscles.)*

Use Visuals Show students photos that capture athletes in motion. Have them use an anatomy book to identify which muscles, bones, and joints are involved in the motion.

Research Interested students may want to do an in depth description of a particular movement, such as throwing a ball. Students can identify the muscles, bones, and joints involved in the motion and identify how to perform the motion most efficiently. Students can make drawings or computer graphics to show the exact components of the motion in a slow-motion series.

Oral Presentation Invite the school's athletic trainer or a local athletic trainer to the classroom as a guest speaker. Have students write out questions to ask the speaker prior to the presentation. Encourage them to ask the speaker to describe a typical day's work.

? How did you get the job with the Steelers?

I started out at Portland State University in Oregon as the women's basketball assistant athletic trainer. Later, when I became the football athletic trainer, I attended an NFL football-injury conference. There I met the head athletic trainer for the Pittsburgh Steelers. He told me to apply to the Steelers' summer internship program for athletic trainers. I ended up working at the Steelers' training camp for two summers. Then in the spring of 2002, the Steelers called and asked if I would be interested in a full-time job.

? What do you do as an athletic trainer?

I do a little bit of everything. I will tape up ankles before a practice or a game. If someone needs help loosening up his muscles, I'll lend a hand. I make sure that the players drink plenty of fluids. If someone gets a small cut, I'll close it up. When someone is injured on the field, it's my job to evaluate the injury and to perform whatever emergency treatment is appropriate. I also need to be able to tell when to call for a doctor or other specialist.

Off the field, my duties include helping the athletes avoid injury. But if a player does get injured, I make sure that his rehabilitation goes as well as possible. An athlete recovering from an anterior cruciate ligament (ACL) injury, for instance, can take up to a year to be completely healthy. It's my job to monitor his progress and make sure he is doing everything he can to speed his recovery.

In the Steelers' training center, Ariko monitors the recovery of injured players.

A Steelers player exercises, using a machine. The computer graphs how much force he is using (above).

Recovering from shoulder surgery, this player exercises and stretches to build strength.

2 ◆

Background

Facts and Figures The knee is one of the largest and most complex joints in the human body. The knee joins together two bones, the end of the femur from the thigh and the top of the tibia from the shin. There are four main ligaments in the knee that hold these two bones together: the medial collateral ligament (MCL), the lateral collateral ligament (LCL), the anterior cruciate ligament (ACL), and the posterior cruciate ligament (PCL). All four of the ligaments help stabilize the knee and keep the joint from moving abnormally. If the ligaments are injured, the knee joint may "give out" unexpectedly during physical activity. In many cases, surgery is needed to fully repair the injured ligament. Basketball, football, soccer, and skiing are sports in which ACL injuries often occur.

What rehabilitation do you give for an ACL injury?

Tearing the anterior cruciate ligament is a big injury. If you sprain your ankle, there is usually no need to operate. But if you tear your anterior cruciate ligament in your knee, reconstruction is recommended. With my athletes, the focus during the first 24 to 48 hours after the surgery is on controlling the pain and swelling with compression and ice. As soon as the pain is bearable, the patient is expected to exercise to regain a range of motion in the knee. The player is walking with crutches within about three days and without crutches within two weeks.

The tissue needs a certain time to heal before beginning rehabilitation. I would probably start with really light weights as soon as the pain and swelling go down and then watch the knee carefully. You begin with no weight, work up to a five-pound weight, and increase the amount of weight from there.

What's the best part of your job?

I like working with athletes over a long time. I can tend to their aches and pains, monitor their training, and oversee their rehabilitation. It's a mentally challenging job, too. It demands a detailed knowledge of how the body works and how best to take care of it. I'd choose this job again!

This Steelers player is exercising with weights in the whirlpool.

Career Path Ariko says that it's important for an athletic trainer to know the science of bone and muscle structures. Think of one simple motion that you use in an activity, such as walking, running, or swimming. In a paragraph, describe the bones and muscles you use and what you'd like to learn about improving your motion.

Go Online
PHSchool.com
For: More on this career
Visit: PHSchool.com
Web Code: ceb-4000

◆ 3

Chapter at a Glance

Chapter at a Glance

 Chapter Project *Is It Really True?*

Technology

Local Standards

All in One Teaching Resources, Unit 1
- Chapter Project Teacher Notes, pp. 40–41
- Chapter Project Student Overview, pp. 42–43
- Chapter Project Student Worksheets, pp. 44–45
- Chapter Project Scoring Rubric, p. 46

Video Preview

Section 1 — What Is Science?
1 period
1/2 block

1.1.1 Identify skills scientists use to learn about the world.

Go Online
PHSchool.com

Section 2 — Scientific Inquiry
1 period
1/2 block

1.2.1 Explain what scientific inquiry involves.

1.2.2 Describe how to develop a hypothesis and design an experiment.

1.2.3 Describe the attitudes, or habits of mind, that are important in science.

Video Field Trip

Go Online
active art

Section 3 — Understanding Technology
1 period
1/2 block

1.3.1 Describe the goal of technology.

1.3.2 Explain how technology differs from science.

1.3.3 Explain how technology affects people in both positive and negative ways.

Go Online
SCiLINKS™
NSTA

Section 4 — Safety in the Science Laboratory
1 period
1/2 block

1.4.1 Explain why preparation is important when carrying out scientific investigations in the lab and in the field.

1.4.2 Describe what you should do if an accident occurs.

Go Online
SCiLINKS™
NSTA

Review and Assessment

All in One Teaching Resources, Unit 1
- Key Terms Review, p. 79
- Transparency LS8
- Performance Assessment Teacher Notes, p. 85
- Performance Assessment Scoring Rubric, p. 86
- Performance Assessment Student Worksheet, p. 87
- Chapter Test, pp. 88–91

Video Assessment

Go Online
PHSchool.com

Test Preparation

Test Preparation Blackline Masters

Chapter Activities Planner

For more activities
LAB ZONE
Easy Planner
CD-ROM

Student Edition	Inquiry	Time	Materials	Skills	Resources
Chapter Project, p. 5	Open-ended	Ongoing (2 weeks)	**All in One Teaching Resources, Unit 1,** p. 40	Developing hypotheses, designing experiments, interpreting data, drawing conclusions, communicating	**Lab zone Easy Planner** **All in One Teaching Resources, Unit 1,** Support, pp. 40–41
Section 1					
Discover Activity, p. 6	Open-ended	10 minutes		Observing	**Lab zone Easy Planner**
At-Home Activity, p. 13	Open-ended	Home		Classifying	**Lab zone Easy Planner**
Section 2					
Discover Activity, p. 14	Open-ended	10 minutes	Mealworms, small trays, magnifying glass	Posing questions	**Lab zone Easy Planner**
Skills Activity, p. 16	Directed	10 minutes		Controlling variables	**Lab zone Easy Planner**
Section 3					
Discover Activity, p. 19	Guided	10 minutes		Forming operational definitions	**Lab zone Easy Planner**
Skills Activity, p. 20	Directed	10 minutes		Predicting	**Lab zone Easy Planner**
Section 4					
Discover Activity, p. 23	Open-ended	15 minutes		Predicting	**Lab zone Easy Planner**
Design Your Own Lab, p. 27	Guided	Prep: 20 minutes; Class: 40 minutes (over 5 days)	Plastic cups, cut flowers, spoon, sugar, water	Developing hypotheses, designing experiments, drawing conclusions	**Lab zone Easy Planner Lab Activity Video** **All in One Teaching Resources, Unit 1,** Design Your Own Lab: *Keeping Flowers Fresh,* pp. 76–78

Section 1 What Is Science?

 1 period, 1/2 block

Objective

1.1.1 Identify skills scientists use to learn about the world.

Local Standards

Key Terms

• science • observing • quantitative observation • qualitative observation
• inferring • predicting • classifying • making models • life science

---

Preteach

Build Background Knowledge

Students describe their experiences in science from previous years that involved observing.

 **Discover Activity** *How Keen Are Your Senses?* **L1**

Targeted Print and Technology Resources

 Teaching Resources, Unit 1

L2 Reading Strategy Transparency
LS1: Asking Questions

PresentationEXPRESS™ CD-ROM

Instruct

Observing Have students make quantitative and qualitative observations of the classroom.

Inferring Ask leading questions for a discussion on making inferences from observations.

Predicting Use the definition of *predicting* to help students understand how predictions are made.

Classifying Teach students about classifying by focusing on Jane Goodall's work with chimps.

Making Models Have groups make a list of models that would be useful in studying chimps.

Working in Life Science Use the scientists shown in the figure to discuss careers in life science and the skills involved.

Targeted Print and Technology Resources

 Teaching Resources, Unit 1

L2 Guided Reading, pp. 49–52

PHSchool.com Web Code: cgd-6011

Student Edition on Audio CD

Assess

Section Assessment Questions

Have students use their completed Asking Questions graphic organizers to answer the questions.

Reteach

Students distinguish between observations and inferences using real-life situations.

Targeted Print and Technology Resources

 Teaching Resources, Unit 1

• Section Summary, p. 48
L1 Review and Reinforce, p. 53
L3 Enrich, p. 54

Section 2 Scientific Inquiry

1 period, 1/2 block

ABILITY LEVELS

L1 Basic to Average
L2 For All Students
L3 Average to Advanced

Objectives

1.2.1 Explain what scientific inquiry involves.
1.2.2 Describe how to develop a hypothesis and design an experiment.
1.2.3 Describe the attitudes, or habits of mind, that are important in science.

Local Standards

Key Terms

• scientific inquiry • hypothesis • variable • controlled experiment
• manipulated variable • responding variable • operational definition
• data • communicating

Preteach

Build Background Knowledge

Students relate the steps they can use in explaining an everyday problem.

 *What Can You Learn About Mealworms?*

Targeted Print and Technology Resources

 **Teaching Resources, Unit 1**

L2 Reading Strategy: Building Vocabulary

PresentationEXPRESS™ CD-ROM

Instruct

The Scientific Process Have students assess questions about how they might lead to scientific inquiry.

Scientific Attitudes Ask leading questions for a discussion on scientists' habits of mind.

Targeted Print and Technology Resources

 **Teaching Resources, Unit 1**

L2 Guided Reading, pp. 57–60
L2 Transparency LS2

DISCOVERY CHANNEL SCHOOL
Video Field Trip

PHSchool.com Web Code: cgp-6012

Student Edition on Audio CD

Assess

Section Assessment Questions

Have students use their completed definitions of each key term to answer the questions.

Reteach

Use a figure to describe the process of scientific inquiry.

Targeted Print and Technology Resources

 **Teaching Resources, Unit 1**

• Section Summary, p. 56
L1 Review and Reinforce, p. 61
L3 Enrich, p. 62

Section 3 **Understanding Technology**

ABILITY LEVELS
L1 Basic to Average
L2 For All Students
L3 Average to Advanced

🕐 *1 period, 1/2 block*

Objectives

1.3.1 Describe the goal of technology.

1.3.2 Explain how technology differs from science.

1.3.3 Explain how technology affects people in both positive and negative ways.

Key Terms

• technology • engineer

Local Standards

Preteach

Build Background Knowledge

Students classify objects according to whether they are examples of technology or not.

 **Discover Activity** *What Are Some Examples of Technology?* L2

Targeted Print and Technology Resources

All in One Teaching Resources, Unit 1

L2 Reading Strategy Transparency
LS3: Previewing Visuals

⊙ **PresentationEXPRESS™ CD-ROM**

Instruct

What Is Technology? Use the definition of *technology* to help students understand what technology is.

Comparing Technology and Science Use examples shown in Figure 12 to clarify how technology relates to science.

Targeted Print and Technology Resources

All in One Teaching Resources, Unit 1

L2 Guided Reading, pp. 65–66
L2 Transparency LS4
www.SciLinks.org Web Code: scn-1631

⊙ **Student Edition on Audio CD**

Assess

Section Assessment Questions

Have students use their completed Previewing Visuals graphic organizers to answer the questions.

Reteach

Use an example to review what technology is.

Targeted Print and Technology Resources

All in One Teaching Resources, Unit 1

• Section Summary, p. 64
L1 Review and Reinforce, p. 67
L3 Enrich, p. 68

Section 4 Safety in the Science Laboratory

 1 period, 1/2 block

ABILITY LEVELS
L1 Basic to Average
L2 For All Students
L3 Average to Advanced

Objectives

1.4.1 Explain why preparation is important when carrying out scientific investigations in the lab and in the field.

1.4.2 Describe what you should do if an accident occurs.

Local Standards

Build Background Knowledge

Students analyze the safety issues involved in fictional scenarios.

 *Where Is the Safety Equipment in Your School?* L1

Targeted Print and Technology Resources

All in One Teaching Resources, Unit 1

L2 Reading Strategy Transparency
LS5: Outlining

 PresentationEXPESS™ CD-ROM

Safety During Investigations Lead a discussion of how to stay safe in a laboratory.

In Case of an Accident Ask students what they would do if an accident happened in the lab.

 Keeping Flowers Fresh L2

Targeted Print and Technology Resources

All in One Teaching Resources, Unit 1

L2 Guided Reading, pp. 71–73
L2 Transparencies LS6, LS7
L2 Design Your Own Lab: *Keeping Flowers Fresh*, pp. 76–78

Lab Activity Video/DVD
Design Your Own Lab: *Keeping Flowers Fresh*

www.SciLinks.org Web Code: scn-1624

 Student Edition on Audio CD

Assess

Section Assessment Questions

Have students use their outlines to answer the questions.

Reteach

Use a flowchart to show students what they should do before, during, and after a lab.

Targeted Print and Technology Resources

All in One Teaching Resources, Unit 1

• Section Summary, p. 70
L1 Review and Reinforce, p. 74
L3 Enrich, p. 75

Chapter 1 **Content Refresher**

Go Online

NSTA-PD_LINKS_

For: Professional Development Support
Visit: www.SciLinks.org/PDLinks
Web Code: scf-1610

Professional Development

Section 1 **What Is Science?**

Scientific Skills A good example of a scientist with the proper skills is Jane Goodall (1934–). She grew up in England and was working as a secretary in Kenya when she was recruited to do research on chimpanzees by famed physical anthropologist Louis Leakey. Goodall began her observations on the shore of Lake Tanganyika in Tanzania in 1960. Among her many important discoveries about these primates was that chimpanzees strip leaves off twigs to make a tool for finding termites in nests. Until this discovery, scientists thought only humans made tools. She also observed that chimps eat meat, disproving the widely accepted notion that they were herbivores. In 1977, she established the Jane Goodall Institute for Wildlife Research, Education, and Conservation. Goodall's field of biology is called ethology, which is the comparative study of animal behavior in the natural environment.

 **Address Misconceptions**

Students may think that if one event follows another, they can always infer that the second event was caused by the first. For a strategy for overcoming this misconception, see **Address Misconceptions** in the section *What Is Science?*

Branches of Life Science There are many areas of study within life science, or biology. Some emphasize the types of organisms being studied. For example, botanists study plants, zoologists study animals, and microbiologists study bacteria and other microorganisms. Parasitologists study organisms that live on or in—and harm—other organisms. Other areas within biology emphasize processes, such as embryological development, chemical reactions within organisms, and animal behavior. Some biologists study life at different levels of organization, such as cells, tissues, populations, communities, and ecosystems.

Section 2 **Scientific Inquiry**

A Process of Inquiry Some textbooks present the process of scientific inquiry in terms of a straight-line "scientific method" instead of the multipath process of scientific inquiry outlined in the section. Versions of the scientific method vary, but in its simplest form it includes the steps shown below.

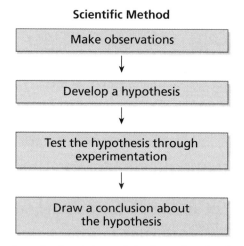

Scientific Method

Make observations

↓

Develop a hypothesis

↓

Test the hypothesis through experimentation

↓

Draw a conclusion about the hypothesis

This general method originated during what has been called the Scientific Revolution in Europe, which occurred during the Renaissance period. Yet, doing science doesn't necessarily involve rigidly following a set method. The actual process of science is less structured than a strict "method" implies. Therefore, this textbook presents a process of scientific inquiry that incorporates the traditional scientific method but has no set path.

Central to this inquiry process—and a common theme in any explanation of how science proceeds—is the idea of using deductive reasoning to test hypotheses. Deduction is reasoning from the general to the specific. A hypothesis is often a general statement. From that hypothesis, a scientist predicts that specific events or data will result under certain conditions. The scientist then sets up an experiment to test whether the predicted results will occur. In practice, a hypothesis is rarely confirmed with just one experiment. The experiment must be duplicated over and over. And the results of those experiments suggest other paths to follow in testing that hypothesis or related hypotheses. When a wide range of hypotheses are confirmed, an overarching scientific theory may be developed that explains a phenomenon. Scientists can also consolidate observations into scientific laws, or predictions of what is expected to happen every time under a certain set of conditions.

Section 3 Understanding Technology

Prosthetic Limbs Herodotus, the famous Greek historian, wrote the first known description of an artificial limb (a wooden foot) in 484 B.C. The first artificial leg to include a knee joint was designed in the 1500s. Today's artificial limbs, or prostheses, offer a range of available options. People today can use different prostheses for varying functions such as everyday use versus recreational or competitive sports. The ability to make better prostheses has come as a result of advances in science and engineering. For example, advances in physics and physiology have increased scientific understanding of the normal functioning of limbs. Materials science has developed better composites and other substances for use in prosthetic design and manufacture.

Recent developments have created prosthetic legs that allow users to be more active than ever before. Most current prostheses have an adjustable socket so that the stump of the leg can fit securely and comfortably into the prosthesis. This makes it much easier for the wearer to walk normally. Advances in understanding of the mechanics of normal gait have led to technical improvements in materials for artificial feet so that they can bend in the same rolling action during walking as the biological foot does. The foot for each wearer can be customized in materials as well as size and form so that it has an elasticity that matches the remaining natural foot. Athletes can have prostheses customized for their sport, and there are many amputee athletes. In 2004, Marlon Shirley, who wears a metal spring leg prosthesis, became the first athlete with a disability to run the 100-meter dash in less than 11.0 seconds.

Section 4 Safety in the Science Laboratory

Safety First Following safety precautions in the science laboratory cannot be overemphasized. Review all safety guidelines from your state and district. In addition to having students follow the safety cautions in their texts, the teacher can take some actions that might further ensure safety. For instance, it is a good idea to lock the laboratory or the lab storeroom when you are not present. This will prevent the enterprising student from continuing an investigation when you are not there to supervise. Also consider having drills on what students should do if a substance catches fire or if there is an accidental chemical exposure or spill. You may want to post the phone numbers of the local poison control center in your laboratory.

Help Students Read

Relating Text and Figures
Using Graphic Elements to Clarify and Extend

Strategy Help students relate figures to text in order to clarify difficult concepts in the text or to understand information beyond that stated in the text. This strategy enables students to focus on their own thought processes as they actively make use of photos and illustrations as tools to support comprehension. Before students begin, choose a subsection, such as *The Scientific Process*.

Example
1. Have students keep their books closed as you read a few paragraphs aloud, including text that refers to a figure. You may want to think aloud as you read, saying, for example, "I wonder what that would be like."
2. Then have the students open their books to the passage that you have read. Tell them to reread it and then study the figure and its caption carefully. Ask what parts of the passage make more sense when students look at the figure.
3. Point out that visuals also sometimes communicate information that is not in the text. Have students identify any new information that can be learned from the figure.
4. Have students work in pairs to discuss how a figure provides additional information or helps them understand a passage.

Interactive Textbook

- Complete student edition
- Video and audio
- Simulations and activities
- Section and chapter activities

Interactive Textbook

This food scientist is busy ▶ at work in a laboratory.

4 ◆

Chapter Project L3

Objectives

Students will design and conduct a scientific experiment to test whether a common belief is true or false. After completing this Chapter Project, students will be able to

- develop a hypothesis about whether a common belief is true or false
- design a controlled experiment that will test the hypothesis
- interpret the data from the experiment and draw a conclusion about the hypothesis
- communicate results to the class

Skills Focus

Developing hypotheses, designing experiments, interpreting data, drawing conclusions, communicating

Project Time Line 2 weeks

All in One Teaching Resources, Unit 1

- Chapter Project Teacher Notes
- Chapter Project Overview
- Chapter Project Worksheet 1
- Chapter Project Worksheet 2
- Chapter Textbook Scoring Rubric

4

Developing a Plan

Students should first brainstorm a list of common beliefs, starting with those described in their text. Others include: the measure of a person's left fingertip to the right fingertip equals that person's height, and an apple a day keeps the doctor away. Then, each student should decide which common belief to investigate. All students should follow the process of scientific inquiry described chnder the section, *Scientific Inquiry*. Have students preview Figure 9 to get an idea about how they should proceed in this project.

Possible Materials

Materials may vary greatly from student to student, depending on the common belief each investigates. For example, to investigate the belief that yawning is contagious, students may not require any materials. An experiment to investigate that belief may focus on observing several groups of students. In contrast, to investigate the idea that fresh eggs sink in water, but older eggs float, students would need several fresh eggs, several stale eggs, and a container of water. As students present their procedures to you,

LabZone™ Chapter **Project**

Is It Really True?

Does fertilizer make plants grow taller? Is yawning contagious? Do fresh eggs sink in water, but older eggs float? Does moss always grow on the north side of trees? Each of these questions relates to a common belief about living things. But are those beliefs true? In this chapter project, you will use scientific methods to find out.

Your Goal To design and conduct a scientific experiment to test whether a common belief about living things is true or false

To complete this project, you must

● select one specific question to investigate
● determine the procedure you will follow to investigate your question
● collect data and use it to draw conclusions
● follow the safety guidelines in Appendix A

Plan It! Make a list of some common beliefs you could explore. Then preview the chapter to learn what types of questions can be explored by scientific methods. When you select a question, write the procedure you will follow. After your teacher approves your plan, begin your experiment.

Chapter 1 ◆ 5

Video Preview

What Is Science?

Show the Video Preview to introduce the Chapter Project and overview the chapter content. Discussion question: **How did the scientists follow the steps of observing, inferring, and modeling in their study of the Iceman?** *(They observed an arrowhead lodged in his back and inferred that he was murdered. They observed his remains and inferred that he was a shepherd and was perhaps killed for his sheep. To test their hypothesis, they re-created a model of his clothes and tough life as an alpine shepherd. Their observations of this model disproved their hypothesis.)*

Performance Assessment

The Chapter Project Scoring Rubric will help you evaluate how well students complete the Chapter Project. You may want to share the scoring rubric with your students so they are clear about what will be expected of them. Students will be assessed on

● how well they develop a hypothesis that can be tested
● how well they plan a procedure for a controlled experiment to test the hypothesis
● how well they carry out the procedure and collect the data that result
● how well they communicate their conclusion to the class
   Students can keep their hypotheses, test data, and conclusions in their portfolios.

Portfolio

discuss what materials are needed to carry out the planned experiment and decide with students how those materials can be obtained.

Possible Shortcuts

● You can make this project shorter by dividing the class into groups rather than having individual students do investigations. All groups could focus on the same common belief.
● You could have groups choose a common belief, develop a hypothesis, and plan a procedure. Then, you could choose one procedure to carry out as a demonstration.

Launching the Project

To introduce the project, lead a discussion about common beliefs concerning people and everyday objects that students have heard expressed among family or peers. Then, explain that they will be investigating whether one of those common beliefs is true using the process of scientific inquiry that they will learn about in this chapter.

Objective

After this lesson, students will be able to
1.1.1 Identify skills scientists use to learn about the world.

Target Reading Skill

Asking Questions Explain that changing a head into a question helps students anticipate the ideas, facts, and events they are about to read.

Answers

Sample questions and answers: **What does observing involve?** (*Observing involves using one or more of your senses to gather information.*) **What is inferring?** (*Inferring means to explain or interpret the things you observe.*) **What does predicting mean?** (*Predicting means making a forecast of what will happen in the future based on past experience or evidence.*) **What does making models involve?** (*Making models involves creating representations of complex objects or processes.*) **What is classifying?** (*Classifying is the process of grouping together items that are alike in some way.*) **What do scientific attitudes include?** (*Scientific attitudes include curiosity, honesty, open-mindedness, skepticism, and creativity.*)

All in One **Teaching Resources, Unit 1**
• Transparency LS1

Preteach

Build Background Knowledge   L2

Experience With Scientific Thinking

Encourage students to describe experiences in science from previous years that involved observing and then making an inference or a prediction from the observations. Then, ask students to draw from those experiences to describe the attitudes that a person should possess when observing or making inferences or predictions.

Reading Preview

Key Concepts
• What skills do scientists use to learn about the world?

Key Terms
• science • observing
• quantitative observation
• qualitative observation
• inferring • predicting
• classifying • making models
• life science

Target Reading Skill

Asking Questions Before you read, preview the red headings. In a graphic organizer like the one below, ask a *what, how,* or *why* question for each heading. As you read, write answers to your questions.

Thinking Like a Scientist

Question	Answer
What does observing involve?	Observing involves . . .

For: More on scientific thinking
Visit: PHSchool.com
Web Code: cgd-6011

6 ◆

Lab zone Discover **Activity**

How Keen Are Your Senses?

1. Your teacher has arranged for an unexpected event to occur. At the count of three, the event will begin.
2. List as many details as you can remember about the event.
3. Compare your list with those of your classmates.

Think It Over
Observing How many details could you list? Which of your senses did you use to gather information?

Once, as I walked through thick forest in a downpour, I suddenly saw a chimp hunched in front of me. Quickly I stopped. Then I heard a sound from above. I looked up and there was a big chimp there, too. When he saw me he gave a loud, clear wailing wraaaaah—a spine-chilling call that is used to threaten a dangerous animal. To my right I saw a large black hand shaking a branch and bright eyes glaring threateningly through the foliage. Then came another savage wraaaah from behind. Up above, the big male began to sway the vegetation. I was surrounded.

These words are from the writings of Jane Goodall, a scientist who studies wild chimpanzees in Gombe National Park in Tanzania, Africa. What would you have done if you were in Jane's shoes? Would you have screamed or tried to run away? Jane did neither of these things. Instead, she crouched down and stayed still so she wouldn't startle the chimps. Not feeling threatened by her, the chimps eventually moved on.

Jane Goodall was determined to learn all she could about chimps. Her studies are an example of science in action. **Science** is a way of learning about the natural world. Science also includes all of the knowledge gained by exploring the natural world. **Scientists use skills such as observing, inferring, predicting, classifying, and making models to learn more about the world.** However, these skills are not unique to scientists. You, too, think like a scientist every day.

Lab zone Discover **Activity**

Skills Focus Observing

Time 10 minutes

Tips Have a school staff member run into and out of the classroom wearing some distinct outfit, ringing a bell, and carrying something that smells strongly, such as a piece of pizza. Advise this person not to do anything that would frighten or disturb students.

L1 **Expected Outcome** Most students will recall in general what occurred, but the details listed among students will vary widely.

Think It Over Some students may list two or three details, while others may list many more. Students may report that they used sight, hearing, and smell in gathering information.

Observing

Jane Goodall has spent countless hours among the chimpanzees—quietly following them, taking notes, and carefully observing. **Observing** means using one or more of your senses to gather information. Your senses include sight, hearing, touch, taste, and smell. By using her senses, Jane learned what chimpanzees eat, what sounds they make, and even what games they play! During her time in Gombe, Jane made many surprising observations. For example, she observed how chimpanzees use stems or long blades of grass as tools to "fish" out a tasty meal from termite mounds.

Like Jane, you use your senses to gather information. Look around you. What do you see? What do you hear and smell? You depend on your observations to help you make decisions throughout the day. For example, if it feels chilly when you wake up, you'll probably dress warmly.

Observations can be either quantitative or qualitative. **Quantitative observations** deal with a number, or amount. Seeing that you have eight new e-mails in your inbox is a quantitative observation. **Qualitative observations,** on the other hand, deal with descriptions that cannot be expressed in numbers. Noticing that a bike is blue or that a grape tastes sour are qualitative observations.

 Reading Checkpoint What senses can the skill of observation involve?

FIGURE 1 Observing
By patiently observing chimpanzees, Jane Goodall learned many things about chimpanzee behavior. The smaller photo shows one of Jane's earliest discoveries—that chimps use sticks as tools to fish for termites.

Chapter 1 ◆ 7

7

Inferring

Teach Key Concepts L2

Interpreting Observations

Focus Tell students that making observations begins the process of learning about the world. A next step may be to explain or interpret one observation or several observations taken together.

Teach Ask: **What observations did Jane Goodall make concerning chimpanzees and tree hollows?** *(She observed a chimp chew leaves, push them in a tree hollow, and then put them back into its mouth. She also observed the gleam of water on the leaves when they were pulled out of the tree hollow.)* **What inference did she make from her observations?** *(She inferred that the chimp was using the leaves like a sponge to soak up water in the tree hollow.)* Emphasize that Goodall's inference was based on reasoning and was not simply a wild guess.

Apply Give students this fictional scenario: A student is missing from his usual bus to school, and when he arrives he looks tired. Then ask students what they might infer from these observations. *(Given these observations as well as past experience, students may infer that the student overslept.)* **learning modality: logical/mathematical**

🚩 Address Misconceptions L1

Testing Inferences for Correctness

Focus Encourage students to explain what they can infer when one event follows another.

Teach Students may think that if one event follows another, the second event was caused by the first. Ask: **What are some pairs of events that may occur together?** *(A hungry person feels full after eating. A soccer team won when the fans wore their lucky jackets.)* Point out that just because one event follows another, the first event does not necessarily cause the second. Eating causes the feeling of fullness, but the wearing of lucky jackets does not cause athletic teams to win. People may infer that one event causes another, but in science, such inferences must be tested before they are accepted as correct. The tests often involve experiments.

Apply Point out that many people take vitamin C whenever they get a cold. Because they've quickly recovered from a cold when taking vitamin C in the past, they infer that the vitamin "cures" colds. Ask: **What is the observation?** *(The person quickly recovered from a cold after taking vitamin C.)* **What is the inference?** *(Vitamin C cured the cold.)* **How could you prove that taking vitamin C cures colds?** *(Carry out experiments testing whether people who took vitamin C recovered from colds faster than those who didn't.)* **learning modality: logical/mathematical**

Inferring

One day, Jane Goodall saw something peculiar. She watched as a chimpanzee peered into a hollow in a tree. The chimp picked off a handful of leaves from the tree and chewed on them. Then it took the leaves out of its mouth and pushed them into the tree hollow. When the chimp pulled the leaves back out, Jane saw the gleam of water. The chimp then put the wet leaves back in its mouth.

What was the chimpanzee doing? Jane reasoned that the chimpanzee might be using the chewed leaves like a sponge to soak up water. Seeing the chimp chew on leaves, put them in the hollow, and then squeeze the liquid out is an example of an observation. But Jane went beyond simply observing when she reasoned why the chimpanzee was doing these things. When you explain or interpret the things you observe, you are **inferring,** or making an inference.

Making an inference doesn't mean guessing wildly. Inferences are based on reasoning from what you already know. Jane knew that chimpanzees, like all other animals, need water, and that rainwater collects in tree hollows. She reasoned that the chimp was using chewed leaves to get the water out of the tree.

You, too, make inferences all the time. Because your brain processes observations and other information so quickly, you may not even realize when you have made an inference. For example, if you see your friend smile after getting back an exam, you might automatically infer that she got a good grade. Inferences are not always correct, however. Your friend's smile might not have anything to do with the test.

✅ **Reading Checkpoint** What is inferring?

FIGURE 2 Inferring
When you explain or interpret your observations, you are making an inference. **Inferring** *List three inferences you can make about this chimp.*

Predicting

Sometimes, Jane could even predict what a chimp was going to do next. **Predicting** means making a forecast of what will happen in the future based on past experience or evidence.

Through her observations, Jane learned that when a chimpanzee is frightened or angry, its hairs stand on end. This response is sometimes followed by threatening gestures such as charging, throwing rocks, and shaking trees, or even an attack. Therefore, if Jane sees a chimp with its hairs on end, she can predict that the chimp might attack her in a short time. She then leaves the area.

Likewise, you would probably move away if you saw a dog growling or baring its teeth. Why? Because predicting is part of your everyday thinking. You might predict, for example, that your basketball team will win tonight's game if you have always beaten the other team in the past. Predictions, of course, are not always correct. New players this year may increase the other team's chances of winning.

Predictions and inferences are closely related. An inference is typically an attempt to explain what is happening or *has* happened. A prediction is a forecast of what *will* happen. If you see a broken egg on the floor by a table, you might infer that the egg had rolled off the table. If, however, you see an egg rolling toward the edge of a table, you can predict that it's about to create a mess.

FIGURE 3
Predicting
Predictions are forecasts of what will happen next. Like many animals, chimps bare their teeth when they are frightened or angry. **Predicting** *What do you think the chimp will do next?*

 Reading Checkpoint What are predictions based on?

Math ▶ Analyzing Data

Chimp Food

This graph shows the diet of chimps at Gombe National Park during May of one year.

1. **Reading Graphs** According to the graph, what foods do chimps eat?
2. **Interpreting Data** Did chimps feed more on seeds or leaves during this month?
3. **Calculating** What percentage of the diet did blossoms, seeds, leaves, and fruit make up?
4. **Predicting** Suppose you learn that November is the main termite-fishing season, when chimps spend a large part of their time eating termites. Predict how the chimp diet might change in November.

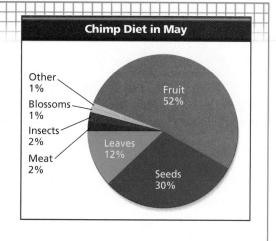

Chimp Diet in May

- Other 1%
- Blossoms 1%
- Insects 2%
- Meat 2%
- Leaves 12%
- Seeds 30%
- Fruit 52%

Classifying

Teach Key Concepts `L2`
Grouping Items

Focus Tell students that one way scientists organize their observations is by classifying.

Teach Ask: **Jane grouped together information about Jomeo's feeding habits. What kind of information would she have classified in that grouping?** *(What foods Jomeo ate and the proportions of each type of food, when Jomeo fed, whether Jomeo ate with other chimps or ate alone, and so on)* **How would this sort of classifying aid her in understanding chimpanzees?** *(By classifying behaviors, Jane could better compare her observations of various chimps. She could also compare her observations of chimps with those of other scientists. She might also better see patterns and trends.)*

Apply Explain the basic difference between evergreen and deciduous plants. Then students can make a survey of all the plants on the school grounds, classifying each plant into one or the other category. **learning modality: visual**

Lab zone Build **Inquiry** `L2`

Classifying Objects

Materials various small objects of different sizes, shapes, and colors

Time 15 minutes

Focus Tell students that scientists often collect a great variety of observations in doing an investigation and classifying what they have observed may be difficult.

Teach Place the objects on a table in the classroom. Challenge students to observe the objects and devise a classification system that might be useful.

Apply After all students have completed their classifications, have students present their systems to the class. Ask: **What is the value of classifying things?** *(Sample answer: Classifying objects helps in understanding the various kinds of objects in a place and the proportions of each kind.)* **learning modality: verbal**

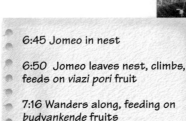

FIGURE 4 Classifying
Field notes like these contain many details about a chimp's daily activities. By grouping together all the information related to resting, climbing, or feeding, Jane can better understand the chimp's behavior.

6:45 Jomeo in nest

6:50 Jomeo leaves nest, climbs, feeds on viazi pori fruit

7:16 Wanders along, feeding on budyankende fruits

8:08 Stops feeding, climbs, and feeds on viazi pori fruit again

8:35 Travels

Resting

Classifying

What do chimps do all day? To find out, Jane and her assistants followed the chimpanzees through the forest. They took detailed field notes about the chimps' behaviors. Figure 4 shows a short section of notes about Jomeo, an adult male chimp.

Suppose Jane wanted to know how much time Jomeo spent feeding or resting that morning. She could find out by classifying Jomeo's actions into several categories. **Classifying** is the process of grouping together items that are alike in some way. For example, Jane could group together all the information about Jomeo's feeding habits or his resting behavior. This would also make it easier to compare Jomeo's actions to those of other chimps. For instance, she could determine if other adult males feed or rest as much as Jomeo does.

You, too, classify objects and information all the time. Classifying things helps you to stay organized so you can easily find and use them later. When you put papers in a notebook, you might classify them by subject or date. And, you might have one drawer in your dresser for shirts and another for socks.

 Reading Checkpoint How is classifying objects useful?

Differentiated Instruction

English Learners/Beginning `L1`
Vocabulary: Science Glossary
Pronounce and define aloud Key Terms for students. Suggest that they start a personal glossary of Key Terms for this and subsequent chapters. They might write each term and its definition in English on one side of an index card and in the student's primary language on the other side. **learning modality: verbal**

English Learners/Intermediate `L2`
Vocabulary: Science Glossary Students can expand on the Beginning activity by adding important terms encountered in the text other than the Key Terms. In this section, they might add *curiosity, support, disprove,* and *scientific journal.* Have students write sentences that use each of these words. **learning modality: verbal**

Climbing

Feeding

Making Models

How far do chimpanzees travel? Where do they go? Sometimes, Jane's research team would follow a particular chimpanzee for many days at a time. Figure 5 illustrates Jomeo's journey through the forest over the course of one day. The diagram is one example of a model. **Making models** involves creating representations of complex objects or processes. Models help people study and understand things that are complex or that can't be observed directly. Using a model like the one in Figure 5, Jane and her assistants could share information that would otherwise be difficult to explain.

Models are all around you. They include physical objects, such as globes or the sets used in filming your favorite TV show. Some models are generated by computer, like the ones some architects use to design new buildings. It's important to keep in mind that models are only representations of the real object or process. Because some information may be missing from a model, you may not be able to understand everything about the object or process the model represents.

 What is a model?

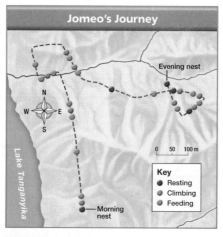

FIGURE 5
Making Models
This map is a model that traces Jomeo's journey through the forest. It represents information that would be hard to explain in words. **Interpreting Maps** *What is the total distance that Jomeo traveled between his morning and evening nests?*

Making Models

Teach Key Concepts   L2
Creating Representations

Focus Tell students that scientists often create models to study natural objects, events, and processes.

Teach Ask: **What is a model?** (*A representation of a complex object or process*) **How does using a model help scientists communicate information?** (*Using a model can communicate information among scientists that would otherwise be difficult to explain.*)

Apply Ask: **What models can you point out in this classroom?** (*Sample answer: A globe, a map, a model of the human body, a labeled diagram of the body*) **learning modality: verbal**

Use Visuals: Figure 5   L2
Making Models

Focus Have students examine Figure 5.

Teach Ask: **What can you tell about the geography of the area in which the chimpanzees live?** (*The map shows a rugged topography, bordered by Lake Tanganyika.*) **What does the map show about Jomeo's day?** (*It shows the chimp left its nest in the morning, traveled near the lake before moving into the interior, and then nested farther from the lake in the evening.*)

Apply Show students a weather map of your region. Discuss the scale of the map and the symbols used. Have students speculate about how meteorologists collect data and make this model. **learning modality: visual**

Monitor Progress   L2

Skills Check Have students make a table that classifies students in the school according to grade, age, gender, neighborhood, and transportation to school.

Answers
Figure 5 The distance is about 1,500 meters.

 Classifying objects helps you stay organized so you can easily find and use them later.

Reading Checkpoint A representation of a complex object or process

Working in Life Science

Teach Key Concepts   `L2`

What Life Science Involves

Focus Have students read the paragraph under the head *Working in Life Science*.

Teach Ask: **What is life science?** *(The study of living things.)* **What is another word for life science?** *(Biology)* **What are some things that life scientists might study?** *(Sample answer: Plants, animals, microorganisms; the ways in which living things relate to their environments; how microorganisms cause disease)* Then call students' attention to the careers shown on these pages. Ask students to explain how life science is involved in each career.

Apply Encourage students to choose one of the careers shown on these pages—or another career related to life science—and investigate it to learn more about it. Students might then prepare reports on the careers and share these reports with other students. **learning modality: verbal**

Use Visuals: Figure 6   `L2`

Relating Text and Figures

On the board, list all the careers shown on these pages. Briefly discuss each career with students. Then, to elicit how science skills might be involved in each career, ask questions such as the following: **How is observing important to physicians?** *(Physicians must observe patients' symptoms; they must listen to patients' descriptions of their illnesses.)* **If ocean water is polluted, what prediction might a marine biologist make about fish?** *(The fish might become ill or die.)* **How might a botanist classify plants?** *(Sample answer: According to how they reproduce)*

Apply Have each student choose one of the careers shown here, or a different science career, and list the skills they think the job involves. **learning modality: logical/ mathematical**

FIGURE 6
Life Science Careers

You can find life scientists at work in such diverse places as forests, laboratories, farms, and animal hospitals. **Comparing and Contrasting** *How are the careers of botanist and forestry technician similar?*

Botanist ◄
Botanists study plants. Many botanists, such as the one shown here, work with farmers to help increase crop yields. Other botanists study plants growing in their natural environment.

Park Rangers ▲
Park rangers work in government parks. These rangers are attaching a tag to a bird so they can track its movements. Other rangers lead tours that educate park visitors.

► Marine Biologist
Marine biologists study living things that are found in oceans. This marine biologist is examining a sample of ocean water.

Working in Life Science

The study of the behavior of animals such as chimpanzees is one branch of life science. **Life science** is the study of living things. Life science is also known as biology, and scientists who study living things are called biologists.

If you are interested in living things, you might one day enjoy working in life science. You don't need to be a biologist to use life science in your career. Many different jobs involve knowing about life science. You can see some of these jobs in Figure 6.

 Reading Checkpoint What is life science?

Forestry Technician ▲
Forestry technicians mostly work outdoors. They determine which trees can be cut down for lumber. They check trees for disease and insect damage. These workers also plant tree seedlings.

Health-Care Workers ▼
Health-care workers do jobs such as examine patients, treat injuries, and research cures for diseases. The doctor (left) and nurse (right) are discussing their notes.

Section 1 Assessment

⊙ **Target Reading Skill** Asking Questions Use the answers to the questions you wrote about the headings to help you answer the questions below.

Reviewing Key Concepts

1. a. Listing Name five skills that are important in scientific thinking.
  b. Comparing and Contrasting How do observations differ from inferences?
  c. Classifying Is this statement an observation or an inference? *The cat must be ill.* Explain your reasoning.
  d. Applying Concepts Choose a career described on these pages. Give examples of how observations and inferences might be important in that career.

Lab zone **At-Home Activity**

"Pastabilities" Collect pasta of various shapes and sizes. You and a family member should each devise a system to classify the pasta into three groups. You and your family member should each identify the characteristics you used in your classifications. How similar were your groupings?

Chapter 1 ◆ 13

Lab zone **Chapter Project**

Keep Students on Track By this time, students should have made a list of possible common beliefs and chosen one to investigate. Check to see that each belief students have chosen to study involves a scientific question. Check the procedures students propose for both soundness and safety.

Lab zone **At Home Activity**

"Pastabilities" **L2** You may want to display some different kinds of pasta in class to give students some idea about the common shapes. Spaghetti, tubes, and bow-tie pasta are examples. Explain that each type of pasta has a common name. Students should avoid these names in making their classification systems.

Objectives

After this lesson, students will be able to

1.2.1 Explain what scientific inquiry involves.

1.2.2 Describe how to develop a hypothesis and design an experiment.

1.2.3 Describe the attitudes, or habits of mind, that are important in science.

Target Reading Skill

Building Vocabulary Explain that knowing the definitions of Key Terms helps students understand what they read.

Answers

Answers should be similar to the text definitions but rewritten in students' own words. Have volunteers read definitions aloud. Correct any misconceptions.

Preteach

Build Background Knowledge   L2

Everyday Inquiry

Ask: **Suppose you make a sandwich, and then leave the kitchen for a few minutes. When you return, the sandwich is gone. How could you find out what happened to the sandwich?** Lead students to discover that they could use some variety of scientific inquiry, e.g., by developing a tentative explanation (hypothesis) and then looking for evidence to support or refute the explanation.

Scientific Inquiry

Reading Preview

Key Concepts
- What is scientific inquiry?
- What makes a hypothesis testable?
- What attitudes are important in science?

Key Terms
- scientific inquiry
- hypothesis • variable
- controlled experiment
- manipulated variable
- responding variable
- operational definition
- data • communicating

Target Reading Skill

Building Vocabulary A definition states the meaning of a word or phrase by telling about its most important feature or function. After you read this section, reread the paragraphs that contain definitions of Key Terms. Use all the information you have learned to write a definition of each Key Term in your own words.

▼ A snowy tree cricket

Lab zone Discover Activity

What Can You Learn About Mealworms?

1. Observe mealworms in a tray. Use a magnifying glass to see them more clearly.
2. Watch the mealworms' behavior—for example, how they move.

Think It Over
Posing Questions Write three questions you have about mealworms and their behavior. How could you find out the answers?

"Chirp, chirp, chirp." It is one of the hottest nights of summer and your bedroom windows are wide open. On most nights, the quiet chirping of crickets gently lulls you to sleep, but not tonight. The noise from the crickets is almost deafening!

Why do all the crickets in your neighborhood seem determined to keep you awake tonight? Could the crickets be chirping more because of the heat? How could you find out?

As you lie awake, you are probably not thinking much about science. But, in fact, you are thinking just as a scientist would. You made observations—you heard the loud chirping of the crickets and felt the heat of the summer night. Your observations led you to infer that heat might cause increased chirping. You might even make a prediction: "If it's cooler tomorrow night, the crickets will be quieter."

The Scientific Process

Although you might not know it, your thinking and questioning can be the start of the **scientific inquiry** process. **Scientific inquiry refers to the diverse ways in which scientists study the natural world and propose explanations based on the evidence they gather.** If you have ever tried to figure out why a plant has wilted, then you have used scientific inquiry. Similarly, you could use scientific inquiry to find out whether there is a relationship between the air temperature and crickets' chirping.

14 ◆

Lab zone Discover Activity

Skills Focus Posing questions   L2

Materials mealworms, small trays, magnifying glass (optional: fine cornmeal)

Time 10 minutes

Tips Obtain mealworms from pet shops or scientific supply houses. For contrast, you might set up one tray without cornmeal and another with cornmeal.

Expected Outcome Mealworms may do such things as move forward and burrow in cornmeal.

Think It Over Sample questions: What happens if you shine a light on mealworms? If you put them in a refrigerator? If you gently prod a mealworm? Discuss and approve plans for finding the answers.

Posing Questions Scientific inquiry often begins with a problem or question about an observation. In the case of the crickets, your question might be: Does the air temperature affect the chirping of crickets? Of course, questions don't just come to you from nowhere. Instead, questions come from experiences that you have and from observations and inferences that you make. Curiosity plays a large role as well. Think of a time that you observed something unusual or unexpected. Chances are good that your curiosity sparked a number of questions.

Some questions cannot be investigated by scientific inquiry. Think about the difference between the two questions below.

- Does my dog eat more food than my cat?
- Which makes a better pet—a cat or a dog?

The first question is a scientific question because it can be answered by making observations and gathering evidence. For example, you could measure the amount of food your cat and dog each eat during a week. In contrast, the second question has to do with personal opinions or values. Scientific inquiry cannot answer questions about personal tastes or judgments.

Developing a Hypothesis How could you explain your observation of noisy crickets on that summer night? "Perhaps crickets chirp more when the temperature is higher," you think. In trying to answer the question, you are in fact developing a hypothesis. A **hypothesis** (plural: *hypotheses*) is a possible explanation for a set of observations or answer to a scientific question. In this case, your hypothesis would be that cricket chirping increases at higher air temperatures.

In science, a hypothesis must be testable. This means that researchers must be able to carry out investigations and gather evidence that will either support or disprove the hypothesis. Many trials will be needed before a hypothesis can be accepted as true.

 Reading Checkpoint What is a hypothesis?

Perhaps crickets chirp more when the temperature is higher.

FIGURE 7 **Developing Hypotheses**
A hypothesis is one possible way to explain a set of observations. A hypothesis must be testable—scientists must be able to carry out investigations to test the hypothesis. **Developing Hypotheses** *Propose another hypothesis that could explain the observation that crickets seem to be noisier on some nights than others.*

Chapter 1 ◆ 15

The Scientific Process

Teach Key Concepts L2
Questions and Possible Explanations
Focus Explain to students that a scientist often begins the process of inquiry by posing questions about an observation. Then the scientist may focus on a possible answer to one question in particular.

Teach Contrast the two questions about cats and dogs, making certain that students understand why only the first one is a scientific question. Then explain what a hypothesis is and ask for a hypothesis related to the amount of food eaten by a cat and dog. (*Sample: My dog eats a greater amount of food than my cat.*) Ask: **What does it mean that a hypothesis must be testable?** (*Researchers must be able to carry out investigations and gather evidence that will either support or disprove the hypothesis.*)

Apply Ask: **How could you test the hypothesis about the amount of food eaten by the cat and dog?** (*Sample answer: By weighing the amount of food eaten by each animal during a week*) **learning modality: logical/mathematical**

Independent Practice L2
 **Teaching Resources, Unit 1**
- Guided Reading and Study Worksheet: *Scientific Inquiry*

⊙ **Student Edition on Audio CD**

Less Proficient Readers L1
Answering Questions Select a passage from the text, such as *Developing a Hypothesis*. Read the passage aloud to students as they follow along in their books. After reading, ask some questions about the passage. If they don't know the answers, help them find the answers in the passage. **learning modality: verbal**

Gifted and Talented L3
Before students read the section on scientific inquiry, ask them to propose in writing a process of scientific inquiry that they think would work best in finding the answer to a scientific question. After they have read the section, ask them to compare the process they proposed with the process described in the text. **learning modality: verbal**

Monitor Progress L2
Writing Show students a wilted plant or a photo of a wilted plant. Ask them to write a hypothesis to account for the wilting.

Answers
Figure 7 Sample answer: Maybe more crickets were around that night.

Reading Checkpoint A possible explanation for a set of observations or an answer to a scientific question

15

Teach Key Concepts

L2

Testing a Hypothesis

Focus Tell students that scientists design an experiment to yield results that will prove or disprove the hypothesis.

Teach Call on volunteers to define *variable, manipulated variable,* and *responding variable.* Ask: **What is the manipulated variable and the responding variable in this experiment?** *(Air temperature and number of cricket chirps, respectively)* **Why is this considered a controlled experiment?** *(Only one variable is being tested: air temperature. All other variables are controlled.)*

Apply Have groups of students design an experiment to test this hypothesis: Crickets are more active at midnight than at noon. The experiment should have a manipulated variable and a responding variable, and other variables should be controlled.
learning modality: logical/mathematical

Help Students Read

Relating Text and Figures Refer to the Content Refresher in this chapter, which provides the guidelines for the Relating Text and Figures strategy.

Have students read the text related to designing an experiment. Then, have them use Figure 8 to identify the variables that were designed as part of the cricket experiment. Ask: **What evidence do you see in the photo of what the manipulated variable was in the cricket experiment?** *(Since each container is labeled with a different temperature, the manipulated variable is air temperature. One container is maintained at room temperature, one is cooled with ice, and one is warmed using a heating pad.)* **What can you see from the photo about variables that were controlled in this experiment?** *(The containers look identical. The environments within the containers look identical or at least very similar. Since only one small container is labeled as a cricket holder, the crickets in each large container are the same species. All the containers are aligned in a row, which means they will all receive the same amount of light.)*

Go Online
active art

For: The Nature of Inquiry activity
Visit: PHSchool.com
Web Code: cgp-6012

Students can interact with the scientific inquiry art online.

Lab zone Skills **Activity**

Controlling Variables
Suppose you are designing an experiment to determine whether birds eat a larger number of sunflower seeds or millet seeds. What is your manipulated variable? What is your responding variable? What other variables would you need to control?

FIGURE 8
A Controlled Experiment
In their controlled experiment, these students are using the same kind of containers, thermometers, leaves, and crickets. The manipulated variable in this experiment is temperature. The responding variable is the number of cricket chirps per minute at each temperature.
Controlling Variables *What other variables must the students keep constant in this experiment?*

Designing an Experiment To test your hypothesis, you will need to observe crickets at different air temperatures. All other **variables,** or factors that can change in an experiment, must be exactly the same. Other variables include the kind of crickets, the type of container you test them in, and the type of thermometer you use. By keeping all of these variables the same, you will know that any difference in cricket chirping must be due to temperature alone.

An experiment in which only one variable is manipulated at a time is called a **controlled experiment.** The one variable that is purposely changed to test a hypothesis is called the **manipulated variable** (also called the independent variable). In your cricket experiment, the manipulated variable is the air temperature. The factor that may change in response to the manipulated variable is called the **responding variable** (also called the dependent variable). The responding variable here is the number of cricket chirps.

Another aspect of a well-designed experiment is having clear operational definitions. An **operational definition** is a statement that describes how to measure a variable or define a term. For example, in this experiment you would need to determine what sounds will count as a single "chirp."

Collecting and Interpreting Data For your experiment, you need a data table in which to record your data. **Data** are the facts, figures, and other evidence gathered through observations. A data table is an organized way to collect and record observations. After the data have been collected, they need to be interpreted. A graph can help you interpret data. Graphs can reveal patterns or trends in data.

 **Reading Checkpoint** What are data?

Lab zone Skills **Activity**

Skills Focus Controlling variables
L3

Time 10 minutes

Expected Outcome The manipulated variable is the type of seed (sunflower or millet); the responding variable is the number of seeds eaten. Variables that need to be controlled include the species of bird, the number of birds, the way in which the seeds are provided (e.g., type of container, location of container), and the time period during which the birds have access to the seeds.

Extend Challenge students to design a controlled experiment to determine whether more seeds germinate (sprout) in light or in darkness, and to identify the manipulated, responding, and controlled variables.

Drawing Conclusions A conclusion is a summary of what you have learned from an experiment. In drawing your conclusion, you should ask yourself whether the data support the hypothesis. You also need to consider whether you collected enough data. After reviewing the data, you decide that the evidence supports your original hypothesis. You conclude that cricket chirping does increase with temperature. It's no wonder that you have trouble sleeping on those warm summer nights!

Scientific inquiry usually doesn't end once a set of experiments is done. Often, a scientific inquiry raises new questions. These new questions can lead to new hypotheses and new experiments. Also, scientific inquiry is not a rigid sequence of steps. Instead, it is a process with many paths, as shown in Figure 9.

Communicating An important part of the scientific inquiry process is communicating your results. **Communicating** is the sharing of ideas and experimental findings with others through writing and speaking. Scientists share their ideas in many ways. For example, they give talks at scientific meetings, exchange information on the Internet, and publish articles in scientific journals. When scientists communicate their research, they describe their procedures in full detail so that other scientists can repeat their experiments.

What Is Science?

Video Preview
▶ Video Field Trip
Video Assessment

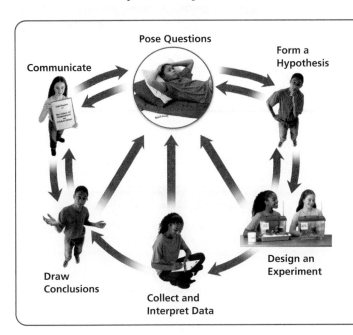

Pose Questions

Form a Hypothesis

Communicate

Design an Experiment

Draw Conclusions

Collect and Interpret Data

Go Online
active art

For: The Nature of Inquiry Activity
Visit: PHSchool.com
Web Code: cgp-6012

FIGURE 9
Scientific Inquiry
There is no set path that a scientific inquiry must follow. Observations at each stage of the process may lead you to modify your hypothesis or experiment. Conclusions from one experiment often lead to new questions and experiments.

Chapter 1 ◆ 17

What Is Science?
Show the Video Field Trip to let students see forensic investigators gathering and interpreting evidence to solve a crime

Preventing Fruits From Discoloring L3

Time 15 minutes to set up; 5 minutes to observe half an hour later

Materials lemon juice, paper towels, and fresh slices of apples and pears

Focus Tell students that they will design an experiment to determine whether lemon juice prevents sliced fruit from discoloring.

Teach Help students decide how to set up the experiment. (They might apply lemon juice to some slices of fruit, while leaving others untreated. Factors to be controlled include the number and approximate sizes of fruit slices, the amount of lemon juice applied to the treated fruit, and the amount of time the fruit is allowed to stand.)

Apply Ask students to draw a conclusion about their results. (*Lemon juice usually prevents fruit from turning brown.*) **learning modality: logical/mathematical**

All in One Teaching Resources, Unit 1
Transparency LS2

Differentiated Instruction

English Learners/Beginning Comprehension: Modified Cloze L1
Distribute a simplified paragraph about designing an experiment, but leave some words blank. Provide students with the correct answers as choices. Model how to fill in the blanks using a sample sentence on the board. **learning modality: verbal**

English Learners/Intermediate Comprehension: Modified Cloze L2
Distribute the same paragraph, but include some additional terms as incorrect answer choices. After students complete the paragraph, have them work together to write definitions for the answer choices that were not used. **learning modality: verbal**

Monitor Progress L2

Oral Presentation Have students explain the relationship between data collected and conclusions drawn.

Answers
Figure 8 Sample answer: Time of day, amount of light, duration of observation

 Reading Checkpoint Facts, figures, and other evidence gathered through observation

Scientific Attitudes

Teach Key Concepts `L2`
Scientists' Habits of Mind

Focus Point out that science is done best with certain attitudes.

Teach List these attitudes on the board: curiosity, honesty, open-mindedness, skepticism, creativity. Call on students to define each attitude and give an example.

Apply Invite students to explain why each attitude would be good for a scientist to have. **learning modality: verbal**

Assess

Reviewing Key Concepts

1. a. Scientific inquiry refers to the diverse ways in which scientists study the natural world and propose explanations based on evidence they gather. **b.** You could, because the hypothesis can be tested. **c.** Comparative growth of pea plants and corn plants

2. a. Researchers must be able to carry out investigations and gather evidence that will either support or disprove the hypothesis. **b.** Sample answer: Studying for an exam while listening to classical music improves exam scores.

3. a. Curiosity, honesty, open-mindedness, skepticism, and creativity **b.** Open-mindedness helps a scientist accept new ideas; skepticism helps the scientist question whether the ideas are correct. **c.** Sample answer: Yes. Open-mindedness helps you accept new ideas; skepticism helps you reject incorrect ideas.

Reteach `L1`

Use Figure 9 to reteach scientific inquiry. Point to each part of the process and carefully paraphrase the text explanation, describing specific examples.

Performance Assessment `L2`
Oral Presentation Call on students to explain each step of scientific inquiry.

All in One Teaching Resources, Unit 1

- Section Summary: *Scientific Inquiry*
- Review and Reinforce: *Scientific Inquiry*
- Enrich: *Scientific Inquiry*

Scientific Attitudes

Why has Jane Goodall been very successful at studying chimps? **Successful scientists possess certain important attitudes, or habits of mind, including curiosity, honesty, open-mindedness, skepticism, and creativity.**

Curiosity An important attitude that drives scientists is curiosity. Successful scientists are eager to learn more about the topics they study. They stick with problems in spite of setbacks.

Honesty Good scientists always report their observations and results truthfully. Honesty is especially important when a scientist's results go against previous ideas or predictions.

Open-Mindedness and Skepticism Scientists need to be open-minded, or capable of accepting new and different ideas. However, open-mindedness should always be balanced by skepticism, which is an attitude of doubt.

Creativity Whether scientists study chimps or earthquakes, problems may arise in their studies. Sometimes, it takes a bit of creativity to find a solution. Creativity means coming up with inventive ways to solve problems or produce new things.

FIGURE 10 Curiosity
Curiosity has led Dr. Daphne Soares to study how alligators interact with their environment.

Section 2 Assessment

Target Reading Skill Building Vocabulary Use your definitions to help answer the questions.

Reviewing Key Concepts

1. a. Defining Define the term *scientific inquiry*.
   b. Explaining A friend claims that pea plants grow faster than corn plants. Could you investigate this idea through scientific inquiry? Explain.
   c. Problem Solving What kind of data would you need to collect to carry out this experiment?

2. a. Reviewing What is meant by saying that a hypothesis must be testable?
   b. Developing Hypotheses Every time you and your friend study for an exam while listening to classical music, both of you do well on the exam. What testable hypothesis can you develop from your observations?

3. a. Identifying What attitudes help scientists succeed in their work?
   b. Explaining Why is it important for scientists to balance open-mindedness and skepticism?
   c. Making Judgments Is it important to be both open-minded and skeptical in your everyday life? Explain.

Writing in Science

Summary Suppose you will be traveling to a convention of cricket scientists from around the world. Write a paragraph describing the results of your cricket experiment. Include questions you'd like to ask other cricket scientists while at the conference.

Understanding Technology

Reading Preview

Key Concepts
• What is the goal of technology?
• How does technology differ from science?
• How does technology affect society?

Key Terms
• technology • engineer

Target Reading Skill
Previewing Visuals When you preview, you look ahead at the material to be read. Preview Figure 12. Then write two questions you have about the diagram. As you read, answer your questions.

Science and Technology

Q.	What does technology have to do with science?
A.	
Q.	

◀ Neil Parry plays football.

Lab zone Discover **Activity**

What Are Some Examples of Technology?
1. Look at the objects in the photographs.
2. With a partner, discuss whether or not each object is an example of technology. Write your reasons for each decision.

Think It Over
Forming Operational Definitions On what basis did you and your partner decide whether an object was an example of technology? What is your definition of the term *technology?*

In the fourth quarter of a football game between San Jose State and Nevada, the crowd went wild. Neil Parry had just joined the San Jose players on the field. Cries of "PAR-ry, PAR-ry, PAR-ry" filled the stadium.

It was Neil's first football game after his right leg below the knee had been amputated, or removed in an operation. Neil now has an artificial leg, or prosthesis. Because of his determination and hard work, Neil Parry can play football again. His ability to run and tackle is also due to the design of his artificial leg.

Chapter 1 ◆ 19

Lab zone Discover **Activity**

Skills Focus Forming operational definitions

Time 10 minutes

Tips Pair students of differing abilities.

Expected Outcome Students who classified all the objects as examples of technology are correct.

L1 **Think It Over** Many students may think that technology consists only of electronic devices such a computers, CD players, and cellular phones. After students have read the section, have them revisit and revise their definitions.

Understanding Technology

Section
3
Understanding Technology

Objectives
After this lesson, students will be able to
1.3.1 Describe the goal of technology.
1.3.2 Explain how technology differs from science.
1.3.3 Explain how technology affects people in both positive and negative ways.

Target Reading Skill
Previewing Visuals Explain that looking at the visuals before they read helps students activate prior knowledge and predict what they are about to read.

Answers
Sample answers:
Q. What does technology have to do with science?
A. Advances in technology contribute to advances in science.
Q. How does science affect technology?
A. Advances in science contribute to advances in technology.

All in One Teaching Resources, Unit 1
• Transparency LS3

Preteach

Build Background Knowledge   **L2**

Science and Technology
Ask: **What is technology?** (*Sample answer: Technology is something complicated or electronic, such as a computer.*) **Is a saw an example of technology?** (*Sample answer: An electric saw may be considered technology, but a handsaw may not be.*) Explain that students will learn that both an electric saw and a handsaw are examples of technology. **What does science have to do with technology?** (*Sample answer: People who make technology use knowledge of science in their designs.*) **Does technology ever affect science?** (*Yes, by providing advanced instruments scientists use to do their research*)

What Is Technology?

Teach Key Concepts L2
Meeting People's Needs

Focus Tell students that most things they do during a day involve technology.

Teach Call on a volunteer to provide the definition of technology. Ask students whether this definition surprises them. (Many students will be surprised, because many people think that technology refers only to complex electronic devices that have been invented fairly recently.) Then ask: **Why is a bird feeder an example of technology?** (*A bird feeder is manufactured by people. A bird feeder meets the need that many people have to feed and observe birds.*) **How does a football helmet improve the way people live?** (*By protecting the head of a football player*)

Apply Have students decide whether or not various objects are examples of technology. (Except for people and other living things, most classroom items will be examples of technology.)

Independent Practice L2

 **Teaching Resources, Unit 1**

- Guided Reading and Study Worksheet: *Understanding Technology*

 **Student Edition on Audio CD**

Go **O**nline
*SC*i*LINKS*™ NSTA

For: Links on technology
Visit: www.SciLinks.org
Web Code: scn-1631

Download a worksheet that will guide students' review of Internet resources on technology.

Lab zone Skills **Activity**

Predicting

Choose a type of technology, such as medical technology or video technology. Talk to older people about how this type of technology has changed during their lives. Then predict how this technology may continue to change.

What Is Technology?

Artificial legs are examples of technology. So are football helmets, shoulder pads, and shoes with cleats. When you see or hear the word *technology*, you may think of such things as electronic scoreboards, computers, and DVD players. But technology consists of more than modern inventions. **Technology** is how people change the world around them to meet their needs and solve practical problems.

Technology includes things people make, such as computers. It also consists of the knowledge needed to design those products. Finally, technology includes the processes, such as manufacturing and transportation, that get products to the people who use them. Figure 11 shows examples of technology. **The goal of technology is to improve the way people live.** Your refrigerator, for example, improves your life by making food stay fresh longer. If you wear glasses or contact lenses, you know that they help people see better. A medical thermometer makes it easier to determine whether you are sick.

 Reading Checkpoint What are some examples of technology?

FIGURE 11
Examples of Technology
Technology includes things people make to meet their needs. **Applying Concepts** *How does farm machinery help people meet their needs?*

▼ Heart monitor

▼ Farm machinery

Lab zone Skills **Activity**

Skills Focus Predicting

Time 10 minutes

Tips Suggest that when making their predictions, students focus on some specific aspect of the technology they have chosen.

Expected Outcome Specific predictions will depend on the technology that

students choose. If they choose medical technology, for example, older people may mention developments in the field of cardiology, such as heart transplants and the first artificial hearts. Students might predict that artificial hearts will be improved to the point where their use may become preferable to heart transplants.
learning modality: verbal

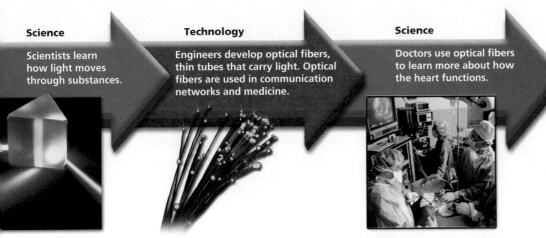

Science	Technology	Science
Scientists learn how light moves through substances.	Engineers develop optical fibers, thin tubes that carry light. Optical fibers are used in communication networks and medicine.	Doctors use optical fibers to learn more about how the heart functions.

Comparing Technology and Science

Science and technology are related, but they are not the same thing. **Science is the study of the natural world to understand how it functions. Technology, on the other hand, changes, or modifies, the natural world to meet human needs or solve problems.**

To understand this difference, contrast the ways in which a biologist and an engineer might study insects. (An **engineer** is a person who is trained to use both technological and scientific knowledge to solve practical problems.) The biologist might investigate the structure of insects' bodies and how insects obtain oxygen. The engineer might study insects to learn how to keep them from damaging crops. In other words, a scientist studies something to learn about the topic itself. An engineer studies a topic to solve a problem or develop a process or product for human use.

Often, advances in science and technology depend on one another, as shown in Figure 12. Endoscopes are tiny medical instruments that allow doctors to view organs within the human body. Endoscopes transmit light using long, thin strands of glass called optical fibers. The design of these fibers would not have been possible without the work of scientists. Once scientists understood how light travels through substances, technologists were able to use this knowledge to design optical fibers and endoscopes. Endoscopes, in turn, have helped scientists learn more about the human body.

 Reading Checkpoint What is an endoscope?

FIGURE 12
Science and Technology
Advances in science contribute to advances in technology, which in turn can contribute to science. Understanding the characteristics of light (science) led to the development of optical fibers and endoscopes (technology).
Relating Cause and Effect *How might endoscopes help scientists learn more about the human body?*

Go Online
SciLINKS
NSTA

For: Links on technology
Visit: www.SciLinks.org
Web Code: scn-1631

Differentiated Instruction

Less Proficient Readers [L1]
Comprehension: Link to Visual To help students understand Figure 12, discuss each frame. Point out that the photo in the first frame shows light traveling through a crystal. Point out that the word *optical* in the second frame usually indicates something to do with light or seeing. Also note that a fiber is a long, threadlike structure, and point out the structure of the optical fiber. To help students understand the third frame, explain that light is involved in seeing, and that optical fibers can carry an image of things that are very small and difficult to see, such as the detailed internal structure of the heart. **learning modality: visual**

Comparing Technology and Science

Teach Key Concepts [L2]
Study vs. Doing

Focus Tell students that the difference between science and technology is the difference between studying the natural world to gain understanding and using knowledge about the natural world to do something to meet a human need.

Teach Ask: **What is the purpose of science?** *(To study the natural world to understand how it functions)* **What is the purpose of technology?** *(To change or modify the natural world to meet human needs or solve problems)* Review the example shown in Figure 12, in which advances in physical science lead to advances in the technology of optical fibers, which lead to advances in life science.

Apply Ask: **How might a marine biologist view the salt water of the ocean, and how might an engineer view that same salt water?** *(Sample answer: A marine biologist might try to determine how the salt affects ocean organisms, while an engineer might study how to remove the salt to produce drinkable water.)* **learning modality: logical/mathematical**

All in One Teaching Resources, Unit 1
• Transparency LS4

Monitor Progress [L2]

Skills Check Have each student make a table with two column heads: *Science* and *Technology*. Ask them to think about what they observed on the way to school this morning. Under *Science*, they can write questions about the things they saw that might be answered by a scientist. Under *Technology*, they can write questions about the things they saw that might be answered by an engineer. Students can keep their tables in their portfolios.

Portfolio

Answers
Figure 11 By helping farmers grow needed crops
Figure 12 By showing more about how a particular organ functions

 Reading Checkpoint Sample answer: Tractors, heart monitors

 Reading Checkpoint An instrument for viewing internal organs

Impact on Society

Teach Key Concepts
Positive and Negative

Teach Ask: **How do pesticides demonstrate both the good and bad effects of technology?** *(Pesticides kill harmful insects but may harm humans and wildlife.)*

Apply Ask students to list the positive and negative effects of other technologies.
learning modality: verbal

Monitor Progress ———— L2
Answer

 Reading Checkpoint Chemicals that kill insects

Assess

Reviewing Key Concepts

1. a. Technology is how people change the world around them to meet their needs or to solve practical problems. **b.** A toothbrush meets the need of cleaning teeth. **c.** To improve the way people live. A toothbrush achieves this by providing an effective method of cleaning teeth.
2. a. Science is the study of the natural world to understand how it functions. Technology changes the natural world to meet human needs. **b.** Technology, because it has been constructed to meet the need of people who have lost a leg **c.** Sample answer: Scientists discovered the properties of the materials in the leg prosthesis; engineers designed and constructed it.
3. a. Positive: farmers can produce more crops and feed more people; negative: pesticides may harm people and animals. **b.** Because technology generally has negative as well as positive consequences. Pesticides have improved people's lives but have also caused environmental damage.

Reteach L1
To help students understand what technology is, explain a very simple example, such as plastic gloves.

Performance Assessment L2
Skills Check Students can create a Venn diagram comparing technology and science.

All in One Teaching Resources, Unit 1
- Section Summary, Review and Reinforce, Enrich: *Understanding Technology*

FIGURE 13
Spraying Pesticide
The airplane is spraying pesticide on a field.

Impact on Society

When you read stories like that of Neil Parry, you might think that technology always benefits people. **However, technology can have both positive and negative consequences for individual people and for society as a whole.** The term *society* refers to any group of people who live together in an area and have certain things in common, such as form of government.

For example, pesticides are chemicals that kill insects, including those that eat crops. Because of pesticides, farmers can produce more crops and feed more people. However, humans and other animals can sometimes be harmed if they eat food containing pesticides. Also, rain can wash pesticides into rivers, streams, and water supplies. The pesticides can then affect plants and animals that live in the water, as well as people who depend on the water supply.

Technology does not provide perfect solutions to the problems it helps solve. People must make informed decisions to use technology wisely.

 Reading Checkpoint What are pesticides?

Section 3 Assessment

Target Reading Skill Previewing Visuals Refer to your questions and answers about Figure 12 to help you answer Question 2 below.

Reviewing Key Concepts

1. a. Defining What is technology?
   b. Explaining Explain why a toothbrush is an example of technology.
   c. Applying Concepts What is the goal of technology? Explain how a toothbrush achieves this goal.
2. a. Comparing and Contrasting Compare science and technology.
   b. Explaining Is a human leg prosthesis an example of science or technology? Explain.
   c. Relating Cause and Effect Explain how both science and technology must have been involved in the development of a leg prosthesis.

3. a. Listing List the positive consequences of using pesticides. Then list the negative consequences.
   b. Explaining Explain the following statement: "Technology does not provide perfect solutions to problems." Use pesticides as an example.

Writing in Science

Technology and You Choose an example of technology that has had an important impact on your life. Describe the technology and explain how it has affected you.

22 ◆

Lab zone Chapter Project

Keep Students on Track Students should have finished collecting data. The next task is to interpret the collected data and draw a conclusion about the common belief. Where appropriate, review how to create graphs, how to determine percentages, or how to construct labeled diagrams.

Writing in Science

Writing Mode Explanation
Scoring Rubric
4 Interesting description and clear explanation
3 Sufficient description and good explanation
2 Some description and explanation
1 Little description or explanation

Safety in the Science Laboratory

Reading Preview

Key Concepts
- Why is preparation important when carrying out scientific investigations in the lab and in the field?
- What should you do if an accident occurs?

 **Target Reading Skill**

Outlining As you read, make an outline about science safety that you can use for review. Use the red headings for the main ideas and the blue headings for supporting ideas.

Safety in the Science Laboratory
I. Safety During Investigations
A. Preparing for the lab
B.
C.
D.
II. In Case of an Accident

Where Is the Safety Equipment in Your School?

1. Look around your classroom or school for any safety-related equipment.
2. Draw a floor plan of the room or building and clearly label where each item is located.

Think It Over

Predicting Why is it important to know where safety equipment is located?

You and your family have just arrived at a mountain cabin for a vacation. The view of the mountaintops is beautiful, and the fresh scent of pine trees fills the air. In the distance, you can glimpse a lake through the pines.

You put on a bathing suit and head down the trail toward the lake. The sparkling, clear water looks inviting. You're tempted to jump in and swim. However, you wait for the rest of your family to join you. It isn't safe for a person to swim alone.

Safety During Investigations

Just as when you go swimming, you have to take steps to be safe during any scientific investigation. **Good preparation helps you stay safe when doing science activities.** Do you know how to use lab equipment? What should you do if something goes wrong? Thinking about these questions ahead of time is an important part of being prepared.

Preparing for the Lab Preparing for a lab should begin the day before you will perform the lab. It is important to read through the procedure carefully and make sure you understand all the directions. Also, review the general safety guidelines in Appendix A, including those related to the specific equipment you will use. If anything is unclear, be prepared to ask your teacher about it before you begin the lab.

Chapter 1 ◆ 23

Safety in the Science Laboratory

Objectives
After this lesson, students will be able to
1.4.1 Explain why preparation is important when carrying out scientific investigations in the lab and in the field.
1.4.2 Describe what you should do if an accident occurs.

Target Reading Skill 🔄

Outlining Explain that an outline helps students organize information.

Answers
Safety in the science laboratory
I. Safety during investigations
  A. Preparing for the lab
  B. Performing the lab
  C. End-of-lab procedures
  D. Safety in the field
II. In case of an accident

All in One Teaching Resources, Unit 1
- Transparency LS5

Preteach

Build Background Knowledge   L2
Real-Life Safety
Discuss swimming and other situations, such as bicycling and in-line skating, in which it is important to take safety precautions.

Skills Focus Predicting   **L1**

Time 15 minutes

Tips Allow pairs of students to search the school and classroom for safety-related equipment. After students have completed their search, discuss as a class what they have found. Then direct students to make their floor plans.

Expected Outcome Students will learn where safety-related equipment is kept in the classroom and in the school building, and they will be better able to access such equipment in an emergency.

Think It Over Sample answer: It is important to know where safety equipment is located because in an emergency there may not be time to ask a teacher or search for the equipment.

Instruct

Safety During Investigations

Teach Key Concepts
Safety in Advance

Focus Tell students that they need to take certain precautions to be safe in a science lab.

Teach Ask: **What is one reason for preparing in advance for labs?** (*To ensure safety*) **What safety issues should you look for when you read a lab?** (*Sample answer: The correct way to perform procedures; how to use lab equipment; any safety cautions*)

Apply Ask students to predict what situations might necessitate the use of safety goggles and a lab apron. (*Sample answer: When working with dangerous chemicals*) **learning modality: logical/ mathematical**

Teach Key Concepts
Following Directions

Focus Remind students that the most important safety rule is to follow the teacher's instructions and the textbook directions.

Teach Ask: **Why is it important to follow directions?** (*To help ensure safety and obtain reliable data*)

Apply Have students skim some of the labs in this book. They should look for situations in which failure to follow directions might produce serious safety issues. **learning modality: logical/mathematical**

All in One Teaching Resources, Unit 1

• Transparency LS6

Go Online
SciLINKS NSTA

For: Links on laboratory safety
Visit: www.SciLinks.org
Web Code: scn-1624

Download a worksheet that will guide students' review of Internet resources on laboratory safety.

Independent Practice L2

All in One Teaching Resources, Unit 1

• Guided Reading and Study Worksheet:
  Safety in the Science Laboratory

 **Student Edition on Audio CD**

Go Online
SciLINKS NSTA

For: Links on laboratory safety
Visit: www.SciLinks.org
Web Code: scn-1624

Performing the Lab Whenever you perform a science lab, always follow your teacher's instructions and the textbook directions exactly. You should never try anything on your own without asking your teacher first. Keep your work area clean and organized. Also, do not rush through any of the steps. Finally, always show respect and courtesy to your teacher and classmates.

Labs and activities in this textbook include the safety symbols shown on the next page. These symbols alert you to possible dangers in performing the lab and remind you to work carefully. They also identify any safety equipment that you should use to protect yourself from potential hazards. The symbols are explained in detail in Appendix A. Make sure you are familiar with each safety symbol and what it means.

FIGURE 14
Safety in the Lab
Good preparation for an experiment helps you stay safe in the laboratory. **Observing** *List three precautions each student is taking while performing the labs.*

End-of-Lab Procedures When you have finished a lab, clean your work area. Turn off and unplug equipment and return it to its proper place. Dispose of any wastes as your teacher instructs you to. Finally, wash your hands thoroughly.

Safety in the Field You work in the "field" whenever you work outdoors—for example, in a forest, park, or schoolyard. Always tell an adult where you will be. Never carry out a field investigation alone. Ask an adult or classmate to go with you.

Possible safety hazards outdoors include such things as severe weather, traffic, wild animals, and poisonous plants. Planning ahead can help you avoid some hazards. For example, the weather report can alert you to severe weather. Use common sense to avoid any potentially dangerous situations.

 Reading Checkpoint What should you do with equipment at the end of a lab?

Wear plastic gloves to protect your skin when handling animals, plants, or chemicals.

Handle live animals and plants with care.

Tie back long hair to keep it away from flames, chemicals, or equipment.

Safety Symbols

- Safety Goggles
- Lab Apron
- Breakage
- Heat-Resistant Gloves
- Plastic Gloves
- Heating
- Flames
- No Flames
- Corrosive Chemical
- Poison
- Fumes
- Sharp Object
- Animal Safety
- Plant Safety
- Electric Shock
- Physical Safety
- Disposal
- Hand Washing
- General Safety Awareness

Use Visuals: Figure 14   L2
Safety Symbols

Focus Tell students that, when carrying out science investigations, they will see safety symbols that caution them about each investigation.

Teach Have students examine the safety symbols listed in Figure 14. Then ask them to turn to laboratory investigations in this and other chapters to see the symbols that are used. Ask: **Where are the symbols explained in detail?** *(In Appendix A)* Have students turn to Appendix A and become familiar with what each symbol stands for.

Apply Ask: **What does the mouse symbol mean when you see it in a laboratory procedure?** *(Caution, animal safety)* **What steps should you take to avoid injury?** *(Treat live or preserved animals with care to avoid harming yourself or the live animals; wash hands when you are finished.)* **learning modality: verbal**

All in One Teaching Resources, Unit 1
- Transparency LS7

Monitor Progress   L3

Oral Presentation Call on students at random to explain what a student should do to prepare for a lab, during a lab, and during a field trip to stay safe.

Answers
Figure 14 Any three of the following: Wearing goggles, wearing heat-resistant gloves, making sure electric cords are untangled and out of the way, wearing an apron, keeping work area clean and uncluttered, wearing closed-toe shoes, handling live animals and plants with care, wearing plastic gloves, tying back long hair

Reading Checkpoint Clean work area; turn off and unplug equipment and return it to its proper place; dispose of wastes as the teacher instructs; wash hands.

Differentiated Instruction

English Learners/Beginning Vocabulary   L1 Use the safety symbols above to help build students' ability to speak and read English words. Pair beginning students with students who speak the same language but are more proficient in English. Point to each symbol and then say the words aloud as you point to each word. Student pairs should then work together to communicate how the symbols relate to the words. **learning modality: visual**

English Learners/Intermediate Vocabulary   L2 Extend the activity for beginners by having students create word webs around drawings of the safety symbols. **learning modality: verbal**

In Case of an Accident

Teach Key Concepts   **L2**

What to Do

Focus Tell students that lab accidents sometimes happen, and they should know what to do in that case.

Teach Ask: **What is the first thing to do after a lab accident?** *(Notify the teacher.)* Then explain and discuss the instructions in Figure 15.

Apply Ask: **After telling your teacher, what would you do in case of a burn?** *(Immerse the burn in cold water.)* **learning modality: verbal**

Assess

Reviewing Key Concepts

1. a. To help ensure safety **b.** Accept any two: read through the procedure; read Appendix A; ask teacher for clarification of anything that is unclear. **c.** Sample answer: You risk an accident; you might not obtain reliable results.
2. a. Notify your teacher. **b.** No. She should have covered the cut with a clean dressing and applied pressure to stop the bleeding. **c.** She may have been able to avoid the cut if she had paid attention to symbols for breakage and/or sharp objects.

Reteach   **L1**

Prepare a partially completed flowchart that shows what students should do before, during, and after a lab. Work with students to complete the flowchart.

Performance Assessment   **L2**

Writing Have students make a list of behaviors that should be done to ensure lab safety, and a second list of behaviors to avoid.

All in One Teaching Resources, Unit 1

- Section Summary: *Safety in the Science Laboratory*
- Review and Reinforce: *Safety in the Science Laboratory*
- Enrich: *Safety in the Science Laboratory*

In Case of Emergency

ALWAYS NOTIFY YOUR TEACHER IMMEDIATELY

Injury	What to Do
Burns	Immerse burns in cold water.
Cuts	Cover cuts with a clean dressing. Apply direct pressure to the wound to stop bleeding.
Spills on Skin	Flush the skin with large amounts of water.
Foreign Object in Eye	Flush the eye with large amounts of water. Seek medical attention.

FIGURE 15 First-Aid Tips
These first-aid tips can help guide your actions during emergency situations. Remember, always notify your teacher immediately if an accident occurs.

In Case of an Accident

Good preparation and careful work habits can go a long way toward making your lab experiences safe ones. But, at some point, an accident may occur. A classmate might accidentally knock over a beaker or a chemical might spill on your sleeve. Would you know what to do?

When any accident occurs, no matter how minor, notify your teacher immediately. Then, listen to your teacher's directions and carry them out quickly. Make sure you know the location and proper use of all the emergency equipment in your lab room. Knowing safety and first-aid procedures beforehand will prepare you to handle accidents properly. Figure 15 lists some first-aid procedures you should know.

 Reading Checkpoint What should you do when an accident occurs?

Section **4** Assessment

Target Reading Skill Outlining Use the information in your outline about science safety to help you answer the questions below.

Reviewing Key Concepts

1. a. Reviewing Why is good preparation important in lab investigations?
  b. Identifying Identify two steps you should take to prepare for a lab.
  c. Predicting What might happen if you did not follow the steps you identified in Question (b)?
2. a. Describing What should you do immediately after any lab accident?
  b. Applying Concepts Your lab partner cuts herself and stops the bleeding with a tissue from her pocket. Did she follow the proper procedure? Explain.

c. Relating Cause and Effect Explain how your partner might have prevented the accident if she had been more familiar with the safety symbols on page 25.

Writing in Science

Field Trip Safety Think of an outdoor area that you know, such as a park, field, or vacant lot, where you might observe wild plants. Write safety instructions that would help students prepare for a field trip to that place. You might add illustrations to help make the instructions clear.

Writing in Science

Writing Mode List
Scoring Rubric
4 Exceeds criteria; detailed, extensive lists
3 Meets criteria; complete lists
2 Meets some criteria; incomplete lists
1 Meets few criteria; few items on lists

Keeping Flowers Fresh

Problem

How can cut flowers stay fresher for a longer period of time?

Skills Focus

developing hypotheses, designing experiments, drawing conclusions

Suggested Materials

- plastic cups • cut flowers • spoon
- water • sugar

Design a Plan

1. You have just been given a bouquet of cut flowers. You remember once seeing a gardener put some sugar into the water in a vase before putting flowers in. You wonder if the gardener did that so that the flowers would stay fresh longer. Write a hypothesis for an experiment you could perform to answer your question.

2. Working with a partner, design a controlled experiment to test your hypothesis. Make a list of all of the variables you will need to control. Also decide what data you will need to collect. For example, you could count the number of petals each flower drops. Then write out a detailed experimental plan for your teacher to review.

3. If necessary, revise your plan according to your teacher's instructions. Then set up your experiment and begin collecting your data.

Analyze and Conclude

1. **Developing Hypotheses** What hypothesis did you decide to test? On what information or experience was your hypothesis based?

2. **Designing Experiments** What was the manipulated variable in the experiment you performed? What was the responding variable? What variables were kept constant?

3. **Graphing** Use the data you collected to create one or more graphs of your experimental results. (For more on creating graphs, see the Skills Handbook.) What patterns or trends do your graphs reveal?

4. **Drawing Conclusions** Based on your graphs, what conclusion can you draw about sugar and cut flowers? Do your results support your hypothesis? Why or why not?

5. **Communicating** In a paragraph, describe which aspects of your experimental plan were difficult to carry out. Were any variables hard to control? Was it difficult to collect accurate data? What changes could you make to improve your experimental plan?

More to Explore

Make a list of some additional questions you would like to investigate about how to keep cut flowers fresh. Choose one of the questions and write a hypothesis for an experiment you could perform. Then design a controlled experiment to test your hypothesis. *Obtain your teacher's permission before carrying out your investigation.*

Analyze and Conclude

1. Sample answer: Hypothesis: Placing cut flowers in sugar water keeps the flowers fresh. The hypothesis is based on seeing a gardener put sugar in the water in a vase.

2. Manipulated variable: the presence of sugar in the water; responding variable: freshness of flowers; controlled variables include amount of water and sunlight and the air temperature.

3. Graphs will vary depending on the responding variable chosen. Graphs may show the number of petals that drop or the number of days flowers stayed fresh. A typical graph will include two bars or lines, one for each flower (or bouquet)—one placed in sugar water, and one in water alone.

4. Students should conclude the sugar in the water keeps flowers fresh.

5. Sample answer: Collecting data about the freshness of the cut flowers was most difficult.

Lab zone Design Your Own **Lab**

Keeping Flowers Fresh L2

Prepare for Inquiry

Key Concept

In a controlled experiment, only one variable is manipulated at a time.

Skills Objectives

After this lab, students will be able to

- develop a testable hypotheses
- design a controlled experiment in which a manipulated variable is tested
- control all variables in an experiment except the manipulated variable

 **Prep Time** 20 minutes

Class Time 40 minutes class time over 5 days

Advance Planning

Collect the appropriate number of flower bouquets and plastic cups ahead of time. Each pair of students can divide one bouquet in half to carry out an experiment.

Safety

Caution students to be careful when handling sharp objects.

All in One **Teaching Resources, Unit 1**

- Lab Worksheet: *Keeping Flowers Fresh*

Guide Inquiry

Introduce the Procedure

Call on students to define the terms *hypothesis, manipulated variable, responding variable,* and *controlled experiment.* Have students then read through the lab and identify the manipulated variable and the responding variable.

Troubleshooting the Experiment

- Review each student's or group's hypothesis and plan before giving the go-ahead to set up the experiment.
- Review how to make a graph.

Expected Outcome

See **Analyze and Conclude,** answer for Question 4.

Extend Inquiry

More to Explore A typical controlled experiment might test a hypothesis that focuses on the air temperature the cut flowers are exposed to.

Study Guide

Interactive Textbook

- Complete student edition
- Section and chapter self-assessments
- Assessment reports for teachers

Help Students Read

Building Vocabulary

Word Origin Have students look up the origin of the word *skeptic*. They will discover that it comes from the Greek word *skeptikos,* meaning "thoughtful." Ask students how being thoughtful is related to being skeptical. *(People who are thoughtful often don't accept explanations without examining them closely with an attitude of doubt.)*

Words in Context Help students learn the meaning of new words or phrases by examining the context. Tell students to look for familiar words or phrases that surround a new term—these are clues to the new term's meaning. Have students reread the second paragraph under the heading Inferring. Ask: **Which word in the paragraph could help you remember the meaning of *inferring?*** *(In the first sentence of the paragraph, Jane "reasoned.")*

Connecting Concepts

Concept Maps Help students develop one way to show how the information in this chapter is related. Biologists use characteristic skills and ways of thinking, and they follow a certain process of inquiry. Have students brainstorm to identify the Key Concepts, Key Terms, details, and examples. Then write each one on a self-sticking note and attach it at random on chart paper or on the board.

Tell students that this concept map will be organized in hierarchical order and to begin at the top with Key Concepts. Ask students these questions to guide them to categorize the information on the self-sticking notes: **What skills do scientists use to learn about the world? What attitudes are important in**

---

① What Is Science?

Key Concepts

- Scientists use skills such as observing, inferring, predicting, classifying, and making models to learn more about the world.

Key Terms

science
observing
quantitative observation
qualitative observation
inferring

predicting
classifying
making models
life science

② Scientific Inquiry

Key Concepts

- Scientific inquiry refers to the diverse ways in which scientists study the natural world and propose explanations based on the evidence they gather.
- In science, a hypothesis must be testable. This means that researchers must be able to carry out investigations and gather evidence that will either support or disprove the hypothesis.
- Successful scientists possess certain attitudes, or habits of mind, including curiosity, honesty, open-mindedness, skepticism, and creativity.

Key Terms

scientific inquiry
hypothesis
variable
controlled experiment
manipulated variable
responding variable
operational definition
data
communicating

③ Understanding Technology

Key Concepts

- The goal of technology is to improve the way people live.
- Science is the study of the natural world to understand how it functions. Technology, on the other hand, changes, or modifies, the natural world to meet human needs or solve problems.
- Technology can have both positive and negative consequences for individual people and for society as a whole.

Key Terms

technology
engineer

④ Safety in the Science Laboratory

Key Concepts

- Good preparation helps you stay safe when doing science activities.
- When any accident occurs, no matter how minor, notify your teacher immediately. Then, listen to your teacher's directions and carry them out quickly.

---

science? **What stages are important in the scientific inquiry process? What is technology? What must you do to be safe in a lab?**

Prompt students by using connecting words such as "use," "possess," and "includes," to indicate the basis for the organization of the map. The phrases should form a sentence between or among a set of concepts.

Answer
Accept logical presentations by students.

All in One Teaching Resources, Unit 1

- Key Terms Review: *Introduction to Life Science*
- Connecting Concepts: *Introduction to Life Science*

Review and Assessment

Organizing Information

Identifying Main Ideas Copy the graphic organizer about scientific skills onto a separate sheet of paper. Then complete it and add a title. (For more on Identifying Main Ideas, see the Skills Handbook.)

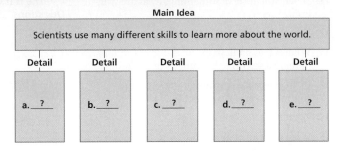

Reviewing Key Terms

Choose the letter of the best answer.

1. When you note that a rabbit has white fur, you are making a
   a. quantitative observation.
   b. qualitative observation.
   c. prediction.
   d. model.

2. Music stores arrange CDs according to the type of music—rock, country, folk, and so on. This is an example of
   a. observation.   b. inferencing.
   c. posing questions.   d. classifying.

3. A statement that describes how to measure a variable or define a term is a(n)
   a. controlled variable.
   b. manipulated variable.
   c. hypothesis.
   d. operational definition.

4. Which of the following is NOT an example of technology?
   a. a teaspoon   b. a computer
   c. a leaf   d. a microscope

5. In labs in this book, which of the following indicates the danger of breakage?

   a.   b.

   c.   d.

If the statement is true, write *true*. If it is false, change the underlined word or words to make the statement true.

6. When you interpret what you have observed, you are <u>inferring</u>.

7. When you <u>pose questions</u>, you create representations of complex objects or processes.

8. The <u>responding variable</u> is changed to test a hypothesis.

9. <u>Technology</u> changes the natural world to meet human needs.

10. You should begin preparing for a lab <u>15 minutes</u> before you perform the lab.

Writing in Science

Description Think about the ways in which the police who investigate crimes act like scientists. In a paragraph, describe the scientific skills that police use in their work.

What Is Science?
Video Preview
Video Field Trip
▶ Video Assessment

Organizing Information
a. Observing
b. Inferring
c. Predicting
d. Classifying
e. Making models

Reviewing Key Terms
1. b 2. d 3. d 4. c 5. d
6. true
7. make models
8. manipulated variable
9. true
10. the day

Writing in Science

Writing Mode Explanation

Scoring Rubric

4 Exceeds criteria; includes many examples and discussion of tools that may be used

3 Meets criteria; clearly describes each skill and applies it to the work of crime investigators; includes examples

2 Lists scientific skills but does not apply them to crime investigators

1 Includes only brief and/or inaccurate information

What Is Science?

Show the Video Assessment to review chapter content and as a prompt for the writing assignment. Discussion questions: **What tools did present-day forensic scientists use to solve this investigation?** *(They used DNA testing and fiber analysis.)* **What observations did modern-day forensic scientists make that helped them determine that John Toms was guilty of this historical crime?** *(They could take photos of the crime scene, take the temperature of the victim, make a plaster cast of a footprint, examine hair and fibers, and analyze blood samples and gunpowder residue.)*

All in One Teaching Resources, Unit 1
• Transparency LS8
• Chapter Test
• Performance Assessment Teacher Notes
• Performance Assessment Student Worksheet
• Performance Assessment Scoring Rubric

 **ExamView® Computer Test Bank CD-ROM**

Checking Concepts

11. When you observe something, you use one or more of your senses to gather information.

12. Life science is the study of living things.

13. A hypothesis is a possible explanation for a set of observations or answer to a scientific question. A hypothesis should be testable to gather evidence that will either support or disprove the hypothesis.

14. By keeping all variables except one (the manipulated variable) the same, the researcher knows that any experimental responses are due to the change in the manipulated variable.

15. Data are facts, figures, and other evidence gathered through observation.

16. An engineer is trained to use both technological and scientific knowledge to solve practical problems.

17. Read the procedure carefully; review the general safety guidelines in Appendix A; if anything is unclear, ask your teacher for clarification.

Thinking Critically

18. Sample answer: The kitten was trying to catch the fish and fell into the tank. When the kitten became wet, it left the fish alone and began to struggle to get out of the tank.

19. Sample answer: The amount of dog food given; the times of feeding; the size and location of the food dish

20. Sample answer: How was the study conducted? What frozen fruits and canned vegetables were involved? How was nutrition measured or determined?

21. This textbook meets the need of providing students with information about life science. It solves the practical problem of combining this information in one source.

Review and Assessment

Checking Concepts

11. When you observe something, what are you doing?

12. What is life science?

13. What is a hypothesis? Why is it important to develop a scientific hypothesis that is testable?

14. In an experiment, why is it important to control all variables except one?

15. What does *data* mean?

16. What does an engineer do?

17. Identify three things that you should do to prepare for a lab.

Thinking Critically

18. **Inferring** Suppose you come home to the scene below. What can you infer happened while you were gone?

19. **Problem Solving** Suppose you would like to find out which dog food your dog likes best. What variables would you need to control in your experiment?

20. **Making Judgments** You read an ad claiming that scientific studies prove that frozen fruit is more nutritious than canned vegetables. What questions would you want answered before you accept this claim?

21. **Applying Concepts** This textbook is an example of technology. What need does it meet? What practical problem does it solve?

Applying Skills

Use the data table below to answer Questions 22–26.

Three students conducted a controlled experiment to find out how walking and running affected their heart rates.

Effect of Activity on Heart Rate (in beats per minute)

Student	Heart Rate (at rest)	Heart Rate (walking)	Heart Rate (running)
1	70	90	115
2	72	80	100
3	80	100	120

22. **Controlling Variables** What is the manipulated variable in this experiment? What is the responding variable?

23. **Developing Hypotheses** What hypothesis might this experiment be testing?

24. **Predicting** Based on this experiment and what you know about exercising, predict how the students' heart rates would change while they are resting after a long run.

25. **Designing Experiments** Design a controlled experiment to determine which activity has more of an effect on a person's heart rate—jumping rope or doing push-ups.

26. **Drawing Conclusions** What do the data indicate about the increased physical activity and heart rate?

Lab zone Chapter **Project**

Performance Assessment Create a poster that summarizes your experiment for the class. Your poster should include the question you tested, how you tested it, the data you collected, and what conclusion you drew from your experiment. What problems did you encounter while carrying out your experiment? Is additional testing necessary?

Lab zone Chapter **Project**   L3

Performance Assessment Students' posters will vary depending on the common belief tested. Each poster should include a statement of the common belief, the hypothesis, a description of the experiment, the data gathered in the form of a table or graph, and the conclusion drawn from that data. In a summary, students should mention any problems encountered as well as state whether additional testing is necessary.

Standardized Test Prep

Choose the letter of the best answer.

1. Your brother has a cold and you think you will probably get a cold, too. Which of the following are you doing?
  A posing a question based on an inference
  B predicting based on an observation
  C making a model based on an observation
  D designing a controlled experiment

Use the table below to answer Questions 2 and 3.

Animals in a Field

Kind of Animal	Number of Animals	
	July	August
Grasshoppers	5,000	1,500
Birds	100	100
Spiders	200	500

2. Which of the following statements about the data is true?
  F In July, there were more grasshoppers than birds.
  G In August, there were more birds than spiders.
  H Between July and August, the number of grasshoppers increased by 500.
  J In both months, there were more spiders than grasshoppers.

3. Which of the following is a logical question that a scientist might pose based on the data in the table?
  A What killed off the spiders in the field?
  B Are spiders feeding on grasshoppers?
  C Do all birds fly south for the winter?
  D Are grasshoppers related to beetles?

4. During a lab, if you spill a chemical on your skin, you should
  F apply pressure to the area.
  G rub the chemical off with a clean tissue.
  H flush the skin with large amounts of water.
  J throw the rest of the chemical in a waste basket.

Constructed Response

5. Advertisements for three brands of plant food each claim that their brand makes plants grow fastest. How would you design an experiment to test which brand works best?

Applying Skills

22. The manipulated variable is the type of activity (at rest, walking, running); the responding variable is heart rate.

23. Sample answer: A person's heart rate while running is greater than that person's heart rate while walking.

24. Their heart rates would decrease as they rested after a long run.

25. Sample answer: The manipulated variable is the type of activity, such as jumping rope or doing push-ups. The responding variable is heart rate. Controlled variables include the same person, time of day, temperature, humidity, and level of physical exertion before the activity.

26. The data indicate that heart rate increases as physical activity increases (becomes more strenuous).

Standardized Test Prep

1. B **2.** F **3.** B **4.** H
5. Sample answer: Grow the same kind of plants in four pots. Add a different brand of plant food to each of three pots. Add no plant food to the fourth pot. Control all other variables, including soil type, amount of water, amount of sunlight, and temperature. Observe the growth of the four plants over a two-week period, measuring and recording the height of the plant each day. After two weeks, compare the growth data from the four plants and draw a conclusion about which plant food works best.

Chapter at a Glance

 Chapter Project *Mystery Object*

Technology

Local Standards

All in One Teaching Resources, Unit 1
- Chapter Project Teacher Notes, pp. 102–103
- Chapter Project Student Overview, pp. 104–105
- Chapter Project Student Worksheets, pp. 106–107
- Chapter Project Scoring Rubric, p. 108

 Section 1

What Is Life?

2 periods
1 block

2.1.1 List the characteristics all living things share
2.1.2 Explain where living things come from
2.1.3 Identify what all living things need to survive

Section 2

Classifying Organisms

1 period
1/2 block

2.2.1 Tell why biologists classify organisms
2.2.2 Relate the levels of organisms to the relationships between organisms
2.2.3 List characteristics used to classify organisms into groups, including domains and kingdoms

Section 3

Discovering Cells

2 periods
1 block

2.3.1 Tell what cells are.
2.3.2 Explain how the invention of the microscope contributed to scientists' understanding of living things.
2.3.3 State the cell theory.
2.3.4 Describe how microscopes produce magnified images.

Section 4

Looking Inside Cells

2 periods
1 block

2.4.1 Identify the role of the cell wall and the cell membrane in the cell.
2.4.2 Describe the functions of cell organelles.
2.4.3 Explain how cells are organized in many-celled organisms.

Review and Assessment

Test Preparation

All in One Teaching Resources, Unit 1
- Key Terms Review, p. 143
- Transparency LS19
- Performance Assessment Teacher Notes, p. 149
- Performance Assessment Scoring Rubric p. 150
- Performance Assessment Student Worksheet, p. 151
- Chapter Test, pp. 152–155

Test Preparation Blackline Masters

Student Edition	Inquiry	Time	Materials	Skills	Resources
Chapter Project p. 33	Open-Ended	1 to 2 weeks	**All in One Teaching Resources, Unit 1**, p. 102	Observing, inferring, classifying	**Lab zone Easy Planner** **All in One Teaching Resources, Unit 1**, Support pp. 102–103
Section 1					
Discover Activity, p. 34	Guided	10 minutes	Wind-up toys	Forming operational definitions	**Lab zone Easy Planner**
Try This Activity, p. 35	Guided	10 minutes	Lemon slices, small mirrors	Classifying	**Lab zone Easy Planner**
Skills Activity, p. 38	Open-Ended	30 minutes	Balance, hair dryer, paper towels, thin potato slices, small mirrors	Designing an experiment	**Lab zone Easy Planner**
Skills Lab, p. 41	Directed	Prep: 20 min Class: 20 min the first day, then 5 min for the next 5 days	Paper plates, plastic dropper, bread without preservatives, sealable plastic bags, tap water, packing tape	Observing, controlling variables	**Lab zone Easy Planner** **Lab Activity Video** **All in One Teaching Resources, Unit 1**, Skills Lab: *Please Pass the Bread*, pp. 117–118
Section 2					
Discover Activity, p. 42	Guided	15 minutes	Items such as envelopes, erasers, paper, paper clips, pencils, rubber bands, stamps, tape	Classifying	**Lab zone Easy Planner**
Skills Activity, p. 47	Guided	10 minutes	None	Classifying	**Lab zone Easy Planner**
Section 3					
Discover Activity, p. 50	Guided	10 minutes	Black and white newspaper photograph, hand lens, microscope, scissors	Observing	**Lab zone Easy Planner**
Skills Activity, p. 55	Guided	10 minutes	Blank slide, coverslip, microscope, plastic dropper, pond water, prepared slide of cork	Observing	**Lab zone Easy Planner**
Technology Lab, pp. 58–59	Open-Ended	40 minutes	Book, 1 low-power magnifying lens, 1 high-power magnifying lens, 2 cardboard tubes from paper towels (or black construction paper), tape	Building a prototype, working with design constraints	**Lab zone Easy Planner** **Lab Activity Video** **All in One Teaching Resources, Unit 1**, Technology Lab: *Design and Build a Microscope*, pp. 134–135
Section 4					
Discover Activity, p. 60	Directed	10 minutes	Calculator, metric ruler	Inferring	**Lab zone Easy Planner**
Try This Activity, p. 62	Open-Ended	10 minutes first day; 10 minutes the next	Packet of colorless gelatin, warm water, stirrer, other craft-type materials, rectangular or round pan	Making models	**Lab zone Easy Planner**
Skills Activity, p. 66	Guided	15 minutes	Microscope, prepared slide of animal cells, prepared slide of plant cells	Observing	**Lab zone Easy Planner**

Section 1 What Is Life?

 2 periods, 1 block

ABILITY LEVELS
L1 Basic to Average
L2 For All Students
L3 Average to Advanced

Objectives

2.1.1 List the characteristics all living things share.
2.1.2 Explain where living things come from.
2.1.3 Identify what all living things need to survive.

Key Terms

• organism • cell • unicellular • multicellular • stimulus • response
• development • spontaneous generation • autotroph • heterotroph
• homeostasis

Local Standards

Preteach

Build Background Knowledge

Invite students to describe the most unusual thing they have seen and describe it as a plant, animal, or other life form.

 **Discover Activity** *Is It Living or Nonliving?* **L1**

Targeted Print and Technology Resources

 Teaching Resources, Unit 1

L2 Reading Strategy Transparency
LS9: Using Prior Knowledge

PresentationEXPRESS™ CD-ROM

Instruct

The Characteristics of Living Things Use questions to link the lesson subheadings with the lesson Key Concept.

Life Comes From Life Use a figure to summarize Redi's experiment.

The Needs of Living Things Describe the four basic needs of living things, and give examples of ways that various organisms fulfill those needs.

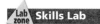 **Skills Lab** *Please Pass the Bread!* **L2**

Targeted Print and Technology Resources

Teaching Resources, Unit 1

L2 Guided Reading, pp. 111–114
L2 Transparencies LS10, LS11
L2 Skills Lab: *Please Pass the Bread!* pp. 117–118

Lab Activity Video/DVD
Skills Lab: *Please Pass the Bread!*

PHSchool.com Web Code: cep-1011

Student Edition on Audio CD

Assess

Section Assessment Questions

Have students use their completed Using Prior Knowledge graphic organizers to help them answer the questions.

Reteach

Use a concept map to identify characteristics of living things.

Targeted Print and Technology Resources

Teaching Resources, Unit 1

• Section Summary, p. 110
L1 Review and Reinforce, p. 115
L3 Enrich, p. 116

Section 2 Classifying Organisms

 1 period, 1/2 block

ABILITY LEVELS
L1 Basic to Average
L2 For All Students
L3 Average to Advanced

Objectives

2.2.1 Explain why biologists classify organisms.

2.2.2 Relate the levels of classification to the relationships between organisms.

2.2.3 List characteristics used to classify organisms into groups, including domains and kingdoms.

Local Standards

Key Terms

• classification • taxonomy • binomial nomenclature • genus • species
• prokaryote • nucleus • eukaryote

Preteach

Build Background Knowledge

Invite students to describe how libraries are organized.

 **Discover Activity** *Can You Organize a Junk Drawer?* L1

Targeted Print and Technology Resources

 Teaching Resources, Unit 1

L2 Reading Strategy Transparency LS12: Asking Questions

PresentationEXPRESS™ CD-ROM

Instruct

Why Do Scientists Classify? Use an imaginary fish to discuss classification.

The Naming System of Linnaeus Define *genus* and *species* and apply to an example.

Levels of Classification Use a drawing to discuss the levels of classification.

Domains and Kingdoms Use the illustration to present the three domains and the four kingdoms of domain Eukarya.

Domain Eukarya Discuss characteristics of the kingdoms that make up Eukarya.

Targeted Print and Technology Resources

 Teaching Resources, Unit 1

L2 Guided Reading, pp. 121–124
L2 Transparency LS13

www.SciLinks.org Web Code: scn-0113

Student Edition on Audio CD

Assess

Section Assessment Questions

Have students use their completed Asking Questions graphic organizers to answer the questions.

Reteach

Have students list the levels of classification from broad to specific.

Targeted Print and Technology Resources

Teaching Resources, Unit 1

• Section Summary, p. 120
L1 Review and Reinforce, p. 125
L3 Enrich, p. 126

Section Lesson Plans

Section 3 **Discovering Cells**

⏱ *2 periods, 1 block*

Objectives

2.3.1 Tell what cells are.

2.3.2 Explain how the invention of the microscope contributed to scientists' understanding of living things.

2.3.3 State the cell theory.

2.3.4 Describe how microscopes produce magnified images.

Key Terms

• cell • microscope • cell theory

Local Standards

Preteach

Build Background Knowledge

Help students appreciate the great number of cells in an organism and the size of individual cells.

Lab zone **Discover Activity** *Is Seeing Believing?* **L1**

Targeted Print and Technology Resources

All in One **Teaching Resources, Unit 1**

L2 Reading Strategy Transparency LS14: Sequencing

⊙ **PresentationEXPRESS™ CD-ROM**

Instruct

An Overview of Cells Ask questions to help students define a cell and its functions.

First Observations of Cells Identify what early scientists learned by studying living things under a microscope.

Development of the Cell Theory Examine the contributions of scientists leading to the cell theory.

Light and Electron Microscopes Use a diagram to explain how microscopes magnify images.

Lab zone **Technology Lab** *Design and Build a Microscope* **L2**

Targeted Print and Technology Resources

All in One **Teaching Resources, Unit 1**

L2 Guided Reading, pp. 129–131
L2 Transparency LS15
L2 Technology Lab: *Design and Build a Microscope*, pp. 134–135

📼 **Lab Activity Video/DVD**
Technology Lab: *Design and Build a Microscope*

www.SciLinks.org Web Code: scn-0311

⊙ **Student Edition on Audio CD**

Assess

Section Assessment Questions

⟳ Have students use their completed Sequencing graphic organizers to answer the questions.

Reteach

Use the Technology and History timeline to discuss the development of microscopes and the development of the cell theory.

Targeted Print and Technology Resources

All in One **Teaching Resources, Unit 1**

• Section Summary, p. 128
L1 Review and Reinforce, p. 132
L3 Enrich, p. 133

Section 4 Looking Inside Cells

 2 periods, 1 block

ABILITY LEVELS
L1 Basic to Average
L2 For All Students
L3 Average to Advanced

Objectives

2.4.1 Identify the role of the cell wall and the cell membrane in the cell.
2.4.2 Describe the functions of cell organelles.
2.4.3 Explain how cells are organized in many-celled organisms.

Key Terms

• organelle • cell wall • cell membrane • cytoplasm • mitochondria
• endoplasmic reticulum • ribosome • Golgi body • chloroplast • vacuole
• lysosome

Local Standards

Preteach

Build Background Knowledge

Relate division of labor among cell structure to division of labor in a community.

 Discover Activity *How Large Are Cells?* L1

Targeted Print and Technology Resources

All in One Teaching Resources, Unit 1

L2 Reading Strategy Transparency
LS16: Previewing Visuals

⊙ **PresentationEXPRESS™ CD-ROM**

Instruct

Enter the Cell Use illustrations to identify the functions of the cell wall and cell membrane.

Sail on to the Nucleus Use a diagram of the nucleus to analyze its functions.

Organelles in the Cytoplasm Ask questions to help students synthesize how organelles work together to perform their functions.

Specialized Cells Explain how cells are organized into tissues, then organs, then organ systems.

Targeted Print and Technology Resources

All in One Teaching Resources, Unit 1

L2 Guided Reading, pp. 138–140
L2 Transparencies LS17, LS18

Discovery CHANNEL SCHOOL
Video Field Trip

PHSchool.com Web Code: cep-3012

Assess

Section Assessment Questions

Have students use their completed Asking Questions graphic organizers to answer the questions.

Reteach

Show photographs of different types of cells for students to classify.

Targeted Print and Technology Resources

All in One Teaching Resources, Unit 1

• Section Summary, p. 137
L1 Review and Reinforce, p. 141
L3 Enrich, p. 142

Chapter 2 Content Refresher

Section 1 What Is Life?

Comparing Growth and Development Growth is an increase in the size of an organism or its parts that can be traced to ongoing mitotic cell division. Each division initially results in two cells that are half the size of the parent cell. Each new cell soon grows to full size, and the combined effect of millions of such cells dividing and enlarging produces a notable increase in an organism's dimensions.

Development, like growth, takes place as cells divide. But while growth involves only an increase in the number of cells, development involves changes in the structures and functions of cells. In plants and animals, development is a complex process. It begins with a fertilized egg and ends with the emergence of an adult organism. At first, after fertilization, there is a period of rapid cell division, without much actual cell growth. At this stage, the cells are very simple and similar in form. They represent the raw material of development.

Next, cells undergo differentiation, in which groups of similar cells begin to differ in appearance from other such groups. These differences are the result of the activation and deactivation of specific genes, and this activation differs from one group of cells to another. Differentiation results in the formation of tissue and organ precursors—the first signs of an emerging plant or animal form.

For example, in the development of a bird or mammal, early differentiation in the embryo produces protrusions of tissue called limb buds. They are precursors to feet, hands, and wings. In time, the outlines of digits—toes or fingers—are seen. Soon, joints begin to form, and the toes and fingers fully separate. At their tips, the rudimentary nails or claws take shape. In humans, fingerprints are one of the last details to emerge.

Both growth and development continue after birth or germination. The growth of many plants, for example, is accompanied by the differentiation of its cells into complex structures such as leaves, roots, and flowers.

Section 2 Classifying Organisms

Described Species To date, scientists have described around 1.8 million species of living organisms. Although the number of described species may seem large, scientists estimate that between 10 million and 100 million species actually exist. Also, millions of additional species have become extinct. We know nothing of most of these extinct species because they did not leave any fossil traces.

In 2000, an international group of scientists and other individuals established All Species Foundation. Its goal is to catalog every living species within 25 years. Currently the group is identifying about 15,000 species a year, but hopes to increase the pace to 60,000 annually.

Section 3 Discovering Cells

Resolution in Light and Electron Microscopes In biological study, resolution, or resolving power, is the capability of lenses to distinguish individual objects within a specimen. In the study of cells, this includes the fine structures such as membranes, ribosomes, and even macromolecules.

The resolving power of both light and electron microscopes is limited by the source of illumination, that is, light waves and streams of vibrating electrons, respectively. In order for two adjacent objects to be resolved as two, light waves or electrons must pass between the objects without being scattered. When scattering occurs, the image is still visible, but the two objects will appear as a single fuzzy one. If objects are closer together than half the wavelength of light or electrons, the waves will be scattered.

Because of this physical limitation, the resolving power of light microscopes turns out to be no greater than half the wavelength of visible light. This translates into a useful magnification of about 1,000 X. You can magnify an image much greater than this by photographic enlargement, but you will not be able to see more detail. For this reason, many biological structures cannot be seen through even the finest light microscopes.

The wavelength of oscillating electrons in their stream is much smaller than the wavelengths of visible light, so electrons will easily pass between and resolve adjacent cell structures. As a result, the electron microscope's useful magnification is in the neighborhood of 250,000 X.

Section 4 Looking Inside Cells

Endosymbiotic Model Some scientists have developed a model that may explain the origins of plant and animal cells. Bacterial cells are prokaryotic organisms, meaning that their genetic information is not enclosed within a nucleus and they do not have membrane-bound organelles, such as mitochondria and chloroplasts. All other cells, including plant and animal cells, are eukaryotic, meaning they have a nucleus and contain membrane-bound organelles.

Address Misconceptions

Some students may think that different types of cells within an organism contain different genetic material. However, every cell of an organism has exactly the same genetic material. For a strategy for overcoming this misconception, see **Address Misconceptions** in the section *Looking Inside Cells*.

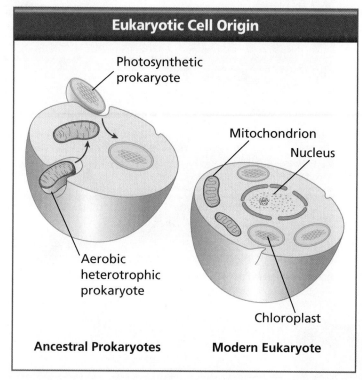

Eukaryotic Cell Origin

- Photosynthetic prokaryote
- Mitochondrion
- Nucleus
- Aerobic heterotrophic prokaryote
- Chloroplast

Ancestral Prokaryotes   **Modern Eukaryote**

The endosymbiotic model suggests that eukaryotic cells came from a mutually beneficial (symbiotic) relationship between different kinds of prokaryotic cells. That is, ancient bacterial cells enveloped smaller bacterial cells, and they functioned together as a unit. The model suggests that they evolved together, eventually becoming present-day eukaryotic cells. This model is supported by the fact that mitochondria and chloroplasts contain enzymes, ribosomes, and membranes that are similar to those of existing prokaryotes. Furthermore, mitochondria and chloroplasts have their own DNA and reproduce themselves within the eukaryotic cell in the same way that bacterial cells do.

Help Students Read

Sequencing
Ordering Events

Strategy Help students understand and visualize the steps in a process, or the order in which events occur. Sequences frequently involve cause-effect relationships. Readers can construct graphic organizers to help them visualize and comprehend a sequence. For most sequences, flowcharts are the graphic of choice. However, cycle diagrams are more appropriate for cyclic events. Before students begin, locate in the text a description of a multi-step process or a chain of causes and effects.

Example
1. Have students read the passage, thinking about what takes place first, second, third, and so on. Point out that the text will not always use order words such as *first, next, then,* and *finally*.
2. Review the passage, listing the steps or events in order.
3. If the passage describes a chain of steps or events, draw a flowchart on the board, having students tell the sequence of events, steps, or causes and effects. Write each part of the process in a separate box.
4. If the passage describes a cycle, use a cycle diagram to show the sequence.
5. Have students locate additional examples of sequential relationships in the text or visuals of the chapter. Students can depict the steps or events using graphic organizers.

Interactive Textbook
- Complete student edition
- Video and audio
- Simulations and activities
- Section and chapter activities

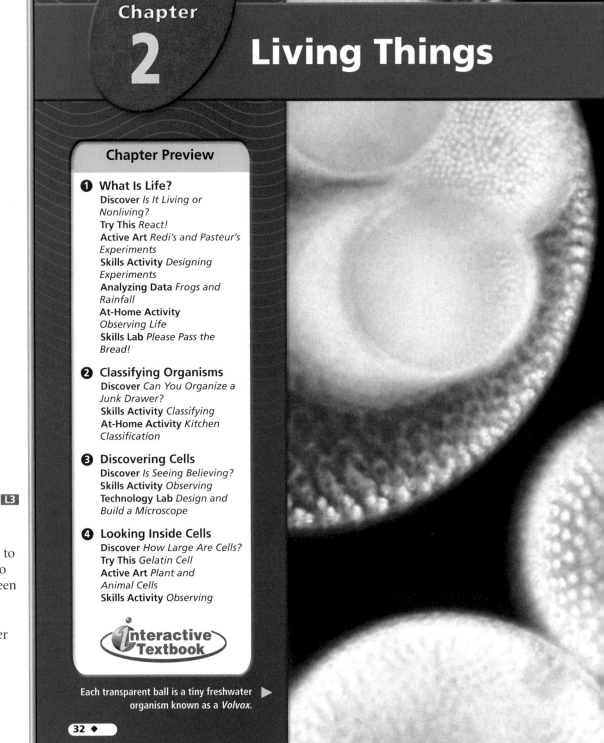

Chapter
2
Living Things

Chapter Preview

Interactive Textbook

Each transparent ball is a tiny freshwater organism known as a *Volvox.* ▶

Lab zone Chapter **Project** ▨ **L3**

Objectives
In this project, students observe an object to determine whether it is alive. Students also develop strategies for distinguishing between living and nonliving objects. After this Chapter Project, students will be able to
- observe characteristics of objects to infer whether they are alive
- carry out tests for signs of life
- classify living things into kingdoms

Skills Focus
Observing, inferring, classifying

Project Time Line 1 to 2 weeks

All in One Teaching Resources, Unit 1
- Chapter Project Teacher Notes
- Chapter Project Overview
- Chapter Project Worksheet 1
- Chapter Project Worksheet 2
- Chapter Project Scoring Rubric

Developing a Plan
During the first two days, students should observe their objects and record their observations. Allow at least three days for students to carry out tests for life characteristics. Students should make data tables and drawings during this stage. Finally, students should analyze their data, classify their objects, and plan a presentation.

Possible Materials
Provide students with living and nonliving objects and instructions on their care.
- Living objects may include brine shrimp, slime mold, bread mold, insect larvae, goldfish, plants, yeast (add one spoonful of baker's yeast and one spoonful of sugar to 250 mL warm water; observe under a microscope), and seeds (soak lentil seeds in water overnight then wrap in wet paper towel; place towel in a plastic bag and store in the dark; observe daily).

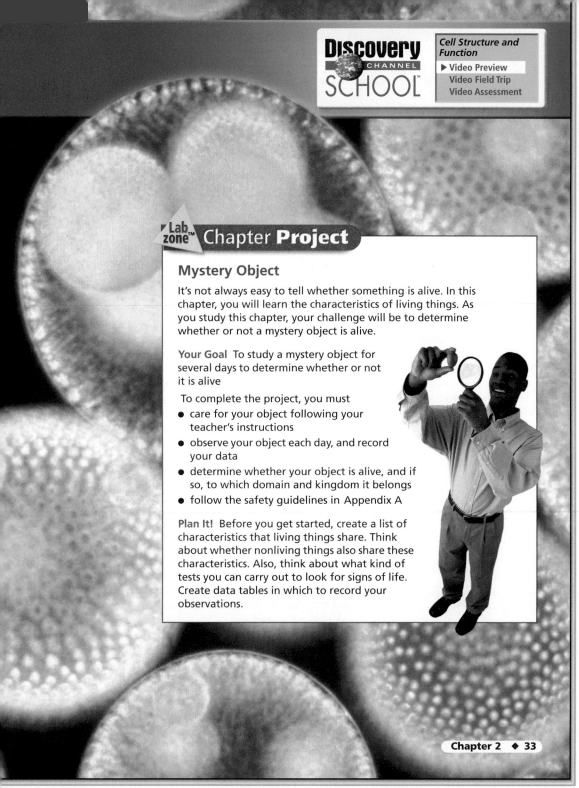

Lab zone™ Chapter **Project**

Mystery Object

It's not always easy to tell whether something is alive. In this chapter, you will learn the characteristics of living things. As you study this chapter, your challenge will be to determine whether or not a mystery object is alive.

Your Goal To study a mystery object for several days to determine whether or not it is alive

To complete the project, you must
- care for your object following your teacher's instructions
- observe your object each day, and record your data
- determine whether your object is alive, and if so, to which domain and kingdom it belongs
- follow the safety guidelines in Appendix A

Plan It! Before you get started, create a list of characteristics that living things share. Think about whether nonliving things also share these characteristics. Also, think about what kind of tests you can carry out to look for signs of life. Create data tables in which to record your observations.

Chapter 2 ◆ 33

Cell Structure and Function

Show the Video Preview to introduce the topic of cells.

Launching the Project

Show students living organisms, such as a plant and a snail. Ask: **What characteristics do these objects have in common?** (*Possible answer: They grow and respond to changes in the environment.*) **What tests could you design that would help you observe the characteristics of these living organisms?** (*Possible answers: Measure size over a period of time; observe under a microscope*) Explain to students that all tests must be approved so that living organisms are not injured.

Performance Assessment

The Chapter Project Scoring Rubric will help you evaluate how well students complete the Chapter Project. You may want to share the rubric with your students so that they will know what is expected. Students will be assessed on
- the detail of their observations
- how well they design tests to determine whether their object is alive and, if it is alive, if they are able to identify which domain and kingdom it belongs to
- the accuracy and organization of their testing and documentation, including how well they follow directions for the care of their objects
- whether they draw appropriate conclusions from their tests and present their results to the class in a clear and organized manner

Portfolio

- Nonliving objects may include pebbles, vermiculite, artificial plants (look real but do not grow or have a cellular structure), soluble salts in a saturated solution (so that "crystal gardens" appear to grow), hair (has cellular structure, but no longer living), and toys with microchips (can have complex responses).
- Plastic petri dishes and paper towels are useful for germinating seeds.

- BTB solution (bromthymol blue) can be used to test for presence of carbon dioxide in water.
- Provide equipment such as a microscope, glass slides, cover slips, scissors, a plastic dropper, a hand lens, and a ruler. Show students how to use a microscope and make a thin cross-section of material for observation under the microscope.

Objectives

After completing the lesson, students will be able to

2.1.1 List the characteristics all living things share.

2.1.2 Explain where living things come from.

2.1.3 Identify what all living things need to survive.

Target Reading Skill 🔄

Using Prior Knowledge Explain that using prior knowledge helps students connect what they already know to what they are about to read.

Answers

Possible answers include:

What You Know

1. Living things grow.

2. Living things are made of cells.

What You Learned

1. Unicellular organisms are composed of only one cell.

2. The cells of living things are composed of chemicals.

3. The cells of organisms use energy to do things they must do.

All in One Teaching Resources, Unit 1

• Transparency LS9

Preteach

Build Background Knowledge   L2

Unusual Living Things

Ask students to describe the most unusual living thing they have seen. Ask: **What did it look like? Where did it live? What was so unusual about it?** Write the heading *Living Things* on the board and list the organisms as students identify them. Have students describe whether they thought the organism was a plant, an animal, or another life form.

Section 1
What Is Life?

Reading Preview

Key Concepts

• What characteristics do all living things share?

• Where do living things come from?

• What do living things need to survive?

Key Terms

• organism • cell • unicellular
• multicellular • stimulus
• response • development
• spontaneous generation
• autotroph • heterotroph
• homeostasis

🔄 Target Reading Skill

Using Prior Knowledge Look at the section headings and visuals to see what this section is about. Then write what you already know about living things in a graphic organizer like the one below. As you read, write what you learn.

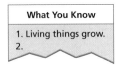

What You Know
1. Living things grow.
2.

What You Learned
1.
2.

Lab zone · Discover **Activity**

Is It Living or Nonliving?

1. Your teacher will give you and a partner a wind-up toy.

2. One of you will look for evidence that the toy is alive and the other will look for evidence that the toy is not alive.

3. Observe the toy. List the evidence that supports your position about whether or not the toy is alive.

4. Share your lists with your classmates.

Think It Over

Forming Operational Definitions Based on what you just learned, create a list of characteristics that living things share.

If you were asked to name some living things, or **organisms,** you might name yourself, a pet, and maybe some insects or plants. You would probably not mention a moss growing in a shady spot, the mildew on bathroom tiles, or the slime molds that oozed across lawns. But all of these things are organisms.

The Characteristics of Living Things

Living things share important characteristics. **All living things have a cellular organization, contain similar chemicals, use energy, respond to their surroundings, grow and develop, and reproduce.**

Cellular Organization All organisms are made of small building blocks called cells. A **cell** is the basic unit of structure and function in an organism. Cells are so small that you need a microscope to see them.

Organisms may be composed of only one cell or of many cells. **Unicellular,** or single-celled organisms, include bacteria (bak TIHR ee uh), the most numerous organisms on Earth. **Multicellular** organisms are composed of many cells that are specialized to do certain tasks. For example, you are made of trillions of cells. Specialized cells in your body, such as muscle and nerve cells, work together to keep you alive.

Lab zone · Discover **Activity**

Skills Focus Forming operational definitions

Materials wind-up toys

Time 10 minutes

Tips Do not wind toys too tightly. Urge students to think of all living things, not just animals, as they make their lists.

L1 Expected Outcome Students could say that the toy is alive because it moves or that it is not alive because it does not eat, grow, or reproduce.

Think It Over All living things grow or change over time, while characteristics such as sleeping or talking are not shared among all organisms.

FIGURE 1
Cellular Organization
Like all living things, the frog is made of cells. Most cells are so small that you need a microscope to see them.

The Chemicals of Life The cells of all living things are composed of chemicals. The most abundant chemical in cells is water. Other chemicals, called carbohydrates (kahr boh HY drayts), are a cell's main energy source. Two other chemicals, proteins (PROH teenz) and lipids, are the building materials of cells. Nucleic (noo KLEE ik) acids are the genetic material—the chemical instructions that direct the cell's activities.

Energy Use The cells of organisms use energy to do what living things must do, such as repairing injured parts. An organism's cells are always hard at work. For example, as you read this paragraph, your eye and brain cells are at work. Your blood cells are busy moving chemicals around your body.

Response to Surroundings Have you noticed that plant stems bend toward the light? Plants and all other organisms react to changes in their environment. A change in an organism's surroundings that causes the organism to react is called a **stimulus** (plural *stimuli*). Stimuli include changes in temperature, light, sound, and other factors. An organism reacts to a stimulus with a **response**—an action or change in behavior. For example, has the sound of a car horn ever startled you? The sound was a stimulus that caused your response.

Growth and Development Living things also grow and develop. Growth is the process of becoming larger. **Development** is the process of change that occurs during an organism's life to produce a more complex organism.

Reproduction Another characteristic of organisms is the ability to reproduce, or produce offspring that are similar to the parents. For example, robins lay eggs that develop into young robins that closely resemble their parents.

Lab zone Try This **Activity**

React!

1. Have a partner clap his or her hands together about 10 centimeters in front of your face. Describe how you react.
2. Look at one of your eyes in a mirror. Cover the eye with your hand for a minute. While looking in the mirror, remove your hand. Observe how the size of your pupil changes.
3. Bring a slice of lemon close to your nose and mouth. Describe what happens.

Classifying For each action performed, name the stimulus and the response.

Lab zone Try This **Activity**

Skills Focus Classifying

Materials lemon slices, small mirrors

Time 10 minutes

Tips Remind students not to taste the lemon.

Expected Outcome clapping hands—sudden motion close to eyes/eyes blink; covering eyes, then uncover—change in light intensity/pupil contracts; lemon—smell/mouth puckers

Extend Challenge students to list 5 other stimulus/response actions of plants or animals. (*Possible answers: see a predator—run away; light source—plant stem turns toward*) **learning modality: kinesthetic**

Instruct

The Characteristics of Living Things

Teach Key Concepts   L2
Characteristics of All Living Things

Focus Tell students that biologists organize living things into groups to make the organisms easier to study. Link this statement with the boldfaced subheadings that follow The Characteristics of Living Things.

Teach Define each characteristic and give an example that relates to humans.

Apply Ask: **Which characteristics apply to trees?** (*All of them*) **To dogs?** (*All*) **learning modality: logical/mathematical**

Use Visuals: Figure 1   L2
Cellular Organization

Focus Tell students that the image in the circle shows cells that have been magnified.

Teach Help students identify individual cells. Ask students to describe the cells. (*The frog's cells are round and have a dark shape in the center.*)

Apply Explain that mushrooms are living things. Ask: **What would you expect to see if you magnified a mushroom?** (*Cellular structures similar to the frog's cells*) **learning modality: visual**

Independent Practice   L2

All in One **Teaching Resources, Unit 1**

• Guided Reading and Study Worksheet: *What Is Life?*

⊙ **Student Edition on Audio CD**

Monitor Progress _____ L2

Skills Check Have each student choose one living thing and explain how he or she knows it is alive.

Life Comes From Life

Teach Key Concepts

Living Things Arise Through Reproduction

Focus Direct students' attention to Figure 2.

Teach Ask: **How many jars did Redi use?** *(2)* Ask: **How do they differ?** *(One is covered; the other is not.)* Ask: **What did Redi conclude from his experiment?** *(The meat did not make maggots; the maggots came from flies.)*

Apply Ask: **If you found a baby mouse, what could you conclude?** *(Possible answer: A mother mouse lives nearby.)* **learning modality: visual**

 **Teaching Resources, Unit 1**

- Transparencies LS10, LS11

 **Lab zone**   Teacher **Demo**   L2

Compare Broth Samples

Materials beef broth that has been exposed to air for 2 to 3 days, beef broth from a freshly opened can

Time 10 minutes

Focus Show students the two cans of broth.

Teach Do not allow students to touch or taste the broth. Ask: **What is the difference between the two cans of broth?** *(The older broth will appear cloudier than the fresh one.)* **Why do you think Redi's and Pasteur's experiments used food?** *(Possible answer: People were concerned about food going bad.)*

Apply Ask: **How can you prevent the spread of germs through food?** *(Possible answers: wash hands before handling food, refrigerate food, cook food thoroughly)* Ask: **How do these behaviors prevent the spread of germs?** *(They kill some germs and prevent others from reproducing in the food.)* **learning modality: logical/mathematical**

Go Online
active art

For: Redi's and Pasteur's Experiments activity
Visit: PHSchool.com
Web Code: cep-1011

Students can interact online with the art of Redi's and Pasteur's experiments.

FIGURE 2
Redi's Experiment

Francesco Redi designed one of the first controlled experiments. In his experiment, Redi showed that flies do not spontaneously arise from decaying meat.
Controlling Variables *What is the manipulated variable in this experiment?*

Uncovered jar   Covered jar

❶ Redi placed meat in two identical jars. He left one jar uncovered. He covered the other jar with a cloth that let in air.

❷ After a few days, Redi saw maggots (young flies) on the decaying meat in the open jar. There were no maggots on the meat in the covered jar.

❸ Redi reasoned that flies had laid eggs on the meat in the open jar. The eggs hatched into maggots. Because flies could not lay eggs on the meat in the covered jar, there were no maggots there. Redi concluded that decaying meat did not produce maggots.

Go Online
active art

For: Redi's and Pasteur's Experiments activity
Visit: PHSchool.com
Web Code: cep-1011

Life Comes From Life

Today, when people see moths fly out of a closet or weeds poking out of cracks in the sidewalk, they know that these organisms are the result of reproduction. **Living things arise from living things through reproduction.** However, four hundred years ago, people believed that life could appear from nonliving material. For example, they thought that flies could arise from rotting meat. The mistaken idea that living things can arise from nonliving sources is called **spontaneous generation.** It took hundreds of years of experiments to convince people that spontaneous generation does not occur.

Redi's Experiment In the 1600s, an Italian doctor named Francesco Redi helped to disprove spontaneous generation. Redi designed a controlled experiment to show that flies do not arise from decaying meat. Recall that in a controlled experiment, a scientist carries out two tests that are identical in every respect except for one factor. The one factor that a scientist changes is called the manipulated variable.

Differentiated Instruction

English Learners/Beginning Comprehension: Key Concept   L1   Write *Characteristics of Living Things* on the board. Direct students' attention to the boldfaced subheadings that follow it in the text. Explain each characteristic. Have students construct a concept circle by connecting each characteristic to the central concept with lines. **learning modality: logical/mathematical**

English Learners/Intermediate Comprehension: Key Concept   L2   After students complete the Beginning activity, ask individuals to identify characteristics that all living things share. Then pair English learners with students who are proficient in English. Each pair should summarize the contents following one of the subheadings. **learning modality: verbal**

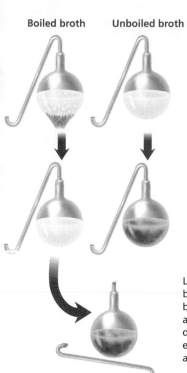

Boiled broth　　Unboiled broth

1 Pasteur put clear broth into two flasks with curved necks. The necks would let in oxygen but keep out bacteria from the air. Pasteur boiled the broth in one flask to kill any bacteria in the broth. He did not boil the broth in the other flask.

2 In a few days, the unboiled broth became cloudy, showing that new bacteria were growing. The boiled broth remained clear. Pasteur concluded that bacteria do not spontaneously arise from the broth. New bacteria appeared only when living bacteria were already present.

Later, Pasteur took the flask with the broth that had remained clear and broke its curved neck. Bacteria from the air could now enter the flask. In a few days, the broth became cloudy. This evidence confirmed that new bacteria arise only from existing bacteria.

FIGURE 3
Pasteur's Experiment
Louis Pasteur's carefully controlled experiment demonstrated that bacteria arise only from existing bacteria.

▲ Pasteur in his laboratory

In Redi's experiment, shown in Figure 2, the manipulated variable was whether or not the jar was covered. Flies were able to enter the uncovered jar and lay their eggs on the meat inside. These eggs hatched into maggots, which developed into new flies. The flies could not enter the covered jar, however. Therefore, no maggots formed on the meat in the covered jar. Through his experiment, Redi was able to conclude that rotting meat does not produce flies.

Pasteur's Experiment Even after Redi's work, many people continued to believe that spontaneous generation could occur. In the mid-1800s, the French chemist Louis Pasteur designed some controlled experiments that finally rejected spontaneous generation. As shown in Figure 3, he demonstrated that new bacteria appeared in broth only when they were produced by existing bacteria. The experiments of Redi and Pasteur helped to convince people that living things do not arise from nonliving material.

Reading Checkpoint What is a controlled experiment?

Chapter 2　◆　37

Differentiated Instruction

Less Proficient Readers L1
Recognizing Word Parts Students may not understand *variable*. Write the prefix *vari-* on the board. Explain that it means "diverse" or "having different characteristics." Have students look up words that begin with *vari*. Ask students to find synonyms that will help them identify *variables* in an experiment. **learning modality: verbal**

Gifted and Talented L3
Summarizing Ask students to explain how Pasteur's experiments led to the development of pasteurization. Students can summarize the process, its impact on society, and its link to Pasteur's experiments in a chart, poster, or report. **learning modality: verbal**

Lab zone Build **Inquiry**　L3

Design a Poster

Materials markers, poster board
Time 30 minutes

Focus Tell students they will design posters to show how Redi's and Pasteur's experiments helped disprove the idea of spontaneous generation. Divide the class into small groups for this purpose.

Teach Have students review the two experiments and choose one to illustrate. Encourage students to brainstorm how they will illustrate the experiment. Posters might show a flowchart, comic strip, or illustrated story, for example. Display the posters and allow students to present them to the class.

Apply Remind students that controlled experiments have a manipulated or independent variable and a dependent variable. Ask: **Which variables in these two experiments are manipulated and which are dependent?** (*Redi's experiment: manipulated—whether or not there was a cover; dependent—whether or not maggots formed on the meat; Pasteur's experiment: independent—whether or not the broth was boiled; dependent—growth of bacteria*)
learning modality: visual

Monitor Progress　L2

Writing Ask students to write a short paragraph explaining how we know that spontaneous generation does not take place.

Students can save their paragraphs in their portfolios. 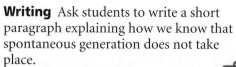 Portfolio

Answers
Figure 2 Whether or not the jar was covered

Reading Checkpoint An experiment in which two tests are identical except for one factor

The Needs of Living Things

Teach Key Concepts L2
Living Things Have Four Basic Needs

Focus Ask students to think of the things they need to live.

Teach Write the boldfaced concept statement on the board and read it aloud. Give students examples of each of the needs listed (food, water, living space, and stable internal conditions). Tell them that all of these things are needed by all living things.

Apply Ask students to choose a living thing and describe how it meets each of these needs. **learning modality: logical/mathematical**

Address Misconceptions L2
"Plant Food" Is Not Food

Focus Students may be confused by hearing the statement that plants make their own food, yet they know that people purchase commercial "plant food." Show students the label from a plant-food package. Point out the ingredients (usually forms of nitrogen, phosphorus, and potassium).

Teach Tell students that these chemicals are not actually food because they are not a source of energy. They are nutrients that plants need to grow, develop, and make food. The "food" that plants make is sugar.

Apply Ask: **List some nutrients people need that do not provide energy.** (*Possible answers: water, vitamins, minerals*) **learning modality: logical/mathematical**

Lab zone Skills **Activity**

Designing Experiments

Your teacher will give you a slice of potato. Predict what percentage of the potato's mass is water. Then come up with a plan to test your prediction. For materials, you will be given a hair dryer and a balance. Obtain your teacher's approval before carrying out your plan. How does your result compare with your prediction?

FIGURE 4
Water, Food, and Living Space

This environment meets the needs of the many animals that live there. **Inferring** *How do plants meet their needs for food?*

The Needs of Living Things

Though it may seem surprising, flies, bacteria, and all other organisms have the same basic needs as you. **All living things must satisfy their basic needs for water, food, living space, and stable internal conditions.**

Water All living things need water to survive. In fact, most organisms can live for only a few days without water. Organisms need water to obtain chemicals from their surroundings, break down food, grow, move substances within their bodies, and reproduce.

Food Recall that organisms need a source of energy to live. They use food as their energy source. Organisms differ in the ways they obtain energy. Some organisms, such as plants, capture the sun's energy and use it to make food. Organisms that make their own food are called **autotrophs** (AW toh trohfs). *Auto-* means "self" and *-troph* means "feeder." Autotrophs use the food they make to carry out their own life functions.

Organisms that cannot make their own food are called **heterotrophs** (HET uh roh trohfs). *Hetero-* means "other." Heterotrophs obtain their energy by feeding on others. Some heterotrophs eat autotrophs and use the energy in the autotroph's stored food. Other heterotrophs consume heterotrophs that eat autotrophs. Therefore, a heterotroph's energy source is also the sun—but in an indirect way. Animals, mushrooms, and slime molds are examples of heterotrophs.

 Reading Checkpoint Why are plants called autotrophs?

The porcupine, a heterotroph, feeds on green plants.

38 ◆

Lab zone Skills **Activity**

Skills Focus Designing experiments L2

Materials balance, hair dryer, paper towels, thin potato slices, small mirrors

Time 30 minutes

Safety Review the Safety Guidelines in Appendix A.

Tips Before class, slice the potatoes thin (but not too thin or they will blow away).

Keep slices in a container of cold water. Tell students to thoroughly dry potato slices.

Expected Outcome Have students find the mass of the wet potato slices, use the hair dryer to dry the slices, find the mass of the dry slices, and subtract to find the mass of the water lost. Have students place the slices on a paper towel on a flat surface and

turn them frequently. The water content of the potato slices is about 40%.

Extend Ask students to find the water content of other fruits or vegetables (apples, carrots, peppers). Encourage students to predict the water content before they begin. **learning modality: kinesthetic**

Frogs and Rainfall

Frogs need a moist environment, such as a pond, to survive. For five years, a scientist counted the frogs in a pond. The scientist also measured the spring rainfall.

1. **Reading Graphs** What data are plotted on the horizontal axis? What units were used?

2. **Interpreting Data** What was the greatest number of frogs that the scientist recorded? How much rain fell that spring?

3. **Making Generalizations** What is the relationship between the number of frogs and the amount of spring rain? What do you know about living things that might help explain that relationship?

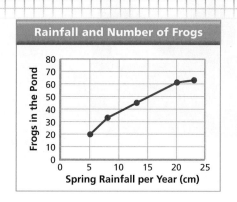

Rainfall and Number of Frogs

Frogs in the Pond (vertical axis, 0–80)
Spring Rainfall per Year (cm) (horizontal axis, 0–25)

Living Space All organisms need a place to live—a place to get food and water and find shelter. Whether an organism lives in the freezing Antarctic or the scorching desert, its surroundings must provide what it needs to survive.

Because there is a limited amount of space on Earth, some organisms must compete for space. Trees in a forest, for example, compete with other trees for sunlight above ground. Below ground, their roots compete for water and minerals.

The stream fulfills the moose's need for water.

The owl finds suitable living space in a tree hollow.

◆ 39

Math Skill Interpreting graphs

Focus Tell students that a line graph can help show whether two variables are related.

Teach Ask: **Does the graph tell which year each frog count was made?** *(No)* **What variable is plotted on the vertical axis?** *(Number of frogs in the pond)* **When was the frog count the lowest?** *(When the spring rainfall was 5 cm.)* **What is the overall trend of the graph?** *(The slope increases.)* **What does the trend indicate?** *(That the greater the rainfall, the larger the number of frogs)*

Answers

1. The spring rainfall per year plotted in centimeters
2. About 63 frogs; about 23 cm
3. The more rain that fell in the spring season, the larger the number of frogs that were observed in the pond. Since frogs require a moist environment, more frogs were able to survive during seasons with greater rainfall.

Monitor Progress _____ L2

Skills Check Have students choose one living thing and give examples of how it meets its basic needs.

Answers

Figure 4 Plants use the sun's energy to make their own food, and then use that food to carry out their life functions.

✓ **Reading Checkpoint** Because they make their own food

39

Monitor Progress

L2

Answer

 Reading Checkpoint The maintenance of stable internal conditions

Assess

Reviewing Key Concepts

1. a. Cellular organization, similar chemicals, energy use, response to surroundings, growth and development, and reproduction **b.** Response to surroundings **c.** It has all the characteristics of life. Movement is not a characteristic of life although many living things move.

2. a. The mistaken idea that living things can arise from nonliving things **b.** Spontaneous generation cannot occur, because living things can only arise from living things. Redi's and Pasteur's experiments help to disprove spontaneous generation. **c.** It showed that new bacteria in broth appeared only when there were existing bacteria.

3. a. A source of energy (food), water, living space, and stable internal conditions **b.** Getting energy by eating food **c.** It helps the fox keep it internal body temperature stable even though the temperature of the fox's surroundings changes.

Reteach

L1

Have each student create a concept map that includes the characteristics and needs of living things.

Performance Assessment

L2

Writing Have students invent a living thing that meets all the criteria in this section. Ask students to write a paragraph describing the characteristics of this new organism.

Portfolio

All in One Teaching Resources, Unit 1

- Section Summary: *What Is Life?*
- Review and Reinforce: *What Is Life?*
- Enrich: *What Is Life?*

FIGURE 5
Homeostasis
Sweating helps your body maintain a steady body temperature. Your body produces sweat during periods of strenuous activity. As the sweat evaporates, it cools your body down.

Stable Internal Conditions Organisms must be able to keep the conditions inside their bodies stable, even when conditions in their surroundings change significantly. For example, your body temperature stays steady despite changes in the air temperature. The maintenance of stable internal conditions is called **homeostasis** (hoh mee oh STAY sis).

Homeostasis keeps internal conditions just right for cells to function. Think about your need for water after a hard workout. When water levels in your body decrease, chemicals in your body send signals to your brain, causing you to feel thirsty.

Other organisms have different mechanisms for maintaining homeostasis. Consider barnacles, which as adults are attached to rocks at the edge of the ocean. At high tide, they are covered by water. At low tide, however, the watery surroundings disappear, and barnacles are exposed to hours of sun and wind. Without a way to keep water in their cells, they would die. Fortunately, a barnacle can close up its hard outer plates, trapping some water inside. In this way, a barnacle can keep its body moist until the next high tide.

 Reading Checkpoint What is homeostasis?

Section 1 Assessment

Target Reading Skill Using Prior Knowledge Review your graphic organizer and revise it based on what you just learned in the section.

Reviewing Key Concepts

1. a. Reviewing List the six characteristics of living things.
   b. Inferring A bird sitting in a tree flies away as you walk by. Which of the life characteristics explains the bird's behavior?
   c. Applying Concepts Explain why the tree, which does not move away, is also considered a living thing.

2. a. Defining What was meant by the idea of *spontaneous generation*?
   b. Explaining Why is this idea incorrect?
   c. Summarizing How did Pasteur's experiment help show that spontaneous generation does not occur?

3. a. Identifying What four things do all organisms need to survive?
   b. Describing Which need is a fox meeting by feeding on berries?
   c. Applying Concepts The arctic fox has thick, dense fur in the winter and much shorter fur in the summer. How does this help the fox maintain homeostasis?

Lab zone At-Home **Activity**

Observing Life With a family member, observe a living thing, such as a family pet, a houseplant, or a bird outside your window. Record your observations as you study the organism. Prepare a chart that shows how the organism meets the four needs of living things discussed in this section.

40 ◆

Lab zone Chapter **Project**

Keep Students on Track Have each student examine their mystery object, record observations, and develop a plan to test for different characteristics and predict how a living thing would respond to each test. Review plans. Work with students to revise plans that do not meet your approval.

Lab zone At-Home **Activity**

Observing Life **L1** Remind students to list the needs of living things and to include them in their charts. Ask students whether their family members agree with the information they recorded in their chart.

Lab zone Skills Lab

Please Pass the Bread!

Problem
What factors are necessary for bread molds to grow?

Skills Focus
observing, controlling variables

Materials
- paper plates
- plastic dropper
- bread without preservatives
- sealable plastic bags
- tap water
- packing tape

Procedure

1. Brainstorm with others to predict which factors might affect the growth of bread mold. Record your ideas.

2. Place two slices of bread of the same size and thickness on separate, clean plates.

3. To test the effect of moisture on bread mold growth, add drops of tap water to one bread slice until the whole slice is moist. Keep the other slice dry. Expose both slices of bread to the air for one hour.

4. Put each slice into its own sealable bag. Press the outside of each bag to remove the air. Seal the bags. Then use packing tape to seal the bags again. Store the bags in a warm, dark place.

5. Copy the data table into your notebook.

6. Every day for at least five days, briefly remove the sealed bags from their storage place. Record whether any mold has grown. Estimate the area of the bread where mold is present. **CAUTION:** *Do not unseal the bags. At the end of the experiment, give the sealed bags to your teacher.*

Analyze and Conclude

1. **Observing** How did the appearance of the two slices of bread change over the course of the experiment?

2. **Inferring** How can you explain any differences in appearance between the two slices?

3. **Controlling Variables** What was the manipulated variable in this experiment? Why was it necessary to control all other variables except this one?

4. **Communicating** Suppose that you lived in Redi's time. A friend tells you that molds just suddenly appear on bread. How would you explain to your friend about Redi's experiment and how it applies to molds and bread?

Design an Experiment

Choose another factor that may affect mold growth, such as temperature or the amount of light. Set up an experiment to test the factor you choose. Remember to keep all conditions the same except for the one you are testing. *Obtain your teacher's permission before carrying out your investigation.*

Data Table				
	Moistened Bread Slice		Unmoistened Bread Slice	
Day	Mold Present?	Area With Mold	Mold Present?	Area With Mold
1				
2				

Prepare for Inquiry

Key Concept
Bread mold needs water to grow.

Skills Objective
After this lab, students will be able to
- make quantitative observations of mold growth by using grids to make estimations
- control variables to determine the effect of different factors

Prep Time 20 minutes
Class Time 20 minutes the first day, then 5 minutes for each of the next 5 days

Advance Planning
Obtain bread without preservatives the day before

Safety
Do not open sealed bags. Released mold spores could aggravate allergies, asthma, or other medical conditions. Review the safety guidelines in Appendix A.

All in One Teaching Resources, Unit 1
- Lab Worksheet: *Please Pass the Bread!*

Guide Inquiry

Introduce the Procedure
Show students how to slide the bread off the side of the plate and into the bag. Students can use a grid containing squares of equal size to record and estimate mold growth. A 5 × 5 grid contains 25 squares, so each represents 4% of the slice.

Expected Outcome
Mold should grow on the moistened bread, but not on the dry bread.

Analyze and Conclude
1. The moistened bread became moldy. The unmoistened bread remained almost the same.
2. Mold grew on the moistened bread because it had the right conditions to grow—water, food (the bread), and living space (a dark, warm place).

3. The manipulated variable was moisture. If the other variables are not controlled, experimenters cannot be sure which variable caused a specific change.
4. Redi showed that spontaneous generation does not occur. Mold is produced only by existing mold and grows when environmental conditions are suitable.

Extend Inquiry

Design an Experiment Students' designs should take account of the fact that bread mold spores are in the air.

41

Classifying Organisms

Objectives
After completing the lesson, students will be able to

2.2.1 Explain why biologists classify organisms.

2.2.2 Relate the levels of classification to the relationships between organisms.

2.2.3 List characteristics used to classify organisms into groups, including domains and kingdoms.

Target Reading Skill 🎯

Asking Questions Explain that changing a head into a question helps students anticipate the ideas, facts, and events they are about to read.

Answers
Possible questions and answers include: **Why do scientists classify?** (*Scientists classify because they want to organize living things into groups so they are easier to study.*) **What system did Linnaeus use to name organisms?** (*He used a system called binomial nomenclature.*) **What are the levels of classification?** (*Domain, kingdom, phylum, class, order, family, genus, species*)

All in One Teaching Resources, Unit 1
• Transparency LS12

Preteach

Build Background Knowledge **L2**
How Libraries Are Organized
Ask: **How do libraries organize their books?** (*First by whether they are fiction or nonfiction, then by subject matter, then in alphabetical order by author's last name, first name, and finally title*) Discuss with students how difficult it would be to find a book in the library without an organizing system.

Section 2

Classifying Organisms

Reading Preview

Key Concepts
• Why do biologists organize living things into groups?
• What do the levels of classification indicate about the relationship between organisms?
• What characteristics are used to classify organisms into domains and kingdoms?

Key Terms
• classification • taxonomy
• binomial nomenclature
• genus • species • prokaryote
• nucleus • eukaryote

🎯 Target Reading Skill
Asking Questions Before you read, preview the red headings. In a graphic organizer like the one below, ask a *what*, *why*, or *how* question for each heading. As you read, write the answers to your questions.

Classifying Organisms

Question	Answer
Why do scientists classify?	Scientists classify because . . .

Lab zone · Discover **Activity**

Can You Organize a Junk Drawer?
1. Your teacher will give you some items that you might find in the junk drawer of a desk. Your job is to organize the items.
2. Examine the objects and decide on three groups into which you can sort them.
3. Place each object into one of the groups, based on how the item's features match the characteristics of the group.
4. Compare your grouping system with those of your classmates.

Think It Over
Classifying Which of your classmates' grouping systems seemed most useful? Why?

Suppose you had only ten minutes to run into a supermarket to get what you needed—milk and tomatoes. Could you do it? In most supermarkets this would be an easy task. You'd probably find out where the dairy and produce sections are, and head straight to those areas. Now imagine if you had to shop for these same items in a market where things were randomly placed throughout the store. Where would you begin? You'd have to search through a lot of things before you found what you needed. You could be there for a long time!

FIGURE 6
Classifying Vegetables
Vegetables in the produce section of a supermarket are neatly organized.

Lab zone · Discover **Activity**

Skills Focus Classifying **L1**

Materials items such as envelopes, erasers, paper, paper clips, pencils, rubber bands, stamps, tape

Time 15 minutes

Tips Avoid using sharp objects. Stress that items in a set must share at least one common trait.

Expected Outcome Students may group the items in a number of ways, such as by function (items you write with) or by shape (round).

Think It Over Each grouping system will have strengths and weaknesses. Criteria for usefulness will vary. Possibilities include systems that emphasize similar functions or that allow objects to be found quickly.

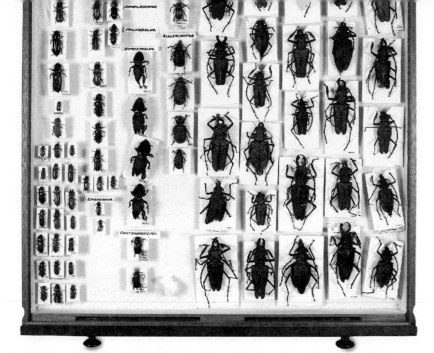

Why Do Scientists Classify?

Just as shopping can be a problem in a disorganized store, finding information about a specific organism can also be a problem. So far, scientists have identified more than one million kinds of organisms on Earth. That's a large number, and it is continually growing as scientists discover new organisms. Imagine how difficult it would be to find information about one particular organism if you had no idea even where to begin. It would be a lot easier if similar organisms were placed into groups.

Organizing living things into groups is exactly what biologists have done. Biologists group organisms based on similarities, just as grocers group milk with dairy products and tomatoes with produce. **Classification** is the process of grouping things based on their similarities.

Biologists use classification to organize living things into groups so that the organisms are easier to study. The scientific study of how living things are classified is called **taxonomy** (tak SAHN uh mee). Taxonomy is useful because once an organism is classified, a scientist knows a lot about that organism. For example, if you know that a crow is classified as a bird, then you know that a crow has wings, feathers, and a beak.

Figure 7
Classifying Beetles
These beetles belong to a large insect collection in a natural history museum. They have been classified according to characteristics they share. *Observing What characteristics may have been used to group these beetles?*

 Reading Checkpoint What is the scientific study of how living things are classified called?

Why Do Scientists Classify?

Teach Key Concepts L2
Organisms Are Organized into Groups

Focus Tell students that like organisms are grouped together. This makes it easier to study them.

Teach Write *kaz* on the board. Tell students this organism is a fish. Ask students to list what they know about *kaz* based on its classification.

Apply Ask: **How might you classify a sunflower, a robin, a lizard, a blue jay, and a tree?** *(Possible answers: sunflower and tree as plants; robin, lizard, and blue jay as animals; robin and blue jay as birds)* **learning modality: logical/mathematical**

Independent Practice L2

All in One Teaching Resources, Unit 1

• Guided Reading and Study Worksheet: *Classifying Organisms*

 Student Edition on Audio CD

Differentiated Instruction

Special Needs L2
Classifying Help students understand the concept of classification by discussing classification of rocks. Give students samples of igneous, metamorphic, and sedimentary rocks. Display a sample of each rock type in front of a labeled box. Ask students to classify their rock samples. **learning modality: kinesthetic**

Monitor Progress L2

Writing Have students describe the difference between classification and taxonomy.

Answers
Figure 7 Sample: Overall body shape, size, number of legs, shape of head and antennae, color

 Reading Checkpoint Taxonomy

43

The Naming System of Linnaeus

Teach Key Concepts [L2]
Scientific Names Have Two Parts

Focus Write these scientific names on the board: *Perognathus californicus, Perognathus nelsoni, Perognathus spinatus.*

Teach Explain that these animals are North American field pocket mice. Ask: **What genus/genera do these animals belong to?** *(Perognathus)* **What are the species of these mice?** *(Perognathus californicus, Perognathus nelsoni, and Perognathus spinatus)* Stress to students that both terms of the scientific name must be used to indicate an organism's species. The first term, the genus, can be used alone, while the second term (known as the specific epithet) cannot.

Extend Challenge students to see how much information they can infer about these animals from their names. *(Possible answers: They are different species, but all belong to the same genus. Mating among them would not produce fertile offspring. Students might infer that P. nelsoni was discovered by someone named Nelson, P. californicus is found in California, and P. spinatus has prickly fur.)* **learning modality: verbal**

Help Students Read [L2]
Analyze the Parts of Binomial
Word Part Analysis/Build Vocabulary

Write the term *binomial nomenclature* on the board. Tell students that *bi-* means "two" and *nomen* means "name." Ask: **What does the term *binomial* mean?** *(Two names)*

The Naming System of Linnaeus

Taxonomy also involves naming organisms. In the 1750s, the Swedish naturalist Carolus Linnaeus devised a system of naming organisms that is still used today. Linnaeus placed organisms in groups based on their observable features. Based on his observations, Linnaeus gave each organism a unique, two-part scientific name. This naming system Linnaeus used is called **binomial nomenclature** (by NOH mee ul NOH men klay chur). The word *binomial* means "two names."

Genus and Species The first word in an organism's scientific name is its genus. A **genus** (JEE nus) (plural *genera*) is a classification grouping that contains similar, closely related organisms. For example, pumas, marbled cats, and house cats are all classified in the genus *Felis*. Organisms that are classified in the genus *Felis* share characteristics such as sharp, retractable claws and behaviors such as hunting other animals.

The second word in a scientific name often describes a distinctive feature of an organism, such as where it lives or its appearance. Together, the two words indicate a unique species. A **species** (SPEE sheez) is a group of similar organisms that can mate with each other and produce offspring that can also mate and reproduce.

 Reading Checkpoint What kind of name did Linnaeus give each organism?

FIGURE 8 **Binomial Nomenclature**
These three species of cats belong to the same genus. Their scientific names, written in Latin, share the same first word, *Felis*. The second word of their names describes a feature of the animal. **Classifying** *What characteristics do these species share?*

Felis concolor (Puma)
Concolor means "the same color." Notice that this animal's coat is mostly the same color.

Felis marmorata (Marbled cat)
Notice the marbled pattern of this animal's coat. *Marmorata* means "marble."

Felis domesticus
(House cat)
Domesticus means "of the house."

44 ◆

Differentiated Instruction

Less Proficient Readers
Communicating Have students use sketches, photographs, and short captions to create a visual display that compares common names and scientific names.

[L1] Students can stick to the general concept or use a specific example. A specific example would be a pill bug/wood louse/roly poly/*Porcellio scaber*. **learning modality: visual**

Using Binomial Nomenclature Notice in Figure 8 that a complete scientific name is written in italics. Only the first letter of the first word is capitalized. Notice also that scientific names contain Latin words. Linnaeus used Latin because it was the language that scientists used during that time.

Binomial nomenclature makes it easy for scientists to communicate because everyone uses the same name for the same organism. Using different names can get confusing. For instance, people call the animal in Figure 9 a woodchuck, groundhog, or whistlepig. Fortunately, it has only one scientific name—*Marmota monax*.

Levels of Classification

The classification system that scientists use today is based on the contributions of Linnaeus. But today's classification system uses a series of many levels to classify organisms.

To help you understand the levels in classification, imagine a room filled with everybody from your state. First, all of the people from your town raise their hands. Then, those from your neighborhood raise their hands. Then, those from your street raise their hands. Finally, those from your house raise their hands. Each time, fewer people raise their hands. But you'd be in all of the groups. The most general group you belong to is the state. The most specific group is the house. The more levels you share with others, the more you have in common with them. Of course, organisms are not grouped by where they live, but rather by their shared characteristics.

The Major Levels of Classification Most biologists today classify organisms into eight levels. First, an organism is placed in a broad group, which in turn is divided into more specific groups. **The more classification levels that two organisms share, the more characteristics they have in common.**

Here are the eight classification levels that biologists commonly use.

- A domain is the highest level of organization.
- Within a domain, there are kingdoms.
- Within kingdoms, there are phyla (FY luh) (singular *phylum*).
- Within phyla are classes.
- Within classes are orders.
- Within orders are families.
- Each family contains one or more genera.
- Each genus contains one or more species.

FIGURE 9
Marmota monax
Although there are many common names for this animal, it has only one scientific name, *Marmota monax*.

Go Online
SciLINKS

For: Links on kingdoms
Visit: www.SciLinks.org
Web Code: scn-0113

Levels of Classification

Teach Key Concepts L2
Organisms Are Grouped into General and Specific Groups

Focus Draw a series of eight concentric circles on the board. Label the outermost circle "Domain." Label the innermost circle "Species."

Teach Correlate the remaining circles with their corresponding classification level. Point out that the broadest group is the domain. Ask: **Which is the most specific group?** *(Species)*

Extend Ask: **Which animals will share the same innermost circle?** *(Only those of the same species)* **Which animals will share the circle around the species circle?** *(Those of the same genus)* **Which animals will share the same kingdom circle?** *(All animals)*
learning modality: logical/mathematical

All in One Teaching Resources, Unit 1
- Transparency LS13

Go Online
SciLINKS

For: Links on kingdoms
Visit: www.SciLinks.org
Web Code: scn-0113

Download a worksheet that will guide students' review of Internet resources on kingdoms.

Monitor Progress _____ L2

Skills Check Ask students to explain which classification level will always have the most different kinds of organisms and which level will always have the fewest different kinds of organisms. *(Domain, species; because domains include some kingdoms, many phyla, classes, orders, families, genera, and species, while a species includes only one specific kind of organism)*

Answers
Figure 8 Sharp, retractable claws and behaviors such as hunting animals

 A unique two-part name

45

Make a Classification Chart

Materials colored pencils; dictionary; glue; list of class, order, and family of common pets; nature magazines; pen; poster board or heavyweight paper; ruler

Time 50 minutes

Focus Tell students to find the level in Figure 10 that would include a specific pet. Ask: **Which levels of Figure 10 would include a house cat?** (*Domain Eukarya; Kingdom Animalia; Phylum Chordata*)

Teach Direct students to create a model classification chart for a pet. Help students find the scientific name of their pet and determine its genus and species.

Apply Ask students how many classification levels the Magellan horned owl, *Bubo magellanicus* shares with *Bubo virginianus*. (*Seven*) **learning modality: visual**

Classifying an Owl Look at Figure 10 to see how the great horned owl is classified. The top row shows a wide variety of organisms that share the owl's domain. Notice that as you move down the levels, there are fewer kinds of organisms in each group. The organisms in each new group have more in common, however. For example, the class Aves includes all birds. The order Strigiformes includes only owls.

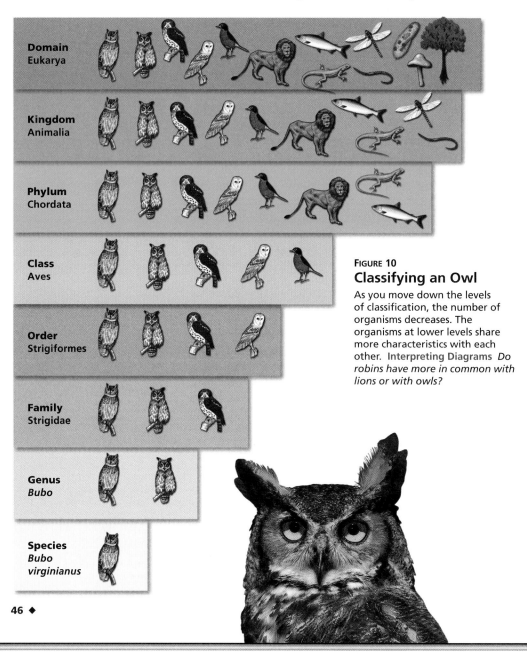

FIGURE 10
Classifying an Owl
As you move down the levels of classification, the number of organisms decreases. The organisms at lower levels share more characteristics with each other. **Interpreting Diagrams** *Do robins have more in common with lions or with owls?*

46 ◆

Domains and Kingdoms

Today, a three-domain system of classification is commonly used. Shown in Figure 11, the three domains are Bacteria, Archaea, and Eukarya. Within the domains are kingdoms. **Organisms are placed into domains and kingdoms based on their cell type, their ability to make food, and the number of cells in their bodies.**

Bacteria Although you may not know it, members of the domain Bacteria are all around you. You can find them in the yogurt you eat, on every surface you touch, and inside your body, both when you are healthy and sick. Some bacteria are autotrophs, while others are heterotrophs.

Members of the domain Bacteria are prokaryotes (proh KA ree ohtz). **Prokaryotes** are organisms whose cells lack a nucleus. A **nucleus** (NOO klee us) (plural *nuclei*) is a dense area in a cell that contains nucleic acids—the chemical instructions that direct the cell's activities. In prokaryotes, nucleic acids are not contained within a nucleus.

Archaea Deep in the Pacific Ocean, hot gases and molten rock spew out from a vent in the ocean floor. Surprisingly, a group of tiny organisms thrives there. They are members of the domain Archaea (ahr KEE uh), whose name comes from the Greek word for "ancient." Archaea can be found in some of the most extreme environments on Earth, including hot springs, very salty water, swamps, and the intestines of cows! Scientists think that the harsh conditions in which archaea live are similar to those of ancient Earth.

Like bacteria, archaea are unicellular prokaryotes. And like bacteria, some archaea are autotrophs while others are heterotrophs. Archaea are classified in their own domain, however, because their structure and chemical makeup differ from that of bacteria.

✔ **Reading Checkpoint** What is a nucleus?

Lab zone | Skills **Activity**

Classifying

Test your classifying skills using Figure 10. Look carefully at the organisms pictured together at the kingdom level. Make a list of the characteristics that the organisms share. Then make two more lists of shared characteristics—one for the organisms at the class level and the other for those at the genus level. How does the number of shared characteristics on your lists change at each level?

Three Domains of Life

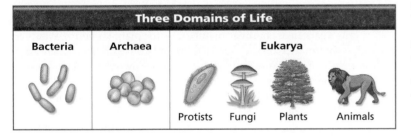

Bacteria	Archaea	Eukarya
		Protists Fungi Plants Animals

FIGURE 11
Three Domains
In the three-domain system of classification, all known organisms belong to one of three domains—Bacteria, Archaea, or Eukarya.

Chapter 2 ◆ **47**

Domains and Kingdoms

Teach Key Concepts   L2
The Three Domains

Focus Ask each student to write down the names of five organisms. Invite students to read their lists aloud. Ask the class how they would classify those living things if they had to put them into just three groups.

Teach Have students examine Figure 11, which names the three domains. Point out that the first two domains are made up of organisms that cannot be seen without a microscope. Ask: **What does it mean to say that those two domains include only unicellular eukaryotes?** *(Every organism is made up of just one cell, and that cell has no nucleus.)* **How do the members of the two domains get food?** *(Some are autotrophs, while others are heterotrophs.)*

Apply Invite students to read any names from their lists that belong in either domain Bacteria or domain Archaea. Ask: **What can you conclude from this reading?** *(Most or all of their lists will probably consist of members of the domain Eukarya.)* **learning modality: verbal**

Monitor Progress _____ L2

Answers
Figure 10 Owls; robins and owls are birds, and so robins share many more levels of classification with owls than they do with lions.

✔ **Reading Checkpoint** A dense area in a cell that contains nucleic acids

---

Lab zone | Skills **Activity**

Skills Focus Classifying   L2

Time 10 minutes

Tips At the kingdom level, ask: **Are these animals unicellular or multicellular?** *(Multicellular)* **Autotrophs or heterotrophs?** *(Heterotrophs)* For the class and genus levels, point out that structural adaptations for movement and obtaining food can be used in classification. If students need more help, question them about adaptations that help birds fly, eat, perch.

Expected Outcome The closer to the species level, the longer the list of shared characteristics. *(Kingdom: multicellular heterotrophs; Class: multicellular heterotrophs with wings, feathers, a beak, feet that grip; Genus: similar body shape,* tufts of feathers, hooked beak, flat, round face, forward facing eyes, talons)

Extend Challenge students to describe some shared characteristics of humans. *(Possible answers: multicellular heterotroph, walks on two legs, has hair, opposable thumb, stands upright)* **learning modality: visual**

Domain Eukarya

Teach Key Concepts L2
Eukarya Are Eukaryotes

Focus List ten different plants, animals, protists, and fungi on the board and direct students' attention to the list. Tell students all these organisms are made of cells that have a nucleus (eukaryotes).

Teach List the kingdoms that make up Eukarya (Animals, Plants, Protists, Fungi). Review the main characteristics of each kingdom. Ask: **What do members of these kingdoms have in common?** *(They are eukaryotes.)*

Extend Have students classify the list of organisms from Focus into the four kingdoms. **learning modality: logical/ mathematical**

Teacher Demo L3

Staining Leaves

Materials alcohol, iodine, light green leaf, petri dish

Focus Tell students that iodine darkens when it touches starch.

Teach Soak the leaf in alcohol for 24 hours. Dry the leaf, place it in a glass dish, and cover it with iodine. Show the leaf to students. Ask: **What can you conclude?** *(The leaf contains starch.)* Explain to students that the food plants make is sugar, stored in the form of starch.

Apply Ask: **How did the starch get in the leaf?** *(The plant made it.)* **learning modality: visual**

▲ Protists: Paramecium
▲ Fungi: Mushrooms

FIGURE 12
Domain Eukarya
You can encounter organisms from all four kingdoms of Eukarya on a hike through the woods.
Making Generalizations *What characteristic do all Eukarya share?*

Domain Eukarya

What do seaweeds, mushrooms, tomatoes, and dogs have in common? They are all members of the domain Eukarya. Organisms in this domain are **eukaryotes** (yoo KA ree ohtz)—organisms with cells that contain nuclei. **Scientists classify organisms in the domain Eukarya into one of four kingdoms: protists, fungi, plants, or animals.**

Protists A protist (PROH tist) is any eukaryotic organism that cannot be classified as an animal, plant, or fungus. Because its members are so different from one another, the protist kingdom is sometimes called the "odds and ends" kingdom. For example, some protists are autotrophs, while other protists are heterotrophs. Most protists are unicellular, but some, such as seaweeds, are large multicellular organisms.

Fungi If you have eaten mushrooms, then you have eaten fungi (FUN jy). Mushrooms, molds, and mildew are all fungi. Most fungi are multicellular eukaryotes. A few, such as the yeast you use for baking, are unicellular eukaryotes. Fungi are found almost everywhere on land, but only a few live in fresh water. All fungi are heterotrophs. Most fungi feed by absorbing nutrients from dead or decaying organisms.

Plants Dandelions on a lawn, mosses in a forest, and peas in a garden are familiar members of the plant kingdom. Plants are all multicellular eukaryotes and most live on land. In addition, plants are autotrophs that make their own food. Plants provide food for most of the heterotrophs on land.

The plant kingdom includes a great variety of organisms. Some plants produce flowers, while others do not. Some plants, such as giant redwood trees, can grow very tall. Others, like mosses, never grow taller than a few centimeters.

Differentiated Instruction

Less Proficient Readers L1
Compare and Contrast Have students work in small groups to prepare a compare and contrast table for the six kingdoms. Suggest these column headings: *Kingdom, Cell Type, Ability to Make Food, Number of Cells, Examples.* Have students list the kingdoms in the first column and fill in information for the remaining columns.

Gifted and Talented L3
Making Connections Ask students to find out how the six kingdoms and three domains are related. Have students summarize their findings in a graphic organizer or phylogenic tree. **learning modality: visual**

▲ Plants: Moss

▲ Animals: Salamander

Animals A dog, a flea on the dog's ear, and a cat that the dog chases have much in common because all are animals. All animals are multicellular eukaryotes. In addition, all animals are heterotrophs. Animals have different adaptations that allow them to locate food, capture it, eat it, and digest it. Members of the animal kingdom live in diverse environments throughout Earth. Animals can be found from ocean depths to mountaintops, from hot, scalding deserts to cold, icy landscapes.

 Reading Checkpoint | Which two kingdoms consist only of heterotrophs?

Section 2 Assessment

⊙ **Target Reading Skill** Asking Questions Use the answers to the questions you wrote about the headings to help you answer the questions below.

Reviewing Key Concepts

1. **a. Reviewing** Why do biologists classify?
   b. Inferring Suppose someone tells you that a jaguarundi is classified in the same genus as a house cat. What characteristics do you think a jaguarundi might have?
   c. Predicting What genus name would you expect a jaguarundi to have? Explain.
2. **a. Listing** List in order the levels of classification, beginning with domain.
   b. Applying Concepts Woodchucks are classified in the same family as squirrels, but in a different family than mice. Do woodchucks have more characteristics in common with squirrels or mice? Explain.

3. **a. Identifying** What are the three domains into which organisms are classified?
   b. Classifying Which two domains include only organisms that are prokaryotes?
   c. Comparing and Contrasting How do the members of the two domains of prokaryotes differ?

Lab zone At-Home **Activity**

Kitchen Classification With a family member, go on a "classification hunt" in the kitchen. Look in your refrigerator, cabinets, and drawers to discover what classification systems your family uses to organize items. Then explain to your family member the importance of classification in biology.

Answers

Figure 12 All organisms that are eukaryotes have cells that contain nuclei.

✔ Reading Checkpoint | Fungi and animals

Assess

Reviewing Key Concepts

1. **a.** To make studying organisms easier
   b. Possible answers: Four legs, fur, sharp, retractable claws, hunts other animals
   c. The name *Felis* because that's the housecat's genus
2. **a.** Domain, kingdom, phylum, class, order, family, genus, species **b.** Squirrels, because organisms in the same family are more similar to each other than to those in different families
3. **a.** Bacteria, Archaea, Eukarya **b.** Bacteria and Archaea **c.** In the structure and chemical makeup of their cells

Reteach L1

As a class, summarize the characteristics of each domain and the kingdoms that make up Eukarya.

All in One Teaching Resources, Unit 1

- Section Summary: *Classifying Organisms*
- Review and Reinforce: *Classifying Organisms*
- Enrich: *Classifying Organisms*

Lab zone Chapter **Project**

Keep Students on Track Encourage students to observe their object each day and record observations and drawings. If students seem bored because their object is not doing anything, encourage them to consider whether the inactivity shows that the object is not alive, or whether they should revise their methods of observation. For example, encourage students to explain how they could be sure that the object is not breathing or growing.

Lab zone At-Home **Activity**

Kitchen Classification L1 Remind students to identify the criteria used to classify kitchen objects in their houses. Families may have organized items by size, function, or location. Ask students whether their family members agreed with their classification systems.

49

Objectives

After this lesson, students will be able to
2.3.1 Tell what cells are.
2.3.2 Explain how the invention of the microscope contributed to scientists' understanding of living things.
2.3.3 State the cell theory.
2.3.4 Describe how microscopes produce magnified images.

Target Reading Skill

Sequencing Explain that organizing information from beginning to end helps students understand a step-by-step process.

Answer

One possible way to complete the flowchart:
Discovering Cells
Hooke sees cells in cork; Leeuwenhoek sees many one-celled organisms; Schleiden concludes that all plants are made of cells; Schwann concludes that all animals (and all living things) are made of cells; Virchow proposes that new cells form only from cells that already exist.

All in One Teaching Resources, Unit 1
• Transparency LS14

Preteach

Build Background Knowledge

Numbers of Cells

Ask: **How many individual grains of sand do you think make up a beach?** (*Students probably will say billions or trillions.*) Point out that humans and many other living things are composed of trillions of tiny components as well. These components, called cells, are too small to be easily seen without a microscope.

Reading Preview

Key Concepts
• What are cells?
• How did the invention of the microscope contribute to knowledge about living things?
• What is the cell theory?
• How do microscopes produce magnified images?

Key Terms
• cell • microscope • cell theory

Target Reading Skill

Sequencing A sequence is the order in which a series of events occurs. As you read, construct a flowchart showing how the work of Hooke, Leeuwenhoek, Schleiden, Schwann, and Virchow contributed to scientific understanding of cells.

Discovering Cells

Hooke sees cells in cork.

↓

↓

Lab zone Discover **Activity**

Is Seeing Believing?

1. Cut a black-and-white photograph out of a page in a newspaper. With only your eyes, closely examine the photo. Record your observations.
2. Examine the same photo with a hand lens. Again, record your observations.
3. Place the photo on the stage of a microscope. Use the clips to hold the photo in place. Shine a light down on the photo. Focus the microscope on part of the photo. (See Appendix B for instructions on using the microscope.) Record your observations.

Think It Over
Observing What did you see in the photo with the hand lens that you could not see with only your eyes? What additional details could you see with the microscope?

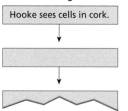

A forest is filled with an amazing variety of living things. Some are easy to see, but you have to look closely to find others. If you look carefully at the floor of a forest, you can often find spots of bright color. A beautiful pink coral fungus grows beneath tall trees. Beside the pink fungus, a tiny red newt perches on a fallen leaf.

What do you think a fungus, a tree, and a red newt have in common? They are all living things, or organisms, and, like all organisms, they are made of cells.

FIGURE 13
Newt and Coral Fungus
All living things are made of cells, including this pink fungus and the red newt that perches next to it.

50 ◆

Lab zone Discover **Activity**

Skills Focus Observing

Materials black and white newspaper photograph, hand lens, microscope, scissors

Time 10 minutes

Tips CAUTION: *Advise students to be careful when using the scissors.* Set up several microscopes around the room and review with students how to use them.

L1

Expected Outcome Students can see the individual dots of ink that make up the photograph. This will help them appreciate how the hand lens and microscope allow them to see very small objects.

Think It Over The black and grey shaded areas in the picture are made up of separate tiny dots of ink. Additional details may include things such as fibers or flaws in the paper.

An Overview of Cells

You are made of cells. **Cells are the basic units of structure and function in living things.** This means that **cells** form the parts of an organism and carry out all of an organism's processes, or functions.

Cells and Structure When you describe the structure of an object, you describe what it is made of and how its parts are put together. The structures of many buildings, for example, are determined by the way in which bricks, steel beams, and other materials are arranged. The structures of living things are determined by the amazing variety of ways in which cells are put together. A tall tree, for example, consists of cells arranged to form a high trunk and leafy branches. A red newt's cells form a body with a head and four legs.

Cells and Function An organism's functions are the processes that enable it to stay alive and reproduce. Some functions in organisms include obtaining oxygen, getting rid of wastes, obtaining food, and growing. Cells are involved in all these functions. For example, cells in your digestive system absorb food. The food provides your body with energy and materials needed for growth.

Many and Small Figure 14 shows human skin cells. One square centimeter of your skin's surface contains more than 100,000 cells. But no matter how closely you look with your eyes alone, you won't be able to see individual skin cells. That is because, like most cells, those of your skin are very small. Until the late 1600s, no one knew cells existed because there was no way to see them.

 **Reading Checkpoint** What are some functions that cells perform in living things?

First Observations of Cells

Around 1590, the invention of the microscope enabled people to look at very small objects. **The invention of the microscope made it possible for people to discover and learn about cells.** A **microscope** is an instrument that makes small objects look larger. Some microscopes do this by using lenses to focus light. The lenses used in light microscopes are similar to the clear, curved pieces of glass or plastic used in eyeglasses. A simple microscope contains only one lens. A light microscope that has more than one lens is called a compound microscope.

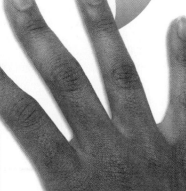

FIGURE 14
Skin Cells
Your skin is made of cells such as these. **Applying Concepts** *What are cells?*

An Overview of Cells

Help Students Read ⬜L2

Active Comprehension Refer to the Content Refresher for guidelines on using Active Comprehension. Have students read the first paragraph in this section. Ask: **What would you like to know about cells?** *(Possible answers: What do cells do? How do microscopes work?)* Write student responses on the board. After students have finished reading the section, ask them to respond to each question.

Teach Key Concepts ⬜L2

Cell Structure and Function

Focus Call students' attention to the photograph of the hand and the close up image of human skin cells.

Teach Ask: **Why do you need a microscope to see most cells?** *(They are too small to be seen with the naked eye.)* **What are cells?** *(The basic units of structure and function in living things)* **What are some functions of cells?** *(Obtaining oxygen, getting rid of waste, obtaining food, growing)*

Apply Explain that cells are so small that scientists use the micron, one thousandth of one millimeter, to measure cells. **learning modality: verbal**

Independent Practice ⬜L2

All in One Teaching Resources, Unit 1
• Guided Reading and Study Worksheet: *Discovering Cells*

 Student Edition on Audio CD

Differentiated Instruction

Special Needs ⬜L1
Magnifying Objects Have students choose a suitable object, such as a strand of human hair, to place on a slide with a coverslip and view under the microscope, first at low and then at high power. For students whose movements are limited,

you can use a microprojector to project the images on a screen, or pair students with students who can adjust and turn the knobs on the microscope. Have students orally describe what they see under each magnification. **learning modality: visual**

Monitor Progress ⬜L2

Writing Ask students to write a definition of cells using an analogy similar to the building materials analogy in the text.

Answers
Figure 14 The basic units of structure and function in living things

Reading Checkpoint Cells obtain oxygen, get rid of wastes, obtain food, and grow.

First Observations of Cells

Teach Key Concepts $\quad$ L2

Discovery of the Cell

Focus Remind students that without instruments to make them visible, cells were unknown until the microscope was invented.

Teach Ask: **What was Robert Hooke's contribution to the study of cells?** *(Hooke was one of the first people to observe cells. He gave them their name.)* **What did Anton van Leeuwenhoek use his microscope to study?** *(Lake water, scrapings from his teeth and gums, water from rain gutters, and tiny, moving organisms that he named animalcules.)* **How did the invention of the microscope help advance the study of life science?** *(The invention of the microscope made it possible to discover and learn about cells.)*

Apply Hooke published drawings of the cells he saw in a book, which became a bestseller. Ask: **Why do you think people were so interested in seeing Hooke's drawings?** *(They were drawings of things that up until then had been invisible, so the book opened up a whole new world to people.)*
learning modality: visual

Classifying Images

Materials Photocopies of images produced by different types of microscopes (available in high school and college-level textbooks)

Time 10 minutes

Focus Review the magnifications of the microscopes featured in the text.

Teach Provide a set of the images to each group of students. Have them classify the images according to which microscope they think took them.

Apply Ask: **Why are light microscopes still used?** *(Possible answer: Light microscopes are less expensive. Also, sometimes you do not want the level of detail you get with higher magnifications, such as when looking at feathers or insect legs. In such cases, you want to look at overall structure.)* **learning modality: visual**

Robert Hooke One of the first people to observe cells was the English scientist and inventor Robert Hooke. Hooke built his own compound microscope, which was one of the best microscopes of his time. In 1663, Hooke used his microscope to observe the structure of a thin slice of cork. Cork, the bark of the cork oak tree, is made up of cells that are no longer alive. To Hooke, the empty spaces in the cork looked like tiny rectangular rooms. Therefore, Hooke called the empty spaces *cells*, which is a word meaning "small rooms."

Hooke described his observations this way: "These pores, or cells, were not very deep, but consisted of a great many little boxes. . . ." What most amazed Hooke was how many cells the cork contained. He calculated that in a cubic inch there were about twelve hundred million cells—a number he described as "almost incredible."

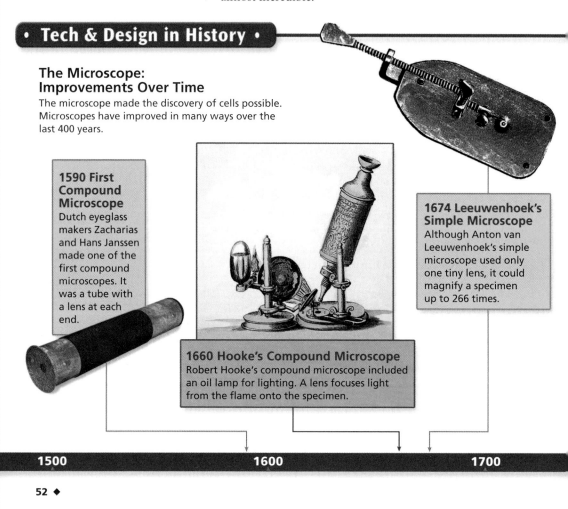

• Tech & Design in History •

The Microscope: Improvements Over Time
The microscope made the discovery of cells possible. Microscopes have improved in many ways over the last 400 years.

1590 First Compound Microscope
Dutch eyeglass makers Zacharias and Hans Janssen made one of the first compound microscopes. It was a tube with a lens at each end.

1660 Hooke's Compound Microscope
Robert Hooke's compound microscope included an oil lamp for lighting. A lens focuses light from the flame onto the specimen.

1674 Leeuwenhoek's Simple Microscope
Although Anton van Leeuwenhoek's simple microscope used only one tiny lens, it could magnify a specimen up to 266 times.

1500	1600	1700

Background

Facts and Figures To differentiate among particular cell structures under a microscope, scientists may stain the tissue to be examined. Different stains color different structures inside cells. For example, a stain called hematoxylin colors the cell's nucleus, the area where most nucleic acids in the cell are found.

After staining the tissue, a scientist shaves off extremely thin slices with a precision cutting instrument called a microtome. The microtome can cut slices so thin that they are less than one cell thick. This allows a clear view of even the tiniest cell structures.

Anton van Leeuwenhoek At about the same time that Robert Hooke made his discovery, Anton van Leeuwenhoek (LAY vun hook) also began to observe tiny objects with microscopes. Leeuwenhoek was a Dutch businessman who sold cloth. In his spare time, he built simple microscopes.

Leeuwenhoek looked at drops of lake water, scrapings from teeth and gums, and water from rain gutters. In many materials, Leeuwenhoek was surprised to find a variety of one-celled organisms. Leeuwenhoek noted that many of these tiny organisms moved. Some whirled, some hopped, and some shot through water like fast fish. He called these moving organisms *animalcules* (an ih MAL kyoolz), meaning "little animals."

 Reading Checkpoint Which type of microscope—simple or compound—did Leeuwenhoek make and use?

Writing in Science

Research and Write Find out more about one of the microscopes. Then write an advertisement for it that might appear in a popular science magazine. Be creative. Emphasize the microscope's usefulness or describe the wonders that can be seen with it.

1886 Modern Compound Light Microscope German scientists Ernst Abbé and Carl Zeiss made a compound light microscope with complex lenses that greatly improved the image. A mirror focuses light up through the specimen. Modern compound microscopes can effectively magnify a specimen up to 1,000 times.

1965 Scanning Electron Microscope (SEM) An SEM sends electrons over the surface of a specimen, rather than through it. The result is a three-dimensional image of the specimen's surface. SEMs can magnify a specimen up to 150,000 times.

1933 Transmission Electron Microscope (TEM) German physicist Ernst Ruska created the first electron microscope. TEMs send electrons through a very thinly sliced specimen. TEMs can magnify a specimen up to 500,000 times.

1981 Scanning Tunneling Microscope (STM) An STM measures electrons that leak, or "tunnel," from the surface of a specimen. STMs can magnify a specimen up to 1,000,000 times.

| 1800 | 1900 | 2000 |

Chapter 2 ◆ 53

Development of the Cell Theory

Teach Key Concepts L2

Understanding the Cell Theory

Focus Remind students that even after Hooke viewed cork cells, scientists still did not understand cells and their importance.

Teach Draw a simple timeline on the board that begins with Hooke's observation of cork cells in 1663. Ask: **How did Schleiden, Schwann, and Virchow contribute to the understanding of cells?** (*In 1838, Schleiden concluded that all plants are made of cells. In 1839, Schwann concluded that all animals are made of cells. In 1855, Virchow proposed that all new cells are formed from existing cells.*) As students answer, add each contribution to the timeline. Point out that almost 200 years separated the contributions of Hooke and Virchow. Ask: **What is the cell theory?** (*All living things are composed of cells. Cells are the basic units of structure and function in living things. All cells are produced from other cells.*)

Apply Ask: **Why do you think it took almost 200 years after cells were discovered for scientists to conclude that all living things consist of cells?** (*Sample answer: There were far fewer scientists and microscopes than there are today, and scientists had to examine thousands of samples of living things before they could reasonably conclude that all living things are made of cells.*) **learning modality: visual**

Animal Cells

54 ◆

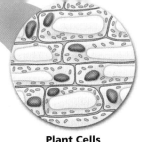

FIGURE 15
Monarch and Milkweed
The monarch butterfly caterpillar and the milkweed leaf that the caterpillar nibbles on are both made of cells.

Plant Cells

Development of the Cell Theory

Leeuwenhoek's exciting discoveries caught the attention of other researchers. Like Hooke, Leeuwenhoek, and all good scientists, these other researchers were curious about the world around them, including things they couldn't normally see. Many other people began to use microscopes to discover what secrets they could learn about cells.

Schleiden, Schwann, and Virchow Three German scientists made especially important contributions to people's knowledge about cells. These scientists were Matthias Schleiden (SHLY dun), Theodor Schwann, and Rudolf Virchow (FUR koh). In 1838, Schleiden concluded that all plants are made of cells. He based this conclusion on his own research and on the research of others before him. The next year, Theodor Schwann concluded that all animals are also made up of cells. Thus, stated Schwann, all living things are made up of cells.

Schleiden and Schwann had made an important discovery about living things. However, they didn't explain where cells came from. Until their time, most people thought that living things could come from nonliving matter. In 1855, Virchow proposed that new cells are formed only from cells that already exist. "All cells come from cells," wrote Virchow.

What the Cell Theory Says Schleiden, Schwann, Virchow, and others helped develop the cell theory. The **cell theory** is a widely accepted explanation of the relationship between cells and living things. **The cell theory states the following:**

- **All living things are composed of cells.**

- **Cells are the basic units of structure and function in living things.**

- **All cells are produced from other cells.**

The cell theory holds true for all living things, no matter how big or how small. Since cells are common to all living things, they can provide information about the functions that living things perform. Because all cells come from other cells, scientists can study cells to learn about growth and reproduction.

 Reading Checkpoint What did Schleiden and Schwann conclude about cells?

Light and Electron Microscopes

The cell theory could not have been developed without microscopes. For a microscope to be useful, it must combine two important properties—magnification and resolution. Scientists today use two kinds of microscopes: light microscopes and electron microscopes.

Magnification and Lenses The first property, magnification, is the ability to make things look larger than they are. **The lenses in light microscopes magnify an object by bending the light that passes through them.** If you examine a hand lens, such as the one in Figure 16, you will see that the lens is curved, not flat. The center of the lens is thicker than the edge. A lens with this curved shape is called a convex lens. The light passing through the sides of the lens bends inward. When this light hits the eye, the eye sees the object as larger than it really is.

Convex lens

Incoming light rays bend as they pass through a convex lens.

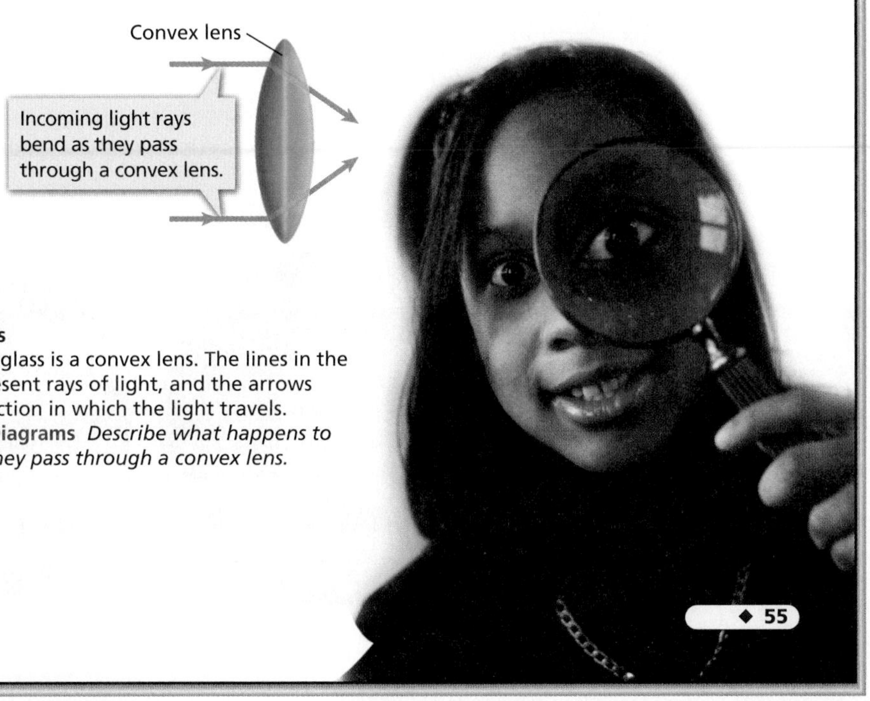

FIGURE 16
A Convex Lens
A magnifying glass is a convex lens. The lines in the diagram represent rays of light, and the arrows show the direction in which the light travels.
Interpreting Diagrams *Describe what happens to light rays as they pass through a convex lens.*

♦ 55

 **Lab zone** Skills **Activity**

Observing

1. Read about using the microscope (Appendix B) before beginning this activity.
2. Place a prepared slide of a thin slice of cork on the stage of a microscope.
3. Observe the slide under low power. Draw what you see.
4. Place a few drops of pond water on another slide and cover it with a coverslip.
5. Observe the slide under low power. Draw what you see. Wash your hands after handling pond water.

How does your drawing in Step 3 compare to Hooke's description of cells on page 52? Based on your observations in Step 5, why did Leeuwenhoek call the organisms he saw "little animals"?

Light and Electron Microscopes

Teach Key Concepts L2
How Microscopes Magnify Images

Focus Remind students that cells were visible only after the invention of microscopes.

Teach Refer students to the inset in Figure 16. Ask: **What shape is the lens?** *(Convex)* **What does it do to light passing through?** *(Bends it inward)* **What two properties does a light microscope need to work?** *(Magnification and resolution)* **How does an electron microscope magnify?** *(By using a beam of electrons)*

Apply Ask: **When might you use a light microscope instead of an electron microscope?** *(When you do not need great magnification)* **learning modality: verbal**

All in One Teaching Resources, Unit 1
• Transparency LS15

 Lab zone Build **Inquiry** L1

Applying How Microscopes Work

Focus Use Appendix B to point out the parts of a microscope.

Teach Have students name its parts and describe its functions.

Apply Ask students to write a paragraph describing how microscopes magnify images. **learning modality: kinesthetic**

Monitor Progress _____ L2

Oral Presentation Call on students to describe the cell theory in their own words.

Answers
Figure 16 The light rays bend inward.

Reading Checkpoint Schleiden: All plants are made of cells; Schwann: all animals are made of cells.

Lab zone Skills **Activity**

Skills Focus Observing L2

Materials blank slide, coverslip, microscope, plastic dropper, pond water, prepared slide of cork

Time 10 minutes

Tips Caution students that glass slides are fragile. Make sure students have focused the microscope and can see the cells clearly before they start their drawings.

Expected Outcome Drawings of cork cells should resemble Hooke's drawing. Leeuwenhoek called the organisms he saw "little animals" because they moved as animals move.

Extend Ask students to examine a drop of tap water under the microscope. Most likely, the water will not contain microorganisms, but it could possibly contain non-disease-causing ones, as treated tap water is not sterile. **learning modality: visual**

Observing with a Microscope

Materials compound microscope, prepared slides of various cells and microscopic organisms

Time 10 minutes

Focus Review how to determine the magnification of an object using a compound microscope.

Teach Caution students that glass slides are fragile. Have students view the slides first at low power and then at high power. Ask them to calculate the magnification of each. Ask: **What does the microscopic view allow you to see that the naked eye does not?** (*The microscope allows you to see the smaller details and tinier parts of the object.*) Point out that smaller magnifications are useful for viewing an entire organism, such as the water flea in Figure 6.

Apply Have students draw and label a simple sketch of what they see under each magnification, then share their drawings with the class. **learning modality: visual**

Integrating Physics

Show students a concave lens and have students contrast its structure to that of a convex lens. Group students in pairs, and instruct one student to hold a hand lens (convex lens) steady at about 10 cm above a page. Tell the other student to move closer to or farther from the lens until the letters on the page come into focus. At this point, have both students note the relative positions of the eye, lens, and page. By moving farther back from the lens, students can see the difference between magnification and resolution. Ask: **How does the object appear now?** (*Even larger but blurry, or out of focus*) Have students switch positions and repeat the activity. **learning modality: kinesthetic**

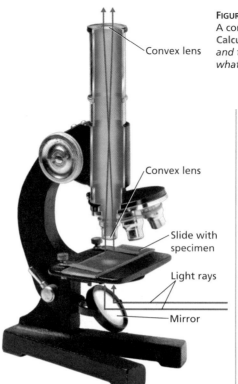

Convex lens

Convex lens

Slide with specimen

Light rays

Mirror

FIGURE 17 A Compound Microscope
A compound microscope has two convex lenses.
Calculating *If one lens has a magnification of 10, and the other lens has a magnification of 50, what is the total magnification?*

Compound Microscope Magnification

A compound microscope uses more than one lens. As a result, it can magnify an object more than one lens by itself. Light passes through a specimen and then through two lenses, as shown in Figure 17. The first lens, near the specimen, magnifies the object. Then a second lens, near the eye, further magnifies the enlarged image. The total magnification of the microscope is equal to the magnifications of the two lenses multiplied together. For example, suppose the first lens makes an object look 10 times bigger than it actually is, and the second lens makes the object look 40 times bigger than it actually is. The total magnification of the microscope is 10×40, or 400.

Resolution To create a useful image, a microscope must also help you see individual parts clearly. The ability to clearly distinguish the individual parts of an object is called resolution. Resolution is another term for the sharpness of an image. For example, a photograph in a newspaper is really made up of a collection of small dots. If you put the photo under a microscope, you can see the dots. You see the dots not only because they are magnified but also because the microscope improves resolution. Good resolution is needed when you study cells.

FIGURE 18
Light Microscope Photos
The pictures of the water flea and the threadlike *Spirogyra* were both taken with a light microscope.

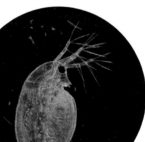

Water flea
40 times actual size

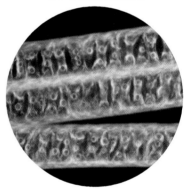

Spirogyra
300 times actual size

Differentiated Instruction

Less Proficient Readers L1
Reading in Pairs Parts of the chapter, such as the paragraphs under the heading Light and Electron Microscopes, contain advanced words and concepts that some students may find difficult. Pair these students with more proficient readers. Have each student read a paragraph in the section independently. Next, have the students discuss what they have read with their partners. Encourage them to discuss the main ideas of what they read as well as any questions they may have about it. Then have them write a paragraph in their own words that describes how microscopes magnify images. **learning modality: verbal**

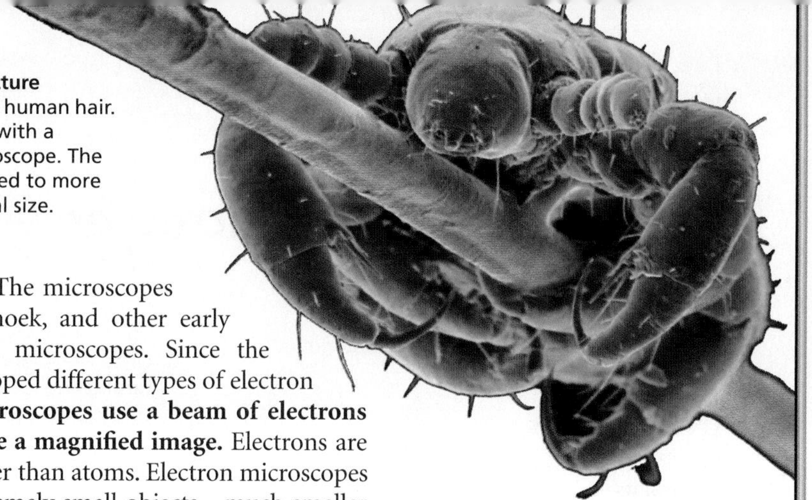

FIGURE 19
Electron Microscope Picture
A head louse clings to a human hair. This picture was taken with a scanning electron microscope. The louse has been magnified to more than 100 times its actual size.

Electron Microscopes The microscopes used by Hooke, Leeuwenhoek, and other early researchers were all light microscopes. Since the 1930s, scientists have developed different types of electron microscopes. **Electron microscopes use a beam of electrons instead of light to produce a magnified image.** Electrons are tiny particles that are smaller than atoms. Electron microscopes can obtain pictures of extremely small objects—much smaller than those that can be seen with light microscopes. The resolution of electron microscopes is much better than the resolution of light microscopes.

Reading Checkpoint **What do electron microscopes use to produce magnified images?**

Section 3 Assessment

Target Reading Skill **Sequencing** Review your flowchart and use it to answer Questions 2 and 3 below.

Reviewing Key Concepts

1. a. **Defining** Define *structure* and *function*.
   b. **Explaining** Explain this statement: Cells are the basic units of structure and function in organisms.
   c. **Applying Concepts** In what important function are the cells in your eyes involved?
2. a. **Reviewing** What does a microscope enable people to do?
   b. **Summarizing** Summarize Hooke's observations of cork under a microscope.
   c. **Relating Cause and Effect** Why would Hooke's discovery have been impossible without a microscope?
3. a. **Reviewing** What are the main ideas of the cell theory?
   b. **Explaining** What did Virchow contribute to the cell theory?
   c. **Applying Concepts** Use the ideas of Virchow to explain why plastic plants and stuffed animals are not alive.
4. a. **Defining** What is magnification?
   b. **Comparing and Contrasting** Contrast the way light microscopes and electron microscopes magnify objects.

Writing in Science

Writing an Award Speech Suppose you are a member of a scientific society that is giving an award to one of the early cell scientists. Choose the scientist, and write a speech that you might give at the award ceremony. Your speech should describe the scientist's accomplishments.

Monitor Progress L2

Answers
Figure 17 10 × 50, or 500
Reading Checkpoint A beam of electrons

Assess

Reviewing Key Concepts

1. a. Structure is what an object or organism is made of and how its parts are put together. A function is a process that enables an organism to stay alive and reproduce. **b.** Cells form the parts of an organism and carry out all of its functions. **c.** Sight
2. a. Microscopes make it possible for people to discover and learn about tiny things, such as cells. **b.** Hooke saw that the cork was made up of many tiny, rectangular spaces, which he called cells. **c.** The human eye is not able to see such small structures.
3. a. All living things are made up of cells, which are the basic units of structure and function in living things. Cells come from other cells. **b.** Virchow proposed that cells are produced from other cells. **c.** Plastic plants and stuffed animals are not made up of cells. Their parts do not produce similar parts in the same way that cells produce other cells. Instead, the parts of plastic plants and stuffed animals are human-made.
4. a. Magnification is the process of making things look larger than they are. **b.** Light microscopes use lenses to bend light rays to magnify objects, while electron microscopes use a beam of electrons.

Reteach L1

Use the Tech & Design in History timeline to present and discuss the different types of microscopes. Have students identify where in the timeline the cell theory was developed.

Performance Assessment L2

Skills Check Have students compare and contrast light microscopes and electron microscopes.

All in One Teaching Resources, Unit 1

- Section Summary: *Discovering Cells*
- Review and Reinforce: *Discovering Cells*
- Enrich: *Discovering Cells*

Writing in Science

Writing Skill Description
Scoring Rubric
4 Includes accomplishments and goes beyond requirements in some way, for example, by researching other accomplishments
3 Includes all criteria but does not go beyond requirements
2 Includes only brief description
1 Includes inaccurate or incomplete description

Design and Build a Microscope L2

Prepare for Inquiry

Key Concept
You can build a working microscope using two different lenses.

Skills Objectives
After this lab, students will be able to
- build a working microscope using high-and low-powered magnifying lenses
- use the microscope to examine objects
- evaluate the usefulness of the design

 Class Time 40 minutes

All in One Teaching Resources, Unit 1
- Lab Worksheet: *Design and Build a Microscope*

Safety
 Review the safety guidelines in Appendix A.

Guide Inquiry

Invitation
Remind students of the general structure of a compound light microscope. Have them examine Figure 5 and conclude that compound microscopes contain two convex lenses.

Introduce the Procedure
Review the terms *magnification* and *resolution* and how they relate to microscopy. Make sure students know how to use a compound microscope. Ask: **If you know the magnification of the two lenses in the microscope, how do you determine the overall magnification?** (*You multiply the magnifications of the lenses.*) **Which of the two lenses has a higher magnification?** (*The lens closer to the eye*) **What do you do if the image you see in a microscope is blurry?** (*You move the lenses closer or farther from the object and from each other.*)

Lab zone Technology **Lab**
· Tech & Design ·

Design and Build a Microscope

Problem
How can you design and build a compound microscope?

Design Skills
building a prototype, evaluating design constraints

Materials
- book
- 2 dual magnifying glasses, each with one high-power and one low-power lens
- metric ruler
- 2 cardboard tubes from paper towels, or black construction paper
- tape

Procedure

PART 1 Research and Investigate

1. Work with a partner. Using only your eyes, examine words in a book. Then use the high-power lens to examine the same words. In your notebook, contrast what you saw with and without the magnifying lens.

2. Hold the high-power lens about 5–6 cm above the words in the book. When you look at the words through the lens, they will look blurry.

3. Keep the high-power lens about 5–6 cm above the words. Hold the low-power lens above the high-power lens, as shown in the photograph on the right.

4. Move the low-power lens up and down until the image is in focus and upside down. (*Hint:* You may have to move the high-power lens up or down slightly too.)

5. Once the image is in focus, experiment with raising and lowering both lenses. Your goal is to produce the highest magnification while keeping the image in clear focus.

6. When the image is in focus at the position of highest magnification, have your lab partner measure and record the distance between the book and the high-power lens. Your lab partner should also measure and record the distance between the two lenses.

7. Write a description of how the magnified words viewed through two lenses compares with the words seen without magnification.

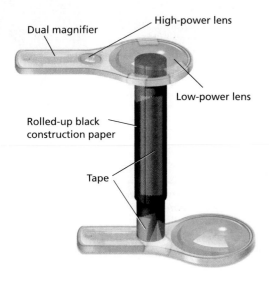

Dual magnifier

High-power lens

Low-power lens

Rolled-up black construction paper

Tape

PART 2 Design and Build

8. Based on what you learned in Part 1, work with a partner to design your own two-lens (compound) microscope. Your microscope should
   - consist of one high-power lens and one low-power lens, each attached to a tube of paper or rolled-up cardboard
   - allow one tube to fit snugly inside the other tube so the distance between the two lenses can be easily adjusted
   - focus to produce a clear, enlarged, upside-down image of the object
   - be made from dual magnifying glasses, cardboard tubes, and tape

9. Sketch your design on a sheet of paper. Obtain your teacher's approval for your design. Then construct your microscope.

PART 3 Evaluate and Redesign

10. Test your microscope by examining printed words or a printed photograph. Then, examine other objects such as a leaf or your skin. Record your observations. Did your microscope meet the criteria listed in Step 8?

11. Examine microscopes made by other students. Based on your tests and your examination of other microscopes, list ways you could improve your microscope.

Analyze and Conclude

1. **Observing** Compare the images you observed using one lens with the image from two lenses.

2. **Evaluating** When you used two lenses, how did moving the top lens up and down affect the image? What was the effect of moving the bottom lens up and down?

3. **Building a Prototype** Describe how you built your microscope and explain why you built it that way.

4. **Evaluating the Impact on Society** Describe some of the ways that microscopes have aided scientists in their work.

Communicate

Imagine it is 1675. Write an explanation that will convince scientists to use your new microscope rather than the single-lens variety used by Leeuwenhoek.

Troubleshooting the Experiment

Remind students to write down all of their observations and to record which lenses they used and in which combinations they used them.

Expected Outcome

The image is blurry and inverted with the high-power lens a few centimeters above the print. When the low-power lens is placed near the print, the image appears in focus and inverted. Holding the high-power lens still and moving the low-power lens upward increases the magnification, causing the print to appear larger. Holding the low-power lens still and moving the high-power lens closer to the print increases the magnification, causing the print to appear larger until you get very close to the page. At that point the image is smaller and no longer inverted. The distances measured will depend on the lenses used.

Analyze and Conclude

1. Images obtained with two lenses were magnified more.

2. Moving the top lens up increased the magnification, while moving the bottom lens down increased magnification.

3. Each lens was attached to a cardboard tube. One tube was then inserted in the other so that the lenses could be moved closer to or farther from one another.

4. Answers might note that increasing magnifications have enabled scientists to make detailed examinations of the structures of cells.

Extend Inquiry

Communicate Explanations should note that the total magnification of a compound microscope is the product of the magnifying power of each lens; therefore, compound microscopes have greater magnifying power than most single-lens microscopes.

Objectives

After this lesson, students will be able to

2.4.1 Identify the role of the cell wall and the cell membrane in the cell.

2.4.2 Describe the functions of cell organelles.

2.4.3 Explain how cells are organized in many-celled organisms.

Target Reading Skill

Previewing Visuals Explain that looking at the visuals before they read helps students activate prior knowledge and predict what they are about to read.

Answers

Possible questions and answers: **How are animal cells different from plants cells?** *(Plants cells have a cell wall and chloroplasts, which animal cells do not have.)* **What do mitochondria do?** *(Mitochondria convert energy in food molecules to energy the cell can use.)*

All in One Teaching Resources, Unit 1

• Transparency LS16

Preteach

Build Background Knowledge

Division of Labor   **L1**

Introduce students to the division of labor among structures in cells by relating it to the division of labor in a community. Ask: **How are jobs in a town divided up among people?** *(Possible answers: Shopkeepers supply food, police officers enforce laws, and the mayor and city council members make decisions.)* **Why is it effective to divide the labor in this way?** *(By dividing labor, people can become specialized at their work and do it more effectively.)* Point out that, like a town and its people, cells have a division of labor among their structures.

Reading Preview

Key Concepts
• What role do the cell wall and cell membrane play in the cell?
• What are the functions of cell organelles?
• How are cells organized in many-celled organisms?

Key Terms
• organelle • cell wall
• cell membrane • cytoplasm
• mitochondria
• endoplasmic reticulum
• ribosome • Golgi body
• chloroplast • vacuole
• lysosome

Target Reading Skill
Previewing Visuals Before you read, preview Figure 24. Then write two questions that you have about the illustrations in a graphic organizer like the one below. As you read, answer your questions.

Plant and Animal Cells

Q.	How are animal cells different from plant cells?
A.	
Q.	

Lab Zone Discover **Activity**

How Large Are Cells?

1. Look at the organism in the photo. The organism is an amoeba (uh MEE buh), a large single-celled organism. This type of amoeba is about 1 mm long.

2. Multiply your height in meters by 1,000 to get your height in millimeters. How many amoebas would you have to stack end-to-end to equal your height?

3. Many of the cells in your body are about 0.01 mm long—one hundredth the size of an amoeba. How many body cells would you have to stack end-to-end to equal your height?

Think It Over
Inferring Look at a metric ruler to see how small 1 mm is. Now imagine a distance one one-hundredth as long, or 0.01 mm. Why can't you see your body's cells without the aid of a microscope?

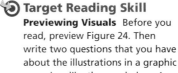

Nasturtiums brighten up many gardens with green leaves and colorful flowers. How do nasturtiums carry out all the functions necessary to stay alive? To answer this question, you are about to take an imaginary journey. You will travel inside a nasturtium leaf, visiting its tiny cells. You will observe some of the structures found in plant cells. You will also learn some differences between plant and animal cells.

As you will discover on your journey, there are even smaller structures inside a cell. These tiny cell structures, called **organelles,** carry out specific functions within the cell. Just as your stomach, lungs, and heart have different functions in your body, each organelle has a different function within the cell. Now it's time to hop aboard your imaginary ship and sail into a typical plant cell.

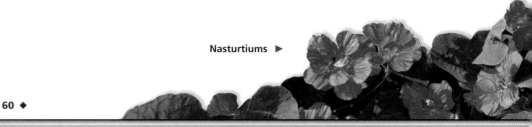

Nasturtiums ▶

Lab Zone Discover **Activity**

Skills Focus Inferring

Materials calculator, metric ruler

Time 10 minutes

Tips If students do not know their height in meters, have partners measure each other's height with a metric ruler.

L1 **Expected Outcome** A student who is 1.5 m tall would be the same height as a stack of 1,500 amoebas. The same student would be 150,000 body cells tall.

Think It Over You cannot see body cells without a microscope because they are too small.

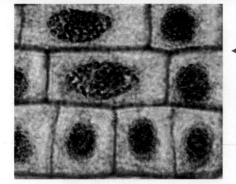
◀ Onion root cells

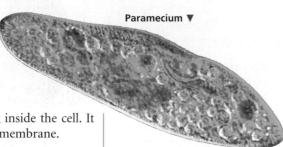
Paramecium ▼

Enter the Cell

Your ship doesn't have an easy time getting inside the cell. It has to pass through the cell wall and the cell membrane.

Cell Wall As you travel through the plant cell, refer to Figure 24 in this section. First, you must slip through the cell wall. The **cell wall** is a rigid layer of nonliving material that surrounds the cells of plants and some other organisms. The cells of animals, in contrast, do not have cell walls. **A plant's cell wall helps to protect and support the cell.** The cell wall is made mostly of a strong material called cellulose. Although the cell wall is tough, many materials, including water and oxygen, can pass through easily.

Cell Membrane After you sail through the cell wall, the next barrier you must cross is the **cell membrane.** All cells have cell membranes. In cells with cell walls, the cell membrane is located just inside the cell wall. In other cells, the cell membrane forms the outside boundary that separates the cell from its environment.

The cell membrane controls what substances come into and out of a cell. Everything the cell needs, from food to oxygen, enters the cell through the cell membrane. Fortunately, your ship can slip through, too. Harmful waste products leave the cell through the cell membrane. For a cell to survive, the cell membrane must allow these materials to pass in and out. In addition, the cell membrane prevents harmful materials from entering the cell. In a sense, the cell membrane is like a window screen. The screen allows air to enter and leave a room, but it keeps insects out.

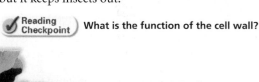 **Reading Checkpoint** What is the function of the cell wall?

FIGURE 20
Cell Wall and Cell Membrane
The onion root cells have both a cell wall and a cell membrane. The single-celled paramecium has only a cell membrane.
Interpreting Photographs *What shape do the cell walls give to the onion root cells?*

DISCOVERY CHANNEL SCHOOL™

Cell Structure and Function

Video Preview
▶ Video Field Trip
Video Assessment

Enter the Cell

Teach Key Concepts L2
Cell Wall and Cell Membrane

Focus Point out that when Hooke observed cork cells, what he saw was the cell wall.

Teach Have students locate the cell wall in Figure 20. Ask: **What is the function of the cell wall?** *(It helps protect and support the cell.)* Have students locate the cell membrane. Ask: **What is the function of the cell membrane?** *(It controls what substances come into and out of a cell.)* **Which two structures do plants have?** *(Both)* **Animal cells?** *(Only cell membranes, not cell walls)*

Apply Point out that cells with cell walls also have a cell membrane. Ask: **Why does a cell with a cell wall need a cell membrane?** *(The cell wall separates the cell from the outside environment, but it cannot control all substances that come into and out of the cell.)* **learning modality: visual**

Independent Practice L2

All in One **Teaching Resources, Unit 1**
• Guided Reading and Study Worksheet: *Looking Inside Cells*

🔘 **Student Edition on Audio CD**

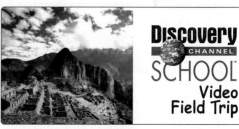

DISCOVERY CHANNEL SCHOOL™
Video Field Trip

Cell Structure and Function
Show the Video Field Trip to let students learn about different kinds of cells.

Differentiated Instruction

English Learners/Beginning L1
Vocabulary: Science Glossary Have students find the terms *cell wall* and *cell membrane* in the text as you read aloud. Use Figure 20 to describe the meanings of the terms. Have students write the meanings in their science glossaries. Then have students draw and label diagrams of the structures. **learning modality: verbal**

English Learners/Intermediate L2
Vocabulary: Science Glossary Have students expand on the *Beginning* activity and add the other key terms to their science glossaries as they read the section. Have students draw structures designated by the terms and write a sentence about each term in their own words. **learning modality: verbal**

Monitor Progress L2

Oral Presentation Call on students to identify differences and similarities between cell walls and cell membranes.

Answers
Figure 20 Rectangular

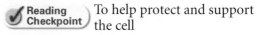 **Reading Checkpoint** To help protect and support the cell

61

Sail on to the Nucleus

Teach Key Concepts `L1`

Functions of the Nucleus

Focus Have students locate the nucleus in Figure 21. Point out the membrane around it, called the nuclear envelope.

Teach Ask: **What is the function of the nucleus?** *(The nucleus directs all of the cell's activities.)* **What keeps material in the nucleus from spilling out?** *(The nucleus is surrounded by the nuclear envelope.)* **How does the nucleus "know" how to direct the cell?** *(Thin strands of chromatin in the nucleus contain genetic material, the instructions for directing the cell's functions.)* **What is the nucleolus?** *(It is where organelles that make proteins are produced.)*

Apply Ask: **How is the nucleus like the manager of a company?** *(The nucleus directs functions of the cell, just as a manager directs functions of a company.)* **learning modality: verbal**

Address Misconceptions `L1`

Cells Have the Same Genetic Material

Focus Students may think that different types of cells within an organism contain different genetic material.

Teach Point out to students that exactly the same genetic material is found in every cell of an organism. Different cells in their bodies, such as skin cells and blood cells, look and function differently because they respond to different genetic instructions. Ask: **How is a cookbook like the genetic code?** *(The same cookbook can be used by different cooks to make different recipes. Different cells contain a copy of the same cookbook or genetic material, yet the cells look and function differently because they follow different recipes.)*

Apply Remind students that Virchow proposed that all cells come from cells. Explain that cells get their genetic material from the cell they came from, and an organism grows as cells divide to make new cells. This explains why all cells in an organism have the same genetic material. **learning modality: verbal**

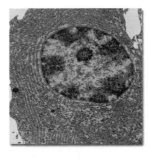 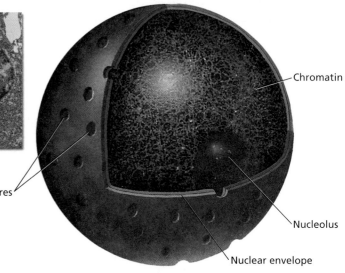

FIGURE 21
The Nucleus
The photo (left) and diagram (right) both show the nucleus, which is the cell's control center. The chromatin in the nucleus contains instructions for carrying out the cell's activities.

Chromatin

Pores

Nucleolus

Nuclear envelope

Lab zone Try This **Activity**

Gelatin Cell
Make your own model of a cell.

1. Dissolve a packet of colorless gelatin in warm water. Pour the gelatin into a rectangular pan (for a plant cell) or a round pan (for an animal cell).
2. Choose different materials that resemble each of the cell structures found in the cell you are modeling. Insert these materials into the gelatin before it begins to solidify.

Making Models On a sheet of paper, develop a key that identifies each cell structure in your model. Describe the function of each structure.

62 ◆

Sail On to the Nucleus

As you sail inside the cell, a large, oval structure comes into view. This structure, the nucleus, acts as the "brain" of the cell. **You can think of the nucleus as the cell's control center, directing all of the cell's activities.**

Nuclear Envelope Notice in Figure 21 that the nucleus is surrounded by a membrane called the nuclear envelope. Just as a mailing envelope protects the letter inside it, the nuclear envelope protects the nucleus. Materials pass in and out of the nucleus through pores in the nuclear envelope. So aim for that pore just ahead and carefully glide into the nucleus.

Chromatin You might wonder how the nucleus "knows" how to direct the cell. The answer lies in those thin strands floating directly ahead in the nucleus. These strands, called chromatin, contain genetic material, the instructions for directing the cell's functions. For example, the instructions in the chromatin ensure that leaf cells grow and divide to form more leaf cells.

Nucleolus As you prepare to leave the nucleus, you spot a small object floating by. This structure, a nucleolus, is where ribosomes are made. Ribosomes are the organelles where proteins are produced. Proteins are important chemicals in cells.

 Where in the nucleus is genetic material found?

Lab zone Try This **Activity**

Skills Focus Making models `L2`

Materials packet of colorless gelatin, warm water, stirrer, craft materials, rectangular or round pan

Time 10 min one day; 10 min the next

Tips Use warm, not hot, water. Students should stir the gelatin until it dissolves completely and chill it for up to an hour before adding the cell structures.

Extend Challenge students to model an animal cell with gelatin in a resealable plastic bag. Ask: **What does the bag represent?** *(The cell membrane)* **Why is this a better model for an animal cell than a pan?** *(There is no "cell wall" to support the cell and make it rigid.)* **learning modality: kinesthetic**

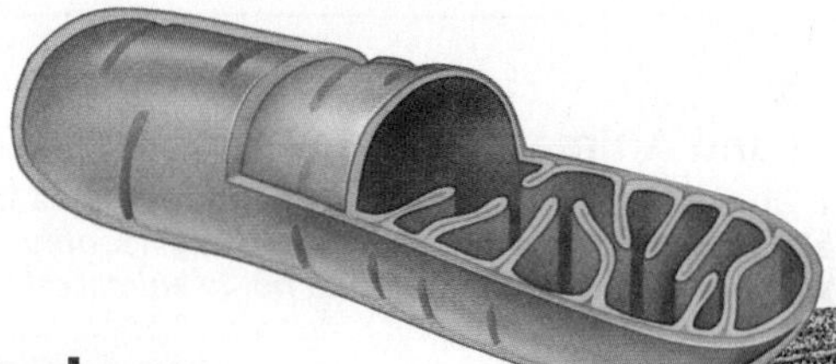

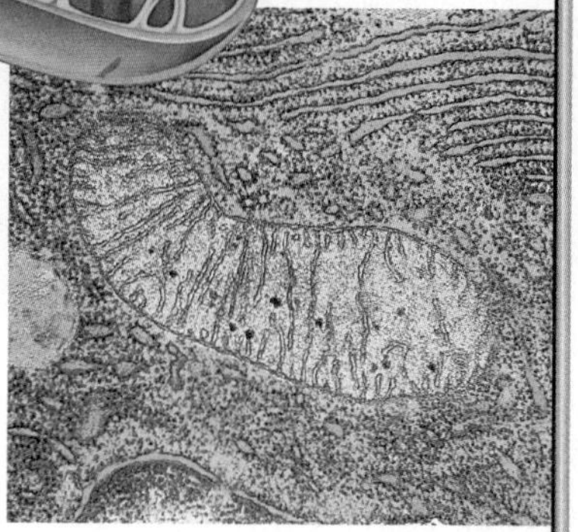

FIGURE 22 Mitochondrion
The mitochondria produce most of the cell's energy. *Inferring In what types of cells would you expect to find a lot of mitochondria?*

Organelles in the Cytoplasm

As you leave the nucleus, you find yourself in the **cytoplasm,** the region between the cell membrane and the nucleus. Your ship floats in a clear, thick, gel-like fluid. The fluid in the cytoplasm is constantly moving, so your ship does not need to propel itself. Many cell organelles are found in the cytoplasm.

Mitochondria Suddenly, rod-shaped structures loom ahead. These organelles are **mitochondria** (my tuh KAHN dree uh) (singular *mitochondrion*). **Mitochondria are known as the "powerhouses" of the cell because they convert energy in food molecules to energy the cell can use to carry out its functions.** Figure 22 shows a mitochondrion up close.

Endoplasmic Reticulum As you sail farther into the cytoplasm, you find yourself in a maze of passageways called the **endoplasmic reticulum** (en duh PLAZ mik rih TIK yuh lum). **The endoplasmic reticulum's passageways carry proteins and other materials from one part of the cell to another.**

Ribosomes Attached to some surfaces of the endoplasmic reticulum are small, grainlike bodies called **ribosomes.** Other ribosomes float in the cytoplasm. **Ribosomes function as factories to produce proteins.** Some newly made proteins are released through the wall of the endoplasmic reticulum. From the interior of the endoplasmic reticulum, the proteins will be transported to the Golgi bodies.

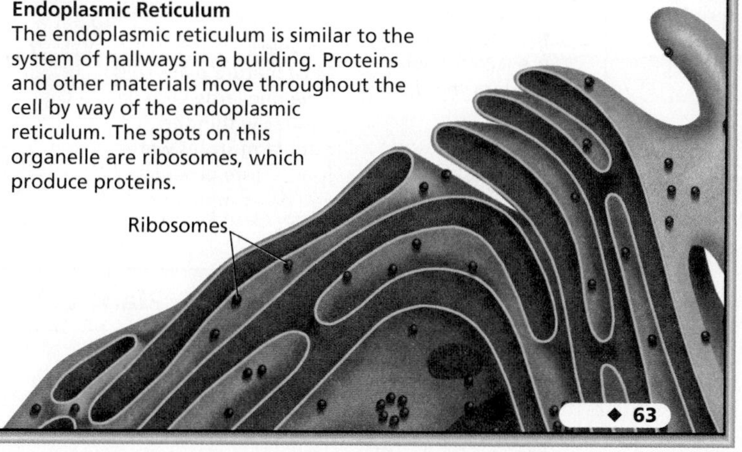

FIGURE 23
Endoplasmic Reticulum
The endoplasmic reticulum is similar to the system of hallways in a building. Proteins and other materials move throughout the cell by way of the endoplasmic reticulum. The spots on this organelle are ribosomes, which produce proteins.

Ribosomes

◆ 63

Organelles in the Cytoplasm

Use Visuals: Figure 24 [L2]

Comparing Plant and Animal Cells

Focus Point out that some cell structures are defined on only one drawing because they are much the same in both plant cells and animal cells.

Teach Help students organize the material in the figure by creating a table on the board titled "Comparison of Plant and Animal Cells." For headings, use *Similarities* and *Differences,* and for rows use *Plants* and *Animals.* Encourage students to examine the diagrams and other information in the figure to help fill in the cells of the table. Complete the table as students volunteer their ideas. When the table is finished, you may want to have students copy it in a notebook and refer to it as they study this section.

Apply Ask: **Which organelles are found only in plant cells? Which are found in both plant and animal cells?** *(Except for cell walls and chloroplasts, most organelles are found in both plant and animal cells.)* **learning modality: visual**

All in One Teaching Resources, Unit 1
• Transparencies LS17, LS18

Help Students Read [L1]

Relating Text and Visuals Have students compare the drawings on these pages with the descriptions of their functions in the passages Sail on to the Nucleus and Organelles in the Cytoplasm. Instruct students to go back and read about each organelle, then locate it on the drawing.

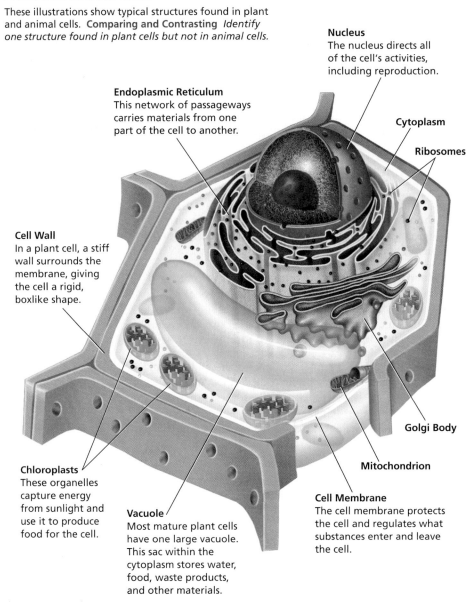

Figure 24
Plant and Animal Cells
These illustrations show typical structures found in plant and animal cells. **Comparing and Contrasting** *Identify one structure found in plant cells but not in animal cells.*

Nucleus
The nucleus directs all of the cell's activities, including reproduction.

Cytoplasm

Ribosomes

Endoplasmic Reticulum
This network of passageways carries materials from one part of the cell to another.

Cell Wall
In a plant cell, a stiff wall surrounds the membrane, giving the cell a rigid, boxlike shape.

Golgi Body

Mitochondrion

Chloroplasts
These organelles capture energy from sunlight and use it to produce food for the cell.

Vacuole
Most mature plant cells have one large vacuole. This sac within the cytoplasm stores water, food, waste products, and other materials.

Cell Membrane
The cell membrane protects the cell and regulates what substances enter and leave the cell.

Plant Cell

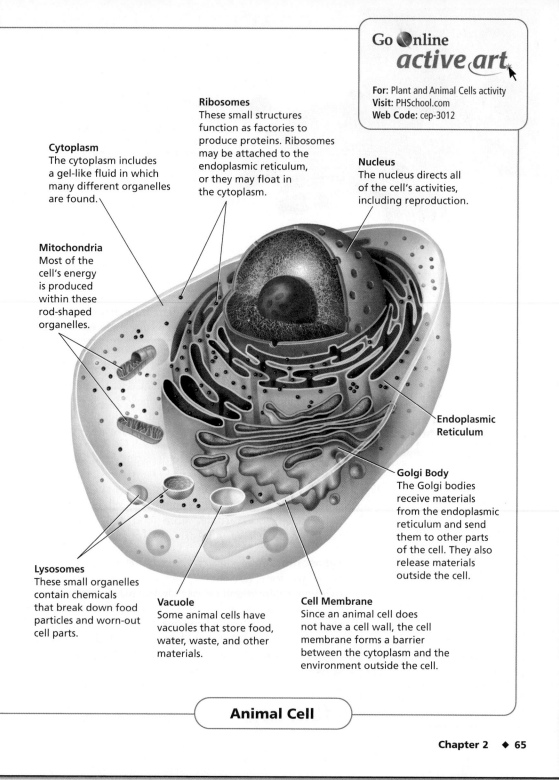

Cytoplasm
The cytoplasm includes a gel-like fluid in which many different organelles are found.

Ribosomes
These small structures function as factories to produce proteins. Ribosomes may be attached to the endoplasmic reticulum, or they may float in the cytoplasm.

Nucleus
The nucleus directs all of the cell's activities, including reproduction.

Mitochondria
Most of the cell's energy is produced within these rod-shaped organelles.

Go Online
active art
For: Plant and Animal Cells activity
Visit: PHSchool.com
Web Code: cep-3012

Endoplasmic Reticulum

Golgi Body
The Golgi bodies receive materials from the endoplasmic reticulum and send them to other parts of the cell. They also release materials outside the cell.

Lysosomes
These small organelles contain chemicals that break down food particles and worn-out cell parts.

Vacuole
Some animal cells have vacuoles that store food, water, waste, and other materials.

Cell Membrane
Since an animal cell does not have a cell wall, the cell membrane forms a barrier between the cytoplasm and the environment outside the cell.

Animal Cell

Go Online
active art
For: Plant and Animal Cells activity
Visit: PHSchool.com
Web Code: cep-3012
Students can interact with the art of cells online.

Lab zone   Teacher Demo   L2

Comparing Slides to Illustrations

Materials microprojector, prepared slide of plant cells, prepared slide of animal cells, drawings of other types of cells (such as leaf and root cells for plants, and muscle and bone cells for animals)

Time 10 minutes

Focus Point out that the drawings of plant and animal cells shown on these pages are generalized representations of cells.

Teach Project the prepared slides, and have students relate the organelles they see to the illustrations. Encourage them to describe how the actual cells vary in shape and structure from the generalized cells in the text. Point out that cells have many different shapes and sizes. They also can vary in the specific organelles they contain.

Apply Ask: **Why do you think different cells look so different from one other?** *(Because they have different functions in the organism)* **learning modality: visual**

Differentiated Instruction

Special Needs   L1
Making Flash Cards Have students use index cards to write the name of a cell structure on one side and the structure's function on the other side. Pair students and have them use their flash cards to quiz each other. **learning modality: verbal**

Less Proficient Readers   L1
Identifying Organelles Make photocopies of the plant and animal cell illustrations in Figure 24. Blank out the labels but leave the taglines. As each organelle is studied and discussed, have students write in the labels. Give students extra copies for practice and as a study aid. **learning modality: visual**

Monitor Progress   L2

Oral Presentation Call out the names of organelles, and have students tell what they do.

Answer
Figure 24 Either one: Cell walls, chloroplasts

Specialized Cells

Teach Key Concepts   L2

How Cells Are Organized

Focus Point out the different shapes and functions of the cells in Figure 26.

Teach Ask: **What is a tissue?** *(A group of similar cells that work together to perform a specific function)* **What are different types of tissues working together called?** *(An organ)* **What is an organ system?** *(A group of organs that work together to perform a major function)*

Apply Blood is able to circulate through the human body because of the heart and blood vessels. Ask: **Is this an example of tissues, organs, or an organ system?** *(This is an organ system called the circulatory system. The heart and blood vessels are organs of this system.)* **learning modality: logical/ mathematical**

Use Visuals: Figure 26   L1

Focus Remind students that cells have different structures because of their functions.

Teach Ask students to compare the nerve cell and the red blood cells. *(The nerve cell has extensions, and the red blood cells look flattened or donut-shaped.)*

Apply Ask: **How do you think each cell's shape helps it do its job?** *(The extensions on nerve cells help them reach out and send messages to other cells; the flatness of red blood cells helps them squeeze through tiny blood vessels.)* **learning modality: visual**

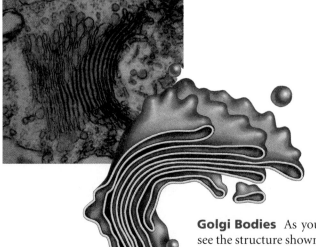

FIGURE 25
A Golgi Body
Golgi bodies are organelles that transport materials.
Applying Concepts Why can a Golgi body be described as a cell's mail room?

Golgi Bodies As you leave the endoplasmic reticulum, you see the structure shown in Figure 25. It looks like flattened sacs and tubes. This structure, called a **Golgi body,** can be thought of as the cell's mail room. **The Golgi bodies receive proteins and other newly formed materials from the endoplasmic reticulum, package them, and distribute them to other parts of the cell.** The Golgi bodies also release materials outside the cell.

Chloroplasts Have you noticed the many large green structures floating in the cytoplasm? Only the cells of plants and some other organisms have these green organelles called **chloroplasts. Chloroplasts capture energy from sunlight and use it to produce food for the cell.** Chloroplasts make leaves green.

Vacuoles Steer past the chloroplasts and head for that large, water-filled sac, called a **vacuole** (VAK yoo ohl), floating in the cytoplasm. **Vacuoles are the storage areas of cells.** Most plant cells have one large vacuole. Some animal cells do not have vacuoles; others do. Vacuoles store food and other materials needed by the cell. Vacuoles can also store waste products.

Lysosomes Your journey through the cell is almost over. Before you leave, take another look around you. If you carefully swing your ship around the vacuole, you may be lucky enough to see a **lysosome** (LY suh sohm). **Lysosomes are small, round structures containing chemicals that break down certain materials in the cell.** Some chemicals break down large food particles into smaller ones. Lysosomes also break down old cell parts and release the substances so they can be used again. In this sense, you can think of lysosomes as the cell's cleanup crew.

Reading Checkpoint What organelle captures the energy of sunlight and uses it to make food for the cell?

Lab zone Skills **Activity**

Observing
Observe the characteristics of plant and animal cells.

1. 🔒 Obtain a prepared slide of plant cells from your teacher. Examine these cells under the low-power and high-power lenses of a microscope.
2. Draw a picture of what you see.
3. Repeat Steps 1 and 2 with a prepared slide of animal cells.

How are plant and animal cells alike? How are they different?

Lab zone Skills **Activity**

Skills Focus Observing   L2

Materials microscope, prepared slide of animal cells, prepared slide of plant cells

Time 15 minutes

Tips Help students identify organelles by looking at Figure 24. Challenge students to locate the cell wall or cell membrane, nucleus, and other organelles on the slides.

Expected Outcome Only plant cells have cell walls and chloroplasts. Most other cell structures are found in both plant and animal cells.

Extend Encourage students to describe how the actual cells vary in shape and structure from the illustrations. **learning modality: visual**

Specialized Cells

Plants and animals (including yourself) contain many cells. In a many-celled organism, the cells are often quite different from each other and are specialized to perform specific functions. Contrast, for example, the nerve cell and red blood cells in Figure 26. Nerve cells are specialized to transmit information from one part of your body to another, and red blood cells carry oxygen throughout your body.

In many-celled organisms, cells are often organized into tissues, organs, and organ systems. A tissue is a group of similar cells that work together to perform a specific function. For example, your brain is made mostly of nervous tissue, which consists of nerve cells. An organ, such as your brain, is made of different kinds of tissues that function together. In addition to nervous tissue, the brain contains other kinds of tissue that support and protect it. Your brain is part of your nervous system, which is an organ system that directs body activities and processes. An organ system is a group of organs that work together to perform a major function.

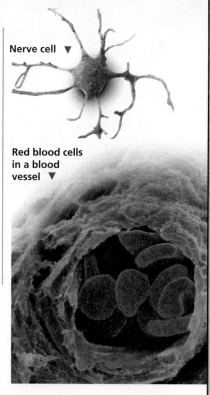

Nerve cell ▼

Red blood cells in a blood vessel ▼

FIGURE 26 Specialized Cells
Nerve cells carry information throughout the human body. Red blood cells carry oxygen.

Section 4 Assessment

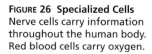

Target Reading Skill Previewing Visuals
Refer to your questions and answers about Figure 24 to help you answer the questions below.

Reviewing Key Concepts

1. **a. Comparing and Contrasting** Compare the functions of the cell wall and the cell membrane.
   b. Inferring How does cellulose help with one function of the cell wall?
2. **a. Identifying** Identify the functions of ribosomes and Golgi bodies.
   b. Describing Describe the characteristics of the endoplasmic reticulum.
   c. Applying Concepts How are the functions of ribosomes, Golgi bodies, and the endoplasmic reticulum related to one another?

3. **a. Reviewing** What is a tissue? What is an organ?
   b. Explaining What is the relationship among cells, tissues, and organs?
   c. Inferring Would a tissue or an organ have more kinds of specialized cells? Explain.

Writing in Science

Writing a Description Write a paragraph describing a typical animal cell. Your paragraph should include all the structures generally found in animal cells and a brief explanation of the functions of those structures.

Chapter 2 ◆ 67

Lab zone Chapter **Project**

Keep Students on Track Have each student analyze the data collected and conclude whether the object is alive. If the object is alive, ask students to determine which domain and kingdom it belongs to.

Writing in Science

Writing Mode Description
Scoring Rubric
4 Includes descriptions of structures and explains their functions; goes beyond requirements in some way, for example, explaining how organelles work together
3 Includes all criteria, but does not go beyond requirements
2 Includes very brief description
1 Includes inaccurate or incomplete information

Monitor Progress ____ L2

Answers
Figure 25 A Golgi body receives newly formed proteins and other materials, packages them, and delivers them to other parts of the cell.

✓ **Reading Checkpoint** The chloroplast

Assess

Reviewing Key Concepts

1. a. The cell membrane separates a cell from its environment and controls what substances go into and come out of the cell. The cell wall protects and supports the cell. **b.** Because cellulose is strong, the cell wall, which is made up of cellulose, can protect the cell and provide support.
2. a. The ribosomes produce proteins. The Golgi bodies distribute these proteins and other materials to different parts of the cell. **b.** The endoplasmic reticulum has many passageways that carry proteins and other materials from one part of the cell to another. **c.** The ribosomes make proteins. The endoplasmic reticulum carries the proteins to the Golgi bodies, which distribute them to other parts of the cell.
3. a. A tissue is a group of similar cells that work together to perform a specific function. An organ is a body structure made up of different kinds of tissues that function together. **b.** Cells make up tissues, which make up organs. **c.** An organ would have more kinds of specialized cells because it is made up of different tissues, each of which consists of the same type of cells.

Reteach L1
Bring in photographs of different types of cells. Ask students to classify them as plant, animal, or bacterial, and identify any visible organelles.

Performance Assessment L2
Have students draw a plant cell, animal cell, and bacterial cell and label their structures.

All in One Teaching Resources, Unit 1
• Section Summary: *Looking Inside Cells*
• Review and Reinforce: *Looking Inside Cells*
• Enrich: *Looking Inside Cells*

Study Guide

nteractive
Textbook

- Complete student edition
- Section and chapter self-assessments
- Assessment reports for teachers

Help Students Read
Building Vocabulary

Vocabulary Rating Chart Have each student construct a chart with four columns labeled Term, Can Define or Use It, Have Heard or Seen It, and Don't Know. Have students copy the Key Terms from this chapter into the first column and rate their knowledge by putting a check in one of the other columns. Then have students read the parts that pertain to the Key Term in question.

Word Origins Help students use word origins to learn Key Terms. Examples: *Uni-* means "one." *Multi-* means "many." *Mitochondrion* comes from the Greek root *chondros,* which means "granule."

Connecting Concepts

Concept Maps Help students develop one way to show how the information in this chapter is related. Cells, the basic units of structure and function in living things, contain structures that help the cell perform its specific tasks within the organism. Have students brainstorm to identify the Key Concepts, Key Terms, details, and examples, and then write each one on a sticky note and attach it at random to chart paper or to the board.

Tell students to begin with the Key Concepts. Ask students questions like these to guide them to organize the information on the stickies: **What is the basic unit of structure in all living things? How are cells involved in the reproduction of living things? What is the cell theory? What are the different structures found in cells and their functions?**

---

① What Is Life?
Key Concepts

- All living things have a cellular organization, contain similar chemicals, use energy, respond to their surroundings, grow and develop, and reproduce.
- Living things arise from living things through reproduction.
- All living things must satisfy their basic needs for water, food, living space, and stable internal conditions.

Key Terms

organism	development
cell	spontaneous
unicellular	generation
multicellular	autotroph
stimulus	heterotroph
response	homeostasis

② Classifying Organisms
Key Concepts

- Biologists use classification to organize living things into groups so that the organisms are easier to study.
- The more classification levels that two organisms share, the more characteristics they have in common.
- Organisms are placed into domains and kingdoms based on their cell type, their ability to make food, and the number of cells in their bodies.

Key Terms

classification
taxonomy
binomial nomenclature
genus
species
prokaryote
nucleus
eukaryote

68 ◆

---

③ Discovering Cells
Key Concepts

- Cells are the basic units of structure and function in living things.
- The cell theory states the following: All living things are composed of cells. Cells are the basic units of structure and function in living things. All cells are produced from other cells.
- The invention of the microscope enabled people to learn about cells. Light microscopes magnify an object by bending light. Electron microscopes use electrons instead of light.

Key Terms

cell	microscope	cell theory

④ Looking Inside Cells
Key Concepts

- A plant's cell wall protects and supports the cell. The cell membrane controls what substances come into and out of a cell.
- The nucleus directs the cell's activities.
- Mitochondria convert energy in food molecules to energy the cell can use.
- The endoplasmic reticulum carries materials throughout the cell.
- Ribosomes produce proteins.
- The Golgi bodies receive materials, package them, and distribute them.
- Chloroplasts capture energy from sunlight and use it to produce food for the cell.
- Vacuoles are the storage areas of cells.
- Lysosomes contain chemicals that break down certain materials in the cell.
- In many-celled organisms, cells are often organized into tissues, organs, and organ systems.

Key Terms

organelle	ribosome
cell wall	Golgi body
cell membrane	chloroplast
cytoplasm	vacuole
mitochondria	lysosome
endoplasmic reticulum	

Prompt students by using connecting words or phrases, such as "are made of," "can contain," "whose function is," and "allow the cell to," to indicate the basis for the organization of the map. The phrases should form a sentence between or among a set of concepts.

Answer Accept logical presentations by students.

All in One **Teaching Resources, Unit 1**
- Key Terms Review: *Living Things*
- Connecting Concepts: *Living Things*

Review and Assessment

Organizing Information

Concept Mapping Copy the concept map about the needs of organisms onto a separate sheet of paper. Then complete it and add a title. (For more on Concept Mapping, see the Skills Handbook.)

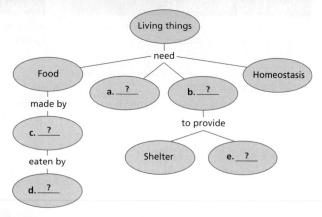

Reviewing Key Terms

Choose the letter of the best answer.

1. The idea that life could spring from nonliving matter is called
   a. development.
   b. spontaneous generation.
   c. homeostasis.
   d. evolution.

2. The scientific study of how living things are classified is called
   a. development.
   b. biology.
   c. taxonomy.
   d. evolution.

3. A genus is divided into
   a. species.   b. phyla.
   c. families.   d. classes.

4. The basic units of structure in all living things are
   a. nuclei.   b. organelles.
   c. tissues.   d. cells.

5. In plant and animal cells, the control center of the cell is the
   a. chloroplast.
   b. cytoplasm.
   c. nucleus.
   d. Golgi body.

If the statement is true, write _true_. If it is false, change the underlined word or words to make the statement true.

6. Bacteria are <u>unicellular</u> organisms.

7. Linnaeus devised a system of naming organisms called <u>binomial nomenclature</u>.

8. The gray wolf, _Canis lupus,_ and the red wolf, _Canis rufus,_ belong to the same <u>species</u>.

9. Cells were discovered using <u>electron</u> microscopes.

10. <u>Ribosomes</u> produce proteins.

Writing in Science

Dialogue A dialogue is a conversation. Write a dialogue that might have taken place between Schleiden and Schwann. The scientists should discuss their observations and conclusions.

Cell Structure and Function
Video Preview
Video Field Trip
▶ Video Assessment

Review and Assessment

Concept Map
a. water
b. living space
c. autotrophs
d. heterotrophs
e. food and water

Reviewing Key Terms
1. b **2.** c **3.** a **4.** d **5.** c

6. true
7. true
8. genus
9. light
10. true

Writing in Science

Writing Skill Dialogue
Scoring Rubric
4 Includes a dialogue that goes beyond requirements, for example, describing the structures of animal and plant cells
3 Includes criteria but does not go beyond requirements
2 Includes factual information that is not written in dialogue form
1 Includes inaccurate information

Video Assessment

Cell Structure and Function

Show the Video Assessment to review chapter content and as a prompt for the writing assignment.

Go Online
PHSchool.com
For: Self-Assessment
Visit: PHSchool.com
Web Code: cha-1020

Students can take a practice test online that is automatically scored.

All in One Teaching Resources, Unit 1
- Transparency LS19
- Chapter Test
- Performance Assessment Teacher Notes
- Performance Assessment Student Worksheet
- Performance Assessment Scoring Rubric

◉ _ExamView®_ **Computer Test Bank CD-ROM**

Checking Concepts

11. Students might point out that plants will bend toward sunlight and that plants grow, develop, and reproduce.

12. Sample answer: My dog gets energy from the food he eats and water from his water bowl. Our house is his living space.

13. A scientific name avoids confusion about the identity of the organism and gives information about an organism's characteristics.

14. The microscope allowed scientists to observe the cells that make up living things. Over the years, they discovered that all living things are made up of cells.

15. The cell wall helps to protect and support the cell in plants and some other organisms.

16. Mitochondria are called the powerhouses of the cell because they convert energy in food molecules to energy the cell can use to carry out its functions.

17. In multicellular organisms, cells are often organized into tissues, groups of similar cells that work together for a specific function. Different kinds of tissues make up organs. Groups of organs form organ systems, which perform major functions.

Thinking Critically

18. Although all robots use energy and some respond to their environments, they do not use energy to grow and develop. Living things are made of cells and are able to reproduce themselves.

19. *Entamoeba histolytica* and *Entamoeba coli*; they are in the same genus.

20. From a plant; the cell has green bodies called choroplasts and rigid, rectangular cell walls.

21. Observing the cells of an organism shows whether the cells have a nucleus. If they do, they belong to domain Eukarya; if they do not, they belong to either domain Bacteria or Archaea. The presence of chloroplasts or a cell wall indicates that the organism is not an animal, but might be a plant or certain other types of organisms.

Checking Concepts

11. Your friend thinks that plants are not alive because they do not move. How would you respond to your friend?

12. Describe how your pet, or a friend's pet, meets its needs as a living thing.

13. What are the advantages of identifying an organism by its scientific name?

14. What role did the microscope play in the development of the cell theory?

15. Describe the function of the cell wall.

16. Which organelles are called the "powerhouses" of the cell? Why are they given that name?

17. How are cells usually organized in large multicellular organisms?

Thinking Critically

18. **Applying Concepts** How do you know that a robot is not alive?

19. **Inferring** Which two of the following organisms are most closely related: *Entamoeba histolytica, Escherichia coli, Entamoeba coli*? Explain your answer.

20. **Applying Concepts** The photograph below has not been artificially colored. Do the cells in the photo come from a plant or an animal? Explain your answer.

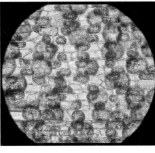

21. **Classifying** If you were trying to classify an unfamiliar organism by looking at its cells, what could the cells tell you?

Applying Skills

Refer to the illustrations below to answer Questions 22–25.

A student designed the experiment pictured below to test how light affects the growth of plants.

22. **Controlling Variables** Is this a controlled experiment? If so, identify the manipulated variable. If not, why not?

23. **Developing Hypotheses** What hypothesis might this experiment be testing?

24. **Predicting** Based on what you know about plants, predict how each plant will change in two weeks.

25. **Designing Experiments** Design a controlled experiment to determine whether the amount of water that a plant receives affects its growth.

Lab zone — Chapter **Project**

Performance Assessment Prepare a display presenting your conclusion about your mystery object. Describe the observations that helped you to reach your conclusion. Compare your ideas with those of other students. If necessary, defend your work.

Lab zone — Chapter **Project** — L3

Performance Assessment Students' displays should be well organized and describe how students tested their hypotheses. Have each student give a brief presentation to the class, describing how the results of their tests support their conclusions. Encourage students to talk about the results that they found surprising.

Reflect and Record Students may have trouble determining whether their object was alive if it was a fungus, a plant, or an animal such as coral that does not move.

Standardized Test Prep

Choose the letter of the best answer.

1. Which of the following statements about cells is *not* true?
  A Cells are the building blocks of living things.
  B Cells carry out the basic life functions of living things.
  C Some organisms are made up of only one cell.
  D Most cells can be seen with the naked eye.

2. Organisms that are autotrophs are classified in which of the following domains?
  F Bacteria
  G Archaea
  H Eukarya
  J all of the above

Use the table below and your knowledge of science to answer Questions 3–4.

Some Types of Trees

Common Name of Tree	Kingdom	Family	Species
Bird cherry	Plants	Rosaceae	*Prunus avium*
Flowering cherry	Plants	Rosaceae	*Prunus serrula*
Smooth-leaved elm	Plants	Ulmaceae	*Ulmus minor*
Whitebeam	Plants	Rosaceae	*Sorbus aria*

3. In the system of binomial nomenclature, what is the name for the whitebeam tree?
  A Rosaceae
  B *Sorbus aria*
  C *Prunus serrula*
  D *Ulmus minor*

4. Which of the following organisms is most different from the other three?
  F *Prunus avium*
  G *Prunus serrula*
  H *Ulmus minor*
  J *Sorbus aria*

5. A compound microscope has two lenses. One lens has a magnification of 15 and the other lens has a magnification of 40. What is the total magnification of the microscope?
  A 55
  B 150
  C 25
  D 600

Constructed Response

6. Name five characteristics that all living things share. Then describe each characteristic or give an example.

Applying Skills

22. Yes, the light is the manipulated variable.

23. Sample hypothesis: If plants do not have enough light, they will die.

24. In two weeks, the plant on the left might be dead, but the plant on the right will be healthy.

25. Sample experiment: Two plants receive the same amount and type of light. One receives one-fourth cup of water a day, and the other one-fourth cup every two days.

Standardized Test Prep

1. D   **2.** J   **3.** B   **4.** H   **5.** D

6. All organisms are made of cells, use energy, grow and develop, respond to their surroundings, and reproduce. Some organisms, such as bacteria, have only one cell, while others are composed of many cells. Animals use the energy from the food they eat to move, repair injured parts, and carry out other life processes. An acorn develops into an oak tree, which grows tall and strong. A person responds to cold temperatures by shivering. Finally, all living things reproduce, or produce offspring that are similar to themselves. Birds lay eggs that hatch into baby birds; bacteria divide to produce more bacteria.

Chapter at a Glance

PRENTICE HALL

TeacherEXPRESS™
Plan • Teach • Assess

Chapter **Project** *Shine On!*

Technology

Local Standards

SCHOOL
Video Preview

All in One Teaching Resources, Unit 1
- Chapter Project Teacher Notes, pp. 164–165
- Chapter Project Student Overview, pp. 166–167
- Chapter Project Student Worksheets, pp. 168–169
- Chapter Project Scoring Rubric, p. 170

Section 1

Chemical Compounds in Cells

2 periods
1 block

3.1.1 Define elements and compounds.

3.1.2 Explain how water is important to the function of cells.

3.1.3 Identify the four main kinds of organic compounds in living things.

Go Online
SCiLINKS NSTA

Section 2

The Cell in Its Environment

1 period
1/2 block

3.2.1 Describe how most small molecules cross the cell membrane.

3.2.2 Explain why osmosis is important to cells.

3.2.3 Tell the difference between passive transport and active transport.

Go Online
PHSchool.com

Section 3

Photosynthesis

1 period
1/2 block

3.3.1 Explain how the sun supplies living things with the energy they need.

3.3.2 Describe what happens during the process of photosynthesis.

Go Online
active art

Section 4

Respiration

1 period
1/2 block

3.4.1 Describe the events that occur during respiration.

3.4.2 Tell what fermentation is.

Go Online
SCiLINKS NSTA

Section 5

Cell Division

3 periods
1 1/2 blocks

3.5.1 Identify the events that take place during the three stages of the cell cycle.

3.5.2 Explain how the structure of DNA helps account for the way in which DNA copies itself.

SCHOOL
Video Field Trip

Go Online
active art

Review and Assessment

Test Preparation

All in One Teaching Resources, Unit 1
- Key Terms Review, p. 210
- Transparency LS34
- Performance Assessment Teacher Notes, p. 219
- Performance Assessment Scoring Rubric, p. 220
- Performance Assessment Student Worksheet, p. 221
- Chapter Test, pp. 222–225

SCHOOL
Video Assessment

Go Online
PHSchool.com

Test Preparation Blackline Masters

Lab zone

Chapter Activities Planner

For more activities

LAB ZONE
Easy Planner
CD-ROM

Student Edition	Inquiry	Time	Materials	Skills	Resources
Chapter Project, p. 73	Open-Ended	3 weeks	**All in One Teaching Resources, Unit 1,** p. 164	Designing an experiment, measuring, observing, graphing, drawing conclusions	**Lab zone Easy Planner** **All in One Teaching Resources, Unit 1,** Support, pp. 164–165
Section 1					
Discover Activity, p. 74	Directed	10 minutes	Labeled containers of chemical compounds such as baking soda, chalk, salt, and zinc oxide	Forming operational definitions	**Lab zone Easy Planner**
Try This Activity p. 77	Guided	5 minutes	Unsalted soda cracker	Inferring	**Lab zone Easy Planner**
Consumer Lab, p. 79	Guided	Prep 20 minutes; Class 30 minutes	Fat-testing test strips, color key, dips containing fat, paper towels, cotton swabs, clock or watch with second hand, permanent marker	Interpreting data, inferring	**Lab zone Easy Planner** **Lab Activity Video** **All in One Teaching Resources, Unit 1,** Consumer Lab: *Which Foods Are Fat-Free?* pp. 178–179
Section 2					
Discover Activity, p. 80	Directed	5 minutes	Air freshener spray	Developing hypotheses	**Lab zone Easy Planner**
Try This Activity, p. 83	Directed	10 minutes	Water; food coloring; cup; dropper	Inferring	**Lab zone Easy Planner**
Section 3					
Discover Activity, p. 86	Directed	5 minutes	Solar-powered calculator that does not use batteries	Inferring	**Lab zone Easy Planner**
Try This Activity, p. 89	Guided	20 minutes	Coffee filter, scissors, leaf, metric ruler, dime, rubbing alcohol, cup	Inferring	**Lab zone Easy Planner**
Section 4					
Discover Activity, p. 91	Directed	20 minutes	2 test tubes with stoppers, warm water, 5 mL sugar, test tube rack, 1.0 mL dried yeast, 2 straws	Observing	**Lab zone Easy Planner**
Section 5					
Discover Activity, p. 95	Guided	15 minutes	Dropper, yeast, stained microscope slide, coverslip, microscope	Developing hypotheses	**Lab zone Easy Planner**
Try This Activity, p. 96	Guided	10 minutes	Construction paper, different colored pipe cleaners	Making models	**Lab zone Easy Planner**
Skills Lab, p. 103	Directed	40 minutes	Microscope, colored pencils, calculator (optional), prepared slides of onion root tip cells undergoing cell division	Observing, calculating, interpreting data	**Lab zone Easy Planner** **All in One Teaching Resources, Unit 1,** Skills Lab: *Multiplying by Dividing,* pp. 208–209

Section 1 Chemical Compounds in Cells

 *2 periods, 1 block*

Objectives

3.1.1 Define elements and compounds.

3.1.2 Explain how water is important to the function of cells.

3.1.3 Identify the four main kinds of organic compounds in living things.

Local Standards

Key Terms

• element • compound • carbohydrate • lipid • protein
• amino acid • enzyme • nucleic acid • DNA • RNA

Preteach

Build Background Knowledge

Model the difference between an element and a compound.

 **Discover Activity** *What Is a Compound?* **L2**

Targeted Print and Technology Resources

All in One Teaching Resources, Unit 1

L2 Reading Strategy Transparency
LS20: Comparing and Contrasting

PresentationEXPRESS™ CD-ROM

Instruct

Elements and Compounds Discuss elements, compounds, and water.

Carbohydrates Discuss which elements make up carbohydrates and the role of carbohydrates.

Lipids Identify the elements in lipids and how lipids function in living things.

Proteins Describe proteins and their various functions in cells.

Nucleic Acids Compare RNA and DNA, and discuss their role in cells.

 **Consumer Lab** *Which Foods Are Fat-Free?* **L2**

Targeted Print and Technology Resources

All in One Teaching Resources, Unit 1

L2 Guided Reading, pp. 173–175
L2 Transparency LS21
L2 Consumer Lab: *Which Foods Are Fat-Free?* pp. 178–179

Lab Activity Video
Consumer Lab: *Which Foods Are Fat-Free?*

www.SciLinks.org Web Code: scn-0313

Assess

Section Assessment Questions

Have students use their graphic organizers comparing and contrasting carbohydrates, proteins, and lipids to answer the questions.

Reteach

Compare and contrast the main types of organic compounds in living things.

Targeted Print and Technology Resources

All in One Teaching Resources, Unit 1

• Section Summary, p. 172
L1 Review and Reinforce, p. 176
L3 Enrich, p. 177

Section 2 The Cell in Its Environment

 1 period, 1/2 block

ABILITY LEVELS
L1 Basic to Average
L2 For All Students
L3 Average to Advanced

Objectives

3.2.1 Describe how most small molecules cross the cell membrane.

3.2.2 Explain why osmosis is important to cells.

3.2.3 Tell the difference between passive transport and active transport.

Key Terms

• selectively permeable • diffusion • osmosis • passive transport
• active transport

Local Standards

Preteach

Build Background Knowledge

Compare the cell membrane to a sieve.

Lab zone Discover Activity *How Do Molecules Move?* L1

Targeted Print and Technology Resources

All in One Teaching Resources, Unit 1
L2 Reading Strategy: Building Vocabulary

○ **PresentationEXPRESS™ CD-ROM**

Instruct

Diffusion Describe how diffusion causes molecules to move in or out of a cell membrane.

Osmosis Use visuals to explain how water moves in osmosis and why this is important.

Active Transport Compare and contrast active and passive transport.

Targeted Print and Technology Resources

All in One Teaching Resources, Unit 1
L2 Guided Reading, pp. 182–183
L2 Transparencies LS22, LS23, LS24

PHSchool.com Web Code: ced-3014

Assess

Section Assessment Questions

Have students use their definitions to answer the questions.

Reteach

Summarize the three ways substances can move into and out of a cell.

Targeted Print and Technology Resources

All in One Teaching Resources, Unit 1
• Section Summary, p. 181
L1 Review and Reinforce, p. 184
L3 Enrich, p. 185

Section 3 **Photosynthesis**

 1 period, 1/2 block

Objectives

3.3.1 Explain how the sun supplies living things with the energy they need.
3.3.2 Describe what happens during the process of photosynthesis.

Key Terms

• photosynthesis • autotroph • heterotroph • pigment • chlorophyll • stomata

Local Standards

Preteach

Build Background Knowledge

Invite students to share what they know about the role of light in caring for houseplants.

 **Discover Activity** *Where Does the Energy Come From?* **L1**

Targeted Print and Technology Resources

 Teaching Resources, Unit 1

L2 Reading Strategy Transparency
LS25: Sequencing

 PresentationEXPRESS™ CD-ROM

Instruct

Sources of Energy Compare and contrast how autotrophs and heterotrophs receive energy from the sun directly and indirectly.

The Two Stages of Photosynthesis Use a diagram to examine what happens during photosynthesis.

Targeted Print and Technology Resources

Teaching Resources, Unit 1

L2 Guided Reading, pp. 188–190
L2 Transparencies LS26, LS27

PHSchool.com Web Code: cep-1042

Student Edition on Audio CD

Assess

Section Assessment Questions

Have students use their completed flowcharts that sequence photosynthesis to help them answer the questions.

Reteach

Use a diagram to review what happens during photosynthesis.

Targeted Print and Technology Resources

Teaching Resources, Unit 1

• Section Summary, p. 187
L1 Review and Reinforce, p. 191
L3 Enrich, p. 192

Section 4 Respiration

1 period, 1/2 block

ABILITY LEVELS
L1 Basic to Average
L2 For All Students
L3 Average to Advanced

Objectives

3.4.1 Describe the events that occur during respiration.

3.4.2 Tell what fermentation is.

Key Terms

• respiration • fermentation

Local Standards

Preteach

Build Background Knowledge

Relate students' knowledge of combustion to the concept of respiration.

 **Discover Activity** *What Is a Product of Respiration?*

Targeted Print and Technology Resources

All in One Teaching Resources, Unit 1

L2 Reading Strategy Transparency LS28: Using Prior Knowledge

⦿ **PresentationEXPRESS™ CD-ROM**

Instruct

What Is Respiration? Analyze respiration and the events that occur during the process.

Fermentation Describe fermentation and its products, and relate it to the familiar situation of exercising.

Targeted Print and Technology Resources

All in One Teaching Resources, Unit 1

L2 Guided Reading, pp. 195–197
L2 Transparency LS29

www.SciLinks.org Web Code: scn-0322

⦿ **Student Edition on Audio CD**

Assess

Section Assessment Questions

⟳ Have students use their completed graphic organizer about respiration to answer the questions.

Reteach

Have students make flowcharts to show what occurs during respiration and fermentation.

Targeted Print and Technology Resources

All in One Teaching Resources, Unit 1

• Section Summary, p. 194
L1 Review and Reinforce, p. 198
L3 Enrich, p. 199

Section 5 Cell Division

 3 periods, 1 1/2 blocks

ABILITY LEVELS
L1 Basic to Average
L2 For All Students
L3 Average to Advanced

Objectives

3.5.1 Identify the events that take place during the three stages of the cell cycle.

3.5.2 Explain how the structure of DNA helps account for the way in which DNA copies itself.

Local Standards

Key Terms

• cell cycle • interphase • replication • mitosis • chromosome • cytokinesis

---

Preteach

Build Background Knowledge

Elicit the stages of the human life cycle, and relate that cycle to the cell cycle.

 **Discover Activity** *What Are the Yeast Cells Doing?* L1

Targeted Print and Technology Resources

All in One Teaching Resources, Unit 1

L2 Reading Strategy Transparency LS30: Sequencing

⊙ **PresentationEXPRESS™ CD-ROM**

Instruct

Stage 1: Interphase Identify the events that occur during interphase, and lead students to infer the role of DNA replication.

Stage 2: Mitosis Examine how the cell's genetic material changes during mitosis.

Stage 3: Cytokinesis Discuss what happens during cytokinesis, and compare and contrast the process in plant and animal cells.

Structure and Replication of DNA Use diagrams of the structure of DNA to discuss how DNA replicates.

 **Skills Lab** *Multiplying by Dividing* L2

Targeted Print and Technology Resources

All in One Teaching Resources, Unit 1

L2 Guided Reading, pp. 202–205
L2 Transparencies LS31, LS32, LS33
L2 Skills Lab: *Multiplying by Dividing,* pp. 208–209

📼 **Lab Activity Video**
Skills Lab: *Multiplying by Dividing*

Discovery CHANNEL SCHOOL
Video Field Trip

PHSchool.com Web Code: cep-3023

⊙ **Student Edition on Audio CD**

Assess

Section Assessment Questions

⟳ Have students use their diagrams showing the sequence in the cell cycle to help them answer the questions.

Reteach

Have students sketch the stages of the cell cycle and exchange with partners to identify each stage.

Targeted Print and Technology Resources

All in One Teaching Resources, Unit 1

• Section Summary, p. 201
L1 Review and Reinforce, p. 206
L3 Enrich, p. 207

Chapter 3 Content Refresher

Section 1 Chemical Compounds in Cells

Biopolymers Complex carbohydrates, proteins, and nucleic acids are often called biopolymers. A biopolymer is a large biological molecule consisting of many similar units bonded together. These units are called monomers. Complex carbohydrates, such as starches, are made up of many simple sugars chemically combined in long strands or branching molecules. Cellulose, a complex carbohydrate that makes up the cell walls of plants, consists of many identical units of glucose (a simple sugar) bonded together in a long, unbranching strand.

Nucleic Acid Structure

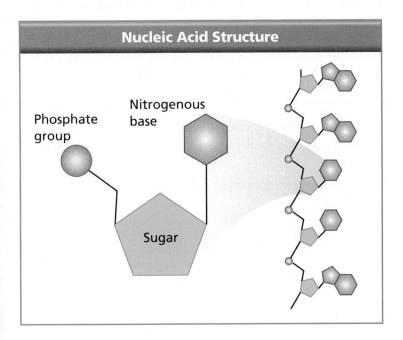

Phosphate group

Nitrogenous base

Sugar

Nucleic acids are polymers made up of nucleotide units. Each nucleotide monomer consists of a sugar, a nitrogen-containing base, and a phosphate group, as you can see in the illustration. The nucleotide units are bonded together by their sugar and phosphate groups, making nucleic acids a sugar-phosphate chain with exposed nitrogenous bases. These nitrogenous bases can attract bases on a nearby chain, giving DNA molecules their double-stranded structure.

Proteins are polymers made up of amino acid monomers. The amino acids that make up proteins vary in structure and therefore chemical characteristics. Thus, the great variety of sequences of amino acids that make up different proteins gives rise to the great variety of protein shapes and functions.

Section 2 The Cell in Its Environment

Transport Proteins The cell membrane is a lipid bilayer, which means that it is composed of two layers of lipid molecules. The structure is such that some molecules (such as oxygen, carbon dioxide, water, and many organic compounds) can easily pass through the cell membrane, while other substances (such as ions and large, water-soluble organic compounds) cannot pass through on their own. Instead, these substances must pass from one side of the cell membrane to the other via transport proteins.

Transport proteins are specific to the substances they allow into and out of the cell. The transport protein simply acts like a key-activated gate—only particles of a specific size, shape, or chemical makeup can use them. Some transport proteins do not require cellular energy. The process by which such transport proteins carry out their function is called facilitated diffusion. Like simple diffusion, the substance that crosses the membrane goes from an area of high concentration to one of low concentration.

Professional Development

72H

Section 3 **Photosynthesis**

Chlorophyll and the Absorption of Light The light that we see consists of a mixture of light having different wavelengths. If light passes through a prism, the light waves are separated according to wavelength and produce a spectrum of different colors, such as the one that forms the background of the graph below.

The pigment chlorophyll absorbs some, but not all, of the wavelengths of light. There are two main types of chlorophyll— chlorophyll *a* and chlorophyll *b*. The graph shows the percentage of different wavelengths absorbed by chlorophyll *a*. Notice that the highest percentage of absorption occurs in the purple/blue and orange/red areas of the spectrum. In contrast, almost no light is absorbed in the green area of the spectrum. This general pattern is also true for the absorption of light by chlorophyll *b*.

Address Misconceptions

Some students may think that soil provides plants with food. However, plants do not take in food; they produce all of their food through photosynthesis. From soil, plants obtain water— one of the raw materials for *making* food—and minerals, which are needed for growth and development. For a strategy for overcoming this misconception, see **Address Misconceptions** in the section *Photosynthesis*.

Chlorophyll makes chloroplasts—and leaves—look green because it reflects green light rather than absorbing it. It is the light reflected by leaves—not the light absorbed by them— that reaches people's eyes.

Light is a form of energy. When chlorophyll absorbs light, energy is transferred to electrons in the chlorophyll molecule. These "energized" electrons provide the energy for photosynthesis.

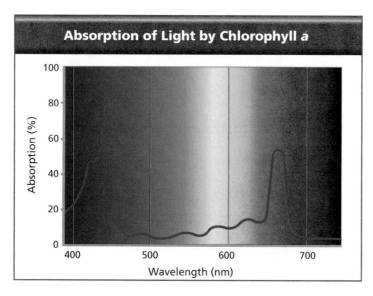

Absorption of Light by Chlorophyll *a*

Section 4 **Respiration**

A Form of Combustion Respiration is often compared to combustion because both processes involve the breakdown of molecules in the presence of oxygen to produce energy and carbon dioxide. However, respiration is a much slower, more controlled process than combustion. If respiration is like carrying a bundle down five flights of stairs, combustion is like dropping it from a fifth-story window.

The discovery of the nature of cellular respiration is attributed jointly to the French chemist Antoine Laurent Lavoisier and the French physicist, mathematician, and astronomer Pierre Laplace. In 1780 they published the results of their experiments showing that animal respiration is a form of combustion.

Energy and ATP Adenosine triphosphate, or ATP, is one of the main chemical compounds that release energy in organisms. The energy released by ATP powers processes such as active transport, muscle contraction, and the synthesis of DNA molecules.

During cellular respiration, cells use the energy stored in food molecules to produce ATP. For each molecule of glucose that undergoes the chemical reactions of cellular respiration, 36 molecules of ATP are formed. The stage of respiration that does not take place in a mitochondrion, which is called glycolysis, produces a net of only 2 ATP molecules. Oxygen is not required for the production of those two molecules. In contrast, the stage of respiration that takes place in the mitochondrion requires oxygen. The reactions that take place within a mitochondrion generate the remaining 34 molecules of ATP.

Section 5 Cell Division

Discovery of Chromosomes With the development of dyes for staining microscope specimens in the 1800s, scientists could see organelles in the nucleus and learn the details of mitosis. Some of the dyes stained the granular material in the nucleus, so it was given the name *chromatin,* from the Greek word *chroma,* meaning "color." With the dye, chromatin could be seen condensing into rodlike structures during cell division. These rodlike structures were called chromosomes, or "colored bodies" (the Greek word *soma* means "body.")

DNA Replication In most eukaryotic cells—that is, cells with nuclei and other membrane-bound organelles—the replication of a DNA molecule does not start at one end and finish at the other end. Instead, replication occurs simultaneously at many sites along the molecule. At each replication site, the two DNA strands separate. The opening that forms between the two strands, which is called a bubble, can be compared to the opening produced in a resealable plastic bag when the bag is opened in the middle of the "zipper" rather than at either end. The points at which the strands separate are called replication forks.

The process of DNA replication is facilitated by many different enzymes as well as other types of protein molecules. Protein molecules called single-strand binding proteins hold the original DNA strands apart. An enzyme called DNA polymerase links individual nucleotides in a chain, one by one, to form the new DNA strand. DNA polymerase also "proofreads" each new nucleotide as it is added to the strand, making sure that the new nucleotide correctly pairs with the corresponding nucleotide on the original strand. If a nucleotide is incorrect, DNA polymerase removes it.

DNA Replication Bubble

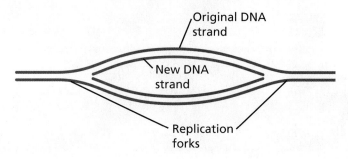

Original DNA strand

New DNA strand

Replication forks

Help Students Read

Visualizing
Forming Mental Pictures

Strategy Help students understand and recall complex text by forming mental pictures as they read. In some cases, visual elements of the text can aid students in visualizing; in other cases, students must rely solely on text descriptions. Choose several paragraphs from this chapter. If possible, include at least one paragraph that has an accompanying figure, such as a diagram, chart, graph, or photograph, and at least one other paragraph that refers to concepts or events that are not illustrated.

Example
1. Have students keep their books closed. Tell them to listen while you read and to visualize, or form mental pictures of, each object or action you read about.
2. Then, read a paragraph or so aloud, pausing frequently to demonstrate, by thinking aloud, how to visualize each thing described. When reading complex or technical text, pausing after each phrase will often be appropriate.
3. Tell students to continue visualizing. Slowly and clearly, read on. Then, select a logical stopping point, and discuss with students the images they visualized.
4. If there is an accompanying figure, have students open to it and see how it compares with their visualizing. Point out that visuals in the text help readers picture what they are reading.
5. Have students work with partners to practice by taking turns reading and visualizing aloud. Tell them to expand on visuals that appear in the text and to describe their own mental images of ideas or events that are not shown in visuals.

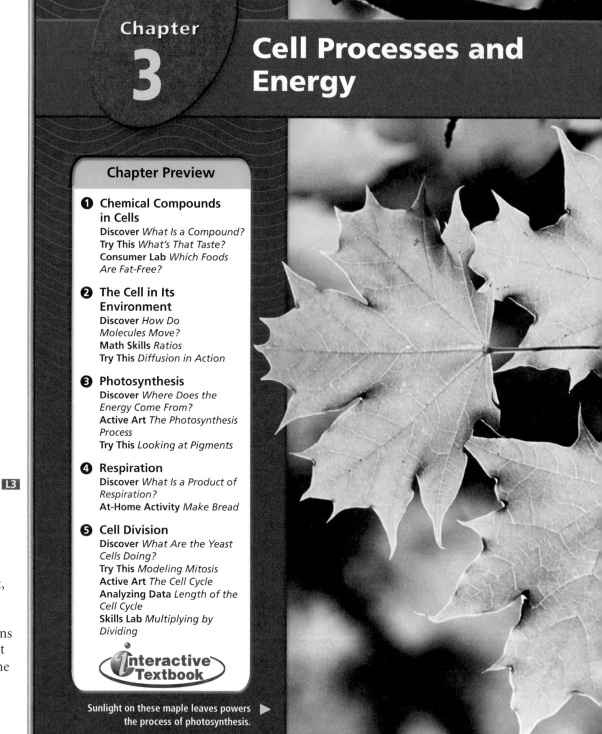

Chapter 3

Cell Processes and Energy

Chapter Preview

❶ Chemical Compounds in Cells
Discover *What Is a Compound?*
Try This *What's That Taste?*
Consumer Lab *Which Foods Are Fat-Free?*

❷ The Cell in Its Environment
Discover *How Do Molecules Move?*
Math Skills *Ratios*
Try This *Diffusion in Action*

❸ Photosynthesis
Discover *Where Does the Energy Come From?*
Active Art *The Photosynthesis Process*
Try This *Looking at Pigments*

❹ Respiration
Discover *What Is a Product of Respiration?*
At-Home Activity *Make Bread*

❺ Cell Division
Discover *What Are the Yeast Cells Doing?*
Try This *Modeling Mitosis*
Active Art *The Cell Cycle*
Analyzing Data *Length of the Cell Cycle*
Skills Lab *Multiplying by Dividing*

i**nteractive** Textbook

Sunlight on these maple leaves powers the process of photosynthesis. ▶

72 ◆

Chapter **Project**   L3

Objectives

This project will give students an opportunity to learn how plants use sunlight to make food in the process of photosynthesis. After this Chapter Project, students will be able to

- design a controlled experiment to grow plants under different lighting conditions while keeping other conditions constant
- observe, measure, and record data on the health and growth of the plants
- graph the data and draw conclusions about the effect of light on plant health and growth

Skills Focus

Designing an experiment, observing, measuring, making and interpreting graphs, drawing conclusions

Project Time Line   3 weeks

All in One Teaching Resources, Unit 1

- Chapter Project Teacher Notes
- Chapter Project Overview
- Chapter Project Worksheet 1
- Chapter Project Worksheet 2
- Chapter Project Scoring Rubric

Developing a Plan

During the first week, students will read and discuss the project, assemble into their groups, write an experimental plan, and begin setting up their experiment. Students continue to measure and record data during the next three weeks. Set aside time at the end of three weeks for students to prepare and deliver their presentations.

Possible Materials

- Provide rapidly growing plants (such as bean seedlings), watering cans, water, and metric rulers.
- Students may achieve different lighting conditions by placing the plants in different areas of the room, or by using plant lights on timers or colored cellophane paper.

DISCOVERY CHANNEL SCHOOL

Cell Processes and
Energy

▶ Video Preview
Video Field Trip
Video Assessment

Cell Processes and Energy

Show the Video Preview to introduce the
video topic and the topic of the cell cycle.

Lab zone™ Chapter **Project**

Shine On!

Every morning at sunrise, tiny living factories start a
manufacturing process called photosynthesis. The
power they use is sunlight. In this project, you will
investigate how light affects one familiar group of
photosynthesizers—plants.

Your Goal To determine how different lighting conditions affect the health and growth of plants

To complete the project, you will

- write up a plan to
  grow plants under
  different lighting
  conditions
- care for your plants
  daily and keep care-
  ful records of their
  health and growth for
  three weeks
- graph your data and draw conclusions about the effect of light on plant growth
- follow the safety guidelines in Appendix A

Plan It! Brainstorm with classmates to answer these
questions: What different light conditions might you
test? What plants will you use? How will you measure
health and growth? How can you be sure your results
are due to the light conditions? Write up your plan
and submit it to your teacher.

Chapter 3 ◆ 73

Suggested Shortcut

Individual students can grow the plants at
home to reduce the amount of class time
and classroom space needed to care for and
measure the plants.

Launching the Project

Ask: **What do plants need to grow?** (Possible
answers include soil, minerals, water, and
light.) Emphasize the importance of light to
plant growth. Point out that plants need
light to make food, which in turn provides
them with the energy they need for growth
and all other life processes. Ask: **What do
you predict would happen to a plant that
did not receive any light?** (Possible answer:
The plant would not be able to make food, so
it probably would die.)

Performance Assessment

The Chapter Project Scoring Rubric will help
you evaluate how well students complete the
Chapter Project. You may want to share the
scoring rubric with your students so they are
clear about what will be expected of them.
Students will be assessed on

- their experimental design and how
  well they control variables
- their record of observations and
  measurements of plant health and growth
- their graphs of the data and their
  conclusions about the effect of light on
  plant health and growth
- their group participation, if they worked
  in groups

Portfolio

Chemical Compounds in Cells

Objectives

After this lesson, students will be able to

3.1.1 Define elements and compounds.

3.1.2 Explain how water is important to the function of cells.

3.1.3 Identify the four main kinds of organic compounds in living things.

Target Reading Skill

Comparing and Contrasting Explain that comparing and contrasting information shows how ideas, facts, and events are similar and different. The results of the comparison can have importance.

Answers

Possible answers:

- *Type of Compound:* Carbohydrate
- *Elements in It:* Carbon, hydrogen, oxygen
- *Its Functions:* Stores and provides energy and makes up cellular parts
- *Type of Compound:* Lipid
- *Elements in It:* Carbon, hydrogen, oxygen
- *Its Functions:* Stores energy
- *Type of Compound:* Protein
- *Elements in It:* Carbon, hydrogen, oxygen, nitrogen, and sometimes sulfur
- *Its Function:* Makes up much of the structure of cells and speeds up chemical reactions

All in One Teaching Resources, Unit 1

- Transparency LS20

Preteach

Build Background Knowledge **L1**

Component Parts

Show students a jar with its lid on. Ask: **Can the lid be separated from the jar?** *(Yes)* Then remove the lid and put it alongside the jar. Ask: **Can the jar be easily divided into two or more parts?** *(No)* **What about the lid?** *(No)* Tell students that the jar and the lid by themselves are something like elements, and the jar with the lid attached is something like a compound. Tell students that they will learn about elements and compounds in this section.

Chemical Compounds in Cells

Reading Preview

Key Concepts

- What are elements and compounds?
- How is water important to the function of cells?
- What are the main kinds of organic molecules in living things?

Key Terms

- element • compound
- carbohydrate • lipid
- protein • amino acid
- enzyme • nucleic acid
- DNA • RNA

Target Reading Skill

Comparing and Contrasting As you read, compare and contrast carbohydrates, lipids, and proteins in a table like the one below.

Type of Compound	Elements	Functions
Carbo-hydrate	Carbon, hydrogen, oxygen	
Lipid		
Protein		

Lab zone Discover **Activity**

WATER
hydrogen and oxygen

SALT
sodium and chlorine

What Is a Compound?

1. Your teacher will provide you with containers filled with various substances. All of the substances are chemical compounds.
2. Examine each substance. Read the label on each container to learn what each substance is made of.

Think It Over

Forming Operational Definitions Write a definition of what you think a chemical compound is.

Watch out—you are surrounded by particles that you can't see! Air is made up of millions of tiny particles. They bump into your skin, hide in the folds of your clothes, and whoosh into your nose every time you take a breath. In fact, you and the world around you, including the cells in your body, are composed of tiny particles. Some of these particles are elements, and others are compounds.

Elements and Compounds

You may not realize it, but air is a mixture of gases. These gases include both elements and compounds. Three gases in the air are oxygen, nitrogen, and carbon dioxide.

Elements Oxygen and nitrogen are examples of **elements. An element is any substance that cannot be broken down into simpler substances.** The smallest unit of an element is called an atom. An element is made up of only one kind of atom. The elements found in living things include carbon, hydrogen, oxygen, nitrogen, phosphorus, and sulfur.

FIGURE 1
An Element
Sulfur is an element. In its pure form, it sometimes forms crystals.

Lab zone Discover **Activity**

Skills Focus Forming operational definitions **L2**

Materials Labeled containers of chemical compounds such as baking soda, chalk, salt, and zinc oxide sun block

Time 10 minutes

Tips Label the compounds with their common and chemical names (sodium bicarbonate for baking soda, calcium

carbonate for chalk, sodium chloride for salt, zinc oxide for sun block).

Expected Outcome Students will discover that all the compounds consist of two or more elements.

Think It Over Students may say that a chemical compound is something that is made up of more than one substance.

Compounds Carbon dioxide is a **compound** made up of the elements carbon and oxygen. **When two or more elements combine chemically, they form a compound.** Most elements in living things occur in the form of compounds. The smallest unit of any compound is called a molecule. A molecule of carbon dioxide consists of one carbon atom and two oxygen atoms.

The Compound Called Water Like carbon dioxide, water is a compound. Each water molecule is made up of two hydrogen atoms and one oxygen atom. Water makes up about two thirds of your body. Water plays many important roles in cells. Water dissolves chemicals that cells need. **Most chemical reactions within cells could not take place without water.** Water also helps cells keep their size and shape. In fact, a cell without water would be like a balloon without air. In addition, because water changes temperature so slowly, it helps keep the temperature of cells from changing rapidly.

Organic and Inorganic Compounds Many compounds in living things contain the element carbon. Most compounds that contain carbon are called organic compounds. Compounds that don't contain carbon are called inorganic compounds. Water and sodium chloride, or table salt, are familiar examples of inorganic compounds.

✔ **Reading Checkpoint** How are inorganic compounds different from organic compounds?

Go Online
SciLINKS NSTA

For: Links on proteins
Visit: www.SciLinks.org
Web Code: scn-0313

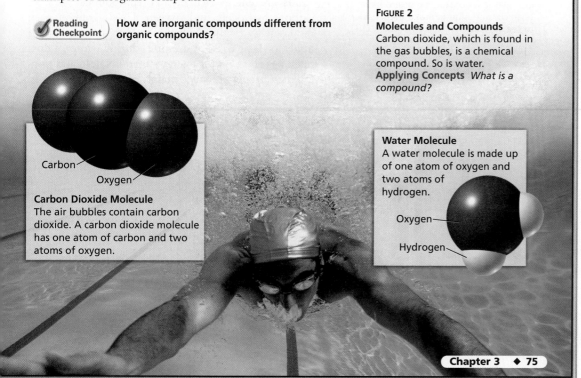

FIGURE 2
Molecules and Compounds
Carbon dioxide, which is found in the gas bubbles, is a chemical compound. So is water.
Applying Concepts *What is a compound?*

Carbon Dioxide Molecule
The air bubbles contain carbon dioxide. A carbon dioxide molecule has one atom of carbon and two atoms of oxygen.

Carbon
Oxygen

Water Molecule
A water molecule is made up of one atom of oxygen and two atoms of hydrogen.

Oxygen
Hydrogen

Go Online
SciLINKS NSTA

For: Links on proteins
Visit: www.SciLinks.org
Web Code: scn-0313

Download a worksheet to guide students' review of proteins.

Elements and Compounds

Teach Key Concepts L2
Elements, Compounds, and Water

Focus Write H_2O on the board. Explain that it is the chemical formula for water.

Teach Ask: **Which is water—an element or a compound?** *(Compound)* **Why?** *(It contains two elements—oxygen and water—that are combined chemically.)* **Why is water so important to living things?** *(Because most chemical reactions in living things couldn't take place without water; water also helps cells retain their size and shape and helps stabilize temperature.)* **How are organic compounds different from inorganic compounds?** *(Organic compounds contain carbon.)*

Apply Ask students to look at the chemical formula for water. Point out that the symbol *H* represents hydrogen and *O* represents oxygen. Ask: **What do you think this formula tells you about water?** As a hint, suggest that students look at the structure of water in the illustration. *(A water molecule has two hydrogen atoms and one oxygen atom.)* **learning modality: visual**

Independent Practice L2

All in One Teaching Resources, Unit 1

• Guided Reading and Study Worksheet: *Chemical Compounds in Cells*
• Transparency LS21

⊙ **Student Edition on Audio CD**

Monitor Progress _____ L1

Skills Check Have students construct a Venn diagram comparing organic and inorganic compounds.

Answers
Figure 2 A chemical combination of two or more elements

✔ **Reading Checkpoint** Organic compounds contain carbon.

Carbohydrates

Teach Key Concepts `L2`

The Role of Carbohydrates

Focus Review the definition of *carbohydrate*.

Teach Ask: **What are the functions of carbohydrates?** *(To store and produce energy and to make up some cell parts)*

Apply Ask students to name foods that are carbohydrates. **learning modality: verbal**

Lipids

Teach Key Concepts `L2`

The Role of Lipids

Focus Review the definition of *lipid*.

Teach Ask: **How do living things use lipids?** *(They use some of the energy contained in lipids and store some energy in lipids for later use.)*

Apply Ask students to name foods that contain lipids. **learning modality: verbal**

Detecting Starch `L2`

Materials dropper, iodine solution, soda crackers, bread, granulated sugar

Time 10 minutes

Focus Tell students that iodine darkens in the presence of starch.

Teach Add three drops of iodine to each sample. Only the sugar will not darken.

Apply Ask students to find out why the iodine changes color when combining with starch. **learning modality: visual**

FIGURE 3 Starch
These potatoes contain a large amount of starch. Starch is a carbohydrate. The blue grains in the close-up are starch granules in a potato. The grains have been colored blue to make them easier to see.

Carbohydrates

Carbohydrates, lipids, proteins, and nucleic acids are important groups of organic compounds in living things. A **carbohydrate** is an energy-rich organic compound made of the elements carbon, hydrogen, and oxygen. Sugars and starches are carbohydrates.

Sugars are produced during the food-making process that takes place in plants. Foods such as fruits and some vegetables have a high sugar content. Sugar molecules can combine, forming large molecules called starches, or complex carbohydrates. Plant cells store excess energy in molecules of starch. Many foods that come from plants contain starch. These foods include potatoes, pasta, rice, and bread. When you eat those foods, your body breaks down the starch into glucose, a sugar that your cells can use to produce energy.

Carbohydrates are important components of some cell parts. For example, the cellulose found in the cell walls of plants is a type of carbohydrate. Carbohydrates are also found in cell membranes.

Lipids

Fats, oils, and waxes are all lipids. Like carbohydrates, **lipids** are energy-rich organic compounds made of carbon, hydrogen, and oxygen. Lipids contain even more energy than carbohydrates. Cells store energy in lipids for later use. For example, during winter, a dormant bear lives on the energy stored in fat. In addition, cell membranes are made mainly of lipids.

Reading Checkpoint What are three kinds of lipids?

FIGURE 4 Lipids
Olive oil, which comes from olives such as those shown here, is made mostly of lipids.
Making Generalizations
What elements are lipids composed of?

76 ◆

Differentiated Instruction

Special Needs `L1`
Modeling Elements and Compounds
Use colored beads or blocks and glue to model elements and compounds and to help students distinguish between the two. Point out the illustration of a water molecule. Explain that it consists of two atoms of hydrogen, which is an element, and one atom of oxygen, which is an element. To demonstrate this, use two

beads of one color to represent hydrogen and another bead of a different color to represent oxygen. First, focus attention on these "elements" as separate entities. Then glue the three element-beads together to represent a water molecule. Explain that the glue represents chemical bonds. Then help students repeat the modeling procedure for carbon dioxide. **learning modality: kinesthetic**

Proteins

What do a bird's feathers, a spider's web, and your fingernails have in common? All of these substances are made mainly of proteins. **Proteins** are large organic molecules made of carbon, hydrogen, oxygen, nitrogen, and, in some cases, sulfur. Foods that are high in protein include meat, eggs, fish, nuts, and beans.

Structure of Proteins Protein molecules are made up of smaller molecules called **amino acids.** Although there are only 20 common amino acids, cells can combine them in different ways to form thousands of different proteins. The kinds of amino acids and the order in which they link together determine the type of protein that forms. You can think of the 20 amino acids as being like the 26 letters of the alphabet. Those 26 letters can form thousands of words. The letters you use and their order determine the words you form. Even a change in one letter, for example, from *rice* to *mice*, creates a new word. Similarly, a change in the type or order of amino acids can result in a different protein.

Functions of Proteins Much of the structure of cells is made up of proteins. Proteins form parts of cell membranes. Proteins also make up many of the organelles within the cell.

The proteins known as enzymes perform important functions in the chemical reactions that take place in cells. An **enzyme** is a type of protein that speeds up a chemical reaction in a living thing. Without enzymes, many chemical reactions that are necessary for life would either take too long or not occur at all. For example, enzymes in your saliva speed up the digestion of food by breaking down starches into sugars in your mouth.

 Reading Checkpoint What is the role of enzymes in cells?

Lab zone Try This **Activity**

What's That Taste?
Use this activity to discover one role that enzymes play in your body.

1. Put an unsalted soda cracker in your mouth. Chew it, but do not swallow. Note what the cracker tastes like.
2. Continue to chew the cracker for a few minutes, mixing it well with your saliva. Note how the taste of the cracker changes.

Inferring Soda crackers are made up mainly of starch, with little sugar. How can you account for the change in taste after you chewed the cracker for a few minutes?

FIGURE 5
Feathers Made of Protein
The feathers of this peacock are made mainly of protein.
Applying Concepts *What smaller molecules make up protein molecules?*

Proteins

Teach Key Concepts [L2]
The Role of Proteins

Focus Point out that proteins make up much of the structure of cells.

Teach Ask: **What elements make up proteins?** *(Carbon, hydrogen, oxygen, nitrogen, and sometimes sulfur)* **What kinds of molecules make up proteins?** *(Amino acids)* **How are proteins used in living things?** *(Proteins form parts of cell membranes and organelles. Proteins known as enzymes speed up many chemical reactions necessary for life.)*

Apply Ask: **What foods that you have eaten today contain proteins?** *(Sample answer: meat, eggs, fish, nuts, and beans.)* **learning modality: verbal**

Lab zone Teacher **Demo**

Modeling Enzymes [L1]

Materials hot plate, 1 package of pudding (not instant), water, spoon
Time 10 minutes

Focus Review the definition of enzyme.

Teach Prepare the pudding according to the package directions. Heat until it thickens. Ask: **What happened to the pudding?** *(It thickened.)* **How long would it have taken the pudding to thicken without heating it?** *(Much longer, perhaps not at all)* **How is the heat like an enzyme?** *(Both speed up chemical reactions.)*

Apply Explain that thrombin is an enzyme in blood that helps blood clot after an injury. Have students infer what would happen if thrombin were missing from blood. *(The blood would clot slowly or not at all.)* **learning modality: visual**

Monitor Progress [L2]

Writing Students can summarize the characteristics of carbohydrates, lipids, and proteins.

Answers
Figure 4 Carbon, hydrogen, and oxygen
Figure 5 Amino acids

 Reading Checkpoint Fats, oils, waxes

 Reading Checkpoint Speeding chemical reactions

Lab zone Try This **Activity**

Skills Focus Inferring [L1]
Materials unsalted soda cracker
Time 5 minutes
Tips *CAUTION: Students with food allergies to ingredients in the cracker should be exempted from this activity.*

Expected Outcome After students have chewed the cracker for a minute or two, it should start to taste slightly sweet. Enzymes in saliva help break down the cracker's starch into sugar.

Extend Ask: **How can you tell that a food is high in sugar?** *(It tastes sweet.)* **learning modality: kinesthetic**

Nucleic Acids

Teach Key Concepts L2

The Roles of DNA and RNA

Focus Remind students that the nucleus directs all the activities of animal and plant cells.

Teach Ask: **What is DNA?** (*The genetic material that carries information about an organism and that is passed from parent to offspring*) **What does RNA do?** (*It plays an important role in the production of proteins.*) **Why are nucleic acids important to all cells in the body?** (*They contain instructions that cells need to carry out all the functions of life.*)

Apply Ask: **How is RNA related to the structure of an organism?** (*RNA is important in the production of proteins, which make up much of the structure of cells.*)
learning modality: verbal

Monitor Progress L2

Answer

Reading Checkpoint DNA—carries genetic material; RNA—is important in production of proteins.

Assess

Reviewing Key Concepts

1. a. Any substance that cannot be broken down into simpler substances **b.** A compound can be broken down into two or more elements. **c.** A compound; it is made of the two elements nitrogen and hydrogen.
2. a. Water helps cells keep their size and shape, helps keep the temperature of cells stable, and helps carry substances into and out of cells. **b.** Chemical reactions could not take place, so enzymes could not function.
3. a. Carbohydrates, proteins, lipids, and nucleic acids **b.** Proteins and nucleic acids **c.** It could be a carbohydrate, but not a protein. All proteins contain nitrogen.

Reteach L1

Help students compare and contrast the four main types of organic compounds.

All in One Teaching Resources, Unit 1

- Section Summary: *Chemical Compounds in Cells*
- Review and Reinforce: *Chemical Compounds in Cells*
- Enrich: *Chemical Compounds in Cells*

Nucleic Acids

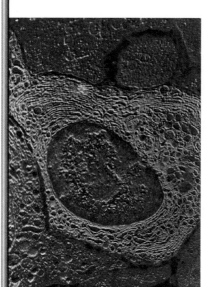

Nucleic acids are very long organic molecules made of carbon, oxygen, hydrogen, nitrogen, and phosphorus. Nucleic acids contain the instructions that cells need to carry out all the functions of life.

There are two kinds of nucleic acids. Deoxyribonucleic acid (dee ahk see ry boh noo KLEE ik), or **DNA,** is the genetic material that carries information about an organism and is passed from parent to offspring. The information in DNA also directs all of the cell's functions. Most of the DNA in a cell is found in the chromatin in the nucleus. Ribonucleic acid (ry boh noo KLEE ik), or **RNA,** plays an important role in the production of proteins. RNA is found in the cytoplasm as well as in the nucleus.

 Reading Checkpoint What are the two kinds of nucleic acids? What are their functions?

FIGURE 6 DNA in the Nucleus
A cell's nucleus (colored purple) contains most of the cell's DNA in its chromatin (colored red and yellow).

Section 1 Assessment

Target Reading Skill

Comparing and Contrasting Use the information in your table to help you answer the questions below.

Reviewing Key Concepts

1. a. Defining What is an element?
 b. Comparing and Contrasting How is a compound different from an element?
 c. Classifying A molecule of ammonia consists of one atom of nitrogen and three atoms of hydrogen. Is ammonia an element or a compound? Explain.
2. a. Reviewing What three important functions does water perform in cells?
 b. Relating Cause and Effect Suppose a cell is seriously deprived of water. How might this lack of water affect the cell's enzymes? Explain.
3. a. Reviewing What are four types of organic molecules found in living things?

 b. Classifying Which of the four types of organic molecules contain the element nitrogen?
 c. Inferring An organic compound contains only the elements carbon, hydrogen, and oxygen. Could this compound be a carbohydrate? Could it be a protein? Explain.

Lab zone At-Home Activity

Compounds in Food With family members, look at the "Nutrition Facts" labels on a variety of food products. Identify foods that contain large amounts of the following organic compounds: carbohydrates, proteins, and fats. Discuss with your family what elements make up each of these compounds and what roles they play in cells and in your body.

78 ◆

Lab zone At-Home Activity

Compounds in Food L2
Before students perform the activity at home, allow class time for them to review the composition and function of the organic compounds. Bring in some empty food containers with labels to model how to find the information.

Lab zone Chapter Project

Keep Students on Track Have students make any necessary revisions to their experimental plans. Make sure students are exposing their plants to different lighting conditions and are controlling all other variables. Check that students have a data table ready to record observations and measurements.

78

Consumer Lab

Which Foods Are Fat-Free?

Problem

Some people want to limit their intake of fats, or lipids. How can you determine whether information about fats on a food label is accurate?

Skills Focus

interpreting data, inferring

Materials

- 5 different snack dips in their containers, including nutrition labels
- 5 fat-testing strips with color key
- permanent marker
- 5 cotton swabs
- 5 small squares of paper towel

Procedure

1. Copy the data table on a sheet of paper. Record the brand names of the five snack dips in the table. **CAUTION:** *Do not taste the dips at any time.*
2. Examine the nutrition label on the container of each dip. Record the percentage of the Daily Value (% DV) of fat that the dip contains.
3. Look at other information on the container to see whether the dip is labeled "fat-free." Record this information in the table.

4. Obtain five fat-testing strips. Label each strip with the name of one of the dips.
5. Use a cotton swab to smear a bit of one dip onto the test square of the corresponding testing strip. After 30 seconds, gently wipe the dip from the strip with a paper towel.
6. To determine whether the sample contains fat, compare the test square with the color key. Record your observation in the table.
7. Repeat Steps 5–6 for each of the sample dips.

Analyze and Conclude

1. **Observing** According to the information on the containers, which dips had 0% fat? Which dips were labeled "fat-free"?
2. **Interpreting Data** Did the result shown on the test square always agree with the information on the dip's container?
3. **Inferring** Based on your results, what can you conclude about the accuracy of labels indicating that foods are fat-free?
4. **Communicating** Write a report for consumers that summarizes your results. Summarize the processes you used.

Design an Experiment

Protein test strips indicate *how much* protein is present in a food sample. Design an experiment to rank five food samples in the order of least protein to most protein. *Obtain your teacher's permission before carrying out your investigation.*

Data Table			
Name of Dip	Percent Fat (% Daily Value)	Labeled Fat-Free?	Result of Test

Chapter 3 ◆ 79

Analyze and Conclude

1. Results will vary. Sometimes a "fat-free" sample will produce a positive result.
2. Answers will vary. The test does not indicate the amount of fat, only the presence or absence of fat. Intermediate results (dark pink) indicate a moderate level of fat.
3. Students will probably say that labels are generally accurate.

4. The report should include the methods used, the limitations of the test, and an explanation to consumers of the meaning of "fat free."

Extend Inquiry

Design an Experiment Designs should include methods for controlling variables such as the amount of the food and the time before reading the result.

 Consumer Lab L2

Which Foods Are Fat-Free?

Prepare for Inquiry

Skills Objectives

Students will be able to

- organize and interpret results on the published values of nutritional labels
- infer the amount of fat present in the samples

🕐 **Prep Time** 20 minutes

Class Time 30 minutes

All in One Teaching Resources, Unit 1

- Lab Worksheet: *Which Foods Are Fat-Free?*

Advance Planning

Suggested foods are mayonnaise, butter, sour cream, olive oil, fat-free sour cream, cream cheese, light cream cheese, and fat-free liquid creamer.

Safety

Warn students to be careful when using the scissors and not to eat any of the foods. Review the safety guidelines in Appendix A.

Guide Inquiry

Introduce the Procedure

Show students how to interpret a food label. Explain that a serving that contains less than 0.5 g of fat/serving is considered "fat free."

Troubleshooting

- These test strips sometimes show false negative results with certain types of fats and those with an acidic pH (for example, vinegar in salad dressing).
- The age of the testing strip may affect its ability to change color.
- Some foods take longer than others to show a positive result.

Expected Outcome

Most foods with greater than 50% fat will show positive results. Some false negatives may occur.

Objectives

After this lesson, students will be able to

3.2.1 Describe how most small molecules cross the cell membrane.

3.2.2 Explain why osmosis is important to cells.

3.2.3 Tell the difference between passive transport and active transport.

Target Reading Skill

Building Vocabulary Explain that knowing the definitions of key terms helps students understand what they read.

Answers

Have students write what they know about each Key Term before reading the definitions in the section. Explain that connecting what they already know about Key Terms helps them to remember the terms. As they read each passage that contains Key Terms, remind them to write the definitions in their own words.

Preteach

Build Background Knowledge `L1`

Comparing a Membrane to a Sieve

Ask: **Why might you use a sieve or colander?** *(Possible answers: Strain lumps out of gravy or drain vegetables or pasta.)* **What do these things have in common?** *(They use a filter to separate large from small particles or solids from liquids.)* Tell students that the cell membrane also acts like a filter. It allows some substances, but not others, to pass in and out of the cell.

Section

2

The Cell in Its Environment

Reading Preview

Key Concepts

- How do most small molecules cross the cell membrane?
- Why is osmosis important to cells?
- What is the difference between passive transport and active transport?

Key Terms

- selectively permeable
- diffusion • osmosis
- passive transport
- active transport

Target Reading Skill

Building Vocabulary

A definition states the meaning of a word or phrase. After you read the section, reread the paragraphs that contain definitions of Key Terms. Use all the information you have learned to write a definition of each Key Term in your own words.

Lab zone — Discover **Activity**

How Do Molecules Move?

1. Stand with your classmates in locations that are evenly spaced throughout the classroom.
2. Your teacher will spray an air freshener into the room. When you first smell the air freshener, raise your hand.
3. Note how long it takes for other students to smell the scent.

Think It Over

Developing Hypotheses How was each student's distance from the teacher related to when he or she smelled the air freshener? Develop a hypothesis about why this pattern occurred.

As darkness fell, the knight urged his horse toward the castle. The weary knight longed for the safety of the castle, with its thick walls of stone and strong metal gates. The castle's gate-keeper opened the gates and slowly lowered the drawbridge. The horse clopped across the bridge, and the knight sighed with relief. Home at last!

Like ancient castles, cells have structures that protect their contents from the world outside. All cells are surrounded by a cell membrane that separates the cell from the outside environment. The cell membrane is **selectively permeable,** which means that some substances can pass through the membrane while others cannot.

80 ◆

Lab zone — Discover **Activity**

Skills Focus Developing hypotheses `L1`

Materials air freshener spray

Time 5 minutes

Tips Spray the air freshener up or down rather than in the direction of students.

Expected Outcome The spray will diffuse evenly throughout the classroom, reaching students at the same distance from the source at about the same time.

Think It Over The farther each student is from the teacher, the longer it takes for the student to smell the air freshener. Students may hypothesize that particles in the spray moved from an area of higher concentration to an area of lower concentration.

Cells, like castles, must let things enter and leave. Cells must let in needed materials, such as oxygen and food molecules. In contrast, waste materials must move out of cells. Oxygen, food molecules, and waste products all must pass through the cell membrane.

Diffusion

Substances that can move into and out of a cell do so by one of three methods: diffusion, osmosis, or active transport. **Diffusion is the main method by which small molecules move across the cell membrane.** Diffusion (dih FYOO zhun) is the process by which molecules move from an area of higher concentration to an area of lower concentration. The concentration of a substance is the amount of the substance in a given volume. For example, suppose you dissolve 1 gram of sugar in 1 liter of water. The concentration of the sugar solution is 1 gram per liter.

If you did the Discover activity, you observed diffusion in action. The area where the air freshener was sprayed had many molecules of freshener. The molecules gradually moved from this area of higher concentration to the other parts of the classroom, where there were fewer molecules of freshener—and thus a lower concentration.

What Causes Diffusion? Molecules are always moving. As they move, the molecules bump into one another. The more molecules there are in an area, the more collisions there will be. Collisions cause molecules to push away from one another. Over time, the molecules of a substance will continue to spread out. Eventually, they will be spread evenly throughout the area.

Math Skills

Ratios
The concentration of a solution can be expressed as a ratio. A ratio compares two numbers. It tells you how much you have of one item in comparison to another. For example, suppose you dissolve 5 g of sugar in 1 L of water. You can express the concentration of the solution in ratio form as 5 g : 1 L, or 5 g/L.

Practice Problem Suppose you dissolve 7 g of salt in 1 L of water. Express the concentration of the solution as a ratio.

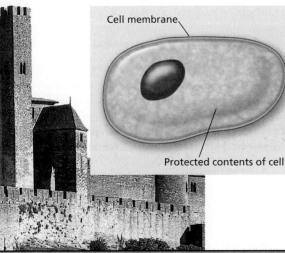
Cell membrane

Protected contents of cell

FIGURE 7
A Selective Barrier
The walls of a castle protected the inhabitants within, and the castle gatekeeper allowed only certain people to pass through. Similarly, the cell membrane protects the contents of the cell and helps control the materials that enter and leave.

Chapter 3 ◆ 81

Differentiated Instruction

Less Proficient Readers L1
Making a Chart Have students make a chart with three headings: *Diffusion, Osmosis,* and *Active Transport.* As they read the section, have students write notes about each process in the chart, paying attention to the relationships among the three topics. **learning modality: visual**

Gifted and Talented L3
Extending the Topic Ask students what happens in a cell once the concentrations of molecules inside and outside the cell are equal. Have students research the concept of dynamic equilibrium. *(Molecules continue to move into and out of a cell, but the numbers entering and leaving are approximately equal.)* **learning modality: logical/mathematical**

Instruct

Diffusion

Teach Key Concepts L2
Diffusion Across a Cell Membrane

Focus Remind students that all cells have a cell membrane.

Teach Ask: **What is the main way small molecules move across the cell membrane?** *(Diffusion)* **In what direction do molecules move during diffusion?** *(Molecules move from an area of higher concentration to an area of lower concentration.)*

Apply Ask: **Suppose a permeable membrane separates sugar solutions with concentrations of 5 g/L and 7 g/L. Which way will the sugar diffuse across the membrane?** *(The sugar will diffuse from the side that has 7 g/L to the side that has 5 g/L.)* **learning modality: logical/mathematical**

All in One Teaching Resources, Unit 1
• Transparency LS22

Math Skills

Math Skill Ratios

Focus Remind students that ratios can compare parts to a whole.

Teach Point out that concentrations that are written in fraction form often express the ratio of the mass of the solute to the volume of the solvent.

Answer
7 g : 1 L or 7 g/L

Independent Practice

All in One Teaching Resources, Unit 1
• Guided Reading and Study Worksheet: *The Cell in Its Environment*

◉ Student Edition on Audio CD

Monitor Progress _____ L2

Drawing Have students make a drawing that explains diffusion. Students can save their drawings in their portfolios. Portfolio

Help Students Read   L2

Outlining This section provides students with an excellent opportunity to practice outlining skills. Tell students to write the heads and subheads, leaving room between each one. As they read, they can list details under each subhead.

   L3

Observing Diffusion

Materials cornstarch, 2 cups, iodine, plastic dropper, resealable plastic bag, tablespoon, water

Time 10 minutes

Focus Tell students that iodine turns purple in the presence of starch.

Teach Explain that iodine molecules are small enough to move through plastic, but starch molecules are too large. Have students stir a tablespoon of cornstarch into half a cup of water and pour the mixture into a plastic bag. Seal the bag, rinse it, and place it in a clean cup half full of water. Add 20 drops of iodine to the water in the cup. Later, observe the cup and its contents. Ask: **Why did the water in the bag turn purple?** *(Iodine molecules passed through the plastic into the bag and interacted with the starch.)* **Why didn't the water in the cup turn purple?** *(The starch molecules were too big to pass through the bag.)*

Apply Ask: **How is this activity a model for a cell?** *(The bag is like a cell membrane.)*
learning modality: visual

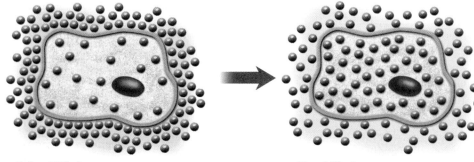

Before Diffusion
There is a higher concentration of oxygen molecules outside the cell than inside the cell.

After Diffusion
The concentration of oxygen molecules is the same outside and inside the cell.

FIGURE 8
Diffusion in Action
Molecules move by diffusion from an area of higher concentration to an area of lower concentration.
Predicting *What would happen if the concentration of oxygen molecules outside the cell was lower than inside the cell?*

Diffusion of Oxygen Have you ever used a microscope to observe one-celled organisms in pond water? These organisms obtain the oxygen they need to survive from the water around them. Luckily for them, there are many more molecules of oxygen in the water outside the cell than there are inside the cell. In other words, there is a higher concentration of oxygen molecules in the water than inside the cell. Remember that the cell membrane is permeable to oxygen molecules. The oxygen molecules diffuse from the area of higher concentration—the pond water—through the cell membrane to the area of lower concentration—the inside of the cell.

 Reading Checkpoint By what process do small molecules move into cells?

Osmosis

Like oxygen, water passes easily into and out of cells through the cell membrane. **Osmosis** is the diffusion of water molecules through a selectively permeable membrane. **Because cells cannot function properly without adequate water, many cellular processes depend on osmosis.**

Osmosis and Diffusion Remember that molecules tend to move from an area of higher concentration to an area of lower concentration. In osmosis, water molecules move by diffusion from an area where they are highly concentrated through the cell membrane to an area where they are less concentrated.

Effects of Osmosis Osmosis can have important consequences for a cell. Look at Figure 9 to see the effect of osmosis on cells. In Figure 9A, a red blood cell is bathed in a solution in which the concentration of water is the same as it is inside the cell. This is the normal shape of a red blood cell.

Contrast this shape to the cell in Figure 9B. The red blood cell is floating in water that contains a large amount of salt. The concentration of water molecules outside the cell is lower than the concentration of water molecules inside the cell. This difference in concentration occurs because the salt takes up space in the salt water. Therefore, there are fewer water molecules in the salt water outside the cell compared to the water inside the cell. As a result, water moves out of the cell by osmosis. When water moves out, cells shrink.

In Figure 9C, the red blood cell is floating in water that contains a very small amount of salt. The water inside the cell contains more salt than the solution outside the cell. Thus, the concentration of water outside the cell is greater than it is inside the cell. The water moves into the cell, causing it to swell.

 Reading Checkpoint How is osmosis related to diffusion?

FIGURE 9
Effects of Osmosis on Cells
In osmosis, water diffuses through a selectively permeable membrane.

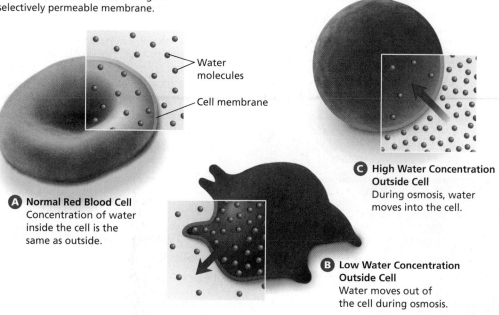

Water molecules

Cell membrane

A Normal Red Blood Cell
Concentration of water inside the cell is the same as outside.

B Low Water Concentration Outside Cell
Water moves out of the cell during osmosis.

C High Water Concentration Outside Cell
During osmosis, water moves into the cell.

Chapter 3 ◆ 83

Osmosis

Teach Key Concepts   L2
The Importance of Osmosis

Focus Point out that one of the substances that must move across a cell membrane is water.

Teach Ask: **What is osmosis?** (*The diffusion of water molecules through a selectively permeable membrane*) **Why is it important?** (*Cells cannot function properly without adequate water.*) Refer students to the illustration showing the effects of osmosis. Ask a student volunteer to read the passage Effects of Osmosis while the class follows by examining the visuals. Then ask: **Is the cell in A gaining or losing water?** (*Neither—the concentration is equal inside and outside.*) **In B, which side of the cell has a higher concentration of water molecules?** (*Inside the cell*) **What might eventually happen to the cell in C?** (*The cell might eventually burst as it continued to fill with more water.*)

Apply Ask: **Why can't people drink large amounts of salt water?** (*The salt water causes water to move out of body cells.*) **learning modality: logical/mathematical**

All in One **Teaching Resources, Unit 1**
• Transparency LS23

Monitor Progress   L2

Skills Check Have students compare and contrast diffusion and osmosis.

Answers
Figure 8 Oxygen molecules inside would diffuse out of the cell.

Reading Checkpoint Diffusion

Reading Checkpoint Diffusion is the proccess by which small molecules move from an area of higher concentration to an area of lower concentration; osmosis is the diffusion of water molecules through a selectively permeable membrane.

Active Transport

Teach Key Concepts L2

Comparing Active and Passive Transport

Focus Have students think about the words *active, passive,* and *transport.* Ask: **What are some ways you have heard all or parts of these words used?** (*Possible answers are* activity, passive smoke, *and* transportation.)

Teach Refer students to the diagram of passive and active transport. Ask: **What are two different types of passive transport?** (*Diffusion and osmosis*) **What is different about the movement of molecules using active transport?** (*It requires cellular energy, while passive transport does not.*) **When would active transport be used?** (*When a cell needs to take in a substance that is in a higher concentration inside the cell than outside*) **Which method of active transport is shown in the illustration?** (*Transport proteins in the cell membrane pick up molecules outside the cell and carry them in.*) **What other method is used in active transport?** (*The cell membrane engulfs a particle, then pinches off and forms a vacuole within the cell.*)

Apply Have students draw a Venn diagram that relates active and passive transport. (*Diagrams should show that active transport requires cellular energy and passive transport does not. The overlap area should indicate that in both processes, materials move in and out of cells.*) **learning modality: visual**

All in One **Teaching Resources, Unit 1**

• Transparency LS24

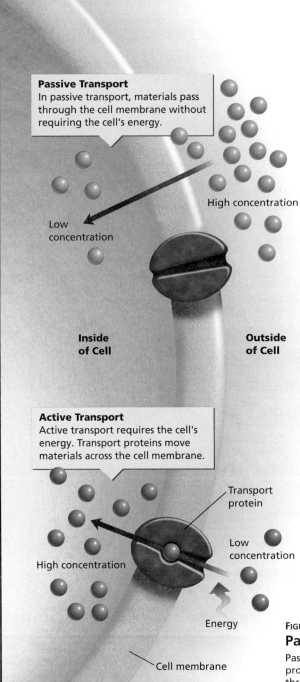

Passive Transport
In passive transport, materials pass through the cell membrane without requiring the cell's energy.

High concentration

Low concentration

Inside of Cell

Outside of Cell

Active Transport
Active transport requires the cell's energy. Transport proteins move materials across the cell membrane.

Transport protein

Low concentration

High concentration

Energy

Cell membrane

FIGURE 10
Passive and Active Transport
Passive and active transport are two processes by which materials pass through the cell membrane.
Interpreting Diagrams *What is the function of a transport protein?*

84 ◆

Active Transport

If you have ever ridden a bicycle down a long hill, you know that it doesn't take any of your energy to go fast. But you do have to use some of your energy to pedal back up the hill. For a cell, moving materials through the cell membrane by diffusion and osmosis is like cycling downhill. These processes do not require the cell to use its own energy. The movement of dissolved materials through a cell membrane without using cellular energy is called **passive transport.**

What if a cell needs to take in a substance that is present in a higher concentration inside the cell than outside? The cell would have to move the molecules in the opposite direction than they naturally move by diffusion. Cells can do this, but they have to use energy—just as you would use energy to pedal back up the hill. **Active transport** is the movement of materials through a cell membrane using cellular energy. **Active transport requires the cell to use its own energy, while passive transport does not.**

Transport Proteins Cells have several ways of moving materials by active transport. In one method, transport proteins in the cell membrane "pick up" molecules outside the cell and carry them in, using energy. Figure 10 illustrates this process. Transport proteins also carry molecules out of cells in a similar way. Some substances that are carried into and out of cells in this way include calcium, potassium, and sodium.

Differentiated Instruction

Special Needs L1
Modeling Active and Passive Transport Provide students with a small board, stack of books, and a toy car. Help pairs of students to model active and passive transport, or model for them. (*The most likely way is to make an inclined plane with the board and books, and then to roll the toy car down the ramp to simulate passive transport and push it up the ramp to* simulate active transport.) Ask: **Why do you need to supply energy to move the toy car up the ramp?** (*To overcome the force of gravity*) Ask: **Why is energy needed to actively transport some substances into the cell?** (*To move the substances from an area of lower to an area of higher concentration*) **learning modality: kinesthetic**

Transport by Engulfing Figure 11 shows another method of active transport. First, the cell membrane surrounds and engulfs, or encloses, a particle. Once the particle is engulfed, the cell membrane wraps around the particle and forms a vacuole within the cell. The cell must use energy in this process.

Why Cells Are Small As you know, most cells are so small that you cannot see them without a microscope. Have you ever wondered why cells are so small? One reason is related to how materials move into and out of cells.

As a cell's size increases, more of its cytoplasm is located farther from the cell membrane. Once a molecule enters a cell, it is carried to its destination by a stream of moving cytoplasm, somewhat like the way currents in the ocean move a raft. But in a very large cell, the streams of cytoplasm must travel farther to bring materials to all parts of the cell. It would take much longer for a molecule to reach the center of a very large cell than it would in a small cell. Likewise, it would take a long time for wastes to be removed. If a cell grew too large, it could not function well enough to survive.

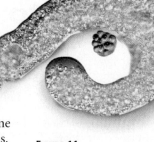

FIGURE 11
Amoeba Engulfing Food
This single-celled amoeba is surrounding a smaller organism. The amoeba will engulf the organism and use it for food. Engulfing is a form of active transport.

Reading Checkpoint **What prevents cells from growing very large?**

Section 2 Assessment

Target Reading Skill **Building Vocabulary** Use your definitions to help answer the questions below.

Reviewing Key Concepts

1. a. **Defining** What is diffusion?
   b. **Relating Cause and Effect** Use diffusion to explain what happens when you drop a sugar cube into a mug of hot tea.
2. a. **Defining** What is osmosis?
   b. **Describing** Describe how water molecules move through the cell membrane during osmosis.
   c. **Applying Concepts** A selectively permeable membrane separates solutions A and B. The concentration of water molecules in Solution B is higher than that in Solution A. Describe how the water molecules will move.
3. a. **Comparing and Contrasting** How is active transport different from passive transport?
   b. **Reviewing** What are transport proteins?
   c. **Explaining** Explain why transport proteins require energy to function in active transport.

Math Practice

A scientist dissolves 60 g of sugar in 3 L of water.

4. **Calculating a Concentration** Calculate the concentration of the solution in grams per liter.
5. **Ratios** Express the concentration as a ratio.

Monitor Progress L2

Answers

Figure 10 A transport protein picks up molecules outside the cell and brings them into the cell, or carries them out in a similar way.

Reading Checkpoint If cells were very large, it would take much longer for molecules entering the cell to reach the center of the cell and for wastes to be removed.

Assess

Reviewing Key Concepts

1. a. The process by which molecules move from an area of higher concentration to an area of lower concentration **b.** The sugar molecules dissolve and move from the area near the cube, where the sugar concentration is high, to the rest of the tea, where the concentration is lower.
2. a. The diffusion of water molecules through a selectively permeable membrane **b.** Water molecules move from the side of the cell membrane with a higher concentration of water to the side with a lower concentration of water. **c.** Water molecules move by osmosis from B to A.
3. a. Active transport requires cellular energy; passive transport does not. **b.** Proteins in the cell membrane that carry molecules from outside the cell to inside **c.** Because they are moving molecules from an area of lower concentration to an area of higher concentration.

Math Practice

4. 20 g/L **5.** 60 g : 3 L or 20 g : 1 L

Reteach L1

Have students summarize the three ways substances can move into and out of a cell and tell whether each requires the cell to use energy.

All in One Teaching Resources, Unit 1

- Section Summary: *The Cell in Its Environment*
- Review and Reinforce: *The Cell in Its Environment*
- Enrich: *The Cell in Its Environment*

Lab zone Chapter Project

Keep Students on Track Make sure students are making and recording daily measurements for at least two weeks. Check that students are doing their best to control variables. Suggest that students make drawings of the plants at different stages and include in their observations the number and length of stems, and the number, size, color, and firmness of the leaves.

Objectives

After this lesson, students will be able to

3.3.1 Explain how the sun supplies living things with the energy they need.

3.3.2 Describe what happens during the process of photosynthesis.

Target Reading Skill

Sequencing Explain that organizing information from beginning to end helps students understand a step-by-step process.

Answer

One possible way to complete the flowchart is to place the following sentence in the third bar: Cells use the energy to produce sugars and oxygen from water and carbon dioxide.

All in One Teaching Resources, Unit 1

• Transparency LS25

Preteach

Build Background Knowledge   L1

Care of Houseplants

Ask: **How many of you have houseplants in your home?** Most will probably say they do. **Where are houseplants usually placed?** *(Near a window or under plant lights)* **What happens if a houseplant doesn't get enough light?** *(They lose their leaves, turn yellow, and may die.)* **Why do plants need light?** Some students may know that plants use light energy to make food. Accept all responses without comment at this time.

Reading Preview

Key Concepts

• How does the sun supply living things with the energy they need?

• What happens during the process of photosynthesis?

Key Terms

• photosynthesis • autotroph
• heterotroph • pigment
• chlorophyll • stomata

Target Reading Skill

Sequencing A sequence is the order in which the steps in a process occur. As you read, create a flowchart that shows the steps in photosynthesis. Put each step in a separate box in the flowchart in the order in which it occurs.

Steps in Photosynthesis

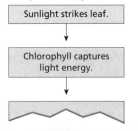

Sunlight strikes leaf.

↓

Chlorophyll captures light energy.

↓

Lab zone Discover Activity

Where Does the Energy Come From?

1. Obtain a solar-powered calculator that does not use batteries. Place the calculator in direct light.

2. Cover the solar cells with your finger. Note how your action affects the number display.

3. Uncover the solar cells. What happens to the number display?

4. Now cover all but one of the solar cells. How does that affect the number display?

Think It Over

Inferring From your observations, what can you infer about the energy that powers the calculator?

On a plain in Africa, dozens of zebras peacefully eat the grass. But watch out—the zebras' grazing will soon be harshly interrupted. A group of lions is about to attack the herd. The lions will kill one of the zebras and eat it.

Both the zebras and the lions use the food they eat to obtain energy. Every living thing needs energy. All cells need energy to carry out their functions, such as making proteins and transporting substances into and out of the cell. The zebra's meat supplies the lion's cells with the energy they need, just as the grass provides the zebra's cells with energy. But plants and certain other organisms, such as algae and some bacteria, obtain their energy in a different way. These organisms use the energy in sunlight to make their own food.

Lab zone Discover Activity

Skills Focus Inferring   L1

Materials solar-powered calculator that does not use batteries

Time 5 minutes

Tips If necessary, show students where the solar cells are located on the calculator.

Expected Outcome When all the solar cells are covered, the number display

should go blank. When all but one of the solar cells are covered, the number display should flicker and fade.

Think It Over Energy to power the calculator comes from sunlight.

The sun is the source of energy for most living things.

Plants such as grass use energy from the sun to make their own food.

The zebra obtains energy by eating grass.

The lion obtains energy by feeding on the zebra.

FIGURE 12
Energy From the Sun
The sun supplies energy for most living things, directly or indirectly. **Relating Cause and Effect** *How does sunlight provide food for the zebra?*

Sources of Energy

The process by which a cell captures energy in sunlight and uses it to make food is called **photosynthesis** (foh toh SIN thuh sis). The term *photosynthesis* comes from the Greek words *photo*, which means "light," and *synthesis*, which means "putting together."

Nearly all living things obtain energy either directly or indirectly from the energy of sunlight captured during photosynthesis. Grass obtains energy directly from sunlight, because it makes its own food during photosynthesis. When the zebra eats the grass, it gets energy that has been stored in the grass. Similarly, the lion obtains energy stored in the zebra. The zebra and lion both obtain the sun's energy indirectly, from the energy that the grass obtained through photosynthesis.

Plants manufacture their own food through the process of photosynthesis. An organism that makes its own food is called an **autotroph** (AWT oh trahf). An organism that cannot make its own food, including animals such as the zebra and the lion, is called a **heterotroph** (HET ur oh trahf). Many heterotrophs obtain food by eating other organisms. Some heterotrophs, such as fungi, absorb their food from other organisms.

Reading Checkpoint What are autotrophs?

FIGURE 13
Autotrophs and Heterotrophs
Grass, which makes its own food during photosynthesis, is an autotroph. Zebras and lions are heterotrophs, because they cannot make their own food.

♦ 87

The Two Stages of Photosynthesis

Go Online
active art

For: The Photosynthesis Process
Visit: PHSchool.com
Web Code: cep-1042

Students can interact with the art of photosynthesis online.

Help Students Read L2

Visualizing Refer to the Content Refresher for guidelines on visualizing. Have students close their eyes and form mental pictures as you slowly read aloud The Two Stages of Photosynthesis. Ask them to think about the role of the different parts of a plant. Then have students look at Figure 14 and see how it compares with their visualizing. Point out that visualizing text helps readers understand what they are reading.

Teach Key Concepts L2

What Happens During Photosynthesis

Focus Refer students to Figure 14.

Teach Ask: **What are the two stages of photosynthesis?** (*Capturing the sun's energy and producing sugars*) **What is the energy captured in the first stage used for?** (*To produce sugars in the second stage*) **What pigment in chloroplasts absorbs light?** (*Chlorophyll*) **How is chlorophyll like a solar cell?** (*Both chlorophyll and solar cells absorb light energy and use it to power a process.*) **What happens in the second stage?** (*Water and carbon dioxide combine chemically to form sugars, and oxygen is released.*) **How are roots and stomata important for photosynthesis?** (*Roots take up water, and stomata take in carbon dioxide, both of which are needed for photosynthesis.*)

Apply Explain that not all the oxygen produced in photosynthesis is released from the plant. Plants use some of the oxygen to break down the sugar molecules they need for their own energy needs. **learning modality: visual**

All in One Teaching Resources, Unit 1
• Transparency LS27

Go Online
active art

For: The Photosynthesis Process
Visit: PHSchool.com
Web Code: cep-1042

FIGURE 14
Two Stages of Photosynthesis

Photosynthesis has two stages, as shown in the diagram.
Interpreting Diagrams *Which stage requires light?*

The Two Stages of Photosynthesis

Photosynthesis is a complex process. **During photosynthesis, plants and some other organisms use energy from the sun to convert carbon dioxide and water into oxygen and sugars.** The process of photosynthesis is shown in Figure 14. You can think of photosynthesis as taking place in two stages: capturing the sun's energy and producing sugars. You're probably familiar with many two-stage processes. To make a cake, for example, the first stage is to combine the ingredients to make the batter. The second stage is to bake the batter. To get the desired result—the cake—both stages must occur in the correct order.

Stage 1: Capturing the Sun's Energy The first stage of photosynthesis involves capturing the energy in sunlight. In plants, this energy-capturing process occurs mostly in the leaves. Recall that chloroplasts are green organelles inside plant cells. The green color comes from **pigments,** colored chemical compounds that absorb light. The main photosynthetic pigment in chloroplasts is **chlorophyll.**

Chlorophyll functions in a manner similar to that of the solar "cells" in a solar-powered calculator. Solar cells capture the energy in light and use it to power the calculator. Similarly, chlorophyll captures light energy and uses it to power the second stage of photosynthesis.

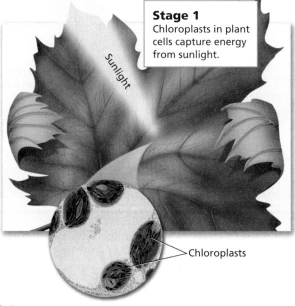

Stage 1
Chloroplasts in plant cells capture energy from sunlight.

Sunlight

Chloroplasts

Stage 2
The captured light energy is used to produce sugars and oxygen from water and carbon dioxide.

Carbon dioxide enters the leaf through openings called stomata.

Water enters the plant through roots and moves upward to the leaf.

88 ◆

Differentiated Instruction

Gifted and Talented L3
Researching Light and Chlorophyll

Help students integrate science concepts by having them research the nature of light, reflection, and absorption. Ask: **Why is chlorophyll green? What does chlorophyll's color have to do with the kind of light that plants grow best in?** (*Visible light consists of all colors of light,* *including red, blue, and green light. Chlorophyll is green because it reflects green light. Red and blue light is absorbed by chlorophyll and used to power photosynthesis. Because chlorophyll does not absorb green light very well, green light does not help power photosynthesis. Red and blue light is best for growing plants.*)
learning modality: logical/mathematical

Stage 2: Using Energy to Make Food In the next stage of photosynthesis, the cell uses the captured energy to produce sugars. The cell needs two raw materials for this stage: water (H_2O) and carbon dioxide (CO_2). In plants, the roots absorb water from the soil. The water then moves up through the plant's stem to the leaves. Carbon dioxide is one of the gases in the air. Carbon dioxide enters the plant through small openings on the undersides of the leaves called **stomata** (STOH muh tuh) (singular *stoma*). Once in the leaves, the water and carbon dioxide move into the chloroplasts.

Inside the chloroplasts, the water and carbon dioxide undergo a complex series of chemical reactions. The reactions are powered by the energy captured in the first stage. These reactions produce chemicals as products. One product is a sugar that has six carbon atoms. Six-carbon sugars have the chemical formula $C_6H_{12}O_6$. Recall that sugars are a type of carbohydrate. Cells can use the energy in the sugar to carry out important cell functions.

The other product of photosynthesis is oxygen (O_2), which exits the leaf through the stomata. In fact, almost all the oxygen in Earth's atmosphere was produced by living things through the process of photosynthesis.

Reading Checkpoint What makes plants green?

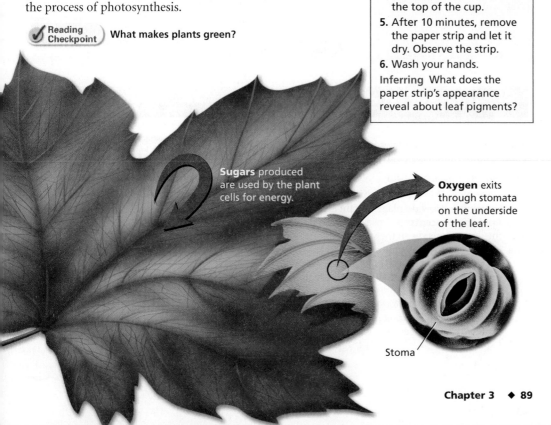

Sugars produced are used by the plant cells for energy.

Oxygen exits through stomata on the underside of the leaf.

Stoma

Chapter 3 ◆ 89

Lab zone **Try This Activity**

Looking at Pigments
You can observe the pigments in a leaf.

1. Cut a strip 5 cm by 20 cm out of a paper coffee filter.
2. Place a leaf on top of the paper strip, about 2 cm from the bottom.
3. Roll the edge of a dime over a section of the leaf, leaving a narrow band of color on the paper strip.
4. Pour rubbing alcohol into a plastic cup to a depth of 1 cm. Stand the paper strip in the cup so the color band is about 1 cm above the alcohol. Hook the other end of the strip over the top of the cup.
5. After 10 minutes, remove the paper strip and let it dry. Observe the strip.
6. Wash your hands.

Inferring What does the paper strip's appearance reveal about leaf pigments?

Lab zone **Build Inquiry**

Observing Stomata **L2**

Materials forceps, lettuce leaf, water, microscope slide, coverslip, microscope

Time 15 minutes

Focus Review the function of stomata.

Teach Have students use forceps to gently pull away a small piece of the thin membrane on the underside of a lettuce leaf, then make a slide and sketch the structures they see. Call their attention to the sausage-shaped guard cells on either side of each stoma, and ask: **What role do you think the guard cells play?** (*They regulate what enters the stomata.*)

Apply Tell students that stomata are not open all the time. Ask: **When do you think the stomata are usually open?** (*During the day when light energy is available for photosynthesis*) **learning modality: visual**

Address Misconceptions **L2**

The Role of Soil in Photosynthesis

Focus Some students may think that soil provides plants with food.

Teach Explain that soil provides one of the raw materials for plants to make food—water. However, plants produce their own food from water plus carbon dioxide and the energy from sunlight; plants do not "take in" food.

Apply Tell students that hydroponics means growing plants in water, without soil. As long as plants are provided with the minerals they need and the materials for making their own food, they do not have to be grown in soil. **learning modality: logical/mathematical**

Lab zone **Try This Activity**

Skills Focus Inferring **L2**

Materials coffee filter, scissors, leaf, metric ruler, dime, rubbing alcohol, plastic cup

Time 20 minutes

Tips CAUTION: *Do not use plants that may cause allergic reactions. Warn students not to taste or inhale the alcohol. Make sure no open flames are present.*
A geranium works well.

Expected Outcome Alcohol dissolves plant pigments and carries them up the paper strip. The paper's appearance reveals that leaves contain several pigments.

Extend Ask: **In the fall, when chlorophyll decreases in some plants, why do leaves change color?** (*As chlorophyll decreases, other pigments that were hidden by the green chlorophyll can then be seen.*) **learning modality: kinesthetic**

Monitor Progress **L2**

Oral Presentation Have students make a flowchart to show what happens during photosynthesis.

Answers
Figure 14 Stage 1

Reading Checkpoint Chloroplasts contain the green pigment chlorophyll.

Answer

Assess

Reviewing Key Concepts

1. a. All living things are made up of cells, which need energy to carry out their functions. **b.** They trap energy from sunlight in the process of photosynthesis. **c.** The leaf has stored food that the plant made using energy from the sun in the process of photosynthesis.

2. a. 6 CO$_2$ (carbon dioxide) + 6 H$_2$O (water) + (light energy) → C$_6$H$_{12}$O$_6$ (a sugar) + 6 O$_2$ (oxygen) **b.** Carbon dioxide, water, and light energy; sugar and oxygen **c.** A plant would likely produce more oxygen on a sunny day, because there would be more sunlight available to the plant for photosynthesis.

Reteach L1

Use Figure 14 to review what happens during photosynthesis. Have students identify how the figure relates to the equation for photosynthesis.

Performance Assessment L2

Writing Have students explain how life on Earth depends on the sun.

All in One Teaching Resources, Unit 1

- Section Summary: *Photosynthesis*
- Review and Reinforce: *Photosynthesis*
- Enrich: *Photosynthesis*

FIGURE 15 Stored Energy
When you eat a carrot, you obtain energy stored during photosynthesis.

The Photosynthesis Equation The events of photosynthesis can be summed up by the following chemical equation:

$$6\ CO_2 \ + \ 6\ H_2O \ \xrightarrow{\text{light energy}} \ C_6H_{12}O_6 \ + \ 6\ O_2$$

carbon dioxide   water   a sugar   oxygen

Notice that the raw materials—six molecules of carbon dioxide and six molecules of water—are on the left side of the equation. The products—one molecule of a sugar and six molecules of oxygen—are on the right side of the equation. An arrow, which you can read as "yields," connects the raw materials to the products. Light energy, which is necessary for the chemical reaction to occur, is written above the arrow.

What happens to the sugar produced in photosynthesis? Plant cells use some of the sugar for food. The cells break down the sugar molecules to release the energy they contain. This energy can then be used to carry out the plant's functions. Some sugar molecules are converted into other compounds, such as cellulose. Other sugar molecules may be stored in the plant's cells for later use. When you eat food from plants, such as potatoes or carrots, you are eating the plant's stored energy.

✓ **Reading Checkpoint** In the photosynthesis equation, what does the arrow mean?

Section 3 Assessment

↻ **Target Reading Skill** Sequencing Use your flowchart about photosynthesis to help answer Question 2.

Reviewing Key Concepts

1. a. **Reviewing** Why do living things need energy?
   b. **Explaining** How do plants obtain energy?
   c. **Applying Concepts** An insect eats a leaf. Explain how the insect depends on the sun for energy.
2. a. **Reviewing** What chemical equation sums up the events of photosynthesis?
   b. **Comparing and Contrasting** What are the substances needed for photosynthesis? What substances are produced during photosynthesis?
   c. **Making Generalizations** Would you expect a plant to produce more oxygen on a cloudy day or a sunny day? Explain.

Writing in Science

Job Qualifications When people apply for jobs, they often must complete a job application form in which they describe their qualifications for a job. Suppose that you are a leaf, and that you are applying for a job in a photosynthesis factory. Write a paragraph in which you summarize your qualifications for the job of photosynthesis. Your paragraph should include the following words: *chloroplasts, chlorophyll, light, energy, water, carbon dioxide,* and *stomata.*

Writing in Science

Writing Mode Description
Scoring Rubric
4 Includes complete description of the stages of photosynthesis written from the point of view of a leaf; description is lively and engaging
3 Includes all criteria, but description is uninteresting
2 Includes incomplete description
1 Includes inaccurate description

Reading Preview

Key Concepts
• What events occur during respiration?
• What is fermentation?

Key Terms
• respiration • fermentation

Target Reading Skill
Using Prior Knowledge Your prior knowledge is what you already know before you read about a topic. Before you read, write a definition of respiration in a graphic organizer like the one below. As you read, revise your definition based on what you learn.

What You Know
1. Definition of respiration:

What You Learned
1.

Lab zone Discover **Activity**

What Is a Product of Respiration?

1. Put on your goggles. Fill two test tubes half full of warm water. Add 5 mL of sugar to one of the test tubes. Put the tubes in a test-tube rack.

2. Add 0.5 mL of dried yeast (a single-celled organism) to each tube. Stir the contents of each tube with a straw. Place a stopper snugly in the top of each tube.

3. Observe the two test tubes over the next 10 to 15 minutes.

Think It Over
Observing How can you account for any changes you observed?

You've been hiking all morning, and you are hungry. You get out the sandwich you packed and begin munching. Why does your body need food?

What Is Respiration?

Food supplies your body with glucose, an energy-rich sugar. **Respiration** is the process by which cells obtain energy from glucose. **During respiration, cells break down simple food molecules such as sugar and release the energy they contain.**

Storing and Releasing Energy Energy stored in cells is something like money in a savings account. During photosynthesis, plants capture energy from sunlight and "save" it in the form of carbohydrates, including sugars and starches. Similarly, when you eat, you add to your body's energy savings account. When cells need energy, they "withdraw" it by breaking down the carbohydrates in the process of respiration.

Breathing and Respiration The term *respiration* has two meanings. You have probably used it to mean "breathing," that is, moving air in and out of your lungs. To avoid confusion, the respiration process that takes place inside cells is sometimes called cellular respiration. Breathing brings oxygen, which is usually necessary for cellular respiration, into your lungs.

Chapter 3 ◆ 91

Lab zone Discover **Activity**

Skills Focus Observing L1

Materials 2 test tubes with stoppers, warm water, 5 mL sugar, test tube rack, 1.0 mL dried yeast, 2 straws

Time 20 minutes

Tips CAUTION: *Advise students to handle the test tubes with care.* If possible, use fast-acting yeast, which you can purchase at a food store. The water should be warm, but not hot.

Expected Outcome Students will observe bubbles in the sugar water but none in the plain water.

Think It Over The bubbles in the test tube containing the sugar are due to some process involving the yeast and the sugar.

Objectives
After this lesson, students will be able to
3.4.1 Describe the events that occur during respiration.
3.4.2 Tell what fermentation is.

Target Reading Skill

Using Prior Knowledge Explain that prior knowledge helps students connect what they already know to what they read.

Possible Answers
What You Know
The definition of respiration is breathing in oxygen by an organism.
What You Learned
Respiration also means the process in which cells break down simple food molecules such as sugar and release the energy they contain.

All in One Teaching Resources, Unit 1
• Transparency LS28

Preteach

Build Background Knowledge L1
Combustion and Respiration
Ask: **What does a fire need to burn?** *(Fuel and oxygen)* **What is released when fuel is burned?** *(Energy in the form of heat and light)* Tell students that like combustion, respiration uses fuel and oxygen to produce energy. The fuel comes from food, and the energy is used for cellular functions.

Instruct

What Is Respiration?

Teach Key Concepts L2

Focus Remind students that food must be broken down to release energy.

Teach Ask: **What process releases energy from food?** *(Respiration)* **Why is respiration important?** *(It provides cells with the energy they need to carry out their functions.)*

Apply Ask: **Why do you think that muscle cells have many mitochondria?** *(The mitochondria supply a great amount of energy for movement.)* **learning modality: verbal**

Measuring Carbon Dioxide [L1]

Materials 100 mL tap water, flask, phenolphthalein, 0.4% sodium hydroxide solution, 2 plastic droppers

Time 20 minutes

Focus Tell students that the carbon dioxide in exhaled breath can be measured.

Teach Breathe for one minute into a flask containing the water. Add five drops of phenolphthalein to the water, and then add the sodium hydroxide solution, drop by drop, until the water turns light pink. Explain that the more sodium hydroxide that is needed to turn the water pink, the greater the concentration of carbon dioxide.

Apply Ask students to infer how exercise affects the amount of carbon dioxide in exhaled breath. *(The amount would be greater because more respiration is needed to provide energy for the activity.)* **learning modality: visual**

Use Visuals: Figure 16 [L2]

Focus Remind students that respiration occurs in plant and animal cells.

Teach Ask students to locate where the first stage of respiration takes place. *(Cytoplasm)* Ask: **What happens in the cytoplasm?** *(Glucose is broken down.)* Have students locate the mitochondrion in the cell. Ask: **Do you think plants have mitochondria?** *(Yes, because they need to break down energy for their functions.)* **In which stage is oxygen involved?** *(The second stage, in the mitochondrion)* **How do most animals get rid of carbon dioxide?** *(They breathe it out.)*

Apply Ask: **How do plants get rid of carbon dioxide and water vapor?** *(Through their stomata)* **learning modality: visual**

Independent Practice [L2]

All in One Teaching Resources, Unit 1

- Guided Reading and Study Worksheet: *Respiration*

- **Student Edition on Audio CD**

For: Links on cellular respiration
Visit: www.SciLinks.org
Web Code: scn-0322

The Two Stages of Respiration Like photosynthesis, respiration is a two-stage process. The first stage takes place in the cytoplasm of the organism's cells. There, molecules of glucose are broken down into smaller molecules. Oxygen is not involved, and only a small amount of energy is released.

The second stage of respiration takes place in the mitochondria. There, the small molecules are broken down into even smaller molecules. These chemical reactions require oxygen, and they release a great deal of energy. This is why the mitochondria are sometimes called the "powerhouses" of the cell.

Trace the steps in the breakdown of glucose in Figure 16. Note that energy is released in both stages. Two other products of respiration are carbon dioxide and water. These products diffuse out of the cell. In most animals, the carbon dioxide and some water leave the body during exhalation, or breathing out. Thus, when you breathe in, you take in oxygen—a raw material for respiration. When you breathe out, you release carbon dioxide and water—products of respiration.

The Respiration Equation Although respiration occurs in a series of complex steps, the overall process can be summarized in the following equation:

$$C_6H_{12}O_6 + 6\,O_2 \longrightarrow 6\,CO_2 + 6\,H_2O + energy$$

sugar　　oxygen　　carbon dioxide　　water

Notice that the raw materials for respiration are sugar and oxygen. Plants and other organisms that undergo photosynthesis make their own sugar. The glucose in the cells of animals and other organisms comes from the food they consume. The oxygen used in respiration comes from the air or water surrounding the organism.

FIGURE 16
Two Stages of Respiration
Respiration, like photosynthesis, takes place in two stages.
Interpreting Diagrams *In which stage is oxygen used?*

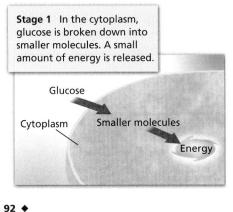

Stage 1 In the cytoplasm, glucose is broken down into smaller molecules. A small amount of energy is released.

Glucose
Cytoplasm
Smaller molecules
Energy

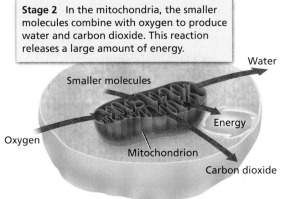

Stage 2 In the mitochondria, the smaller molecules combine with oxygen to produce water and carbon dioxide. This reaction releases a large amount of energy.

Water
Smaller molecules
Energy
Oxygen
Mitochondrion
Carbon dioxide

92 ◆

Differentiated Instruction

Less Proficient Readers [L1]

Comparing Breathing and Cellular Respiration Make a copy of What Is Respiration? and have students read and highlight phrases that will help to answer the following questions: **How are breathing and cellular respiration similar?** *(Both involve using or taking in oxygen and releasing carbon dioxide and water.)* **How are breathing and cellular respiration different?** *(Breathing takes place in the lungs and provides the body with oxygen, whereas cellular respiration takes place inside cells and provides the cells with energy.)* **learning modality: verbal**

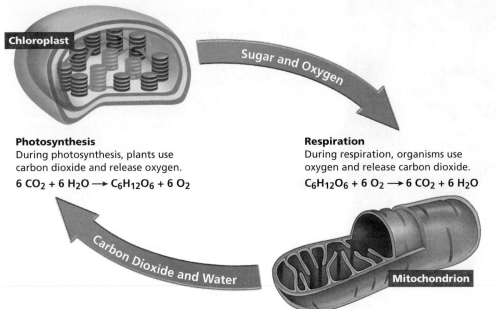

Chloroplast

Sugar and Oxygen

Photosynthesis
During photosynthesis, plants use carbon dioxide and release oxygen.

$$6\ CO_2 + 6\ H_2O \longrightarrow C_6H_{12}O_6 + 6\ O_2$$

Respiration
During respiration, organisms use oxygen and release carbon dioxide.

$$C_6H_{12}O_6 + 6\ O_2 \longrightarrow 6\ CO_2 + 6\ H_2O$$

Carbon Dioxide and Water

Mitochondrion

FIGURE 17
Photosynthesis and Respiration
You can think of photosynthesis and respiration as opposite processes.
Comparing and Contrasting
Which process uses oxygen? Which uses carbon dioxide?

Comparing Photosynthesis and Respiration Can you notice anything familiar about the equation for respiration? You are quite right if you said it is the opposite of the equation for photosynthesis. This is an important point. During photosynthesis, carbon dioxide and water are used to produce sugars and oxygen. During respiration, the sugar glucose and oxygen are used to produce carbon dioxide and water. Photosynthesis and respiration can be thought of as opposite processes.

Together, these two processes form a cycle that keeps the levels of oxygen and carbon dioxide fairly constant in Earth's atmosphere. As you can see in Figure 17, living things use both gases over and over again.

 Reading Checkpoint Which process—photosynthesis or respiration—produces water?

Fermentation

Some cells are able to obtain energy from food without using oxygen. For example, some single-celled organisms live where there is no oxygen, such as deep in the ocean or in the mud of lakes or swamps. These organisms obtain their energy through **fermentation,** an energy-releasing process that does not require oxygen. **Fermentation provides energy for cells without using oxygen.** The amount of energy released from each sugar molecule during fermentation, however, is much lower than the amount released during respiration.

Fermentation

Teach Key Concepts ![L2]
Obtaining Energy Without Oxygen

Focus Tell students that some organisms, such as yeasts, are able to release energy without oxygen.

Teach Ask: **What is the process in which energy is released without using oxygen?** (*Fermentation*) **What are the products of alcoholic fermentation?** (*Alcohol, carbon dioxide, and energy*) **What is a product of lactic-acid fermentation?** (*Lactic acid*) **When might your body release energy using fermentation?** (*If you are exercising so hard or long that your muscle cells cannot take up oxygen faster than it is being used*)

Apply Ask students to compare and contrast fermentation and respiration. (*Both produce energy. Respiration uses oxygen and produces more energy, while fermentation does not use oxygen and produces less energy.*)
learning modality: verbal

All in One Teaching Resources, Unit 1
• Transparency LS29

Monitor Progress _____ ![L2]

Skills Check Have students create a compare-and-contrast table of the two stages of cellular respiration.

Answers
Figure 16 The second stage

Figure 17 Respiration uses oxygen, and photosynthesis uses carbon dioxide.

 Reading Checkpoint Respiration

Differentiated Instruction

English Learners/Beginning ![L1]
Comprehension: Ask Questions Write the chemical equations for photosynthesis and respiration on the board. Read the equations aloud, pointing to the chemical symbols and labels. Ask students questions such as: **What is one product of respiration? What do plants use to make food?** Have students answer orally. Then

help them to write the answers. **learning modality: visual**

English Learners/Intermediate ![L2]
Comprehension: Ask Questions Have students do the *Beginning* activity. Then, ask questions that cannot be answered directly from the equation, such as: **What part of the equation represents what you breathe out? learning modality: visual**

Reviewing Key Concepts

1. a. Cells break down simple food molecules such as sugar and release the energy they contain. **b.** $C_6H_{12}O_6$ (sugar) + 6 O_2 (oxygen) → 6 CO_2 (carbon dioxide) + 6 H_2O (water) + energy **c.** Both involve the same chemical compounds, but they are reverse processes. **d.** Cellular respiration produces carbon dioxide, while photosynthesis uses up carbon dioxide. **2. a.** Fermentation **b.** If an athlete's muscles ran out of oxygen and fermentation did not occur, the athlete would not be able to continue the activity. **c.** Fermentation is more likely to take place during a short, fast run than in a long, less intense walk. For the short run, the athlete is pushing the muscles hard to run very fast, so the muscles will use up oxygen sooner.

Reteach   L1

As a class, make flowcharts showing what happens during respiration and fermentation.

Performance Assessment   L2

Writing Have students describe how plants maintain the level of oxygen in the atmosphere.

All in One Teaching Resources, Unit 1

- Section Summary: *Respiration*
- Review and Reinforce: *Respiration*
- Enrich: *Respiration*

FIGURE 18
Lactic Acid Fermentation
When an athlete's muscles run out of oxygen, lactic acid fermentation supplies the cells with energy.

Alcoholic Fermentation One type of fermentation occurs when yeast and some other single-celled organisms break down sugars. This process is sometimes called alcoholic fermentation because alcohol is one of the products. The other products are carbon dioxide and a small amount of energy.

Alcoholic fermentation is important to bakers and brewers. The carbon dioxide produced by yeast creates air pockets in bread dough, causing it to rise. Carbon dioxide is also the source of bubbles in alcoholic drinks such as beer.

Lactic Acid Fermentation Another type of fermentation takes place at times in your body. You've probably felt its effects. Think of a time when you ran as fast as you could for as long as you could. Your leg muscles were pushing hard against the ground, and you were breathing quickly.

No matter how hard you breathed, your muscle cells used up the oxygen faster than it could be replaced. Because your cells lacked oxygen, fermentation occurred. The fermentation supplied your cells with energy. One product of this type of fermentation is an acid known as lactic acid. When lactic acid builds up, you feel a painful sensation in your muscles. Your muscles feel weak and sore.

Section 4 Assessment

Target Reading Skill

Using Prior Knowledge Review your graphic organizer about respiration. List two things that you learned about respiration.

Reviewing Key Concepts

1. a. Reviewing What happens during respiration?
  b. Reviewing What is the equation for respiration?
  c. Comparing and Contrasting Compare the equations for respiration and photosynthesis.
  d. Relating Cause and Effect Explain why cellular respiration adds carbon dioxide to the atmosphere, but photosynthesis does not.

2. a. Identifying What is the process in which cells obtain energy without using oxygen?
  b. Inferring How would athletes be affected if this process could not take place?
  c. Predicting Is this process more likely to occur during a short run or a long walk? Explain your answer.

Lab zone At-Home **Activity**

Make Bread With an adult family member, follow a recipe in a cookbook to make a loaf of bread using yeast. Explain to your family what causes the dough to rise. After you bake the bread, observe a slice and look for evidence that fermentation occurred.

Lab zone At-Home **Activity**

Make Bread L2 Students will explain that yeast cells use the sugar in the dough for alcoholic fermentation, which releases carbon dioxide. The carbon dioxide, in turn, causes the dough to rise and small holes to form in the baked bread.

Reading Preview

Key Concepts
- What events take place during the three stages of the cell cycle?
- How does the structure of DNA help account for the way in which DNA copies itself?

Key Terms
- cell cycle
- interphase
- replication
- mitosis
- chromosome
- cytokinesis

Target Reading Skill
Sequencing As you read, make a cycle diagram that shows the events in the cell cycle, including the phases of mitosis. Write each event in a separate circle.

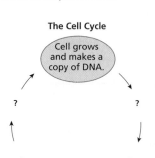

The Cell Cycle

Cell grows and makes a copy of DNA.

? ? ? ? ?

Lab zone Discover Activity

What Are the Yeast Cells Doing?

1. Use a plastic dropper to transfer some yeast cells from a yeast culture to a microscope slide. Your teacher has prepared the slide by drying methylene blue stain onto it. Add a coverslip and place the slide under a microscope.

2. Examine the cells on the slide. Use low power first and then high power. Look for what appear to be two cells attached to each other. One cell may be larger than the other. Draw what you see.

Think It Over
Developing Hypotheses What process do you think the "double cells" are undergoing? Develop a hypothesis that might explain what you see.

In the early autumn, many local fairs run pumpkin contests. Proud growers enter their largest pumpkins, hoping to win a prize. The pumpkin below has a mass greater than 600 kilograms! This giant pumpkin began as a small flower. How did the pumpkin grow so big?

A pumpkin grows in size by increasing both the size and the number of its cells. A single cell grows and then divides, forming two cells. Then two cells grow and divide, forming four, and so on. This process of cell growth and division does not occur only in pumpkins, though. In fact, many cells in your body are dividing as you read this page.

Prize-winning pumpkin ▲

Chapter 3 ◆ 95

Objectives
After this lesson, students will be able to
3.5.1 Identify the events that take place during the three stages of the cell cycle.
3.5.2 Explain how the structure of DNA helps account for the way in which DNA copies itself.

Target Reading Skill

Sequencing Explain that organizing information in sequence helps students understand a step-by-step process.

Answers
One possible way to complete the graphic organizer:
The Cell Cycle

1. Cell grows, makes a copy of DNA.

2. Chromosomes and spindle fibers form; nuclear envelope breaks down.

3. Chromosomes line up across the center and attach to a spindle fiber.

4. Centromeres split; chromatids separate and move to opposite ends.

5. Chromosomes stretch out; new nuclear envelope forms around chromosomes.

6. Cell pinches in two; each daughter cell has same number of identical chromosomes.

All in One Teaching Resources, Unit 1
- Transparency LS30

Preteach

Build Background Knowledge   L1

Comparing Different Cycles
Ask: **What are the stages that people go through during their life, starting with infancy and ending with old age?** Students are likely to name or describe the additional stages of childhood, adolescence, and adulthood. Point out that cells, like people, undergo a life cycle, called the cell cycle. During the stages of the cell cycle, cells grow and mature. But unlike the human life cycle, the cell cycle starts over when the cell divides.

Lab zone Discover Activity

Skills Focus Developing hypotheses **L1**

Materials plastic dropper, yeast culture, stained microscope slide, coverslip, microscope

Time 15 minutes

Tips CAUTION: *Students must handle the glass and microscope carefully.* Prepare culture by stirring dry yeast and sugar into warm water. Stain each slide with a drop of methylene blue, and let it dry. Or use prepared slides.

Expected Outcome Students will observe yeast cells budding.

Think It Over Students may say that the cells are dividing, and hypothesize that yeast cells split in two to reproduce.

Instruct

Stage 1: Interphase

Teach Key Concepts `L2`
Events in Interphase

Focus Remind students that living things grow by producing more cells rather than the cells becoming larger.

Teach Ask: **What is the cell cycle?** *(The regular sequence of growth and division that cells undergo)* **What are daughter cells?** *(The cells that result when a cell divides)* **What happens during interphase?** *(The cell grows, makes a copy of its DNA, and prepares to divide into two cells.)* **In what process does the cell make a copy of the DNA?** *(Replication)* **How does the cell prepare for cell division?** *(It produces structures that it will use to divide.)*

Apply Ask students to infer what would happen if cell division occurred without DNA replication occurring first. Ask: **How would this affect the daughter cells?** *(Each daughter cell would have only half the DNA of the parent cell and would be unable to direct all cell activities. The cells probably would not survive.)* **learning modality: logical/mathematical**

Independent Practice `L2`

 **Teaching Resources, Unit 1**

- Guided Reading and Study Worksheet: *Cell Division*

 Student Edition on Audio CD

Help Students Read `L2`

Outlining Instruct students to outline this section, writing the subheads and leaving room between each one. As students read, they can list details under each subhead.

Video Field Trip

Cell Processes and Energy

Show the Video Field Trip to let students explore the relationship between the cell cycle and cancer.

Stage 1: Interphase

How do little pigs get to be big pigs? Their cells grow and divide, over and over. The regular sequence of growth and division that cells undergo is known as the **cell cycle.** During the cell cycle, a cell grows, prepares for division, and divides into two new cells, which are called "daughter cells." Each of the daughter cells then begins the cell cycle again. You can see details of the cell cycle in Figure 21. Notice that the cell cycle is divided into three main stages: interphase, mitosis, and cytokinesis.

The first stage of the cell cycle is called **interphase.** Interphase is the period before cell division. **During interphase, the cell grows, makes a copy of its DNA, and prepares to divide into two cells.**

Growing During the first part of interphase, the cell grows to its full size and produces structures it needs. For example, the cell makes new ribosomes and produces enzymes. Copies are made of both mitochondria and chloroplasts.

Copying DNA In the next part of interphase, the cell makes an exact copy of the DNA in its nucleus in a process called **replication.** Recall that DNA is found in the chromatin in the nucleus. DNA holds all the information that the cell needs to carry out its functions. Replication of DNA is very important, since each daughter cell must have a complete set of DNA to survive. At the end of DNA replication, the cell contains two identical sets of DNA. You will learn the details of DNA replication later in this section.

Preparing for Division Once the DNA has replicated, preparation for cell division begins. The cell produces structures that it will use to divide into two new cells. At the end of interphase, the cell is ready to divide.

 Reading Checkpoint What is replication?

Lab zone Try This Activity

Modeling Mitosis
Refer to Figure 21 as you carry out this activity.

1. Construct a model of a cell that has four chromosomes. Use a piece of construction paper to represent the cell. Use different-colored pipe cleaners to represent the chromosomes. Make sure that the chromosomes look like double rods.

2. Position the chromosomes in the cell where they would be during prophase.

3. Repeat Step 2 for metaphase, anaphase, and telophase.

Making Models How did the model help you understand the events of mitosis?

96 ◆

Lab zone Try This Activity

Skills Focus Making models `L1`

Materials construction paper, different colored pipe cleaners

Time 10 minutes

Expected Outcome Prophase: Join pipe cleaners in each pair at center. Cluster paired pipe cleaners. Metaphase: Align paired pipe cleaners across center. Anaphase: Separate pipe cleaners in each pair and move them toward opposite ends. Telophase: Move separated pipe cleaners to opposite ends. The model helps students see mitosis as a continuous process.

Extend Ask: **How could you show the next stage of the cell cycle?** *(Cut the paper into two halves and place half the pipe cleaners on each piece to model cytokinesis.)* **learning modality: kinesthetic**

Stage 2: Mitosis

Once interphase is complete, the second stage of the cell cycle begins. **Mitosis** (my TOH sis) is the stage during which the cell's nucleus divides into two new nuclei. **During mitosis, one copy of the DNA is distributed into each of the two daughter cells.**

Scientists divide mitosis into four parts, or phases: prophase, metaphase, anaphase, and telophase. During prophase, the threadlike chromatin in the nucleus condenses to form double-rod structures called **chromosomes.** Each chromosome has two rods because the cell's DNA has replicated, and each rod in a chromosome is an exact copy of the other. Each identical rod in a chromosome is called a chromatid. Notice in Figure 20 that the two chromatids are held together by a structure called a centromere.

As the cell progresses through metaphase, anaphase, and telophase, the chromatids separate from each other and move to opposite ends of the cell. Then two nuclei form around the new chromosomes at the two ends of the cell.

FIGURE 19
Bigger Pig, More Cells
The mother pig has more cells in her body than her small piglets.

FIGURE 20
Chromosomes
During mitosis, the chromatin condenses to form chromosomes. Each chromosome consists of two identical strands, or chromatids.
Applying Concepts *During which phase of mitosis do the chromosomes form?*

Chromosomes ▼

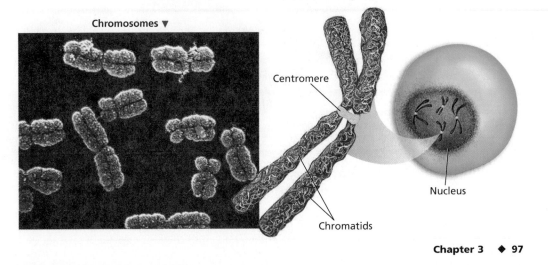

Centromere

Nucleus

Chromatids

Chapter 3 ◆ 97

Use Visuals: Figure 21

L2

Visualizing the Cell Cycle

Focus Point out that the cell cycle shown is moving clockwise and that the photographs show actual cells.

Teach Ask: **Where is the chromatin in the interphase stage?** *(In the nucleus)* Point out that, in prophase, each pair of chromatids consists of the original DNA of the parent cell plus a copy of the DNA, which is made during interphase. Have students trace the movement of chromosomes through the cycle. Ask: **When are the chromosomes completely separated in their own nuclear envelope?** *(During telophase)*

Apply Ask: **How does the genetic material of each of the daughter cells in the cytokinesis stage compare to the genetic material of the cell shown in prophase?** *(The cell in prophase has condensed genetic material.)* **learning modality: visual**

 **Teaching Resources, Unit 1**

• Transparency LS31

Lab zone Build **Inquiry**

L2

Modeling the Cell Cycle

Materials poster board, colored markers, index cards, dice, small objects such as colored erasers or game tokens

Time 20 minutes

Focus Challenge students to create a board game that models the cell cycle.

Teach Divide the class into groups and provide game materials. To get from "start" to "finish" on the game board, players must advance through each stage of the cell cycle by correctly answering questions about that stage.

Apply Ask a student volunteer to compile all questions into a list that all students can use as a study guide. **learning modality: kinesthetic**

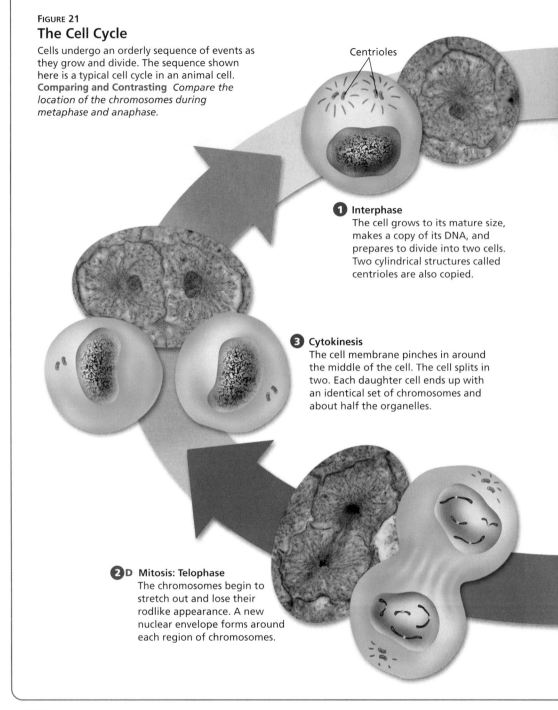

FIGURE 21

The Cell Cycle

Cells undergo an orderly sequence of events as they grow and divide. The sequence shown here is a typical cell cycle in an animal cell. **Comparing and Contrasting** *Compare the location of the chromosomes during metaphase and anaphase.*

Centrioles

1 Interphase
The cell grows to its mature size, makes a copy of its DNA, and prepares to divide into two cells. Two cylindrical structures called centrioles are also copied.

3 Cytokinesis
The cell membrane pinches in around the middle of the cell. The cell splits in two. Each daughter cell ends up with an identical set of chromosomes and about half the organelles.

2 D Mitosis: Telophase
The chromosomes begin to stretch out and lose their rodlike appearance. A new nuclear envelope forms around each region of chromosomes.

98 ◆

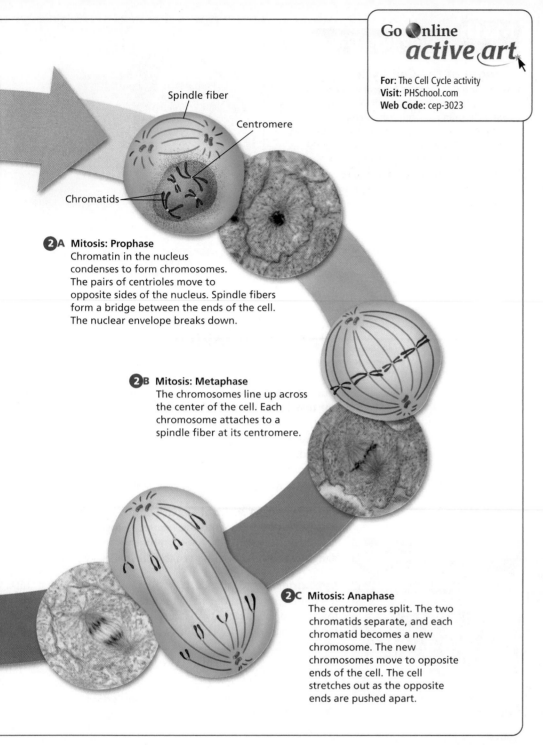

Go Online
active art

For: The Cell Cycle activity
Visit: PHSchool.com
Web Code: cep-3023

Spindle fiber

Centromere

Chromatids

2A Mitosis: Prophase
Chromatin in the nucleus condenses to form chromosomes. The pairs of centrioles move to opposite sides of the nucleus. Spindle fibers form a bridge between the ends of the cell. The nuclear envelope breaks down.

2B Mitosis: Metaphase
The chromosomes line up across the center of the cell. Each chromosome attaches to a spindle fiber at its centromere.

2C Mitosis: Anaphase
The centromeres split. The two chromatids separate, and each chromatid becomes a new chromosome. The new chromosomes move to opposite ends of the cell. The cell stretches out as the opposite ends are pushed apart.

Go Online
active art

For: The Cell Cycle activity
Visit: PHSchool.com
Web Code: cep-3023

Students can interact with the art of mitosis online.

Lab zone Build Inquiry ⬜L1

Modeling Mitosis

Materials construction paper, colored markers, tape or safety pins

Time 15 minutes

Focus Review the four parts of mitosis.

Teach Challenge the class to describe how to make a human model of the nucleus to show how mitosis occurs. *(To start out, a few pairs of students, representing paired chromatids, might stand face to face and join hands, while the other students, representing the nuclear envelope, join hands in a circle around them.)* Have students make and wear signs that show which part of the nucleus they represent, then move in ways to model the parts.

Apply Ask students to model the chromatin inside the nucleus during the other stages of the cell cycle. *(The formerly paired students might stand at random inside the "nuclear envelope" and no longer hold hands.)*
learning modality: kinesthetic

Monitor Progress _____ L2

Writing Have students list in chronological order the major events that occur during mitosis and describe each event in their own words. Students may place their lists in their portfolios.

Answer
Figure 21 The chromosomes are lined up across the center of the cell during metaphase, while they are moving to the opposite ends of the cell during anaphase.

⌐ Differentiated Instruction ─

English Learners/Beginning L1
Comprehension: Word-Part Analysis Pair students with English-proficient students. To help them identify and remember the stages and parts, explain the prefixes *inter-, meta-, ana-, telo-,* and *cyto-,* and then describe how those prefixes relate to each stage or part. **learning modality: verbal**

English Learners/Intermediate L2
Comprehension: Link to Visual
Make copies of Figure 21, and cut out each step showing the cells and the caption. Have students place the steps in order and write a sentence about each step to summarize what is happening. **learning modality: visual**

Math Skill Interpreting graphs

Focus Remind students that the sections of a circle graph show portions of a whole.

Teach Ask: **What does the circle represent?** *(The time it takes a human liver cell to go through the entire cell cycle)* **Which parts of the circle are included in interphase?** *(Growth, DNA replication, and Preparation for division)* **Which stages of the cell cycle does cell division include?** *(Mitosis and cytokinesis)*

Answers

1. The longest curved arrow represents the cell's interphase; the shortest represents cytokinesis; and the middle one represents mitosis.

2. Interphase

3. 10 hours

4. Interphase

Stage 3: Cytokinesis

Teach Key Concepts   L2

The Cell Divides

Focus Review that during mitosis the nucleus of a cell divides, but the cell is still one cell.

Teach Ask: **What happens during cytokinesis?** *(The cytoplasm divides, distributing the organelles into each of the two new cells.)* **What happens during cytokinesis of animal cells?** *(The cell membrane squeezes together around the middle of the cell.)* **Plant cells?** *(A cell plate forms across the middle of the cell and gradually develops into new cell membranes, and new cell walls form around the cell membranes.)*

Apply Explain that there are many variations of the basic pattern of cytokinesis. For example, yeast cells divide, though not equally. A small daughter cell, or bud, pinches off of the parent cell. The bud then grows into a full-sized yeast cell. **learning modality: verbal**

Length of the Cell Cycle

How long does it take for a cell to go through one cell cycle? It all depends on the cell. A human liver cell, for example, completes one cell cycle in about 22 hours, as shown in the graph. Study the graph and then answer the following questions.

1. **Reading Graphs** What do the three curved arrows outside the circle represent?
2. **Reading Graphs** In what stage of the cell cycle is the wedge representing growth?
3. **Interpreting Data** In human liver cells, how long does it take DNA replication to occur?
4. **Drawing Conclusions** In human liver cells, what stage in the cell cycle takes the longest time?

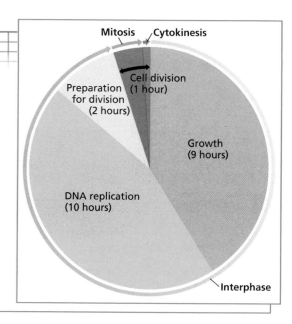

Mitosis Cytokinesis
Cell division (1 hour)
Preparation for division (2 hours)
Growth (9 hours)
DNA replication (10 hours)
Interphase

FIGURE 22
Cytokinesis in Plant Cells
During cytokinesis in plant cells, a cell plate forms between the two new nuclei.

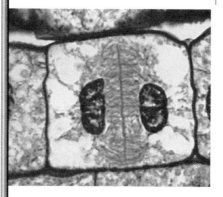

100 ◆

Stage 3: Cytokinesis

The final stage of the cell cycle, which is called **cytokinesis** (sy toh kih NEE sis), completes the process of cell division. **During cytokinesis, the cytoplasm divides. The organelles are distributed into each of the two new cells.** Cytokinesis usually starts at about the same time as telophase. When cytokinesis is complete, two new cells, or daughter cells, have formed. Each daughter cell has the same number of chromosomes as the original parent cell. At the end of cytokinesis, each cell enters interphase, and the cycle begins again.

Cytokinesis in Animal Cells During cytokinesis in animal cells, the cell membrane squeezes together around the middle of the cell. The cytoplasm pinches into two cells. Each daughter cell gets about half of the organelles.

Cytokinesis in Plant Cells Cytokinesis is somewhat different in plant cells. A plant cell's rigid cell wall cannot squeeze together in the same way that a cell membrane can. Instead, a structure called a cell plate forms across the middle of the cell. The cell plate gradually develops into new cell membranes between the two daughter cells. New cell walls then form around the cell membranes.

 Reading Checkpoint   **During what phase of mitosis does cytokinesis begin?**

Structure and Replication of DNA

DNA replication ensures that each daughter cell will have the genetic information it needs to carry out its activities. Before scientists could understand how DNA replicates, they had to know its structure. In 1952, Rosalind Franklin used an X-ray method to photograph DNA molecules. Her photographs helped James Watson and Francis Crick figure out the structure of DNA in 1953.

The Structure of DNA Notice in Figure 23 that a DNA molecule looks like a twisted ladder, or spiral staircase. The two sides of the DNA ladder are made up of molecules of a sugar called deoxyribose, alternating with molecules known as phosphates.

Each rung is made up of a pair of molecules called nitrogen bases. Nitrogen bases are molecules that contain the element nitrogen and other elements. DNA has four kinds of nitrogen bases: adenine (AD uh neen), thymine (THY meen), guanine (GWAH neen), and cytosine (SY tuh seen). The capital letters A, T, G, and C are used to represent the four bases.

The bases on one side of the ladder pair with the bases on the other side. Adenine (A) only pairs with thymine (T), while guanine (G) only pairs with cytosine (C). This pairing pattern is the key to understanding how DNA replication occurs.

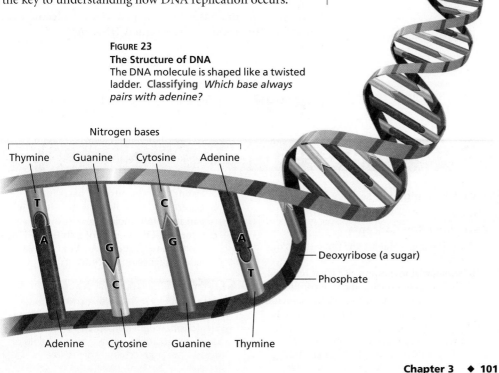

FIGURE 23
The Structure of DNA
The DNA molecule is shaped like a twisted ladder. **Classifying** *Which base always pairs with adenine?*

Nitrogen bases
Thymine   Guanine   Cytosine   Adenine

Deoxyribose (a sugar)
Phosphate

Adenine   Cytosine   Guanine   Thymine

Teach Key Concepts   L2
How DNA Copies Itself

Focus Review with students that DNA is replicated during interphase.

Teach Refer students to Figure 23. Ask: **What do you notice about the nitrogen bases?** *(The same ones always pair. Adenine pairs with thymine, and guanine pairs with cytosine.)* **How does this pairing determine how DNA replication occurs?** *(The order of the bases in each new DNA molecule exactly matches the order of the bases in the original DNA molecule.)* **What happens in DNA replication?** *(The two strands in one molecule separate, and then new nitrogen bases pair up with each strand to form two molecules of DNA.)*

Apply Ask: **If you had one strand of DNA, could you make a molecule with it?** *(Yes; the rules of base pairing would allow you to reconstruct the base sequence of the other strand to make a complete molecule.)*
learning modality: logical/mathematical

All in One Teaching Resources, Unit 1
• Transparencies LS32

Lab zone **Build Inquiry**

Modeling DNA Molecules   L2

Materials toothpicks, white and colored miniature marshmallows

Time 15 minutes

Focus Review how nitrogen bases pair in a DNA molecule.

Teach Have students make a three-dimensional model of a DNA molecule.

Apply Have students use their models to demonstrate how a molecule of DNA is replicated. **learning modality: kinesthetic**

Monitor Progress _____   L2

Writing Have students explain why the pairing of nitrogen bases is the key to understanding DNA replication.

Answers
Figure 23 Thymine

 Reading Checkpoint Telophase

Differentiated Instruction

Less Proficient Readers   L1
Organizing Information Urge students to create flash cards for the stages of the cell cycle and the phases of mitosis. Suggest that they write the name of each stage or phase on one side of an index card, and describe it in their own words on the other side. After students have finished making their flash cards, check to see that they have included all the stages of the cell cycle and all the phases of mitosis. Also make sure that students have correctly described each stage or phase. Encourage pairs of students of quiz each other using their flash cards. **learning modality: verbal**

Answer

 Reading Checkpoint) Cytosine

Assess

Reviewing Key Concepts

1. a. Interphase, mitosis, and cytokinesis
b. In prophase, the chromatin condenses to form chromosomes. In metaphase, the chromosomes line up across the center of the cell and attach to the spindle fibers. In anaphase, the chromatids separate, and each moves to an opposite end of the cell. In telophase, the chromosomes begin to stretch out and lose their rodlike appearance.
c. The chromosomes move along the spindle fibers to the ends of the cell.
2. a. Adenine, thymine, cytosine, and guanine **b.** Adenine pairs with thymine, and cytosine pairs with guanine. **c.** TCTAAG

Reteach L1

Have students make sketches of each stage of the cell cycle on separate pieces of paper. Then have them shuffle their drawings and exchange with a partner to place in the correct order and identify each stage.

Performance Assessment L2

Skills Check Have students create a concept map that includes the following terms: *DNA structure, phosphate molecules, sugar molecules, nitrogen bases, adenine, thymine, guanine,* and *cytosine.*

All in One Teaching Resources, Unit 1

• Transparency LS33
• Section Summary: *Cell Division*
• Review and Reinforce: *Cell Division*
• Enrich: *Cell Division*

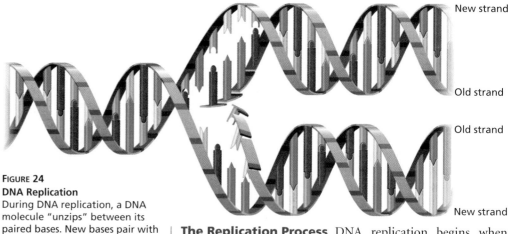

New strand
Old strand
Old strand
New strand

FIGURE 24
DNA Replication
During DNA replication, a DNA molecule "unzips" between its paired bases. New bases pair with the bases on each old strand. As a result, two identical DNA strands form.

The Replication Process DNA replication begins when the two sides of the DNA molecule unwind and separate, somewhat like a zipper unzipping. As you can see in Figure 24, the molecule separates between the paired nitrogen bases.

Next, nitrogen bases that are floating in the nucleus pair up with the bases on each half of the DNA molecule. **Because of the way in which the nitrogen bases pair with one another, the order of the bases in each new DNA molecule exactly matches the order in the original DNA molecule.** Adenine always pairs with thymine, while guanine always pairs with cytosine. Once the new bases are attached, two new DNA molecules are formed.

 Reading Checkpoint) **During DNA replication, which base pairs with guanine?**

Section 5 Assessment

Target Reading Skill Sequencing Your cycle diagram will help you answer Question 1.

Reviewing Key Concepts

1. a. Reviewing What are the three stages of the cell cycle?
b. Summarizing Summarize what happens to chromosomes during the stage of the cell cycle in which the nucleus divides. Include the terms *prophase, metaphase, anaphase,* and *telophase.*
c. Interpreting Diagrams Look at Figure 21. What is the role of spindle fibers during cell division?

2. a. Listing List the nitrogen bases in DNA.
b. Describing Describe how the nitrogen bases pair in a DNA molecule.
c. Inferring One section of a strand of DNA has the base sequence AGATTC. What is the base sequence on the other strand?

Writing in Science

Writing Instructions Imagine that you work in a factory where cells are manufactured. Write instructions for newly forming cells on how to carry out cytokinesis. Provide instructions for both plant and animal cells.

Writing in Science

Writing Mode Exposition (how to)
Scoring Rubric
4 Includes complete description of the steps in cytokinesis for plant and animal cells and is written as instructions to the cells
3 Includes all criteria, but is not written to the cells
2 Includes incomplete description
1 Includes inaccuracies

Multiplying by Dividing

Problem

How long do the stages of the cell cycle take?

Skills Focus

observing, calculating

Materials

- microscope
- colored pencils
- calculator (optional)
- prepared slides of onion root tip cells undergoing cell division

Procedure

1. Place the slide on the stage of a microscope. Use low power to locate a cell in interphase. Then switch to high power, and make a labeled drawing of the cell. **CAUTION:** *Slides and coverslips break easily. Do not allow the objective to touch the slide. If the slide breaks, notify your teacher. Do not touch broken glass.*

2. Repeat Step 1 to find cells in prophase, metaphase, anaphase, and telophase. Then copy the data table into your notebook.

3. Return to low power. Find an area of the slide with many cells undergoing cell division. Switch to the magnification that lets you see about 50 cells at once (for example, 100 ×).

4. Examine the cells row by row, and count the cells that are in interphase. Record that number in the data table under *First Sample*.

5. Examine the cells row by row four more times to count the cells in prophase, metaphase, anaphase, and telophase. Record the results.

6. Move to a new area on the slide. Repeat Steps 3–5 and record your counts in the column labeled *Second Sample*.

7. Fill in the column labeled *Total Number* by adding the numbers across each row in your data table.

8. Add the totals for the five stages to find the total number of cells counted.

Analyze and Conclude

1. **Observing** Which stage of the cell cycle did you observe most often?

2. **Calculating** The cell cycle for onion root tips takes about 720 minutes (12 hours). Use your data and the formula below to find the number of minutes each stage takes.

$$\text{Time for each stage} = \frac{\text{Number of cells at each stage}}{\text{Total number of cells counted}} \times 720 \text{ min}$$

3. **Communicating** Use the data to compare the amount of time spent in mitosis with the total time for the whole cell cycle. Write your answer in the form of a paragraph.

More to Explore

Examine prepared slides of animal cells undergoing cell division. Use drawings and descriptions to compare plant and animal mitosis.

Data Table

Stage of Cell Cycle	First Sample	Second Sample	Total Number
Interphase			
Mitosis:			
Prophase			
Metaphase			
Anaphase			
Telophase			
Total number of cells counted			

Extend Inquiry

More to Explore Interphase and mitosis are very similar in plant and animal cells, except that the centrioles appear during prophase in animal cells. Challenge students to predict whether animal or plant cells spend a longer time in mitosis. Then have them design an experiment to test their prediction.

Sample Data Table

Stages of Cell Cycle	First Sample	Second Sample	Total Number
Interphase	43	46	89
Mitosis: Prophase	3	4	7
Metaphase	1	1	2
Anaphase	1	0	1
Telophase	0	1	1
Total number of cells counted			100

Lab zone Skills Lab L2

Multiplying by Dividing

Prepare for Inquiry

Key Concept

Mitosis occurs quickly, and cells spend most of their time in interphase.

Skills Objectives

Students will be able to
- observe cells in different stages of the cell cycle
- calculate the amount of time cells spend in each stage of the cell cycle

Class Time 40 minutes

All in One Teaching Resources, Unit 1
- Lab Worksheet: *Multiplying by Dividing*

Safety

Remind students to handle slides and coverslips carefully. Review the safety guidelines in Appendix A.

Guide Inquiry

Expected Outcome

Most of the cells students count should be in the interphase stage of the cell cycle, but errors in counting and differences in samples may give varying results.

Analyze and Conclude

1. The most likely answer is interphase.
2. Answers will vary depending on students' data. Answers for the sample data are: Interphase, 641 minutes; prophase, 50 minutes; metaphase, 14 minutes; anaphase, 7 minutes; telophase, 7 minutes.
3. Based on the sample data, the amount of time spent in mitosis is 11%. Students' answers will vary.

Help Students Read

Building Vocabulary

Word-Part Analysis Explain that the term *chlorophyll* comes from the Greek words *khloros,* which means "green" and *phullon,* which means "leaf." The term *autotroph* comes from the Greek words *autos,* meaning "self," and *trophe,* meaning "food." *Heteros* means "other." Ask students to relate these word parts to key terms. *(Chlorophyll is found in green leaves. An autotroph makes food for itself. A heterotroph gets food from others.)*

Vocabulary Knowledge Rating Chart

Have students construct a chart with four columns: *Term, Can Define or Use It, Have Heard or Seen It,* and *Don't Know.* Students can copy the vocabulary terms for this chapter under Column 1, then place a check mark under one of the other columns for each term. If students did not check the *Can Define or Use It* column, have them reread passages with those terms.

Connecting Concepts

Concept Maps Help students develop one way to show how the information in this chapter is related. Chemical compounds found in cells include carbohydrates, lipids, proteins, nucleic acids, and water. Materials enter the cell by means of passive transport or active transport. Cells require energy, which they manufacture and release in the processes of photosynthesis and respiration, and grow and reproduce in a sequence called the cell cycle. Have students brainstorm to identify the Key Concepts, Key Terms, details, and examples, and then write each one on a sticky note and attach it at random on chart paper or on the board.

Tell students that this concept map will be organized in hierarchical order. Ask students

Chapter 3 Study Guide

① Chemical Compounds in Cells

Key Concepts

- An element is any substance that cannot be broken down into simpler substances.
- When two or more elements combine chemically, they form a compound.
- Most chemical reactions in cells could not take place without water.
- Carbohydrates, lipids, proteins, and nucleic acids are important groups of organic compounds in living things.

Key Terms

- element • compound • carbohydrate
- lipid • protein • amino acid • enzyme
- nucleic acid • DNA • RNA

② The Cell in Its Environment

Key Concepts

- Diffusion is the main method by which small molecules move across cell membranes.
- Osmosis is important because cells cannot function properly without adequate water.
- Active transport requires the cell to use its own energy, while passive transport does not.

Key Terms

- selectively permeable • diffusion • osmosis
- passive transport • active transport

③ Photosynthesis

Key Concepts

- Nearly all living things obtain energy either directly or indirectly from the energy of sunlight captured during photosynthesis.
- During photosynthesis, plants and some other organisms use energy from the sun to convert carbon dioxide and water into oxygen and sugars. The equation for photosynthesis is

$$6\,CO_2 + 6\,H_2O \longrightarrow C_6H_{12}O_6 + 6\,O_2.$$

Key Terms

- photosynthesis • autotroph • heterotroph
- pigment • chlorophyll • stomata

④ Respiration

Key Concepts

- During respiration, cells break down simple food molecules such as sugar and release their stored energy. The respiration equation is

$$C_6H_{12}O_6 + 6\,O_2 \longrightarrow$$
$$6\,CO_2 + 6\,H_2O + energy.$$

- Fermentation provides energy for cells without using oxygen.

Key Terms

- respiration • fermentation

⑤ Cell Division

Key Concepts

- During interphase, the cell grows, makes a copy of its DNA, and prepares to divide into two cells. During mitosis, one copy of the DNA is distributed into each of the two daughter cells. During cytokinesis, the cytoplasm divides. The organelles are distributed into the new cells.
- Because of the way in which the nitrogen bases pair with one another, the order of the bases in each new DNA molecule exactly matches the order in the original DNA molecule.

Key Terms

- cell cycle • interphase • replication
- mitosis • chromosome • cytokinesis

questions such as these to guide them to categorize the information on the stickies: **What are the main kinds of organic molecules in living things? How do substances pass through cell membranes? What is photosynthesis? What is respiration, and how is it related to photosynthesis? What are the stages of the cell cycle?**

Answer Accept logical presentations by students.

All in One Teaching Resources, Unit 1

- Key Terms Review: *Cell Processes and Energy*
- Connecting Concepts: *Cell Processes and Energy*

Review and Assessment

Go Online
PHSchool.com
For: Self-Assessment
Visit: PHSchool.com
Web Code: cha-1030

Organizing Information

Comparing and Contrasting
Copy the compare and contrast table about photosynthesis and respiration. Complete the table to compare these processes. (For more information on compare and contrast tables, see the Skills Handbook.)

Comparing Photosynthesis and Respiration

Feature	Photosynthesis	Respiration
Raw materials	Water and carbon dioxide	a. ___?___
Products	b. ___?___	c. ___?___
Is energy released?	d. ___?___	Yes

Reviewing Key Terms

Choose the letter of the best answer.

1. Starch is an example of a
   a. nucleic acid.
   b. protein.
   c. lipid.
   d. carbohydrate.

2. The process by which water moves across a cell membrane is called
   a. osmosis.
   b. active transport.
   c. enzyme.
   d. carbohydrate.

3. The organelle in which photosynthesis takes place is the
   a. mitochondrion.
   b. chloroplast.
   c. chlorophyll.
   d. nucleus.

4. What process produces carbon dioxide?
   a. photosynthesis
   b. replication
   c. mutation
   d. respiration

5. What happens during cytokinesis?
   a. A spindle forms.
   b. Chloroplasts release energy.
   c. The cytoplasm divides.
   d. Chromosomes divide.

If the statement is true, write *true*. If it is false, change the underlined word or words to make the statement true.

6. Both DNA and RNA are <u>proteins</u>.

7. The cell membrane is <u>selectively permeable</u>.

8. During <u>respiration</u>, most energy is released in the mitochondria.

9. An energy-releasing process that does not require oxygen is <u>replication</u>.

10. The stage of the cell cycle when DNA replication occurs is called <u>telophase</u>.

Writing in Science

Brochure Cancer is a disease in which the cell cycle is disrupted. Suppose you are a volunteer who works with cancer patients. Write a brochure that could be given to cancer patients and their families. The brochure should explain the cell cycle.

Discovery CHANNEL SCHOOL
Cell Processes and Energy
Video Preview
Video Field Trip
▶ Video Assessment

Review and Assessment

Organizing Information

a. Oxygen and sugars
b. Oxygen and sugars
c. Water and carbon dioxide
d. No

Reviewing Key Terms

1. d 2. a 3. b 4. d 5. c
6. nucleic acids
7. true
8. true
9. fermentation
10. interphase

Writing in Science

Writing Mode Explanation

Scoring Rubric

4 Includes complete and accurate information with many details; writing is clear and organized
3 Includes all criteria but fewer details
2 Includes all criteria but writing is disorganized
1 Includes inaccurate or incomplete information

Discovery CHANNEL SCHOOL Video Assessment

Cell Processes and Energy

Show the Video Assessment to review chapter content and as a prompt for the writing assignment.

Go Online
PHSchool.com
For: Self-Assessment
Visit: PHSchool.com
Web Code: cha-1030

Students can take a practice test online that is automatically scored.

All in One Teaching Resources, Unit 1
- Transparency LS34
- Chapter Test
- Performance Assessment Teacher Notes
- Performance Assessment Student Worksheet
- Performance Assessment Scoring Rubric

ExamView® Computer Test Bank CD-ROM

Checking Concepts

11. An element is any substance that cannot be broken down into simpler substances. A compound is made up of two or more elements.

12. Enzymes speed up chemical reactions in living things. Without enzymes, many of the chemical reactions that are necessary for life would either take too long or not occur at all.

13. During photosynthesis, energy from sunlight is changed into chemical energy, which is used to convert carbon dioxide and water into oxygen and sugars.

14. The raw materials are carbon dioxide and water. The products are oxygen and sugars.

15. Organisms need to carry out respiration to provide energy for cell processes.

16. During interphase, the cell grows, DNA is replicated, and the cell prepares to divide.

17. During interphase, exact copies of the DNA are made. During mitosis, the DNA and cell organelles are divided equally between the daughter cells.

Review and Assessment

Checking Concepts

11. Explain the difference between elements and compounds.

12. How are enzymes important to living things?

13. Briefly explain what happens to energy from the sun during photosynthesis.

14. What are the raw materials needed for photosynthesis? What are the products?

15. Why do organisms need to carry out the process of respiration?

16. Describe what happens during interphase.

17. How do the events in the cell cycle ensure that the genetic information in the daughter cells will be identical to that of the parent cell?

Thinking Critically

18. Predicting Suppose a volcano threw so much ash into the air that it blocked most of the sunlight that usually strikes Earth. How might this affect the ability of animals to obtain the energy they need to live?

19. Comparing and Contrasting Explain the relationship between the processes of breathing and cellular respiration.

20. Relating Cause and Effect Do plant cells need to carry out respiration? Explain.

21. Inferring The diagram below shows part of one strand of a DNA molecule. What would the bases on the other strand be?

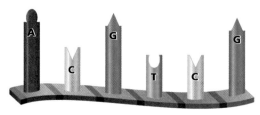

22. Comparing and Contrasting Explain how active transport is different from osmosis.

Applying Skills

Use the table below to answer Questions 23–26.

Percentages of Nitrogen Bases in the DNA of Various Organisms

Nitrogen Base	Human	Wheat	E. coli Bacterium
Adenine	30%	27%	24%
Guanine	20%	23%	26%
Thymine	30%	27%	24%
Cytosine	20%	23%	26%

23. Graphing For each organism, draw a bar graph to show the percentages of each nitrogen base in its DNA.

24. Interpreting Data What is the relationship between the amounts of adenine and thymine in the DNA of each organism? What is the relationship between the amounts of guanine and cytosine?

25. Inferring Based on your answer to Question 24, what can you infer about the structure of DNA in these three organisms?

26. Applying Concepts Suppose cytosine made up 28% of the nitrogen bases in an organism. What percentage of the organism's nitrogen bases should be thymine? Explain.

Lab zone Chapter **Project**

Performance Assessment Bring in your plants, recorded observations, and graphs to share with the class. Be prepared to describe your experimental plan and explain your results. How well did you follow your experimental plan? What did you learn about photosynthesis and light from the experiment you performed?

Lab zone Chapter **Project** ▪ L3

Performance Assessment Advise students to describe how they varied lighting conditions and controlled other variables, as well as how they assessed plant health and growth. One learning outcome is that plants cannot carry out normal photosynthesis without adequate light.

Reflect and Record Students may not have varied the lighting conditions enough to affect plant growth. In another study, students might vary the color of light plants receive.

Standardized Test Prep

Choose the letter of the best answer.

1. Which statement best describes chromosomes?

A They carry out respiration.

B They consist mostly of the pigment chlorophyll.

C Their structure is visible only during interphase.

D They consist of tightly coiled strands of DNA and proteins.

2. A scientist performed an experiment to determine the effect of temperature on the length of the cell cycle. On the basis of the data in the table below, how long would you expect the cell cycle to be at 5°C ?

F less than 13.3 hours

G more than 54.6 hours

H between 29.8 and 54.6 hours

J about 20 hours

Effect of Temperature on Length of Onion Cell Cycle

Temperature (°C)	Length of Cell Cycle (hours)
10	54.6
15	29.8
20	18.8
25	13.3

3. Which of the following statements is true?

A Plants cannot respire because they have no mitochondria.

B Photosynthesis produces energy.

C Animals cannot photosynthesize.

D Only plants photosynthesize and only animals respire.

4. Which of the following nitrogen base pairs can be found in DNA?

F A-G

G T-C

H G-T

J A-T

Constructed Response

5. Explain why water is important in the cell. Include a description of the ways osmosis can affect a cell.

Thinking Critically

18. The ash from the volcano would block the sun and prevent plants from using its energy to make food. Plants would die out, and the animals and other organisms that get their energy from plants would die out as well.

19. Breathing brings oxygen into the body for respiration. Cellular respiration uses the oxygen to break down food and provide energy for the body's needs.

20. Yes, plants need to carry out respiration to get the energy they need for their cell processes. Photosynthesis provides sugars, which are used in respiration to generate energy.

21. The bases on the other strand would be TGCAGC.

22. Active transport and osmosis are both ways that molecules cross cell membranes, but osmosis is a passive form of transport that requires no cellular energy, whereas active transport requires energy to take place. In addition, osmosis refers specifically to the transfer of water across the cell membrane, whereas active transport involves other kinds of molecules.

Applying Skills

23. The bars in the graph should correspond to the percentages in the table. There should be four bars for each organism.

24. The percents of adenine and thymine are equal. The percents of guanine and cytosine also are equal.

25. Sample: In all of the organisms, adenine is paired with thymine and guanine is paired with cytosine.

26. The percentage of nitrogen bases that are thymine would be 22%. The percentages of cytosine must equal the percentage of guanine. The percentages of all four must add up to 100%. The percentage of thymine must be half of the remaining bases.

Standardized Test Prep

1. D **2.** G **3.** C **4.** J

5. Sample answer: Water is important in a cell because water is needed for most chemical reactions in a cell. Water also helps keep the temperature of the cell about the same because water changes temperature slowly. Finally, water helps a cell maintain its shape. Osmosis can affect the cell because water enters and leaves the cell through the process of osmosis.

Chapter at a Glance

PRENTICE HALL
TeacherEXPRESS™
Plan • Teach • Assess

 Chapter **Project**   *All in the Family*

Technology

Local Standards

All in One Teaching Resources, Unit 1
- Chapter Project Teacher Notes, pp. 236–237
- Chapter Project Student Overview, pp. 238–239
- Chapter Project Student Worksheets, pp. 240–241
- Chapter Project Scoring Rubric, p. 242

 Section 1

2 periods
1 block

Mendel's Work
4.1.1   Describe the results of Mendel's experiments.
4.1.2   Identify what controls the inheritance of traits in organisms.

 Section 2

2 periods
1 block

Probability and Heredity
4.2.1   Define probability and describe how it helps explain the results of genetic crosses.
4.2.2   Explain what is meant by genotype and phenotype.
4.2.3   Tell what codominance is.

 Section 3

1 period
1/2 block

The Cell and Inheritance
4.3.1   Describe the role chromosomes play in inheritance.
4.3.2   Identify the events that occur during meiosis.
4.3.3   Explain the relationship between chromosomes and genes.

 Section 4

2 periods
1 block

The DNA Connection
4.4.1   Explain what forms the genetic code.
4.4.2   Describe how a cell produces proteins.
4.4.3   Identify how mutations can affect an organism.

Discovery CHANNEL SCHOOL
Video Field Trip

Review and Assessment

All in One Teaching Resources, Unit 1
- Key Terms Review, p. 277
- Transparency LS43
- Performance Assessment Teacher Notes, p. 284
- Performance Assessment Scoring Rubric, p. 285
- Performance Assessment Student Worksheets, p. 286
- Chapter Test, pp. 287–290

Discovery CHANNEL SCHOOL
Video Assesment

Test Preparation

Test Preparation Blackline Masters

Lab zone Chapter Activities Planner

Student Edition	Inquiry	Time	Materials	Skills	Resources
Chapter Project, p. 109	Open-Ended	2 to 3 weeks	**All in One Teaching Resources, Unit 1,** p. 236	Making models, inferring, predicting, communicating	**Lab zone Easy Planner** **All in One Teaching Resources, Unit 1,** Support pp. 236–237
Section 1					
Discover Activity, p. 110	Guided	10 minutes	none	Inferring	**Lab zone Easy Planner**
Skills Activity, p. 114	Guided	5 minutes	none	Predicting	**Lab zone Easy Planner**
Skills Lab, pp. 116–117	Directed	40 minutes	mirror (optional)	Observing, interpreting data, developing hypotheses	**Lab zone Easy Planner** **All in One Teaching Resources, Unit 1,** Skills Lab: *Take a Class Survey,* pp. 250–252
Section 2					
Discover Activity, p. 118	Directed	15 minutes	coin	Predicting	**Lab zone Easy Planner**
Try This Activity, p. 120	Directed	15 minutes	2 coins, masking tape, scissors	Interpreting data	**Lab zone Easy Planner**
Skills Lab, pp. 124–125	Guided	40 minutes	2 small paper bags, marking pen, 3 blue marbles, 3 white marbles	Making models, interpreting data, predicting, communicating inferring	**Lab zone Easy Planner** **All in One Teaching Resources, Unit 1,** Skills Lab: *Make the Right Call!,* pp. 260–262
Section 3					
Discover Activity, p. 126	Directed	10 minutes	4 craft sticks, 3 pieces of paper, marking pen	Making models	**Lab zone Easy Planner**
Section 4					
Discover Activity, p. 131	Guided	15 minutes	none	Forming operational definitions	**Lab zone Easy Planner**
Skills Activity, p. 133	Guided	5 minutes	none	Drawing conclusions	**Lab zone Easy Planner**

Section 1 Mendel's Work

 2 periods, 1 block

ABILITY LEVELS
- **L1** Basic to Average
- **L2** For All Students
- **L3** Average to Advanced

Objectives

4.1.1 Describe the results of Mendel's experiments.

4.1.2 Identify what controls the inheritance of traits in organisms.

Local Standards

Key Terms

• heredity • trait • genetics • fertilization • purebred • gene • alleles
• dominant allele • recessive allele • hybrid

 **Preteach**

Build Background Knowledge

Invite students to share observations about the physical similarities and differences among family members.

Lab zone Discover Activity *What Does the Father Look Like?* **L1**

 Targeted Print and Technology Resources

All in One Teaching Resources, Unit 1
- **L2** Reading Strategy Transparency LS35: Outlining

○ PresentationEXPRESS™ CD-ROM

 Instruct

Mendel's Experiments Discuss the results of Mendel's experiments.

Dominant and Recessive Alleles Ask leading questions to identify the role of genes in inheritance.

Lab zone Skills Lab *Take a Class Survey* **L2**

 Targeted Print and Technology Resources

All in One Teaching Resources, Unit 1
- **L2** Guided Reading, pp. 245–247
- **L2** Transparency LS36
- **L2** Skills Lab: *Take a Class Survey,* pp. 250–252

📼 Lab Activity Video/DVD
Skills Lab: *Take a Class Survey*

PHSchool.com Web Code: ced-3031

○ Student Edition on Audio CD

Assess

Section Assessment Questions

🔄 Have students use their completed outlines of the section to help them answer the questions.

Reteach

As a class, construct the crosses for the F_1 and F_2 generation for a particular trait.

Targeted Print and Technology Resources

All in One Teaching Resources, Unit 1
- Section Summary, p. 244
- **L1** Review and Reinforce, p. 248
- **L3** Enrich, p. 249

Section 2 Probability and Heredity

 2 periods, 1 block

Objectives

4.2.1 Define probability and describe how it helps explain the results of genetic crosses.

4.2.2 Explain what is meant by genotype and phenotype.

4.2.3 Tell what codominance is.

Key Terms

• probability • Punnett square • phenotype • genotype • homozygous
• heterozygous • codominance

Local Standards

Preteach

Build Background Knowledge

Invite students to describe situations in which they have used a coin toss to decide an issue.

 **Discover Activity** *What's the Chance?* **L1**

Targeted Print and Technology Resources

All in One Teaching Resources, Unit 1
L2 Reading Strategy: Building Vocabulary

⊙ **PresentationEXPRESS™ CD-ROM**

Instruct

Principles of Probability Define probability and apply it to a coin toss.

Probability and Genetics Use diagrams to explain how Punnett squares use probability to predict the results of genetic crosses.

Phenotypes and Genotypes Define phenotype and genotype, and apply to an example.

Codominance Define codominance and contrast to complete dominance by creating patterns.

 Skills Lab *Make the Right Call!*

Targeted Print and Technology Resources

All in One Teaching Resources, Unit 1
L2 Guided Reading, pp. 255–257
L2 Skills Lab: *Make the Right Call!* pp. 260–262
L2 Transparency LS37

📼 **Lab Activity Video/DVD**
Skills Lab: *Make the Right Call!*

www.SciLinks.org Web Code: scn-0332

⊙ **Student Edition on Audio CD**

Assess

Section Assessment Questions

↻ Have students use their definitions to answer the questions.

Reteach

Use Punnett squares to review the principles of probability.

Targeted Print and Technology Resources

All in One Teaching Resources, Unit 1
• Section Summary, p. 254
L1 Review and Reinforce, p. 258
L3 Enrich, p. 259

Section 3 The Cell and Inheritance

 *1 period, 1/2 block*

ABILITY LEVELS
L1 Basic to Average
L2 For All Students
L3 Average to Advanced

Objectives

4.3.1 Describe the role chromosomes play in inheritance.
4.3.2 Identify the events that occur during meiosis.
4.3.3 Explain the relationship between chromosomes and genes.

Local Standards

Key Terms

• meiosis

Preteach

Build Background Knowledge

Have students predict the location of hereditary factors in the cell.

 Discover Activity *Which Chromosome Is Which?* **L2**

Targeted Print and Technology Resources

All in One Teaching Resources, Unit 1

L2 Reading Strategy Transparency
LS38: Identifying Supporting Evidence

PresentationEXPRESS™ CD-ROM

Instruct

Chromosomes and Inheritance Explain the chromosomal theory of inheritance.

Meiosis Use a labeled diagram to describe how cells divide in each stage of meiosis.

A Lineup of Genes Use a diagram to explain how chromosomes and genes are related.

Targeted Print and Technology Resources

All in One Teaching Resources, Unit 1

L2 Guided Reading, pp. 265–266
L2 Transparency LS39

www.SciLinks.org Web Code: scn-0333

Student Edition on Audio CD

Assess

Section Assessment Questions

Have students use their graphic organizers with evidence that chromosomes play a role in inheritance to help them answer the questions.

Reteach

Have students sketch the stages of meiosis, exchange with a partner, and put the sketches in order.

Targeted Print and Technology Resources

All in One Teaching Resources, Unit 1

• Section Summary, p. 264
L1 Review and Reinforce, p. 267
L3 Enrich, p. 268

Section 4 The DNA Connection

 2 periods, 1 block

ABILITY LEVELS
L1 Basic to Average
L2 For All Students
L3 Average to Advanced

Objectives

4.4.1 Explain what forms the genetic code.

4.4.2 Describe how a cell produces proteins.

4.4.3 Identify how mutations can affect an organism.

Local Standards

Key Terms

• messenger RNA • transfer RNA • mutation

Preteach

Build Background Knowledge

Ask students to recall what they have learned about inheritance, DNA, and cell division, and to predict how genes determine traits.

 Discover Activity *Can You Crack the Code?* **L2**

Targeted Print and Technology Resources

 Teaching Resources, Unit 1

L2 Reading Strategy Transparency
LS40: Sequencing

O **PresentationEXPRESS™ CD-ROM**

Instruct

The Genetic Code Ask students questions to help them understand that genes carry genetic codes for making proteins.

How Cells Make Proteins Guide a discussion on how cells produce proteins.

Mutations Have students analyze how mutations occur and apply that knowledge by making models.

Targeted Print and Technology Resources

 Teaching Resources, Unit 1

L2 Guided Reading, pp. 271–274
L2 Transparencies LS41, LS42

PHSchool.com Web Code: cep-3034

DISCOVERY
CHANNEL
SCHOOL
Video Field Trip

O **Student Edition on Audio CD**

Assess

Section Assessment Questions

Have students use their flowcharts sequencing the steps in protein synthesis to answer the questions.

Reteach

Use diagrams to summarize the structure of DNA and how cells make proteins.

Targeted Print and Technology Resources

Teaching Resources, Unit 1

• Section Summary, p. 270
L1 Review and Reinforce, p. 275
L3 Enrich, p. 276

Chapter 4 **Content Refresher**

Section 1 **Mendel's Work**

The Law of Segregation As the textbook indicates, when Mendel saw the recessive short-stem trait reappear in the F_2 generation of pea plants, he suspected that each trait was controlled by two factors, now called alleles, one coming from each parent. He also thought that some alleles are dominant and others are recessive.

Mendel then reasoned that the each tall F_2 pea plant must have one of two allele combinations, *TT* or *Tt*. Mendel's next cross was inspired. He carefully self-pollinated each tall F_2 plant to produce an F_3 generation. Mendel predicted that if he was right about genes being paired and how they were passed along, some F_2 tall plants, when self-pollinated, should produce some short plants in the F_3 generation. Sure enough, a portion of the F_3 offspring were short.

Mendel's final conclusions, later formally codified into Mendel's First Law, or The Law of Segregation and Dominance, were as follows.

a. Each of the selected garden pea traits is controlled by a pair of alleles.
b. For each trait, an offspring receives one allele from one parent and one allele from the other.
c. The chance of offspring receiving one or the other allele from each pair is equal.
d. The expression of a dominant trait requires only one dominant allele; the expression of a recessive trait requires two recessive alleles.

Before Mendel, no plant breeder had even come close to understanding these basic principles of heredity. His conclusions qualify for the status of scientific law because after 150 years of testing, they are known to apply dependably to all sexually reproducing organisms, including humans.

Section 2 **Probability and Heredity**

Reginald C. Punnett The Punnett square was devised in the early 1900s by the English geneticist Reginald C. Punnett. Punnett studied at the University of Cambridge under the biologist William Bateson. Bateson had recognized that the results of his breeding experiments were perfectly explained by Mendel's principles. Bateson and Punnett were among the first to show that Mendel's principles were also applied to animals. Punnett wrote the first textbook on the subject of Mendel's principles of genetics, called *Mendelism,* in 1905.

Incomplete Dominance Incomplete dominance is a pattern of inheritance in which neither allele is fully dominant. This is different from codominance, in which both alleles are fully expressed, resulting in organisms that display the characteristics of both parents. Incomplete dominance results in organisms that have an intermediate phenotype. For example, in four o'clock flowers, a cross between a homozygous red-flowered plant and a homozygous white flowered plant produces F_1 offspring with pink flowers. When the F_1 offspring are crossed, the F_2 offspring are in a ratio of 1 red : 2 pink : 1 white.

Incomplete Dominance

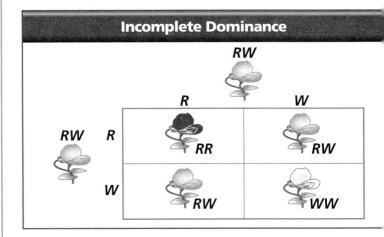

Section 3 **The Cell and Inheritance**

Crossing Over Before the first division of meiosis occurs, an important event, called crossing over, takes place. In crossing over, corresponding segments of chromosome pairs are exchanged, as shown in the illustration on the following page. In effect, the organism's maternal and paternal chromosomes exchange some alleles, producing some chromosomes that are genetically different from those of either parent of the organism. This increases the genetic diversity of a species.

Crossing over occurs randomly, but the farther apart genes are located on their chromosomes, the more often crossing over will occur between them. Geneticists use this principle to map the location of genes on chromosomes.

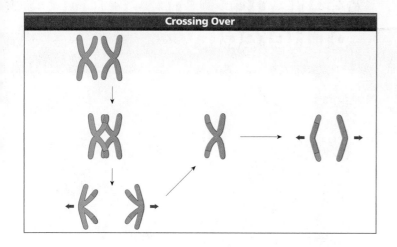

Crossing Over

amino acids are encoded by more than one codon. The protein may have a reduced function because one amino acid is substituted for the correct one. Other times the protein will not work at all, either because the codon has been changed to a stop codon or the amino acid that is substituted completely changes the nature of the protein.

Address Misconceptions

Some students may think that mutations can only be harmful to organisms. However, some mutations can be harmless or even helpful to an organism. For a strategy for helping to overcome this misconception, see **Address Misconceptions** in the section *The DNA Connection.*

Section 4 The DNA Connection

Transcription and Translation Transcription is the process by which RNA is produced using a single-stranded DNA template. Messenger RNA, transfer RNA, and ribosomal RNA are all transcribed in the nuclei of eukaryotic cells and then pass into the cytoplasm. Ribosomal RNA and proteins make up the structures of ribosomes, the organelles where proteins are made.

Translation is the production of proteins on the ribosomes. Often, several ribosomes are attached to the same messenger RNA molecule. The ribosome holds both the messenger RNA with its genetic information and the transfer RNAs with their attached amino acids in position to allow a specific protein chain to form.

Mutations in DNA Different types of changes in the base sequence of DNA affect the organism in different ways. A frameshift mutation occurs when a base is inserted or deleted from a gene. To understand what happens to a gene that has undergone a frameshift mutation, consider the following sentence:

THE DOG WAS TOO FAT.

Note that each word in the sentence consists of three letters; this is similar to the code in DNA, in which a three-base sequence codes for an amino acid. If one letter in the sentence above, the E, is lost, the sentence might be read as follows:

THD OGW AST OOF AT.

As you can see, the sentence no longer makes sense. Similarly, when one base is lost from a gene or added to it, the gene's code may no longer function normally. The result of a frameshift mutation may be a nonfunctional protein.

Sometimes one base is substituted for another. This kind of mutation affects only one codon, which has variable effects on the protein product. Sometimes it has no effect because most

Help Students Read

Think Aloud

Verbalize Thought Processes While Reading

Strategy Model processes that students can use to build meaning, self-correct, and monitor their own comprehension. Choose part of a section for this chapter, and preview it. As you do so, imagine that you are reading these paragraphs for the first time, just as your students will be. Make a copy of the section, and on it write comments and questions that you can use as "think-aloud" models.

Example

1. Read several paragraphs aloud and have your students follow along silently. Have them listen to how you pause to check your own comprehension and to determine meaning at trouble spots. You might model some of the following strategies aloud as you read:
- Make a prediction, then revise or verify it.
- Describe mental pictures as they form.
- Connect new information with prior knowledge or related ideas; share an analogy.
- Verbalize confusing points and work out steps to clarify their meanings; adjust your reading pace if needed.

2. Select a logical stopping point. Distribute copies of the annotated section you prepared earlier.

3. Then, have students read the next paragraph silently and apply similar strategies internally. Afterward, ask students to share the strategies they used. Repeat this step several times.

interactive Textbook
- Complete student edition
- Video and audio
- Simulations and activities
- Section and chapter reviews

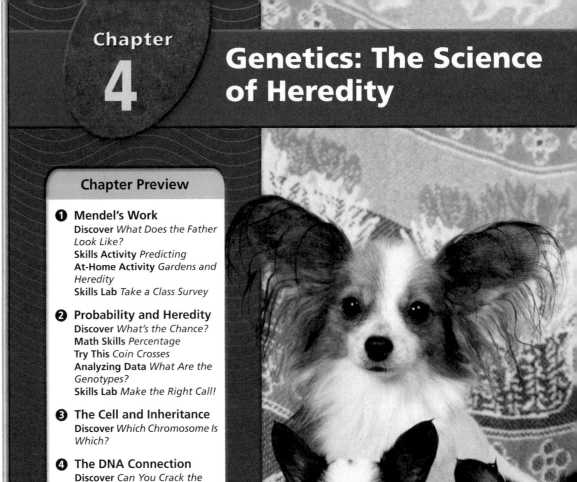

Chapter

4

Genetics: The Science of Heredity

Chapter Preview

❶ Mendel's Work
Discover *What Does the Father Look Like?*
Skills Activity *Predicting*
At-Home Activity *Gardens and Heredity*
Skills Lab *Take a Class Survey*

❷ Probability and Heredity
Discover *What's the Chance?*
Math Skills *Percentage*
Try This *Coin Crosses*
Analyzing Data *What Are the Genotypes?*
Skills Lab *Make the Right Call!*

❸ The Cell and Inheritance
Discover *Which Chromosome Is Which?*

❹ The DNA Connection
Discover *Can You Crack the Code?*
Skills Activity *Drawing Conclusions*
Active Art *Protein Synthesis*

interactive Textbook

These spaniel puppies and their mother resemble each other in many ways. ▶

108 ◆

Lab zone Chapter **Project**   L3

Objectives

This project will give students an opportunity to create a family of "paper pets" based on phenotypes they have selected. Students will learn how traits are passed from parent to offspring and how it is possible to predict the outcomes of genetic crosses. After this Chapter Project, students will be able to

- model the inheritance of traits using a paper pet
- infer their pets' genotypes
- predict the genotypes and phenotypes of their pets' offspring
- communicate the results of genetic crosses in a class presentation

Skills Focus

Making models, inferring, predicting, communicating

Project Time Line 2 to 3 weeks

All in One Teaching Resources, Unit 1

- Chapter Project Teacher Notes
- Chapter Project Overview
- Chapter Project Worksheet 1
- Chapter Project Worksheet 2
- Chapter Project Scoring Rubric

Developing a Plan

Discuss the project with students and the materials they will need. Once they have created their pets, allow class time for students to set up crosses with another pet. Each pair can simply assume that one of their pets is female and the other is male. Then have students work with partners to determine the results of the crosses between their pets and create the offspring. Provide class time for students to prepare displays.

Possible Materials

- Students need blue or yellow construction paper for the pet's body, scissors, colored pencils, glue, markers, and posterboard.
- Encourage students to decorate their pets with additional materials that you provide or students bring from home, such as glitter, beads, feathers, sequins, yarn, and buttons.

Genetics: The Science of Heredity

Show the Video Preview to introduce the topic of genetics.

Lab zone — Chapter Project

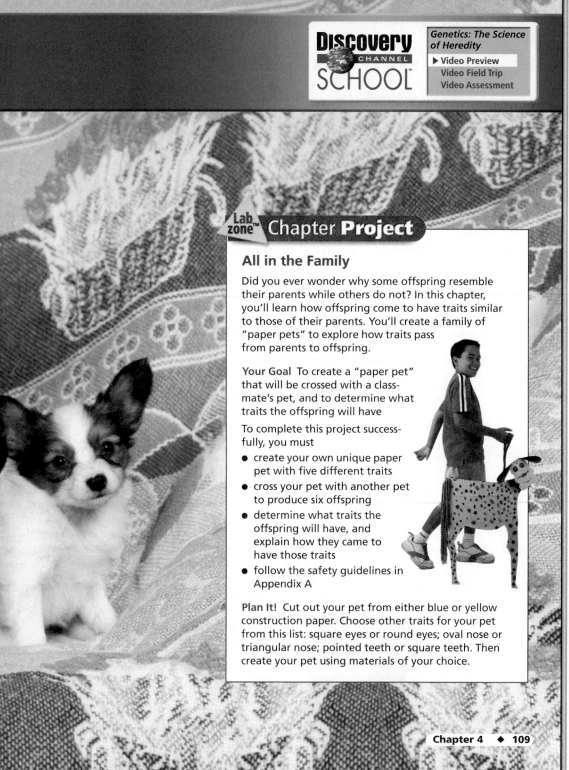

All in the Family

Did you ever wonder why some offspring resemble their parents while others do not? In this chapter, you'll learn how offspring come to have traits similar to those of their parents. You'll create a family of "paper pets" to explore how traits pass from parents to offspring.

Your Goal To create a "paper pet" that will be crossed with a class-mate's pet, and to determine what traits the offspring will have

To complete this project success-fully, you must

- create your own unique paper pet with five different traits
- cross your pet with another pet to produce six offspring
- determine what traits the offspring will have, and explain how they came to have those traits
- follow the safety guidelines in Appendix A

Plan It! Cut out your pet from either blue or yellow construction paper. Choose other traits for your pet from this list: square eyes or round eyes; oval nose or triangular nose; pointed teeth or square teeth. Then create your pet using materials of your choice.

Chapter 4 ◆ 109

Possible Shortcuts

You can simplify this project by having students record the phenotype and genotype of their pets on paper. Student pairs can set up Punnett squares for the crosses without making paper models of the pet parents and offspring.

Launching the Project

Invite students to look at the Chapter Opener photo. Ask: **How are these puppies similar to one other and to their mother? How are they different?** (*Accept all answers. Most students will describe similarities in the shape of the nose and ears and differences in color.*) Encourage students to offer explanations for these similarities and differences.

Performance Assessment

The Chapter Project Scoring Rubric will help you evaluate how well students complete the Chapter Project. You may want to share the scoring rubric with your students so they are clear about what will be expected of them. Students will be assessed on

- how neatly and creatively they design their paper pets
- how accurately they identify the phenotypes and genotypes of their pets and their offspring
- how effectively they design their display and explain it to the class

Objectives

After this lesson, students will be able to
4.1.1 Describe the results of Mendel's experiments.
4.1.2 Identify what controls the inheritance of traits in organisms.

Target Reading Skill

Outlining Explain that using an outline format helps students organize information by main topic, subtopic, and details.

Answer

Check students' outlines to make sure they include significant details. The beginning of the outlines should resemble the following:

I. Mendel's Experiments
   A. Crossing Pea Plants
     1. crossed plants with contrasting traits
     2. used only purebred plants

All in One Teaching Resources, Unit 1

• Transparency LS35

Preteach

Build Background Knowledge   L1

Family Resemblances

Invite students to share observations they have made about the physical similarities and differences among family members. Ask: **Have you ever wondered why some family members look very similar while others look very different?** (*Many students will have considered this in one way or another.*) Encourage students to share their ideas about the inheritance of traits in families. Be alert for misconceptions students might have, and address these throughout the section.

Reading Preview

Key Concepts

• What were the results of Mendel's experiments, or crosses?
• What controls the inheritance of traits in organisms?

Key Terms

• heredity • trait • genetics
• fertilization • purebred • gene
• alleles • dominant allele
• recessive allele • hybrid

Target Reading Skill

Outlining As you read, make an outline about Mendel's work. Use the red headings for the main ideas and the blue headings for the supporting ideas.

Mendel's Work
I. Mendel's experiments
A. Crossing pea plants
B.
C.

Lab zone Discover **Activity**

What Does the Father Look Like?

1. Observe the colors of the kitten in the photo. Record the kitten's coat colors and pattern. Include as many details as you can.
2. Observe the mother cat in the photo. Record her coat color and pattern.

Think It Over

Inferring Based on your observations, describe what you think the kitten's father might look like. Identify the evidence on which you based your inference.

In the mid nineteenth century, a priest named Gregor Mendel tended a garden in a central European monastery. Mendel's experiments in that peaceful garden would one day revolutionize the study of heredity. **Heredity** is the passing of physical characteristics from parents to offspring.

Mendel wondered why different pea plants had different characteristics. Some pea plants grew tall, while others were short. Some plants produced green seeds, while others had yellow seeds. Each different form of a characteristic, such as stem height or seed color, is called a **trait.** Mendel observed that the pea plants' traits were often similar to those of their parents. Sometimes, however, the plants had different traits from those of their parents.

Mendel experimented with thousands of pea plants to understand the process of heredity. Today, Mendel's discoveries form the foundation of **genetics,** the scientific study of heredity.

◀ Gregor Mendel

Lab zone Discover **Activity**

Skills Focus Inferring   L1

Time 10 minutes

Materials none

Expected Outcome The mother cat's coat is gray and has a tiger pattern. The kitten's coat is orange and has a tiger pattern.

Think It Over Students will probably infer that the father may have orange fur. They may infer that the kitten has inherited its color from the father.

Mendel's Experiments

Figure 1 shows a pea plant's flower. The flower's petals surround the pistil and the stamens. The pistil produces female sex cells, or eggs. The stamens produce pollen, which contains the male sex cells, or sperm. A new organism begins to form when egg and sperm join in the process called **fertilization**. Before fertilization can happen in pea plants, pollen must reach the pistil of a pea flower. This process is called pollination.

Pea plants are usually self-pollinating. In self-pollination, pollen from a flower lands on the pistil of the same flower. Mendel developed a method by which he cross-pollinated, or "crossed," pea plants. To cross two plants, he removed pollen from a flower on one plant. He then brushed the pollen onto a flower on a second plant.

Crossing Pea Plants Suppose you wanted to study the inheritance of traits in pea plants. What could you do? Mendel decided to cross plants with contrasting traits—for example, tall plants and short plants. He started his experiments with purebred plants. A **purebred** organism is the offspring of many generations that have the same trait. For example, purebred short pea plants always come from short parent plants.

FIGURE 1
Crossing Pea Plants
Gregor Mendel crossed pea plants that had different traits. The illustrations show how he did this. **Interpreting Diagrams** *How did Mendel prevent self-pollination?*

1 To prevent self-pollination, Mendel removed the pollen-producing structures from a pink flower.

2 He used a brush to remove pollen from a white flower on another plant. He brushed this pollen onto the pink flower.

3 The egg cells in the pink flower were then fertilized by sperm from the white flower. After a time, peas formed in the pod.

◆ 111

Observing Pistils and Stamens

Materials tulip or lily flower, hand lens, small blunt-tipped scissors

Time 15 minutes

Focus Remind students that the pistil produces female sex cells and the stamens produce pollen, which contains male sex cells.

Teach Have students observe the intact flower with a hand lens, then snip apart the pistil and stamens with scissors and examine these parts individually. Ask students to draw a labeled diagram of the flower and its parts, and compare their diagrams with Figure 1.

Apply Ask: **Why are self-pollinating plants a better choice for studying inheritance?** *(Because it is easier to obtain purebreeding plants from them.)* **learning modality: kinesthetic**

Dominant and Recessive Alleles

Teach Key Concepts   L2
Factors That Control Inheritance

Focus Remind students that the trait of shortness did not disappear in the F_1 generation of pea plants.

Teach Explain that the factors that control traits exist in pairs. One factor can hide the other factor. Ask: **What are the factors that control inheritance of traits?** *(Genes)* **What are alleles?** *(The different forms of a gene.)* **What is a dominant allele?** *(An allele whose trait always shows up in the organism when it is present)* **What kind of allele can be hidden when a dominant allele is present?** *(A recessive allele)* **What kind of alleles does a hybrid organism have?** *(Both a dominant allele and a recessive allele)*

Apply Ask: **Why were purebred pea plants important for Mendel's experiments?** *(They have two identical alleles for a gene, so in a cross, each parent contributes one allele, making the inheritance pattern easier to detect.)* **learning modality: logical/mathematical**

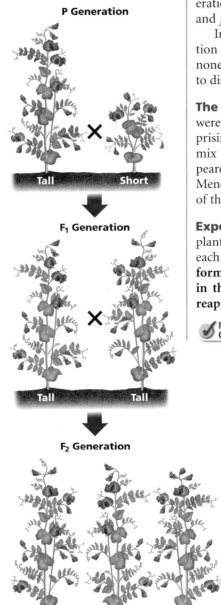

P Generation

Tall   Short

F_1 Generation

Tall   Tall

F_2 Generation

Tall   Tall   Tall   Short

112 ◆

The F_1 Offspring In one experiment, Mendel crossed pure-bred tall plants with purebred short plants. Scientists today call these parent plants the parental generation, or P generation. The offspring from this cross are the first filial (FIL ee ul) generation, or the F_1 generation. The word *filial* comes from *filia* and *filius*, the Latin words for "daughter" and "son."

In Figure 2, notice that all the offspring in the F_1 generation were tall. Even though one of the parent plants was short, none of the offspring were short. The shortness trait seemed to disappear!

The F_2 Offspring When the plants in the F_1 generation were full-grown, Mendel allowed them to self-pollinate. Surprisingly, the plants in the F_2 (second filial) generation were a mix of tall and short plants. The shortness trait had reappeared, even though none of the F_1 parent plants were short. Mendel counted the tall and short plants. About three fourths of the plants were tall, while one fourth were short.

Experiments With Other Traits Mendel also crossed pea plants with other contrasting traits. Compare the two forms of each trait in Figure 3. **In all of Mendel's crosses, only one form of the trait appeared in the F_1 generation. However, in the F_2 generation, the "lost" form of the trait always reappeared in about one fourth of the plants.**

Reading Checkpoint   What did Mendel observe about the F_2 plants?

FIGURE 2
Results of a Cross
When Mendel crossed purebred tall-stemmed plants with purebred short-stemmed plants, the first-generation offspring all had tall stems. Then he allowed the first-generation plants to self-pollinate. About 75 percent of the offspring had tall stems, and about 25 percent had short stems.

Genetics of Pea Plants							
Traits	Seed Shape	Seed Color	Seed Coat Color	Pod Shape	Pod Color	Flower Position	Stem Height
Controlled by Dominant Allele	Round	Yellow	Gray	Smooth	Green	Side	Tall
Controlled by Recessive Allele	Wrinkled	Green	White	Pinched	Yellow	End	Short

Dominant and Recessive Alleles

Mendel reached several conclusions on the basis of his experimental results. He reasoned that individual factors, or sets of genetic "information," must control the inheritance of traits in peas. The factors that control each trait exist in pairs. The female parent contributes one factor, while the male parent contributes the other factor. Finally, one factor in a pair can mask, or hide, the other factor. The tallness factor, for example, masked the shortness factor.

Genes and Alleles Today, scientists use the word **gene** for the factors that control a trait. **Alleles** (uh LEELZ) are the different forms of a gene. The gene that controls stem height in peas, for example, has one allele for tall stems and one allele for short stems. Each pea plant inherits two alleles from its parents—one allele from the egg and the other from the sperm. A pea plant may inherit two alleles for tall stems, two alleles for short stems, or one of each.

An organism's traits are controlled by the alleles it inherits from its parents. Some alleles are dominant, while other alleles are recessive. A **dominant allele** is one whose trait always shows up in the organism when the allele is present. A **recessive allele,** on the other hand, is hidden whenever the dominant allele is present. A trait controlled by a recessive allele will only show up if the organism does not have the dominant allele. Figure 3 shows dominant and recessive alleles in Mendel's crosses.

FIGURE 3
Mendel studied several traits in pea plants.
Interpreting Diagrams *Is yellow seed color controlled by a dominant allele or a recessive allele?*

Chapter 4 ◆ 113

Use Visuals: Figure 3 [L2]
Pea Plant Crosses

Focus Remind students that the traits in pea plants have two distinct forms.

Teach Direct students' attention to the trait of seed shape. Ask: **What does it mean for this trait to be dominant?** *(If a plant has two alleles for round or one allele for round and one for wrinkled, you would get a pea plant that has a round seed shape.)*

Apply Have students choose a pea trait and use the symbols for alleles to diagram the crosses that Mendel made. **learning modality: visual**

All in One Teaching Resources, Unit 1
• Transparency LS36

Lab zone Build Inquiry [L3]

Inferring the Parent Generation

Materials F_2 ear of corn with purple and yellow kernels (available from science supply companies)

Time 15 minutes

Focus Explain that the ears were produced by F_2 generation plants. The purple color is controlled by the dominant allele, and yellow is controlled by the recessive allele.

Teach Give each small group an ear of corn. Challenge them to trace the inheritance of the dominant and recessive alleles for kernel color by working backward from the F_2 ear to the F_1 cross and finally to the parental cross. *(F_1 parents: both purple (—Pp; P parents: one purple —PP, one yellow —pp)*

Apply Ask: **What kind of corn can you conclude looks like what you normally eat?** *(Yellow corn, which has two recessive alleles, (pp))* **learning modality: logical/ mathematical**

Differentiated Instruction

Gifted and Talented [L3]
Describing the Scientific Method
Challenge students to create a poster on which they identify Mendel's question and hypothesis and outline his experimental design. Groups can also include a summary of their opinions about Mendel's procedures. **learning modality: visual**

Less Proficient Readers [L1]
Mapping Key Terms Help students make a concept map in which they show the relationships among the key terms in this section. Ask them to include the definitions on the map. You may wish to pair students with more proficient readers to construct the map. **learning modality: visual**

Monitor Progress [L2]

Skills Check Have students compare and contrast dominant and recessive alleles.

Answers
Figure 3 Dominant

 Reading Checkpoint The "lost" form of the trait reappeared in about one-fourth of the plants.

Observing Crosses in Fruit Flies

Materials 2 *Drosophila melanogaster* cultures—wild-type and ebony, culture vials and plugs, *Drosophila* media, nonether anesthesia kit, hand lens, paint brush, white index card, marking pen (Note: *Drosophila* cultures are available from science supply companies.)

Advance Preparation

Set up the parental cross about two weeks in advance by placing 2 to 3 ebony males with 2 to 3 wild-type virgin females in each of three vials. To collect virgin females, remove all adult flies from the culture vial. Then, within 4 to 6 hours, collect the newly emerged females. Females have pointed abdomens with stripes almost to the end. Males have rounded abdomens that are black at the end. Anesthetize flies to sort them and to set up the crosses. Place vials on their sides until the flies wake up. Remove parent flies from the vials when pupae begin to develop. When F_1 adults begin to emerge, remove the flies daily to prevent F_2 offspring from mixing with F_1 offspring. Dispose of flies in a jar of mineral oil. Empty this "morgue" into a garbage disposal.

Time 20 minutes

Focus Review that a recessive trait can show only if two recessive alleles for the trait are present in a gene.

Teach Anesthetize the parent flies and place them on index cards for students to examine. *CAUTION: Students should not work with anesthesia.* Ask: **How do these flies differ?** *(Ebony flies have darker bodies than wild-type flies.)* Challenge students to predict which trait is controlled by a dominant allele and which is controlled by a recessive allele. Then anesthetize the F_1 flies and place them on index cards for students to count. Ask: **Which trait is controlled by a dominant allele?** *(Lighter body color)* **How do you know?** *(None of the F_1 flies have ebony bodies.)* **What body color will F_2 flies have?** *(Some will have ebony bodies, but most will have lighter bodies.)*

Apply Ask students to use symbols for alleles to write out the cross that you have demonstrated and the cross that would produce an F_2 generation. **learning modality: logical/mathematical**

Skills Activity

Predicting

In fruit flies, long wings are dominant over short wings. A scientist crossed a purebred long-winged male fruit fly with a purebred short-winged female. Predict the wing length of the F_1 offspring. If the scientist crossed a hybrid male F_1 fruit fly with a hybrid F_1 female, what would their offspring probably be like?

FIGURE 4
Black Fur, White Fur
In rabbits, the allele for black fur is dominant over the allele for white fur. **Inferring** *What combination of alleles must the white rabbit have?*

114 ◆

In pea plants, the allele for tall stems is dominant over the allele for short stems. Pea plants with one allele for tall stems and one allele for short stems will be tall. The allele for tall stems masks the allele for short stems. Only pea plants that inherit two recessive alleles for short stems will be short.

Alleles in Mendel's Crosses In Mendel's cross for stem height, the purebred tall plants in the P generation had two alleles for tall stems. The purebred short plants had two alleles for short stems. The F_1 plants each inherited an allele for tall stems from the tall parent and an allele for short stems from the short parent. Therefore, each F_1 plant had one allele for tall stems and one for short stems. The F_1 plants are called hybrids. A **hybrid** (HY brid) organism has two different alleles for a trait. All the F_1 plants are tall because the dominant allele for tall stems masks the recessive allele for short stems.

When Mendel crossed the F_1 plants, some of the offspring in the F_2 generation inherited two dominant alleles for tall stems. These plants were tall. Other F_2 plants inherited one dominant allele for tall stems and one recessive allele for short stems. These plants were also tall. The rest of the F_2 plants inherited two recessive alleles for short stems. These plants were short.

Symbols for Alleles Geneticists use letters to represent alleles. A dominant allele is represented by a capital letter. For example, the allele for tall stems is represented by T. A recessive allele is represented by the lowercase version of the letter. So, the allele for short stems would be represented by t. When a plant inherits two dominant alleles for tall stems, its alleles are written as TT. When a plant inherits two recessive alleles for short stems, its alleles are written as tt. When a plant inherits one allele for tall stems and one allele for short stems, its alleles are written as Tt.

Skills Activity

Skills Focus Predicting

Materials none

Time 5 minutes

Tips Have students write out the crosses using L for the dominant allele and l for the recessive allele.

Expected Outcome The F_1 offspring will all have long wings. The F_2 generation will produce three fourths with long wings and one fourth with short wings.

Extend Have students determine what kind of cross would produce half the offspring with long wings and half with short wings. *(A hybrid fruit fly and a purebred short-winged fruit fly)* **learning modality: logical/mathematical**

Significance of Mendel's Contribution Mendel's discovery of genes and alleles eventually changed scientists' ideas about heredity. Before Mendel, most people thought that the traits of an individual organism were simply a blend of their parents' characteristics. According to this idea, if a tall plant and a short plant were crossed, the offspring would all have medium height.

However, when Mendel crossed purebred tall and purebred short pea plants, the offspring were all tall. Mendel's experiments demonstrated that parents' traits do not simply blend in the offspring. Instead, traits are determined by individual, separate alleles inherited from each parent. Some of these alleles, such as the allele for short height in pea plants, are recessive. If a trait is determined by a recessive allele, the trait can seem to disappear in the offspring.

Unfortunately, the importance of Mendel's discovery was not recognized during his lifetime. Then, in 1900, three different scientists rediscovered Mendel's work. These scientists quickly recognized the importance of Mendel's ideas. Because of his work, Mendel is often called the Father of Genetics.

 Reading Checkpoint If an allele is represented by a capital letter, what does this indicate?

FIGURE 5
The Mendel Medal
Every year, to honor the memory of Gregor Mendel, an outstanding scientist is awarded the Mendel Medal.

Section 1 Assessment

Target Reading Skill Outlining Use the information in your outline about Mendel's work to help you answer the questions below.

Reviewing Key Concepts

1. **a. Identifying** In Mendel's cross for stem height, what contrasting traits did the pea plants in the P generation exhibit?
   b. Explaining What trait or traits did the plants in the F₁ generation exhibit? When you think of the traits of the parent plants, why is this result surprising?
   c. Comparing and Contrasting Contrast the offspring in the F₁ generation to the offspring in the F₂ generation. What did the differences in the F₁ and F₂ offspring show Mendel?
2. **a. Defining** What is a dominant allele? What is a recessive allele?

   b. Relating Cause and Effect Explain how dominant and recessive alleles for the trait of stem height determine whether a pea plant will be tall or short.
   c. Applying Concepts Can a short pea plant ever be a hybrid for the trait of stem height? Why or why not? As part of your explanation, write the letters that represent the alleles for stem height of a short pea plant.

Lab zone At-Home **Activity**

Gardens and Heredity Some gardeners save the seeds produced by flowers and plant them in the spring. If there are gardeners in your family, ask them how closely the plants that grow from these seeds resemble the parent plants. Are the offspring's traits ever different from those of the parents?

Prepare for Inquiry

Key Concept
Human traits are controlled by dominant and recessive alleles, causing many different combinations of traits among a group of people.

Skills Objectives
Students will be able to
- develop hypotheses about whether traits controlled by dominant alleles are more common than traits controlled by recessive alleles
- make observations and interpret data about certain traits controlled by dominant and recessive alleles in humans

 **Class Time** 40 minutes

All in One Teaching Resources, Unit 1
- Lab Worksheet: *Take a Class Survey*

Advance Planning
Gather mirrors, or invite students to bring some from home. You might wish to make photocopies of the circle chart and the data table.

Alternative Materials
If you do not have mirrors, students can observe one other.

Guide Inquiry

Invitation
Ask: **Why do you think people often look very similar to other family members, but also different?** (*Students should realize that children inherit both dominant and recessive alleles from each parent. The combination of these alleles determines the child's physical appearance.*)

Lab zone Skills Lab

Take a Class Survey

Problem
Are traits controlled by dominant alleles more common than traits controlled by recessive alleles?

Skills Focus
developing hypotheses, interpreting data

Materials
- mirror (optional)

Procedure

PART 1 Dominant and Recessive Alleles

1. Write a hypothesis reflecting your ideas about the problem. Then copy the data table.
2. For each of the traits listed in the data table, work with a partner to determine which trait you have. Circle that trait in your data table.
3. Count the number of students in your class who have each trait. Record that number in your data table. Also record the total number of students.

PART 2 Are Your Traits Unique?

4. Look at the circle of traits on the opposite page. All the traits in your data table appear in the circle. Place the eraser end of your pencil on the trait in the small central circle that applies to you—either free ear lobes or attached ear lobes.
5. Look at the two traits touching the space your eraser is on. Move your eraser onto the next description that applies to you. Continue using your eraser to trace your traits until you reach a number on the outside rim of the circle. Share that number with your classmates.

Analyze and Conclude

1. **Observing** The traits listed under Trait 1 in the data table are controlled by dominant alleles. The traits listed under Trait 2 are controlled by recessive alleles. Which traits controlled by dominant alleles were shown by a majority of students? Which traits controlled by recessive alleles were shown by a majority of students?

Free ear lobe

Widow's peak

Cleft chin

Dimple

Attached ear lobe

No widow's peak

No cleft chin

No dimple

Introduce the Procedure
- Have students read through the entire procedure. Then review with them what each trait looks like. Refer students to the photos in the text, or find examples of each trait among the class. Tell students that curly hair includes wavy hair or any hair that is not straight.
- Make sure students know how to use the circle of traits in Part 2. Point out how to use the color-coding, starting at the center of the circle.

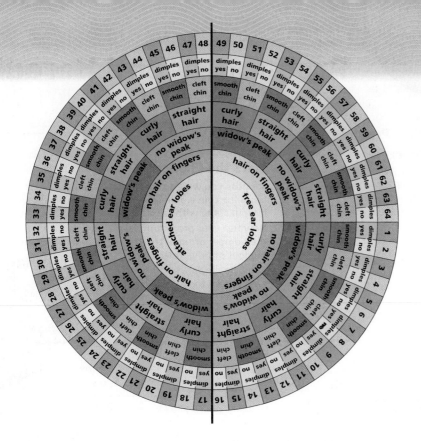

2. **Interpreting Data** How many students ended up on the same number on the circle of traits? How many students were the only ones to have their number? What do the results suggest about each person's combination of traits?

3. **Developing Hypotheses** Do your data support the hypothesis you proposed in Step 1? Write an answer with examples.

Design an Experiment

Do people who are related to each other show more genetic similarity than unrelated people? Write a hypothesis. Then design an experiment to test your hypothesis. *Obtain your teacher's permission before carrying out your investigation.*

	Data Table			
	Total Number of Students _____			
	Trait 1	Number	Trait 2	Number
A	Free ear lobes		Attached ear lobes	
B	Hair on fingers		No hair on fingers	
C	Widow's peak		No widow's peak	
D	Curly hair		Straight hair	
E	Cleft chin		Smooth chin	
F	Smile dimples		No smile dimples	

Chapter 4 ♦ 117

Troubleshooting the Experiment

• Monitor students as they work to make sure they correctly identify each trait.
• The class can record their results on a large data table on the chalkboard by writing their initials in the appropriate columns.

Expected Outcome

Students will show a great variation in traits. Few, if any, will have the same number on the circle of traits.

Analyze and Conclude

1. One trait controlled by a dominant allele that is usually more common is free earlobes. Some traits controlled by recessive alleles that are usually more common include smooth chin, straight hair, no widow's peak, and no mid-finger hair. However, any class's results may vary from the overall population patterns because of the small sample size.

2. Answers will vary, but usually few or no students have the same number when six traits are studied. The more traits that are considered, the smaller the chance that any two people in a class will have the same number. Even siblings, except identical twins, have different combinations of traits.

3. Answers will vary, but answers should include examples from the lab to explain that neither traits controlled by dominant alleles nor traits controlled by recessive alleles are automatically more common in a population.

Extend Inquiry

Design an Experiment Students' hypotheses will vary. *Possible hypothesis:* A group of related people will share more numbers on the circle of traits than a group of unrelated people. Student experiments can follow the same procedure as this lab, except students would observe the traits in people from a single family.

For: Data sharing
Visit: PHSchool.com
Web Code: ced-3031

Students can share data online.

Objectives

After this lesson, students will be able to

4.2.1 Define probability and describe how it helps explain the results of genetic crosses.

4.2.2 Explain what is meant by genotype and phenotype.

4.2.3 Tell what codominance is.

Target Reading Skill

Building Vocabulary Explain that knowing the definitions of key-concept words helps students understand what they read.

Answers

Call on volunteers to read their definitions aloud. Make sure that students have explained the definitions in their own words.

Preteach

Build Background Knowledge

L1

Coin Tosses and Probability

Invite students to describe situations in which they have used a coin toss to decide an issue. Ask: **Why did you toss a coin in these situations?** (*Possible answer: It was the fairest way to make a decision.*) **Why is a coin toss fair?** (*Each person has a 50–50 chance of winning.*)

Go Online
SciLINKS NSTA

For: Links on probability and genetics
Visit: www.SciLinks.org
Web Code: scn-0332

Download a worksheet to guide students' review of probability and genetics.

Reading Preview

Key Concepts

- What is probability and how does it help explain the results of genetic crosses?
- What is meant by genotype and phenotype?
- What is codominance?

Key Terms

- probability
- Punnett square
- phenotype
- genotype
- homozygous
- heterozygous
- codominance

 **Target Reading Skill**

Building Vocabulary After you read the section, reread the paragraphs that contain definitions of Key Terms. Use all the information you have learned to write a definition of each Key Term in your own words.

Go Online
SciLINKS NSTA

For: Links on probability and genetics
Visit: www.SciLinks.org
Web Code: scn-0332

Lab zone Discover **Activity**

What's the Chance?

1. Suppose you were to toss a coin 20 times. Predict how many times the coin would land with heads up and how many times it would land with tails up.

2. Now test your prediction by tossing a coin 20 times. Record the number of times the coin lands with heads up and the number of times it lands with tails up.

3. Combine the data from the entire class. Record the total number of tosses, the number of heads, and the number of tails.

Think It Over

Predicting How did your results in Step 2 compare to your prediction? How can you account for any differences between your results and the class results?

On a brisk fall afternoon, the stands are packed with cheering football fans. Today is the big game between Riverton's North and South high schools, and it's almost time for the kickoff. Suddenly, the crowd becomes silent, as the referee is about to toss a coin. The outcome of the coin toss will decide which team kicks the ball and which receives it. The captain of the visiting North High team says "heads." If the coin lands with heads up, North High wins the toss and the right to decide whether to kick or receive the ball.

What is the chance that North High will win the coin toss? To answer this question, you need to understand the principles of probability.

Principles of Probability

If you did the Discover activity, you used the principles of **probability** to predict the results of a particular event. In this case, the event was the toss of a coin. **Probability is a number that describes how likely it is that an event will occur.**

Lab zone Discover **Activity**

Skills Focus Predicting

Materials coin

Time 15 minutes

Expected Outcome The outcome of the coin tosses will vary. The more data, the closer the outcome will be to the expected ratio of one "heads" to one "tails."

L1 **Think It Over** For most students, their results were slightly different from their predictions. The combined class data should be closer to the expected ratio of one "heads" to one "tails." Students might infer that the difference is due to chance or that the more coin tosses they make, the closer they will come to the predicted outcome.

Mathematics of Probability Each time you toss a coin, there are two possible ways that the coin can land—heads up or tails up. Each of these two events is equally likely to occur. In mathematical terms, you can say that the probability that a tossed coin will land with heads up is 1 in 2. There is also a 1 in 2 probability that the coin will land with tails up. A 1 in 2 probability can also be expressed as the fraction $\frac{1}{2}$ or as a percent—50 percent.

The laws of probability predict what is likely to occur, not necessarily what will occur. If you tossed a coin 20 times, you might expect it to land with heads up 10 times and with tails up 10 times. However, you might not get these results. You might get 11 heads and 9 tails, or 8 heads and 12 tails. The more tosses you make, the closer your actual results will be to the results predicted by probability.

 Reading Checkpoint What is probability?

Independence of Events When you toss a coin more than once, the results of one toss do not affect the results of the next toss. Each event occurs independently. For example, suppose you toss a coin five times and it lands with heads up each time. What is the probability that it will land with heads up on the next toss? Because the coin landed heads up on the previous five tosses, you might think that it would be likely to land heads up on the next toss. However, this is not the case. The probability of the coin landing heads up on the next toss is still 1 in 2, or 50 percent. The results of the first five tosses do not affect the result of the sixth toss.

FIGURE 6
A Coin Toss
The result of a coin toss can be explained by probability.

◆ 119

119

Probability and Genetics

Help Students Read   L2

Active Comprehension Read the first paragraph on this page. Ask: **What more would you like to know about probability and genetics?** Help students make connections between probability and their daily lives, such as weather forecasts. As students read the section, have them consider their questions. After reading, have students discuss the section, making sure each question is answered or that students know where to look for the answer.

Teach Key Concepts   L2

Probability Explains Genetic Crosses

Focus Remind students that the outcome of tossing a coin is based on probability.

Teach Ask: **How is this similar to the outcome of a genetic cross?** (*The allele that each parent will pass on to its offspring is based on probability.*) **What tool can be used to predict the results of a cross?** (*A Punnett square, a chart that shows all the possible combinations of alleles that can result from a genetic cross*) Refer students to Figure 7, and have student volunteers read each step. Point out that combinations are simply pairings of the male and female alleles from a particular row and column.

Apply Challenge students to devise a Punnett square that illustrates the possible offspring in a cross between a purebred pea plant whose seeds have gray coats and a purebred pea plant whose seeds have white coats. Students can also make Punnett squares showing a cross between the hybrid offspring of the first cross. **learning modality: logical/mathematical**

All in One Teaching Resources, Unit 1
• Transparency LS37

---

❶ Start by drawing a box and dividing it into four squares.

❷ Write the male parent's alleles along the top of the square and the female parent's alleles along the left side.

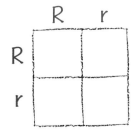

FIGURE 7

How to Make a Punnett Square

The diagrams show how to make a Punnett square. In this cross, both parents are heterozygous for the trait of seed shape. *R* represents the dominant round allele, and *r* represents the recessive wrinkled allele.

Probability and Genetics

How is probability related to genetics? To answer this question, think back to Mendel's experiments with peas. Remember that Mendel carefully counted the offspring from every cross that he carried out. When Mendel crossed two plants that were hybrid for stem height (Tt), three fourths of the F_1 plants had tall stems. One fourth of the plants had short stems.

Each time Mendel repeated the cross, he obtained similar results. Mendel realized that the mathematical principles of probability applied to his work. He could say that the probability of such a cross producing a tall plant was 3 in 4. The probability of producing a short plant was 1 in 4. Mendel was the first scientist to recognize that the principles of probability can be used to predict the results of genetic crosses.

Punnett Squares A tool that can help you understand how the laws of probability apply to genetics is called a Punnett square. A **Punnett square** is a chart that shows all the possible combinations of alleles that can result from a genetic cross. Geneticists use Punnett squares to show all the possible outcomes of a genetic cross, and to determine the probability of a particular outcome.

Figure 7 shows how to construct a Punnett square. In this case, the Punnett square shows a cross between two hybrid pea plants with round seeds (Rr). The allele for round seeds (R) is dominant over the allele for wrinkled seeds (r). Each parent can pass either of its alleles, R or r, to its offspring. The boxes in the Punnett square represent the possible combinations of alleles that the offspring can inherit.

Reading Checkpoint What is a Punnett square?

Lab zone Try This Activity

Coin Crosses

Here's how you can use coins to model Mendel's cross between two Tt pea plants.

1. Place a small piece of masking tape on each side of two coins.

2. Write a T (for tall) on one side of each coin and a t (for short) on the other.

3. Toss both coins together 20 times. Record the letter combinations that you obtain from each toss.

Interpreting Data How many of the offspring would be tall plants? (*Hint:* What different letter combinations would result in a tall plant?) How many would be short? Convert your results to percentages. Then compare your results to Mendel's.

Lab zone Try This Activity

Skills Focus Interpreting data   L1

Materials 2 coins, masking tape, scissors

Time 15 minutes

Expected Outcome 5 TT, 10 Tt, 5 tt; All plants that are TT and Tt will be tall, approximately 15, or 75%. All tt plants will be short, approximately 5, or 25%. Some students might observe that

their results are similar to Mendel's results.

Extend Let students toss both coins another 20 times and observe whether their percentages are closer to Mendel's results. **learning modality: logical/ mathematical**

③ Copy the female parent's alleles into the boxes to their right.

④ Copy the male parent's alleles into the boxes beneath them.

⑤ The completed Punnett square shows all the possible allele combinations in the offspring.

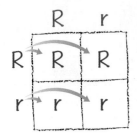

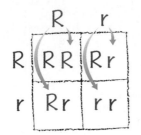

R R r
R RR Rr
r Rr rr

Using a Punnett Square

You can use a Punnett square to calculate the probability that offspring with a certain combination of alleles will result. **In a genetic cross, the allele that each parent will pass on to its offspring is based on probability.** The completed Punnett square in Figure 7 shows four possible combinations of alleles. The probability that an offspring will be *RR* is 1 in 4, or 25 percent. The probability that an offspring will be *rr* is also 1 in 4, or 25 percent. Notice, however, that the *Rr* allele combination appears in two boxes in the Punnett square. This is because there are two possible ways in which this combination can occur. So the probability that an offspring will be *Rr* is 2 in 4, or 50 percent.

When Mendel crossed hybrid plants with round seeds, he discovered that about three fourths of the plants (75 percent) had round seeds. The remaining one fourth of the plants (25 percent) produced wrinkled seeds. Plants with the *RR* allele combination would produce round seeds. So too would those plants with the *Rr* allele combination. Remember that the dominant allele masks the recessive allele. Only those plants with the *rr* allele combination would have wrinkled seeds.

Predicting Probabilities

You can use a Punnett square to predict probabilities. For example, Figure 8 shows a cross between a purebred black guinea pig and a purebred white guinea pig. The allele for black fur is dominant over the allele for white fur. Notice that only one allele combination is possible in the offspring—*Bb*. All of the offspring will inherit the dominant allele for black fur. Because of this, all of the offspring will have black fur. There is a 100 percent probability that the offspring will have black fur.

FIGURE 8
Guinea Pig Punnett Square
This Punnett square shows a cross between a black guinea pig (*BB*) and a white guinea pig (*bb*). *Calculating* What is the probability that an offspring will have white fur?

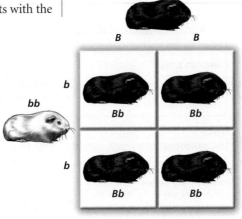

Chapter 4 ◆ 121

Use Visuals: Figure 8   L2
Interpreting Punnett Squares

Focus Remind students that a Punnett square identifies possible gene combinations.

Teach Have students identify the alleles that each parent could pass on to the offspring. (*BB* and bb) Walk through each column and row to make sure students understand how the alleles combine. Ask: **Why are all the offspring black?** (*Black is the dominant allele, and all the offspring have it.*)

Apply Ask: What percent of the F$_2$ offspring are likely to be black? (*75%*)
learning modality: visual

Observing Crosses in Tobacco Plants

Materials F$_2$ tobacco seeds that produce green (*GG, Gg*) and albino (*gg*) seedlings in a ratio of 3:1, seed starting soil, shallow pan, plastic wrap, water. Order the seeds from a science supply house, and plant them 7 to 14 days in advance, or as directed on the packet.

Time 15 minutes

Focus Explain that a cross between two hybrid green tobacco plants (*Gg* and *Gg*) produces both green and white offspring.

Teach Draw a Punnett square of this cross; 75% of the seedlings are likely to be green and 25% are likely to be white. Have students count the numbers of green and white seedlings from the F$_2$ seeds you planted and compare those numbers to the predictions.

Apply Ask students to explain why the numbers may not match. (*The Punnett square just predicts the probability. The actual combinations could be different.*) **learning modality: logical/mathematical**

Differentiated Instruction

Special Needs   L1
Understanding Independence of Events Provide one student in a pair with four pipe cleaners of different lengths, but all the same color. Ask the student to hold them so that they all appear to be the same length. Ask: **What is the chance that the longest pipe cleaner will be chosen?** (*1 out of 4, or 25%*) Have the other student test

this answer, and then replace the pipe cleaner. Ask if the probability is still 25% that the same pipe cleaner will be chosen if he or she draws again. (*Yes*) Explain that this models how events occur independently. Have students repeat this exercise as needed to understand the concept. **learning modality: kinesthetic**

Monitor Progress   L2

Drawing Have students draw a Punnett square for a cross between any two hybrids (*Aa* × *Aa*) and include the probabilities of each offspring type.

Answers
Figure 8 0%

✓ **Reading Checkpoint** A chart that shows all the possible combinations of alleles that can result from a genetic cross

121

Phenotypes and Genotypes

Teach Key Concepts **L2**

Comparing Phenotype and Genotype

Focus Review that a hybrid has a recessive allele but shows the dominant trait.

Teach Ask: **What is a phenotype?** *(An organism's physical appearance)* **What is a genotype?** *(An organism's genetic makeup)* **What is the term used to describe an organism whose genotype consists of two identical alleles for a trait?** *(Homozygous)* **What term is used to describe an organism whose genotype consists of two different alleles for a trait?** *(Heterozygous)*

Apply Ask: **Why can you be certain of the genotype of an organism that shows a recessive trait?** *(It must have a homozygous recessive genotype, because the recessive allele is not hidden by a dominant allele.)* **learning modality: logical/mathematical**

Math ▶ Analyzing Data

Math Skill Making and interpreting graphs

Focus Point out that bar graphs are often used to compare different types of data.

Teach Ask: **What two types of data are being compared in the graph?** *(Numbers of plants with yellow seeds and with green seeds)*

Answers
1. 6,000 yellow; 2,000 green
2. 8,000; 75% have yellow peas and 25% have green peas.
3. Both parents probably had the genotype *Bb*.

Codominance

Teach Key Concepts **L2**

Focus Refer students to Figure 10.

Teach Ask: **Which alleles are expressed in these offspring?** *(Both)* **What is codominance?** *(In codominance, the alleles are neither dominant nor recessive.)*

Apply Have students create colored patterns comparing genotypes and phenotypes in simple dominance and in codominance.
learning modality: visual

Math ▶ Analyzing Data

What Are the Genotypes?
Mendel allowed several F$_1$ pea plants with yellow seeds to self-pollinate. The graph shows the approximate numbers of the F$_2$ offspring with yellow seeds and with green seeds.

1. **Reading Graphs** How many F$_2$ offspring had yellow seeds? How many had green seeds?

2. **Calculating** Use the information in the graph to calculate the total number of offspring that resulted from this cross. Then calculate the percentage of the offspring with yellow peas, and the percentage with green peas.

3. **Inferring** Use the answers to Question 2 to infer the probable genotypes of the parent plants.

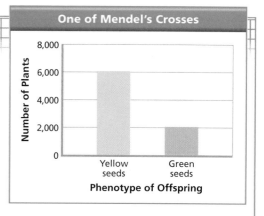

One of Mendel's Crosses

(Hint: Construct Punnett squares with the possible genotypes of the parents.)

Phenotypes and Genotypes

Two useful terms that geneticists use are **phenotype** (FEE noh typ) and **genotype** (JEN uh typ). **An organism's phenotype is its physical appearance, or visible traits. An organism's genotype is its genetic makeup, or allele combinations.**

To understand the difference between phenotype and genotype, look at Figure 9. The allele for smooth pea pods (*S*) is dominant over the allele for pinched pea pods (*s*). All of the plants with at least one dominant allele have the same phenotype—they all produce smooth pods. However, the plants can have two different genotypes—*SS* or *Ss*. If you were to look at the plants with smooth pods, you would not be able to tell the difference between those with the *SS* genotype and those with the *Ss* genotype. The plants with pinched pods, on the other hand, would all have the same phenotype—pinched pods—as well as the same genotype—*ss*.

Geneticists use two additional terms to describe an organism's genotype. An organism that has two identical alleles for a trait is said to be **homozygous** (hoh moh ZY gus) for that trait. A smooth-pod plant that has the alleles *SS* and a pinched-pod plant with the alleles *ss* are both homozygous. An organism that has two different alleles for a trait is **heterozygous** (het ur oh ZY gus) for that trait. A smooth-pod plant with the alleles *Ss* is heterozygous. Mendel used the term *hybrid* to describe heterozygous pea plants.

Reading Checkpoint If a pea plant's genotype is *Ss*, what is its phenotype?

SS   *Ss*   *ss*

Phenotypes and Genotypes	
Phenotype	**Genotype**
Smooth pods	*SS*
Smooth pods	*Ss*
Pinched pods	*ss*

FIGURE 9
The phenotype of an organism is its physical appearance. Its genotype is its genetic makeup.
Interpreting Tables *How many genotypes are there for the smooth-pod phenotype?*

Codominance

For all of the traits that Mendel studied, one allele was dominant while the other was recessive. This is not always the case. For some alleles, an inheritance pattern called **codominance** exists. **In codominance, the alleles are neither dominant nor recessive. As a result, both alleles are expressed in the offspring.**

Look at Figure 10. Mendel's principle of dominant and recessive alleles does not explain why the heterozygous chickens have both black and white feathers. The alleles for feather color are codominant—neither dominant nor recessive. As you can see, neither allele is masked in the heterozygous chickens. Notice also that the codominant alleles are written as capital letters with superscripts—F^B for black feathers and F^W for white feathers. As the Punnett square shows, heterozygous chickens have the $F^B F^W$ allele combination.

 Reading Checkpoint How are the symbols for codominant alleles written?

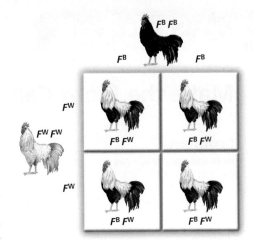

FIGURE 10
Codominance
The offspring of the cross in this Punnett square will have both black and white feathers.
Classifying *Will the offspring be heterozygous or homozygous? Explain your answer.*

Section 2 Assessment

Target Reading Skill Building Vocabulary Use your definitions to help you answer the questions.

Reviewing Key Concepts

1. a. **Reviewing** What is probability?
   b. **Explaining** If you know the parents' alleles for a trait, how can you use a Punnett square to predict the probable genotypes of the offspring?
   c. **Predicting** A pea plant with round seeds has the genotype *Rr*. You cross this plant with a wrinkled-seed plant, genotype *rr*. What is the probability that the offspring will have wrinkled seeds? (Use a Punnett square to help with the prediction.)

2. a. **Defining** Define *genotype* and *phenotype*.
   b. **Relating Cause and Effect** Explain how two organisms can have the same phenotype but different genotypes. Give an example.
   c. **Applying Concepts** A pea plant has a tall stem. What are its possible genotypes?

3. a. **Explaining** What is codominance? Give an example of codominant alleles and explain why they are codominant.
   b. **Applying Concepts** What is the phenotype of a chicken with the genotype $F^B F^W$?

Math Practice

4. **Ratios** A scientist crossed a tall pea plant with a short pea plant. Of the offspring, 13 were tall and 12 were short. Write the ratio of each phenotype to the total number of offspring. Express the ratios as fractions.

5. **Percentage** Use the fractions to calculate the percentage of the offspring that were tall and the percentage that were short.

Chapter 4 ◆ 123

123

Make the Right Call! L2

Prepare for Inquiry

Key Concept
Punnett squares can predict the results of a genetic cross when the genotypes of both parents are known.

Skills Objectives
Students will be able to
- model the combination of alleles in a genetic cross
- predict the offspring of a genetic cross
- interpret data from models of genetic crosses

Class Time 40 minutes

All in One Teaching Resources, Unit 1
- Lab Worksheet: *Make the Right Call!*

Alternative Materials
Marbles of other colors may be substituted, but use two easily distinguishable colors. (Some students may be colorblind.) Other small colored objects that have a uniform shape and texture, such as buttons, can be used.

Guide Inquiry

Invitation
Discuss circumstances in which students make predictions in their lives. Then ask: **Why is it helpful to scientists to make accurate predictions in their experiments?** *(Accurate predictions make scientists more confident that they are asking the right questions and correctly understanding the phenomena that they are studying; they also help scientists to better plan their experiments.)*

Make the Right Call!

Problem
How can you predict the possible results of genetic crosses?

Skills Focus
making models, interpreting data

Materials
- 2 small paper bags
- marking pen
- 3 blue marbles
- 3 white marbles

Procedure
1. Label one bag "Bag 1, Female Parent." Label the other bag "Bag 2, Male Parent." Then read over Part 1, Part 2, and Part 3 of this lab. Write a prediction about the kinds of offspring you expect from each cross.

PART 1 Crossing Two Homozygous Parents

2. Copy the data table and label it *Data Table 1.* Then place two blue marbles in Bag 1. This pair of marbles represents the female parent's alleles. Use the letter *B* to represent the dominant allele for blue color.

3. Place two white marbles in Bag 2. Use the letter *b* to represent the recessive allele for white color.

4. For Trial 1, remove one marble from Bag 1 without looking in the bag. Record the result in your data table. Return the marble to the bag. Again, without looking in the bag, remove one marble from Bag 2. Record the result in your data table. Return the marble to the bag.

5. In the column labeled Offspring's Alleles, write *BB* if you removed two blue marbles, *bb* if you removed two white marbles, or *Bb* if you removed one blue marble and one white marble.

6. Repeat Steps 4 and 5 nine more times.

PART 2 Crossing Homozygous and Heterozygous Parents

7. Place two blue marbles in Bag 1. Place one white marble and one blue marble in Bag 2. Copy the data table again, and label it *Data Table 2.*

8. Repeat Steps 4 and 5 ten times.

Data Table			
Number _____			
Trial	Allele From Bag 1 (Female Parent)	Allele From Bag 2 (Male Parent)	Offspring's Alleles
1			
2			
3			
4			
5			
6			

Introduce the Procedure
Have students read the entire procedure. Ask: **What do the marbles represent?** *(The alleles from each parent)* **Why should you not look inside the bag when you remove the marbles?** *(To make sure the combinations occur randomly)*

Expected Outcome
In the first cross (*BB* × *bb*), students observe that all offspring are *Bb*. In the second cross (*BB* × *Bb*), all offspring are blue, but some are homozygous (*BB*) and some are heterozygous (*Bb*). In the third cross (*Bb* × *Bb*), some offspring are blue and some are white. All white offspring are homozygous (*bb*). Blue offspring are either homozygous (*BB*) or heterozygous (*Bb*).

PART 3   Crossing Two Heterozygous Parents

9. Place one blue marble and one white marble in Bag 1. Place one blue marble and one white marble in Bag 2. Copy the data table again and label it *Data Table 3*.

10. Repeat Steps 4 and 5 ten times.

Analyze and Conclude

1. **Making Models** Make a Punnett square for each of the crosses you modeled in Part 1, Part 2, and Part 3.

2. **Interpreting Data** According to your results in Part 1, how many different kinds of offspring are possible when the homozygous parents (*BB* and *bb*) are crossed? Do the results you obtained using the marble model agree with the results shown by a Punnett square?

3. **Predicting** According to your results in Part 2, what percentage of offspring are likely to be homozygous when a homozygous parent (*BB*) and a heterozygous parent (*Bb*) are crossed? What percentage of offspring are likely to be heterozygous? Does the model agree with the results shown by a Punnett square?

4. **Making Models** According to your results in Part 3, what different kinds of offspring are possible when two heterozygous parents (*Bb* × *Bb*) are crossed? What percentage of each type of offspring are likely to be produced? Does the model agree with the results of a Punnett square?

5. **Inferring** For Part 3, if you did 100 trials instead of 10 trials, would your results be closer to the results shown in a Punnett square? Explain.

6. **Communicating** In a paragraph, explain how the marble model compares with a Punnett square. How are the two methods alike? How are they different?

More to Explore

In peas, the allele for yellow seeds (*Y*) is dominant over the allele for green seeds (*y*). What possible crosses do you think could produce a heterozygous plant with yellow seeds (*Yy*)? Use the marble model and Punnett squares to test your predictions.

◆ 125

Extend Inquiry

More to Explore Crosses that will produce a heterozygous plant (*Yy*) include *YY* × *yy*, *YY* × *Yy*, *Yy* × *Yy*, and *Yy* × *yy*.

Analyze and Conclude

1. Punnett square for Part 1:

	b	b
B	Bb	Bb
B	Bb	Bb

Punnett square for Part 2:

	B	b
B	BB	Bb
B	BB	Bb

Punnett square for Part 3:

	B	b
B	BB	Bb
b	Bb	bb

2. Only heterozygous blue offspring (*Bb*) are possible. The Punnett square shows the same results.

3. Student results may produce slightly different answers. As the number of trials increases, the results will more likely show that 50 percent of the offspring are likely to be homozygous (*BB*), while 50 percent are likely to be heterozygous (*Bb*). The Punnett square shows that 50 percent will be homozygous and 50 percent will be heterozygous.

4. Student results may vary due to chance, but all should observe that three different genotypes are possible: *BB*, *Bb*, and *bb*. From the Punnett square, students can predict that 25 percent are likely to be *BB*, 50 percent are likely to be *Bb*, and 25 percent are likely to be *bb*. The marble model will probably not totally agree with the Punnett square due to chance.

5. Probably; as the number of trials is increased, the results are more likely to match those predicted in a Punnett square because of chance.

6. Sample answer: The marble model and the Punnett square both show the genotypes of the parents and offspring, and demonstrate how the parent can donate one of two possible alleles to the offspring. The Punnett square gives all the possible genotypes of the offspring and their probabilities of occurring. The model gives the genotypes of the offspring based on chance, much like the actual combining of alleles in a real genetic cross.

Objectives

After this lesson, students will be able to

4.3.1 Describe the role chromosomes play in inheritance.

4.3.2 Identify the events that occur during meiosis.

4.3.3 Explain the relationship between chromosomes and genes.

Target Reading Skill 🔄

Identifying Supporting Evidence

Explain that identifying supporting evidence helps students understand the relationship between the facts and the hypothesis.

Answers

One possible way to complete the graphic organizer:

Detail: Grasshoppers: 24 chromosomes in body cells, 12 in sex cells

Detail: Fertilized egg has 24 chromosomes.

Detail: Alleles exist in pairs in organisms.

All in One Teaching Resources, Unit 1

• Transparency LS38

Preteach

Build Background Knowledge **L1**

Relating Genetics and the Cell Cycle

Have students recall what they know about cells and cell structure. Challenge them to predict the location of Mendel's hereditary factors, or genes, within the cell. You might wish to record students' predictions on the board and have the class evaluate them as you study the section.

Reading Preview

Key Concepts

• What role do chromosomes play in inheritance?

• What events occur during meiosis?

• What is the relationship between chromosomes and genes?

Key Term

• meiosis

🔄 Target Reading Skill

Identifying Supporting Evidence As you read, identify the evidence that supports the hypothesis that chromosomes are important in inheritance. Write the evidence in a graphic organizer.

Evidence

Grasshoppers: 24 chromosomes in body cells, 12 in sex cells

Hypothesis

Chromosomes are important in inheritance.

Lab zone Discover Activity

Which Chromosome Is Which?

Mendel did not know about chromosomes or their role in genetics. Today we know that genes are located on chromosomes.

1. Label two craft sticks with the letter *A*. The craft sticks represent a pair of chromosomes in the female parent. Turn the sticks face down on a piece of paper.

2. Label two more craft sticks with the letter *a*. These represent a pair of chromosomes in the male parent. Turn the sticks face down on another piece of paper.

3. Turn over one craft stick "chromosome" from each piece of paper. Move both sticks to a third piece of paper. These represent a pair of chromosomes in the offspring. Note the allele combination that the offspring received.

Think It Over

Making Models Use this model to explain how chromosomes are involved in the inheritance of alleles.

Mendel's work showed that genes exist. But scientists in the early twentieth century did not know what structures in cells contained genes. The search for the answer to this puzzle is something like a mystery story. The story could be called "The Clue in the Grasshopper's Cells."

In 1903, Walter Sutton, an American geneticist, was studying the cells of grasshoppers. He wanted to understand how sex cells (sperm and egg) form. Sutton focused on the movement of chromosomes during the formation of sex cells. He hypothesized that chromosomes were the key to understanding how offspring have traits similar to those of their parents.

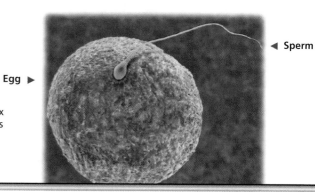

◀ Sperm

Egg ▶

FIGURE 11
Sex Cells
The large egg is a female sex cell, and the smaller sperm is a male sex cell.

Lab zone Discover Activity

Skills Focus Making models

Materials 4 craft sticks, 3 pieces of paper, marking pen

Time 10 minutes

Tips Receives only one allele from each parent.

Expected Outcome Students will realize that parents contribute only one of their two chromosomes to the offspring.

L2 The idea is to get students thinking about genes being carried on chromosomes and that the cell has a process to make sure only one allele of a gene is contributed to offspring.

Think It Over Genes are located on chromosomes, which must divide and separate so that the offspring get only one chromosome, or one allele, from each parent.

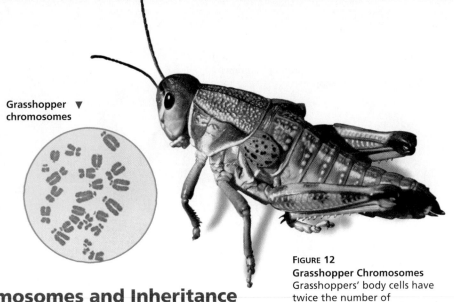

Grasshopper ▼
chromosomes

FIGURE 12
Grasshopper Chromosomes
Grasshoppers' body cells have twice the number of chromosomes as their sex cells.
Applying Concepts *What is the function of chromosomes?*

Chromosomes and Inheritance

Sutton needed evidence to support his hypothesis that chromosomes were important in the inheritance of traits. He found that evidence in grasshoppers' cells. The body cells of a grasshopper have 24 chromosomes. To his surprise, Sutton found that the grasshopper's sex cells have only 12 chromosomes. In other words, a grasshopper's sex cells have exactly half the number of chromosomes found in its body cells.

Chromosome Pairs Sutton observed what happened when a sperm cell and an egg cell joined during fertilization. The fertilized egg that formed had 24 chromosomes. As a result, the grasshopper offspring had exactly the same number of chromosomes in its cells as did each of its parents. The 24 chromosomes existed in 12 pairs. One chromosome in each pair came from the male parent, while the other chromosome came from the female parent.

Genes on Chromosomes Recall that alleles are different forms of a gene. Because of Mendel's work, Sutton knew that alleles exist in pairs in an organism. One allele in a pair comes from the organism's female parent and the other allele comes from the male parent. Sutton realized that paired alleles were carried on paired chromosomes. Sutton's idea came to be known as the chromosome theory of inheritance. **According to the chromosome theory of inheritance, genes are carried from parents to their offspring on chromosomes.**

 Reading Checkpoint What is the relationship between alleles and chromosomes?

Chapter 4 ◆ 127

Instruct

Chromosomes and Inheritance

Teach Key Concepts L2
The Role of Chromosomes

Focus Review the definition and location of chromosomes.

Teach Ask: **What did Sutton observe about the relative numbers of chromosomes in the body cells and sex cells of grasshoppers?** *(The sex cells have half the number of chromosomes as body cells.)* **How many chromosomes does the fertilized egg receive from each parent?** *(The number that is present in each sex cell)* **How are genes passed from parent to offspring?** *(Sex cells contain half of each parent's chromosomes, which include the parent's genes. When the sex cells from each parent join during fertilization, the offspring receives a full set of genes.)* **What is the chromosomal theory of inheritance?** *(Genes are carried from parents to their offspring on chromosomes.)*

Apply Ask: **If human body cells each have 46 chromosomes, how many chromosomes do human sex cells have?** *(23)* **learning modality: logical/mathematical**

Independent Practice

 Teaching Resources, Unit 1 L2

• Guided Reading and Study Worksheet: *The Cell and Inheritance*

⊙ **Student Edition on Audio CD**

Differentiated Instruction

Gifted and Talented L3
Modeling the Function of Meiosis
Provide various art materials to students, and challenge them to illustrate what might happen if sex cells did not have half the number of chromosomes in body cells. Have groups present their models to the class and explain why sex cells have half the chromosomes of body cells. **learning modality: visual**

Special Needs L1
Visualizing Chromosomes Show a picture of a cell and point out the chromosomes. Diagram two cells, each with one pair of chromosomes. Work backward to show how one chromosome came from the mother and one from the father. Point out the location of a gene. Show how it can have two alleles. **learning modality: visual**

Monitor Progress _____ L2

Drawing Have students draw a diagram of a grasshopper body cell and sex cell and show the number of chromosomes in each of these cells.

Answers
Figure 12 Chromosomes carry genes from parents to offspring.

 Paired alleles are carried on paired chromosomes.

127

Meiosis

Help Students Read L2

Use Prior Knowledge Students absorb new material more quickly when they can relate it to previously learned concepts. Before they read about meiosis, have them write a paragraph explaining the steps in mitosis. As they read about meiosis, have them compare and contrast mitosis with meiosis, using what they have written.

Teach Key Concepts L2

Events in Meiosis

Focus Remind students that sex cells have half the number of chromosomes as body cells.

Teach Refer students to Figure 13. Point out that before meiosis occurs, every chromosome is copied, so the cell has four copies of each chromosome. Ask: **What happens during Meiosis I?** (*The chromosome pairs separate into two different cells.*) **What happens during Meiosis II?** (*The centromeres split and the chromosome copies separate.*) **How many sex cells are produced at the end of the meiosis?** (*Four*) **How do the sex cells differ from the parent cell?** (*The sex cells have half the number of chromosomes of the parent cell.*)

Apply Ask: **How is meiosis similar to mitosis?** (*Chromosomes are copied and line up to move to opposite sides of the cell. The cell divides.*) **Different?** (*In meiosis, the body cell divides twice, producing 4 sex cells that have half the number of chromosomes of the original body cell. Mitosis produces only 2 body cells, each with the same number of chromosomes as the parent cell.*) **learning modality: visual**

All in One Teaching Resources, Unit 1

• Transparency LS39

FIGURE 13
Meiosis

During meiosis, a cell produces sex cells with half the number of chromosomes. **Interpreting Diagrams** *What happens before meiosis?*

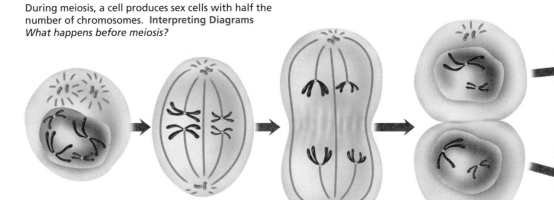

❶ Before Meiosis
Before meiosis begins, every chromosome in the parent cell is copied. Centromeres hold the two chromatids together.

❷ Meiosis I
A The chromosome pairs line up in the center of the cell.

B The pairs separate and move to opposite ends of the cell.

C Two cells form, each with half the number of chromosomes. Each chromosome still has two chromatids.

Meiosis

How do sex cells end up with half the number of chromosomes as body cells? To answer this question, you need to understand the events that occur during meiosis. **Meiosis** (my OH sis) is the process by which the number of chromosomes is reduced by half to form sex cells—sperm and eggs.

What Happens During Meiosis You can trace the events of meiosis in Figure 13. In this example, each parent cell has four chromosomes arranged in two pairs. **During meiosis, the chromosome pairs separate and are distributed to two different cells. The resulting sex cells have only half as many chromosomes as the other cells in the organism.** The sex cells end up with only two chromosomes each—half the number found in the parent cell. Each sex cell has one chromosome from each original pair.

When sex cells combine to form an organism, each sex cell contributes half the normal number of chromosomes. Thus, the offspring gets the normal number of chromosomes—half from each parent.

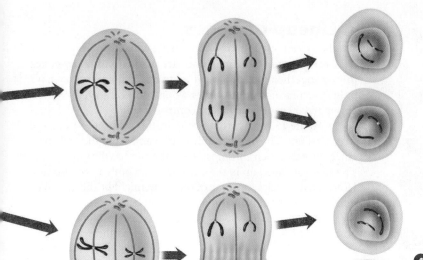

3 **Meiosis II**

A The chromosomes with their two chromatids move to the center of the cell.

B The centromeres split, and the chromatids separate. Single chromosomes move to opposite ends of the cell.

4 **End of Meiosis**
Four sex cells have been produced. Each cell has only half the number of chromosomes that the parent cell had at the beginning of meiosis. Each cell has only one chromosome from each original pair.

Modeling Chromosomes During Meiosis

Materials 8 pipe cleaners (4 of one color and 4 of another), 4 beads

Time 15 minutes

Focus Review the steps in meiosis.

Teach Challenge students to model the steps in meiosis using the pipe cleaners to represent two chromosomes in a cell. Students use pipe cleaners of the same color to represent chromosome pairs, with different chromosome pairs having different colors. Monitor students to make sure they double each chromosome before meiosis begins by adding another pipe cleaner of the same color to each pipe cleaner chromosome. Students can use beads to hold the chromosome copies together or twist the pipe cleaners together at one point. Make sure students separate the chromosome pairs during Meiosis I and the chromosome copies during Meiosis II.

Apply Have students use pipe cleaners to model mitosis. Have them compare the number of total chromosomes that result in meiosis vs. mitosis. *(The total number of chromosomes that results is the same. However, they are distributed in the resulting cells in different ways. In meiosis, the result is 8 chromosomes distributed into 4 sex cells. In mitosis, the result is 8 chromosomes distributed into 2 body cells.)* **learning modality: kinesthetic**

Meiosis and Punnett Squares A Punnett square is actually a way to show the events that occur at meiosis. When the chromosome pairs separate and go into two different sex cells, so do the alleles carried on each chromosome. One allele from each pair goes to each sex cell.

In Figure 14, you can see how the Punnett square accounts for the separation of alleles during meiosis. As shown across the top of the Punnett square, half of the sperm cells from the male parent will receive the chromosome with the *T* allele. The other half of the sperm cells will receive the chromosome with the *t* allele. In this example, the same is true for the egg cells from the female parent, as shown down the left side of the Punnett square. Depending on which sperm cell combines with which egg cell, one of the allele combinations shown in the boxes will result.

FIGURE 14
Meiosis Punnett Square
Both parents are heterozygous for the trait of stem height. The Punnett square shows the possible allele combinations after fertilization.

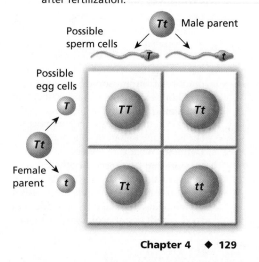

Differentiated Instruction

English Learners/Beginning L1
Comprehension: Link to Visual
Pair beginners with more advanced English learners. Have the pairs of students go over each step in Figure 13, with the more advanced student helping the beginner understand what goes on in each step. The beginner can make sketches and take notes in his or her first language.
learning modality: visual

English Learners/Intermediate L2
Comprehension: Link to Visual
Have students prepare two-column written explanations of each step in meiosis as shown in Figure 13. The first column should explain each step in the student's first language. The second column should have a corresponding explanation in English. The student can make a copy of this two-column explanation to share with a beginner.
learning modality: visual

Monitor Progress _____ L2

Writing Have students write an outline of meiosis in which each major step is a main heading in the outline. Students can save their outlines in their portfolios.

Portfolio

Answer
Figure 13 Every chromosome in the cell is copied.

A Lineup of Genes

Teach Key Concepts L2
Chromosomes and Genes

Focus Refer students to Figure 15.

Teach Ask: **How are chromosomes and genes related?** (*Chromosomes are made up of many genes joined together.*)

Apply Have students show two ways to make a chromosome pair heterozygous for all genes. **learning modality: visual**

Monitor Progress _____ L2
Answer
Figure 15 Homozygous: C, e, F, G, I; Heterozygous: A, B, D, H

Assess

Reviewing Key Concepts
1. a. Body cells have twice the number of chromosomes (24) as sex cells (12). **b.** The fertilized egg gets 24 chromosomes. **c.** Just as the offspring get one allele from each parent for every gene, the offspring get half their chromosomes from one parent and half from the other parent.
2. a. The process by which the number of chromosomes is reduced by half to form sex cells **b.** Meiosis I: The duplicate chromosomes divide into two cells, each with half the number of chromosomes. Meiosis II: The two cells divide once more, producing sex cells that have half as many chromosomes as the body cells. **c.** In meiosis I, the members of each chromosome pair separate and end up in different cells.
3. a. They are joined together like beads on a string. **b.** They are lined up in the same order on both chromosomes.

Reteach L1
Have students sketch the stages of meiosis on separate pieces of paper, then exchange with a partner. Each student should then put the sketches in order.

All in One Teaching Resources, Unit 1
- Section Summary: *The Cell and Inheritance*
- Review and Reinforce: *The Cell and Inheritance*
- Enrich: *The Cell and Inheritance*

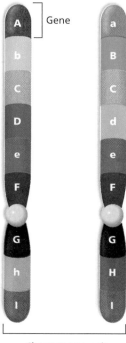

Gene

A Lineup of Genes
The body cells of humans contain 23 chromosome pairs, or 46 chromosomes. **Chromosomes are made up of many genes joined together like beads on a string.** Although you have only 23 pairs of chromosomes, your body cells each contain about 35,000 genes. Each gene controls a trait.

In Figure 15, one chromosome in the pair came from the female parent. The other chromosome came from the male parent. Notice that each chromosome in the pair has the same genes. The genes are lined up in the same order on both chromosomes. However, the alleles for some of the genes might be different. For example, the organism has the *A* allele on one chromosome and the *a* allele on the other. As you can see, this organism is heterozygous for some traits and homozygous for others.

FIGURE 15
Genes on Chromosomes
Genes are located on chromosomes. The chromosomes in a pair may have different alleles for some genes and the same alleles for others.
Classifying *For which genes is this organism homozygous? For which genes is it heterozygous?*

Chromosome pair

Section 3 Assessment

🎯 **Target Reading Skill** Identifying Supporting Evidence Refer to your graphic organizer about the chromosome theory of inheritance as you answer Question 1 below.

Reviewing Key Concepts
1. a. Comparing and Contrasting According to Sutton's observations, how does the number of chromosomes in a grasshopper's body cells compare to the number in its sex cells?
   b. Describing Describe what happens to the number of chromosomes when two grasshopper sex cells join in fertilization.
   c. Explaining How do Sutton's observations about chromosome number support the chromosome theory of inheritance?
2. a. Defining What is meiosis?
   b. Interpreting Diagrams Briefly describe meiosis I and meiosis II. Refer to Figure 13.
   c. Sequencing Use the events of meiosis to explain why a sex cell normally does not receive both chromosomes from a pair.

3. a. Describing How are genes arranged on a chromosome?
   b. Comparing and Contrasting How does the order of genes in one member of a chromosome pair compare to the order of genes on the other chromosome?

Writing in Science

Newspaper Interview You are a newspaper reporter in the early 1900s. You want to interview Walter Sutton about his work with chromosomes. Write three questions you would like to ask Sutton. Then, for each question, write answers that Sutton might have given.

130 ◆

Lab zone Chapter Project

Keep Students on Track Students will determine the traits inherited from each parent for six offspring by using a coin toss. They will write a genotype for each trait on each parent's back. Then they will construct a paper pet for each offspring, showing the traits that each one has inherited.

Writing in Science

Writing Mode Questions and answers
Scoring Rubric
4 Includes complete description of Sutton's work and is written in the format of an interview with the scientist; questions require critical thinking
3 Includes all criteria, but questions are low-level comprehension type
2 Includes only two questions
1 Includes inaccurate information

Reading Preview

Key Concepts
- What forms the genetic code?
- How does a cell produce proteins?
- How can mutations affect an organism?

Key Terms
- messenger RNA
- transfer RNA
- mutation

Target Reading Skill

Sequencing A sequence is the order in which the steps in a process occur. As you read, make a flowchart that shows protein synthesis. Put the steps of the process in separate boxes in the flowchart in the order in which they occur.

Protein Synthesis

DNA provides code to form messenger RNA.

↓

Messenger RNA attaches to ribosome.

↓

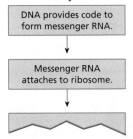

Lab zone Discover **Activity**

Can You Crack the Code?

1. Use the Morse code in the chart to decode the question in the message below. The letters are separated by slash marks.

• – – / • • • • / • / • – • / • / • – / • – • /
• / – – • / • / – • / • / • • • / • – • • / – – – /
– • – • / • – / – / • • / – • •

2. Write your answer to the question in Morse code.

3. Exchange your coded answer with a partner. Then decode your partner's answer.

Think It Over

Forming Operational Definitions Based on your results from this activity, write a definition of the word *code*. Then compare your definition to one in a dictionary.

A • –	N – •
B – • • •	O – – –
C – • – •	P • – – •
D – • •	Q – – • –
E •	R • – •
F • • – •	S • • •
G – – •	T –
H • • • •	U • • –
I • •	V • • • –
J • – – –	W • – –
K – • –	X – • • –
L • – • •	Y – • – –
M – –	Z – – • •

The young, white, ring-tailed lemur in the photograph below was born in a forest in southern Madagascar. White lemurs are extremely rare. Why was this lemur born with such an uncommon phenotype? To answer this question, you need to know how the genes on a chromosome control an organism's traits.

A white lemur and its mother ▶

◆ 131

Section 4

The DNA Connection

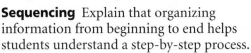

Objectives
After this lesson, students will be able to

4.4.1 Explain what forms the genetic code.

4.4.2 Describe how a cell produces proteins.

4.4.3 Identify how mutations can affect an organism.

Target Reading Skill

Sequencing Explain that organizing information from beginning to end helps students understand a step-by-step process.

Answers
Possible way to complete the graphic organizer:

DNA provides code to form messenger RNA.

↓

Messenger RNA attaches to ribosome.

↓

Transfer RNA "reads" the messenger RNA.

↓

Amino acids are added to the growing protein.

All in One Teaching Resources, Unit 1
- Transparency LS40

Preteach

Build Background Knowledge

Genes and Traits
Invite students to recall what they have learned about inheritance, DNA, and cell division up to this point. Then ask: **How do genes determine the traits of an organism?** *(Accept all answers without comment.)* Explain that students will learn more about this process in the section.

Lab zone Discover **Activity**

Skills Focus Forming operational definitions

Time 15 minutes

Tips Some students may require extra help in deciphering the code; you may want to pair students.

Expected Outcome The coded question is "Where are genes located?" The answer, "on chromosomes," is encoded here:

L2 – – – / – • / – • • • / • • • • / • – – / – – – / – – – /
• • • / – – – / – – / • / • / • • • /

Think It Over Students might define *code* as a set of symbols with specific meanings used to send messages. Some dictionaries define *code* as a system of symbols, letters, or words given arbitrary meanings, used for transmitting messages requiring secrecy or brevity.

The Genetic Code

Help Students Read L1

Think Aloud Refer to the Content Refresher for guidelines on Think Aloud. Read the paragraphs on the genetic code aloud. As you read, pause and make a prediction, for example, you might predict that DNA provides the information to make proteins. Describe mental pictures of the order of the bases, and sketch them on the board. Ask students to stop you at any point at which they are confused so that the meaning can be clarified. Then have students read the next passage silently and apply the strategies you modeled. Ask students to share their strategies with the class.

Teach Key Concepts L2

How the Genetic Code Works

Focus Have students recall that chromosomes are made of genes.

Teach Ask: **What are chromosomes composed of?** *(DNA)* **What are genes?** *(Sections of a DNA molecule)* Refer students to Figure 16. Ask: **What forms the rungs of the DNA ladder?** *(The nitrogen bases adenine, thymine, guanine, and cytosine)* **Why is the sequence of bases important?** *(The sequence forms a code that tells the cell what protein to produce.)*

Apply Ask: **How are the nitrogen bases of DNA like the letters of the alphabet?** *(Like groups of letters that make up specific words, a group of three bases indicates a specific amino acid.)* **learning modality: logical/ mathematical**

Independent Practice

All in One Teaching Resources, Unit 1

- Guided Reading and Study Worksheet: *The DNA Connection*

🔘 **Student Edition on Audio CD**

The Genetic Code

The main function of genes is to control the production of proteins in an organism's cells. Proteins help to determine the size, shape, color, and many other traits of an organism.

Genes and DNA Recall that chromosomes are composed mostly of DNA. In Figure 16, you can see the relationship between chromosomes and DNA. Notice that a DNA molecule is made up of four different nitrogen bases—adenine (A), thymine (T), guanine (G), and cytosine (C). These bases form the rungs of the DNA "ladder."

A gene is a section of a DNA molecule that contains the information to code for one specific protein. A gene is made up of a series of bases in a row. The bases in a gene are arranged in a specific order—for example, ATGACGTAC. A single gene on a chromosome may contain anywhere from several hundred to a million or more of these bases. Each gene is located at a specific place on a chromosome.

Order of the Bases A gene contains the code that determines the structure of a protein. **The order of the nitrogen bases along a gene forms a genetic code that specifies what type of protein will be produced.** Remember that proteins are long-chain molecules made of individual amino acids. In the genetic code, a group of three DNA bases codes for one specific amino acid. For example, the base sequence CGT (cytosine-guanine-thymine) always codes for the amino acid alanine. The order of the three-base code units determines the order in which amino acids are put together to form a protein.

FIGURE 16
The DNA Code

Chromosomes are made of DNA. Each chromosome contains thousands of genes. The sequence of bases in a gene forms a code that tells the cell what protein to produce. **Interpreting Diagrams** *Where in the cell are chromosomes located?*

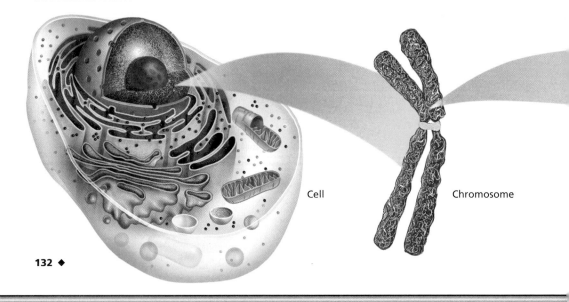

Cell   Chromosome

132 ◆

Differentiated Instruction

**Less Proficient Readers L3
Understanding DNA and RNA**
Provide students with the section on Student Edition on Audio CD and a copy of the passage The Genetic Code. Have them listen to this passage as they read along and highlight key phrases and sentences that explain the relationships

among genes, chromosomes, and DNA. Then pair students with more proficient readers. Have them construct a concept map that includes and defines the terms *gene, chromosome, DNA, genetic code, nitrogen base,* and other words. **learning modality: verbal**

How Cells Make Proteins

The production of proteins is called protein synthesis. **During protein synthesis, the cell uses information from a gene on a chromosome to produce a specific protein.** Protein synthesis takes place on the ribosomes in the cytoplasm of a cell. As you know, the cytoplasm is outside the nucleus. The chromosomes, however, are found inside the nucleus. How, then, does the information needed to produce proteins get out of the nucleus and into the cytoplasm?

The Role of RNA Before protein synthesis can take place, a "messenger" must first carry the genetic code from the DNA inside the nucleus into the cytoplasm. This genetic messenger is called ribonucleic acid, or RNA.

Although RNA is similar to DNA, the two molecules differ in some important ways. Unlike DNA, which has two strands, RNA has only one strand. RNA also contains a different sugar molecule from the sugar found in DNA. Another difference between DNA and RNA is in their nitrogen bases. Like DNA, RNA contains adenine, guanine, and cytosine. However, instead of thymine, RNA contains uracil (YOOR uh sil).

Types of RNA There are several types of RNA involved in protein synthesis. **Messenger RNA** copies the coded message from the DNA in the nucleus, and carries the message to the ribosome in the cytoplasm. Another type of RNA, called **transfer RNA,** carries amino acids to the ribosome and adds them to the growing protein.

> **Reading Checkpoint** How is RNA different from DNA?

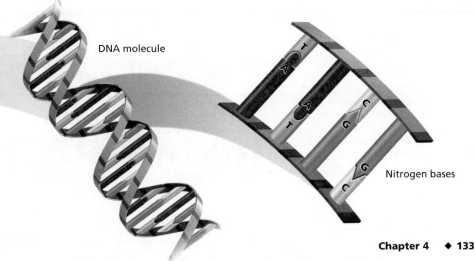

DNA molecule

Nitrogen bases

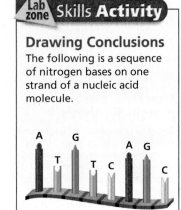

Lab zone Skills **Activity**

Skills Focus Drawing conclusions

Time 5 minutes

Tips You may wish to have students reread the passage The Role of RNA to help them answer the question.

Expected Outcome The strand comes from DNA because it contains thymine.

Extend Ask: **What base would the strand contain if it were RNA?** *(Uracil instead of thymine)* **What RNA bases would pair with this strand of DNA?** (A U G U C A G C) **learning modality: verbal**

Lab zone Build **Inquiry** L1

Modeling the Genetic Code

Materials various craft materials, such as yarn, construction paper, tape, markers, pipe cleaners, and beads

Time 20 minutes

Focus Remind students that particular base sequences code for specific proteins.

Teach Challenge groups of students to make a model of DNA and invent a code in which base sequences stand for words. When the sequences are in order, the words make a sentence.

Apply Ask: **What would happen to your sentence if the order of the base sequences were changed?** *(The sentence might not make sense.)* **learning modality: kinesthetic**

How Cells Make Proteins

Teach Key Concepts L2
Understanding Protein Synthesis

Focus Ask: **What do genes code for?** *(The production of proteins)*

Teach Ask: **What happens during protein synthesis?** *(The cell uses information from a gene on a chromosome to produce a specific protein.)* **What is the role of messenger RNA?** *(To copy the coded message from the DNA in the nucleus and carry the message to the ribosome in the cytoplasm)* **Transfer RNA?** *(To carry amino acids to the ribosome and add them to the growing protein chain)*

Apply Ask students to infer why proteins are made in the cytoplasm instead of the nucleus. *(The cytoplasm has ribosomes, which are needed to carry out protein synthesis.)* **learning modality: verbal**

Monitor Progress _____ L2

Oral Presentation Call on students to describe the role and types of RNA.

Answers
Figure 16 In the nucleus

> **Reading Checkpoint** RNA has only one strand; it has a different sugar molecule; instead of thymine, it contains uracil.

Use Visuals: Figure 17 L2
Visualizing Protein Synthesis

Focus Review the definitions of messenger RNA and transfer RNA.

Teach Direct students' attention to Step 1. Point out that DNA always stays inside the cell nucleus. Ask: **What is the first step in protein synthesis?** *(For the strands of the DNA molecule to separate)* **Why is this important?** *(The messenger RNA bases have to pair up with a single strand of DNA to form the messenger RNA strand.)* **What does the messenger RNA do in Step 2?** *(It leaves the nucleus, enters the cytoplasm, attaches to a ribosome, and provides the code for the protein molecule.)* **In Step 3, how is a protein chain formed?** *(Molecules of transfer RNA pick up the amino acids specified by each three-letter code. Each transfer RNA molecule puts the amino acid it is carrying in the correct order along the growing protein chain.)* Explain that in Step 4, more than one ribosome can attach to a single messenger RNA at one time.

Apply Ask: **Why is it important that protein synthesis be so carefully organized and carried out?** *(Proteins determine many traits of an organism and how that organism will function.)* **learning modality: visual**

All in One Teaching Resources, Unit 1

• Transparency LS41

Translating the Code The process of protein synthesis is shown in Figure 17. Look at the illustration as you read the following steps.

❶ The first step is for a DNA molecule to "unzip" between its base pairs. Then one of the strands of DNA directs the production of a strand of messenger RNA. To form the RNA strand, RNA bases pair up with the DNA bases. The process is similar to the process in which DNA replicates. Cytosine always pairs with guanine. However, uracil—not thymine— pairs with adenine.

❷ The messenger RNA then leaves the nucleus and enters the cytoplasm. In the cytoplasm, messenger RNA attaches to a ribosome. On the ribosome, the messenger RNA provides the code for the protein molecule that will form. During protein synthesis, the ribosome moves along the messenger RNA strand.

FIGURE 17
Protein Synthesis

To make proteins, messenger RNA copies information from DNA in the nucleus. Messenger RNA and transfer RNA then use this information to produce proteins. **Interpreting Diagrams** *In which organelle of the cell are proteins manufactured?*

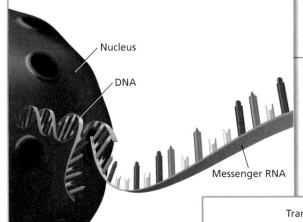

❶ **Messenger RNA Production ▲**
In the nucleus, a DNA molecule serves as a "pattern" for making messenger RNA. The DNA molecule "unzips" between base pairs. RNA bases match up along one of the DNA strands. The genetic information in the DNA is transferred to the messenger RNA strand.

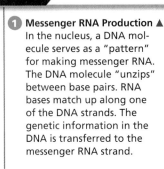

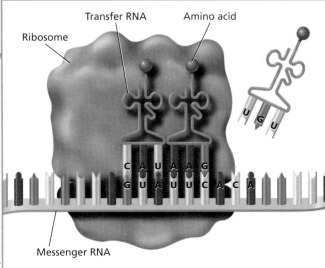

❷ **Messenger RNA Attaches to a Ribosome ▼**
When the messenger RNA enters the cytoplasm, it attaches to a ribosome, where production of the protein chain begins. The ribosome moves along the messenger RNA strand.

Molecules of transfer RNA attach to the messenger RNA. The bases on the transfer RNA "read" the message by pairing up three-letter codes to bases on the messenger RNA. For example, you can see that a molecule of transfer RNA with the bases AAG pairs with the bases UUC on the messenger RNA. The molecules of transfer RNA carry specific amino acids. The amino acids link in a chain. The order of the amino acids in the chain is determined by the order of the three-letter codes on the messenger RNA.

 The protein molecule grows longer as each transfer RNA molecule puts the amino acid it is carrying along the growing protein chain. Once an amino acid is added to the protein chain, the transfer RNA is released into the cytoplasm and can pick up another amino acid. Each transfer RNA molecule always picks up the same kind of amino acid.

Reading Checkpoint What is the function of transfer RNA?

Go Online
active art

For: Protein Synthesis activity
Visit: PHSchool.com
Web Code: cep-3034

❸ Transfer RNA Attaches to Messenger RNA ▼
Transfer RNA molecules carry specific amino acids to the ribosome. There they "read" the message in messenger RNA by matching up with three-letter codes of bases. The protein chain grows as each amino acid is attached.

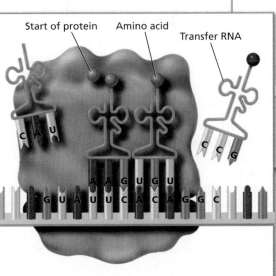

Start of protein   Amino acid   Transfer RNA

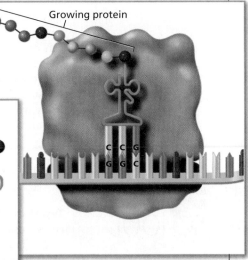

Growing protein

❹ Protein Production Continues ▲
The protein chain continues to grow until the ribosome reaches a three-letter code that acts as a stop sign. The ribosome then releases the completed protein.

Chapter 4   ◆   135

— Differentiated Instruction —

Gifted and Talented   **L3**
Researching the Causes of Cancer
Explain that cancer is a disease in which DNA is damaged, and body cells grow out of control. Some types of cancer are inherited, but most are thought to develop as a result of exposure to cancer-causing agents or random events in a cell. Ask

interested students to research how these agents damage DNA: tobacco, ultraviolet light, and the hepatitis B virus. These agents cause the majority of lung, skin, and liver cancers, respectively. Have students report their results to the class and describe behaviors to reduce the risk of these cancers.   **learning modality: verbal**

Lab zone   Build Inquiry   **L2**

Modeling Protein Synthesis

Materials various craft materials
Time 20 minutes

Focus Summarize the steps in protein synthesis on the board.

Teach Challenge groups of students to make a "human" model of protein synthesis by having members assume the roles of DNA, messenger RNA, transfer RNA, and a ribosome. Students may use craft materials for props and to identify themselves. Ask groups to present their models to the class and explain what is happening in each step.

Apply Ask: **How are molecules of transfer RNA like workers in a factory?** (*Each type of transfer RNA has a different job in the making of proteins.*) **learning modality: kinesthetic**

Monitor Progress   **L2**

Writing Have students write instructions to a cell on how to make proteins. Instructions should include the roles of messenger RNA and transfer RNA, and the cell structures involved in protein synthesis. Students may place their instructions in their portfolio.

Answers
Figure 17 The ribosome

Reading Checkpoint To carry amino acids and add them to the growing protein chain

Mutations

Genetics: The Science of Heredity

Show the Video Field Trip to let students understand human genes and DNA.

Teach Key Concepts **L2**

How Mutations Affect an Organism

Focus Remind students that protein synthesis is a very precise process.

Teach Ask: **In what ways can a mistake be made in this process?** (*A single base may be substituted, added, or deleted during replication; chromosomes may not separate correctly during meiosis.*) **What are these mistakes called?** (*Mutations*) **How can mutations affect an organism?** (*They can be helpful or harmful depending on the environment.*)

Apply Have students make models of the mutations shown in the text and show why mutations in body cells do not affect offspring. **learning modality: kinesthetic**

All in One Teaching Resources, Unit 1
• Transparency LS42

Address Misconceptions **L1**

Mutations Can Be Harmless or Helpful

Focus Some students may think that mutations can be only harmful.

Teach Ask a student to read the last paragraph under "Effects of Mutations" aloud. Explain what antibiotic resistance is. Ask: **How are the mutations that produce antibiotic resistance helpful to bacteria?** (*They enable bacteria to survive in the presence of antibiotics.*)

Apply Ask: **What kind of mutation might help an animal survive in a desert?** (*Possible answer: a mutation that reduced the animal's need for water.*) **learning modality: visual**

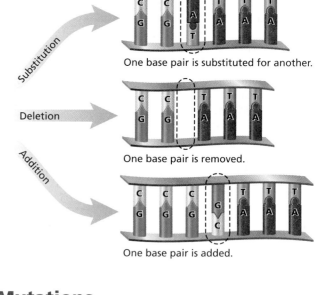

Substitution — One base pair is substituted for another.

Deletion — One base pair is removed.

Addition — One base pair is added.

Original DNA sequence

FIGURE 18
Mutations in Genes
The illustration shows three types of mutations that can occur in genes. *Comparing and Contrasting How are these mutations different from the mutations that occur when chromosomes do not separate during meiosis?*

Mutations

Suppose that a mistake occurred in one gene of a chromosome. Instead of the base A, for example, the DNA molecule might have the base G. Such a mistake is one type of mutation that can occur in a cell's hereditary material. A **mutation** is any change in a gene or chromosome. **Mutations can cause a cell to produce an incorrect protein during protein synthesis. As a result, the organism's trait, or phenotype, may be different from what it normally would have been.** In fact, the term *mutation* comes from a Latin word that means "change."

If a mutation occurs in a body cell, such as a skin cell, the mutation will not be passed on to the organism's offspring. If, however, a mutation occurs in a sex cell, the mutation can be passed on to an offspring and affect the offspring's phenotype.

Types of Mutations Some mutations are the result of small changes in an organism's hereditary material. For example, a single base may be substituted for another, or one or more bases may be removed from a section of DNA. This type of mutation can occur during the DNA replication process. Other mutations may occur when chromosomes don't separate correctly during meiosis. When this type of mutation occurs, a cell can end up with too many or too few chromosomes. The cell could also end up with extra segments of chromosomes.

Effects of Mutations Because mutations can introduce changes in an organism, they can be a source of genetic variety. Some mutations are harmful to an organism. A few mutations, however, are helpful, and others are neither harmful nor helpful. A mutation is harmful to an organism if it reduces the organism's chance for survival and reproduction.

Whether a mutation is harmful or not depends partly on the organism's environment. The mutation that led to the production of a white lemur would probably be harmful to an organism in the wild. The lemur's white color would make it more visible, and thus easier for predators to find. However, a white lemur in a zoo has the same chance for survival as a brown lemur. In a zoo, the mutation neither helps nor harms the lemur.

Helpful mutations, on the other hand, improve an organism's chances for survival and reproduction. Antibiotic resistance in bacteria is an example. Antibiotics are chemicals that kill bacteria. Gene mutations have enabled some kinds of bacteria to become resistant to certain antibiotics—that is, the antibiotics do not kill the bacteria that have the mutations. The mutations have improved the bacteria's ability to survive and reproduce.

 Reading Checkpoint What are two types of mutations?

FIGURE 19
Six-Toed Cat
Because of a mutation in one of its ancestors, this cat has six toes on each front paw.

Section 4 Assessment

🎯 **Target Reading Skill** Sequencing Refer to your flowchart as you answer Question 2.

Reviewing Key Concepts

1. a. **Explaining** What is the relationship between a gene, a DNA molecule, and a protein?
   b. **Relating Cause and Effect** How does a DNA molecule determine the structure of a specific protein?
   c. **Inferring** The DNA base sequence GGG codes for the amino acid proline. Could this same base sequence code for a different amino acid? Why or why not?
2. a. **Listing** List the sequence of events that happens during protein synthesis.
   b. **Describing** What is messenger RNA? Describe how it performs its function.

   c. **Inferring** Does transfer RNA perform its function in the nucleus or cytoplasm? Explain your answer.
3. a. **Reviewing** How does a mutation in a gene affect the order of DNA bases?
   b. **Relating Cause and Effect** How can a mutation in a gene cause a change in an organism's phenotype?

Writing in Science

Compare/Contrast Paragraph Write a paragraph comparing and contrasting gene mutations and chromosome mutations. In your paragraph, explain what the two types of mutations are, and how they are similar and different.

Chapter 4 ◆ 137

Study Guide

interactive Textbook

- Complete student edition
- Section and chapter self-assessments
- Assessment reports for teachers

Help Students Read

Building Vocabulary

Word-Part Analysis Show students that the term *homozygous* is made up of the Greek words *homos,* meaning "same" and *zygos,* meaning "yoked" or "paired." Taken together, these words describe a cell formed from two gametes that have the same genetic makeup. In *heterozygous, heteros* is the Greek word meaning "other" or "different." This word describes a cell formed from two gametes that have a different genetic makeup.

Words in Context Select Key Terms from the chapter. Have students write a sentence for each term that places the term in a correct context. Provide them with one example before they begin: *Gene: A gene contains instructions for making proteins.*

Connecting Concepts

Concept Maps Help students develop one way to show how the information in this chapter is related. The inheritance of traits is determined by genes that are passed from parents to offspring in a predictable manner and that carry instructions for the synthesis of proteins. Have students brainstorm to identify the Key Concepts, Key Terms, details, and examples, and then write each one on a sticky note and attach it at random on chart paper or on the board.

Tell students that this concept map will be organized in hierarchical order and to begin at the top with the Key Concepts. Ask students these questions to guide them to categorize the information on the stickies: **What controls the inheritance of traits in organisms? How does probability help explain the results of a genetic cross? How does a cell produce proteins?**

① Mendel's Work

Key Concepts

- In all of Mendel's crosses, only one form of the trait appeared in the F_1 generation. However, in the F_2 generation, the "lost" form of the trait always reappeared in about one fourth of the plants.
- An organism's traits are controlled by the alleles it inherits from its parents. Some alleles are dominant, while other alleles are recessive.

Key Terms

heredity	gene
trait	alleles
genetics	dominant allele
fertilization	recessive allele
purebred	hybrid

② Probability and Heredity

Key Concepts

- Probability is the likelihood that a particular event will occur.
- In a genetic cross, the allele that each parent will pass on to its offspring is based on probability.
- An organism's phenotype is its physical appearance, or visible traits. An organism's genotype is its genetic makeup, or allele combinations.
- In codominance, the alleles are neither dominant nor recessive. As a result, both alleles are expressed in the offspring.

Key Terms

probability
Punnett square
phenotype
genotype
homozygous
heterozygous
codominance

③ The Cell and Inheritance

Key Concepts

- According to the chromosome theory of inheritance, genes are carried from parents to their offspring on chromosomes.
- During meiosis, the chromosome pairs separate and are distributed to two different cells. The resulting sex cells have only half as many chromosomes as the other cells in the organism.
- Chromosomes are made up of many genes joined together like beads on a string.

Key Term

meiosis

④ The DNA Connection

Key Concepts

- The order of the nitrogen bases along a gene forms a genetic code that specifies what type of protein will be produced.
- During protein synthesis, the cell uses information from a gene on a chromosome to produce a specific protein.
- Mutations can cause a cell to produce an incorrect protein during protein synthesis. As a result, the organism's trait, or phenotype, may be different from what it normally would have been.

Key Terms

messenger RNA
transfer RNA
mutation

Prompt students by using connecting words or phrases, such as "was revolutionized by," "which have the same," and "which show all the possible combinations of," to indicate the basis for the organization of the map. The phrases should form a sentence between or among a set of concepts.

Answer

Accept logical presentations by students.

All in One Teaching Resources, Unit 1

- Key Terms Review: *Genetics: The Science of Heredity*
- Connecting Concepts: *Genetics: The Science of Heredity*

Review and Assessment

Go Online
PHSchool.com

For: Self-Assessment
Visit: PHSchool.com
Web Code: cea-3030

Organizing Information

Concept Mapping Copy the concept map onto a separate sheet of paper. Then complete the concept map. (For more on Concept Mapping, see the Skills Handbook.)

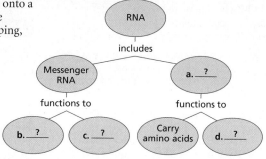

Reviewing Key Terms

Choose the letter of the best answer.

1. The different forms of a gene are called
   a. alleles.   b. chromosomes.
   c. phenotypes.   d. genotypes.

2. The likelihood that a particular event will occur is called
   a. chance.
   b. Punnett square.
   c. probability.
   d. recessive.

3. An organism with two identical alleles for a trait is
   a. heterozygous.
   b. homozygous.
   c. recessive.
   d. dominant.

4. If the body cells of an organism have 10 chromosomes, then the sex cells produced during meiosis would have
   a. 5 chromosomes.
   b. 10 chromosomes.
   c. 15 chromosomes.
   d. 20 chromosomes.

5. During protein synthesis, messenger RNA
   a. links one amino acid to another.
   b. releases the completed protein chain.
   c. provides a code from DNA in the nucleus.
   d. carries amino acids to the ribosome.

If the statement is true, write *true*. If it is false, change the underlined word or words to make the statement true.

6. The scientific study of heredity is called <u>genetics</u>.

7. An organism's physical appearance is its <u>genotype</u>.

8. In <u>codominance</u>, neither of the alleles is dominant or recessive.

9. Each transfer RNA molecule picks up one kind of <u>protein</u>.

10. Mutations in <u>body cells</u> are passed to offspring.

Writing in Science

Science Article You are a science reporter for a newspaper. Write an article about gene mutations. Explain what a mutation is and what determines whether it is helpful or harmful.

Discovery CHANNEL **SCHOOL**

Genetics: The Science of Heredity
Video Preview
Video Field Trip
▶ Video Assessment

Review and Assessment

Organizing Information

a. Transfer RNA
b. Copy the coded message from the DNA
c. Carry the message to the ribosome in the cytoplasm
d. Add amino acids to the growing protein

Reviewing Key Terms

1. a 2. c 3. b 4. a 5. c
6. true
7. phenotype
8. true
9. amino acid
10. sex cells

Writing in Science

Writing Mode Description

Scoring Rubric

4 Includes definition of a mutation and what determines whether it is helpful or harmful; goes beyond requirements to explain details of the two types of mutations

3 Includes criteria but does not go beyond requirements to include the types of mutations

2 Includes only part of the criteria

1 Includes inaccurate information

Go Online
PHSchool.com

For: Self-Assessment
Visit: PHSchool.com
Web Code: cea-3030

Students can take a practice test online that is automatically scored.

All in One Teaching Resources, Unit 1
- Transparency LS43
- Chapter Test
- Performance Assessment Teacher Notes
- Performance Assessment Student Worksheet
- Performance Assessment Scoring Rubric

 **ExamView® Computer Test Bank CD-ROM**

Checking Concepts

11. All the first generation offspring were tall.

12. There is a 1 in 2, or 50% chance, that the coin will land heads up on the sixth toss because each coin toss is an independent event. The result of one toss does not affect the following coin tosses.

13. There is a 50 percent (2 in 4) chance that an offspring will have a white coat (*bb*). The Punnett square should look like the following:

	B	b
b	Bb	bb
b	Bb	bb

14. Transfer RNA carries the amino acid that corresponds to the code in the messenger RNA and adds it to the growing protein chain.

15. Mutations can cause a cell to produce an incorrect protein during protein synthesis by the substitution of a single base for another, or by adding or removing one or more bases from a section of DNA.

Review and Assessment

Checking Concepts

11. Describe what happened when Mendel crossed purebred tall pea plants with purebred short pea plants.

12. You toss a coin five times and it lands heads up each time. What is the probability that it will land heads up on the sixth toss? Explain your answer.

13. In guinea pigs, the allele for black fur (*B*) is dominant over the allele for white fur (*b*). In a cross between a heterozygous black guinea pig (*Bb*) and a homozygous white guinea pig (*bb*), what is the probability that an offspring will have white fur? Use a Punnett square to answer the question.

14. Describe the role of transfer RNA in protein synthesis.

15. How can mutations affect protein synthesis?

Thinking Critically

16. Applying Concepts In rabbits, the allele for a spotted coat is dominant over the allele for a solid-colored coat. A spotted rabbit was crossed with a solid-colored rabbit. The offspring all had spotted coats. What are the probable genotypes of the parents? Explain.

17. Interpreting Diagrams The diagram below shows a chromosome pair. For which genes is the organism heterozygous?

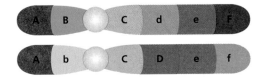

18. Predicting A new mutation in mice causes the coat to be twice as thick as normal. In what environments would this mutation be helpful? Why?

19. Applying Concepts If the body cells have 12 chromosomes, how many will the sex cells have?

20. Relating Cause and Effect Why are mutations that occur in an organism's body cells not passed on to its offspring?

Math Practice

21. Percentage A garden has 80 pea plants. Of the plants, 20 have short stems and 60 have tall stems. What percentage of the plants have short stems? What percentage have tall stems?

Applying Skills

Use the information in the table to answer Questions 22–24.

In peas, the allele for green pods (G) is dominant over the allele for yellow pods (g). The table shows the phenotypes of offspring produced from a cross of two plants with green pods.

Phenotype	Number of Offspring
Green pods	27
Yellow pods	9

22. Calculating Percent Calculate what percent of the offspring produce green pods. Calculate what percent have yellow pods.

23. Inferring What is the genotype of the offspring with yellow pods? What are the possible genotypes of the offspring with green pods?

24. Drawing Conclusions What are the genotypes of the parents? How do you know?

Lab zone Chapter **Project**

Performance Assessment Finalize your display of your pet's family. Be prepared to discuss the inheritance patterns in your pet's family. Examine your classmates' exhibits. See which offspring look most like, and least like, their parents. Can you find any offspring that "break the laws" of inheritance?

Lab zone Chapter **Project**   L3

Performance Assessment Make sure students understand that "breaking the laws" of inheritance refers to proposed inheritance patterns that violate the principles of heredity. This could happen, for example, when students propose that two homozygous recessive parents produce offspring with one or two dominant alleles.

Reflect and Record Encourage students to record how their paper pets helped them understand specific concepts and principles of genetics. For example, students could describe how the inheritance patterns of their paper pets demonstrated the inheritance of dominant and recessive alleles, or showed the relationship between genotype and phenotype.

Standardized Test Prep

Choose the letter of the best answer.

1. Which of the following is the first step in the formation of sex cells in an organism that has eight chromosomes?
- **A** The two chromatids of each chromosome separate.
- **B** Chromosome pairs line up next to each other in the center of the cell.
- **C** The DNA in the eight chromosomes is copied.
- **D** The chromatids move apart, producing cells with four chromosomes each.

The Punnett square below shows a cross between two pea plants, each with round seeds. Use the Punnett square to answer Questions 2–4.

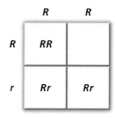

	R	R
R	RR	
r	Rr	Rr

2. The missing genotype in the empty square is correctly written as
- **F** Rr.
- **G** rR.
- **H** rr.
- **J** RR.

3. Which statement is true about the cross shown in the Punnett square?
- **A** Both parents are heterozygous for the trait.
- **B** Both parents are homozygous for the trait.
- **C** One parent is heterozygous and the other is homozygous for the trait.
- **D** The trait is controlled by codominant alleles.

4. What percentage of the offspring of this cross will produce round seeds?
- **F** 0%
- **G** 25%
- **H** 50%
- **J** 100%

5. A section of DNA has the base sequence GCTTAA. The corresponding messenger RNA base sequence will be
- **A** GCTTAA.
- **B** CGAAUU.
- **C** CGAATT.
- **D** UUTTCG.

Constructed Response

6. Compare the processes and outcomes of mitosis and meiosis.

Thinking Critically

16. The solid-colored parent must be homozygous for the recessive allele (*ss*), and the spotted parent is probably homozygous for the dominant allele (*SS*). If the spotted parent were heterozygous (*Ss*), then 50% of the offspring would probably have been solid-colored.

17. B, D, F

18. A thicker coat is a helpful mutation in a very cold environment because it provides extra insulation to keep the mouse warm.

19. Six

20. Mutations in body cells do not affect sex cells. Only sex cells carry alleles to offspring.

Math Practice

21. 25% have short stems, and 75% have tall stems.

Applying Skills

22. 75% green pods; 25% yellow pods

23. Yellow pods: *gg*; green pods: *GG* or *Gg*

24. Both parents are *Gg*. If both parents were *GG*, then none of the offspring would have yellow pods. If one parent were *GG* and the other were *Gg*, then again, none of the offspring would have yellow pods. Neither parent could be *gg*, because both parents have green pods, and *g* is a recessive allele for yellow pods.

Standardized Test Prep

1. C **2.** J **3.** C **4.** J **5.** B

6. Sample answer: In mitosis, a cell divides to form two daughter cells that have sets of chromosomes that are complete and identical to each other and to the parent cell. Mitosis allows an organism's body to grow and replace cells. In meiosis, a cell divides twice to eventually produce cells with half the number of chromosomes as the parent cell. Meiosis is how sex cells are produced.

Chapter **5** **Modern Genetics**

Chapter at a Glance

PRENTICE HALL
Teacher EXPRESS™
Plan • Teach • Assess

  Chapter **Project** *Teach Others About a Trait*

Technology

Local Standards

All in One Teaching Resources, Unit 1
- Chapter Project Teacher Notes, pp. 300–301
- Chapter Project Student Overview, pp. 302–303
- Chapter Project Student Worksheets, pp. 304–305
- Chapter Project Scoring Rubric, p. 306

Discovery CHANNEL SCHOOL
Video Preview

Section 1

2 periods
1 block

Human Inheritance
5.1.1 Identify some patterns of inheritance in humans.
5.1.2 Describe the functions of the sex chromosomes.
5.1.3 Explain the relationship between genes and the environment.

Go Online
SciLINKS NSTA

Section 2

2 periods
1 block

Human Genetic Disorders
5.2.1 Identify two major causes of genetic disorders in humans.
5.2.2 Explain how geneticists trace the inheritance of traits.
5.2.3 Describe how genetic disorders are diagnosed and treated.

Go Online
active art

Section 3

2 periods
1 block

Advances in Genetics
5.3.1 Describe three ways of producing organisms with desired traits.
5.3.2 State the goal of the Human Genome Project.

Discovery CHANNEL SCHOOL
Video Field Trip

Go Online
SciLINKS NSTA

Review and Assessment

Test Preparation

All in One Teaching Resources, Unit 1
- Key Terms Review, p. 330
- Transparency LS50
- Performance Assessment Teacher Notes, p. 340
- Performance Assessment Scoring Rubric , p. 341
- Performance Assessment Student Worksheet, p. 342
- Chapter Test, pp. 343–346

Go Online
PHSchool.com

Discovery CHANNEL SCHOOL
Video Assessment

Test Preparation
Blackline Masters

Chapter Activities Planner

Student Edition	Inquiry	Time	Materials	Skills	Resources
Chapter Project, p. 143	Open-Ended	Ongoing (2 to 3 weeks)	**All in One** Teaching Resources, **Unit 1**, p. 300	Applying concepts, making models, communicating	**Lab zone Easy Planner** **All in One** Teaching Resources, **Unit 1**, Support pp. 300–301
Section 1					
Discover Activity, p. 144	Guided	15 minutes	Metric ruler, graph paper	Inferring	**Lab zone Easy Planner**
Try This Activity, p. 147	Guided	10 minutes	None	Designing experiments	**Lab zone Easy Planner**
Section 2					
Discover Activity, p. 151	Directed	10 minutes	None	Inferring	**Lab zone Easy Planner**
Skills Activity, p. 152	Guided	10 minutes	None	Predicting	**Lab zone Easy Planner**
Skills Lab, p. 156	Guided	40 minutes	12 index cards, scissors, marker	Interpreting data, predicting	**Lab zone Easy Planner** **Lab Activity Video** **All in One** Teaching Resources, **Unit 1**, Skills Lab: *Family Puzzle*, pp. 320–321
Section 3					
Discover Activity, p. 157	Guided	15 minutes	Plain white paper, ink pad, hand lens	Observing	**Lab zone Easy Planner**
Skills Activity, p. 161	Guided	15 minutes	Writing materials	Communicating	**Lab zone Easy Planner**
At-Home Activity, p. 162	Open-Ended	Home		Communicating	**Lab zone Easy Planner**
Skills Lab, p. 163	Guided	20 minutes	4–6 bar codes, hand lens	Drawing conclusions, inferring	**Lab zone Easy Planner** **Lab Activity Video** **All in One** Teaching Resources, **Unit 1**, Skills Lab: *Guilty or Innocent?*, pp. 328–329

Section Lesson Plans

Section 1 Human Inheritance

🕐 *2 periods, 1 block*

ABILITY LEVELS
L1 Basic to Average
L2 For All Students
L3 Average to Advanced

Objectives

5.1.1 Identify some patterns of inheritance in humans.
5.1.2 Describe the functions of the sex chromosomes.
5.1.3 Explain the relationship between genes and the environment.

Key Terms

• multiple alleles • sex chromosomes • sex-linked gene • carrier

Local Standards

Preteach

Build Background Knowledge

Students share observations they have made about inherited traits.

 **Discover Activity** *How Tall Is Tall?* **L1**

Targeted Print and Technology Resources

 Teaching Resources, Unit 1

L2 Reading Strategy Transparency
LS44: Identifying Main Ideas

 PresentationEXPRESS™ CD-ROM

Instruct

Patterns of Human Inheritance Ask questions about the number of genes or alleles controlling traits to distinguish patterns of inheritance.

The Sex Chromosomes Use a Punnett square to explain the functions of sex chromosomes.

The Effect of Environment Use examples to explain how genes and the environment interact to determine the characteristics of an organism.

Targeted Print and Technology Resources

Teaching Resources, Unit 1

L2 Guided Reading, pp. 309–311
L2 Transparency LS45

www.SciLinks.org Web Code: scn-0341

Student Edition on Audio CD

Assess

Section Assessment Questions

Have students use their graphic organizers with main ideas and details to help them answer the questions.

Reteach

Use the figures in the section to review how sex is determined and how a sex-linked trait is inherited.

Targeted Print and Technology Resources

Teaching Resources, Unit 1

• Section Summary, p. 308
L1 Review and Reinforce, p. 312
L3 Enrich, p. 313

142C

Section 2 Human Genetic Disorders

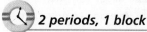 *2 periods, 1 block*

Objectives

5.2.1 Identify two major causes of genetic disorders in humans.
5.2.2 Explain how geneticists trace the inheritance of traits.
5.2.3 Describe how genetic disorders are diagnosed and treated.

Key Terms

• genetic disorder • pedigree • karyotype

Local Standards

Preteach

Build Background Knowledge

Invite students to discuss the definition of a genetic disorder and to name examples.

 Discover Activity *How Many Chromosomes?* **L1**

Targeted Print and Technology Resources

 **Teaching Resources, Unit 1**

L2 Reading Strategy Transparency
LS46: Comparing and Contrasting

⊙ **PresentationEXPRESS™ CD-ROM**

Instruct

Causes of Genetic Disorders Discuss four genetic disorders in terms of their causes.

Pedigrees Use a pedigree to explain how inheritance is traced.

Managing Genetic Disorders Ask questions to help students consider how genetic disorders are diagnosed and treated.

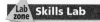 **Skills Lab** *Family Puzzle* **L2**

Targeted Print and Technology Resources

Teaching Resources, Unit 1

L2 Guided Reading, pp. 316–317
L2 Transparency LS47
L2 Skills Lab: *Family Puzzle*, pp. 320–321

Lab Activity Video/DVD
Skills Lab: *Family Puzzle*

PHSchool.com Web Code: cep-3042

⊙ **Student Edition on Audio CD**

Assess

Section Assessment Questions

⊙ Have students use their graphic organizers comparing and contrasting genetic disorders to answer the questions.

Reteach

Use pedigrees to review how inheritance of traits can be traced in a family.

Targeted Print and Technology Resources

Teaching Resources, Unit 1

• Section Summary, p. 315
L1 Review and Reinforce, p. 318
L3 Enrich, p. 319

Section 3 Advances in Genetics

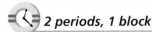 *2 periods, 1 block*

Objectives

5.3.1 Describe three ways of producing organisms with desired traits.
5.3.2 State the goal of the Human Genome Project.

Local Standards

Key Terms

• selective breeding • inbreeding • hybridization • clone
• genetic engineering • gene therapy • genome

Preteach

Build Background Knowledge

Relate selective breeding to different breeds of dogs.

 **Discover Activity** *What Do Fingerprints Reveal?*   **L1**

Targeted Print and Technology Resources

All in One Teaching Resources, Unit 1

L2 Reading Strategy Transparency
LS48: Asking Questions

○ **PresentationEXPRESS™ CD-ROM**

Instruct

Selective Breeding Use an example to define selective breeding, and discuss the different methods.

Cloning Explain how plants and animals can be cloned.

Genetic Engineering Use a diagram with ordered steps to describe genetic engineering.

Learning About Human Genetics Discuss the goal of the Human Genome Project.

 Skills Lab *Guilty or Innocent?*   **L2**

Targeted Print and Technology Resources

All in One Teaching Resources, Unit 1

L2 Guided Reading, pp. 324–325
L2 Transparency LS49
L2 Skills Lab: *Guilty or Innocent?*, pp. 328–329

■ **Lab Activity Video/DVD**
Skills Lab: *Guilty or Innocent?*

DISCOVERY CHANNEL
SCHOOL
Video Field Trip

www.SciLinks.org Web Code: scn-0343

PHSchool.com Web Code: ceh-3040

○ **Student Edition on Audio CD**

Assess

Section Assessment Questions

 Have students use their graphic organizers to help them answer the questions.

Reteach

Ask students to orally describe the different methods of producing organisms with desirable traits.

Targeted Print and Technology Resources

All in One Teaching Resources, Unit 1

• Section Summary, p. 323
L1 Review and Reinforce, p. 326
L3 Enrich, p. 327

Go Online

NSTA-PD_LINKS

For: Professional development support
Visit: www.SciLinks.org/PDLinks
Web Code: scf-0340

Professional Development

Professional Development

Section 1 Human Inheritance

Sex-Linked Inheritance Patterns Traits controlled by sex-linked recessive alleles often appear to skip generations in a pedigree. Such traits may pass from a man through his daughters, who do not have the trait but are carriers, to his grandsons. When a trait shows this inheritance pattern, it is likely to be controlled by a sex-linked recessive allele carried on the X chromosome.

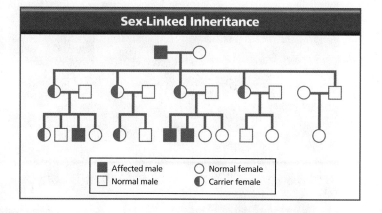

Sex-Linked Inheritance

■ Affected male   ○ Normal female
□ Normal male   ◐ Carrier female

Section 2 Human Genetic Disorders

Too Many Chromosomes In addition to Down syndrome, a number of other syndromes are caused by extra chromosomes in a person's cells. Edwards syndrome is caused by an extra copy of chromosome 18. It occurs about once in every 8,000 live births. Symptoms include mental retardation and malformations of the head, heart, and kidneys. Death usually occurs in the first year. Patau syndrome is caused by an extra copy of chromosome 13. It occurs about once in every 20,000 live births. Symptoms include mental retardation and defects of the hands, heart, and genitals. Death typically occurs by age one. Klinefelter's syndrome is caused by an extra X chromosome in males. It occurs about once in every 500 live male births. Symptoms may include feminine features, sterility, and behavioral problems.

Address Misconceptions

Students may think that all genetic disorders will soon be cured with gene therapy. However, many genetic diseases cannot be cured in this way. For a strategy for overcoming this misconception, see **Address Misconceptions** in the section *Advances in Genetics.*

Section 3 Advances in Genetics

Gene Technology Two major problems must be solved in developing gene therapy for a particular genetic disorder. The first problem is finding the best way to correct the genetic defect that is causing the disorder. Options may include correcting a defective cell product, increasing the production of a cell product that is lacking, making diseased cells weaker, or blocking the operation of diseased cells. The other problem that must be solved is finding a way to carry the genetically engineered DNA to target cells. Viruses make excellent candidates for this role because of their ability to infect living cells. However, before a virus can be used safely, the viral DNA must be genetically engineered to make the virus harmless to the human patient.

Help Students Read

Directed Reading/Thinking Activity
Predict, Read, Confirm, Revise Predictions

Strategy Help students develop their own reading and thinking processes by setting a purpose for reading. Select a section of this chapter for students to read. Before modeling the strategy with students, divide the targeted section into approximately four equal portions. Present the steps as in the example below.

Example
1. Preview Tell students to survey the section by analyzing the titles, headings, visual elements, and boldfaced type. Have students also read the introductory and concluding paragraphs.
2. Predict/Generate Questions Ask students to predict and describe what they will learn, and to formulate their own questions that a teacher might ask. List students' questions on the board.
3. Read/Evaluate and Refine Predictions Have students read a portion of the section. Pause afterward for students to evaluate their predictions. Discuss any questions the text answered and prior misconceptions the text clarified. Ask students to formulate refined predictions and questions based on the new information.
4. Repeat the process for the remaining text portions.

Chapter

5

Modern Genetics

Chapter Preview

❶ Human Inheritance
Discover *How Tall Is Tall?*
Try This *The Eyes Have It*

❷ Human Genetic Disorders
Discover *How Many Chromosomes?*
Skills Activity *Predicting*
Active Art *A Pedigree*
Skills Lab *Family Puzzle*

❸ Advances in Genetics
Discover *What Do Fingerprints Reveal?*
Analyzing Data *Changing Rice Production*
Skills Activity *Communicating*
At-Home Activity *Foods and Selective Breeding*
Skills Lab *Guilty or Innocent?*

interactive
Textbook

The members of this family resemble one ▶
another because they share some alleles.

142 ◆

Lab zone **Chapter Project** ▪ **L3**

Objectives

This project will give students an opportunity to learn about a genetically inherited trait. Students will design a display that communicates their findings visually to young children. After this Chapter Project, students will be able to

- apply genetic concepts to describe inheritance patterns for a specific trait
- make a visual display showing how a trait is inherited and whom it can affect
- communicate information concerning inheritance of genes

Skills Focus

Applying concepts, making models, communicating

Project Time Line 2 to 3 weeks

All in One Teaching Resources, Unit 1

- Chapter Project Teacher Notes
- Chapter Project Overview
- Chapter Project Worksheet 1
- Chapter Project Worksheet 2
- Chapter Project Scoring Rubric

Developing a Plan

On the first day, allow class time for research and the exchange of ideas. On the second day, have students work on ideas for creating the displays. Request detailed sketches of plans during the next few days. After your approval, students will spend eight to ten days researching the traits and building their displays. Allow one or two class periods for students to present their displays to the class or to younger children.

Possible Materials

- Encourage students to use videos, computers, and art media.
- For posters, provide poster board, colored pens, construction paper, and an assortment of magazines and newspapers.

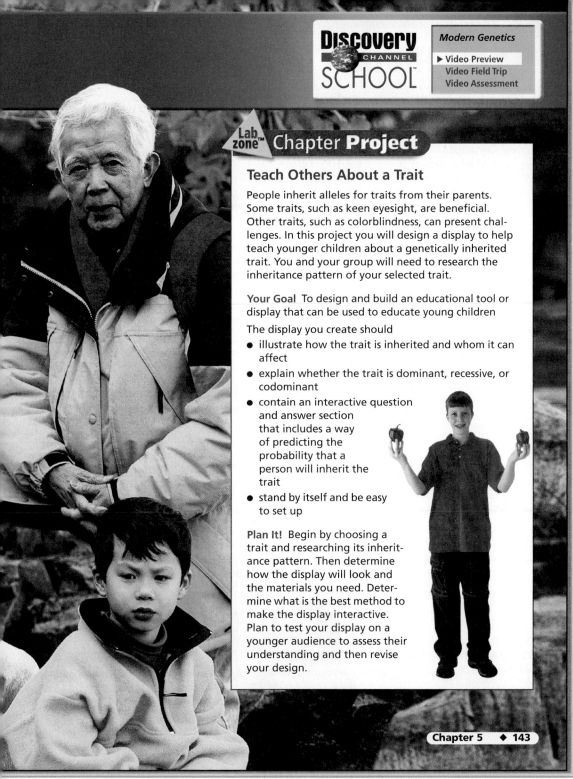

 Video Preview

Modern Genetics

Show the Video Preview to introduce a topic related to the chapter.

Lab zone™ Chapter **Project**

Teach Others About a Trait

People inherit alleles for traits from their parents. Some traits, such as keen eyesight, are beneficial. Other traits, such as colorblindness, can present challenges. In this project you will design a display to help teach younger children about a genetically inherited trait. You and your group will need to research the inheritance pattern of your selected trait.

Your Goal To design and build an educational tool or display that can be used to educate young children

The display you create should

- illustrate how the trait is inherited and whom it can affect
- explain whether the trait is dominant, recessive, or codominant
- contain an interactive question and answer section that includes a way of predicting the probability that a person will inherit the trait
- stand by itself and be easy to set up

Plan It! Begin by choosing a trait and researching its inheritance pattern. Then determine how the display will look and the materials you need. Determine what is the best method to make the display interactive. Plan to test your display on a younger audience to assess their understanding and then revise your design.

Chapter 5 ◆ 143

Launching the Project

Call students' attention to the family photograph on these pages and ask: **What are some traits that the children in this family appear to share with their parents?** (*Students are likely to name obvious physical traits such as hair color or nose shape.*) Point out that in addition to traits such as these, children inherit thousands of other traits from their parents, including many traits that are not so apparent. Tell students that in this project, they will research how genetic traits pass from one generation to the next.

Performance Assessment

The Chapter Project Scoring Rubric will help you evaluate how well students complete the Chapter Project. You may want to share the scoring rubric with your students so they are clear about what will be expected of them. Students will be assessed on

- the thoroughness of their research on the genetically inherited trait
- the accuracy and creativity of their display
- the thoroughness and organization of their presentation of the display to a younger audience
- how well students work with others

 Portfolio

Objectives

After this lesson, students will be able to
5.1.1 Identify some patterns of inheritance in humans.
5.1.2 Describe the functions of the sex chromosomes.
5.1.3 Explain the relationship between genes and the environment.

Target Reading Skill ↻

Identifying Main Ideas Explain that identifying main ideas and details helps students sort information into groups. Each group can have a main topic, subtopics, and details.

Answers

Possible answers:
Main Idea: Human traits are controlled by single genes with two alleles, single genes with multiple alleles, and multiple genes.
Details: Human traits controlled by single genes with two alleles have two distinctly different phenotypes; though a single gene can have multiple alleles, a person can carry only two of these alleles; multiple genes that control a trait act together to produce a single trait with a large number of phenotypes.

All in One Teaching Resources, Unit 1
• Transparency LS44

Preteach

Build Background Knowledge L1

Recognizing Inherited Traits
Help students think of examples of inherited traits by asking: **What are some traits that children may share with one or both of their parents?** (*Students are likely to identify traits such as hair color, nose shape, or eye color.*)

Human Inheritance

Reading Preview

Key Concepts
• What are some patterns of inheritance in humans?
• What are the functions of the sex chromosomes?
• What is the relationship between genes and the environment?

Key Terms
• multiple alleles
• sex chromosomes
• sex-linked gene
• carrier

↻ Target Reading Skill
Identifying Main Ideas
As you read the Patterns of Human Inheritance section, write the main idea—the biggest or most important idea—in a graphic organizer like the one below. Then write three supporting details that further explain the main idea.

Main Idea

Human traits are controlled by single genes with two alleles, single genes with . . .

Detail	Detail	Detail

FIGURE 1
Family Resemblance
Because children inherit alleles for traits from their mother and father, children often look like their parents.

144 ◆

Lab zone Discover Activity

How Tall Is Tall?

1. Choose a partner. Measure each other's height to the nearest 5 centimeters. Record your measurements on the chalkboard.
2. Create a bar graph showing the number of students at each height. Plot the heights on the horizontal axis and the number of students on the vertical axis.

Think It Over
Inferring Do you think height in humans is controlled by a single gene, as it is in peas? Explain your answer.

The arrival of a baby is a happy event. Eagerly, the parents and grandparents gather around to admire the newborn baby. "Don't you think she looks like her father?" "Yes, but she has her mother's eyes."

When a baby is born, the parents, their families, and their friends try to determine whom the baby resembles. Chances are good that the baby will look a little bit like both parents. That is because both parents pass alleles for traits on to their offspring.

Lab zone Discover Activity

Skills Focus Inferring L1

Materials metric ruler, graph paper

Time 15 minutes

Tips If any students are in wheelchairs, you might want to have the class measure sitting height, which is the height from the base of the spine to the top of the head.

Expected Outcome The graph of students' heights is likely to include

several bars, but not as many as there are students in the class.

Think It Over Students may infer that height in humans is controlled by more than one gene because the graph of students' heights has more bars than the two-bar graph Mendel would have drawn for the traits he studied.

Patterns of Human Inheritance

Take a few seconds to look at the other students in your classroom. Some people have curly hair; others have straight hair. Some people are tall, some are short, and many others are in between. You'll probably see eyes of many different colors, ranging from pale blue to dark brown. The different traits you see are determined by a variety of inheritance patterns. **Some human traits are controlled by single genes with two alleles, and others by single genes with multiple alleles. Still other traits are controlled by many genes that act together.**

Single Genes With Two Alleles A number of human traits are controlled by a single gene with one dominant allele and one recessive allele. These human traits have two distinctly different phenotypes, or physical appearances.

For example, a widow's peak is a hairline that comes to a point in the middle of the forehead. The allele for a widow's peak is dominant over the allele for a straight hairline. The Punnett square in Figure 2 illustrates a cross between two parents who are heterozygous for a widow's peak. Trace the possible combinations of alleles that a child may inherit. Notice that each child has a 3 in 4, or 75 percent, probability of having a widow's peak. There is only a 1 in 4, or 25 percent, probability that a child will have a straight hairline. When Mendel crossed peas that were heterozygous for a trait, he obtained similar percentages in the offspring.

FIGURE 2
Widow's Peak Punnett Square
This Punnett square shows a cross between two parents with widow's peaks.
Interpreting Diagrams *What are the possible genotypes of the offspring? What percentage of the offspring will have each genotype?*

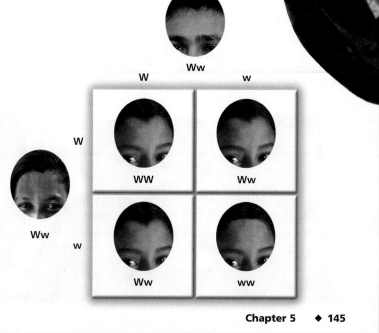

Patterns of Human Inheritance

Teach Key Concepts 〔L2〕
The Different Patterns of Inheritance

Focus Review the meanings of genotype and phenotype.

Teach Refer students to Figure 2. Ask: **What are the two alleles that parents could pass to their offspring?** *(Ww)* **How many genes control the inheritance of a widow's peak?** *(One)* **How many different alleles are involved?** *(Two)* Explain that one gene with two alleles is one pattern of inheritance. Another pattern is traits that are controlled by one gene with more than two alleles. Ask: **How many genes control the inheritance of blood type?** *(One)* **How many different alleles are involved?** *(Three)* **What is a third pattern of inheritance?** *(Traits controlled by many genes)* **How might you know that a trait is controlled by many genes?** *(It has a large number of phenotypes.)*

Apply Explain that human genes are inherited according to the same principles that Mendel discovered. Traits are determined by dominance or codominance regardless of the number of genes involved. **learning modality: verbal**

Independent Practice 〔L2〕

〔All in One〕 **Teaching Resources, Unit 1**
• Guided Reading and Study Worksheet: *Human Inheritance*

 **Student Edition on Audio CD**

Monitor Progress _____ 〔L2〕

Drawing Have students draw a Punnett square that shows a cross between two heterozygotes for smile dimples (a trait controlled by a dominant allele).

Answer
Figure 2 *WW, Ww,* and *ww;* 25% will possibly have the *WW* genotype, 50% the *Ww* genotype, and 25% the *ww* genotype.

⌐ Differentiated Instruction ⌐

Less Proficient Readers 〔L1〕
Making a Picture Dictionary Before students read this section, have them review the meanings of the terms *chromosome, gene, allele, trait, dominant, recessive, phenotype, genotype,* and *codominance.* Have students work in pairs to come up with simple definitions of each term using words they are familiar with. Then have them illustrate each term and

use their terms and illustrations to create a picture dictionary. Encourage students to share their pictures with one another to reinforce their understanding. **learning modality: visual**

145

Help Students Read

L2

Directed Reading/Thinking Activity
(DRTA) Refer to the Content Refresher for guidelines on DRTA. Have students read the main headings and subheadings for the rest of this section. Then, have them make predictions about the main ideas that will be presented. For example, they may predict that some genes are found in males only or in females only. They may also form questions about the text, such as "How is colorblindness inherited?" Record all ideas on the board. After students have finished reading the section, have students confirm which of their predictions were correct, and provide answers to questions that were addressed in the passage.

Use Visuals: Figure 3

L2

Understanding Blood Types

Focus Remind students that some genes have more than two alleles.

Teach Make sure that students understand that the superscripts in Figure 3 are not exponents but labels that distinguish the two codominant alleles, I^A and I^B. Ask: **Which column in the table lists the genotypes? Which lists the phenotypes for blood types?** *(The right column lists the genotypes; the left column the phenotypes.)* **Which alleles are codominant?** *(I^A and I^B)* **What kind of allele is the *i*?** *(Recessive)*

Apply Ask: **Why are there more genotypes than phenotypes for blood types?** *(Two different genotypes—I^AI^A and I^Ai—result in the A phenotype, and two other genotypes—I^BI^B and I^Bi—result in the B phenotype.)* **learning modality: visual**

FIGURE 3
Inheritance of Blood Type
Blood type is determined by a single gene with three alleles. This chart shows which combinations of alleles result in each blood type.

Alleles of Blood Types	
Blood Type	**Combination of Alleles**
A	I^AI^A or I^Ai
B	I^BI^B or I^Bi
AB	I^AI^B
O	ii

FIGURE 4
Many Phenotypes
Skin color in humans is determined by three or more genes. Different combinations of alleles for each of the genes result in a wide range of possible skin colors.

Single Genes With Multiple Alleles Some human traits are controlled by a single gene that has more than two alleles. Such a gene is said to have **multiple alleles**—three or more forms of a gene that code for a single trait. Even though a gene may have multiple alleles, a person can carry only two of those alleles. This is because chromosomes exist in pairs. Each chromosome in a pair carries only one allele for each gene.

Human blood type is controlled by a gene with multiple alleles. There are four main blood types—A, B, AB, and O. Three alleles control the inheritance of blood types. The allele for blood type A and the allele for blood type B are codominant. The allele for blood type A is written as I^A. The allele for blood type B is written I^B. The allele for blood type O—written i—is recessive. Recall that when two codominant alleles are inherited, neither allele is masked. A person who inherits an I^A allele from one parent and an I^B allele from the other parent will have type AB blood. Figure 3 shows the allele combinations that result in each blood type. Notice that only people who inherit two i alleles have type O blood.

Traits Controlled by Many Genes If you completed the Discover activity, you saw that height in humans has more than two distinct phenotypes. In fact, there is an enormous variety of phenotypes for height. Some human traits show a large number of phenotypes because the traits are controlled by many genes. The genes act together as a group to produce a single trait. At least four genes control height in humans, so there are many possible combinations of genes and alleles. Skin color is another human trait that is controlled by many genes.

 Reading Checkpoint Why do some traits exhibit a large number of phenotypes?

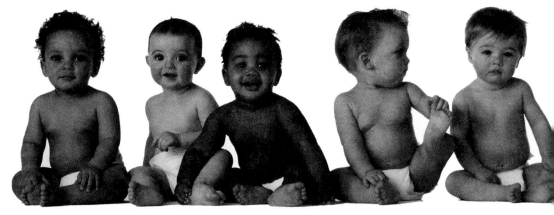

146 ◆

146

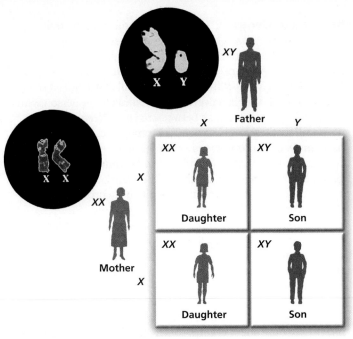

FIGURE 5
Male or Female?
As this Punnett square shows, there is a 50 percent probability that a child will be a girl and a 50 percent probability that a child will be a boy.
Interpreting Diagrams *What sex will the child be if a sperm with a Y chromosome fertilizes an egg?*

The Sex Chromosomes

The **sex chromosomes** are one of the 23 pairs of chromosomes in each body cell. **The sex chromosomes carry genes that determine whether a person is male or female. They also carry genes that determine other traits.**

Girl or Boy? The sex chromosomes are the only chromosome pair that do not always match. If you are a girl, your two sex chromosomes match. The two chromosomes are called X chromosomes. If you are a boy, your sex chromosomes do not match. One of them is an X chromosome, and the other is a Y chromosome. The Y chromosome is much smaller than the X chromosome.

Sex Chromosomes and Fertilization What happens to the sex chromosomes when egg and sperm cells form? Since both of a female's sex chromosomes are X chromosomes, all eggs carry one X chromosome. Males, however, have two different sex chromosomes. Therefore, half of a male's sperm cells carry an X chromosome, while half carry a Y chromosome.

When a sperm cell with an X chromosome fertilizes an egg, the egg has two X chromosomes. The fertilized egg will develop into a girl. When a sperm with a Y chromosome fertilizes an egg, the egg has one X chromosome and one Y chromosome. The fertilized egg will develop into a boy.

 **Try This Activity**

The Eyes Have It
One inherited trait is eye dominance—the tendency to use one eye more than the other. Here's how you can test yourself for this trait.

1. Hold your hand out in front of you at arm's length. Point your finger at an object across the room.
2. Close your right eye. With only your left eye open, observe how far your finger appears to move.
3. Repeat Step 2 with the right eye open. With which eye did your finger seem to remain closer to the object? That eye is dominant.

Designing Experiments
Is eye dominance related to hand dominance—whether a person is right-handed or left-handed? Design an experiment to find out. *Obtain your teacher's permission before carrying out your experiment.*

The Sex Chromosomes

Teach Key Concepts [L2]
Functions of Sex Chromosomes
Focus Refer students to Figure 5.

Teach Ask: **What determines whether a person is male or female?** (*Sex chromosomes*) **What combinations result in a male and in a female?** (*XY and XX*) Ask: **What other role do the sex chromosomes play?** (*They carry genes that determine other traits.*) **How is inheritance different between recessive genes on sex chromosomes and on other chromosomes?** (*It is rarer for a female to have the trait than a male.*)

Apply Ask: **If the man in Figure 5 had an allele *A* on his *X* chromosome, who would inherit it?** (*Only the daughters; the man's sons inherit only the Y chromosome from their father.*) **learning modality: logical/mathematical**

All in One Teaching Resources, Unit 1
• Transparency LS45

Lab zone Build Inquiry [L2]

Applying Concepts of Inheritance
Materials colored pencils
Time 15 minutes

Focus Review the steps in meiosis.

Teach Challenge students to draw two simple diagrams of meiosis, contrasting the formation of sex cells in males and in females.

Apply Ask: **How do your diagrams show that the sperm determines the sex of a child?** (*Male sex cells contain an X or a Y chromosome, whereas female sex cells contain only an X chromosome.*) **learning modality: visual**

Monitor Progress _____ [L2]
Writing Have students explain in their own words why about half of all babies born are boys and about half are girls. Students can place their paragraphs in their portfolios.

Portfolio

Answers
Figure 5 Male

 Reading Checkpoint The traits are controlled by many genes.

Lab zone Try This Activity

Skills Focus Designing experiments
Materials none [L2]
Time 10 minutes

Tips Make sure students focus on an object that is at least a few meters away from them.

Expected Outcome When students close one eye, their finger appears to be stationary; when they close the other eye, their finger appears to move. The right eye is dominant if the finger appears stationary when looking at it with the right eye, the left eye if looking at it with the left eye. One possible design for an experiment is to determine eye and hand dominance for a large sample of people, and look for patterns.

Use Visuals: Figure 7 ▪L2▪

Determining Colorblindness

Focus Remind students that for a recessive allele to show up in females, there must be one on each of the two X chromosomes that she inherits.

Teach Discuss the symbols used in the Punnett square. Then ask: **Why is the box for one son shaded?** (*He is colorblind.*) **Would you expect the son who is colorblind to have sons who are colorblind?** (*No; he can pass only the* Y *chromosome to his sons.*)

Apply Ask students to determine the alleles of both parents if there is a 50% chance that either a son or a daughter will be colorblind. (*The father would be colorblind and have alleles* X^cY. *The mother would be a carrier and have the alleles* X^CX^c.) **learning modality: visual**

Modeling Sex-Linked Inheritance ▪L2▪

Materials white, red, and green pipe cleaners

Time 15 minutes

Focus Remind students that all X-linked alleles are expressed in males, even if they are recessive, because males have just one X chromosome.

Teach Have students twist together two white pipe cleaners to represent a normal X chromosome, a red pipe cleaner and a green pipe cleaner to represent an X chromosome with the allele for red-green colorblindness, and a single white pipe cleaner to represent a Y chromosome. Encourage students to use their models to represent several different crosses and their expected outcomes.

Apply Have students use their models to answer these questions: **If the mother is colorblind and the father has normal vision, what is the probability that their sons will be colorblind?** (*100%*) **If the father is colorblind and the mother has normal vision, what is the probability that their daughters will be colorblind?** (*0%*) **learning modality: kinesthetic**

Sex-Linked Genes The genes for some human traits are carried on the sex chromosomes. Genes on the X and Y chromosomes are often called **sex-linked genes** because their alleles are passed from parent to child on a sex chromosome. Traits controlled by sex-linked genes are called sex-linked traits. One sex-linked trait is red-green colorblindness. A person with this trait cannot distinguish between red and green.

Recall that females have two X chromosomes, whereas males have one X chromosome and one Y chromosome. Unlike most chromosome pairs, the X and Y chromosomes have different genes. Most of the genes on the X chromosome are not on the Y chromosome. Therefore, an allele on an X chromosome may have no corresponding allele on a Y chromosome.

Like other genes, sex-linked genes can have dominant and recessive alleles. In females, a dominant allele on one X chromosome will mask a recessive allele on the other X chromosome. But in males, there is usually no matching allele on the Y chromosome to mask the allele on the X chromosome. As a result, any allele on the X chromosome—even a recessive allele—will produce the trait in a male who inherits it. Because males have only one X chromosome, males are more likely than females to have a sex-linked trait that is controlled by a recessive allele.

FIGURE 6
Colorblindness
The lower photo shows how a red barn and green fields look to a person with red-green colorblindness.

Normal vision
▼

Red-green colorblind vision
▼

Inheritance of Colorblindness Colorblindness is a trait controlled by a recessive allele on the X chromosome. Many more males than females have red-green colorblindness. You can understand why this is the case by examining the Punnett square in Figure 7. Both parents in this example have normal color vision. Notice, however, that the mother is a carrier of colorblindness. A **carrier** is a person who has one recessive allele for a trait and one dominant allele. A carrier of a trait controlled by a recessive allele does not have the trait. However, the carrier can pass the recessive allele on to his or her offspring. In the case of sex-linked traits, only females can be carriers.

As you can see in Figure 7, there is a 25 percent probability that this couple will have a colorblind child. Notice that none of the couple's daughters will be colorblind. On the other hand, the sons have a 50 percent probability of being colorblind. For a female to be colorblind, she must inherit two recessive alleles for colorblindness, one from each parent. A male needs to inherit only one recessive allele. This is because there is no gene for color vision on the Y chromosome. Thus, there is no allele that could mask the recessive allele on the X chromosome.

Reading Checkpoint What is the sex of a person who is a carrier for colorblindness?

For: Links on genetics
Visit: www.SciLinks.org
Web Code: scn-0341

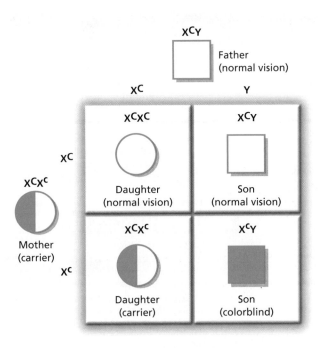

$X^C Y$
Father (normal vision)

X^C Y

X^C

$X^C X^C$ $X^C Y$

Daughter (normal vision)   Son (normal vision)

$X^C X^c$

Mother (carrier)

X^c

$X^C X^c$ $X^c Y$

Daughter (carrier)   Son (colorblind)

FIGURE 7
Colorblindness Punnett Square
Red-green colorblindness is a sex-linked trait. A girl who receives only one recessive allele (written X^c) for red-green colorblindness will not have the trait. However, a boy who receives one recessive allele will be colorblind.
Applying Concepts *What allele combination would a daughter need to inherit to be colorblind?*

◆ 149

For: Links on genetics
Visit: www.SciLinks.org
Web Code: scn-0341

Download a worksheet to guide students' review of genetics.

The Effect of Environment

Teach Key Concepts   L2

Genes and the Environment

Focus Provide this example for students: Tell them to imagine two plants. One receives more sunlight than the other and grows taller and fuller. Ask: **If the two plants have the same genes, what is the difference in how they grow?** *(They are exposed to different environments.)*

Teach Ask: **What does this example demonstrate about the relationship between genes and environment?** *(Genes and the environment interact to determine characteristics.)* **What are some human traits that are influenced by the environment?** *(Height and skills such as playing a musical instrument)*

Apply Ask students how their speech represents the interaction of genetics and environment. *(The way their voice sounds is a combination of the structure of their vocal cords and mouth, which is genetic, and the way their family speaks [slowly or quickly, soft or loud], which is environmental. Language, accent, and dialect are determined by environment.)* **learning modality: logical/mathematical**

Monitor Progress _____ L2

Skills Check Have students solve the following problem: **Mary and her mother are both colorblind. Is Mary's father colorblind, too? How do you know?** *(Because Mary is colorblind, she must have inherited an X^c allele from each parent. Therefore, Mary's father's genotype must be $X^c Y$, so he is colorblind, too.)*

Answers

Figure 7 $X^c X^c$

Reading Checkpoint Female

Differentiated Instruction

Gifted and Talented   L3
Inferring Inheritance Patterns
Challenge students to infer how the inheritance of a sex-linked trait controlled by a dominant allele would differ from the inheritance of a sex-linked trait controlled by a recessive allele. *(A sex-linked trait controlled by a recessive allele is more common in males because males need to inherit just one recessive allele to have the*

trait. A trait controlled by a dominant allele would be equally common in males and females because females, like males, would need to inherit only one dominant allele to have the trait.) Have students make a Punnett Square to show how a sex-linked dominant allele would be passed to offspring. **learning modality: logical/mathematical**

Answer

✓ **Reading Checkpoint** A poor diet could prevent a person from growing as tall as possible, as genetically determined.

Assess

Reviewing Key Concepts

1. a. Single genes with two alleles: widow's peak; single genes with multiple alleles: blood type; and multiple genes: skin color **b.** Four: A, B, AB, and O; the alleles for blood types A and B are codominant, and the allele for blood type O is recessive. Type A blood results from two *A* alleles or one *A* and one *i*; type B blood results from two *B* alleles or one *B* and one *i*; type AB blood results from one *A* allele and one *B* allele; and type O results from two *i* alleles. **c.** No; blood type AB has the genotype $I^A I^B$, while blood type O has the genotype *ii*. Each of his parents passed on an *i* allele, so neither could have blood type AB.

2. a. To carry genes that determine whether a person is male or female, and to carry other traits **b.** The *Y* chromosome is much smaller than the *X* chromosome. Females have two *X* chromosomes, and males have an *X* and a *Y* chromosome. **c.** Red-green colorblindness is determined by a recessive allele on the *X* chromosome. The condition is more common among males because males need to inherit only one recessive allele to express the trait, while females need two.

3. a. No; genes and the environment interact to determine many of a person's characteristics. **b.** Athletic build and coordination may be inherited abilities that work together with environmental factors of practice, instruction, and exercises that strengthen muscles.

Reteach L1

Use Figures 5 and 7 to review how sex is determined and how a sex-linked trait is inherited.

All in One Teaching Resources, Unit 1

- Section Summary: *Human Inheritance*
- Review and Reinforce: *Human Inheritance*
- Enrich: *Human Inheritance*

FIGURE 8
Heredity and Environment
When a person plays a violin, genetically determined traits such as muscle coordination interact with environmental factors such as time spent in practice.

The Effect of Environment

In humans and other organisms, the effects of genes are often influenced by the environment—an organism's surroundings. **Many of a person's characteristics are determined by an interaction between genes and the environment.**

You have learned that several genes work together to help determine human height. However, people's heights are also influenced by their environments. People's diets can affect their height. A diet lacking in protein, certain minerals, or certain vitamins can prevent a person from growing as tall as might be possible.

Environmental factors can also affect human skills, such as playing a musical instrument. For example, physical traits such as muscle coordination and a good sense of hearing will help a musician play well. But the musician also needs instruction on how to play the instrument. Musical instruction is an environmental factor.

✓ **Reading Checkpoint** How can environmental factors affect a person's height?

Section 1 Assessment

🎯 **Target Reading Skill** Identifying Main Ideas Use your graphic organizer to help you answer Question 1 below.

Reviewing Key Concepts

1. a. Identifying Identify three patterns of inheritance in humans. Give an example of a trait that follows each pattern.
   b. Summarizing How many human blood types are there? Summarize how blood type is inherited.
   c. Drawing Conclusions Aaron has blood type O. Can either of his parents have blood type AB? Explain your answer.

2. a. Reviewing What are the functions of the sex chromosomes?
   b. Comparing and Contrasting Contrast the sex chromosomes found in human females and human males.

c. Relating Cause and Effect Explain how red-green colorblindness is inherited. Why is the condition more common in males than in females?

3. a. Reviewing Are a person's characteristics determined only by genes? Explain.
   b. Applying Concepts Explain what factors might work together to enable a great soccer player to kick a ball a long distance.

Writing in Science

Heredity and Environment Think of an ability you admire, such as painting, dancing, snowboarding, or playing games skillfully. Write a paragraph explaining how genes and the environment might work together to enable a person to develop this ability.

🧪 **Chapter Project**

Keep Students on Track Check that students have sketched a plan for displaying their information and that the plan is realistic. Advise students to keep a running list of materials or equipment they will need. Remind them that displays should include an interactive portion that helps the viewer predict the probability that a person will inherit the trait.

Writing in Science

Writing Mode Explanation
Scoring Rubric
4 Includes complete explanation and goes beyond requirements, for example, by including many environmental factors
3 Includes all criteria but does not go beyond requirements
2 Only brief explanation
1 Incomplete or inaccurate explanation

2 Human Genetic Disorders

Reading Preview

Key Concepts
• What are two major causes of genetic disorders in humans?
• How do geneticists trace the inheritance of traits?
• How are genetic disorders diagnosed and treated?

Key Terms
• genetic disorder • pedigree
• karyotype

Target Reading Skill
Comparing and Contrasting As you read, compare and contrast the types of genetic disorders by completing a table like the one below.

Disorder	Description	Cause
Cystic fibrosis	Abnormally thick mucus	Loss of three DNA bases

Lab zone Discover **Activity**

How Many Chromosomes?
The photo at right shows the chromosomes from a cell of a person with Down syndrome, a genetic disorder. The chromosomes have been sorted into pairs.

1. Count the number of chromosomes in the photo.
2. How does the number of chromosomes compare to the usual number of chromosomes in human cells?

Think It Over
Inferring How do you think a cell could have ended up with this number of chromosomes? (*Hint:* Think about the events that occur during meiosis.)

The air inside the stadium was hot and still. The crowd cheered loudly as the runners approached the starting blocks. At the crack of the starter's gun, the runners leaped into motion and sprinted down the track. Seconds later, the race was over. The runners, bursting with pride, hugged each other and their coaches. These athletes were running in the Special Olympics, a competition for people with disabilities. Many of the athletes who compete in the Special Olympics have disabilities that result from genetic disorders.

◀ Runners in the Special Olympics

◆ 151

Lab zone Discover **Activity**

Skills Focus Inferring
Materials none
Time 10 minutes
Tips Provide any students who have vision impairments with a hand lens for examining the photo.
Expected Outcome Students will count 47 chromosomes in the photo, or one

L1

more than the 46 chromosomes normally found in human cells, because there is an extra copy of chromosome 21.

Think It Over Students may correctly say that the extra chromosome is due to failure of the chromosomes to separate during meiosis.

Section 2 Human Genetic Disorders

Objectives
After this lesson, students will be able to
5.2.1 Identify two major causes of genetic disorders in humans.
5.2.2 Explain how geneticists trace the inheritance of traits.
5.2.3 Describe how genetic disorders are diagnosed and treated.

Target Reading Skill

Comparing and Contrasting Explain that comparing and contrasting information shows how ideas, facts, and events are similar and different. The results of the comparison can have importance.

Answers
Possible answers:
Disorder: Cystic fibrosis; *Description:* Body produces abnormally thick mucus; *Cause:* Recessive allele due to removal of three DNA bases
Disorder: Sickle-cell disease; *Description:* Red blood cells are sickle-shaped and have reduced ability to hold oxygen; *Cause:* Codominant allele
Disorder: Hemophilia; *Description:* Blood clots slowly or not at all; *Cause:* Recessive allele on X chromosome
Disorder: Down syndrome; *Description:* Mental retardation and heart defects; *Cause:* An extra copy of chromosome 21

All in One Teaching Resources, Unit 1
• Transparency LS46

Preteach

Build Background Knowledge   **L1**

Discussing Genetic Disorders
Ask: **What do you think a genetic disorder is?** (*An abnormal condition that is inherited*) **What are some genetic disorders you have heard about?** (*Accept all student responses without comment at this time.*)

Instruct

Help Students Read L1

KWL Have students make a chart with columns titled *What I Know, What I Want to Know,* and *What I Learned.* In the first column, they write what they know about the four disorders in the text. They fill out the second column with what they want to know. After reading the text, they complete the third column.

Causes of Genetic Disorders

Teach Key Concepts L2
Common Genetic Disorders

Focus Review with students the different ways that mutations can occur.

Teach Explain that the four diseases discussed result from a mutation in the DNA or a gene, or a change in the structure or number of chromosomes. Ask: **What causes cystic fibrosis?** *(A mutation in which three bases are removed from a DNA molecule)* **What causes sickle-cell disease?** *(A mutation that affects the protein hemoglobin)* **What causes hemophilia?** *(A recessive allele on the X chromosome)* **Why is it more common in males?** *(The allele that causes it is on the X chromosome.)* **What causes Down syndrome?** *(A person's cells have an extra copy of chromosome 21.)*

Apply How could a genetic disorder like cystic fibrosis be cured? *(By changing or replacing the gene that causes the disease)* **learning modality: verbal**

Independent Practice L2

 **Teaching Resources, Unit 1**

- Guided Reading and Study Worksheet: *Human Genetic Disorders*

Student Edition on Audio CD

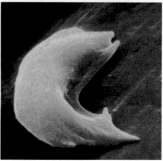

FIGURE 9
Sickle-Cell Disease
Normally, red blood cells are shaped like round disks (top). In a person with sickle-cell disease, red blood cells can become sickle-shaped (bottom).

Lab zone Skills **Activity**

Predicting
A man has sickle-cell disease. His wife does not have the disease, but is heterozygous for the sickle-cell trait. Predict the probability that their child will have sickle-cell disease. (*Hint:* Construct a Punnett square.)

Causes of Genetic Disorders

A **genetic disorder** is an abnormal condition that a person inherits through genes or chromosomes. **Some genetic disorders are caused by mutations in the DNA of genes. Other disorders are caused by changes in the overall structure or number of chromosomes.** In this section, you will learn about some common genetic disorders.

Cystic Fibrosis Cystic fibrosis is a genetic disorder in which the body produces abnormally thick mucus in the lungs and intestines. The thick mucus fills the lungs, making it hard for the affected person to breathe. Cystic fibrosis is caused by a recessive allele on one chromosome. The recessive allele is the result of a mutation in which three bases are removed from a DNA molecule.

Sickle-Cell Disease Sickle-cell disease affects hemoglobin, a protein in red blood cells that carries oxygen. When oxygen concentrations are low, the red blood cells of people with the disease have an unusual sickle shape. Sickle-shaped red blood cells clog blood vessels and cannot carry as much oxygen as normal cells. The allele for the sickle-cell trait is codominant with the normal allele. A person with two sickle-cell alleles will have the disease. A person with one sickle-cell allele will produce both normal hemoglobin and abnormal hemoglobin. This person usually will not have symptoms of the disease.

Hemophilia Hemophilia is a genetic disorder in which a person's blood clots very slowly or not at all. People with the disorder do not produce one of the proteins needed for normal blood clotting. The danger of internal bleeding from small bumps and bruises is very high. Hemophilia is caused by a recessive allele on the X chromosome. Because hemophilia is a sex-linked disorder, it occurs more frequently in males than in females.

Down Syndrome In Down syndrome, a person's cells have an extra copy of chromosome 21. In other words, instead of a pair of chromosomes, a person with Down syndrome has three of that chromosome. Down syndrome most often occurs when chromosomes fail to separate properly during meiosis. People with Down syndrome have some degree of mental retardation. Heart defects are also common, but can be treated.

 Reading Checkpoint How is the DNA in the sickle-cell allele different from the normal allele?

Lab zone Skills **Activity**

Skills Focus Predicting

Materials none

Time 10 minutes

Expected Outcome The probability that their child will have sickle-cell disease is 50%.

Extend Ask: If the couple has a son who does not have symptoms of sickle-cell

L2 disease, could he still have abnormal hemoglobin? *(Yes; he is heterozygous for the sickle-cell trait. A person with only one sickle-cell allele will produce both normal and abnormal hemoglobin but will not have symptoms of the disease.)* **learning modality: logical/mathematical**

Pedigrees

Imagine that you are a geneticist who is interested in tracing the occurrence of a genetic disorder through several generations of a family. What would you do? **One important tool that geneticists use to trace the inheritance of traits in humans is a pedigree.** A **pedigree** is a chart or "family tree" that tracks which members of a family have a particular trait.

The trait in a pedigree can be an ordinary trait, such as a widow's peak, or a genetic disorder, such as cystic fibrosis. Figure 10 shows a pedigree for albinism, a condition in which a person's skin, hair, and eyes lack normal coloring.

Go Online
active art

For: Pedigree activity
Visit: PHSchool.com
Web Code: cep-3042

FIGURE 10
A Pedigree
The father in the photograph has albinism. The pedigree shows the inheritance of the allele for albinism in three generations of a family. **Interpreting Diagrams** *Where is an albino male shown in the pedigree?*

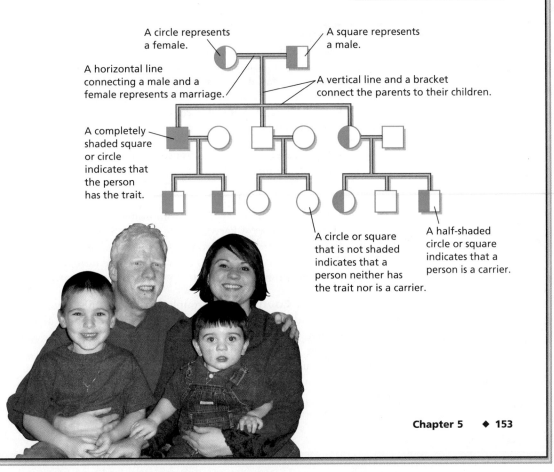

A circle represents a female.

A square represents a male.

A horizontal line connecting a male and a female represents a marriage.

A vertical line and a bracket connect the parents to their children.

A completely shaded square or circle indicates that the person has the trait.

A circle or square that is not shaded indicates that a person neither has the trait nor is a carrier.

A half-shaded circle or square indicates that a person is a carrier.

Chapter 5 ◆ 153

Pedigrees

Go Online
active art

For: Pedigree activity
Visit: PHSchool.com
Web Code: cep-3042

Students can interact with the art of a pedigree online.

Teach Key Concepts L2

How Inheritance Is Traced

Focus Refer students to Figure 10.

Teach Have volunteers read the captions in the figure, then identify the genotypes and phenotypes for each individual.

Apply Have students make a Punnett square to show all possible genotypes of the children of the couple in the first generation of the pedigree. **learning modality: visual**

All in One Teaching Resources, Unit 1
• Transparency LS47

Lab zone **Build Inquiry** L2

Interpreting a Pedigree

Materials poster board, marker

Time 15 minutes

Focus Review the meaning of codominance.

Teach Have students construct a two-generation pedigree for sickle-cell disease, starting with $Ss \times Ss$.

Apply Have students explain why the phenotype for having one sickle-cell allele is different from the phenotype for having one allele for cystic fibrosis. **learning modality: visual**

Monitor Progress L2

Skills Check Have students draw a pedigree that shows the inheritance of cystic fibrosis in a family. Students can place these pedigrees in their portfolio.

Portfolio

Answers
Figure 10 The male in the second generation on the far left

Reading Checkpoint It codes for a hemoglobin of a different shape from the normal allele.

Differentiated Instruction

English Learners/Beginning L1
Comprehension: Link to Visual Draw a pedigree showing the trait of widow's peak, and explain each line, square, and circle as you draw it. Write the symbols for the genotypes beside each figure, and draw faces that show the trait in the circles and squares. Then have students draw their own pedigree for another trait and explain it to you. **learning modality: visual**

English Learners/Intermediate L2
Comprehension: Link to Visual Have students do the Beginning activity, then write sentences in their own words explaining how to interpret the pedigree. **learning modality: visual**

Managing Genetic Disorders

Teach Key Concepts L2

Diagnosing and Treating Genetic Disorders

Focus Tell students that genetic testing is now available for hundreds of disorders.

Teach Ask: **What is a karyotype?** (*A karyotype is a picture of all of the chromosomes in a cell, arranged in pairs.*) **What type of genetic disorders can be determined by looking at a karyotype?** (*Disorders resulting from a change in the number or structure of chromosomes*) **How do counselors help people who have a family history of a genetic disorder?** (*They help couples understand their chances of passing the genes or traits on to offspring.*) **How do people who have genetic disorders deal with them?** (*There are treatments for some disorders, and education and training helps many people live active, productive lives.*)

Apply Have students imagine they are genetic counselors who must determine the chance of a couple having a child with cystic fibrosis, when both husband and wife are carriers. (*Students draw a Punnett square for two heterozygotes. The Punnett square should show that 25% of the couple's children would be likely to inherit two recessive alleles.*) Ask: **If the couple has two children without cystic fibrosis, what is the chance that their third child will have it? Their fourth child?** (*Each child has a 25% chance of having cystic fibrosis.*) **learning modality: logical/mathematical**

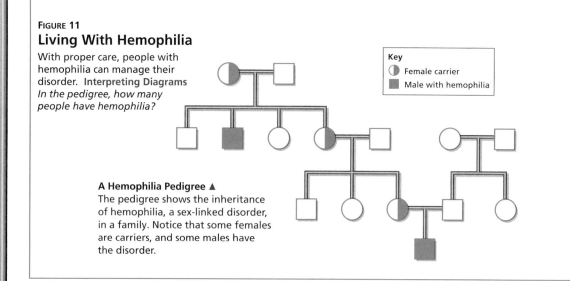

FIGURE 11
Living With Hemophilia
With proper care, people with hemophilia can manage their disorder. Interpreting Diagrams *In the pedigree, how many people have hemophilia?*

Key
◗ Female carrier
■ Male with hemophilia

A Hemophilia Pedigree ▲
The pedigree shows the inheritance of hemophilia, a sex-linked disorder, in a family. Notice that some females are carriers, and some males have the disorder.

Managing Genetic Disorders

Years ago, doctors had only Punnett squares and pedigrees to help them predict whether a child might have a genetic disorder. **Today, doctors use tools such as karyotypes to help diagnose genetic disorders. People with genetic disorders are helped through medical care, education, job training, and other methods.**

Karyotypes To detect chromosomal disorders such as Down syndrome, a doctor examines the chromosomes from a person's cells. The doctor uses a karyotype to examine the chromosomes. A **karyotype** (KA ree uh typ) is a picture of all the chromosomes in a cell. The chromosomes in a karyotype are arranged in pairs. A karyotype can reveal whether a person has the correct number of chromosomes in his or her cells. If you did the Discover activity, you saw a karyotype from a girl with Down syndrome.

Genetic Counseling A couple that has a family history of a genetic disorder may turn to a genetic counselor for advice. Genetic counselors help couples understand their chances of having a child with a particular genetic disorder. Genetic counselors use tools such as karyotypes, pedigree charts, and Punnett squares to help them in their work.

 Reading Checkpoint **What do genetic counselors do?**

154 ◆

Differentiated Instruction

Special Needs L1
Illustrating the Cause of Down's Syndrome Help students use colored pipe cleaners and the diagrams from a previous section to illustrate the chromosomes as the cell goes through Meiosis I and Meiosis II. Point out that the chromosome pairs can fail to separate correctly in either stage.

Students end up with four sets of pipe cleaners to represent the possible individuals formed when sex cells unite. Two individuals should be normal, one should contain only one chromosome of a certain color, and one should contain three chromosomes of that color. **learning modality: visual**

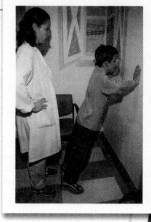

◄ Physical Therapy Trained medical workers help hemophilia patients cope with their disorder. Here, a boy receives physical therapy.

Sports ►
A boy with hemophilia learns how to play golf. The disorder does not stop people from living active lives.

Dealing With Genetic Disorders People with genetic disorders face serious challenges, but help is available. Medical treatments help people with some disorders. For example, physical therapy helps remove mucus from the lungs of people with cystic fibrosis. People with sickle-cell disease take folic acid, a vitamin, to help their bodies manufacture red blood cells. Because of education and job training, adults with Down syndrome can find work in hotels, banks, restaurants, and other places of employment. Fortunately, most genetic disorders do not prevent people from living active, productive lives.

Section 2 Assessment

Target Reading Skill
Comparing and Contrasting Use the information in your table to help you answer Question 1 below.

Reviewing Key Concepts
1. a. **Identifying** Identify the two major causes of genetic disorders in humans.
   b. **Explaining** Which of those two major causes is responsible for Down syndrome?
   c. **Describing** How are the cells of a person with Down syndrome different from those of a person without the disorder?
2. a. **Defining** What is a pedigree?
   b. **Inferring** Why are pedigrees helpful in understanding genetic disorders?

   c. **Applying Concepts** Sam has hemophilia. Sam's brother, mother, and father do not have hemophilia. Draw a pedigree showing who has the disorder and who is a carrier.
3. a. **Reviewing** What is a karyotype?
   b. **Inferring** Would a karyotype reveal the presence of sickle-cell disease? Why or why not?

Writing in Science

Creating a Web Site Create an imaginary Web site to inform the public about genetic disorders. Write a description of one disorder for the Web site.

Chapter 5 ◆ 155

Lab zone Chapter Project

Writing in Science

155

Family Puzzle [L2]

Prepare for Inquiry

Skills Objectives
Students will be able to
- interpret data on phenotypes to construct a family pedigree
- predict the probability of having cystic fibrosis based on the pedigree

 Class Time 40 minutes

All in One Teaching Resources, Unit 1
- Lab Worksheet: *Family Puzzle*

Guide Inquiry

Invitation
Draw a pedigree on the board showing a wife with a genetic disorder and a healthy husband who have an affected daughter and a healthy son. Ask: **Can you tell if the trait is controlled by a dominant or recessive allele?** *(No)* Extend the pedigree back one generation by adding two healthy parents for the wife. Then ask the same question. *(Recessive; otherwise, at least one of the wife's parents would also have the trait.)* Point out that the more generations a pedigree has, the more obvious the pattern of inheritance.

Introduce the Procedure
Check that students know how to construct pedigrees. Have students review the part of the chapter that discusses how to interpret pedigrees.

Troubleshooting the Experiment
- Check that students have drawn and labeled the pedigree correctly.
- Tell students they will need to draw Punnett squares to answer Question 2.

Analyze and Conclude
1. Joshua's parents are both heterozygous (*Nn*); the genotypes of Bella's parents cannot be determined for certain, but at least one must be heterozygous, and the other could be either heterozygous or homozygous for the normal allele (*NN*).
2. Because both parents are heterozygous (*Nn*), there is a 25 percent chance of each child inheriting two *n* alleles and having cystic fibrosis.
3. Genetic counselors cannot usually draw firm conclusions about a hereditary condition with information about just one

---

Family Puzzle

Problem
A husband and wife want to understand the probability that their children might inherit cystic fibrosis. How can you use the information in the box labeled Case Study to predict the probability?

Skills Focus
interpreting data, predicting

Materials
- 12 index cards
- scissors
- marker

Procedure
1. Read the Case Study. In your notebook, draw a pedigree that shows all the family members. Use circles to represent the females, and squares to represent the males. Shade in the circles or squares representing the individuals who have cystic fibrosis.
2. You know that cystic fibrosis is controlled by a recessive allele. To help you figure out Joshua and Bella's family pattern, create a set of cards to represent the alleles. Cut each of six index cards into four smaller cards. On 12 of the small cards, write *N* to represent the dominant normal allele. On the other 12 small cards, write *n* for the recessive allele.

> **Case Study:**
> **Joshua and Bella**
> - Joshua and Bella have a son named Ian. Ian has been diagnosed with cystic fibrosis.
> - Joshua and Bella are both healthy.
> - Bella's parents are both healthy.
> - Joshua's parents are both healthy.
> - Joshua's sister, Sara, has cystic fibrosis.

156 ◆

3. Begin by using the cards to represent Ian's alleles. Since he has cystic fibrosis, what alleles must he have? Write in this genotype next to the pedigree symbol for Ian.
4. Joshua's sister, Sara, also has cystic fibrosis. What alleles does she have? Write in this genotype next to the pedigree symbol that represents Sara.
5. Now use the cards to figure out what genotypes Joshua and Bella must have. Write their genotypes next to their symbols in the pedigree.
6. Work with the cards to figure out the genotypes of all other family members. Fill in each person's genotype next to his or her symbol in the pedigree. If more than one genotype is possible, write in both genotypes.

Analyze and Conclude
1. **Interpreting Data** What were the possible genotypes of Joshua's parents? What were the genotypes of Bella's parents?
2. **Predicting** Joshua also has a brother. What is the probability that he has cystic fibrosis? Explain.
3. **Communicating** Imagine that you are a genetic counselor. A couple asks why you need information about many generations of their families to draw conclusions about a hereditary condition. Write an explanation you can give to them.

More to Explore
Review the pedigree that you just studied. What data suggest that the traits are not sex-linked? Explain.

---

or two generations; more than one inheritance pattern may explain the facts when the information is limited. For example, both sex-linked traits and recessive traits can skip generations.

Extend Inquiry

More to Explore The traits affect males and females about equally. If cystic fibrosis in the case study were sex-linked, Ian would have inherited the disorder from his mother, not from both parents, as appears to have been the case. Also, Joshua's sister probably would not have the disease.

Reading Preview

Key Concepts
- What are three ways of producing organisms with desired traits?
- What is the goal of the Human Genome Project?

Key Terms
- selective breeding
- inbreeding • hybridization
- clone • genetic engineering
- gene therapy • genome

⊙ Target Reading Skill
Asking Questions Before you read, preview the red headings. In a graphic organizer like the one below, ask a question for each heading. As you read, write answers to your questions.

Advances in Genetics

Question	Answer
What is selective breeding?	Selective breeding is . . .

Lab zone Discover Activity

What Do Fingerprints Reveal?

1. Label a sheet of paper with your name. Then roll one of your fingers from side to side on an ink pad. Make a fingerprint by carefully rolling your inked finger on the paper.

2. Divide into groups. Each group should choose one member to use the same finger to make a second fingerprint on a sheet of paper. Leave the paper unlabeled.

3. Exchange your group's fingerprints with those from another group. Compare each labeled fingerprint with the fingerprint on the unlabeled paper. Decide whose fingerprint it is.

4. Wash your hands after completing this activity.

Think It Over
Observing Why are fingerprints used to identify people?

Would you like to have your picture taken with a 9,000-year-old family member? Adrian Targett, a history teacher in the village of Cheddar in England, has actually done that. All that's left of his ancient relative, known as "Cheddar Man," is a skeleton. The skeleton was discovered in a cave near the village. DNA analysis indicates that Targett and Cheddar Man are relatives.

Like your fingerprints, your DNA is different from everyone else's. Because of advances in genetics, DNA evidence can show many things, such as family relationships.

FIGURE 12
Distant Relatives
Adrian Targett visits his distant relative, Cheddar Man. Unfortunately, Cheddar Man cannot respond to questions about life 9,000 years ago.

◆ 157

Lab zone Discover Activity

Skills Focus Observing **L1**

Materials plain white paper, ink pad, hand lens

Time 15 minutes

Tips Help students recognize similarities and differences among the fingerprints by pointing out examples of whirls, loops, and other standard features of fingerprints.

Expected Outcome By comparing a group's unlabeled fingerprints with its labeled fingerprints, students identify who made the unlabeled print.

Think It Over Each person's fingerprints are unique.

Objectives
After this lesson, students will be able to
5.3.1 Describe three ways of producing organisms with desired traits.
5.3.2 State the goal of the Human Genome Project.

Target Reading Skill ⊙

Asking Questions Explain that changing a heading into a question helps students anticipate the ideas, facts, and events they are about to read.

Answers
Possible questions and answers include:
What is selective breeding? (*Selective breeding is the process of selecting organisms with desired traits to be parents of the next generation.*) **Why are organisms cloned?** (*To produce offspring with desired traits*) **What is genetic engineering?** (*A process in which genes from one organism are transferred into the DNA of another organism*) **What advance has helped us learn about human genetics?** (*The Human Genome Project*)

All in One Teaching Resources, Unit 1
- Transparency LS48

Preteach

Build Background Knowledge **L1**
Selective Breeding
Ask: **What are some breeds of dogs that have very different characteristics?** (*Possible answers: Dachshund, Chihuahua, and Great Dane*) Explain that the different breeds were produced by mating animals that have certain traits. In this section, students will learn about selective breeding and other ways of producing organisms with desirable traits.

Selective Breeding

Teach Key Concepts L2

Producing Selected Traits

Focus Tell students that dog breeders use selective breeding to produce purebred dogs that are good hunters or retrievers, for example.

Teach Ask: **Based on this example, what is selective breeding?** *(A technique to produce offspring with desirable traits)* **What are inbreeding and hybridization?** *(Inbreeding is crossing two individuals that have similar characteristics. Hybridization is crossing two genetically different individuals.)*

Apply Have students imagine they have a purebred tall pea plant with yellow pods and a purebred short pea plant with green pods. Ask: **What technique would produce a tall pea plant with yellow pods?** *(Inbreeding)* **learning modality: logical/mathematical**

Independent Practice L2

 **Teaching Resources, Unit 1**

• Guided Reading and Study Worksheet: *Advances in Genetics*

 **Student Edition on Audio CD**

Lab zone **Build Inquiry** L1

Applying Concepts of Hybridization

Materials seed catalogs

Time 10 minutes

Focus Review hybridization.

Teach Have students use the catalogs to list the characteristics of two different hybrid varieties of a certain plant.

Apply Ask students to infer how selective breeding of food plants has benefited people. *(It has increased the amount of food available so people can be better fed or more people can be fed.)* **learning modality: verbal**

FIGURE 13
Inbreeding
Turkeys such as the one with white feathers were developed by inbreeding. Breeders started with wild turkeys.

Wild turkey

Domestic turkey

FIGURE 14
Hybridization
McIntosh and Red Delicious apples were crossed to produce Empire apples.
Applying Concepts *What desirable traits might breeders have been trying to produce?*

Selective Breeding

Genetic techniques have enabled people to produce organisms with desirable traits. **Selective breeding, cloning, and genetic engineering are three methods for developing organisms with desirable traits.**

The process of selecting organisms with desired traits to be parents of the next generation is called **selective breeding**. Thousands of years ago, in what is now Mexico, the food that we call corn was developed in this way. Every year, farmers saved seeds from the healthiest plants that produced the best food. In the spring, they planted those seeds. By repeating this process over and over, farmers developed plants that produced better corn. People have used selective breeding with many different plants and animals. Two selective breeding techniques are inbreeding and hybridization.

Inbreeding The technique of **inbreeding** involves crossing two individuals that have similar characteristics. For example, suppose a male and a female turkey are both plump and grow quickly. Their offspring will probably also have those desirable qualities. Inbred organisms have alleles that are very similar to those of their parents.

Inbred organisms are genetically very similar. Therefore, inbreeding increases the probability that organisms may inherit alleles that lead to genetic disorders. For example, inherited hip problems are common in many breeds of dogs.

Hybridization In **hybridization** (hy brid ih ZAY shun), breeders cross two genetically different individuals. The hybrid organism that results is bred to have the best traits from both parents. For example, a farmer might cross corn that produces many kernels with corn that is resistant to disease. The result might be a hybrid corn plant with both of the desired traits.

 Reading Checkpoint **What is the goal of hybridization?**

McIntosh **Red Delicious** **Empire**

 ×  =

Changing Rice Production

The graph shows how worldwide rice production changed between 1965 and 2000. New, hybrid varieties of rice plants are one factor that has affected the amount of rice produced.

Worldwide Rice Production

1. **Reading Graphs** According to the graph, how did rice production change between 1965 and 2000?

2. **Reading Graphs** How many metric tons of rice per hectare were produced in 1965? How many were produced in 2000?

3. **Calculating** Calculate the approximate difference between rice production in 1965 and 2000.

4. **Developing Hypotheses** What factors besides new varieties of plants might help account for the difference in rice production between 1965 and 2000?

Cloning

For some organisms, a technique called cloning can be used to produce offspring with desired traits. A **clone** is an organism that has exactly the same genes as the organism from which it was produced. It isn't hard to clone some kinds of plants, such as an African violet. Just cut a stem from one plant, and put the stem in soil. Water it, and soon you will have a whole new plant. The new plant is genetically identical to the plant from which the stem was cut.

Researchers have also cloned animals such as sheep and pigs. The methods for cloning these animals are complex. They involve taking the nucleus of an animal's body cell and using that nucleus to produce a new animal.

 Reading Checkpoint How can a clone of a plant be produced?

Discovery CHANNEL SCHOOL

Modern Genetics

Video Preview
▶ Video Field Trip
Video Assessment

FIGURE 15
Cloned Goats
These goats were produced by cloning.

◆ 159

Differentiated Instruction

English Learners/Beginning L1
Comprehension: Modified Cloze
Give students a list of simple sentences that describe the methods for producing organisms with desirable traits, but leave some key words blank. For example, "Different breeds of dogs are produced by _____." Provide students with a list of correct answers, and have them fill in each blank. Model how to do the first one. **learning modality: verbal**

English Learners/Intermediate L2
Comprehension: Modified Cloze Give students the cloze sentences described for the Beginning activity, but fill in incorrect answers and have students correct them. **learning modality: verbal**

Discovery CHANNEL SCHOOL Video Field Trip

Modern Genetics

Show the Video Field Trip to let students learn more about cloning.

Math ► Analyzing Data

Math Skill Making and interpreting graphs

Focus Explain that line graphs are often used to analyze a trend over time.

Teach Ask students what the *x* and the *y* axes represent. (*x: Year; y: Rice production in metric tons per hectare*)

Answers
1. Rice production increased (doubled).
2. 2 in 1965; 4 in 2000
3. 2 metric tons/hectare
4. Possible answer: genetic advances, fertilizers, improved harvesting methods

Cloning

Teach Key Concepts L2
Cloning in Plants and Animals

Focus Tell students that the first clone of an adult mammal was a sheep named Dolly.

Teach Ask: **How is a plant cloned?** (*Cut a stem from one plant and grow it.*) **An animal?** (*Use the nucleus of a body cell to produce a new animal.*)

Apply Ask: **Why are identical twins not clones by the text definition?** (*They are not genetically identical to their parents.*)
learning modality: logical/mathematical

Monitor Progress L2

Skills Check Have students compare inbreeding and hybridization.

Answers
Figure 14 Possible answer: Taste, shelf life, resistance to insects

 Reading Checkpoint To produce an organism with the best traits from both parents

 Reading Checkpoint Grow a cutting of the original plant.

Genetic Engineering

Help Students Read   L2

Monitoring Your Understanding Before students read *Genetic Engineering*, ask them to stop and monitor their understanding after each paragraph. Explain that if they have not fully understood it, they can apply one of the reading techniques that has worked for them in the past, such as outlining, summarizing, or identifying main ideas.

Teach Key Concepts   L2

Selecting an Organism's Traits

Focus Have students look at Figure 16. Give them time to read the captions.

Teach Explain that in genetic engineering, specific genes are transferred into the DNA of another organism. Refer students to Figure 16, and have students trace the steps in creating bacteria that produce insulin. Ask questions such as **What is a plasmid?** (*A small ring of DNA in a bacterial cell*) **Why are the bacteria in step 5 able to produce insulin?** (*They contain copies of the human insulin gene.*)

Apply Challenge students to think of advantages that genetic engineering has over selective breeding. (*Producing the desired traits may be more difficult with breeding; genetic engineering can target the specific genes coding for a trait.*) **learning modality: logical/mathematical**

All in One Teaching Resources, Unit 1

• Transparency LS49

Go Online
SciLINKS NSTA

For: Links on genetic engineering
Visit: www.SciLinks.org
Web Code: scn-0343

Download a worksheet to guide students' review of genetic engineering.

Genetic Engineering

Geneticists have developed another powerful technique for producing organisms with desired traits. In this process, called **genetic engineering**, genes from one organism are transferred into the DNA of another organism. Genetic engineering can produce medicines and improve food crops.

Genetic Engineering in Bacteria One type of genetically engineered bacteria produces a protein called insulin. Injections of insulin are needed by many people with diabetes. Recall that bacteria have a single DNA molecule in the cytoplasm. Some bacterial cells also contain small circular pieces of DNA called plasmids. In Figure 16, you can see how scientists insert the DNA for a human gene into the plasmid of a bacterium.

FIGURE 16
Genetic Engineering
Scientists use genetic engineering to create bacterial cells that produce important human proteins such as insulin.
Interpreting Diagrams *How does a human insulin gene become part of a plasmid?*

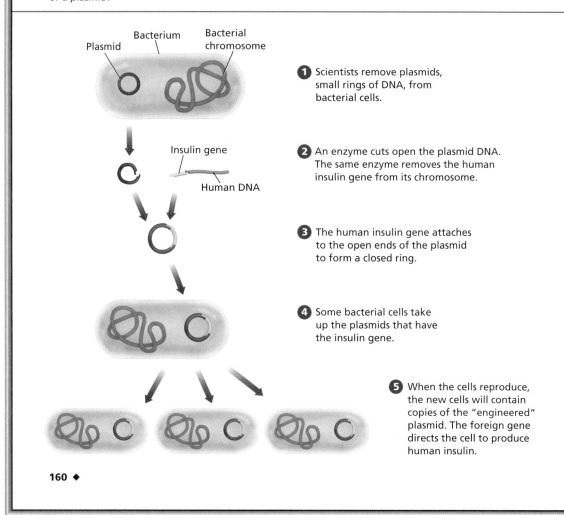

1 Scientists remove plasmids, small rings of DNA, from bacterial cells.

2 An enzyme cuts open the plasmid DNA. The same enzyme removes the human insulin gene from its chromosome.

3 The human insulin gene attaches to the open ends of the plasmid to form a closed ring.

4 Some bacterial cells take up the plasmids that have the insulin gene.

5 When the cells reproduce, the new cells will contain copies of the "engineered" plasmid. The foreign gene directs the cell to produce human insulin.

Labels in figure: Plasmid, Bacterium, Bacterial chromosome, Insulin gene, Human DNA

160 ◆

Differentiated Instruction

Less Proficient Readers   L1
Drawing Diagrams Have students draw simple diagrams that illustrate selective breeding, cloning, and genetic engineering on three separate index cards. Ask them to label the diagrams in their own words. Then have students use their diagrams to make a chart that compares and contrasts the methods. **learning modality: verbal**

Gifted and Talented   L3
Researching the Human Genome Project Have students search for more information about the Human Genome Project via Web sites sponsored by the U.S. Department of Energy and the National Institutes of Health, the two government agencies that coordinate the project, and report their findings to the class. **learning modality: verbal**

Normal zebra danio ▲

Genetically ▶ engineered zebra danios

Once the gene is inserted into the plasmid, the bacterial cell and all its offspring will contain this human gene. As a result, the bacteria produce the protein that the human gene codes for—in this case, insulin. Because bacteria reproduce quickly, large amounts of insulin can be produced in a short time.

Genetic Engineering in Other Organisms Scientists can also use genetic engineering techniques to insert genes into animals. For example, human genes can be inserted into the cells of cows. The cows then produce the human protein for which the gene codes in their milk. Scientists have used this technique to produce the blood clotting protein needed by people with hemophilia.

Genes have also been inserted into the cells of plants, such as tomatoes and rice. Some of the genes enable the plants to survive in cold temperatures or in poor soil. Other genetically engineered crops can resist insect pests.

Gene Therapy Someday it may be possible to use genetic engineering to correct some genetic disorders in humans. This process, called **gene therapy**, will involve inserting copies of a gene directly into a person's cells. For example, doctors may be able to treat hemophilia by replacing the defective allele on the X chromosome. The person's blood would then clot normally.

Concerns About Genetic Engineering Some people are concerned about the long-term effects of genetic engineering. For example, some people think that genetically engineered crops may not be entirely safe. People fear that these crops may harm the environment or cause health problems in humans. To address such concerns, scientists are trying to learn more about the effects of genetic engineering.

Reading Checkpoint How do genetic engineering techniques enable scientists to produce clotting proteins?

FIGURE 17
Genetically Engineered Fish
The bright red zebra danios are the result of genetic engineering.

Go Online
SciLINKS™ NSTA

For: Links on genetic engineering
Visit: www.SciLinks.org
Web Code: scn-0343

Lab zone Skills **Activity**

Communicating
Suppose you work for a drug company that uses genetically engineered bacteria to produce insulin. Write an advertisement for the drug that includes a simplified explanation of how the drug is produced.

Lab zone Skills **Activity**

Skills Focus Communicating **L3**
Materials writing materials
Time 15 minutes
Expected Outcome Students will write an advertisement explaining how insulin is produced through genetically engineered bacteria. Scientists insert the human gene for insulin into the plasmid

of a bacterium, and the bacterium and all of its offspring will produce the protein.
Extend Ask: **Why do the bacteria have to be genetically engineered in order to produce insulin?** *(The bacteria do not naturally produce insulin. The gene must be inserted into their DNA in order for them to make the human protein.)* **learning modality: verbal**

Lab zone Build **Inquiry** **L2**

Modeling Gene Splicing

Materials two pieces of yarn of different colors, blunt scissors, tape, art materials
Time 10 minutes

Focus Remind students that DNA is found in the cytoplasm of bacterial cells.

Teach Challenge students to create a model of DNA with yarn and then to use the model to demonstrate the steps in genetic engineering as illustrated in Figure 16. They might make and cut out large, simple shapes to represent a human cell and a bacterial cell, and arrange the DNA within the "cells" as part of the model.

Apply Remind students that enzymes act on specific sites. Ask: **Do the restriction enzymes have to be the same for both the plasmid and the human gene?** *(Yes; the DNA ends must match for them to join.)* **learning modality: kinesthetic**

Address Misconceptions **L1**
The Future of Gene Therapy

Focus Students may think that all genetic disorders will soon be cured with gene therapy.

Teach Point out that gene therapy is unlikely to be used extensively in the near future because the techniques are new and still being tested.

Apply Ask: **Why is a disease such as hemophilia a good candidate for gene therapy?** *(It is caused by a defect in a single gene.)* **learning modality: logical/ mathematical**

Monitor Progress **L2**

Oral Presentation Call on students to describe ways that genetic engineering is being used.

Answers
Figure 16 The human gene is removed from a chromosome and attaches to the open ends of a cut plasmid in a bacterial cell to form a closed ring.

Reading Checkpoint Human genes are inserted into the cells of cows so that the cows produce milk that contains blood clotting proteins.

Learning About Human Genetics

Teach Key Concepts   L2

Goal of the Human Genome Project

Focus Remind students that genetic engineering depends on identifying what specific genes code for.

Teach Ask: **What is the goal of the Human Genome Project?** (*To identify the DNA sequence of every human gene*)

Apply Tell students that more than 1,400 disease genes have been identified through this project. **learning modality: verbal**

Monitor Progress _____ L2

Answer

 At least 30,000

Assess

Reviewing Key Concepts

1. a. Selective breeding, cloning, and genetic engineering **b.** Selective breeding—crossing two individuals to obtain particular characteristics; cloning—producing an organism with the same genes as another organism; genetic engineering—transferring genes from one organism into the DNA of another **c.** Cloning; many houseplants can be cloned by cutting the stem from one plant and putting the stem in soil.
2. a. All the DNA in one cell of an organism **b.** A research study with the goal of identifying the DNA sequence of every gene in the human genome. **c.** Scientists may eventually be able to insert copies of the normal gene into the genes of people with a genetic disorder.

Reteach   L1

Call on students to explain the different methods of producing organisms with desirable traits.

All in One Teaching Resources, Unit 1

- Section Summary: *Advances in Genetics*
- Review and Reinforce: *Advances in Genetics*
- Enrich: *Advances in Genetics*

FIGURE 18

The Human Genome Project
Scientists on the Human Genome Project continue to study human DNA.

Learning About Human Genetics

Recent advances have enabled scientists to learn a great deal about human genetics. The Human Genome Project and DNA fingerprinting are two applications of this new knowledge.

The Human Genome Project Imagine trying to crack a code that is 6 billion letters long. That's exactly what scientists working on the Human Genome Project have been doing. A **genome** is all the DNA in one cell of an organism. **The main goal of the Human Genome Project has been to identify the DNA sequence of every gene in the human genome.** The Human Genome Project has completed a "first draft" of the human genome. The scientists have learned that the DNA of humans has at least 30,000 genes. The average gene has about 3,000 bases. Scientists will some day know the DNA sequence of every human gene.

DNA Fingerprinting DNA technology used in the Human Genome Project can also identify people and show whether people are related. DNA from a person's cells is broken down into small pieces, or fragments. Selected fragments are used to produce a pattern called a DNA fingerprint. Except for identical twins, no two people have exactly the same DNA fingerprint. You will learn more about DNA fingerprinting in Technology and Society.

 About how many genes are in the human genome?

Section 3 Assessment

Target Reading Skill Asking Questions Work with a partner to check your answers in your graphic organizer.

Reviewing Key Concepts

1. a. Listing List three methods that scientists can use to develop organisms with desirable traits.
   b. Describing Briefly describe each method.
   c. Applying Concepts Lupita has a houseplant. Which method would be the best way of producing a similar plant for a friend? Explain your answer.
2. a. Defining What is a genome?
   b. Explaining What is the Human Genome Project?

c. Relating Cause and Effect How might knowledge gained from the Human Genome Project be used in gene therapy?

Lab zone At-Home **Activity**

Food and Selective Breeding Go to a grocery store with a parent or other family member. Discuss how fruits and vegetables have been produced by selective breeding. Choose a fruit or vegetable, and identify the traits that make it valuable.

Lab zone At-Home **Activity**

Food and Selective Breeding L1
Vegetables and fruits that students might focus on because of their variety are squash and pears. Suggest that students ask the store's produce manager what traits each variety is known for.

Lab zone Chapter **Project**

Keep Students on Track Check that students are completing their displays. Have them write out their presentations using correct terms they have learned in the chapter. Advise students to practice their presentations. Remind them to check their final written descriptions against their displays to make sure that they match and both are correct.

Guilty or Innocent?

Problem

A crime scene may contain hair, skin, or blood from a criminal. These materials all contain DNA that can be used to make a DNA fingerprint. A DNA fingerprint, which consists of a series of bands, is something like a bar code. How can a DNA fingerprint identify individuals?

Skills Focus

drawing conclusions, inferring

Materials

• 4–6 bar codes
• hand lens

Procedure

1. Look at the photograph of DNA band patterns shown at right. Each person's DNA produces a unique pattern of these bands.

2. Now look at the Universal Product Code, also called a bar code, shown below the DNA bands. A bar code can be used as a model of a DNA band pattern. Compare the bar code with the DNA bands to see what they have in common. Record your observations.

3. Suppose that a burglary has taken place, and you're the detective leading the investigation. Your teacher will give you a bar code that represents DNA from blood found at the crime scene. You arrange to have DNA samples taken from several suspects. Write a sentence describing what you will look for as you try to match each suspect's DNA to the DNA sample from the crime scene.

4. You will now be given bar codes representing DNA samples taken from the suspects. Compare those bar codes with the bar code that represents DNA from the crime scene.

5. Use your comparisons to determine whether any of the suspects was present at the crime scene.

Analyze and Conclude

1. **Drawing Conclusions** Based on your findings, were any of the suspects present at the crime scene? Support your conclusion with specific evidence.

2. **Inferring** Why do people's DNA patterns differ so greatly?

3. **Drawing Conclusions** How would your conclusions be affected if you learned that the suspect whose DNA matched the evidence had an identical twin?

4. **Communicating** Suppose you are a defense lawyer. DNA evidence indicates that the bloodstain at the scene of a crime belongs to your client. Do you think this DNA evidence should be enough to convict your client? Write a speech you might give to the jury in defense of your client.

More to Explore

Do you think the DNA fingerprints of a parent and a child would show any similarities? Explain your thinking.

Analyze and Conclude

1. Yes—the suspect whose DNA sample matches the DNA sample from the crime scene

2. No two people, except for identical twins, have the same sequence of bases in their DNA.

3. It would be impossible to conclude which twin was at the crime scene.

4. Students may say no because DNA evidence identifies only who was at the crime scene and not who committed the crime. Students also may say that errors can be made in analyzing the DNA evidence.

Extend Inquiry

More to Explore The DNA fingerprints should look more similar than the DNA fingerprints of unrelated people because parents and children share many genes.

Guilty or Innocent? L2

Prepare for Inquiry

Key Concept

A person's DNA forms a unique pattern of bands that can be used to identify the person.

Skills Objectives

Students will be able to
• draw conclusions about which suspect was present at the crime scene based on the comparisons
• infer why people's DNA patterns differ so greatly

Class Time 20 minutes

All in One Teaching Resources, Unit 1
• Lab Worksheet: *Guilty or Innocent?*

Advance Planning

Remove bar codes from commercial products and cut the numbers from them. Each student's set of bar codes should contain one that is identical to the bar code from the crime scene. You could mount the bar codes on heavy paper and laminate them so they can be reused.

Alternative Materials

If you can obtain actual DNA fingerprints, the lab will be more realistic. Provide a hand lens for any student who has vision impairments.

Guide Inquiry

Troubleshooting the Experiment

Advise students to examine the patterns of bands very carefully because the differences may be minor and easily overlooked.

Expected Outcome

One of the suspect DNA samples is identical to the DNA sample from the crime scene.

Technology and Society

DNA Fingerprinting

Key Concept
DNA fingerprinting is used in many situations. Students research and analyze the use of this technology.

Build Background Knowledge
Ask: **What is the function of genes in a cell?** *(A gene contains the code that determines the structure of a protein.)* **What determines what type of protein will be produced?** *(The order of the nitrogen bases along a gene)* Have a student volunteer read the first paragraph, and then review the steps in producing a DNA fingerprint. Explain that only a portion of the DNA is identified, not the entire genome. The chance that two individuals will have a matching DNA portion varies from one in 800,000 to one in one billion.

Introduce the Debate
Have a student volunteer read the paragraphs *Analyzing DNA* and *Limitations of DNA Fingerprinting.* Explain that in the U.S., a national database of DNA fingerprints is maintained only of adult convicted criminals. Some people have advocated for the DNA fingerprints of all citizens to be maintained. Critics point out that the greater the number of people in the database, the greater the chance of similar profiles. They cite privacy issues and the variability of the quality of DNA fingerprinting from lab to lab. Proponents argue that DNA fingerprints are simply a means of identification, like birth certificates and dental records. Laws are already in place to protect against using genetic information to discriminate against people. A national database would make it easier to fight crime and terrorism.

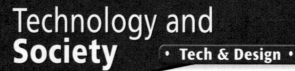

DNA Fingerprinting

What do you have that no one else has? Unless you are an identical twin, your DNA is unique. Because one person's DNA is like no one else's, it can be used to produce genetic "fingerprints." These fingerprints can tie a person to the scene of a crime. They can prevent the wrong person from going to jail. They can also be used to identify skeletal remains. Today, soldiers and sailors give blood and saliva samples so their DNA fingerprints can be saved. Like the identification tags that soldiers wear, DNA records can be used to identify the bodies of unknown soldiers or civilians.

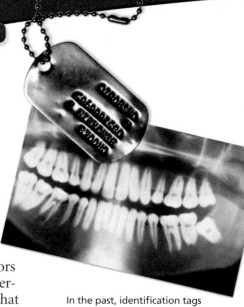

In the past, identification tags and dental records were the main methods for identifying skeletal remains.

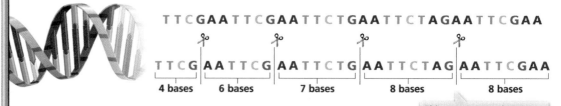

TTCGAATTCGAATTCTGAATTCTAGAATTCGAA

TTCG | AATTCG | AATTCTG | AATTCTAG | AATTCGAA
4 bases · 6 bases · 7 bases · 8 bases · 8 bases

This enzyme cuts the DNA every time it encounters the DNA sequence GAATTC.

1 After a sample of DNA is extracted from the body, an enzyme cuts the DNA strand into several smaller pieces.

2 The cut-up DNA fragments are loaded into a gel that uses electric current to separate fragments. Larger fragments of DNA move through the gel more slowly than the smaller fragments.

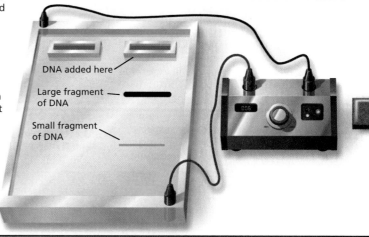

DNA added here

Large fragment of DNA

Small fragment of DNA

164 ◆

Background

History of Science
DNA fingerprinting was invented in 1984 by Professor Sir Alec Jeffreys at the University of Leicester in the United Kingdom. It was first used in an immigration dispute to prove that a boy returning to the UK from Ghana really was the son of legal immigrants. In 1987 in Leicester, the first criminal case involving DNA evidence resulted in the conviction of the true murderer and exoneration of an innocent person. One very interesting use of the technique confirmed that a skeleton was the remains of an Auschwitz camp doctor, Josef Mengele, who escaped to South America in 1979. DNA from the skeleton was compared with DNA from Mengele's wife and son, who were still alive in Germany.

Analyzing DNA

In one method of DNA analysis, DNA from saliva, blood, bones, teeth, or other fluids or tissues is taken from cells. Special enzymes are added to cut the DNA into small pieces. Selected pieces are put into a machine that runs an electric current through the DNA and sorts the pieces by size. The DNA then gets stained and photographed. When developed, a unique banded pattern, similar to a product bar code, is revealed. The pattern can be compared to other samples of DNA to determine a match.

Limitations of DNA Fingerprinting

Like all technology, DNA fingerprinting has its limitations. DNA is very fragile and the films produced can be difficult to read if the DNA samples are old. In rare instances, DNA from the people testing the samples can become mixed in with the test samples and produce inaccurate results. DNA testing is also time consuming and expensive.

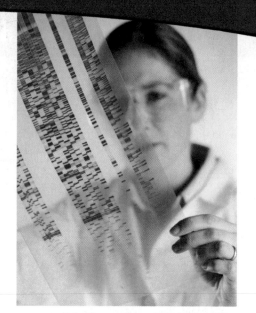

▲ **Scientist reading a DNA fingerprint**

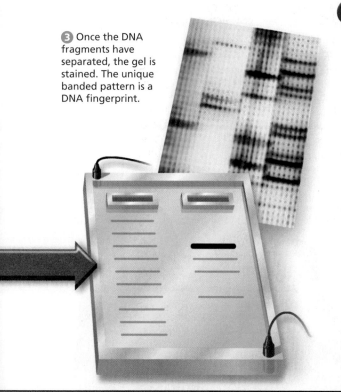

❸ Once the DNA fragments have separated, the gel is stained. The unique banded pattern is a DNA fingerprint.

Weigh the Impact

1. Identify the Need
Make a list of at least five situations in which DNA fingerprinting could be useful.

2. Research
Research the situations you listed in Question 1 to find out if DNA analysis is or can be used in each.

3. Write
Choose one application of DNA analysis and write one or two paragraphs to explain when the application can be used.

Go Online
PHSchool.com

For: More on DNA fingerprinting
Visit: PHSchool.com
Web Code: ceh-3040

Facilitate the Discussion

- Have students participate in a mock hearing to decide whether a national DNA fingerprinting database should be established. This would require every citizen to have DNA samples taken and stored. Students can role-play medical insurance companies, people with genetic disorders, judges who try criminal cases, victims of crimes in which the criminal was never identified, and citizens on both sides of the issue.
- After the hearing, ask students to try to reach a compromise on the fairest way to use DNA fingerprinting.

Weigh the Impact

1. Students may provide a situation using an example from the feature. Other situations include finding out whether people are related and diagnosing a genetic disorder.
2. Require students to access at least three sources for their answers.
3. Paragraphs should include specific situations in which DNA fingerprinting is being used and the limitations of using DNA fingerprinting for that application.

Go Online
PHSchool.com

For: More on DNA fingerprinting
Visit: PHSchool.com
Web Code: ceh-3040

Students can research this issue online.

Extend

Encourage students to investigate the laws in your state regarding the admissibility of DNA evidence in a court of law. Students may also want to find out more about the outcomes in which DNA was used in real-life situations.

Interactive Textbook

- Complete student edition
- Section and chapter self-assessments
- Assessment reports for teachers

Help Students Read

Building Vocabulary

Word Analysis Have students look up the meaning of the word *engineering*. (*The application of scientific and mathematical principles to design ways of solving practical problems*) Then have students use this information to write a definition for *genetic engineering*. (*The application of genetic principles to design processes for inserting the DNA for certain traits in an organism*)

Words in Context Select key terms from the chapter. Have students write a sentence for each term that uses the term in a correct context. Provide them with one example before they begin: *Carrier: Because the boy had hemophilia and neither of his parents showed symptoms of the disease, his mother must have been a carrier.*

Connecting Concepts

Concept Maps Help students develop a concept map to show how the information in this chapter is related. Have students brainstorm to identify the key concepts, key terms, details, and examples, then write each one on a sticky note. They will use these sticky notes to construct the concept map.

Tell students that this concept map will be organized in hierarchical order and to begin at the top with the key concepts. Ask students these questions to guide them to categorize the information on the stickies: **In what ways are human traits controlled by genes? What are two causes of genetic disorders? What are some examples disorders that can be inherited? How can scientists develop organisms with desirable traits?**

Chapter 5 Study Guide

① Human Inheritance

Key Concepts

- Some human traits are controlled by single genes with two alleles, and others by single genes with multiple alleles. Still other traits are controlled by many genes that act together.
- The sex chromosomes carry genes that determine whether a person is male or female. They also carry genes that determine other traits.
- Many of a person's characteristics are determined by an interaction between genes and the environment.

Key Terms

multiple alleles
sex chromosomes
sex-linked gene
carrier

② Human Genetic Disorders

Key Concepts

- Some genetic disorders are caused by mutations in the DNA of genes. Other disorders are caused by changes in the overall structure or number of chromosomes.
- One important tool that geneticists use to trace the inheritance of traits in humans is a pedigree.
- Today doctors use tools such as karyotypes to help detect genetic disorders. People with genetic disorders are helped through medical care, education, job training, and other methods.

Key Terms

genetic disorder
pedigree
karyotype

③ Advances in Genetics

Key Concepts

- Selective breeding, cloning, and genetic engineering are three methods for developing organisms with desirable traits.
- The main goal of the Human Genome Project has been to identify the DNA sequence of every gene in the human genome.

Key Terms

selective breeding
inbreeding
hybridization
clone
genetic engineering
gene therapy
genome

166 ◆

Prompt students by using connecting words or phrases, such as "involves the study of," "which can be caused by," and "which includes diseases such as," to indicate the basis for the organization of the map. The phrases should form a sentence between or among a set of concepts.

Answer
Accept logical presentations by students.

All in One Teaching Resources, Unit 1

- Key Terms Review: *Modern Genetics*
- Connecting Concepts: *Modern Genetics*

Review and Assessment

Organizing Information

Concept Mapping Copy the concept map about human traits onto a separate sheet of paper. Then complete it and add a title. (For more on Concept Mapping, see the Skills Handbook.)

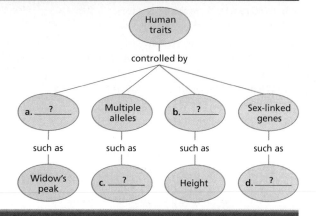

Reviewing Key Terms

Choose the letter of the best answer.

1. A human trait that is controlled by a single gene with multiple alleles is
   a. dimples.   **b.** blood type.
   c. height.   **d.** skin color.

2. A sex-linked disorder is
   a. cystic fibrosis.
   b. sickle-cell disease.
   c. hemophilia.
   d. Down syndrome.

3. Which of the following would most likely be used to diagnose Down syndrome?
   a. a karyotype
   b. a pedigree
   c. a blood-clotting test
   d. a Punnett square

4. Inserting a human gene into a bacterial plasmid is an example of
   a. inbreeding.
   b. selective breeding.
   c. DNA fingerprinting.
   d. genetic engineering.

5. An organism that has the same genes as the organism from which it was produced is called a
   a. clone.   **b.** hybrid.
   c. genome.   **d.** pedigree.

If the statement is true, write *true*. If it is false, change the underlined word or words to make the statement true.

6. A widow's peak is a human trait that is controlled by <u>a single gene</u>.

7. A <u>male</u> inherits two X chromosomes.

8. A <u>karyotype</u> tracks which members of a family have a trait.

9. <u>Hybridization</u> is the crossing of two genetically similar organisms.

10. A <u>genome</u> is all the DNA in one cell of an organism.

Writing in Science

Fact Sheet You are a scientist in a cloning lab. Write a fact sheet that explains what the process of cloning involves. Describe at least one example.

Discovery CHANNEL SCHOOL

Modern Genetics
Video Preview
Video Field Trip
▶ Video Assessment

Chapter 5 ◆ **167**

Review and Assessment

Organizing Information
   a. Single genes with two alleles
   b. Many genes
   c. Blood type (or skin color)
   d. Colorblindness (or Hemophilia)
   Sample title: The Inheritance of Human Traits

Reviewing Key Terms
   1. b **2.** c **3.** a **4.** d **5.** a
   6. true
   7. female
   8. pedigree
   9. Inbreeding
   10. true

Writing in Science

Writing Mode Explanation
Scoring Rubric
4 Includes description of the cloning process and goes beyond requirements in some way, for example, describes more than one example
3 Includes criteria but does not go beyond requirements
2 Includes only brief description
1 Includes incomplete or inaccurate information

Discovery CHANNEL SCHOOL Video Assessment

Modern Genetics

Show the Video Assessment to review chapter content and as a prompt for the writing assignment.

Go Online
For: Self-Assessment
Visit: PHSchool.com
Web Code: cea-3040

Students can take a practice test online that is automatically scored.

All in One Teaching Resources, Unit 1
• Transparency LS50
• Chapter Test
• Performance Assessment Teacher Notes
• Performance Assessment Student Worksheet
• Performance Assessment Scoring Rubric

◉ *ExamView*® **Computer Test Bank CD-ROM**

Checking Concepts

11. Skin color in humans is controlled by many genes.

12. Males need to inherit just one allele to have the trait, whereas females need to inherit two alleles.

13. Sickle-cell disease is a genetic disorder in which red blood cells contain an abnormal form of hemoglobin. People who have the disease inherit a copy of a recessive allele from each parent.

14. A pedigree is a chart that tracks which members of a family have a particular trait. Geneticists use pedigrees to trace the inheritance of traits.

15. Sample answer: Physical therapy can help remove mucus from the lungs of people with cystic fibrosis. People with sickle-cell disease can take folic acid to help their bodies manufacture red blood cells.

16. The horse breeder would mate only horses that have golden coats. The breeder would always select offspring with golden coats to be parents of the next generation.

17. Doctors would replace the defective allele on the X chromosome with a copy of a normal allele.

18. The Human Genome Project is a research study with the goal of identifying the DNA sequence of every gene in the human genome.

Thinking Critically

19. The mother has normal color vision but is a carrier of the colorblindness allele. Her genotype is $X^C X^c$. The father is colorblind. His genotype is $X^c Y$.

20. The father does not have the allele for hemophilia on his X chromosome, so he does not contribute the trait. If the mother is a carrier of hemophilia, one of her X chromosomes has the allele for normal clotting and the other X chromosome has the allele for hemophilia. The son has a 50 percent chance of inheriting an X chromosome that carries the allele for hemophilia and therefore of having hemophilia. Note: The question asks about the sons only, so there are two possible genotypes, not four.

21. Emily has cystic fibrosis. The mother, the father, and Sarah are carriers.

Review and Assessment

Checking Concepts

11. Explain why there are a wide variety of phenotypes for skin color in humans.

12. Traits controlled by recessive alleles on the X chromosome are more common in males than in females. Explain why.

13. What is sickle-cell disease? How is this disorder inherited?

14. What is a pedigree? How do geneticists use pedigrees?

15. Describe two ways in which people with genetic disorders can be helped.

16. Explain how a horse breeder might use selective breeding to produce horses that have golden coats.

17. Describe how gene therapy might be used in the future to treat a person with hemophilia.

18. What is the Human Genome Project?

Thinking Critically

19. Problem Solving A woman with normal color vision has a colorblind daughter. What are the genotypes and phenotypes of both parents?

20. Calculating If a mother is a carrier of hemophilia and the father does not have hemophilia, what is the probability that their son will have the trait? Explain your answer.

21. Interpreting Diagrams The allele for cystic fibrosis is recessive. Identify which members of the family in the pedigree have cystic fibrosis and which are carriers.

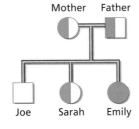

Mother   Father

Joe   Sarah   Emily

Applying Skills

Use the Punnett square to answer Questions 22–24.

The Punnett square below shows how muscular dystrophy, a sex-linked recessive disorder, is inherited.

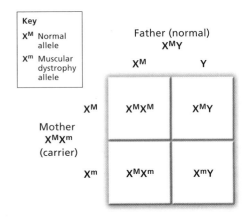

22. Interpreting Data What is the probability that a daughter of these parents will have muscular dystrophy? Explain your answer.

23. Interpreting Data What is the probability that a son of these parents will have muscular dystrophy? Explain your answer.

24. Inferring Is it possible for a woman to have muscular dystrophy? Why or why not?

Lab zone | Chapter **Project**

Performance Assessment Present your display board to your class. Highlight important facts about the genetic trait you selected. Discuss the innovative designs you incorporated into the display board. In your presentation, highlight the interactive part of your project.

Lab zone | Chapter **Project**   L3

Performance Assessment Encourage students to provide constructive feedback to help each other improve their presentations and displays. If possible, arrange for students to present their displays to a younger audience. The display should include an interactive portion that shows the probability of inheriting the trait. Encourage the young children to ask questions about each display as it is presented.

Reflect and Record After all presentations, have students evaluate their own displays in light of their classmates' displays. Students can identify what was most effective in conveying the material and make suggestions they think would have made their display better.

Standardized Test Prep

Choose the letter of the best answer.

1. A woman is heterozygous for the trait of hemophilia. Her husband does not have hemophilia. What is the probability that their son will have hemophilia?

  A 0%

  B 25%

  C 50%

  D 100%

2. Down syndrome is an example of a genetic disorder in which

  F one DNA base has been added.

  G one DNA base has been deleted.

  H one chromosome is substituted for another.

  J an extra chromosome is added to a pair.

Use the pedigree to answer Questions 3–4.

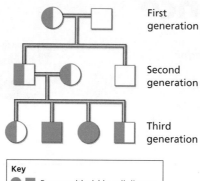

First generation

Second generation

Third generation

Key
- ● ■ Person with sickle-cell disease
- ◐ ◧ Carrier of sickle-cell disease

3. How many people in the second generation have sickle-cell disease?

  A none   **B** one person

  C two people   **D** three people

4. Which statement is true about the third generation in the pedigree?

  F No one has sickle-cell disease.

  G Everyone has sickle-cell disease.

  H Everyone has at least one allele for sickle-cell disease.

  J No one has any alleles for sickle-cell disease.

5. To produce a human protein through genetic engineering, scientists use

  A a bacterial gene inserted into a human chromosome.

  B a human gene inserted into a plasmid.

  C a bacterial gene inserted into a plasmid.

  D a human gene inserted into a human chromosome.

Constructed Response

6. Explain why, for each pregnancy, human parents have a 50 percent probability of having a boy and a 50 percent probability of having a girl. Your answer should include the terms *X chromosome* and *Y chromosome*.

Applying Skills

22. The probability is 0%; the father cannot contribute a recessive allele for muscular dystrophy, so it is not possible for a daughter to receive two X chromosomes with the recessive allele.

23. The probability is 50%; the mother is a carrier of muscular dystrophy, so one of her X chromosomes has the allele for normal health and the other X chromosome has the allele for muscular dystrophy. A son has a 50% chance of inheriting an X chromosome that carries the allele for muscular dystrophy and therefore of having muscular dystrophy.

24. It is possible for a woman to have muscular dystrophy if her father has it and her mother is a carrier. It is a recessive disorder, so she would have to inherit the allele for muscular dystrophy on the X chromosomes of both her parents.

Standardized Test Prep

1. C   **2.** J   **3.** A   **4.** H   **5.** B

6. The mother always contributes an X chromosome to the baby's genome. The father has an X chromosome and a Y chromosome, so the child has a 50% chance of receiving a Y chromosome and therefore a 50% chance of being a boy.

169

Chapter at a Glance

PRENTICE HALL
TeacherEXPRESS™
Plan · Teach · Assess

 Lab zone Chapter **Project** *Life's Long Calendar*

Technology

Local Standards

All in One Teaching Resources, Unit 1
- Chapter Project Teacher Notes, pp. 356–357
- Chapter Project Student Overview, pp. 358–359
- Chapter Project Student Worksheets, pp. 360–361
- Chapter Project Scoring Rubric, p. 362

Discovery CHANNEL SCHOOL
Video Preview

Section 1 **Darwin's Theory**

6.1.1 Describe important observations Darwin made on his voyage.

6.1.2 State the hypothesis Darwin made to explain differences between similar species.

6.1.3 Explain how natural selection leads to evolution.

2 periods
1 block

Go Online SC*LINKS* NSTA

Discovery CHANNEL SCHOOL
Video Field Trip

Section 2 **Evidence of Evolution**

6.2.1 State evidence that supports the theory of evolution.

6.2.2 Explain how scientists infer evolutionary relationships among organisms.

6.2.3 Describe how new species form.

2 periods
1 block

Go Online SC*LINKS* NSTA

Section 3 **The Fossil Record**

6.3.1 Describe how most fossils form.

6.3.2 Explain how scientists can determine a fossil's age.

6.3.3 State what the Geologic Time Scale is.

6.3.4 Identify some unanswered questions about evolution.

2 periods
1 block

Go Online *active art*

Review and Assessment

All in One Teaching Resources, Unit 1
- Key Terms Review, p. 388
- Transparency LS57
- Performance Assessment Teacher Notes, p. 395
- Performance Assessment Scoring Rubric p. 396
- Performance Assessment Student Worksheet, p. 397
- Chapter Test, pp. 398–401

Go Online PHSchool.com

Discovery CHANNEL SCHOOL
Video Assessment

Test Preparation

Test Preparation Blackline Masters

Lab zone Chapter Activities Planner

For more activities

LAB ZONE Easy Planner CD-ROM

Student Edition	Inquiry	Time	Materials	Skills	Resources
Chapter Project, p. 171	Open-Ended	Ongoing (2 to 3 weeks)	**All in One** Teaching Resources, **Unit 1**, p. 356	Calculating, making models, communicating	**Lab zone Easy Planner** **All in One** Teaching Resources, **Unit 1**, Support pp. 356–357
Section 1					
Discover Activity, p. 172	Guided	15 minutes	Metric ruler, 10 sunflower seeds, hand lens	Classifying	**Lab zone Easy Planner**
Try This Activity, p. 175	Guided	10 minutes	Bird seed, paper plate, 20 raisins, tweezers, hair clips, hairpins, clothes pins, stopwatch, paper cup	Inferring	**Lab zone Easy Planner**
Skills Activity, p. 177	Guided	10 minutes	15 black buttons, 15 white buttons, large sheet of plain white paper, stopwatch	Making models	**Lab zone Easy Planner**
Skills Lab, pp. 180–181	Guided	40 minutes	Scissors, marking pen, construction paper, 2 colors	Predicting, making models	**Lab zone Easy Planner** **Lab Activity Video** **All in One** Teaching Resources, **Unit 1**, Skills Lab: *Nature at Work*, pp. 370–372
Section 2					
Discover Activity, p. 182	Open-Ended	10 minutes	6 to 8 pens	Classifying	**Lab zone Easy Planner**
Skills Activity, p. 184	Guided	5 minutes	None	Drawing conclusions	**Lab zone Easy Planner**
Skills Lab, p. 188	Guided	30 minutes	None	Interpreting data, drawing conclusions	**Lab zone Easy Planner** **Lab Activity Video** **All in One** Teaching Resources, **Unit 1**, Skills Lab: *Telltale Molecules*, pp. 379–380
Section 3					
Discover Activity, p. 189	Open-Ended	5 minutes	None	Inferring	**Lab zone Easy Planner**
Try This Activity, p. 190	Guided	10 minutes	Fresh fruit, two plastic containers, water	Inferring	**Lab zone Easy Planner**

Section 1 **Darwin's Theory**

⏱ *2 periods, 1 block*

ABILITY LEVELS
L1 Basic to Average
L2 For All Students
L3 Average to Advanced

Objectives

6.1.1 Describe important observations Darwin made on his voyage.

6.1.2 State the hypothesis Darwin made to explain differences between similar species.

6.1.3 Explain how natural selection leads to evolution.

Local Standards

Key Terms

• species • fossil • adaptation • evolution • scientific theory
• natural selection • variation

 **Preteach**

Build Background Knowledge

Students share knowledge they have about Charles Darwin.

 Discover Activity *How Do Living Things Vary?* **L1**

Targeted Print and Technology Resources

All in One **Teaching Resources, Unit 1**

L2 Reading Strategy
Transparency LS51: Relating
Cause and Effect

◉ **PresentationEXPRESS™ CD-ROM**

Instruct

Darwin's Observations Discuss observations Darwin made on his voyage and why they were significant.

Galápagos Organisms Examine the conclusions Darwin drew from his observations of the organisms on the Galápagos Islands.

Evolution State Darwin's theory of evolution and how he arrived at it.

Natural Selection Explain how natural selection relates to evolution, and apply to an example.

 **Skills Lab** *Nature at Work* **L2**

Targeted Print and Technology Resources

All in One **Teaching Resources, Unit 1**

L2 Guided Reading, pp. 365–367
L2 Skills Lab: *Nature at Work,* pp. 370–372

📼 **Lab Activity Video/DVD**
Skills Lab: *Nature at Work*

www.SciLinks.org Web Code: scn-0351

◉ **Student Edition on Audio CD**

Assess

Section Assessment Questions

🔄 Have students use their graphic organizers with the causes of natural selection to help them answer the questions.

Reteach

Examine figures to review how variation in a species relates to natural selection.

Targeted Print and Technology Resources

All in One **Teaching Resources, Unit 1**

• Section Summary, p. 364
L1 Review and Reinforce, p. 368
L3 Enrich, p. 369

Section 2 Evidence of Evolution

 2 periods, 1 block

Objectives

6.2.1 State evidence that supports the theory of evolution.

6.2.2 Explain how scientists infer evolutionary relationships among organisms.

6.2.3 Describe how new species form.

Key Terms

• homologous structures • branching tree

Local Standards

 **Section Lesson Plans**

Preteach

Build Background Knowledge

Invite students to classify familiar animals.

 **Discover Activity** *How Can You Classify Species?* **L1**

Targeted Print and Technology Resources

All in One Teaching Resources, Unit 1

L2 Reading Strategy
Transparency LS52: Identifying
Supporting Evidence

 PresentationEXPRESS™ CD-ROM

Instruct

Interpreting the Evidence Analyze how fossils, early development, and body structures support the theory of evolution.

Inferring Species Relationships Examine how scientists infer evolutionary relationships among species from evidence.

How Do New Species Form? Describe how separation of organisms leads to the formation of a new species, and apply to an example.

 **Skills Lab** *Telltale Molecules*   **L2**

Targeted Print and Technology Resources

All in One Teaching Resources, Unit 1

L2 Guided Reading, pp. 375–376
L2 Transparency LS53
L2 Skills Lab: *Telltale Molecules*, pp. 379–380

Lab Activity Video/DVD
Skills Lab: *Telltale Molecules*

www.SciLinks.org Web Code: scn-0352

Student Edition on Audio CD

Assess

Section Assessment Questions

Have students use their graphic organizers with evidence supporting the theory of evolution to answer the questions.

Reteach

Use figures in this section to discuss how evidence for evolution can be used to show how species are related.

Targeted Print and Technology Resources

All in One Teaching Resources, Unit 1

• Section Summary, p. 374
L1 Review and Reinforce, p. 377
L3 Enrich, p. 378

Section 3 The Fossil Record

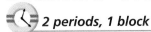 *2 periods, 1 block*

ABILITY LEVELS
L1 Basic to Average
L2 For All Students
L3 Average to Advanced

Objectives

6.3.1 Describe how most fossils form.

6.3.2 Explain how scientists can determine a fossil's age.

6.3.3 State what the Geologic Time Scale is.

6.3.4 Identify some unanswered questions about evolution.

Key Terms

- petrified fossil • mold • cast • relative dating • radioactive dating
- radioactive element • half-life • fossil record • extinct • gradualism
- punctuated equilibria

Local Standards

Preteach

Build Background Knowledge

Ask students to discuss how scientists can know some much about dinosaurs.

Lab zone Discover Activity *What Can You Learn From Fossils?* **L1**

Targeted Print and Technology Resources

All in One Teaching Resources, Unit 1

L2 Reading Strategy: Building Vocabulary

PresentationEXPRESS™ CD-ROM

Instruct

How Do Fossils Form? Explain how most fossils form, and distinguish the types of fossils.

Determining a Fossil's Age Compare and contrast relative dating and radioactive dating.

What Do Fossils Reveal? Explain the Geologic Time Scale, and apply to an example.

Unanswered Questions Ask questions to help students examine unknowns about mass extinctions and the rate of evolution.

Targeted Print and Technology Resources

All in One Teaching Resources, Unit 1

L2 Guided Reading, pp. 383–385

L2 Transparencies LS54, LS55, LS56

PHSchool.com Web Code: cep-3053

Student Edition on Audio CD

Assess

Section Assessment Questions

Have students use their definitions to help them answer the questions.

Reteach

Use the visuals to summarize how fossils are formed and what they tell us about life on Earth.

Targeted Print and Technology Resources

All in One Teaching Resources, Unit 1

- Section Summary, p. 382
L1 Review and Reinforce, p. 386
L3 Enrich, p. 387

Chapter 6 Content Refresher

Go Online

NSTA-PDi LINKS

For: Professional development support
Visit: www.SciLinks.org/PDLinks
Web Code: scf-0350

Professional Development

Section 1 Darwin's Theory

Lamarck's Theory of Evolution Darwin was not the first person to propose a theory of evolution. In the early 1800s, a well-known French naturalist named Jean-Baptiste Lamarck also developed a theory of evolution. Lamarck thought that changes in an organism during its lifetime could be passed on to its offspring. For example, Lamarck thought that giraffes could stretch their necks to feed on the leaves of tall trees. These giraffes would have offspring with longer necks. This idea is often called "the inheritance of acquired characteristics," and it is now known to be incorrect. Changes in an organism cannot be passed on to its offspring unless they are controlled by genes.

Section 2 Evidence of Evolution

Vestigial Organs Vestigial organs are one type of homologous structure. A vestigial organ is a structure that has little or no apparent function in the organism that possesses it, even though corresponding structures are fully functional in other organisms. For example, certain snake species have vestiges of leg bones. Since snakes crawl rather than walk, the leg bones have no function. The snakes with vestigial leg bones probably descended from a vertebrate ancestor that used legs to move.

Section 3 The Fossil Record

Index Fossils and Relative Dating

An index fossil is the fossil of an extinct species, such as trilobites and ammonites, that existed for a relatively short period but over a large area. Scientists use index fossils as a way of estimating the ages of other fossils. For example, if a fossil of an unknown age is found near a trilobite in the same rock layer, such as in Layer A in the illustration, scientists assume that the fossil is approximately the same age as the trilobite.

Address Misconceptions

Many students think that most species that have existed on Earth have left fossil remains. However, only a fraction of one percent is likely to have been preserved as fossils. For a strategy for overcoming this misconception, see **Address Misconceptions** in the section *The Fossil Record*.

Scientists also use index fossils to match up rock layers that may be at a distance from one another or have become separated. For example, in the illustration, the left and right sides of Layers A, B, and C are separated by a valley. The presence of trilobites in Layer A on both sides of the valley indicate that those layers are the same age; likewise, the ammonites in Layer C indicate that these layers match on both sides of the valley.

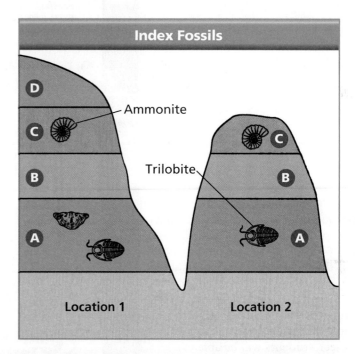

Index Fossils

D

C — Ammonite

B — Trilobite

A

Location 1   Location 2

Help Students Read

Outlining

Understanding Text Structure

Strategy Outlining using headings as major divisions is a good strategy to apply to an entire section, if it is not excessively long. Outlining is best applied to sections in which the headings are parallel, and in which there are main headings and subheadings.

Example

1. Before students read, have them preview a section's title and headings. Make a skeleton outline for the section.
2. Have students copy the skeleton outline and fill in details under each main heading and subheading as they read.

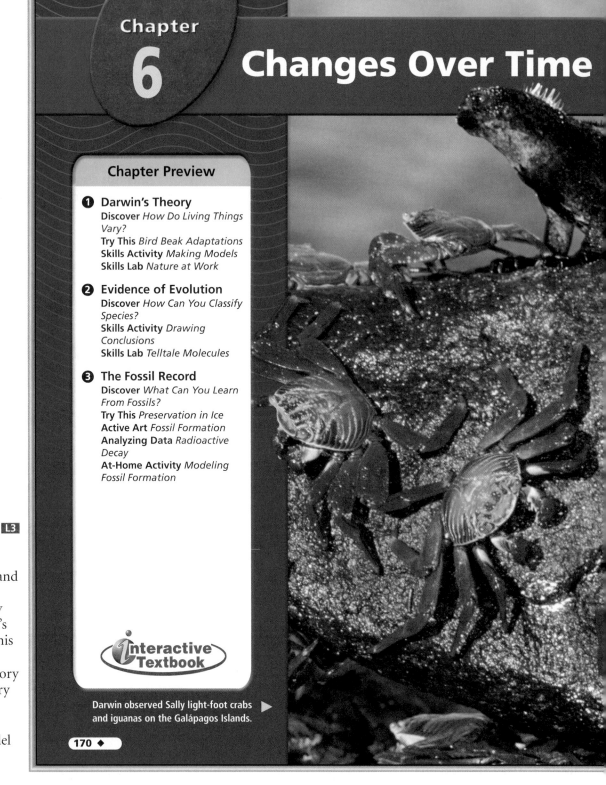

Interactive Textbook

- Complete student edition
- Video and audio
- Simulations and activities
- Section and chapter reviews

Chapter 6
Changes Over Time

Chapter Preview

❶ Darwin's Theory
Discover *How Do Living Things Vary?*
Try This *Bird Beak Adaptations*
Skills Activity *Making Models*
Skills Lab *Nature at Work*

❷ Evidence of Evolution
Discover *How Can You Classify Species?*
Skills Activity *Drawing Conclusions*
Skills Lab *Telltale Molecules*

❸ The Fossil Record
Discover *What Can You Learn From Fossils?*
Try This *Preservation in Ice*
Active Art *Fossil Formation*
Analyzing Data *Radioactive Decay*
At-Home Activity *Modeling Fossil Formation*

Interactive Textbook

Darwin observed Sally light-foot crabs ▶
and iguanas on the Galápagos Islands.

Lab zone Chapter Project L3

Objectives
This project will help students to understand the large time spans involved in geologic time and to place significant evolutionary events within an accurate model of Earth's history: a timeline drawn to scale. After this Chapter Project, students will be able to
- make scale models representing the history of life on Earth, with major evolutionary events included
- calculate the scale of a model
- communicate the features of their model to the class

Skills Focus
Calculating, making models, communicating

Project Time Line 2 to 3 weeks

All in One Teaching Resources, Unit 1
- Chapter Project Teacher Notes
- Chapter Project Overview
- Chapter Project Worksheet 1
- Chapter Project Worksheet 2
- Chapter Project Scoring Rubric

Developing a Plan
On the first day, have students review the project rules and procedures. Invite questions and comments. Then divide the class into groups of three or four students each, and let the groups meet to discuss the types of timelines they could make.

Possible Materials
- Students will need calculators, meter sticks, and metric tape to construct all models that use units of length to represent millions of years.
- Provide a variety of source materials for students to research additional evolutionary events to include in their timelines.
- Other materials will vary depending on the formats that students choose.

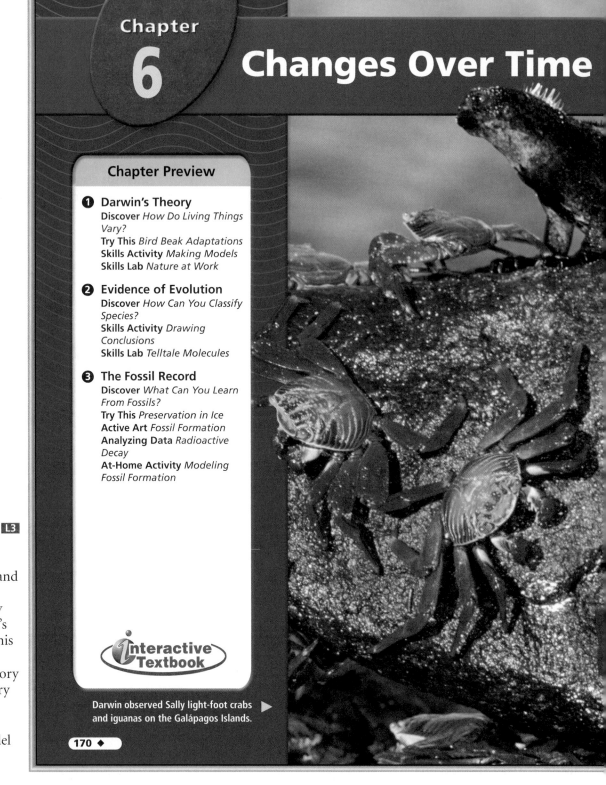

Chapter Project

Life's Long Calendar

Earth's history goes back billions of years. This chapter project will help you understand this huge time span. In this project, you'll find a way to convert enormous time periods into a more familiar scale.

Your Goal To use a familiar measurement scale to create two timelines for Earth's history

To complete the project you must

- represent Earth's history using a familiar scale, such as months on a calendar or yards on a football field
- use your chosen scale twice, once to plot out 5 billion years of history, and once to focus on the past 600 million years
- include markers on both scales to show important events in the history of life

Plan It! Preview Figure 16 in this chapter to see what events occurred during the two time periods. In a small group, discuss some familiar scales you might use for your timelines. You could select a time interval such as a year or a day. Alternatively, you could choose a distance interval such as the length of your schoolyard or the walls in your classroom. Decide on the kind of timelines you will make. Then plan and construct your timelines.

Chapter 6 ◆ 171

Changes Over Time

Show the Video Preview to introduce the Galápagos Islands.

Performance Assessment

The Chapter Project Scoring Rubric will help you evaluate how well students complete the Chapter Project. You may want to share the scoring rubric with your students so they are clear about what will be expected of them. Students will be assessed on

- their accuracy in calculating the scales for the two models
- their ability to construct two scale models of Earth's history with important evolutionary events accurately marked
- their effectiveness in communicating the model-making process and results to others
- their participation in their groups

Launching the Project

Draw a long line across the board, and label the left end *Beginning of Earth* and the right end *Present*. Have students preview Figure 16. Ask: **How long ago did Earth begin?** (*about 4.6 billion years ago*) Write 4,600,000,000 on the board. **When did the first animals appear on Earth?** (*about 600 million years ago*) Write 600,000,000 below the first number with place values aligned. Ask: **Where should I mark the line to show when the first animals appeared?** (*Close to the "Present" end*) Point out that if students made only one timeline to scale, all the events that happened from the beginning of the Paleozoic Era to the present would be crowded into a very small section. Explain that to solve this problem, they will make two timelines in this project.

Objectives

After this lesson, students will be able to
6.1.1 Describe important observations Darwin made on his voyage.
6.1.2 State the hypothesis Darwin made to explain differences between similar species.
6.1.3 Explain how natural selection leads to evolution.

Target Reading Skill

Relating Cause and Effect Explain that cause is the reason for what happens. The effect is what happens because of the cause. Relating cause and effect helps students relate the reason for what happens to what happens as a result.

Answer

Possible answers:

Causes

Overproduction: More offspring are produced than can survive.
Variations: Members of the same species differ.
Competition: Offspring compete for survival.
Selection: Some variations make individuals better fit for survival.
Environmental Change: Changes in environment can affect an individual's survival.
Genes: Genes that help determine survival are passed from parent to offspring.

All in One Teaching Resources, Unit 1

• Transparency LS51

Preteach

Build Background Knowledge   L1

Discussing Darwin

Many students will have read articles or seen television specials about Darwin or the Galápagos Islands. Ask: **Who was Charles Darwin?** *(A scientist who came up with the idea of evolution by natural selection)* **What interested Darwin about the Galápagos Islands?** *(They have a lot of unusual organisms, such as giant lizards and tortoises.)*

Reading Preview

Key Concepts

• What important observations did Darwin make on his voyage?
• What hypothesis did Darwin make to explain the differences between similar species?
• How does natural selection lead to evolution?

Key Terms

• species • fossil • adaptation
• evolution • scientific theory
• natural selection • variation

Target Reading Skill

Relating Cause and Effect In a graphic organizer, identify factors that cause natural selection.

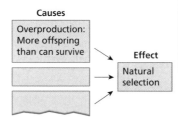

Causes

Overproduction: More offspring than can survive → Effect: Natural selection

FIGURE 1
The Voyage of the *Beagle*

Charles Darwin sailed on the *Beagle* to the Galápagos Islands. He saw many unusual organisms on the islands, such as giant tortoises and the blue-footed booby.
Interpreting Maps *After leaving South America, where did the Beagle go?*

Replica of the *Beagle* ▶

172 ◆

Lab zone Discover Activity

How Do Living Things Vary?

1. Use a ruler to measure the length and width of 10 sunflower seeds. Record each measurement.
2. Now use a hand lens to carefully examine each seed. Record each seed's shape, color, and number of stripes.

Think It Over

Classifying In what ways are the seeds in your sample different from one another? In what ways are they similar? How could you group the seeds based on their similarities and differences?

In December 1831, the British ship HMS *Beagle* set sail from England on a five-year trip around the world. On board was a 22-year-old named Charles Darwin. Darwin eventually became the ship's naturalist—a person who studies the natural world. His job was to learn as much as he could about the living things he saw on the voyage. Darwin observed plants and animals he had never seen before. He wondered why they were so different from those in England. Darwin's observations led him to develop one of the most important scientific theories of all time: the theory of evolution by natural selection.

Asia

Pacific Ocean

Australia

New Zealand

Lab zone Discover Activity

Skills Focus Classifying   L1

Materials metric ruler, 10 sunflower seeds, hand lens

Time 15 minutes

Tips Tell students that differences among seeds in their sample may be slight and hard to detect. Advise them to examine the seeds carefully.

Expected Outcome Students will observe that the seeds in their sample differ in such traits as size, shape, color, or number of stripes.

Think It Over The seeds in each sample may differ in some traits and be similar in others. Depending on the makeup of their sample, students may group seeds that are similar in size, shape, color, number of stripes, or other traits.

Darwin's Observations

As you can see in Figure 1, the *Beagle* made many stops along the coast of South America. From there, the ship traveled to the Galápagos Islands. Darwin observed living things as he traveled. He thought about relationships among those organisms. **Darwin's important observations included the diversity of living things, the remains of ancient organisms, and the characteristics of organisms on the Galápagos Islands.**

Diversity Darwin was amazed by the tremendous diversity of living things that he saw. In Brazil, he saw insects that looked like flowers and ants that marched across the forest floor like huge armies. In Argentina, he saw sloths, animals that moved very slowly and spent much of their time hanging in trees.

Today scientists know that organisms are even more diverse than Darwin could ever have imagined. Scientists have identified more than 1.7 million species of organisms on Earth. A **species** is a group of similar organisms that can mate with each other and produce fertile offspring.

Fossils Darwin saw the fossil bones of animals that had died long ago. A **fossil** is the preserved remains or traces of an organism that lived in the past. Darwin was puzzled by some of the fossils he observed. For example, he saw fossil bones that resembled the bones of living sloths. The fossil bones were much larger than those of the sloths that were alive in Darwin's time. He wondered what had happened to the giant creatures from the past.

Reading Checkpoint What is a fossil?

Changes Over Time
Video Preview
▶ Video Field Trip
Video Assessment

▲ Giant tortoise

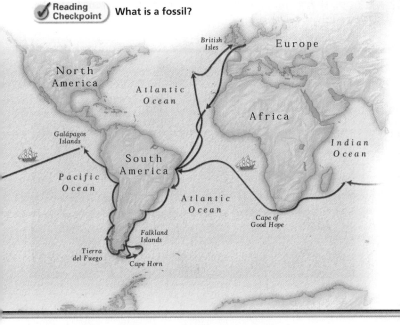

▲ Blue-footed booby

Chapter 6 ◆ 173

Instruct

Changes Over Time
Show the Video Field Trip to let students preview Darwin's ideas.

Darwin's Observations

Teach Key Concepts L2

Darwin's Voyage

Focus Remind students that the variety of living things on Earth is called biological diversity.

Teach Ask: **What observations did Darwin make?** *(He noted the diversity of living things, the remains of ancient organisms, and the characteristics of organisms on the Galápagos Islands.)* **What struck him about these observations?** *(He was amazed by the tremendous diversity he saw, and he wondered what had happened to the animals that left fossil bones.)*

Apply Explain that in Darwin's day, most people believed that all living things were created at the same time and that they never changed. Darwin's observations led him to wonder about these ideas. **learning modality: verbal**

Independent Practice L2

All in One Teaching Resources, Unit 1

• Guided Reading and Study Worksheet: *Darwin's Theory*

⊙ **Student Edition on Audio CD**

Differentiated Instruction

Special Needs L1
Working With a Partner Partner students who have difficulty reading and processing information with more able students. As students read each section, have them rewrite in their own words each of the boldfaced statements and the statements defining key terms. Then have

them write questions about each of the statements they have written. After students have finished reading the section, have them exchange their questions with other pairs of students, and answer one another's questions. **learning modality: verbal**

Monitor Progress L2

Writing Have students describe in their own words the insights that Darwin gained from his voyage.

Answers
Figure 1 The Galápagos Islands

Reading Checkpoint The preserved remains or traces of an organism that lived in the past

Galápagos Organisms

Teach Key Concepts L2

Comparing Organisms

Focus Have students look back at Figure 1 and note that the Galápagos Islands were isolated from the mainland.

Teach Point out that islands make good places for studying how organisms change over time. Ask: **What kinds of comparisons did Darwin make on his voyage?** *(He compared Galápagos organisms to South American organisms, and he compared organisms among the islands.)* **What did Darwin conclude from these observations?** *(He hypothesized that the animals on the islands came from the mainland but had changed over time.)* **What did Darwin notice about slight differences between species?** *(The differences made it possible for the organisms to survive and reproduce in their particular environment.)*

Apply Have students examine Figure 2. Point out that variations in a trait such as color may make organisms better suited for their environment. Ask: **What difference in the environment do you think might make the color of each species an adaptation?** *(Students may say the colors in the environment: the green iguana's color helps it blend in with its leafy environment, and the marine iguana's color helps it blend in with its rocky environment.)* **learning modality: logical/mathematical**

FIGURE 2
Comparing Iguanas
Iguanas on mainland South America (above) have smaller claws than iguanas on the Galápagos Islands. **Comparing and Contrasting** *In what other ways are the iguanas different?*

Galápagos Organisms

In 1835, the *Beagle* reached the Galápagos Islands. Darwin observed many unusual life forms on these small islands, such as giant tortoises, or land turtles. Some of these tortoises could look him in the eye! After returning to England, Darwin thought about the organisms he had seen. He compared Galápagos organisms to organisms that lived elsewhere. He also compared organisms on different islands in the Galápagos group. He was surprised by some of the similarities and differences he saw.

Comparisons to South American Organisms Darwin found many similarities between Galápagos organisms and those in South America. Many of the birds on the islands, including hawks, mockingbirds, and finches, resembled those on the mainland. Many of the plants were similar to plants Darwin had collected on the mainland.

However, there were important differences between the organisms on the islands and those on the mainland. The iguanas on the Galápagos Islands had large claws that allowed them to grip slippery rocks, where they fed on seaweed. The iguanas on the mainland had smaller claws. Smaller claws allowed the mainland iguanas to climb trees, where they ate leaves. You can see these differences in Figure 2.

From his observations, Darwin hypothesized that a small number of different plant and animal species had come to the Galápagos Islands from the mainland. They might have been blown out to sea during a storm or set adrift on a fallen log. Once the plants and animals reached the islands, they reproduced. Eventually, their offspring became different from their mainland relatives.

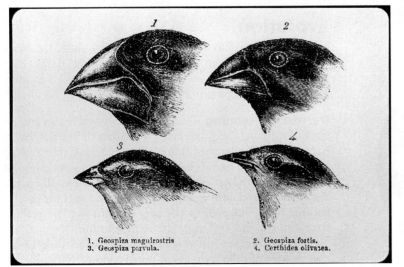

FIGURE 3
Galápagos Finches Darwin made these drawings of four species of Galápagos finches. The structure of each bird's beak is an adaptation related to the type of food the bird eats. **Comparing and Contrasting** *Identify some specific differences in these finches' beaks.*

1. *Geospiza magnirostris*
3. *Geospiza parvula*
2. *Geospiza fortis*.
4. *Certhidea olivacea*.

Comparisons Among the Islands As he traveled from one Galápagos island to the next, Darwin also noticed many differences among organisms. For example, the tortoises on one island had dome-shaped shells. Those on another island had saddle-shaped shells. A government official in the islands told Darwin that he could tell which island a tortoise came from just by looking at its shell.

Adaptations Like the tortoises, the finches on the Galápagos were noticeably different from one island to the next. The most obvious differences were the varied sizes and shapes of the birds' beaks, as shown in Figure 3. An examination of the different finches showed that each species was well suited to the life it led. Finches that ate insects had narrow, needle-like beaks. Finches that ate seeds had strong, wide beaks.

Beak shape is an example of an **adaptation,** a trait that helps an organism survive and reproduce. The finches' beak structures help in obtaining food. Other adaptations help organisms avoid being eaten. For example, some plants, such as milkweed, are poisonous or have a bad taste. A variety of adaptations aid in reproduction. The bright colors of some flowers attract insects. When an insect lands on a flower, the insect may pick up pollen grains, which produce sperm. The insect then may carry the pollen grains to another flower, enabling fertilization to take place.

Reading Checkpoint How did the beaks of Galápagos finches differ from one island to another?

Lab zone Try This **Activity**

Bird Beak Adaptations
Use this activity to explore adaptations in birds.

1. Scatter a small amount of bird seed on a paper plate. Scatter 20 raisins on the plate to represent insects.
2. Obtain a variety of objects such as tweezers, hair clips, and clothespins. Pick one object to use as a "beak."
3. See how many seeds you can pick up and drop into a cup in 10 seconds.
4. Now see how many "insects" you can pick up and drop into a cup in 10 seconds.
5. Use a different "beak" and repeat Steps 3 and 4.

Inferring What type of beak worked well for seeds? For insects? How are different-shaped beaks useful for eating different foods?

Lab zone Build **Inquiry** L2

Interpreting Scientific Drawings

Materials drawings of related bird species from a field identification guide

Time 10 minutes

Focus Point out that much of Darwin's time during the voyage of the *Beagle* was spent observing and comparing different organisms.

Teach Provide students with drawings from a field guide that show several related species of birds, such as several species of ducks, warblers, herons, or woodpeckers. Have students examine the drawings carefully and make lists of all the similarities and differences they observe among the species pictured. Then, have pairs of students compare lists. Emphasize that being a good observer requires care and skill.

Apply Ask: **What are some other ways these birds might be similar or different that you cannot observe visually?** (*Possible ways include their songs and the texture of their feathers.*) **learning modality: visual**

Monitor Progress L2

Oral Presentation Call on students to name examples of the diversity that Darwin observed.

Answers
Figure 2 One iguana is green and lives in a tree and the other iguana is gray and lives on rocks.

Figure 3 The beaks differ in their degree of pointedness and their size. Species 1 and 2 have wider beaks than species 3 and 4. Species 3 has a short beak, and species 4 has a long, narrow beak.

Reading Checkpoint They differed in size and shape. Some were narrow and needle-like, while others were strong and wide.

Lab zone Try This **Activity**

Skills Focus Inferring L2

Materials bird seed, paper plate, 20 raisins, tweezers, hair clips, hairpins, clothes pins, stopwatch, paper cup

Time 10 minutes

Tips Have students work in pairs so one student picks up objects while the other watches the clock.

Expected Outcome Some objects are better for picking up seeds and others for raisins. Likewise, some beaks are better for seeds and others for insects.

Extend Ask: **Which species in Figure 3 appear to be adapted to a diet of seeds, and which to a diet of insects?** (*Seeds: 1, 2, and possibly 3; insects: 4*) **learning modality: kinesthetic**

Evolution

Teach Key Concepts L2

Development of the Theory of Evolution

Focus Review with students that Darwin observed adaptations that helped organisms survive and reproduce in different environments.

Teach Ask: **What did Darwin believe led to the different adaptations in species on the Galápagos Islands?** *(He reasoned that the organisms that arrived on the islands faced conditions that were different from those on the mainland. Over many generations, the species became better adapted to the new conditions.)* **What did Darwin's ideas come to be known as?** *(The theory of evolution)* **What is evolution?** *(Evolution is the gradual change in a species over time.)*

Apply Ask: **How is the way that traits are inherited related to the theory of evolution?** *(If traits were not inherited, evolution would not occur; evolution depends upon passing traits to offspring with the result that the species gradually changes over many generations.)* **learning modality: logical/ mathematical**

Help Students Read L2

Compare and Contrast Have students read the passages on Evolution and Natural Selection. Then have students describe the similarities and differences between selective breeding and natural selection.

▲ Seattle Slew, great-grandfather of Funny Cide

Distorted Humor, ▲ father of Funny Cide

Funny Cide ▶

FIGURE 4
Selective Breeding
Race horses are selectively bred to obtain the trait of speed. Funny Cide's father, Distorted Humor, and great-grandfather, Seattle Slew, were known for their speed.

176 ◆

Evolution

After he returned to England, Darwin continued to think about what he had seen during his voyage on the *Beagle*. Darwin spent the next 20 years consulting with other scientists, gathering more information, and thinking through his ideas.

Darwin's Reasoning Darwin especially wanted to understand the different adaptations of organisms on the Galápagos Islands. **Darwin reasoned that plants or animals that arrived on the Galápagos Islands faced conditions that were different from those on the mainland. Perhaps, Darwin hypothesized, the species gradually changed over many generations and became better adapted to the new conditions.** The gradual change in a species over time is called **evolution**.

Darwin's ideas are often referred to as the theory of evolution. A **scientific theory** is a well-tested concept that explains a wide range of observations. From the evidence he collected, Darwin concluded that organisms on the Galápagos Islands had changed over time. However, Darwin did not know how the changes had happened.

Selective Breeding Darwin studied other examples of changes in living things to help him understand how evolution might occur. One example that Darwin studied was the offspring of animals produced by selective breeding. English farmers in Darwin's time used selective breeding to produce sheep with fine wool. Darwin himself had bred pigeons with large, fan-shaped tails. By repeatedly allowing only those pigeons with many tail feathers to mate, breeders had produced pigeons with two or three times the usual number of tail feathers. Darwin thought that a process similar to selective breeding might happen in nature. But he wondered what process selected certain traits.

 Reading Checkpoint) **What is a scientific theory?**

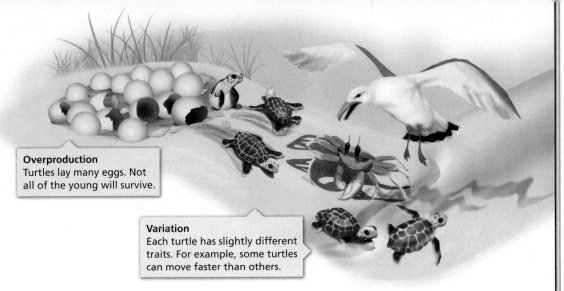

Overproduction
Turtles lay many eggs. Not all of the young will survive.

Variation
Each turtle has slightly different traits. For example, some turtles can move faster than others.

Natural Selection

In 1858, Darwin and another British biologist, Alfred Russel Wallace, each proposed an explanation for how evolution could occur in nature. The next year, Darwin described this mechanism in a book entitled *The Origin of Species*. In his book, Darwin proposed that evolution occurs by means of natural selection. **Natural selection** is the process by which individuals that are better adapted to their environment are more likely to survive and reproduce than other members of the same species. Darwin identified factors that affect the process of natural selection: overproduction, competition, and variations. Figure 5 and Figure 6 show how natural selection might happen in a group of turtles.

Overproduction Darwin knew that most species produce far more offspring than can possibly survive. In many species, so many offspring are produced that there are not enough resources—food, water, and living space—for all of them. Many female insects, for example, lay thousands of eggs. If all newly hatched insects survived, they would soon crowd out all other plants and animals. Darwin knew that this doesn't happen. Why not?

Variations As you learned in your study of genetics, members of a species differ from one another in many of their traits. Any difference between individuals of the same species is called a **variation.** For example, certain insects may be able to eat foods that other insects of their species avoid. The color of a few insects may be different from that of most other insects in their species.

FIGURE 5
Overproduction and Variation
Like actual sea turtles, the turtles in this illustration produce many more offspring than will survive. Some turtles are better adapted than others to survive in their environment.
Relating Cause and Effect *What adaptations might help young sea turtles survive?*

Lab zone · Skills Activity

Making Models

Scatter 15 black buttons and 15 white buttons on a sheet of white paper. Have a partner time you to see how many buttons you can pick up in 10 seconds. Pick up the buttons one at a time. Did you collect more buttons of one color than the other? Why? How can a variation such as color affect the process of natural selection?

Lab zone · Skills Activity

Skills Focus Making models   **L1**

Materials 15 black buttons, 15 white buttons, plain white paper, stopwatch

Time 10 minutes

Tips All the buttons should be identical except for color.

Expected Outcome Students are likely to pick up more black buttons. A

variation such as color can affect natural selection by making an organism more or less likely to be seen by a predator.

Extend Ask: **What other variations might affect whether an organism is captured by a predator?** (*Sample: intelligence and acuteness of senses.*)
learning modality: kinesthetic

Natural Selection

Teach Key Concepts   L2
Natural Selection Can Lead to Evolution

Focus Remind students that Darwin thought that a kind of selective breeding process occurred naturally.

Teach Ask: **What did Darwin call this idea?** (*Natural selection*) **Explain his proposal that natural selection leads to evolution.** (*Helpful variations gradually accumulate in a species over many generations, while unfavorable ones disappear.*)

Apply Ask: **How might natural selection have led from shorter-necked giraffes to long-necked ones?** (*Mutations produced some giraffes with slightly longer necks. Those giraffes could reach plants that other giraffes could not reach and had a better chance of surviving and passing on their genes. Over many generations, longer necks evolved.*) **learning modality: logical/mathematical**

Lab zone · Build Inquiry   L2

Observing Favorable Traits

Materials nature magazines or biology textbooks

Time 15 minutes

Focus Ask students to brainstorm types of adaptations.

Teach Have students identify and record adaptations that allow plants and animals to better survive in their environment.

Apply Ask students to describe some characteristics that are adaptations in some environments but harmful in others. (*Example: white fur*) **learning modality: visual**

Monitor Progress _____   L2

Writing Have students summarize the factors in natural selection.

Answers
Figure 5 Sample answer: Hard shells, ability to swim quickly, and keen eyesight

 Reading Checkpoint A well-tested concept that explains a wide range of observations

Use Visuals: Figures 5 and 6 L2

Factors of Natural Selection

Focus Have students review the factors of natural selection.

Teach Ask: **What factors of natural selection are demonstrated in Figures 5 and 6?** (*Overproduction—there are more turtles than will survive; variation—the turtles have different swimming abilities; and competition—the turtles are competing to escape from a predator; selection—some turtles are better able to survive in their environment; survival and reproduction—only some turtles reproduce.*)

Apply Ask: **What is the outcome of this selection process?** (*The turtle that is not eaten survives and passes its traits on to the next generation.*) **learning modality: visual**

 Lab zone Build **Inquiry** L3

Designing an Experiment

Materials markers and poster board

Time 20 minutes

Focus Remind students that only traits that are controlled by genes can result in evolution.

Teach Divide the class into groups, and challenge students in each group to brainstorm an experiment to demonstrate that traits acquired during an organism's lifetime are not passed on to the next generation. Have each group draw diagrams that show how the group would test the hypothesis and illustrate the steps of the experiment. (*One way is to change experimental organisms in some way, for example, by dyeing the hair of lab rats, and then observing whether the changed trait appears in their offspring.*) Have each group elect a spokesperson to present its poster and describe its experimental plan to the rest of the class. Urge the class to give the group feedback on its ideas.

Apply Ask: **Why don't acquired traits result in evolution?** (*Because only genes, not acquired characteristics, are passed from parents to their offspring*) **learning modality: logical/mathematical**

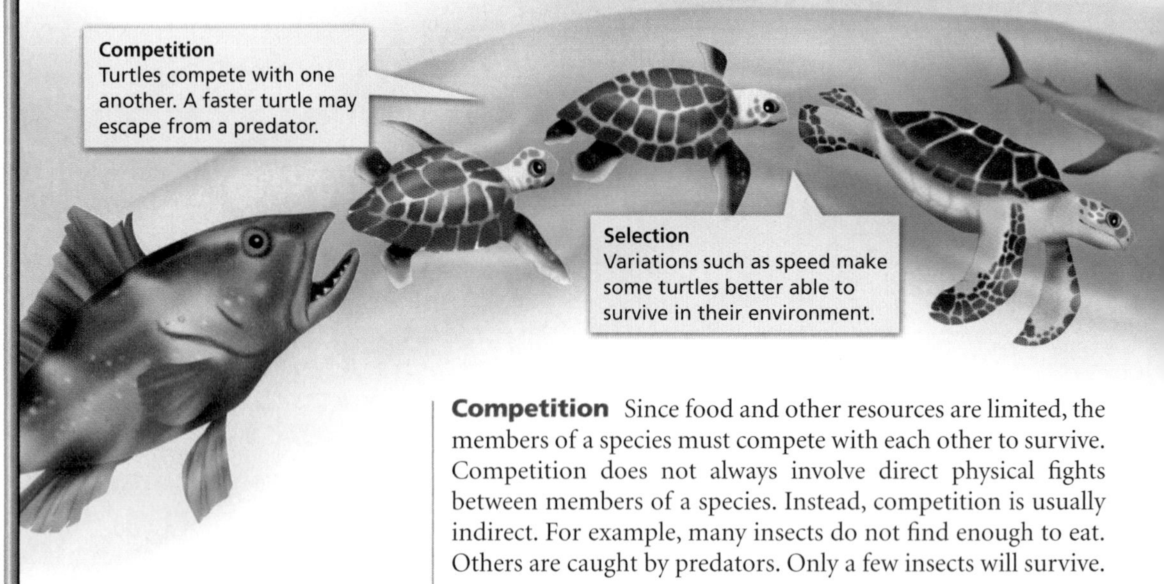

Competition
Turtles compete with one another. A faster turtle may escape from a predator.

Selection
Variations such as speed make some turtles better able to survive in their environment.

FIGURE 6
Competition and Selection
Variations among turtles make some of them better able to survive. Turtles that survive to become adults will be able to reproduce.
Applying Concepts *What are some variations that sea turtles might exhibit?*

Competition Since food and other resources are limited, the members of a species must compete with each other to survive. Competition does not always involve direct physical fights between members of a species. Instead, competition is usually indirect. For example, many insects do not find enough to eat. Others are caught by predators. Only a few insects will survive.

Selection Darwin observed that some variations make individuals better adapted to their environment. Those individuals are more likely to survive and reproduce. Their offspring may inherit the helpful characteristic. The offspring, in turn, will be more likely to survive and reproduce, and thus pass on the characteristic to their offspring. After many generations, more members of the species will have the helpful characteristic.

In effect, the environment has "selected" organisms with helpful traits to become parents of the next generation. **Darwin proposed that, over a long time, natural selection can lead to change. Helpful variations may gradually accumulate in a species, while unfavorable ones may disappear.**

Environmental Change A change in the environment can affect an organism's ability to survive. The environmental change can therefore lead to selection. For example, monkey flowers are a type of plant. Most monkey flowers cannot grow in soil that has a high concentration of copper. However, because of genetic variation, some varieties of monkey flower now grow near copper mines, in spite of the copper in the soil.

Here is how natural selection might have resulted in monkey flowers that can grow in copper-contaminated soil. When the soil around a mine first became contaminated, a small number of monkey-flower plants may have been able to survive in the high level of copper. These plants grew and reproduced. After many generations, most of the seeds that sprouted in the soil produced monkey flowers that could withstand the copper.

Go Online
SciLINKS NSTA

For: Links on Charles Darwin
Visit: www.SciLinks.org
Web Code: scn-0351

Go Online
SCLINKS NSTA

For: Links on Charles Darwin
Visit: www.SciLinks.org
Web Code: scn-0351

Download a worksheet to guide students' review of Darwin's work.

Survival and Reproduction
Only a few turtles survive long enough to reproduce. The offspring may inherit the favorable traits of the parents.

Genes and Natural Selection Without variations, all the members of a species would have the same traits. Natural selection would not occur because all individuals would have an equal chance of surviving and reproducing. But where do variations come from? How are they passed on from parents to offspring?

Darwin could not explain what caused variations or how they were passed on. As scientists later learned, variations can result from mutation and the shuffling of alleles during meiosis. Genes are passed from parents to their offspring. Because of this, only traits that are inherited, or controlled by genes, can be acted upon by natural selection.

Section 1 Assessment

Target Reading Skill
Relating Cause and Effect Work with a partner to check the information in your graphic organizer.

Reviewing Key Concepts
1. a. **Listing** List three general kinds of observations that Darwin made during the voyage of the *Beagle*.
   b. **Comparing and Contrasting** Contrast Galápagos iguanas to South American iguanas.
   c. **Applying Concepts** What is an adaptation? Explain how the claws of the Galápagos and South American iguanas are adaptations.
2. a. **Reviewing** How did Darwin explain why Galápagos species had different adaptations than similar South American species?
   b. **Developing Hypotheses** How does selective breeding support Darwin's hypothesis?

3. a. **Defining** What is variation? What is natural selection?
   b. **Relating Cause and Effect** How do variation and natural selection work together to help cause evolution?
   c. **Applying Concepts** Suppose the climate in an area becomes much drier than it was before. What kinds of variations in the area's plants might be acted on by natural selection?

Writing in Science

Interview You are a nineteenth-century reporter interviewing Charles Darwin about his theory of evolution. Write three questions you would ask him. Then write answers that Darwin might have given.

Chapter 6 ◆ 179

Lab zone Chapter **Project**

Keep Students on Track Review students' plans to make sure they have chosen workable models. In preparation, you might have students make a scale model of their own life history to date. When students are comfortable with the process, let each group start its first timeline.

Writing in Science

Writing Mode Interview
Scoring Rubric
4 Includes criteria and goes beyond requirements, for example, writing questions from the point of view of most people in Darwin's day
3 Includes criteria but does not go beyond requirements
2 Includes only brief information
1 Includes inaccurate or incomplete information

Monitor Progress L2
Answer
Figure 6 Sample answer: Size, color, ability to swim fast

Assess

Reviewing Key Concepts
1. a. The diversity of living things, fossils, and the characteristics of organisms on the Galápagos Islands **b.** The Galápagos iguanas had large claws that allowed them to grip slippery rocks. The South American iguanas had smaller claws that were used for climbing trees. **c.** A trait that helps an organism survive and reproduce; Galápagos iguanas have claws that enable them to cling to rocks to eat seaweed. South American iguanas have claws that enable them to cling to trees to eat leaves.
2. a. He hypothesized that species changed over many generations and became better adapted to their new conditions. **b.** Like natural selection, selective breeding changes a species' traits over many generations.
3. a. Variation: any difference between individuals of the same species; natural selection: the process by which individuals that are better adapted to their environment are more likely to survive and reproduce than other members of the same species
b. With variation, members of a species will have different traits. In the process of natural selection, helpful variations gradually accumulate in a species while unfavorable ones disappear. **c.** Sample answer: Plants that could store water more easily, for example, plants with thicker leaves, would survive and produce more plants like themselves.

Reteach L1
Use the figures to review how variation in a species relates to natural selection.

All in One Teaching Resources, Unit 1
• Section Summary: *Darwin's Theory*
• Review and Reinforce: *Darwin's Theory*
• Enrich: *Darwin's Theory*

Nature at Work L2

Prepare for Inquiry

Key Concept
Natural selection can lead to changes in a species' traits over time.

Skills Objectives
Students will be able to
- predict how changing environmental conditions will affect natural selection in the model
- make a dynamic model of natural selection in mice

 Class Time 40 minutes

All in One Teaching Resources, Unit 1
- Lab Worksheet: *Nature at Work*

Advance Planning
Prepare enough mouse and event cards so each group of students has a complete set.

Guide Inquiry

Invitation
Tell students that they will simulate natural selection in mice of two different colors. Ask: **How do you think variation of color in a species might affect natural selection?** *(Some colors might make individuals better able to hide from predators, making them more likely to survive and reproduce. Other colors might make it more difficult for individuals to hide from predators, making them less likely to survive and reproduce.)*

Nature at Work

Problem
How do species change over time?

Skills Focus
predicting, making models

Materials
- scissors
- marking pen
- construction paper, 2 colors

Procedure

1. Work on this lab with two other students. One student should choose construction paper of one color and make the team's 50 "mouse" cards, as described in Table 1. The second student should choose a different color construction paper and make the team's 25 "event" cards, as described in Table 2. The third student should copy the data table and record all the data.

PART 1   A White Sand Environment

2. Mix up the mouse cards.

3. Begin by using the cards to model what might happen to a group of mice in an environment of white sand dunes. Choose two mouse cards. Allele pairs *WW* and *Ww* produce a white mouse. Allele pair *ww* produces a brown mouse. Record the color of the mouse with a tally mark in the data table.

4. Choose an event card. An "S" card means the mouse survives. A "D" or a "P" card means the mouse dies. A "C" card means the mouse dies if its color contrasts with the white sand dunes. (Only brown mice will die when a "C" card is drawn.) Record each death with a tally mark in the data table.

5. If the mouse lives, put the two mouse cards in a "live mice" pile. If the mouse dies, put the cards in a "dead mice" pile. Put the event card at the bottom of its pack.

6. Repeat Steps 3 through 5 with the remaining mouse cards to study the first generation of mice. Record your results.

7. Leave the dead mice cards untouched. Mix up the cards from the live mice pile. Mix up the events cards.

8. Repeat Steps 3 through 7 for the second generation. Then repeat Steps 3 through 6 for the third generation.

PART 2   A Forest Floor Environment

9. How would the data differ if the mice in this model lived on a dark brown forest floor? Record your prediction in your notebook.

10. Make a new copy of the data table. Then use the cards to test your prediction. Remember that a "C" card now means that any mouse with white fur will die.

Data Table				
Type of Environment:				
Generation	Population		Deaths	
	White Mice	Brown Mice	White Mice	Brown Mice
1				
2				
3				

Introduce the Procedure
Ask: **Why do the mouse cards represent alleles rather than phenotypes?** *(Alleles are passed on to the next generation, not phenotypes)* Point out that choosing alleles to make up the next generation is a realistic way to model reproduction and the inheritance of traits; choosing phenotypes is not.

Troubleshooting the Experiment
Check that students are assigning the right phenotype to each genotype. Remind them that the *W* allele for white fur is dominant to the *w* allele for brown fur.

Table 1: Mouse Cards		
Number	Label	Meaning
25	*W*	Dominant allele for white fur
25	*w*	Recessive allele for brown fur

Table 2: Event Cards		
Number	Label	Meaning
5	S	Mouse survives.
1	D	Disease kills mouse.
1	P	Predator kills mice of all colors.
18	C	Predator kills mice that contrast with the environment.

Analyze and Conclude

1. **Calculating** In Part 1, how many white mice were there in each generation? How many brown mice? In each generation, which color mouse had the higher death rate? (*Hint:* To calculate the death rate for white mice, divide the number of white mice that died by the total number of white mice, then multiply by 100%.)

2. **Predicting** If the events in Part 1 occurred in nature, how would the group of mice change over time?

3. **Observing** How did the results in Part 2 differ from those in Part 1?

4. **Making Models** How would it affect your model if you increased the number of "C" cards? What would happen if you decreased the number of "C" cards?

5. **Communicating** Imagine that you are trying to explain the point of this lab to Charles Darwin. Write an explanation that you could give to him. To prepare to write, answer the following questions: What are some ways in which this investigation models natural selection? What are some ways in which natural selection differs from this model?

Design an Experiment

Choose a different species with a trait that interests you. Make a set of cards similar to these cards to investigate how natural selection might bring about the evolution of that species. *Obtain your teacher's permission before carrying out your investigation.*

◆ 181

Sample Data Table

Type of Environment: White Sand				
Gener–ation	White Mice	Brown Mice	Deaths of White Mice	Deaths of Brown Mice
1	18	7	2	5
2	16	2	2	1
3	14	1	1	1

Expected Outcome

The number of mice declines with each generation, with the number of brown mice declining faster than the number of white mice in Part 1, and the number of white mice declining faster than the number of brown mice in Part 2.

Analyze and Conclude

1. Answers will depend on the genotypes of the mice in each generation and the order in which the mouse and event cards are drawn. For the sample data, there were 18 white mice in the first generation, of which 2 died, yielding a death rate of 11% for the white mice. There were also 7 brown mice in the first generation, of which 5 died, yielding a death rate of 71% for the brown mice.

2. The population of mice would contain more and more mice with white fur.

3. In Part 2, the population contains more brown mice each generation because white mice are selected against, whereas in Part 1, the population contains more white mice each generation because the brown mice are selected against.

4. If you increased the number of "C" cards, natural selection against mice that contrast with the environment would be stronger and contrasting-color mice would decrease in number more quickly. If you decreased the number of "C" cards, natural selection against mice that contrast with the environment would be weaker and contrasting-color mice would decrease in number more slowly.

5. This investigation models natural selection in that an organism's chances of surviving and reproducing depend both on the organism's inherited traits and on the environment in which the organism lives. Natural selection differs from the model in that other environmental factors besides predators and disease, and other traits besides fur color, are likely to influence an organism's chances of surviving and reproducing.

Extend Inquiry

Design an Experiment Urge students to select a trait that is controlled by a recessive allele so they can see how dominance affects the rate at which natural selection changes the genetic makeup of the population. The trait they choose to model may be real or hypothetical.

Objectives

After this lesson, students will be able to

6.2.1 State evidence that supports the theory of evolution.

6.2.2 Explain how scientists infer evolutionary relationships among organisms.

6.2.3 Describe how new species form.

Target Reading Skill

Identifying Supporting Evidence

Explain that identifying supporting evidence helps students understand the relationship between the facts and the hypothesis.

Answers

Possible answers: Theory—Evolution; Evidence—Fossils show that organisms that lived in the past were very different from organisms alive today; patterns of early development show that some different organisms look similar during their early stages; similar body structures in different species show that the organisms shared a common ancestor.

All in One Teaching Resources, Unit 1

• Transparency LS52

Preteach

Build Background Knowledge   **L1**

Comparing Species of Animals

On the board write the following list: horse, rabbit, zebra, squirrel, donkey, deer, chipmunk, and mouse. Then ask: **Which animals would you group together based on their similarities?** (*Students are likely to place the horse, zebra, donkey, and deer in one group and the rabbit, squirrel, chipmunk, and mouse in another.*) Tell students that in this section, they will see how scientists use similarities among living species to infer how the species evolved.

Reading Preview

Key Concepts

• What evidence supports the theory of evolution?

• How do scientists infer evolutionary relationships among organisms?

• How do new species form?

Key Terms

• homologous structures

• branching tree

Target Reading Skill

Identifying Supporting Evidence Evidence consists of facts that can be confirmed by testing or observation. As you read, identify the evidence that supports the theory of evolution. Write the evidence in a graphic organizer like the one below.

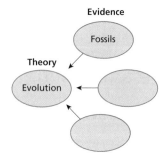

Evidence

Fossils

Theory

Evolution

FIGURE 7
Pesticide Resistance
Many insects, including cockroaches such as these, are no longer killed by some pesticides. Increased pesticide resistance is evidence that natural selection is happening.

182 ◆

Lab zone Discover Activity

How Can You Classify Species?

1. Collect six to eight different pens. Each pen will represent a different species of similar organisms.

2. Choose a trait that varies among your pen species, such as size or ink color. Using this trait, try to divide the pen species into two groups.

3. Now choose another trait. Divide each group into two smaller groups.

Think It Over

Classifying Which of the pen species share the most characteristics? What might the similarities suggest about how the pen species evolved?

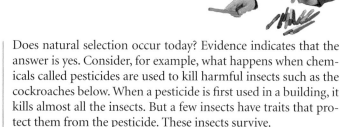

Does natural selection occur today? Evidence indicates that the answer is yes. Consider, for example, what happens when chemicals called pesticides are used to kill harmful insects such as the cockroaches below. When a pesticide is first used in a building, it kills almost all the insects. But a few insects have traits that protect them from the pesticide. These insects survive.

The surviving insects reproduce. Some of their offspring inherit the pesticide protection. The surviving offspring, in turn, reproduce. Every time the pesticide is used, the only insects that survive are those that are resistant to the harmful effects of the pesticide. After many years, most of the cockroaches in the building are resistant to the pesticide. Therefore, the pesticide is no longer effective in controlling the insects. The development of pesticide resistance is one type of evidence that supports Darwin's theory of evolution.

Lab zone Discover Activity

Skills Focus Classifying

Materials 6 to 8 pens

Time 10 minutes

Tips Have extra pens to guarantee enough for each student. Include pens that are somewhat different from one other.

L1   **Expected Outcome** How students classify their pens will depend on their particular sample of pens and the traits they choose for classification.

Think It Over Students may say that the pen species that are most similar evolved from a common ancestor.

Interpreting the Evidence

Since Darwin's time, scientists have found a great deal of evidence that supports the theory of evolution. **Fossils, patterns of early development, and similar body structures all provide evidence that organisms have changed over time.**

Fossils By examining fossils, scientists can infer the structures of ancient organisms. Fossils show that, in many cases, organisms that lived in the past were very different than organisms alive today. You will learn more about the importance of fossils in the next section.

Similarities in Early Development Scientists also make inferences about evolutionary relationships by comparing the early development of different organisms. Suppose you were asked to compare an adult fish, salamander, chicken, and opossum. You would probably say they look quite different from each other. However, during early development, these four organisms are similar, as you can see in Figure 8. For example, during the early stages of development all four organisms have a tail and a row of tiny slits along their throats. These similarities suggest that these vertebrate species are related and share a common ancestor.

FIGURE 8
Similarities in Development
These animals look similar during their early development.
Comparing and Contrasting *What are some similarities you observe? What are some differences?*

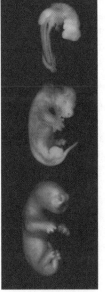
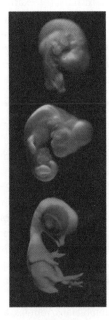

| Opossum | Chicken | Fish | Salamander |

Instruct

Interpreting the Evidence

Teach Key Concepts L2
Evidence in Support of Evolution

Focus Read the boldfaced sentence aloud.

Teach Ask: **How do fossils support the theory of evolution?** *(They show that organisms changed over time.)* **What can you learn from studying embryos about how species are related?** *(During the early stages of development, embryos of related species might share common characteristics.)* **What can body structures tell you about how species might be related?** *(Organisms with homologous structures might have evolved from a common ancestor.)*

Apply Have students examine the homologous structures in Figure 9. Ask them to infer why the structures evolved differently. *(Each limb is an adaptation that helps the organism survive in a different environment.)* **learning modality: visual**

Independent Practice L2

All in One Teaching Resources, Unit 1

• Guided Reading and Study Worksheet: *Evidence of Evolution*

◉ **Student Edition on Audio CD**

Differentiated Instruction

English Learners/Beginning Comprehension: Key Concepts L1
Rewrite the boldfaced statement in Interpreting the Evidence into three sentences and the boldfaced sentence in Inferring Species Relationships into five sentences. Pair students with students who are proficient in English. After students read the sections, have them use the captions, visuals, and text to identify a real-life example of each piece of evidence supporting evolution and species relationships. **learning modality: visual**

English Learners/Intermediate Comprehension: Key Concepts L2 Have students do the Beginning activity, then write in their own words how each example relates to the evidence. **learning modality: verbal**

Monitor Progress L2

Oral Presentation Call on students to describe similarities in living species that indicate evolutionary relationships.

Answer
Figure 8 Possible answers: similarities include large heads, curved backs, tails. Differences: in the later stages, some have developed limbs, while others have not. Heads have acquired distinctive shapes.

Help Students Read

L2

Visualizing Have students read the section on similarities in body structure and homologous structures. Then have students close their eyes and imagine what the bones of the forelimb of a common ancestor of the bird, dolphin, and dog shown in Figure 9 might look like. Have them speculate what that ancestor used its forelimb for. Then have them compare and contrast how each animal shown uses its forelimb.

Build Inquiry

L2

Observing Similar Species

Materials illustrations of vertebrate skeletons from zoology and anatomy textbooks and encyclopedias

Time 15 minutes

Focus Use a taxonomic chart to point out that all vertebrates are classified together, in a subphylum of the phylum Chordata.

Teach Ask students to use the resources to identify similar, important features of the body plan and internal functions of vertebrates. Make sure they examine images of a variety of vertebrates—fish, amphibians, reptiles, birds, and mammals. Challenge them to write a brief paragraph that compares the skeletal structures and explains how such similarities are used to infer evolutionary relationships.

Apply Ask: **What evidence suggests that all of these animals share a common ancestor?** (*Sample answer: all the animals have a backbone, skull, and ribcage. Many have four limbs.*) **learning modality: visual**

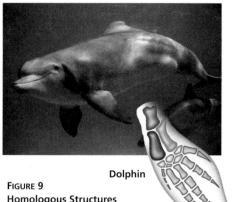
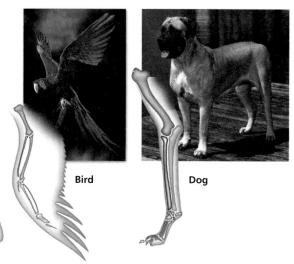

Dolphin   **Bird**   **Dog**

FIGURE 9
Homologous Structures
The structure of the bones in a dolphin's flipper, a bird's wing, and a dog's leg is similar. Homologous bones are shown in the same color. *Interpreting Diagrams How are all three orange bones similar?*

Skills Activity

Drawing Conclusions
Look at the drawing below of the bones in a crocodile's leg. Compare this drawing to Figure 9. Do you think that crocodiles share a common ancestor with birds, dolphins, and dogs? Support your answer with evidence.

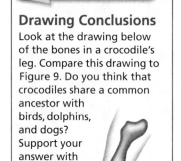

Crocodile

184 ◆

Similarities in Body Structure Long ago, scientists began to compare the body structures of living species to look for clues about evolution. In fact, this is how Darwin came to understand that evolution had occurred on the Galápagos Islands. An organism's body structure is its basic body plan, such as how its bones are arranged. Fishes, amphibians, reptiles, birds, and mammals, for example, all have a similar body structure—an internal skeleton with a backbone. This is why scientists classify all five groups of animals together as vertebrates. All of these groups probably inherited a similar structure from an early vertebrate ancestor that they shared.

Look closely at the structure of the bones in the bird's wing, dolphin's flipper, and dog's leg that are shown in Figure 9. Notice that the bones in the forelimbs of these three animals are arranged in a similar way. These similarities provide evidence that these three organisms all evolved from a common ancestor. Similar structures that related species have inherited from a common ancestor are known as **homologous structures** (hoh MAHL uh gus).

Sometimes scientists find fossils that support the evidence provided by homologous structures. For example, scientists have recently found fossils of ancient whalelike creatures. The fossils show that the ancestors of today's whales had legs and walked on land. This evidence supports other evidence that whales and humans share a common ancestor.

Reading Checkpoint In what way are the body structures of fishes, amphibians, reptiles, and mammals similar?

Skills Activity

Skills Focus Drawing conclusions   L2

Materials none

Time 5 minutes

Tips If students have difficulty identifying similarities, advise them to focus on the number and arrangement of bones.

Expected Outcome Students are likely to say that crocodiles share a common ancestor with birds, dolphins, and dogs

because of the similar structure of the bones in their legs.

Extend Ask: **What other animals do you think would have forelimbs similar in structure to those of crocodiles, birds, dolphins, and dogs?** (*Possible answers include other reptiles, birds, or mammals.*) **learning modality: logical/mathematical**

Inferring Species Relationships

Fossils, early development patterns, and body structure provide evidence that evolution has occurred. Scientists have also used these kinds of evidence to infer how organisms are related to one another. Not too long ago, fossils, embryos, and body structures were the only tools that scientists had to determine how species were related. Today, scientists can also compare the DNA and protein sequences of different species. **Scientists have combined the evidence from DNA, protein structure, fossils, early development, and body structure to determine the evolutionary relationships among species.**

Similarities in DNA Why do some species have similar body structures and development patterns? Scientists infer that the species inherited many of the same genes from a common ancestor. Recently, scientists have begun to compare the genes of different species to determine how closely related the species are.

Recall that genes are made of DNA. By comparing the sequence of nitrogen bases in the DNA of different species, scientists can infer how closely related the two species are. The more similar the DNA sequences, the more closely related the species are. For example, DNA analysis has shown that elephants and tiny elephant shrews, shown in Figure 10, are closely related.

The DNA bases along a gene specify what type of protein will be produced. Therefore, scientists can also compare the order of amino acids in a protein to see how closely related two species are.

Combining Evidence In most cases, evidence from DNA and protein structure has confirmed conclusions based on fossils, embryos, and body structure. For example, recent DNA comparisons show that dogs are more similar to wolves than they are to coyotes. Scientists had already reached this conclusion based on similarities in the structure and development of these three species.

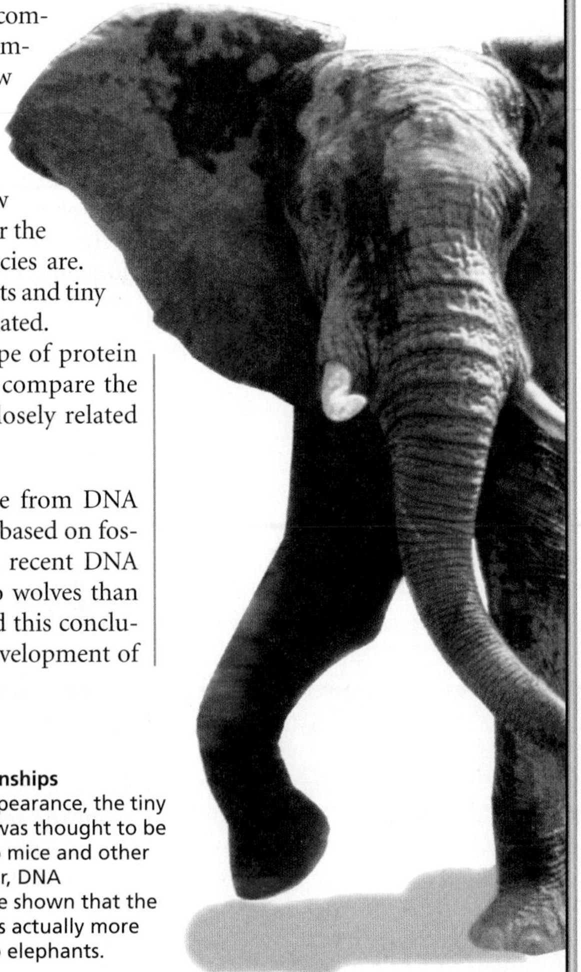

FIGURE 10
DNA and Relationships
Because of its appearance, the tiny elephant shrew was thought to be closely related to mice and other rodents. However, DNA comparisons have shown that the elephant shrew is actually more closely related to elephants.

Chapter 6 ◆ **185**

Differentiated Instruction

Special Needs L1
Understanding Branching Trees Help students construct their family tree with three generations. If they are unable to do this, use your own family or create a fictitious one. Explain that the family tree and the branching tree show relationships among descendants of a common ancestor. Point out that species with a recent common ancestor are like siblings in a family, and species with a remote common ancestor are like distant cousins. **learning modality: visual**

Inferring Species Relationships

Teach Key Concepts L2
Evidence for Species Relationships

Focus Review the evidence for evolution.

Teach Point out that evidence from DNA has helped scientists determine evolutionary relationships among species. Ask: **What does DNA tell you about how similar two species are?** *(The more similar their DNA sequences, the more closely related they are.)* Explain that the more closely related the DNA of two species, the more recently they shared a common ancestor. Scientists use all of this information to construct branching trees. Ask: **What is a branching tree?** *(A diagram that shows how scientists think different groups of organism are related)*

Apply Provide the following scenario: Tell students to imagine three hypothetical species—A, B, and C. A and C are more similar in body structure than A and B or B and C. A and B are more similar in their early development than A and C or B and C. The DNA base sequences of A and B are more similar than the DNA base sequences of A and C or B and C. Challenge students to explain the evolutionary relationships among the three species. *(A and B are more closely related to each other than either species is related to C because of the similarities in their early development and DNA.)* Have students draw a branching tree to illustrate these relationships. **learning modality: logical/mathematical**

All in One Teaching Resources, Unit 1
• Transparency LS53

Monitor Progress L2

Drawing Have students draw a branching tree that shows how dogs, wolves, and coyotes are related. Students can place their drawings in their portfolios.

Answers
Figure 9 They are all in the same position relative to the other limb bones; they are all relatively short and thick compared to the other limb bones.

Reading Checkpoint They all have an internal skeleton with a backbone.

How Do New Species Form?

Teach Key Concepts
Formation of Species

Focus Remind students that a species is a group of similar organisms that can mate with each other and produce fertile offspring.

Teach Ask: **How can separation of organisms within the same species lead to the formation of a new species?** *(The environments for each group may be different. Each group might then evolve with different traits.)* Emphasize that genetic variations that occur in one group and spread through the population could be different from variations in the other group.

Apply Tell students to suppose that the Grand Canyon were suddenly filled in. Ask: **Would the Abert's squirrel and the Kaibab squirrel continue to evolve differently?** *(Possibly not; they are still the same species and might start interbreeding.)* Ask students to predict what would happen to the genotypes and phenotypes of the two types of squirrels. *(They would gradually become more similar.)* **learning modality: logical/mathematical**

Large Scale Isolation

Materials map of Pangaea

Time 10 minutes

Focus Tell students that Pangaea was a landmass in which all the continents were once connected.

Teach Display a map of Pangaea. Point out that Australia broke away from Pangaea 250 million years ago, while other continents were still joined as recently as 50 million years ago.

Apply Ask: **How might the breaking away of Australia have led to the formation of new species?** *(Marsupial species such as kangaroos, koala, and wombats might have formed when a group of individuals remained isolated from the rest of Pangaean mammals long enough to evolve different traits.)* **learning modality: visual**

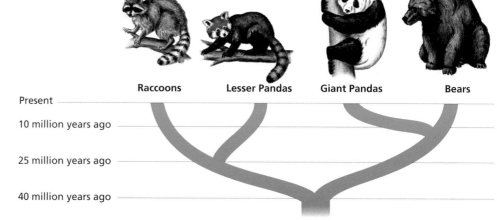

| Raccoons | Lesser Pandas | Giant Pandas | Bears |

Present —
10 million years ago —
25 million years ago —
40 million years ago —

Common Ancestor

FIGURE 11
A Branching Tree
This branching tree shows how scientists now think that raccoons, lesser pandas, giant pandas, and bears are related.
Interpreting Diagrams *Are giant pandas more closely related to lesser pandas or to bears?*

Sometimes, however, scientists have changed their hypotheses about species relationships. For example, lesser pandas were once thought to be closely related to giant pandas. Recently, however, DNA analysis and other methods have shown that giant pandas and lesser pandas are not closely related. Instead, giant pandas are more closely related to bears, while lesser pandas are more closely related to raccoons.

Branching Trees Scientists use the combined evidence of species relationships to draw branching trees. A **branching tree** is a diagram that shows how scientists think different groups of organisms are related. Figure 11 shows how raccoons, lesser pandas, giant pandas, and bears may be related.

 Reading Checkpoint What is a branching tree?

How Do New Species Form?
Natural selection explains how variations can lead to changes in a species. But how could an entirely new species form? **A new species can form when a group of individuals remains isolated from the rest of its species long enough to evolve different traits.** Isolation, or complete separation, occurs when some members of a species become cut off from the rest of the species. Group members may be separated by such things as a river, a volcano, or a mountain range.

186 ◆

Abert's squirrel and the Kaibab squirrel both live in forests in the Southwest. As you can see in Figure 12, the populations of the two kinds of squirrel are separated by the Grand Canyon. The Kaibab and Abert's squirrels belong to the same species, but they have slightly different characteristics. For example, the Kaibab squirrel has a black belly, while Abert's squirrel has a white belly. It is possible that one day Abert's squirrel and the Kaibab squirrel will become so different from each other that they will be separate species.

Kaibab squirrel ▼

Abert's squirrel ▼

FIGURE 12
Kaibab and Abert's Squirrels
These two kinds of squirrels have been isolated from one another for a long time. Eventually, this isolation may result in two different species.

Section 2 Assessment

Target Reading Skill

Identifying Supporting Evidence Refer to your graphic organizer about the theory of evolution as you answer Question 1 below.

Reviewing Key Concepts

1. **a. Listing** List three kinds of evidence that support the theory of evolution.
   b. Comparing and Contrasting What major difference have scientists discovered between today's whales and the fossils of whales' ancient ancestors?
   c. Drawing Conclusions How does this difference show that whales and animals with four legs are probably descended from a common ancestor?
2. **a. Identifying** When scientists try to determine how closely related species are, what evidence do they examine?
   b. Inferring Of the kinds of evidence you listed above, which are probably the most reliable? Explain your answer.

c. Applying Concepts Insects and birds both have wings. What kinds of evidence might show whether or not insects and birds are closely related? Explain your answer.
3. **a. Reviewing** How can isolation lead to the formation of new species?
   b. Predicting A species of snake lives in a forest. A new road separates one group of the snakes from another. Is it likely that these two groups of snakes will become separate species? Why or why not?

Writing in Science

Explaining a Branching Tree Suppose the branching tree in Figure 11 is part of a museum exhibit. Write an explanation of the branching tree for museum visitors. Describe the relationships shown on the tree and identify evidence supporting the relationships.

Monitor Progress _____ L2

Answers
Figure 11 Bears

✔ **Reading Checkpoint** A diagram that shows how scientists think different groups of organisms are related

Assess

Reviewing Key Concepts

1. **a.** Any three: Fossils, similarities in early development, similarities in body structure, DNA, and protein structure **b.** Whales' ancient ancestors had legs and walked on land, while modern whales do not. **c.** The four legs of ancient whales are homologous structures of the legs of modern land animals.
2. **a.** Evidence from DNA, protein structure, fossils, early development, and body structure **b.** DNA and protein structure are probably most reliable because they show specific distinct patterns that can be easily compared. **c.** DNA, protein structure, and early development would probably show that insects and birds are not closely related.
3. **a.** When a group of individuals remains isolated from the rest of its species long enough to evolve different traits, a new species can form. **b.** It is not likely because a road is not wide enough to prevent the snakes from crossing the road and mating with one another.

Reteach L1

Use the figures in this section to discuss how similarities in early development, body structure, and DNA sequences can be used to map out how species are related to one another.

Performance Assessment L2

Writing Have students explain how species can change using the Galápagos finches as an example.

All in One Teaching Resources, Unit 1
- Section Summary: *Evidence of Evolution*
- Review and Reinforce: *Evidence of Evolution*
- Enrich: *Evidence of Evolution*

Writing in Science

Writing Mode Explanation

Scoring Rubric
4 Includes all criteria and goes beyond requirements, for example, writing simply for a general audience
3 Includes all criteria, but does not consider the background of the audience
2 Includes only brief description
1 Includes inaccurate or incomplete information

Telltale Molecules L2

Prepare for Inquiry

Key Concept
The more similar the amino acid sequence in proteins of different species, the more closely the species are related.

Skills Objectives
Students will be able to
- interpret data on amino acid sequences in proteins
- draw conclusions about how the species are related

 Class Time 30 minutes

All in One Teaching Resources, Unit 1
- Lab Worksheet: *Telltale Molecules*

Guide Inquiry

Invitation
Ask: **What is a genetic code?** (*The order of the nitrogen bases along a gene*) **How do cells use a genetic code to make proteins?** (*The nitrogen bases code for the production of specific amino acids, which are the building blocks of proteins.*) **What are genes made of?** (*DNA*)

Introduce the Procedure
Have students read the entire lab, and then ask: **What is the objective of this lab activity?** (*To use the amino acid sequence of a protein to determine the evolutionary relationship among several animals*) **What do the letters in the table represent?** (*Each letter represents a different amino acid.*) Suggest that students create a table to record the number of differences between the horse and each of the other animals.

Expected Outcome
Students infer which species are most closely related and which are least closely related to the horse.

Telltale Molecules

Problem
What information can protein structure reveal about evolutionary relationships among organisms?

Skills Focus
interpreting data, drawing conclusions

Procedure
1. Examine the table below. It shows the sequence of amino acids in one region of a protein, cytochrome c, for six different animals.
2. Predict which of the five other animals is most closely related to the horse. Which animal do you think is most distantly related?
3. Compare the amino acid sequence of the horse to that of the donkey. How many amino acids differ between the two species? Record that number in your notebook.
4. Compare the amino acid sequences of each of the other animals to that of the horse. Record the number of differences in your notebook.

Analyze and Conclude
1. **Interpreting Data** Which animal's amino acid sequence was most similar to that of the horse? What similarities and difference(s) did you observe?
2. **Drawing Conclusions** Based on these data, which species is most closely related to the horse? Which is most distantly related?
3. **Interpreting Data** For the entire protein, the horse's amino acid sequence differs from the other animals' as follows: donkey, 1 difference; rabbit, 6; snake, 22; turtle, 11; and whale, 5. How do the relationships indicated by the entire protein compare with those for the region you examined?
4. **Communicating** Write a paragraph explaining why data about amino acid sequences can provide information about evolutionary relationships among organisms.

More to Explore
Use the amino acid data to construct a branching tree that includes horses, donkeys, and snakes. The tree should show one way that the three species could have evolved from a common ancestor.

Section of Cytochrome c Protein in Animals															
Animal	Amino Acid Position														
	39	40	41	42	43	44	45	46	47	48	49	50	51	52	53
Horse	A	B	C	D	E	F	G	H	I	J	K	L	M	N	O
Donkey	A	B	C	D	E	F	G	H	Z	J	K	L	M	N	O
Rabbit	A	B	C	D	E	Y	G	H	Z	J	K	L	M	N	O
Snake	A	B	C	D	E	Y	G	H	Z	J	K	W	M	N	O
Turtle	A	B	C	D	E	V	G	H	Z	J	K	U	M	N	O
Whale	A	B	C	D	E	Y	G	H	Z	J	K	L	M	N	O

Analyze and Conclude
1. The donkey's; it was similar in all amino acid positions except position 47.
2. The donkey is most closely related; the turtle and snake are least closely related.
3. They are very similar.
4. As two or more species evolve from a common ancestor, their DNA may undergo different mutations, causing changes in the amino acids making up common proteins. The fewer differences in the amino acids, the more closely the given species are related.

Extend Inquiry

More to Explore The branching trees should show that the horse and donkey have the most recent common ancestor and that the horse and snake have the most distant common ancestor.

The Fossil Record

Reading Preview

Key Concepts
- How do most fossils form?
- How can scientists determine a fossil's age?
- What is the Geologic Time Scale?
- What are some unanswered questions about evolution?

Key Terms
- petrified fossil
- mold
- cast
- relative dating
- radioactive dating
- radioactive element
- half-life
- fossil record
- extinct
- gradualism
- punctuated equilibria

Target Reading Skill
Building Vocabulary After you read the section, write a definition of each Key Term in your own words.

Lab zone Discover **Activity**

What Can You Learn From Fossils?

1. Look at the fossil in the photograph. Describe the fossil's characteristics in as much detail as you can.
2. From your description in Step 1, try to figure out how the organism lived. How did it move? Where did it live?

Think It Over
Inferring What type of present-day organism do you think is related to the fossil? Why?

The fossil dinosaur below has been nicknamed "Sue." If fossils could talk, Sue might say something like this: "I don't mind that museum visitors call me 'Sue,' but I do get annoyed when they refer to me as 'that old fossil.' I'm a 67-million-year old *Tyrannosaurus rex*, and I should get some respect. I was fearsome. My skull is one and a half meters long, and my longest tooth is more than 30 centimeters. Ah, the stories I could tell! But I'll have to let my bones speak for themselves. Scientists can learn a lot from studying fossils like me."

Of course, fossils can't really talk or think. But fossils such as Sue reveal life's history.

FIGURE 13 Dinosaur Fossil
The dinosaur nicknamed "Sue" was discovered in 1990 in South Dakota. Sue is now in the Field Museum in Chicago.

◆ 189

Lab zone Discover **Activity**

Skills Focus Inferring

Time 5 minutes

Tips Provide a hand lens for students who need or want it. After the activity, inform students that the fossil pictured is a trilobite, an ocean-bottom-dwelling animal that existed about 540 to 250 million years ago.

L1

Expected Outcome Students are likely to describe the overall shape and obvious physical features of the fossil, including what appear to be a shell and numerous legs.

Think It Over Students may say the fossil is related to present-day insects or crabs because it resembles them in its physical features.

The Fossil Record

Objectives
After this lesson, students will be able to
6.3.1 Describe how most fossils form.
6.3.2 Explain how scientists can determine a fossil's age.
6.3.3 State what the Geologic Time Scale is.
6.3.4 Identify some unanswered questions about evolution.

Target Reading Skill

Building Vocabulary Explain that knowing the definitions of Key Terms helps students understand what they read.

Answers
Have students write what they know about each Key Term before reading the definitions in the section. Explain that connecting what they already know about Key Terms helps them to remember the terms. As they read each passage that contains Key Terms, remind them to write the definitions in their own words.

Preteach

Build Background Knowledge

Evidence of Dinosaurs L1
Most students are likely to know a lot about dinosaurs. Ask: **How do we know so much about dinosaurs if none of them is alive now?** (*From their remains, which have been preserved as fossils*) Tell students they will learn how fossils are formed and how they are used to understand evolution.

Instruct

How Do Fossils Form?

Teach Key Concepts **L2**

Fossil Formation

Focus Remind students that fossils are the remains of organisms or physical evidence of their existence, such as tracks.

Teach Ask: **How do most fossils form?** *(When organisms die and become buried in sediments)* **What must happen for a petrified fossil to form?** *(The organism's remains must become buried in sediment and then be replaced by minerals.)* **How can you tell a mold from a cast?** *(The mold is a hollow shape, while the cast is a solid form that looks like the organism that formed the mold.)*

Apply Ask: **Why do preserved remains often provide more information about an animal than a petrified fossil?** *(Preserved remains can include soft and hard body parts, while a petrified fossil shows the structure of only the hard parts.)* **learning modality: logical/mathematical**

All in One Teaching Resources, Unit 1

• Transparency LS54

Help Students Read **L2**

Outlining Refer to the Content Refresher for guidelines on Outlining. Have students create an outline of this section as they read.

Independent Practice

All in One Teaching Resources, Unit 1

• Guided Reading and Study Worksheet: *The Fossil Record*

⊙ Student Edition on Audio CD

An ancient crocodile dies and sinks to the bottom of a river.

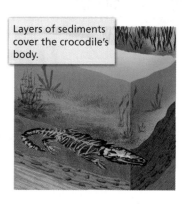
Layers of sediments cover the crocodile's body.

FIGURE 14
Fossil Formation
Most fossils, such as the fossil crocodile shown here, form in sedimentary rock. **Relating Cause and Effect** *In the process of fossil formation, what materials replace the crocodile's remains?*

Lab zone Try This Activity

Preservation in Ice

1. Place fresh fruit, such as apple slices, strawberries, and blueberries, in an open plastic container.
2. Completely cover the fruit with water. Put the container in a freezer.
3. Place the same type and amount of fresh fruit in another open container. Leave it somewhere where no one will disturb it.
4. After three days, observe the contents of both containers.

Inferring Use your observations to explain why fossils preserved in ice can include soft, fleshy body parts.

190 ◆

How Do Fossils Form?

The formation of any fossil is a rare event. Usually only the hard parts of the organism, such as the bones or shells of animals, form fossils. **Most fossils form when organisms that die become buried in sediments.** Sediments are particles of soil and rock. When a river flows into a lake or ocean, the sediments that the river carries settle to the bottom. Layers of sediments may cover the dead organisms. Over millions of years, the layers may harden to become sedimentary rock. Figure 14 shows how a fossil can form.

Petrified Fossils Some remains that become buried in sediments are actually changed to rock. Minerals dissolved in the water soak into the buried remains. Gradually, the minerals replace the remains, changing them into rock. Fossils that form in this way are called **petrified fossils.**

Molds and Casts Sometimes shells or other hard parts buried by sediments gradually dissolve. An empty space remains in the place that the hard part once occupied. A hollow space in sediment in the shape of an organism or part of an organism is called a **mold.** A mold may become filled with hardened minerals, forming a cast. A **cast** is a copy of the shape of the organism that made the mold.

Preserved Remains Organisms can also be preserved in substances other than sediments. For example, entire organisms, such as huge elephant-like mammoths that lived thousands of years ago, have been preserved in ice.

✓ Reading Checkpoint What is the difference between a mold and a cast?

Lab zone Try This Activity

Skills Focus Inferring **L1**

Materials fresh fruit, two plastic containers, water

Time 10 minutes

Tips Make sure students find a place to put the container of fruit that is left out so it will not be disturbed. Warn students not to eat the fruit that has been left out.

Expected Outcome The frozen fruit is well preserved, whereas the fruit that was left out is starting to spoil. Freezing prevents the soft parts from drying out and/or rotting.

Extend Ask: **How do you think a mammoth or other animal might get preserved in this way?** *(Accept any reasonable response, such as an avalanche burying the animal or the animal falling into a crevice in a glacier.)* **learning modality: visual**

Over millions of years, the sediments harden to become rock. The crocodile is preserved as a fossil.

The rock erodes. The fossil is exposed on the surface of a rock.

Go Online
active art
For: Fossil Formation activity
Visit: PHSchool.com
Web Code: cep-3053

Determining a Fossil's Age

To understand how living things have changed through time, scientists need to be able to determine the ages of fossils. They can then determine the order in which past events occurred. This information can be used to reconstruct the history of life on Earth.

For example, suppose a scientist is studying two fossils of ancient snails, Snail A and Snail B. The fossils are similar, but they are different enough that they are not the same species. Perhaps, the scientist hypothesizes, Snail A's species changed over time and eventually gave rise to Snail B's species. To help determine whether this hypothesis could be valid, the scientist must first learn which fossil—A or B—is older. **Scientists can determine a fossil's age in two ways: relative dating and radioactive dating.**

Relative Dating Scientists use **relative dating** to determine which of two fossils is older. To understand how relative dating works, imagine that a river has cut down through layers of sedimentary rock to form a canyon. If you look at the canyon walls, you can see the layers of sedimentary rock piled up one on top of another. The layers near the top of the canyon were formed most recently. These layers are the youngest rock layers. The lower down the canyon wall you go, the older the layers are. Therefore, fossils found in layers near the top of the canyon are younger than fossils found near the bottom of the canyon.

Relative dating can only be used when the rock layers have been preserved in their original sequence. Relative dating can help scientists determine whether one fossil is older than another. However, relative dating does not tell scientists the fossil's actual age.

191

Math Skill Making and interpreting graphs

Focus Point out that a line graph is often used to show change in quantities over time.

Teach Tell students that the two lines are representing the same sample: One slope is negative and one slope is positive to indicate that one type of element is changing into another.

Answers

1. The red line represents the amount of potassium-40. The blue line represents the amount of argon-40.

2. Potassium-40: 1 gram; argon-40: 0 grams

3. About 1.3 billion years

4. 0.5 gram (50%) of each; the half-life of potassium-40 is 1.3 billion years, which means that half will break down into argon-40 every 1.3 billion years

What Do Fossils Reveal?

Teach Key Concepts   L2

Understanding Geologic Time

Focus Explain that because the Earth is billions of years old, years or centuries are not helpful for thinking about Earth's long history.

Teach Use Figure 16 to help explain that Earth's history is called the Geologic Time Scale. Ask: **What is this time scale based on?** (*The ages of many different fossils and rocks and when new groups of organisms evolved*) **What are the units of the Geologic Time Scale?** (*Eras and periods*)

Apply Ask students to calculate what percentage of Earth's history is Precambrian Time. (*About 87%—4 billion years ÷ 4.6 billion years*) Refer students to Figure 15. Ask: **At what position on the clock face would Precambrian Time end?** (*About 10:30 P.M.—12 hours × 87%*)
learning modality: logical/mathematical

Radioactive Decay

The half-life of potassium-40, a radioactive element, is 1.3 billion years. This means that half of the potassium-40 in a sample will break down into argon-40 every 1.3 billion years. The graph shows the breakdown of a 1-gram sample of potassium-40 into argon-40 over billions of years.

1. **Reading Graphs** What does the red line represent? What does the blue line represent?

2. **Reading Graphs** At 2.6 billion years ago, how much of the sample consisted of potassium 40? How much of the sample consisted of argon-40?

3. **Reading Graphs** At what point in time do the two graph lines cross?

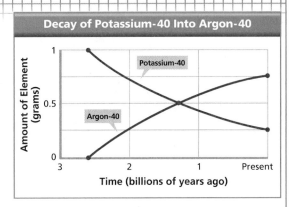

Decay of Potassium-40 Into Argon-40

4. **Interpreting Data** At the point where the graph lines cross, how much of the sample consisted of potassium-40? How much consisted of argon-40? Explain why this is the case.

Radioactive Dating A technique called **radioactive dating** allows scientists to determine the actual age of fossils. The rocks that fossils are found near contain **radioactive elements,** which are unstable elements that decay, or break down, into different elements. The **half-life** of a radioactive element is the time it takes for half of the atoms in a sample to decay. The graph in Analyzing Data shows how a sample of potassium-40, a radioactive element, breaks down into argon-40 over time.

Scientists can compare the amount of a radioactive element in a sample to the amount of the element into which it breaks down. This information can be used to calculate the age of the rock, and thus the age of the fossil.

Reading Checkpoint What is a half-life?

What Do Fossils Reveal?

Like pieces in a jigsaw puzzle, fossils can help scientists piece together information about Earth's past. From the fossil record, scientists have learned information about the history of life on Earth. The millions of fossils that scientists have collected are called the **fossil record.**

Extinct Organisms Almost all of the species preserved as fossils are now extinct. A species is **extinct** if no members of that species are still alive. Most of what scientists know about extinct species is based on the fossil record.

The Geologic Time Scale The fossil record provides clues about how and when new groups of organisms evolved. Using radioactive dating, scientists have calculated the ages of many different fossils and rocks. From this information, scientists have created a "calendar" of Earth's history that spans more than 4.6 billion years. Scientists have divided this large time span into smaller units called eras and periods. **This calendar of Earth's history is sometimes called the Geologic Time Scale.**

The largest span of time in the Geologic Time Scale is Precambrian Time, also called the Precambrian (pree KAM bree un). It covers the first 4 billion years of Earth's history. Scientists know very little about the Precambrian because there are few fossils from these ancient times. After the Precambrian, the Geologic Time Scale is divided into three major blocks of time, or eras. Each era is further divided into shorter periods. In Figure 16 on the next two pages, you can see the events that occurred during each time period.

 Reading Checkpoint What is the largest span in the Geologic Time Scale?

FIGURE 15
Earth's History as a Clock
Fossils found in rock layers tell the history of life on Earth. The history of life can be compared to 12 hours on a clock.
Interpreting Diagrams *At what time on a 12-hour time scale did plants appear on land?*

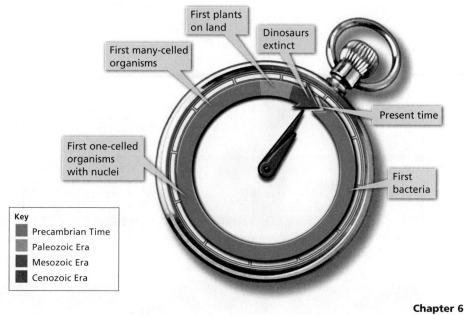

First plants on land

First many-celled organisms

Dinosaurs extinct

Present time

First one-celled organisms with nuclei

First bacteria

Key
- Precambrian Time
- Paleozoic Era
- Mesozoic Era
- Cenozoic Era

Chapter 6 ◆ 193

Differentiated Instruction

English Learners/Beginning **L1**
Vocabulary: Science Glossary Explain that the word "relative" as in *relative dating* is used as a means of comparison. Point out the rock layers in Figure 14 and use the term to describe each one. Discuss the meanings of the other Key Terms in this section. Have students write the definitions in their science glossaries in English and in their native languages.

Encourage them to illustrate the terms. **learning modality: verbal**

English Learners/Intermediate **L2**
Vocabulary: Science Glossary Ask students to write sentences in their own words using each key term. **learning modality: visual**

Modeling the Geologic Time Scale

Materials map of your local area, bulletin board, pushpins, small strips of paper
Time 20 minutes

Focus Refer students to Figure 16. Point out that the length of periods varies because the Geologic Time Scale is divided based on major events in the history of life, not a set number of years.

Teach Have students use Figure 16 to determine how long ago each period and era in the history of Earth occurred. Then have them calculate the distance in kilometers that is proportionate to each length of time. For example, the Cambrian Period began 544 million years ago, so it could be represented by 5.44 km on the map. Hang the map on a bulletin board. Place pushpins labeled with strips of paper on the map to represent each time period. Have the starting point be the school. Explain that as you move away from the school, you are going back in time. For example, the beginning of the Cambrian Period will be located 5.44 km from the school. The beginning of Precambrian Time will not likely fit on the map. Have students use the map's scale to determine where in the room or building its label would go.

Apply Ask students to think of other ways to graphically represent the Geologic Time Scale. **learning modality: kinesthetic**

Monitor Progress _____ **L2**

Skills Check Have students create a table that compares and contrasts relative and radioactive dating. Students can save their tables in their portfolios.

Portfolio

Answers
Figure 15 about 11:00

 Reading Checkpoint The time it takes for half the atoms of a sample of a radioactive element to decay, or break down

 Reading Checkpoint Precambrian Time

Use Visuals: Figure 16 L2

Exploring Life's History

Focus Remind students that geologic eras are based on major events.

Teach Point out that this timeline is different from other timelines because the numbers from left to right are decreasing rather than increasing. Ask student volunteers to read the captions at the bottom. Inform students that the earliest life forms on Earth were confined to the water. Ask questions about the timeline such as: **When did the first land plants and animals appear on Earth?** *(During the Silurian Period, about 430 million years ago)* **Which evolved first, reptiles or amphibians?** *(Amphibians)* **When did the first dinosaurs and mammals evolve?** *(In the Triassic Period, about 220 million years ago)*

Apply Ask: **What evolutionary development made it possible for animals to move from the oceans to land?** *(Plant life developed on land.)* **learning modality: visual**

All in One Teaching Resources, Unit 1

- Transparencies LS55, LS56

◼ Address Misconceptions L2

Fossils Are Rare

Focus Many students think that most species that have existed on Earth have left fossil remains.

Teach Explain that of the millions of extinct species, only a fraction of one percent is likely to have been preserved as fossils. During much of Earth's history, organisms were one-celled or invertebrates.

Apply Ask: **Why have many more fossils of organisms that lived after Precambrian Time been discovered?** *(After Precambrian Time, organisms with hard body parts started appearing. They were more likely to form fossils. Also, organisms in general became more abundant.)* **learning modality: logical/ mathematical**

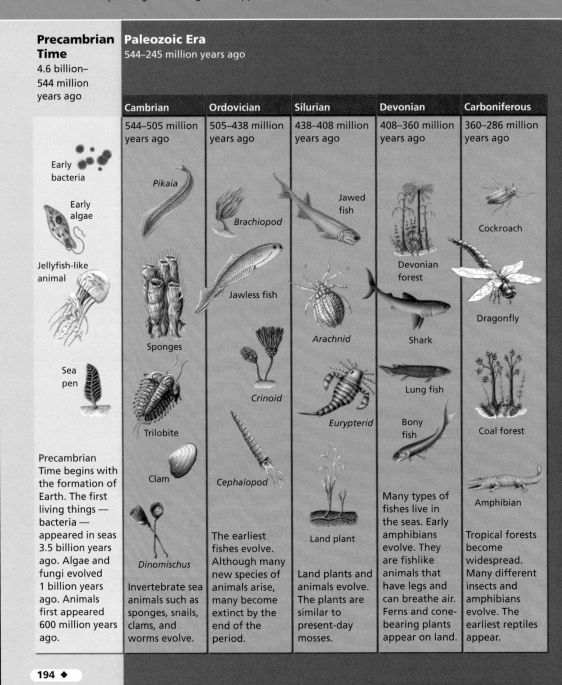

FIGURE 16
The Geologic Time Scale

Sequencing *Which organisms appeared first—amphibians or fishes?*

	Mesozoic Era 245–66 million years ago			Cenozoic Era 66 million years ago to the present	
Permian	**Triassic**	**Jurassic**	**Cretaceous**	**Tertiary**	**Quaternary**
286–245 million years ago	245–208 million years ago	208–144 million years ago	144–66 million years ago	66–1.8 million years ago	1.8 million years ago to the present
Conifer Dimetrodon Dicynodon	Cycad Early mammal Coelophysis	Morganucodon Diplodocus Archaeopteryx	Triceratops Magnolia Tyrannosaurus rex Creodont	Uintatherium Plesiadapis Hyracotherium	Saber-toothed cat Megatherium Homo sapiens
Seed plants, insects, and reptiles become common. Reptile-like mammals appear. At the end of the period, most sea animals and amphibians become extinct.	The first dinosaurs evolve. First turtles and crocodiles appear. Mammals first appear. Cone-bearing trees and palmlike trees dominate forests.	Large dinosaurs roam the world. The first birds appear. Mammals become more common and varied.	The first flowering plants appear. At the end of the period, a mass extinction causes the disappearance of many organisms, including the dinosaurs.	New groups of animals, including the first monkeys and apes, appear. Flowering plants become the most common kinds of plants. First grasses appear.	Mammals, flowering plants, and insects dominate land. Humans appear. Later in the period, many large mammals, including mammoths, become extinct.

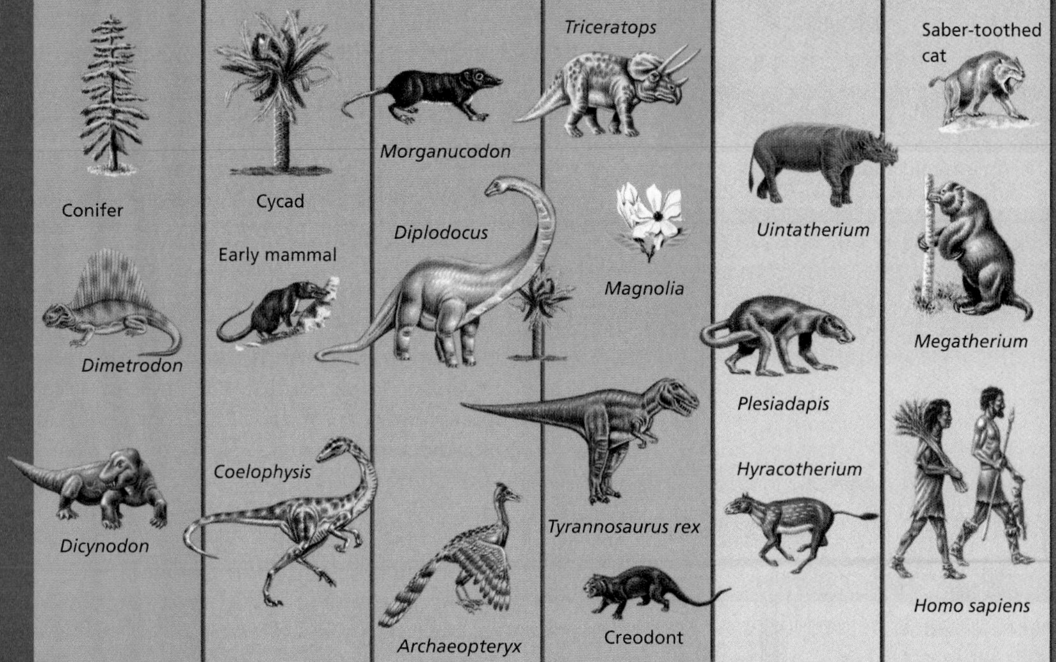

◆ 195

Applying Concepts of Geologic Time

Materials poster board, dice, index cards, markers, small toys or other items for game tokens

Time 30 minutes

Focus Divide the class into groups, and challenge each group to create a board game called *A Trip Through Geologic Time* to reinforce their knowledge of Earth's life history.

Teach The game board should start in Precambrian Time and continue to the present. To advance around the game board (and through time), players are required to answer questions, perhaps written on chance cards, about each period. Escaping from carnivorous dinosaurs, skirting around treacherous tar pits, or avoiding similar relevant obstacles in particular time periods might be included on the game board to add excitement to the game and require students to apply more of the information from Figure 16. After groups have played their own games, urge them to exchange and play one another's games.

Apply Ask: **Is the timeline in your board game to scale?** *(It is not likely because the major events in life's history would be too crowded or the game board would be too large.)* Ask students to explain how they dealt with scale. **learning modality: kinesthetic**

L2

Differentiated Instruction

Gifted and Talented L3
Communicating Ask students to imagine they have traveled to an earlier period in Earth's history. Have them write an eyewitness report, modeled on a television or newspaper story. Encourage them to use additional references for more information, such as descriptions of climate. Ask volunteers to present their reports, and challenge other students to identify the time periods described. **learning modality: verbal**

Less Proficient Readers L1
Creating Study Aids Pair students with more proficient readers. Have them make flash cards with the periods, events, and organisms of the Geologic Time Scale, and use them to quiz each other. **learning modality: verbal**

Monitor Progress L2

Oral Presentation Call on students to describe an event in the evolution of plants or animals, based on the information in Figure 16.

Answer
Figure 16 Fishes appeared in the Ordovician Period, before amphibians, which appeared in the Devonian Period.

Unanswered Questions

Teach Key Concepts

L2

Gaps in the Fossil Record

Focus Tell students that the end of the Paleozoic Era and the Mesozoic Era were marked by major extinctions.

Teach Ask: **What is a mass extinction?** *(A mass extinction occurs when many types of organisms become extinct at the same time.)* **What question do scientists have about mass extinctions?** *(What caused them?)* **How could an asteroid hitting Earth cause a mass extinction?** *(The impact could throw up huge clouds of dust which would block sunlight, making the climate cooler and killing plants. With fewer plants, many animals would starve.)* **What other event do scientists think could cause a mass extinction?** *(Volcanic eruptions)* **What is another unanswered question about evolution?** *(At what rate does evolution occur?)* **Which theories explain how rapidly species change?** *(Gradualism, which is the theory that proposes that evolution occurs slowly but steadily, and punctuated equilibria, which is the theory that evolution occurs quickly during relatively short periods.)*

Apply Explain that an intermediate life form is an organism that is a link between a more modern organism and its ancestor. Ask: **Why are fossils of intermediate life forms likely to be rare if the theory of punctuated equilibria explains how evolution occurs?** *(The theory proposes that new species evolve rapidly over a short period of time, so the chances of fossils of intermediate species forming are reduced.)* **learning modality: logical/mathematical**

FIGURE 17
Mass Extinctions

An asteroid may have caused the mass extinction that occurred about 65 million years ago.
Relating Cause and Effect *How could an asteroid have caused climate change?*

▲ An asteroid zooms toward Earth.

The asteroid ▲ hits Earth, sending up clouds of dust.

Many plants and animals die from ▼ the effects of the collision.

Unanswered Questions

The fossil record has provided scientists with a lot of important information about past life on Earth. The fossil record, however, is incomplete, because most organisms died without leaving fossils behind. These gaps in the fossil record leave many questions unanswered. **Two unanswered questions about evolution involve the causes of mass extinctions and the rate at which evolution occurs.**

Mass Extinctions When many types of organisms become extinct at the same time, a mass extinction has occurred. Several mass extinctions have taken place during the history of life. One mass extinction, for example, occurred at the end of the Cretaceous Period, about 65 million years ago. During the Cretaceous mass extinction, many kinds of plants and animals, including the dinosaurs, disappeared forever.

Scientists are not sure what causes mass extinctions, but they hypothesize that major climate changes may be responsible. For example, a climate change may have caused the mass extinction at the end of the Cretaceous Period. An asteroid, which is a rocky mass from space, may have hit Earth, throwing huge clouds of dust and other materials into the air. The dust clouds would have blocked sunlight, making the climate cooler, and killing plants. If there were fewer plants, many animals would have starved. Some scientists, however, think volcanic eruptions, not an asteroid, caused the climate change.

Gradualism Scientists also are not sure how rapidly species change. One theory, called **gradualism,** proposes that evolution occurs slowly but steadily. According to this theory, tiny changes in a species gradually add up to major changes over very long periods of time. This is how Darwin thought evolution occurred.

If the theory of gradualism is correct, the fossil record should include intermediate forms between a fossil organism and its descendants. However, there are often long periods of time in which fossils show little or no change. Then, quite suddenly, fossils appear that are distinctly different. One possible explanation for the lack of intermediate forms is that the fossil record is incomplete. Scientists may eventually find more fossils to fill the gaps.

Punctuated Equilibria The theory of **punctuated equilibria** accounts for the gaps in the fossil record. According to this theory, species evolve quickly during relatively short periods. These periods of rapid change are separated by long periods of little or no change. Today most scientists think that evolution can occur gradually at some times and more rapidly at others.

 **Reading Checkpoint** What theory proposes that evolution occurs slowly but steadily?

FIGURE 18
Trilobite
Trilobites were once common in Earth's oceans, but they were destroyed in a mass extinction.

Section 3 Assessment

 Target Reading Skill Building Vocabulary Use your definitions to help you answer the questions below.

Reviewing Key Concepts

1. a. Reviewing What are sediments? How are they involved in the formation of fossils?
 b. Classifying Identify three types of fossils.
 c. Comparing and Contrasting Which of the major types of fossils do not form in sediments? Describe how this type can form.
2. a. Identifying What are the two methods of determining a fossil's age?
 b. Describing Describe each method.
 c. Applying Concepts Some fossil organisms are frozen rather than preserved in sediment. Which method of dating would you use with frozen fossils? Why?
3. a. Defining What is the Geologic Time Scale? Into what smaller units is it divided?

 b. Interpreting Diagrams Look at Figure 16. Did the organisms during Precambrian Time have hard body parts?
 c. Relating Cause and Effect Give one reason why there are few Precambrian fossils.
4. a. Reviewing What are two unanswered questions about evolution?
 b. Comparing and Contrasting How are the theories of gradualism and punctuated equilibria different? How are they similar?

Lab zone At-Home Activity

Modeling Fossil Formation With an adult family member, spread some mud in a shallow pan. Use your fingertips to make "footprints" across the mud. Let the mud dry and harden. Explain how this is similar to fossil formation.

Chapter 6 ◆ 197

Lab zone At-Home Activity

Modeling Fossil Formation [L1]
Advise students to use mud that contains a lot of clay and enough water to make it the consistency of yogurt or pudding.

Lab zone Chapter Project

Keep Students on Track Review each group's first timeline, and offer comments before the group starts its second timeline. Confirm that students understand that because the second timeline is an enlargement of one section of the first timeline, its scale will be different. Provide source materials for students to use.

Interactive Textbook

- Complete student edition
- Section and chapter self-assessments
- Assessment reports for teachers

Help Students Read

Building Vocabulary

Word-Part Analysis Help students to learn the names of the eras in the Geologic Time Scale by explaining the word roots. The combining form *-zoic* comes from the Greek word for "life," *paleo-* from the Greek word for "ancient," *meso-* from the Greek word for "middle," and *ceno-* from the Greek word for "recent." After students have learned the meanings of the combining forms, check their understanding by asking: **What do the terms *Paleozoic, Mesozoic,* and *Cenozoic* mean?** *(Ancient life, middle life, and recent life)*

Plural Forms Students may think that the term *species* is plural and that the singular form is *specie*. Explain that the term *species* is both singular and plural. Then have them use the word in a sentence to illustrate this fact. For example, they might say, "All humans belong to one species, but humans and chimpanzees belong to two different species."

Connecting Concepts

Concept Maps Help students develop a concept map to show how the information in this chapter is related. The theory of evolution explains how organisms have changed through time and is supported by evidence from fossils, early development of animals, physiological structures, and DNA sequences. Have students brainstorm to identify the Key Concepts, Key Terms, details, and examples, then write each one on a sticky note and attach it at random on chart paper or on the board. They will use these notes to construct the concept map.

① Darwin's Theory

Key Concepts

- Darwin's important observations included the diversity of living things, the remains of ancient organisms, and the characteristics of organisms on the Galápagos Islands.

- Darwin reasoned that plants or animals that arrived on the Galápagos Islands faced conditions that were different from those on the mainland. Perhaps, Darwin hypothesized, the species gradually changed over many generations and became better adapted to the new conditions.

- Darwin proposed that, over a long period of time, natural selection can lead to change. Helpful variations may gradually accumulate in a species, while unfavorable ones may disappear.

Key Terms

species
fossil
adaptation
evolution
scientific theory
natural selection
variation

198 ◆

② Evidence of Evolution

Key Concepts

- Fossils, patterns of early development, and similar body structures all provide evidence that organisms have changed over time.

- Scientists have combined the evidence from DNA, protein structure, fossils, early development, and body structure to determine the evolutionary relationships among species.

- A new species can form when a group of individuals remains separated from the rest of its species long enough to evolve different traits.

Key Terms

homologous structures
branching tree

③ The Fossil Record

Key Concepts

- Most fossils form when organisms that die become buried in sediments.

- Scientists can determine a fossil's age in two ways: relative dating and radioactive dating.

- The calendar of Earth's history is sometimes called the Geologic Time Scale.

- Two unanswered questions about evolution involve mass extinctions and the rate at which evolution occurs.

Key Terms

petrified fossil
mold
cast
relative dating
radioactive dating
radioactive element
half-life
fossil record
extinct
gradualism
punctuated equilibria

Tell students that this concept map will be organized in hierarchical order and to begin at the top with the Key Concepts. Ask students these questions to guide them to categorize the information on the stickies: **What factors affect natural selection? What kinds of evidence support the theory of evolution? How do scientists summarize the history of life on Earth?**

Prompt students by using connecting words or phrases, such as "is supported by," "is affected by," and "can be broken into," to indicate the basis for the organization of the map. The phrases should form a sentence between or among a set of concepts.

Answer
Accept logical presentations by students.

All in One Teaching Resources, Unit 1

- Key Terms Review: *Changes Over Time*
- Connecting Concepts: *Changes Over Time*

Review and Assessment

Go Online
PHSchool.com
For: Self-Assessment
Visit: PHSchool.com
Web Code: cea-3050

Organizing Information

Sequencing Copy the flowchart about fossil formation onto a separate sheet of paper. Complete the flowchart by writing a sentence describing each stage in the process of fossil formation. Then add a title. (For more on Sequencing, see the Skills Handbook.)

An organism dies in water.

a. _____?

b. _____?

c. _____?

Reviewing Key Terms

Choose the letter of the best answer.

1. Changes in a species over long periods of time are called
   a. half-life.
   b. evolution.
   c. homologous structures.
   d. developmental stages.

2. A trait that helps an organism survive and reproduce is called a(n)
   a. variation.
   b. adaptation.
   c. species.
   d. selection.

3. Similar structures that related species have inherited from a common ancestor are called
   a. adaptations.
   b. punctuated equilibria.
   c. ancestral structures.
   d. homologous structures.

4. Fossils formed when an organism dissolves and leaves an empty space in a rock are called
   a. casts.
   b. mold.
   c. preserved remains.
   d. petrified fossils.

5. The rate of decay of a radioactive element is measured by its
   a. year.
   b. era.
   c. period.
   d. half-life.

If the statement is true, write *true*. If it is false, change the underlined word or words to make the statement true.

6. Darwin's idea about how evolution occurs is called <u>natural selection</u>.

7. Most members of a species show differences, or <u>variations</u>.

8. A diagram that shows how organisms might be related is called <u>gradualism</u>.

9. The technique of <u>relative dating</u> can be used to determine the actual age of a fossil.

10. According to the theory of <u>punctuated equilibria</u>, evolution occurs slowly but steadily.

Writing in Science

Notebook Entry Imagine that you are a biologist exploring the Galápagos Islands. Write a notebook entry on one of the unusual species you have found on the islands. Include a description of how it is adapted to its environment.

DISCOVERY CHANNEL SCHOOL

Changes Over Time
Video Preview
Video Field Trip
▶ Video Assessment

Review and Assessment

Organizing Information

Sample answer:
a. The organism is buried under sediment.
b. Over millions of years, the sediments harden and become rock, and the hard parts of the organism are replaced by minerals.
c. The fossil becomes exposed on the surface of a rock.
   Sample title: Fossil Formation

Reviewing Key Terms

1. b 2. b 3. d 4. b 5. d
6. true
7. true
8. a branching tree
9. radioactive dating
10. gradualism

Writing in Science

Writing Mode Description
Scoring Rubric
4 Includes complete description of an unusual species on the Galápagos written in the format of a notebook entry; goes beyond requirements, for example, providing extensive detail
3 Includes all criteria but does not go beyond requirements
2 Includes only brief description
1 Includes incomplete and inaccurate description

DISCOVERY CHANNEL SCHOOL
Video Assessment

Changes Over Time

Show the Video Assessment to review chapter content and as a prompt for the writing assignment.

Go Online
PHSchool.com
For: Self-Assessment
Visit: PHSchool.com
Web Code: cea-3050

Students can take a practice test online that is automatically scored.

All in One Teaching Resources, Unit 1
- Transparency LS57
- Chapter Test
- Performance Assessment Teacher Notes
- Performance Assessment Student Worksheet
- Performance Assessment Scoring Rubric

 *ExamView®* **Computer Test Bank CD-ROM**

Checking Concepts

11. The overproduction of offspring leads to competition in which only the better adapted organisms survive and reproduce.

12. Examples will vary. Possible answer: A large number of turtles are born every year but only a few will be able to swim fast enough to escape predators. Because being able to swim faster makes the turtles more likely to survive and reproduce, natural selection leads to an increase through time in the fast-swimming trait.

13. A new species can form when a group of individuals remains geographically isolated from the rest of its species long enough to reproduce separately and evolve different traits. Geographic isolation can be caused by the formation of features such as rivers and mountain ranges.

14. They could look for similarities in the DNA or protein structures of the organisms.

15. Related species inherit the same basic developmental plan from their common ancestor.

16. When a species is extinct, none of its members are alive. Scientists obtain information about extinct species from fossils.

17. A mass extinction occurs when many types of organisms become extinct at the same time. Mass extinctions may be caused by major climate changes due to events such as an asteroid hitting Earth.

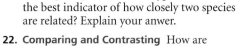

Review and Assessment

Checking Concepts

11. What role does the overproduction of organisms play in natural selection?

12. Use an example to explain how natural selection can lead to evolution.

13. Explain how geographic isolation can result in the formation of a new species.

14. On the basis of similar body structures, scientists hypothesize that two species are closely related. What other evidence would the scientists look for to support their hypothesis?

15. Explain why similarities in the early development of different species suggest that the species are related.

16. What is meant by *extinct*? How do scientists obtain information about extinct species?

17. What are mass extinctions? What may cause mass extinction?

Thinking Critically

18. Relating Cause and Effect Why did Darwin's visit to the Galápagos Islands have such an important influence on his development of the theory of evolution?

19. Applying Concepts Some insects look just like sticks. How could this be an advantage to the insects? How could this trait have evolved through natural selection?

20. Predicting Which of the organisms shown below is least likely to become a fossil? Explain your answer.

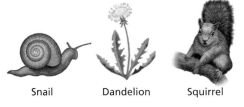

Snail Dandelion Squirrel

21. Making Judgments What type of evidence is the best indicator of how closely two species are related? Explain your anwer.

22. Comparing and Contrasting How are selective breeding and natural selection similar? How are they different?

Applying Skills

Use the data in the table below to answer Questions 23–25.

Radioactive carbon-14 decays to nitrogen with a half-life of 5,730 years. The table contains information about the amounts of carbon-14 and nitrogen in three fossils. The table also gives information about the position of each fossil in rock layers.

Fossil	Amount of Carbon-14 in Fossil	Amount of Nitrogen in Fossil	Position of Fossil in Rock Layers
A	1 gram	7 grams	Bottom layer
B	4 grams	4 grams	Top layer
C	2 grams	6 grams	Middle layer

23. Inferring Use the positions of the fossils in the rock layers to put the fossils in their probable order from the youngest to the oldest.

24. Calculating Calculate the age of each fossil using the data about carbon-14 and nitrogen.

25. Drawing Conclusions Do your answers to Questions 23 and 24 agree or disagree with each other? Explain.

Lab zone Chapter **Project**

Performance Assessment Complete both your timelines. Display your completed timelines for the class. Be prepared to explain why you chose the scale that you did. Also, describe how your timelines are related to each other.

Lab zone Chapter **Project**   L3

Performance Assessment Give each group an opportunity to show its two timelines to the rest of the class, describe how the models were made, and explain how the second timeline relates to the first timeline. Ask each group to point out any evolutionary events that were not included in the textbook's timeline. Encourage the rest of the class to ask questions.

Reflect and Record Ask students to describe how the timelines helped them to understand the long periods involved in the evolution of life. Students will probably realize that making a second timeline for the past 600 million years allowed them to see the time spans and placements of evolutionary events much more clearly. Let students share their ideas in a class discussion.

Standardized Test Prep

Choose the letter of the best answer.

1. The process by which individuals that are better adapted to their environment are more likely to survive and reproduce than other members of the same species is called
   A natural selection.
   B evolution.
   C competition.
   D overproduction.

2. Which of the following is the best example of an adaptation that helps an organism survive in its environment?
   F green coloring in a lizard living on gray rocks
   G a thick coat of fur on an animal that lives in the desert
   H extensive root system in a desert plant
   J thin, delicate leaves on a plant in a cold climate

3. Which of the following is the weakest evidence supporting a close evolutionary relationship between two animals?
   A The bones of a bird's wings are similar to the bones of a dog's legs.
   B Human embryos look like turtle embryos in their early development.
   C Lesser pandas look like bears.
   D The amino acid sequence in mouse hemoglobin is similar to the amino acid sequence in chimpanzee hemoglobin.

Use the diagram below and your knowledge of science to answer Questions 4–5.

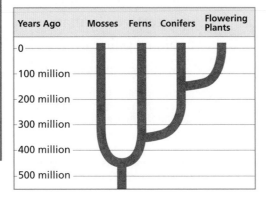

4. About how long ago did mosses first appear?
   F 100 million years ago
   G 150 million years ago
   H 350 million years ago
   J 450 million years ago

5. Which group of plants would have DNA that is most similar to the DNA of flowering plants?
   A mosses
   B ferns
   C conifers
   D They would all be equally alike.

Constructed Response

6. Relative dating and radioactive dating are two methods for determining the age of a fossil. Compare and contrast these two methods.

Thinking Critically

18. The islands were characterized by a great diversity of environments containing generally similar species that exhibited different adaptations suited to each particular environment. This had the effect of leading Darwin to develop his theory.

19. Insects that look like sticks are camouflaged among twigs and may be overlooked by predators. If the trait increases the insect's chances of surviving and reproducing, then insects with the trait would become more common than insects without it.

20. The dandelion is least likely to become a fossil because it does not have hard parts, such as bones, teeth, or a shell.

21. DNA similarities and similarities in amino acid sequence in protein; DNA and proteins have highly specific structures.

22. Both involve passing on desired traits to the next generation of organisms. In selective breeding, humans choose the traits and which organisms to cross or mate. In natural selection, the process occurs through competition and survival of the fittest.

Applying Skills

23. Based on the positions of the fossils in rock layers, B is the youngest, C is intermediate in age, and A is the oldest.

24. Based on the carbon-14 and nitrogen data, A is 17,190 years old, B is 5,730 years old, and C is 11,460 years old.

25. The answers agree because C is 5,730 years older than B, and A is 5,730 older than C. This places the fossils in the same order age-wise as relative dating.

Standardized Test Prep

1. A **2.** H **3.** C **4.** J **5.** C
6. Relative dating involves looking at the rock layers that the fossils are in to see which layer was deposited first, while radioactive dating involves comparing the amount of a radioactive element in a sample to the amount of the element into which it breaks down. Both methods are used to determine the ages of rocks, but relative dating only tells which of two or more rocks is older or younger, while radioactive dating gives the actual age of the rock.

Dogs—Loyal Companions

This interdisciplinary feature presents the central theme of domestic dogs by connecting four different disciplines: science, social studies, language arts, and mathematics. The four explorations are designed to capture students' interest and help them see how the content they are studying in science relates to other school subjects and real-world events. Share with others for a team-teaching experience.

All in One Teaching Resources, Unit 1

- Interdisciplinary Exploration: *Science*
- Interdisciplinary Exploration: *Social Studies*
- Interdisciplinary Exploration: *Language Arts*
- Interdisciplinary Exploration: *Mathematics*

Build Background Knowledge

Dogs as Companions

Ask: **What are some different types of dogs?** *(German shepherd, Labrador retriever, poodle, rottweiler, sheep dog.)* **For what reasons do people have dogs?** *(As pets, as guard dogs, as hunting dogs, as police dogs, to herd sheep, to pull sleds, to be companions for people who are visually impaired or hearing impaired)*

Introduce the Exploration

Have students think about the early mutualistic relationship between humans and wolves over 10,000 years ago. Ask: **How would the wolves benefit from being near humans?** *(They may be able to find food more easily by eating scraps and garbage)* **How would humans benefit from having wolves nearby?** *(The wolves may bark as a warning when strangers were near, the wolves helped keep the living area clean by eating scraps and garbage.)*

Egyptian Art
More than 3,000 years ago, an artist drew three dogs chasing a hyena.

Dogs— Loyal Companions

What's your image of a dog?

- A powerful Great Dane?
- A tiny, lively Chihuahua?
- A protective German shepherd guide dog?
- A friendly, lovable mutt?

Most dogs are descendants of the gray wolf, which was originally found throughout Europe, Asia, and North America. Dogs were the first animals to be domesticated, or tamed. As far back as 9,000 years ago, farmers who raised sheep, cattle, and goats tamed dogs to herd and guard the livestock.

After taming dogs, people began to breed them for traits that people valued. Early herding dogs helped shepherds. Speedy hunting dogs learned to chase deer and other game. Strong, sturdy working dogs pulled sleds and even rescued people. Small, quick terriers hunted animals, such as rats. "Toy" dogs were companions to people of wealth and leisure. More recently, sporting dogs were trained to flush out and retrieve birds. Still others were bred to be guard dogs. But perhaps the real reasons people bred dogs were for loyalty and companionship.

Girl with dalmatian

202 ◆

From Wolf to Purebred

About 10,000 years ago, some wolves may have been attracted to human settlements. They may have found it easier to feed on food scraps than to hunt for themselves. Gradually the wolves came to depend on people for food. The wolves, in turn, kept the campsites clean and safe. They ate the garbage and barked to warn of approaching strangers. These wolves were the ancestors of the dogs you know today.

Over time, dogs became more and more a part of human society. People began to breed dogs for the traits needed for tasks such as herding sheep and hunting. Large, aggressive dogs, for example, were bred to be herding dogs, while fast dogs with a keen sense of smell were bred to be hunting dogs. Today, there are hundreds of breeds. They range from the tiny Chihuahua to the massive Saint Bernard, one of which can weigh as much as 50 Chihuahuas.

Today, people breed dogs mostly for their appearance and personality. Physical features such as long ears or a narrow snout are valued in particular breeds of dogs. To create "pure" breeds of dogs, breeders use a method known as inbreeding. Inbreeding involves mating dogs that are genetically very similar. Inbreeding is the surest way to produce dogs with a uniform physical appearance.

One undesirable result of inbreeding is an increase in genetic disorders. Experts estimate that 25 percent of all purebred dogs have a genetic disorder. Dalmatians, for example, often inherit deafness. German shepherds may develop severe hip problems. Mixed-breed dogs, in contrast, are less likely to inherit genetic disorders.

Fur Color in Retrievers
In Labrador retrievers, the allele for dark-colored fur is dominant over the allele for yellow fur.

Science Activity

Most traits that dogs are bred for are controlled by more than one gene. A few traits, however, show simpler inheritance patterns. For example, in Labrador retrievers, a single gene with one dominant and one recessive allele determines whether the dog's fur will be dark or yellow. The allele for dark fur (D) is dominant over the allele for yellow fur (d).

- Construct a Punnett square for a cross between two Labrador retrievers that are both heterozygous for dark fur (Dd).

- Suppose there were eight puppies in the litter. Predict how many would have dark fur and how many would have yellow fur.

- Construct a second Punnett square for a cross between a Labrador retriever with yellow fur (dd) and one with dark fur (Dd). In a litter with six puppies, predict how many would have dark fur and how many would have yellow fur.

♦ 203

Background

Facts and Figures *Canis familiaris* is the scientific name for the domestic dog. The dog is believed to be the first animal to be domesticated. The domestic dog is a descendent of the wolf, *Canis rufus*. After thousands of years of selective breeding there are more than 300 breeds of dogs. The American Kennel Club (AKC) recognizes 150 breeds of dogs and divides them into seven categories: terrier, working, sporting, hound, herding, toy, and nonsporting. Working dogs include Doberman pinschers, rottweilers, Great Danes, and Alaskan malamutes. Sporting dogs include Labrador retrievers, weimaraners, and Irish setters. Herding dogs include sheep dogs, German shepherds, and Welsh corgis.

Science

Explore Science Concepts

Review Help students recall that traits are passed from parent to offspring through genetic material. By breeding two dogs that both have a desired trait, the chances of their offspring having the desired trait increases.

Discuss Ask: **For what reasons do people breed dogs?** (So that they have traits that allow them to hunt, herd, guard, or run better; also for appearance and personality) **What traits would you want a hunting dog to have?** (Possible answers: to be able to run quickly, to have a good sense of smell, to be able to retrieve, to be able to swim well) **What traits would you want a herding dog to have?** (To be aggressive and be able to herd, to have a lot of energy, to be able to be outside in extreme weather) **What is inbreeding?** (Inbreeding involves mating dogs that are genetically similar to each other.) **What is a disadvantage of inbreeding?** (It increases the chances of genetic disorders in the offspring.)

Science Activity

Focus Students should recall that they are being given the genotypes of the dogs to use in the Punnett squares. Each genotype will be expressed as a phenotype, in this case either dark or yellow fur.

Teach Remind students how to construct a Punnett square. Students should make the Punnett square, then examine the genotypes to determine what percentage of offspring will have each phenotype.

Expected Outcome In the cross between the dogs that are both heterozygous for dark fur, 75 percent of the offspring will probably have dark fur and 25 percent will have yellow fur. Out of eight puppies, six will probably have dark fur and two will have yellow fur. In the cross between the yellow-fur dog and the heterozygous dark-fur dog, 50 percent of the offspring will probably have dark fur and 50 percent will probably have yellow fur. Out of six puppies, three will probably have dark fur and three will probably have yellow fur.

Explore Social Studies Concepts

Use Maps Provide students with copies of world maps on 11 x 17 sheets of paper. The maps can be pre-labeled or students can label them as an extra challenge. Have students use encyclopedias, library resources, and the Internet to research the geographic origin of different dog breeds. Students can label their maps with the dog breeds and the corresponding area or country from which they originate. *(Sample answers: Alaskan malamute—northwestern Alaska; Basenji—Africa; Belgian sheepdog—Belgium; Chihuahua—Mexico; Collie—Scotland; Mastiff—England; Pomeranian—Germany; Portuguese water dog—Portugal; Samoyed—Siberia)*

Teach Key Concepts

Review Some dogs have characteristics that make them better adapted to living in a cold climate. Some dogs have characteristics that make them well adapted for certain activities, such as hunting.

Discuss Ask: **How is the Lhasa Apso well adapted for cold conditions?** *(The breed has a long, thick coat that protects it from cold air.)* **How are the basset hound and the dachshund well adapted for hunting?** *(The basset hound has short legs and a compact body that help it run through underbrush. The dachshund has short legs and a long body that can fit into the burrows of animals such as badgers and rats.)*

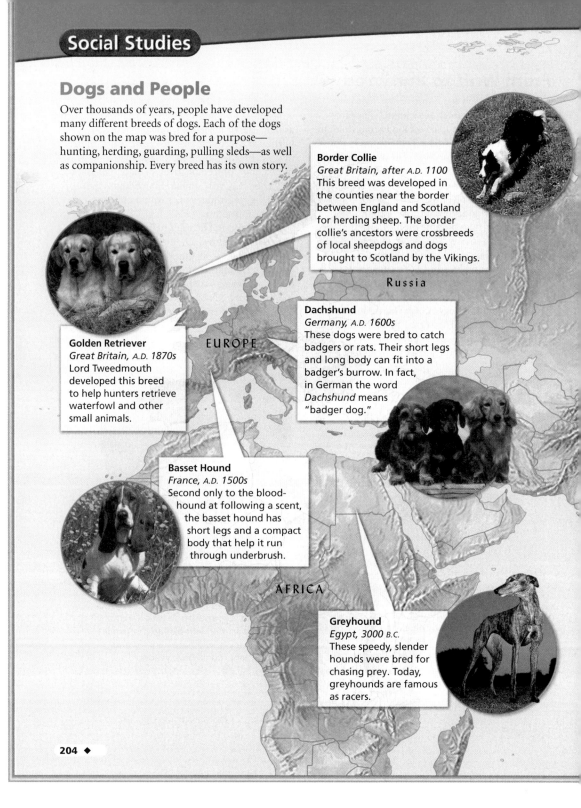

Dogs and People

Over thousands of years, people have developed many different breeds of dogs. Each of the dogs shown on the map was bred for a purpose—hunting, herding, guarding, pulling sleds—as well as companionship. Every breed has its own story.

Border Collie
Great Britain, after A.D. 1100
This breed was developed in the counties near the border between England and Scotland for herding sheep. The border collie's ancestors were crossbreeds of local sheepdogs and dogs brought to Scotland by the Vikings.

Russia

Golden Retriever
Great Britain, A.D. 1870s
Lord Tweedmouth developed this breed to help hunters retrieve waterfowl and other small animals.

EUROPE

Dachshund
Germany, A.D. 1600s
These dogs were bred to catch badgers or rats. Their short legs and long body can fit into a badger's burrow. In fact, in German the word *Dachshund* means "badger dog."

Basset Hound
France, A.D. 1500s
Second only to the bloodhound at following a scent, the basset hound has short legs and a compact body that help it run through underbrush.

AFRICA

Greyhound
Egypt, 3000 B.C.
These speedy, slender hounds were bred for chasing prey. Today, greyhounds are famous as racers.

204 ◆

Siberian Husky
Siberia, 1000 B.C.
The Chukchi people of northeastern Siberia used these strong working dogs to pull sleds long distances across the snow.

Pekingese
China, A.D. 700s
These lapdogs were bred as pets in ancient China. One Chinese name for a Pekingese means "lion dog," which refers to the dog's long, golden mane.

Chow Chow
China, 150 B.C.
Chow chows, the working dogs of ancient China, worked as hunters, herders, and guard dogs.

Akita
Japan, A.D. 1600s
This breed was developed in the cold mountains of northern Japan as a guard dog and hunting dog. The Akita is able to hunt in deep snow and is also a powerful swimmer.

Lhasa Apso
Tibet, A.D. 1100
This breed has a long, thick coat that protects it from the cold air of the high Tibetan plateau. In spite of its small size, the Lhasa apso guarded homes and temples.

China

Japan

Social Studies Activity

Draw a timeline that shows the approximate date of origin of different breeds of domestic dogs from 3000 B.C. to the present. Use the information on the map to fill out your timeline. Include information about where each breed was developed.

◆ 205

Class Activity

Have students think about the impact that dogs have on our society in the United States. Have students look through the phone directory, research on the Internet, magazines, and newspapers, and think about television and radio to find examples of how much dogs are a part of people's lives. Encourage students to look for services and products such as doggie day care, dog groomers, dog sitters, dog walkers, dog food, dog snacks, dog beds, and dog seat belts. Students can make a collage out of advertisements they find in magazines and include drawings of their own to represent other services and products they discovered.

Guest Speaker

Arrange for the trainer of a working dog, such as a companion animal or a police dog, to speak to the class. Encourage students to write down questions for the speaker before the presentation. Questions about how the dog is trained and a typical day "at work" are important.

Social Studies Activity

Focus Students should reorganize the material presented on the pages into a timeline.

Teach Have students read the pages carefully to determine at which date their timelines should begin. Remind students that the timeline will be similar to a number line with negative numbers. The date 3500 B.C. will be on the far left with dates progressing towards zero. The A.D. dates should increase after zero.

Expected Outcome The dates and breeds should be organized as follows: 3000 B.C. — Greyhound; 1000 B.C. —Siberian husky; 150 B.C. —Chow Chow; A.D. 700 —Pekingese; A.D. 1100 —Lhasa Apso; after A.D. 1100 — border collie; A.D. 1500s —basset hound; A.D. 1600s —Akita; A.D. 1600s —dachshund; A.D. 1870s —golden retriever.

Background

Facts and Figures Dogs are trained to help people in many different ways. Dogs can be trained to be guide dogs for people that are visually impaired. They can be companion animals for hearing-impaired people or people who are physically challenged. Dogs are used by the police to search for both perpetrators and victims of crimes. Police dogs can be trained to respond to the smell of drugs or money and used in airports or at border patrols. Some dogs are trained as rescue dogs to search for disaster victims such as after an earthquake or an avalanche. Some dogs work pulling sleds or herding sheep or cattle. Dogs are also used as part of therapy for autistic children or people confined to a hospital or nursing home.

Explore Language Arts Concepts

Discuss James Herriot's writing was descriptive. He uses adjectives, adverbs, and descriptive phrases to bring the reader to a faraway scene. Ask: **How do you think his wife feels in the first paragraph of the story?** *(She is excited, possibly frustrated and worried about losing the dog. She is frustrated and in a rush because her husband has been gone so long.)* **How do you know this?** *(Herriot uses the adverb "agitatedly" to describe his wife's tone of voice. She scolds him by saying, "What a long time you've been out there," and he uses an exclamation point at the end of her statement.)* **What words and phrases does he use to describe the puppy?** *(tiny, brindle, twisting, writhing, tail wagging furiously, pink tongue)* **Would you infer that the puppy's mother and grandmother had a lot of energy or that they were lethargic dogs? Why?** *(They had lots of energy. The dogs "darted out and stood up at our legs, tails lashing, mouths panting in delight.")*

Oral Presentation Bring in several of James Herriot's books. Have students take turns reading aloud from the books to the class. Ask: **How does Herriot's writing transport the reader to the scene? How does reading his stories make you feel?**

Focus Have students identify an event they would like to write about. Have them take a few minutes to quietly recall the event and their feelings surrounding it.

Teach Encourage students to use vivid adjectives to describe the event and their feelings.

Scoring Rubric

4 Includes detailed description of event, including their emotions at the time, how they made a decision; correctly punctuated dialog and well-constructed paragraphs
3 Includes all criteria but details are somewhat sketchy; writing style is good
2 Includes some criteria; writing style is minimally acceptable
1 Includes few details; poorly written

Picking a Puppy

People look for different traits in the dogs they choose. Here is how one expert selected his dog based on good breeding and personality.

James Herriot, a country veterinarian in Yorkshire, England, had owned several dogs during his lifetime. But he had always wanted a Border terrier. These small, sturdy dogs are descendants of working terrier breeds that lived on the border of England and Scotland. For centuries they were used to hunt foxes, rats, and other small animals. In this story, Herriot and his wife, Helen, follow up on an advertisement for Border terrier puppies.

James Herriot
In several popular books published in the 1970s and 1980s, James Herriot wrote warm, humorous stories about the animals he cared for.

◀ **Border terriers**

She [Helen, his wife] turned to me and spoke agitatedly, "I've got Mrs. Mason on the line now. There's only one pup left out of the litter and there are people coming from as far as eighty miles away to see it. We'll have to hurry. What a long time you've been out there!"

We bolted our lunch and Helen, Rosie, granddaughter Emma and I drove out to Bedale. Mrs. Mason led us into the kitchen and pointed to a tiny brindle creature twisting and writhing under the table.

"That's him," she said.

I reached down and lifted the puppy as he curled his little body round, apparently trying to touch his tail with his nose. But that tail wagged furiously and the pink tongue was busy at my hand. I knew he was ours before my quick examination for hernia and overshot jaw.

The deal was quickly struck and we went outside to inspect the puppy's relations. His mother and grandmother were out there.

They lived in little barrels which served as kennels and both of them darted out and stood up at our legs, tails lashing, mouths panting in delight. I felt vastly reassured. With happy, healthy ancestors like those I knew we had every chance of a first rate dog.

As we drove home with the puppy in Emma's arms, the warm thought came to me. The wheel had indeed turned. After nearly fifty years I had my Border terrier.

James Herriot describes this scene using dialog and first-person narrative. The narrative describes Herriot's feelings about a memorable event—finally finding the dog he had wanted for so long. Write a first-person narrative describing a memorable event in your life. You might choose a childhood memory or a personal achievement at school. What emotions did you feel? How did you make your decision? If possible, use dialog in your writing.

206 ◆

Background

Facts and Figures James Alfred Wight (1916–1995) wrote under the pseudonym James Herriot. Born in England, but raised in Scotland, Wight graduated from Glasgow Veterinary College in 1939. He established his veterinary practice in England, where he lived for the remainder of his life. Wight wrote books about his experiences as a vet in the English countryside. Works such as *All Creatures Great and Small* and *All Things Bright and Beautiful* relay tales of his animal care in a small, quiet English town. His books were made into a television series in England in the late 1970s. Wight also published several children's books. In 2001, his son, Jim Wight, published a biography about his father entitled *The Real James Herriot: A Memoir to My Father.*

Popular Breeds

The popularity of different breeds of dogs changes over time. For example, the line graph shows how the number of poodles registered with the American Kennel Club changed between 1970 and 2000.

Standard poodle and puppy ▶

Math Activity

Use the table below to create your own line graph for Labrador retrievers and cocker spaniels. Which breed was more popular in 1980, Labrador retrievers or cocker spaniels?

How has the number of Labrador retrievers changed from 1970 to 2000? How has the number of cocker spaniels changed over the same time?

Dog Populations

Breed	1970	1980	1990	2000
Poodle	265,879	92,250	71,757	45,868
Labrador Retriever	25,667	52,398	95,768	172,841
Cocker Spaniel	21,811	76,113	105,642	29,393

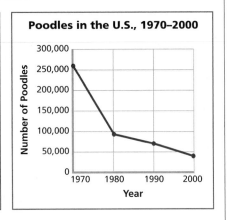

Poodles in the U.S., 1970–2000

Tie It Together

Best-of-Breed Show

In many places, proud dog owners of all ages bring their animals to compete in dog shows.

Organize your own dog show.

With a partner, choose one specific breed of dog. Pick a breed shown on the map on the previous page, or use library resources to research another breed.

• Find out what the breed looks like, the time and place where it originated, and what traits it was first bred for.

• List your breed's characteristics, height, weight, and coloring.

• Research the breed's personality and behavior.

• Find out your breed's strengths. Learn what weaknesses may develop as a result of inbreeding.

• Make a poster for your breed. Include a drawing or photo and the information that you researched.

• With your class, organize the dog displays into categories of breeds, such as hunting dogs, herding dogs, and toy dogs.

◆ 207

Explore Mathematics Concepts

Discuss Encourage students to describe how a graph can successfully *picture* information from a data table. They can use the information about poodles in the table and graph to illustrate their point.

Math Activity

Focus Remind students to plot the year on the horizontal axis and the number of dogs on the vertical axis. Students can use the graph on this page as a model.

Teach Students can put both sets of data on one graph by using a different color pencil for each. Remind them to make a key for the graph if they choose to do this.

Expected Outcome Check students' graphs for appropriate titles and accurate labeling of axes. Answers: In 1980, cocker spaniels were more popular; the number of Labrador retrievers increased from 1970 to 2000; the number of cocker spaniels increased until 1990, and then significantly decreased by 2000.

Tie It Together

Best-of-Breed Show

Time 3 class periods (1 for research, 1 for designing and making the posters, 1 to organize the display of posters)

Tips Have students work in groups of two. Provide students with examples of dogs from each of the seven categories of dogs: terrier, working, sporting, hound, herding, toy, and nonsporting. Once students have chosen which dog they would like to research, review with students the information they need to complete the assignment.

• Check with each group to make sure no breed of dog is repeated. Make sure that at least one breed from each of the seven categories is represented.

• Provide students with poster board, colored markers, construction paper, and other materials they might need to make their posters.

• Students may be able to use computer graphics to design parts of their posters.

• If possible, have students make color copies of the photos for their posters.

Chapter at a Glance

PRENTICE HALL

TeacherEXPRESS™
Plan • Teach • Assess

Technology

Local Standards

 Lab zone Chapter **Project** *A Mushroom Farm*

All in One Teaching Resources, Unit 2
- Chapter Project Teacher Notes, pp. 24–25
- Chapter Project Student Overview, pp. 26–27
- Chapter Project Student Worksheets, pp. 28–29
- Chapter Project Scoring Rubric, p. 30

Discovery CHANNEL SCHOOL
Video Preview

Section 1 Viruses

2 periods
1 block

7.1.1 List characteristics of viruses and state reasons why viruses are considered to be nonliving.

7.1.2 Describe the components of the basic structure of a virus.

7.1.3 Explain how both active and hidden viruses multiply.

7.1.4 Discuss how viral diseases are treated.

Go Online
active art

Section 2 Bacteria

2 periods
1 block

7.2.1 Name and describe structures, sizes, and shapes of a bacterial cell.

7.2.2 Compare autotrophs to heterotrophs, and explain how energy is released through respiration.

7.2.3 Describe the conditions under which bacteria thrive and reproduce frequently.

7.2.4 Explain the roles of bacteria in the production of oxygen and food, in environmental recycling and cleanup, and in health and medicine.

Go Online
PHSchool.com

Section 3 Protists

2 periods
1 block

7.3.1 Describe the characteristics of animal-like protists and give examples.

7.3.2 Describe the characteristics of plantlike protists and give examples.

7.3.3 Describe the characteristics of funguslike protists and give examples.

Go Online
active art

Section 4 Fungi

2 periods
1 block

7.4.1 Name the characteristics fungi share.

7.4.2 Explain how fungi reproduce.

7.4.3 Describe the roles fungi play in nature.

Discovery CHANNEL SCHOOL
Video Field Trip

Go Online
SciLINKS NSTA

Review and Assessment

Test Preparation

All in One Teaching Resources, Unit 2
- Key Terms Review, p. 66
- Transparency LS70
- Performance Assessment Teacher Notes, p. 73
- Performance Assessment Scoring Rubric, p.74
- Performance Assessment Student Worksheet, p. 75
- Chapter Test, pp. 76–79

Discovery CHANNEL SCHOOL
Video Assessment

Go Online
PHSchool.com

**Test Preparation
Blackline Masters**

Lab zone Chapter Activities Planner

For more activities
LAB ZONE
Easy Planner
CD-ROM

Student Edition	Inquiry	Time	Materials	Skills	Resources
Chapter Project, p. 209	Open-Ended	4–5 weeks	**All in One Teaching Resources, Unit 2**, p. 24	Developing hypotheses, designing experiments, drawing conclusions, communicating	**Lab zone Easy Planner** **All in One Teaching Resources, Unit 2**, Support pp. 24–25
Section 1					
Discover Activity, p. 210	Guided	10 minutes	1 key for each student or each group of students	Inferring	**Lab zone Easy Planner**
Skills Lab, p. 216	Guided	Prep: 45 minutes Class: 40 minutes	Straight pin, meter stick, calculator (optional), long strips of paper, scissors, pencil, tape	Calculating, making models	**Lab zone Easy Planner Lab Activity Video** **All in One Teaching Resources, Unit 2**, Skills Lab: *How Many Viruses Fit on a Pin?* pp. 39–40
Section 2					
Discover Activity, p. 217	Guided	20 minutes	Dried beans, paper cups	Calculating, inferring	**Lab zone Easy Planner**
Try This Activity, p. 219	Guided	20 minutes	Unpasteurized yogurt, plastic dropper, methylene blue, glass slide, cover slip, microscope, lab apron	Observing	**Lab zone Easy Planner**
Section 3					
Discover Activity, p. 226	Guided	25 minutes	Plastic dropper, pond water, microscope slide, coverslip, microscope	Observing	**Lab zone Easy Planner**
Try This Activity, p. 231	Directed	15 minutes	Paramecium culture, *Chlorella* culture, plastic dropper, microscope and slide, cotton fibers	Inferring	**Lab zone Easy Planner**
Skills Activity, p. 232	Guided	20 minutes	Euglena culture, plastic petri dish, aluminum foil, compound microscope	Predicting	**Lab zone Easy Planner**
Section 4					
Discover Activity, p. 236	Guided	15 minutes	Sealable bags, tape, hand lens, old bread, fruit	Observing	**Lab zone Easy Planner**
Try This Activity, p. 238	Directed	25 minutes	Round balloon, cotton balls, tape, stick or ruler about 30 cm long, modeling clay, pin	Making models	**Lab zone Easy Planner**
Skills Lab, pp. 242–243	Directed	Prep: 20 minutes Class: 45 minutes	5 plastic narrow-necked bottles, 5 round balloons, 5 plastic straws, dry powered yeast, sugar, salt, warm water, marking pen, beaker, graduated cylinder, metric ruler, string	Measuring, inferring, drawing conclusions	**Lab zone Easy Planner Lab Activity Video** **All in One Teaching Resources, Unit 2**, Skills Lab: *What's for Lunch?* pp. 63–65

Section 1 Viruses

2 periods, 1 block

ABILITY LEVELS
L1 Basic to Average
L2 For All Students
L3 Average to Advanced

Objectives

7.1.1 List characteristics of viruses and state reasons why viruses are considered to be nonliving.

7.1.2 Describe the components of the basic structure of a virus.

7.1.3 Explain how both active and hidden viruses multiply.

7.1.4 Discuss how viral diseases are treated.

Key Terms

• virus • host • parasite • bacteriophage • vaccine

Local Standards

Preteach

Build Background Knowledge

Invite students to name diseases, as you list them on the board. Ask them to identify any they know are caused by viruses. *(Sample: cold, flu, smallpox, measles, mumps, polio)*

 **Discover Activity** *Which Lock Does the Key Fit?* **L1**

Targeted Print and Technology Resources

All in One Teaching Resources, Unit 2

L2 Reading Strategy Transparency LS58: Sequencing

PresentationEXPRESS™ CD-ROM

Instruct

What Is a Virus? Students discuss the characteristics, shapes, and sizes of viruses. They compare the similarities and differences in viral structures.

How Viruses Multiply Students learn how a virus takes over a host cell to reproduce viruses.

Viruses and Diseases Students learn about the spread, treatment, and prevention of viral diseases.

 Skills Lab *How Many Viruses Fit on a Pin?* **L2**

Targeted Print and Technology Resources

All in One Teaching Resources, Unit 2

L2 Guided Reading, pp. 33–36
L2 Transparencies LS59, LS60, LS61
L2 Skills Lab: *How Many Viruses Fit on a Pin?*, pp. 39–40

Lab Activity Video/DVD
Skills Lab: *How Many Viruses Fit on a Pin?*

PHSchool.com Web Code: cep-1021

Student Edition on Audio CD

Assess

Section Assessment Questions

 Have students use their Sequencing graphic organizers to answer questions.

Reteach

Students review flowchart about viruses with a partner, adding any necessary information.

Targeted Print and Technology Resources

All in One Teaching Resources, Unit 2

• Section Summary, p. 32
L1 Review and Reinforce, p. 37
L3 Enrich, p. 38

Section 2 Bacteria

🕐 *2 periods, 1 block*

ABILITY LEVELS
L1 Basic to Average
L2 For All Students
L3 Average to Advanced

Objectives

7.2.1 Name and describe structures, sizes, and shapes of a bacterial cell.

7.2.2 Compare autotrophs to heterotrophs, and explain how energy is released through respiration.

7.2.3 Describe the conditions under which bacteria thrive and reproduce frequently.

7.2.4 Explain the roles of bacteria in the production of oxygen and food, in environmental recycling and cleanup, and in health and medicine.

Local Standards

Key Terms

• bacteria • flagellum • binary fission • asexual reproduction
• sexual reproduction • conjugation • endospore • pasteurization
• decomposer

Preteach

Build Background Knowledge

Students discuss samples of yogurt and Swiss cheese displayed in classroom. Students infer that they are all produced with the help of certain kinds of bacteria.

 **Discover Activity** *How Quickly Can Bacteria Multiply?* **L1**

Targeted Print and Technology Resources

All in One Teaching Resources, Unit 2

L2 Reading Strategy: Building Vocabulary

💿 **PresentationEXPRESS™ CD-ROM**

Instruct

The Bacterial Cell Students discuss structures, shapes, and sizes of bacteria.

Obtaining Food and Energy Students compare autotrophs to heterotrophs and then discuss energy released through respiration.

Reproduction Students study the conditions needed for bacteria to reproduce, comparing and contrasting asexual and sexual methods of bacterial reproduction.

The Role of Bacteria in Nature Students discuss roles of bacteria in the production of oxygen and food, in health care, and in the manufacture of medicine.

Targeted Print and Technology Resources

All in One Teaching Resources, Unit 2

L2 Guided Reading, pp. 43–45

L2 Transparency LS62

PHSchool.com Web Code: ced-1022

💿 **Student Edition on Audio CD**

Assess

Section Assessment Questions

Have students use Building Vocabulary definitions to write sentences about Key Terms.

Reteach

Students answer the assessment questions using their Building Vocabulary definitions.

Targeted Print and Technology Resources

All in One Teaching Resources, Unit 2

• Section Summary, p. 42

L1 Review and Reinforce, p. 46

L3 Enrich, p. 47

Section 3 **Protists**

 2 periods, 1 block

Objectives

Local Standards

7.3.1 Describe the characteristics of animal-like protists and give examples.
7.3.2 Describe the characteristics of plantlike protists and give examples.
7.3.3 Describe the characteristics of funguslike protists and give examples.

Key Terms

• protist • protozoan • pseudopod • contractile vacuole • cilia • symbiosis
• mutualism • algae • spore

Preteach

Build Background Knowledge

Students discuss which characteristics must be considered to determine whether or not "blobs" in a dish are alive.

 **Discover Activity** *What Lives in a Drop of Pond Water?* **L1**

Targeted Print and Technology Resources

All in One Teaching Resources, Unit 2
L2 Reading Strategy Transparency LS63: Outlining

PresentationEXPRESS™ CD-ROM

Instruct

What Is a Protist? Students explore the shared characteristics and tremendous diversity of organisms in the protist kingdom

Animal-Like Protists Students discuss the general traits of animal-like protists and the differences that divide them into four distinct groups.

Plantlike Protists Students identify traits of plantlike protists, called algae, and distinguish the various types, exploring differences in pigments, size, structures, habitats, and functions.

Funguslike Protists Students determine shared characteristics among and differences between the three groups of funguslike protists.

Targeted Print and Technology Resources

All in One Teaching Resources, Unit 2
L2 Guided Reading, pp. 50–53
L2 Transparencies LS65, LS66, LS67

PHSchool.com Web Code: cep-1031

Student Edition on Audio CD

Assess

Section Assessment Questions

Have students use their completed outlines to help answer the questions.

Reteach

Students name features shared by protists and identify the many differences that make the group so diverse.

Targeted Print and Technology Resources

All in One Teaching Resources, Unit 2
• Section Summary, p. 49
L1 Review and Reinforce, p. 54
L3 Enrich, p. 55

Section 4 Fungi

 2 periods, 1 block

ABILITY LEVELS
L1 Basic to Average
L2 For All Students
L3 Average to Advanced

Objectives

7.4.1 Name the characteristics that all fungi share.

7.4.2 Explain how fungi reproduce.

7.4.3 Describe the roles fungi play in nature.

Key Terms

• fungi • hyphae • fruiting body • budding • lichen

Local Standards

Preteach

Build Background Knowledge

Students discuss what they know about mushrooms, both those cultivated and those in natural habitats, and begin to consider their similarities to plants.

 **Discover Activity** *Do All Molds Look Alike?* L1

Targeted Print and Technology Resources

 Teaching Resources, Unit 2

L2 Reading Strategy Transparency LS68: Asking Questions

 PresentationEXPRESS™ CD-ROM

Instruct

What Are Fungi? Students consider traits shared by fungi and examine their habitats, cell structure, and means of obtaining food.

Reproduction in Fungi Students discuss fungal spores and the fruiting bodies that release them, and determine when and how fungi reproduce either sexually or asexually, and how fungi are characterized this way.

The Role of Fungi in Nature Students explore the many roles of fungi on Earth: decomposers, recyclers, disease agents, disease fighters, and organisms living in symbiosis with other organisms.

 Skills Lab *What's for Lunch?* L2

Targeted Print and Technology Resources

 Teaching Resources, Unit 2

L2 Guided Reading, pp. 58–60
L2 Transparency LS69
L2 Skills Lab: *What's for Lunch?*, pp. 63–65

 Lab Activity Video/DVD
Skills Lab: *What's for Lunch?*

PHSchool.com Web Code: ced-1033

www.SciLinks.org Web Code: scn-0133

 DISCOVERY CHANNEL **SCHOOL**
Video Field Trip

 Student Edition on Audio CD

Assess

Section Assessment Questions

Have students use their Asking Questions graphic organizers to help answer the questions.

Reteach

Students produce a chart or diagram illustrating basic characteristics of fungi, how they reproduce and obtain food, and the roles they play in nature.

Targeted Print and Technology Resources

Teaching Resources, Unit 2

• Section Summary, p. 57
L1 Review and Reinforce, p. 61
L3 Enrich, p. 62

Chapter 7 Content Refresher

Go Online
NSTA—PDi LINKS

For: Professional development support
Visit: www.SciLinks.org/PDLinks
Web Code: scf-0120

Professional
Development

Section 1 Viruses

Characteristics of Viruses Viruses vary widely in size and shape. However, all viruses share a similar structure. A virus particle consists of a protein capsid enclosing a nucleic acid core. Some viruses are also surrounded by a membrane envelope, which derives from its host but also contains viral proteins. The illustration below shows the structures of two viruses.

Viruses can be classified according to the type of nucleic acid they contain. The genetic material may be double-stranded DNA, single-stranded DNA, double-stranded RNA, or single-stranded RNA. Viruses are also classified according to their structure and the host organisms they infect. Viruses infect organisms from all three domains. However, because the interaction between a virus' proteins and the proteins on a host's cell is highly specific, a particular virus is able to infect only certain types of cells.

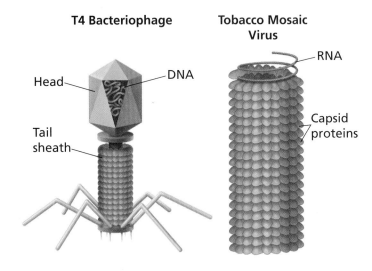

T4 Bacteriophage

Head — DNA

Tail sheath

Tobacco Mosaic Virus

RNA

Capsid proteins

Section 2 Bacteria

Bacteria in the Body Bacteria are part of the normal flora of humans. Found on the skin and in the mouth, intestines, and other sites, these bacteria are part of the mixture of the microorganisms that regularly live in or on the body without causing harm. The normal flora of humans consists of more than 200 species of bacteria. In normal health, the interaction between the bacteria and the human host are thought to be mutualistic. The host provides the bacteria with a stable shelter and temperature, and a supply of nutrients. In return, the bacteria provide the host with benefits including aid in digesting, production of certain vitamins, stimulation of the immune system, and competition against other pathogens.

Section 3 Protists

Diversity of Protists The protists are an extremely diverse group of organisms. In fact, it is probably easier to describe what they are not rather than what they are. A protist is a eukaryote that is not an animal, plant, or fungus. The traditional approach is to group these hard-to-classify organisms under one kingdom—Protista.

However, protists are so incredibly varied that many taxonomists debate whether a kingdom Protista still makes sense. There are currently 30 to 40 phyla of protists recognized by most taxonomists. However, the groups are so different from one another that some biologists have proposed classifying protists into several kingdoms. This idea is supported by recent comparisons of cell physiology and DNA, especially ribosomal RNA sequences. At present, there are many unanswered questions about the protists; the evolutionary history of many of the groups is unclear. Therefore, many people still adopt the traditional classification of protists as one kingdom.

An informal way to classify protists, which does not reflect their evolutionary histories, is according to the way they obtain nutrition. The three nutritional categories are animal-like protists, plantlike protists, and funguslike protists. Animal-like protists are heterotrophs. Plantlike protists are autotrophs, producing their own food through photosynthesis. Funguslike protists, like fungi, are heterotophs that obtain their nutrients by external digestion; they absorb nutrients from dead or decaying organic matter.

 **Address Misconceptions**

Students may think that all red algae look red, or that all green algae look green. Red, green, and brown algae all contain various pigments, so they don't always appear the color they are named. For more on this misconception, see **Address Misconceptions** in the section *Protists*.

Section 4 Fungi

Molds Molds are some of the more familiar members of the fungi kingdom. Molds are found within the club fungi and zygote fungi phyla. One of the best-known molds, the common black bread mold *Rhizopus stolonifer*, is a zygote fungus. *Rhizopus*, like other molds, grows quickly. A growth of *Rhizopus* appears as a layer of dark fuzz. But upon closer inspection, various types of hyphae are visible. Types of hyphae include stolons, rhizoids, and sporangiophores.

Stolons are stemlike, horizontal hyphae that run along the surface of the bread. Rhizoids are rootlike hyphae that anchor the fungus to the bread. They penetrate the surface of the bread, release digestive chemicals, and absorb the nutrients into the fungus. Sporangiophores are upright hyphae that develop tiny, black, pinheadlike spore cases at their tips. Within each spore case, or sporangium, are thousands of spores. These spores are dispersed through the air and grow into new fungi if they land in a favorable environment.

As well as producing spores asexually in its sporangiophores, *Rhizopus* can also produce spores sexually. During sexual reproduction, neighboring hyphae of opposite mating types can come together and join to form a tough, thick-walled structure called a zygospore. Zygospores are very resistant and can survive long periods of freezing, drying, and other harsh environmental conditions. When conditions become favorable again, the zygospores germinate into sporangia. The sporangia release spores that can grow into a new generation of fungi.

Stolon, Rhizoids, and Sporangia

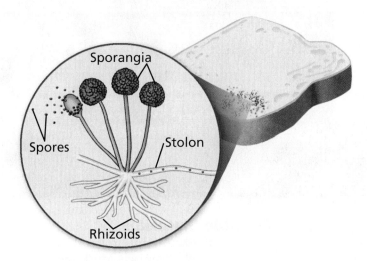

Help Students Read

Comparing and Contrasting
Identifying Similarities and Differences

Strategy Help students read and understand material that discusses two or more related topics or concepts. Identifying similarities and differences enables them to link prior knowledge with new information.

Example

1. Have students compare two or more topics under a heading. Tell them that when they compare, they should focus on both similarities and differences. Remind them to look for signal words: similarities—*similar, also, just as, like, likewise, in the same way;* differences—*but, however, although, whereas, on the other hand, different, unlike.*

2. Have students contrast two or more topics or concepts. Remind them that when they contrast, they should focus only on differences.

3. Have students create a chart or diagram comparing or contrasting two or more topics or concepts they read about in a section. Suggest that they create either a compare/contrast table or a Venn diagram.

Interactive Textbook

• Complete student edition
• Video and audio
• Simulations and activities
• Section and chapter activities

Chapter 7

Viruses, Bacteria, Protists, and Fungi

Chapter Preview

❶ Viruses
Discover *Which Lock Does the Key Fit?*
Active Art *Active and Hidden Viruses*
Skills Lab *How Many Viruses Fit on a Pin?*

❷ Bacteria
Discover *How Quickly Can Bacteria Multiply?*
Try This *Bacteria for Breakfast*
Analyzing Data *Population Explosion*
Science and History *Bacteria and Foods of the World*
At-Home Activity *Edible Bacteria*

❸ Protists
Discover *What Lives in a Drop of Pond Water?*
Active Art *Amoeba and Paramecium*
Try This *Watching Protists*
Skills Activity *Predicting*
At-Home Activity *Algae Scavenger Hunt*

❹ Fungi
Discover *Do All Molds Look Alike?*
Try This *Spreading Spores*
Skills Lab *What's for Lunch?*

Interactive Textbook

Bacteria (blue and purple rods) and other microorganisms lurk in a kitchen sponge. ▶

208 ◆

Chapter **Project**   L3

Objectives
This project will allow students to determine the effect of changing a single variable on the growth of mushrooms. After this Chapter Project, students will be able to
• develop a hypothesis concerning how a variable affects mushroom growth;
• design and perform an experiment to test their hypotheses;
• draw conclusions based on their results;
• communicate their results in the form of a poster.

Skills Focus
Developing hypotheses, designing experiments, drawing conclusions, communicating

Project Time Line 4–5 weeks

All in One Teaching Resources, Unit 2
• Chapter Project Teacher Notes
• Chapter Project Overview
• Chapter Project Worksheet 1
• Chapter Project Worksheet 2
• Chapter Project Scoring Rubric

Developing a Plan
Students first discuss mushrooms, decide which variable to test, and develop experimental designs to test their variables. Depending on conditions tested, the experiment will take 2–3 weeks. Allow one week following the end of the project for data analysis and poster preparation.

Possible Materials
It is difficult to grow mushrooms from spores you collect yourself. Mushroom growing kits, available from most biological supply companies, provide all the materials necessary to complete this project. You may need additional pots and peat moss. You can use milk cartons, two-liter plastic bottle bottoms, or other such containers with holes cut in the bottom. A spray bottle works

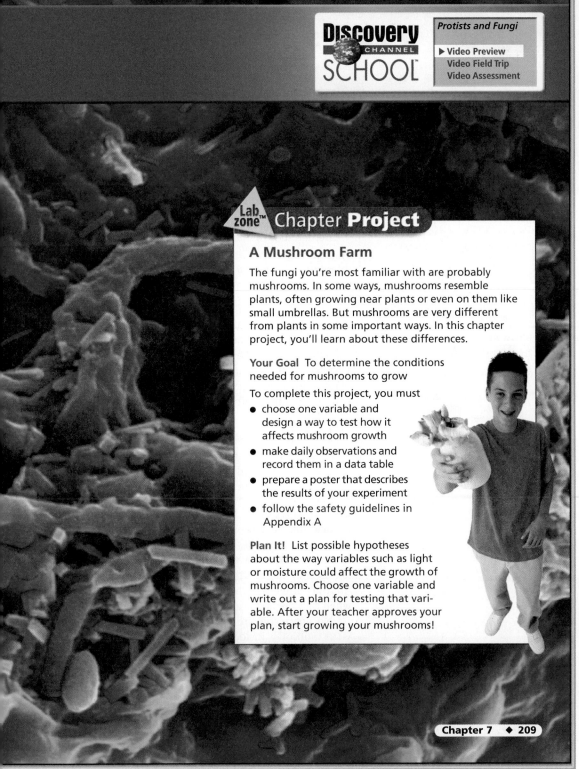

DISCOVERY CHANNEL SCHOOL Video Preview

Protists and Fungi

Show the Video Preview to introduce the Chapter Project and overview the chapter content. Discussion question: **How do epiphytes and lichen contribute to the tree canopy ecosystem?** *(When epiphytes and lichen die, they decompose and form a rich humus soil within the canopy where other organisms can live)*

Discuss experimental design; emphasize the difference between manipulated and responding variables, and why other variables must be controlled. Have students form groups, choose variables, and develop hypotheses about how mushroom growth will be affected by their variable. Check that some groups choose different variables.

Performance Assessment

The Chapter Project Scoring Rubric will help you evaluate how well students complete the Chapter Project. You may wish to share the scoring rubric with your students so they are clear about what will be expected of them. Students will be assessed on

- how well they define and control the variables in their experiment;
- how well their experimental design tests their hypotheses, and the thoroughness of their data collection;
- their analysis of the results, and the clarity and organization of their poster;
- their ability to work cooperatively as a group.

  Students can save their posters in their portfolios.

Portfolio

Lab zone™ Chapter Project

A Mushroom Farm

The fungi you're most familiar with are probably mushrooms. In some ways, mushrooms resemble plants, often growing near plants or even on them like small umbrellas. But mushrooms are very different from plants in some important ways. In this chapter project, you'll learn about these differences.

Your Goal To determine the conditions needed for mushrooms to grow

To complete this project, you must

- choose one variable and design a way to test how it affects mushroom growth
- make daily observations and record them in a data table
- prepare a poster that describes the results of your experiment
- follow the safety guidelines in Appendix A

Plan It! List possible hypotheses about the way variables such as light or moisture could affect the growth of mushrooms. Choose one variable and write out a plan for testing that variable. After your teacher approves your plan, start growing your mushrooms!

Chapter 7 ◆ 209

---

well for watering the containers. For testing variables you will need

- a dark location and a light source (to test light);
- a thermometer and a warm and a cool location (to test temperature);
- substrate lacking nutrients and some fertilizer (to test nutrients).

Launching the Project

To introduce the project, ask: **How do you think mushrooms grow?** *(In damp and warm places, such as in the forest after a rain.)* **Are they like plants?** Students may know that mushrooms are fungi but may also think of them as plants. Encourage students to discuss similarities and differences between mushrooms and plants. Have students read the project description above.

Objectives

After this lesson, students will be able to

7.1.1 List characteristics of viruses and state reasons why viruses are considered to be nonliving.

7.1.2 Describe the components of the basic structure of a virus.

7.1.3 Explain how both active and hidden viruses multiply.

7.1.4 Discuss how viral diseases are treated.

Target Reading Skill ↻

Sequencing Explain that organizing information from beginning to end helps students understand a step-by-step process.

Answer

One way students might organize the information is: How Active Viruses Multiply—1. Virus attaches to the surface of a living cell. 2. Virus injects genetic material into cell. 3. Cell produces viral proteins and genetic material. 4. Viruses assemble. 5. Cell bursts, releasing viruses. How Hidden Viruses Multiply—1. Virus attaches to cell. 2. Virus injects its genetic material. 3. Virus's genetic material becomes part of cell's genetic material. 4. Later, virus's genetic material becomes active. 5. Cell produces viral proteins and genetic material; viruses are assembled. 6. Cell bursts, releasing viruses.

All in One Teaching Resources, Unit 2

• Transparency LS58

Preteach

Build Background Knowledge L2

Identifying Viral Diseases

Invite students to name diseases they are familiar with. List the diseases on the board. Tell students that viruses are the cause of some diseases. Encourage them to identify any diseases on the list that they know are caused by viruses. (*Sample: cold, flu, smallpox, measles, mumps, polio*)

Reading Preview

Key Concepts

• How are viruses like organisms?
• What is the structure of a virus?
• How do viruses multiply?
• How can you treat a viral disease?

Key Terms

• virus • host • parasite
• bacteriophage • vaccine

↻ Target Reading Skill

Sequencing As you read, make two flowcharts that show how active and hidden viruses multiply.

How Active Viruses Multiply

Virus attaches to the surface of a living cell

↓

Virus injects genetic material into cell

↓

Lab zone — Discover Activity

Which Lock Does the Key Fit?

1. Your teacher will give you a key.
2. Study the key closely. Think about what shape the keyhole on its lock must have. On a piece of paper, draw the shape of the keyhole.
3. The lock for your key is contained in the group of locks your teacher will provide. Try to match your key to its lock without inserting the key into the keyhole.

Think It Over

Inferring How might a unique "lock" on its surface help a cell protect itself from invading organisms?

It is a dark and quiet night. An enemy spy slips silently across the border. Invisible to the guards, the spy creeps cautiously along the edge of the road, heading toward the command center. Undetected, the spy sneaks by the center's security system and reaches the door. Breaking into the control room, the spy takes command of the central computer. The enemy is in control.

What Is a Virus?

Although this spy story may read like a movie script, it describes events similar to those that can occur in your body. The spy acts very much like a virus invading an organism.

Characteristics of Viruses A **virus** is a tiny, nonliving particle that invades and then multiplies inside a living cell. Viruses are not cells. They do not have the characteristics of organisms. **The only way in which viruses are like organisms is that they can multiply.** Although viruses can multiply, they multiply differently than organisms. Viruses can only multiply when they are inside a living cell.

No organisms are safe from viruses. The organism that a virus multiplies inside is called a host. A **host** is a living thing that provides a source of energy for a virus or an organism. Viruses act like **parasites** (PA ruh syts), organisms that live on or in a host and cause it harm. Almost all viruses destroy their host cells.

Lab zone — Discover Activity

Skills Focus Inferring   **L1**

Materials key for each group of students, locks that match the keys given to the students

Time 10 minutes

Tips This activity will create interest and anticipation for the concept of virus specificity.

Expected Outcome Students will gain interest in and understanding of the lock-and-key concept and be ready to apply it to the fit between a virus's protein coat and its host cell.

Think It Over An invading organism would not be able to "enter" a cell unless it had a unique "key" that fits the "lock" on the cell's surface.

The Structure of Viruses Viruses are smaller than cells and vary in size and shape. Some viruses are round. Others are shaped like rods, bricks, threads, or bullets. There are even viruses that have complex, robot-like shapes, such as the bacteriophage in Figure 1. A **bacteriophage** (bak TEER ee oh fayj) is a virus that infects bacteria. In fact, its name means "bacteria eater."

Although viruses may look different from one another, they all have a similar structure. **All viruses have two basic parts: a protein coat that protects the virus and an inner core made of genetic material.** A virus's genetic material contains the instructions for making new viruses. Some viruses are also surrounded by an additional outer membrane, or envelope.

The proteins on the surface of a virus play an important role during the invasion of a host cell. Each virus contains unique surface proteins. The shape of the surface proteins allows the virus to attach to certain cells in the host. Like keys, a virus's proteins fit only into certain "locks," or proteins, on the surface of a host's cells. Figure 2 shows how the lock-and-key action works.

Because the lock-and-key action of a virus is specific, a certain virus can attach only to one or a few types of cells. For example, most cold viruses infect cells only in the nose and throat of humans. These cells are the ones with proteins on their surface that complement or "fit" those on the virus.

 Reading Checkpoint What information does a virus's genetic material contain?

FIGURE 1
Bacteriophage
This robot-like virus infects bacteria.

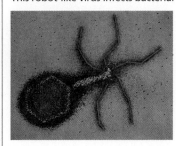

FIGURE 2

Virus Structure and Infection

All viruses consist of genetic material surrounded by a protein coat. Some viruses, like the ones shown here, are surrounded by an outer membrane envelope. A virus can attach to a cell only if the virus' surface proteins can fit those on the cell.

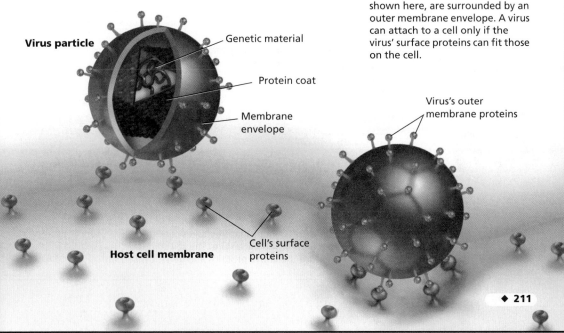

Virus particle

Genetic material

Protein coat

Membrane envelope

Host cell membrane

Cell's surface proteins

Virus's outer membrane proteins

◆ 211

Differentiated Instruction

Gifted and Talented `L3`
Creating Displays Have students briefly research viruses to choose one aspect of viruses they would like to present to the class. You may want their presentations to include posters to make them more interesting and more informative. Give students a deadline for submitting their topics for approval before proceeding with the project. Try to have each student present a different aspect of viruses.

Challenge students to make their presentations very interesting for the class. You may choose to add some competition to the project by asking the class to vote on the presentations. The goal is to make this project especially valuable for the gifted and talented students but also beneficial for the rest of the class. **learning modality: verbal**

Instruct

What Is a Virus?

Teach Key Concepts `L2`
Two Structural Components

Focus Tell students that every virus has two basic structural components.

Teach Ask: **What two structural components does every virus have?** (*A protein coat and an inner core of genetic material*) **How does a virus's protein coat relate to the host cells?** (*The proteins on the outer surface of the virus can attach to proteins on the surface of certain host cells.*)

Apply Ask: **How does this apply to the location where a virus is likely to be found?** (*A virus for a certain disease attaches itself to a specific type of cell, often found in a specific part of the body.*) **learning modality: visual**

All in One Teaching Resources, Unit 2
• Transparency LS59

Independent Practice `L2`

All in One Teaching Resources, Unit 2
• Guided Reading and Study Worksheet: *Viruses*

◉ **Student Edition on Audio CD**

Lab zone Teacher Demo

Predicting Fit of Virus and Cell `L2`

Materials clothing snaps or fasteners
Time 5 minutes

Focus Direct students' attention to Figure 2.

Teach Ask students to observe the way the clothing snaps attach to each other. Fasten and unfasten them as you allow all students to see. Ask: **Would one of these snaps fit other types of snaps or fastener?** (*No, it fits only the unique partner it was made to fit.*)

Apply Ask: **How does that relate to the viral protein coat and the host cell's surface?** (*The fit between the viral proteins and cell proteins is very specific, just as these kinds of snaps fit with only each other.*) **learning modality: visual**

Monitor Progress _____ `L2`

Answer
 Reading Checkpoint Instructions for making new viruses

How Viruses Multiply

Teach Key Concepts

Viruses Take Over

Focus Ask students to look at the visuals under the heading *How Viruses Multiply.*

Teach Ask: **What are the similarities and the differences between the active and the hidden viruses?** (*Similarity: Both inject their genetic material into a host cell. Both burst open the cell after they multiply. Difference: An active virus multiplies immediately, while a hidden virus hides and later multiplies. The genetic material of a hidden virus becomes a part of the host cell's genetic material for a time while it hides.*)

Apply Ask: **What is the difference in the effects of the active and the hidden viruses?** (*The effects of an active virus infection are immediate; the effects of a hidden virus infection take a while to appear. Both eventually burst and kill the host cell.*)
learning modality: visual

All in One Teaching Resources, Unit 2

• Transparencies LS60, LS61

Go Online
active art

For: Active and Hidden Viruses activity
Visit: PHSchool.com
Web Code: cep-1021

Students explore online the two methods viruses use to multiply.

How Viruses Multiply

After a virus attaches to a host cell, it enters the cell. **Once inside a cell, a virus's genetic material takes over many of the cell's functions. It instructs the cell to produce the virus's proteins and genetic material. These proteins and genetic material then assemble into new viruses.** Some viruses take over cell functions immediately. Other viruses wait for a while.

Active Viruses After entering a cell, an active virus immediately goes into action. The virus's genetic material takes over cell functions, and the cell quickly begins to produce the virus's proteins and genetic material. Then these parts assemble into new viruses. Like a photocopy machine left in the "on" position, the invaded cell makes copy after copy of new viruses. When it is full of new viruses, the host cell bursts open, releasing hundreds of new viruses as it dies.

FIGURE 3
Active and Hidden Viruses

Active viruses enter cells and immediately begin to multiply, leading to the quick death of the invaded cells. Hidden viruses "hide" for a while inside host cells before becoming active.

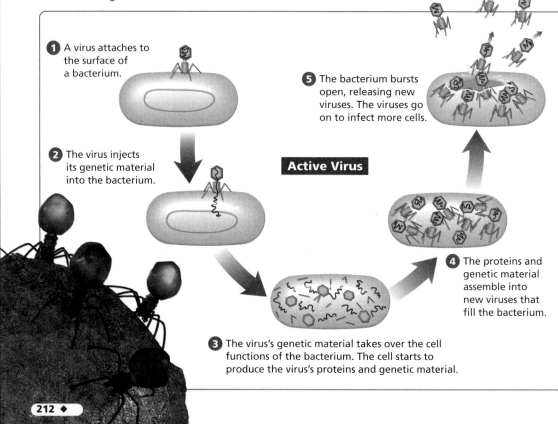

1 A virus attaches to the surface of a bacterium.

2 The virus injects its genetic material into the bacterium.

3 The virus's genetic material takes over the cell functions of the bacterium. The cell starts to produce the virus's proteins and genetic material.

4 The proteins and genetic material assemble into new viruses that fill the bacterium.

5 The bacterium bursts open, releasing new viruses. The viruses go on to infect more cells.

Active Virus

212 ◆

Hidden Viruses Other viruses do not immediately become active. Instead, they "hide" for a while. After a hidden virus enters a host cell, its genetic material becomes part of the cell's genetic material. The virus does not appear to affect the cell's functions and may stay in this inactive state for years. Each time the host cell divides, the virus's genetic material is copied along with the host's genetic material. Then, under certain conditions, the virus's genetic material suddenly becomes active. It takes over the cell's functions in much the same way that active viruses do. Soon, the cell is full of new viruses and bursts open.

The virus that causes cold sores is an example of a hidden virus. It can remain inactive for months or years inside nerve cells in the face. While hidden, the virus causes no symptoms. When it becomes active, the virus causes a swollen, painful sore to form near the mouth. Strong sunlight and stress are two factors that scientists believe may activate a cold sore virus. After an active period, the virus once again "hides" in the nerve cells until it becomes active again.

 Reading Checkpoint Where in a host cell does a hidden virus "hide" while it is inactive?

Go Online
active art

For: Active and Hidden Viruses activity
Visit: PHSchool.com
Web Code: cep-1021

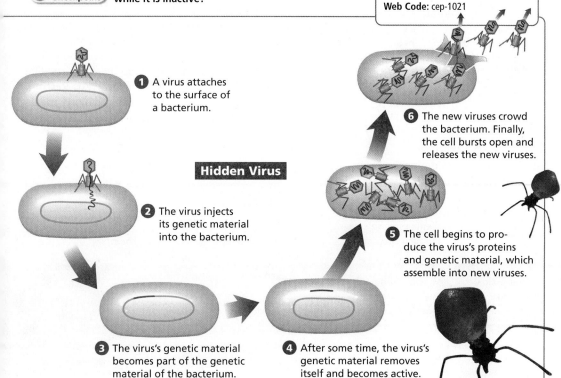

❶ A virus attaches to the surface of a bacterium.

❷ The virus injects its genetic material into the bacterium.

Hidden Virus

❸ The virus's genetic material becomes part of the genetic material of the bacterium.

❹ After some time, the virus's genetic material removes itself and becomes active.

❺ The cell begins to produce the virus's proteins and genetic material, which assemble into new viruses.

❻ The new viruses crowd the bacterium. Finally, the cell bursts open and releases the new viruses.

Chapter 7 ◆ 213

Communicating Differences

Materials per group: 1 package of colored markers, 2 large poster boards, textbook

Time 30 minutes

Focus Review the differences between active and hidden viruses.

Teach Have students work in groups. While volunteers read aloud the descriptions of active viruses, have each group create a flowchart that shows each step of viral reproduction and its result. Repeat the process for hidden viruses. Ask: **At what stage in their cycles do the active and hidden viruses begin to differ?** *(Stage 3).* **What does the active virus do at the point at which the two cycles differ?** *(Its host cell begins to produce the virus's proteins and genetic material.)* **What does the hidden virus do before it becomes active?** *(Its genetic material becomes part of the host's genetic material.)*

Apply Ask **How does this relate to the way a virus affects you?** *(It means that, if the virus is an active virus, the disease symptoms may appear soon. If it is a hidden virus, those symptoms may not appear for a long time.)*
learning modality: visual

Integrating Science

Computer viruses are quite different from biological viruses. Invite a computer science instructor or software programmer to talk to the class about computer viruses. Before the visit, tell students that after a computer virus enters a computer via a disk, e-mail, or online file, the computer may infect all other computers or disks with which it comes into contact by copying the virus onto them. Encourage students to develop a list of questions about computer viruses before the visit. **learning modality: verbal**

Differentiated Instruction

Special Needs L1
Interpreting Visuals Ask students to study Figure 3. Ask them what they understand about active and hidden virus cycles. Use simple language to summarize the text under the sub-headings *Active Viruses* and *Hidden Viruses*. Have them look at the visuals again. Ask what these two visuals communicate. Explain to them that a visual communicates information in

a variety of ways. In this diagram, they can learn from the colored arrows that show the sequence of steps as well as from the numbers preceding each step. Show them how to compare and contrast the two cycles.

Monitor Progress L2

Oral Presentation Ask students to explain the difference between an active and a hidden virus.

Answer
 Reading Checkpoint In the host cell's genetic material

Viruses and Disease

Teach Key Concepts
Treatment of Viral Diseases

Focus Stress to students that there are currently no medicines that can cure viral illnesses. Viral diseases, therefore, can only be managed.

Teach Ask: **How might over-the-counter medications help in the treatment of a viral illness?** (*They help relieve symptoms of the disease.*) Point out to students that, on the other hand, these medications can also hide symptoms that would normally prompt someone to go see a doctor.

Apply Tell students that the best treatment for a viral disease is often getting plenty of rest, eating well-balanced meals, and drinking plenty of fluids. These actions help the body fight and recover from the illness. **learning modality: verbal**

Use Visuals: Figure 4
Two Viral Diseases

Focus Students become familiar with the symptoms, spread, and treatment of two common viral diseases.

Teach Ask: **What advantage would there be in learning how these diseases spread?** (*If you know how a disease spreads, then you would be better able to prevent the disease or avoiding getting it.*)

Apply Call students' attention to the prevention of these diseases. Emphasize that prevention is better than cure. **learning modality: verbal**

FIGURE 4
Viral Diseases
Although there is currently no cure for viral diseases, there are ways to treat the symptoms and prevent their transmission.
Relating Cause and Effect *Why does the flu often pass quickly from one family member to another?*

Viruses and Disease

If you've ever had a cold sore or been sick with the flu, you know that viruses can cause disease. Some diseases, such as colds, are mild—people are sick for a short time but soon recover. Other diseases, such as acquired immunodeficiency syndrome, or AIDS, have much more serious consequences on the body.

Viruses also cause diseases in organisms other than humans. For example, apple trees infected by the apple mosaic virus may produce less fruit. House pets, such as dogs and cats, can get deadly viral diseases, such as rabies and distemper.

The Spread of Viral Diseases Viral diseases can be spread in various ways. For example, some viral diseases can be spread through contact with a contaminated object, while others are spread through the bite of an infected animal. Some viruses, such as cold and flu viruses, can travel in tiny drops of moisture that an infected person sneezes or coughs into the air. Other viruses can spread only through contact with body fluids, such as blood.

Treating Viral Diseases There are currently no cures for viral diseases. However, many over-the-counter medications can help relieve symptoms of a viral infection. While they can make you feel better, these medications can also delay your recovery if you resume your normal routine while you are still sick. The best treatment for viral infections is often bed rest. **Resting, drinking plenty of fluids, and eating well-balanced meals may be all you can do while you recover from a viral disease.**

INFLUENZA (Flu)

Symptoms:	High fever; sore throat; headache; cough
How It Spreads:	Contact with contaminated objects; inhaling droplets
Treatment:	Bed rest; fluids
Prevention:	Vaccine (mainly for the high-risk ill, elderly, and young)

CHICKENPOX

Symptoms:	Fever; red, itchy rash
How It Spreads:	Contact with the rash; inhaling droplets
Treatment:	Antiviral drug (for adults)
Prevention:	Vaccine

Chickenpox virus ▶

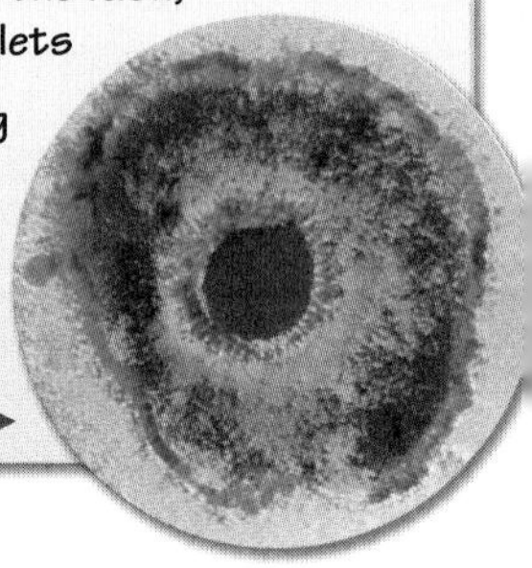

214 ◆

214

Preventing Viral Diseases Of course, you'd probably rather not get sick in the first place. An important tool that helps prevent the spread of many viral diseases is vaccines. A **vaccine** is a substance introduced into the body to stimulate the production of chemicals that destroy specific disease-causing viruses and organisms. A viral vaccine may be made from weakened or altered viruses. Because they have been weakened or altered, the viruses in the vaccine do not cause disease. Instead, they trigger the body's natural defenses. In effect, the vaccine puts the body "on alert." If that disease-causing virus ever invades the body, it is destroyed before it can cause disease. You may have been vaccinated against diseases such as polio, measles, and chickenpox.

Another important way to protect against viral diseases is to keep your body healthy. You need to eat nutritious food, as well as get enough sleep, fluids, and exercise. You can also protect yourself by washing your hands often and by not sharing eating or drinking utensils.

Unfortunately, despite your best efforts, you'll probably get viral infections, such as colds, from time to time. When you do get ill, get plenty of rest, and follow your doctor's recommendations. Also, it's very important to try not to infect others.

 Reading Checkpoint Why don't vaccines cause disease themselves?

FIGURE 5
Vaccines
Veterinarians can give pets vaccine injections that protect the animals against many viral diseases.

Section 1 Assessment

Target Reading Skill **Sequencing** Refer to your flowcharts about how viruses multiply as you answer Question 3.

Reviewing Key Concepts

1. a. Defining What is a virus?
  b. Comparing and Contrasting How are viruses similar to organisms?
  c. Inferring Scientists hypothesize that viruses could not have existed on Earth before organisms appeared. Use what you know about viruses to support this hypothesis.

2. a. Identifying What basic structure do all viruses share?
  b. Relating Cause and Effect What role do the proteins in a virus's outer coat play in the invasion of a host cell?

3. a. Reviewing How does an active virus multiply?
  b. Sequencing List the additional steps that occur when a hidden virus multiplies.
  c. Classifying Do you think that the cold virus is an active virus or a hidden virus? Explain.

4. a. Reviewing What is often the best treatment for viral diseases?
  b. Explaining How are vaccines important in preventing viral diseases?

Writing in Science

Public Service Announcement Write a public service announcement for a radio show that teaches young children how to stay healthy during cold and flu season.

Chapter 7 ◆ 215

Writing in Science

Writing Mode Persuasion

Scoring Rubric

4 Includes complete and accurate persuasive writing at a child's level
3 Includes accurate persuasive writing but lacks some required criteria
2 Includes very brief but accurate persuasive writing
1 Includes poor persuasive writing

Portfolio

How Many Viruses Fit on a Pin? **L2**

Prepare for Inquiry

Key Concept
To help appreciate the small size of viruses, people often compare them to known objects.

Skills Objectives
Students will be able to
- make a model showing a virus's size compared to the head of a pin
- calculate the number of viruses that could fit on a pin's head

Prep Time 45 minutes

Class Time 40 minutes

Alternative Materials
To make the 10-m strip, obtain long rolls of paper such as adding machine tape.

Teaching Resources, Unit 2
- Lab Worksheet: *How Many Viruses Fit on a Pin?*

Guide Inquiry

Invitation
Point out that references to how many items fit on a pinhead are often made when discussing things that are very small or very numerous.

Introduce the Procedure
Review metric measurements to ensure that students remember the metric units of measurement. Review the idea of scale. Remind students of everyday examples of the ways in which scale is used.

Troubleshooting the Experiment
Remind students that there are often different ways to solve specific calculation problems. Match up students who are using similar methods, then let different groups share their strategies.

Expected Outcome
Area of the enlarged pinhead: $\pi \times radius^2 = 3.1 \times 25 = 77.5 \ m^2$; area of enlarged virus: $0.002 \times 0.002 = 0.000004 \ m^2$; could fit $77.5/0.000004 = 19,375,000$ viruses on pinhead

---

Lab zone Skills Lab

How Many Viruses Fit on a Pin?

Problem
How can a model help you understand how small viruses are?

Skills Focus
calculating, making models

Materials
- straight pin • long strips of paper • pencil
- meter stick • scissors • tape
- calculator (optional)

Procedure

1. Examine the head of a straight pin. Write a prediction about the number of viruses that could fit on the pinhead. **CAUTION:** *Avoid pushing the pin against anyone's skin.*

2. Assume that the pinhead has a diameter of about 1 mm. If the pinhead were enlarged 10,000 times, then its diameter would measure 10 m. Create a model of the pinhead by cutting and taping together narrow strips of paper to make a strip that is 10 m long. The strip of paper represents the diameter of the enlarged pinhead.

3. Lay the 10-m strip of paper on the floor of your classroom or in the hall. Imagine creating a large circle that had the strip as its diameter. The circle would be the pinhead at the enlarged size. Calculate the area of the enlarged pinhead using this formula:

   $$Area = \pi \times Radius^2$$

   Remember that you can find the radius by dividing the diameter by 2.

4. A virus particle may measure 200 nm on each side (1 nm equals a billionth of a meter). If the virus were enlarged 10,000 times, each side would measure 0.002 m. Cut out a square 0.002 m by 0.002 m to serve as a model for a virus. (*Hint*: 0.002 m = 2 mm.)

216 ◆

5. Next, find the area in meters of one virus particle at the enlarged size. Remember that the area of a square equals side × side.

6. Now divide the area of the pinhead that you calculated in Step 3 by the area of one virus particle to find out how many viruses could fit on the pinhead.

7. Exchange your work with a partner, and check each other's calculations.

Analyze and Conclude

1. **Calculating** Approximately how many viruses can fit on the head of a pin?

2. **Predicting** How does your calculation compare with the prediction you made? If the two numbers are very different, explain why your prediction may have been inaccurate.

3. **Making Models** What did you learn about the size of viruses by magnifying both the viruses and pinhead to 10,000 times their actual size?

4. **Communicating** In a paragraph, explain why scientists sometimes make and use enlarged models of very small things such as viruses.

More to Explore
Think of another everyday object that you could use to model some other facts about viruses, such as their shapes or how they infect cells. Describe your model and explain why the object would be a good choice.

These papilloma viruses, which cause warts, are about 50 nm in diameter. ▼

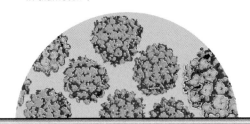

Analyze and Conclude
1. About 20 million
2. Have students explain whether their predictions were based on reasoning or whether they "just guessed."
3. When magnified, the pinhead was very large while the virus size was still very small.
4. The enlarged models help them to understand details of scale and structure.

Extend Inquiry

More to Explore
Have students compare their models with what they know about viruses to determine models' strengths and weaknesses.

Safety
Remind students not to harm anyone with the pins. Caution students not to lose pins. Review the safety guidelines in Appendix A.

Reading Preview

Key Concepts
- How do the cells of bacteria differ from those of eukaryotes?
- What do bacteria need to survive?
- Under what conditions do bacteria thrive and reproduce?
- What positive roles do bacteria play in people's lives?

Key Terms
- bacteria • flagellum
- binary fission
- asexual reproduction
- sexual reproduction
- conjugation • endospore
- pasteurization • decomposer

 **Target Reading Skill**

Building Vocabulary After you read the section, reread the paragraphs that contain definitions of Key Terms. Use all the information you have learned to write a definition of each Key Term in your own words.

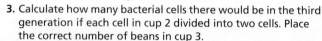 **Discover Activity**

How Quickly Can Bacteria Multiply?

1. Your teacher will give you some beans and paper cups. Number the cups 1 through 8. Each bean will represent a bacterial cell.

2. Put one bean into cup 1 to represent the first generation of bacteria. Approximately every 20 minutes, a bacterial cell reproduces by dividing into two cells. Put two beans into cup 2 to represent the second generation of bacteria.

3. Calculate how many bacterial cells there would be in the third generation if each cell in cup 2 divided into two cells. Place the correct number of beans in cup 3.

4. Repeat Step 3 five more times. All the cups should now contain beans. How many cells are in the eighth generation? How much time has elapsed since the first generation?

Think It Over
Inferring Based on this activity, explain why the number of bacteria can increase rapidly in a short period of time.

They thrive in your container of yogurt. They lurk in your kitchen sponge. They coat your skin and swarm inside your nose. You cannot escape them because they live almost everywhere—under rocks, in the ocean, and all over your body. In fact, there are more of these organisms in your mouth than there are people on Earth! You don't notice them because they are very small. These organisms are bacteria.

The Bacterial Cell

Although there are billions of bacteria on Earth, they were not discovered until the late 1600s. A Dutch merchant named Anton van Leeuwenhoek (LAY vun hook) found them by accident. Leeuwenhoek made microscopes as a hobby. One day, while using one of his microscopes to look at scrapings from his teeth, he saw some tiny, wormlike organisms in the sample. However, Leeuwenhoek's microscopes were not powerful enough to see any details inside these organisms.

Chapter 7 ◆ 217

Objectives

After this lesson, students will be able to

7.2.1 Name and describe structures, shapes, and sizes of a bacterial cell.

7.2.2 Compare autotrophs to heterotrophs, and explain how energy is released through respiration.

7.2.3 Describe the conditions under which bacteria thrive and reproduce frequently.

7.2.4 Explain the roles of bacteria in the production of oxygen and food, in environmental recycling and cleanup, and in health and medicine.

Target Reading Skill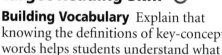

Building Vocabulary Explain that knowing the definitions of key-concept words helps students understand what they read.

Answers

One way students might organize the information is: Students may write one or two descriptive phrases to help them remember the key term. Call on students to share their definitions.

Preteach

Build Background Knowledge `L1`

Helpful Bacteria
Display samples of yogurt and Swiss cheese. Ask students what these foods have in common. Then, record their responses on the board. Tell students that these products are all produced with the help of certain kinds of bacteria. Ask: **What other foods can you think of that might be prepared with the aid of bacteria?** (*Accept all reasonable answers, such as buttermilk, sauerkraut, and sour cream.*)

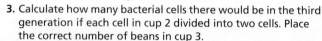 **Discover Activity**

Skills Focus Calculating, inferring

Materials dried beans; paper cups

Time 20 minutes

Tips Remind students to calculate the elapsed time based on the fact that it takes 20 minutes for bacteria to divide.

Expected Outcome Cup 1—1 bean; Cup 2—2 beans; Cup 3—4 beans;

Cup 4—8 beans; Cup 5—16 beans; Cup 6—32 beans; Cup 7—64 beans; Cup 8—128 beans. There are 128 cells in the eighth generation. Two hours and 20 minutes have passed since only 1 bacterium existed.

Think It Over Students will infer that the numbers increase rapidly because each bacterium can double every 20 minutes.

The Bacterial Cell

Teach Key Concepts **L2**

What Are Bacteria?

Focus Students learn what distinguishes bacterial cells from the cells of other organisms.

Teach Write the terms *prokaryote* and *eukaryote* on the board, and invite students to recall their meanings. Ask: **What are the similarities and differences between the cells of prokaryotes and eukaryotes?** *(Both have genetic material and ribosomes. Prokaryotic cells do not have a nucleus or other membrane-bound organelles; eukaryotic cells do.)* **Why do you need a microscope to study bacteria?** *(Because they are tiny, unicellular organisms.)* Explain that bacteria vary in appearance, size, and shape. Show students photos of spherical, rodlike, and spiral-shaped bacteria.

Apply Ask: **How might studying bacteria under a microscope help scientists identify bacteria?** *(Because different bacteria have different appearances, sizes, and shapes, scientists can identify bacteria according to these characteristics.)* **learning modality: visual**

All in One Teaching Resources, Unit 2

• Transparency LS62

Independent Practice **L2**

All in One Teaching Resources, Unit 2

• Guided Reading and Study Worksheet: *Bacteria*

◎ Student Edition on Audio CD

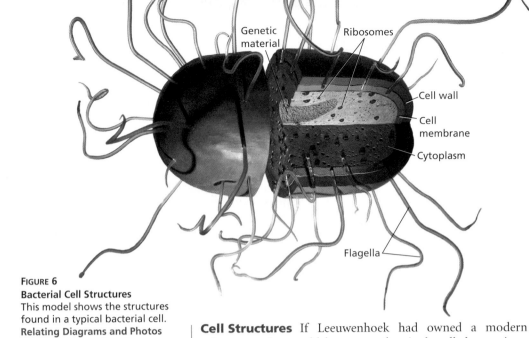

FIGURE 6
Bacterial Cell Structures
This model shows the structures found in a typical bacterial cell.
Relating Diagrams and Photos *What structures does the Salmonella bacterium in the photograph use to move?*

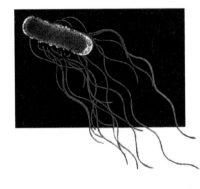

Cell Structures If Leeuwenhoek had owned a modern microscope, he would have seen the single-celled organisms known as **bacteria** (singular *bacterium*) in detail. **Bacteria are prokaryotes. The genetic material in their cells is not contained in a nucleus.** A bacterial cell lacks a nucleus and also lacks many other structures, such as mitochondria and Golgi bodies, that are found in the cells of eukaryotes.

Most bacterial cells, like plant cells, are surrounded by a rigid cell wall. Just inside the cell wall is the cell membrane. The region inside the cell mambrane is called the cytoplasm. Located in the cytoplasm are ribosomes and the genetic material, which looks like a tangled string. If you could untangle the genetic material, you would see that it forms a circular shape.

A bacterial cell may also have a **flagellum** (fluh JEL um) (plural *flagella*), a long, whiplike structure that helps a cell to move. A flagellum moves the cell by spinning in place like a propeller. A bacterial cell can have many flagella, one, or none. Most bacteria that do not have flagella cannot move on their own. Instead, they are carried from place to place by the air, water currents, objects, or other methods.

Cell Sizes Bacteria vary greatly in size. The largest known bacterium is about as big as the period at the end of this sentence. An average bacterium, however, is much smaller. For example, strep throat bacteria are about 0.5 to 1 micrometer in diameter. A micrometer is one millionth of a meter.

218 ◆

Differentiated Instruction

English Learners/Beginning **L1**
Vocabulary: Science Glossary
Pronounce and define aloud the vocabulary words. Have students start a glossary on index cards, with each term and its definition in English on one side and in the student's primary language on the other side. Students may want to draw and label diagrams on their cards. **learning modality: verbal**

English Learners/Intermediate **L2**
Vocabulary: Science Glossary Students may expand on the activity described at left by adding other terms in this section. Have students write sentences using these words. Give students an opportunity to practice pronunciation by calling on individuals to read their sentences aloud. **learning modality: verbal**

Cell Shapes If you observed bacteria under a microscope, you would notice that most bacterial cells have one of three basic shapes: spherical, rodlike, or spiral. The chemical makeup of the cell wall determines the shape of a bacterial cell. The shape of the cell helps scientists identify the type of bacteria. For example, bacteria that cause strep throat are spherical.

Obtaining Food and Energy

From the bacteria that live in soil to those that live in the pores of your skin, all bacteria need certain things to survive. **Bacteria must have a source of food and a way of breaking down the food to release its energy.**

Obtaining Food Some bacteria are autotrophs and make their own food. Autotrophic bacteria make food in one of two ways. Some capture and use the sun's energy as plants do. Others, such as bacteria that live deep in mud, do not use the sun's energy. Instead, these bacteria use the energy from chemical substances in their environment to make their food.

Some bacteria are heterotrophs and cannot make their own food. Instead, these bacteria consume other organisms or the food that other organisms make. Heterotrophic bacteria consume a variety of foods—from milk and meat, which you might also eat, to the decaying leaves on a forest floor.

Respiration Like all organisms, bacteria need a constant supply of energy. This energy comes from breaking down food in the process of respiration. Like many other organisms, most bacteria need oxygen to break down their food. But a few kinds of bacteria do not need oxygen for respiration. In fact, those bacteria die if oxygen is present in their surroundings.

Reading Checkpoint Where does the energy that bacteria need come from?

Lab zone Try This **Activity**

Bacteria for Breakfast

1. Put on your apron. Add water to plain yogurt to make a thin mixture.
2. With a plastic dropper, place a drop of the mixture on a glass slide.
3. Use another plastic dropper to add one drop of methylene blue dye to the slide. **CAUTION:** *This dye can stain your skin.*
4. Put a coverslip on the slide. Observe the slide under both the low- and high-power lenses of a microscope.

Observing Draw what you see under high power.

FIGURE 7
Obtaining Food
Bacteria obtain food in several ways.

▲ These heterotrophic bacteria, found in yogurt, break down the sugars in milk for food.

▲ The autotrophic bacteria that cause the green, cloudy scum in some ponds use the sun's energy to make food.

▲ These autotrophic bacteria, found in hot springs, use chemical energy from their environment to make food.

Chapter 7 ◆ 219

Lab zone Try This **Activity**

Skills Focus Observing **L2**
Materials yogurt containing active (or living) cultures, plastic dropper, methylene blue, glass slide, cover slip, microscope, lab apron
Time 20 minutes
Tips Students will need to use the highest powers of the microscope. As they observe the bacteria in yogurt, have students classify the bacteria according to shape. Caution them not to drop the glass slides, and to avoid getting methylene blue on their skin or clothing.
Expected Outcome The bacteria appear as dark blue dots against a cloudy, pale blue background. Bacteria are so small that students will be unable to see them unless they are using high-powered microscopes.
Extend Challenge students to observe yogurt that contains added *Lactobacillus acidophilus* (the contents will be listed on the label) and to draw what they observe under the microscope. **learning modality: visual**

Obtaining Food and Energy

Teach Key Concepts **L2**
Food Becomes Energy

Focus Point out that bacteria, like all organisms, need a source of energy.

Teach Ask: **What are two sources of energy for autotrophic bacteria?** (*The sun and chemical substances in the environment*) **What is a source of energy for heterotrophic bacteria?** (*Consuming other organisms or food other organisms make*)

Apply Ask: **What benefit is there in knowing how bacteria obtain and utilize their food?** (*Understanding how bacteria obtain and utilize food enables us to help useful bacteria and to kill harmful bacteria.*)
learning modality: verbal

Lab zone Build **Inquiry** **L1**

Classifying Bacteria

Materials light microscope, prepared slides of bacterial species that exhibit these shapes: rodlike (*bacilli*), spherical (*cocci*), and spiral-shaped (*spirilla*)

Time 20 minutes

Focus Tell students that they are going to identify the three main bacterial cell shapes.

Teach Caution students that glass slides are very fragile. Invite students to view Figure 7. Then, as students view the various slides, have them sketch what they observe. Have pairs of students compare sketches and classify the bacteria as rod-shaped (*bacilli*), spherical (*cocci*), or spiral-shaped (*spirilla*).

Apply Tell students that the shapes they saw are also seen in medical labs. When a patient is sick, a health care provider might send a patient's tissue sample to a medical lab to identify any harmful bacteria that are present. **learning modality: visual**

Monitor Progress _____ **L2**
Answers
Figure 6 Flagella

Reading Checkpoint From the sun, from food or other chemicals in the environment, or from consuming other organisms

219

Reproduction

Teach Key Concepts   L2
When Conditions Are Right

Focus Tell students that the conditions bacteria need to reproduce include sufficient food and the right temperature.

Teach Ask: **What are two types of reproduction in bacteria?** *(Asexual reproduction, sexual reproduction)* **How can bacteria survive when conditions are not good enough for reproduction?** *(Endospores, which contain genetic material, are produced by bacteria. Endospores can endure unfavorable conditions. Later, when conditions are favorable, endospores open up, and the bacteria can begin to grow and multiply.)*

Apply Ask: **What benefit is there in knowing how bacteria reproduce?** *(If we understand how bacteria reproduce, we can promote the growth of good bacteria and prevent the reproduction of harmful bacteria.)* **learning modality: verbal**

Go Online
PHSchool.com

For: More on bacteria
Visit: PHSchool.com
Web Code: ced-1022

Students can review bacteria in an online activity.

Go Online
PHSchool.com

For: More on bacteria
Visit: PHSchool.com
Web Code: ced-1022

Reproduction

When bacteria have plenty of food, the right temperature, and other suitable conditions, they thrive and reproduce frequently. Under these ideal conditions, some bacteria can reproduce as often as once every 20 minutes. So it's a good thing that growing conditions for bacteria are rarely ideal!

Asexual Reproduction Bacteria reproduce by a process called **binary fission,** in which one cell divides to form two identical cells. Binary fission is a form of asexual reproduction. **Asexual reproduction** is a reproductive process that involves only one parent and produces offspring that are identical to the parent. During binary fission, a cell first duplicates its genetic material and then divides into two separate cells. Each new cell gets its own complete copy of the parent cell's genetic material as well as some of the parent's ribosomes and cytoplasm.

Sexual Reproduction Some bacteria may at times undergo a form of sexual reproduction. In **sexual reproduction,** two parents combine their genetic material to produce a new organism, which differs from both parents. During a process called **conjugation** (kahn juh GAY shun), one bacterium transfers some genetic material to another bacterium through a threadlike bridge. After the transfer, the cells separate.

Conjugation results in bacteria with new combinations of genetic material. Then, when these bacteria divide by binary fission, the new combinations of genetic material pass to the offspring. Conjugation does not increase the number of bacteria. However, it does result in bacteria that are genetically different.

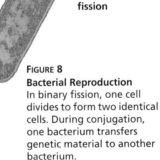

◀ **Binary fission**

FIGURE 8
Bacterial Reproduction
In binary fission, one cell divides to form two identical cells. During conjugation, one bacterium transfers genetic material to another bacterium.

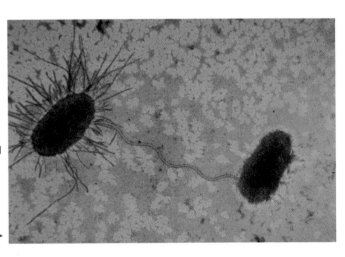

Conjugation ▶

220 ◆

Population Explosion

Suppose a bacterium reproduces by binary fission every 20 minutes. The new cells survive and reproduce at the same rate. This graph shows how the bacterial population would grow from a single bacterium.

1. **Reading Graphs** What variable is being plotted on the horizontal axis? What is being plotted on the vertical axis?

2. **Interpreting Data** According to the graph, how many cells are there after 20 minutes? After 1 hour? After 2 hours?

3. **Drawing Conclusions** Describe the pattern you see in the way the bacterial population increases over 2 hours.

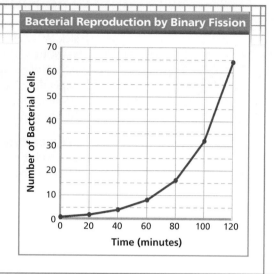

Bacterial Reproduction by Binary Fission

Number of Bacterial Cells (vertical axis, 0 to 70)
Time (minutes) (horizontal axis, 0 to 120)

Endospore Formation Sometimes, conditions in the environment become unfavorable for the growth of bacteria. For example, food sources can disappear, water can dry up, or the temperature can fall or rise dramatically. Some bacteria can survive harsh conditions by forming endospores like those in Figure 9. An **endospore** is a small, rounded, thick-walled, resting cell that forms inside a bacterial cell. It contains the cell's genetic material and some of its cytoplasm.

Because endospores can resist freezing, heating, and drying, they can survive for many years. For example, the bacteria that cause botulism, *Clostridium botulinum*, produce heat-resistant endospores that can survive in improperly canned foods. Endospores are also light—a breeze can lift and carry them to new places. If an endospore lands in a place where conditions are suitable, it opens up. Then the bacterium can begin to grow and multiply.

 Reading Checkpoint Under what conditions do endospores form?

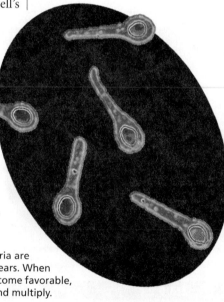

FIGURE 9
Endospores
The red circles within these bacteria are endospores that can survive for years. When conditions in the environment become favorable, the bacteria can begin to grow and multiply.

Chapter 7 ◆ 221

Math Skill Interpreting graphs

Focus Tell students that line graphs can show change over time.

Teach Remind students that a graph is a way of visualizing numerical information. Ask: **How does the slope of the line after 100 minutes compare to its slope the first 20 minutes?** (*The slope is much steeper after 100 minutes than it is during the first 20 minutes.*) **What is the reason for the difference in the slope?** (*More bacteria are doubling in number with time. The number of bacteria dividing increases with each division.*)

Answers
1. Time (minutes); number of bacterial cells
2. 2 cells after 20 minutes; 8 cells after 1 hour; 64 cells after 2 hours
3. The number of cells doubles with each division.

 **Build Inquiry** L3

Designing Experiments

Materials beakers, dried beans, water
Time 20 minutes

Focus Ask: **What do bacteria need to survive?** (*Food, energy, favorable environment*)

Teach Tell students they will design an experiment to show the conditions that bacteria need in order to grow. Students should formulate a hypothesis, have a control, and design a method of observing and recording results. (*Designs will vary. When dried beans are placed in water, the water will become cloudy after about 48 hours because of the growth of bacteria.*)

Apply Have students design a test for the effects of environmental conditions such as temperature. **learning modality: verbal**

Monitor Progress L2

Oral Presentation Have students describe conditions bacteria need in order to survive and explain how some bacteria survive when the conditions are not present.

Answer
 Reading Checkpoint Harsh conditions, such as extreme temperatures or lack of food

---

⌐ Differentiated Instruction

Special Needs L1
Classifying Bacteria by Shape Have students title three poster boards *Spherical*, *Rod-shaped*, and *Spiral-shaped*. Then have them collect copies of photographs of these shapes of bacteria, and mount them on the appropriate poster boards. Have reference books (and/or Internet access), scissors, and poster board available. Use the boards to review bacterial shapes.
learning modality: visual

Gifted and Talented L3
Research Reproduction Have each gifted and talented student research a different aspect of bacterial reproduction and write a report summarizing their findings. They could choose from sexual reproduction or asexual reproduction. Reports could also include information on conjugation or endospore formation.
learning modality: verbal

The Role of Bacteria in Nature

Teach Key Concepts
The Value of Bacteria

Focus Tell students that bacteria can be both helpful and harmful.

Teach Ask: **What kind of bacteria help provide oxygen for breathing?** (*Autotrophic bacteria use the sun's energy to produce food, releasing oxygen.*) **What are some negative ways that bacteria affect food?** (*Some kinds of bacteria cause food to spoil.*)

Apply Ask: **How did Louis Pasteur help to prevent harmful bacteria from growing in food?** (*Louis Pasteur invented the process of pasteurization, heating food to a temperature high enough to kill most harmful bacteria.*) **How are bacteria beneficial as decomposers in the soil?** (*As decomposers, bacteria in soil break down dead organisms, returning basic chemicals to the environment for other living things to reuse.*) **learning modality: verbal**

Build Inquiry L3

Drawing Conclusions

Materials empty boil-in bags, bottles, cans, freezer packages, jars, vacuum-sealed packages, and other containers from a variety of prepared foods with labels included

Time 20 minutes

Focus Review various methods of food preparation and spoilage prevention with students.

Teach Prior to the activity, ask students to bring in various clean and empty food packages. Tell students they will examine some modern ways to preserve food. Organize students into groups; provide each group with two or three packages. **CAUTION:** *Be sure packaging materials are clean. Have students wash their hands with soap and water after handling packaging materials.* Challenge students to draw conclusions about food preparation and spoilage prevention.

Apply Ask students to infer how each spoilage-prevention method inhibits the growth of bacteria. Have a reporter from each group share findings with the class. **learning modality: verbal**

The Role of Bacteria in Nature

When you hear the word *bacteria*, you may think about getting sick. After all, strep throat, many ear infections, and other diseases are caused by bacteria. However, most bacteria are either harmless or helpful to people. In fact, in many ways, people depend on bacteria. **Bacteria are involved in oxygen and food production, environmental recycling and cleanup, and in health maintenance and medicine production.**

Oxygen Production Would it surprise you to learn that the air you breathe depends in part on bacteria? As autotrophic bacteria use the sun's energy to produce food, they also release oxygen into the air. Billions of years ago, there was little oxygen in Earth's atmosphere. Scientists think that autotrophic bacteria were responsible for first adding oxygen to Earth's atmosphere. Today, the distant offspring of those bacteria help keep oxygen levels in the air stable.

Science and History

Bacteria and Foods of the World
Ancient cultures lacked refrigeration and other modern methods of preventing food spoilage. People in these cultures developed ways of using bacteria to preserve foods. You may enjoy some of these foods today.

2300 B.C. Cheese
Ancient Egyptians made cheese from milk. Cheese-making begins when bacteria feed on the sugars in milk. The milk separates into solid curds and liquid whey. The curds are processed into cheeses, which keep longer than milk.

1000 B.C. Pickled Vegetables
The Chinese salted vegetables and packed them in containers. Naturally occurring bacteria fed on the vegetables and produced a sour taste. The salt pulled water out of the vegetables and left them crisp. These vegetables were part of the food rations given to workers who built the Great Wall of China.

500 B.C. Dried Meat
People who lived in the regions around the Mediterranean Sea chopped meat, seasoned it with salt and spices, rolled it, and hung it to dry. Bacteria in the drying meat gave unique flavors to the food. The rolled meat would keep for weeks in cool places.

| 2500 B.C. | 1500 B.C. | 500 B.C. |

Background

History of Science Canning as a method of food preservation was developed in 1810 by a Frenchman named Nicolas Appert. The first food-processing plant began operating in England in 1813. The plant sealed meats, vegetables, and soups in tin canisters, then heated the "cans" to a certain temperature for the correct amount of time.

Freezing food to preserve it was not possible until mechanical refrigeration systems were perfected. About 1880, fish were frozen and sold in the United States and Europe. At that time, New Zealand began to freeze mutton and ship it to England. Frozen fruits appeared in the United States in 1905 and frozen vegetables in 1923.

Dehydration, or drying food, became commercially important during World War I, when soldiers were given dehydrated foods.

Food Production Do you like cheese, sauerkraut, or pickles? The activities of helpful bacteria produce all of these foods and more. For example, bacteria that grow in apple cider change the cider to vinegar. Bacteria that grow in milk produce dairy products such as buttermilk, yogurt, sour cream, and cheeses.

However, some bacteria cause food to spoil when they break down the food's chemicals. Spoiled food usually smells or tastes foul and can make you very sick. Refrigerating and heating foods are two ways to slow down food spoilage. Another method, called pasteurization, is most often used to treat beverages such as milk and juice. During **pasteurization,** the food is heated to a temperature that is high enough to kill most harmful bacteria without changing the taste of the food. As you might have guessed, this process was named after Louis Pasteur, its inventor.

Writing in Science

Research and Write Find out more about one of these ancient food-production methods and the culture that developed it. Write a report about the importance of the food to the culture.

A.D. 500
Soy Sauce
People in China crushed soybeans into mixtures of wheat, salt, bacteria, and other microorganisms. The microorganisms fed on the proteins in the wheat and soybeans. The salt pulled water out of the mixture. The protein-rich soy paste that remained was used to flavor foods. The soy sauce you may use today is made in a similar manner.

A.D. 1500
Chocolate Beverage
People in the West Indies mixed beans from the cocoa plant with bacteria and other microorganisms and then dried and roasted them. The roasted beans were then brewed to produce a beverage with a chocolate flavor. The drink was served cold with honey, spices, and vanilla.

A.D. 1850
Sourdough Bread
Gold prospectors in California ate sourdough bread. The *Lactobacillus sanfrancisco* bacteria gave the bread its sour taste. Each day before baking, cooks would set aside some dough that contained the bacteria to use in the next day's bread.

A.D. 500	A.D. 1500	A.D. 2500

Teacher **Demo**

L2

Drawing Conclusions

Materials several lettuce leaves, two plates

Time 5 minutes today; 10 minutes 4 days later

Focus Show students how bacteria act as decomposers.

Teach *First day:* Put several leaves of lettuce on each of two plates. Place one plate in a refrigerator. Place the other in a warm place. Allow the plates to sit for several days.

Four days later: Show the plates to students and give them time to observe the lettuce and describe what they see. (*The lettuce that was left out has become rotten and slimy.*) Ask: **What made the lettuce change as it did?** (*Bacteria*) **How does temperature affect the growth of some bacteria?** (*Lower temperatures may slow the rate of growth.*) Explain that bacteria broke down the components of the lettuce for food.

Apply Ask: **How are the bacteria in the lettuce similar to the bacteria that act as decomposers in the environment?** (*Like other decomposers, bacteria in the lettuce feed on dead matter and convert it into different forms.*) **learning modality: visual**

Use Visuals: Figure 11

L1

Environmental Cleanup

Focus Tell students that Figure 11 shows people using a substance that contains *Ochrobactrum anthropi,* bacteria that break down oil from oil spills, converting it to harmless substances.

Teach Explain that oil-eating bacteria have become very helpful in cleaning up oil and grease in many locations, such as those with major oil spills.

Apply Ask: **What are some other ways these bacteria might be useful?** (*Substances containing oil-eating or grease-eating bacteria are now sold for cleaning driveways, parking lots, and even drains.*) **learning modality: visual**

FIGURE 10
Environmental Recycling
Decomposing bacteria are at work recycling the chemicals in these leaves. **Predicting** *What might a forest be like if there were no decomposing bacteria in the soil?*

Environmental Recycling If you recycle glass or plastic, then you have something in common with some heterotrophic bacteria. These bacteria, which live in the soil, are **decomposers**—organisms that break down large chemicals in dead organisms into small chemicals.

Decomposers are "nature's recyclers." They return basic chemicals to the environment for other living things to reuse. For example, the leaves of many trees die in autumn and drop to the ground. Decomposing bacteria spend the next months breaking down the chemicals in the dead leaves. The broken-down chemicals mix with the soil and can then be absorbed by the roots of nearby plants.

Another type of recycling bacteria, called nitrogen-fixing bacteria, help plants survive. Nitrogen-fixing bacteria live in the soil and in swellings on the roots of certain plants, such as peanut, pea, and soybean. These helpful bacteria convert nitrogen gas from the air into nitrogen products that plants need to grow. On their own, plants cannot use nitrogen present in the air. Therefore, nitrogen-fixing bacteria are vital to the plants' survival.

Environmental Cleanup Some bacteria help to clean up Earth's land and water. Can you imagine having a bowl of oil for dinner instead of soup? Well, some bacteria prefer the oil. They convert the poisonous chemicals in oil into harmless substances. Scientists have put these bacteria to work cleaning up oil spills in oceans and gasoline leaks in the soil under gas stations.

 Reading Checkpoint What role do bacterial decomposers play in the environment?

FIGURE 11
Environmental Cleanup
Scientists use bacteria such as these *Ochrobactrum anthropi* to help clean up oil spills.

224 ◆

Health and Medicine Did you know that many of the bacteria living in your body actually keep you healthy? In your digestive system, for example, your intestines teem with bacteria. Some help you digest your food. Some make vitamins that your body needs. Others compete for space with disease-causing organisms, preventing the harmful bacteria from attaching to your intestines and making you sick.

Scientists have put some bacteria to work making medicines and other substances. The first medicine-producing bacteria were made in the 1970s. By manipulating the bacteria's genetic material, scientists engineered bacteria to produce human insulin. Although healthy people can make their own insulin, those with some types of diabetes cannot. Many people with diabetes need to take insulin daily. Thanks to bacteria's fast rate of reproduction, large numbers of insulin-making bacteria can be grown in huge vats. The human insulin they produce is then purified and made into medicine.

FIGURE 12
Bacteria and Digestion
Bacteria living naturally in your intestines help you digest food.

Section 2 Assessment

Target Reading Skill Building Vocabulary Use your definitions to help answer the questions below.

Reviewing Key Concepts

1. a. Reviewing Where is the genetic material located in a bacterial cell?
   b. Describing What is the role of flagella in a bacterial cell?
2. a. Listing What are the three ways in which bacteria obtain food?
   b. Describing How do bacteria obtain energy to carry out their functions?
   c. Inferring You have just discovered a new bacterium that lives inside sealed cans of food. How do you think these bacteria obtain food and energy?
3. a. Defining What is binary fission?
   b. Explaining Under what conditions do bacteria thrive and reproduce frequently by binary fission?

   c. Inferring Why might bacteria that undergo conjugation be better able to survive when conditions become less than ideal?
4. a. Listing A friend states that all bacteria are harmful to people. List three reasons why this statement is inaccurate.
   b. Applying Concepts In what ways might bacteria contribute to the success of a garden in which pea plants are growing?

Lab zone At-Home Activity

Edible Bacteria With a family member, look around your kitchen for foods that are made using bacteria. Read the food labels to see if bacteria are used in the food's production. Discuss with your family member the helpful roles that bacteria play in people's lives.

Lab zone At-Home Activity

Edible Bacteria L2 Provide students with a list of keywords (for example, *cultures, live cultures, active cultures,* or *enzymes*) to look for on food labels to help them identify bacteria in products such as cheese, yogurt, buttermilk, or sour cream. You may also want them to further research the terms *cultures* and *enzymes*. Students will observe that bacteria play a large role in the foods they eat.

Monitor Progress _____ L2

Answers
Figure 10 Nothing would decay. Debris would accumulate deeper and deeper. Eventually nothing would be able to grow.

✓ **Reading Checkpoint** They break down dead organisms into basic chemicals that other organisms can reuse.

Assess

Reviewing Key Concepts

1. a. In the cytoplasm **b.** Flagella help bacterial cells move.
2. a. Making food from the sun's energy, using energy from chemicals in the environment, and consuming other organisms or food that other organisms make **b.** Bacteria obtain their energy from food, whether they are autotrophs or heterotrophs. **c.** They probably make food from the chemicals in the food in the can.
3. a. A form of asexual reproduction; one cell divides to form two identical cells **b.** When food is plentiful, temperatures are right, and other conditions are suitable **c.** These bacteria will contain new combinations of genetic material.
4. a. Many bacteria are helpful. Bacteria are involved in oxygen and food production, in environmental recycling and cleanup, and in health maintenance and medicine production. **b.** Bacteria that live on the roots of peas can convert nitrogen from the air into nitrogen that plants need to grow.

Reteach L1

List ways that bacteria are involved in oxygen and food production, in environmental cleanup, and in health maintenance and medicine production.

Performance Assessment L2

Writing Have students describe bacteria that are helpful or harmful to humans.

All in One Teaching Resources, Unit 2

• Section Summary: *Bacteria*
• Review and Reinforce: *Bacteria*
• Enrich: *Bacteria*

Section
3 Protists

Objectives

After completing the lesson, students will be able to

7.3.1 Describe the characteristics of animal-like protists and give examples.

7.3.2 Describe the characteristics of plantlike protists and give examples.

7.3.3 Describe the characteristics of funguslike protists and give examples.

Target Reading Skill

Outlining Explain that using an outline format helps organize information by main topic, subtopic, and details.

Answers

Protists

  I. What is a Protist?

 II. Animal-Like Protists

    A. Protozoans With Pseudopods

    B. Protozoans With Cilia

    C. Protozoans With Flagella

    D. Protozoans That Are Parasites

III. Plantlike Protists

    A. Diatoms

    B. Dinoflagellates

    C. Euglenoids

    D. Red Algae

    E. Green Algae

    F. Brown Algae

IV. Funguslike Protists

    A. Slime Molds

    B. Water Molds

    C. Downy Mildews

All in One Teaching Resources, Unit 2

• Transparency LS63

Preteach

Build Background Knowledge   L2

Characterizing Living Organisms

Review characteristics of living things. Before class, place several drops of vegetable oil in a small dish of water. Add a few drops of green food coloring to the water. Place the dish on an overhead projector. Ask students: **How can you tell whether the blobs you see are alive?** *(Sample answer: Check for reaction to stimuli, taking in food, breathing, and movement.)*

226

Reading Preview

Key Concept

• What are the characteristics of animal-like, plantlike, and funguslike protists?

Key Terms

• protist • protozoan
• pseudopod
• contractile vacuole • cilia
• symbiosis • mutualism
• algae • spore

Target Reading Skill

Outlining As you read, make an outline about protists that you can use for review. Use the red section headings for the main topics and the blue headings for the subtopics.

Protists
I. What is a protist?
II. Animal-like protists
A. Protozoans with pseudopods
B.
C.

Lab zone Discover **Activity**

What Lives in a Drop of Pond Water?

1. Use a plastic dropper to place a drop of pond water on a microscope slide.
2. Put the slide under your microscope's low-power lens. Focus on the objects you see.
3. Find at least three different objects that you think might be organisms. Observe them for a few minutes.
4. Draw the three organisms in your notebook. Below each sketch, describe the movements or behaviors of the organism. Wash your hands thoroughly when you have finished.

Think It Over
Observing What characteristics did you observe that made you think that each organism was alive?

Look at the objects in Figure 13. What do they look like to you? Jewels? Beads? Stained glass ornaments? You might be surprised to learn that these beautiful, delicate structures are the walls of unicellular organisms called diatoms. Diatoms live in both fresh water and salt water and are an important food source for many marine organisms. They have been called the "jewels of the sea."

FIGURE 13
Diatoms
These glasslike organisms are classified as protists.

Lab zone Discover **Activity**

Skills Focus Observing

Materials plastic dropper, pond water, microscope slide, cover slip, microscope

Time 25 minutes

Tips Have students predict what they might observe in the water. Suggest students use their high-power objective lenses if they have them.

L1 **Expected Outcome** Both algae and protozoans should be visible. Green algae have a greenish tint, but most organisms appear colorless. Organisms with flagella or pseudopods could be either protozoans or algae.

Think It Over Students will probably associate movement with life.

These shells are the remains of unicellular, animal-like protists called foraminifera.

FIGURE 14 Protists
Protists include animal-like, plantlike, and funguslike organisms.
Comparing and Contrasting *In what ways do protists differ from one another?*

This red alga is a multicellular, plantlike protist found on ocean floors.

The yellow slime mold oozing off the leaf is a funguslike protist.

What Is a Protist?

Diatoms are only one of the vast varieties of protists. **Protists** are eukaryotes that cannot be classified as animals, plants, or fungi. Because protists are so different from one another, you can think of them as the "odds and ends" kingdom. However, protists do share some characteristics. In addition to being eukaryotes, all protists live in moist surroundings.

The word that best describes protists is *diversity*. For example, most protists are unicellular, but some are multicellular. Some are heterotrophs, some are autotrophs, and others are both. Some protists cannot move, while others zoom around their moist surroundings.

Because of the great variety of protists, scientists have proposed several ways of grouping these organisms. One useful way of grouping protists is to divide them into three categories, based on characteristics they share with organisms in other kingdoms: animal-like protists, plantlike protists, and funguslike protists.

 Reading Checkpoint In what kind of environment do all protists live?

Animal-Like Protists

What image pops into your head when you think of an animal? A tiger chasing its prey? A snake slithering onto a rock? Most people immediately associate animals with movement. In fact, movement is often involved with an important characteristic of animals—obtaining food. All animals are heterotrophs that must obtain food by eating other organisms.

Like animals, animal-like protists are heterotrophs, and most are able to move from place to place to obtain food. But unlike animals, animal-like protists, or **protozoans** (proh tuh ZOH unz), are unicellular. Protozoans can be classified into four groups, based on the way they move and live.

Chapter 7 ◆ 227

Help Students Read

Previewing Visuals Before students read the section on protozoans with pseudopods and protozoans with cilia, have them study Figures 15 and 16 and read the labels. Call on student volunteers to name protozoan structures used for locomotion (*Cilia, pseudopods*), feeding (*Food vacuole, oral groove*), and reproduction (*Nucleus*). Have students read the text in this section, then together discuss the functions of the structures observed prior to reading.

L1

Observing Pseudopod Movement

Materials plastic dropper, amoeba culture, microscope slide, cover slip, microscope

Time 20 minutes

Focus Review with students the function of an amoeba's pseudopods.

Teach Have students place a drop of the amoeba culture on a slide, carefully add a cover slip, and then observe the organisms under low and high power.

Apply Ask: **Can you tell when the amoeba is using its pseudopods to eat and when it is using them to move?** (*Students may say that when the amoeba is eating, it wraps two pseudopods around the food; when it is moving, it puts out a pseudopod and flows into it.*) Students can sketch what they observe and label the parts of the amoeba. Observations should include the organism's shape, size, and motion. **learning modality: visual**

For: Amoeba and Paramecium activity
Visit: PHSchool.com
Web Code: cep-1031

Students learn about two types of protozoans, the amoeba and the paramecium.

FIGURE 15
Amoeba

Amoebas are sarcodines that live in either water or soil. They feed on bacteria and smaller protists.

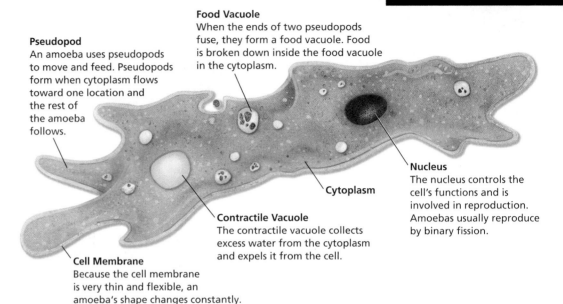

Pseudopod
An amoeba uses pseudopods to move and feed. Pseudopods form when cytoplasm flows toward one location and the rest of the amoeba follows.

Food Vacuole
When the ends of two pseudopods fuse, they form a food vacuole. Food is broken down inside the food vacuole in the cytoplasm.

Nucleus
The nucleus controls the cell's functions and is involved in reproduction. Amoebas usually reproduce by binary fission.

Cytoplasm

Contractile Vacuole
The contractile vacuole collects excess water from the cytoplasm and expels it from the cell.

Cell Membrane
Because the cell membrane is very thin and flexible, an amoeba's shape changes constantly.

For: Amoeba and Paramecium activity
Visit: PHSchool.com
Web Code: cep-1031

Protozoans With Pseudopods The amoeba in Figure 15 belongs to the group of protozoans called sarcodines. Sarcodines move and feed by forming **pseudopods** (SOO duh pahdz)—temporary bulges of the cell. The word *pseudopod* means "false foot." Pseudopods form when cytoplasm flows toward one location and the rest of the organism follows. Pseudopods enable sarcodines to move. For example, amoebas use pseudopods to move away from bright light. Sarcodines also use pseudopods to trap food. The organism extends a pseudopod on each side of the food particle. The two pseudopods then join together, trapping the particle inside.

Protozoans that live in fresh water, such as amoebas, have a problem. Small particles, like those of water, pass easily through the cell membrane into the cytoplasm. If excess water were to build up inside the cell, the amoeba would burst. Fortunately, amoebas have a **contractile vacuole** (kun TRAK til VAK yoo ohl), a structure that collects the extra water and then expels it from the cell.

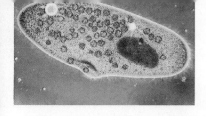

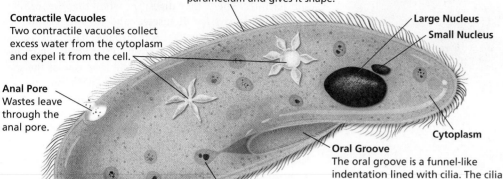

Contractile Vacuoles
Two contractile vacuoles collect excess water from the cytoplasm and expel it from the cell.

Anal Pore
Wastes leave through the anal pore.

Cilia
Thousands of cilia project through the pellicle. The beating cilia enable a paramecium to move smoothly in one direction.

Pellicle
A stiff but flexible covering, called the pellicle, surrounds a paramecium and gives it shape.

Large Nucleus

Small Nucleus

Cytoplasm

Oral Groove
The oral groove is a funnel-like indentation lined with cilia. The cilia move water containing food into the vacuole that forms at the end of the oral groove.

Food Vacuole
A food vacuole forms and pinches off from the oral groove. It moves into the cytoplasm. Inside the vacuole, the food is broken down and then distributed.

FIGURE 16
Paramecium
Paramecia are ciliates that live mostly in fresh water. Like amoebas, paramecia feed on bacteria and smaller protists.

Protozoans With Cilia The second group of animal-like protists are the ciliates. Ciliates have structures called **cilia** (SIL ee uh), which are hairlike projections from cells that move with a wavelike motion. Ciliates use their cilia to move and obtain food. Cilia act something like tiny oars to move a ciliate. Their movement sweeps food into the organism.

The cells of ciliates, like the paramecium in Figure 16, are complex. Notice that the paramecium has two contractile vacuoles that expel water from the cell. It also has more than one nucleus. The large nucleus controls the everyday tasks of the cell. The small nucleus functions in reproduction.

Paramecia usually reproduce asexually by binary fission. Sometimes, however, paramecia reproduce by conjugation. This occurs when two paramecia join together and exchange some of their genetic material.

 Reading Checkpoint What are cilia?

Differentiated Instruction

Gifted and Talented L3
Investigating Protozoan Groups
Provide books or online sources on ciliate and sarcodine (amoeba) protozoans. Have students prepare and present a visual display that highlights the features of one of the two groups: the variety of protozoans in the group, what they eat, whether any cause disease to humans, and so forth. **learning modality: visual**

Less Proficient Readers L1
Identifying Protozoan Structures
Provide students with a list of amoeba and paramecium structures presented in Figures 15 and 16, and an accompanying list of their descriptions. Have students match structures with descriptions as they observe Figures 15 and 16 or the relevant transparencies. **learning modality: visual**

Use Visuals: Figures 15 and 16 L1
Amoeba and Paramecium

Focus Have students observe the figures.

Teach Ask: **What do these two protists have in common?** (*They eat the same things, and they both have nuclei, cytoplasm, food vacuoles, and contractile vacuoles.*) Ask: **What is different about them?** (*Amoebas live in soil and water, paramecia only in water; paramecia move with cilia, amoebas move with pseudopods; paramecia ingest food into an oral groove, amoebas surround food with pseudopods; amoebas have one nucleus, paramecia have two.*)

Apply Ask: **What characteristics make the amoeba suited to life in either soil or water?** (*Sample answer: It can change its shape and flow easily through different substances. The contractile vacuole allows excess water to be expelled.*) **What characteristics make the paramecium suited to living only in water?** (*Sample answer: Its two contractile vacuoles remove excess water from the cell. Their cilia, which move the paramecium through water and sweep food into the oral groove, may not be as effective in a solid environment such as soil. Their rigid shape may hinder movement through compact soil.*) **learning modality: visual**

All in One **Teaching Resources, Unit 2**
• Transparencies LS64, LS65

Monitor Progress L2

Oral Presentation Have students compare and contrast the characteristics of an amoeba and a paramecium.

Answer

Reading Checkpoint Hairlike projections from cells that move with a wavelike motion

Lab zone Build **Inquiry** `L2`

Modeling Animal-Like Protists

Materials clay, paint, string, pipe cleaners, cardboard, and other materials of students' choice

Time 30 minutes

Focus Challenge small groups to design models of one of the four kinds of animal-like protists.

Teach Have students consult photos in the text or in reference materials. Models should include unique details for each organism, with labels. Have students compare and contrast the models, explaining similarities and differences. They should note the structures, shapes, and methods of movement of the various animal-like protozoans.

Apply Challenge groups to use their models to demonstrate how these organisms move or feed. **learning modality: kinesthetic**

Integrating Health `L1`

Avoiding Health Threats of Parasites in Water

Ask students to describe ways that hikers can avoid ingesting *Giardia*. *(Sample answers: Carry enough water, use water purifying treatments, boil water before using.)* Inform students that the safest way to purify water of organisms is to boil it for at least three minutes. This will kill the organisms, but it will not necessarily make the water safe if the water also contains chemical pollutants. **learning modality: verbal**

FIGURE 17
Giardia
When people drink from freshwater streams and lakes, they can get hiker's disease. *Giardia intestinalis* (inset) is the protozoan responsible for this disease.
Inferring *Why is it important for hikers to filter stream water?*

FIGURE 18
Malaria Mosquito
Anopheles mosquitoes can carry the parasitic protozoan *Plasmodium,* which causes malaria in people.

Protozoans With Flagella The third group of protozoans are flagellates (FLAJ uh lits), protists that use long, whiplike flagella to move. A flagellate may have one or more flagella.

Some of these protozoans live inside the bodies of other organisms. For example, one type of flagellate lives in the intestines of termites. There, they digest the wood that the termites eat, producing sugars for themselves and for the termites. In turn, the termites protect the protozoans. The interaction between these two species is an example of **symbiosis** (sim bee OH sis)—a close relationship in which at least one of the species benefits. When both partners benefit from living together, the relationship is a type of symbiosis called **mutualism.**

Sometimes, however, a protozoan harms its host. For example, *Giardia* is a parasite in humans. Wild animals, such as beavers, deposit *Giardia* in freshwater streams, rivers, and lakes. When a person drinks water containing *Giardia*, these protozoans attach to the person's intestine, where they feed and reproduce. The person develops a serious intestinal condition commonly called hiker's disease.

Protozoans That Are Parasites The fourth type of protozoans are characterized more by the way they live than by the way they move. They are all parasites that feed on the cells and body fluids of their hosts. These protozoans move in a variety of ways. Some have flagella, and some depend on hosts for transport. One even produces a layer of slime that allows it to slide from place to place!

Many of these parasites have more than one host. For example, *Plasmodium* is a protozoan that causes malaria, a disease of the blood. Two hosts are involved in *Plasmodium's* life cycle—humans and a species of mosquitoes found in tropical areas. The disease spreads when a healthy mosquito bites a person with malaria, becomes infected, and then bites a healthy person. Symptoms of malaria include high fevers that alternate with severe chills. These symptoms can last for weeks, then disappear, only to reappear a few months later.

✓ **Reading Checkpoint** **What is symbiosis?**

230 ◆

Plantlike Protists

Plantlike protists, which are commonly called **algae** (AL jee), are extremely diverse. **Like plants, algae are autotrophs.** Most are able to use the sun's energy to make their own food.

Algae play a significant role in many environments. For example, algae that live near the surface of ponds, lakes, and oceans are an important food source for other organisms in the water. In addition, much of the oxygen in Earth's atmosphere is made by these algae.

Algae vary greatly in size. Some algae are unicellular, while others are multicellular. Still others are groups of unicellular organisms that live together in colonies. Colonies can contain from a few cells up to thousands of cells. In a colony, most cells carry out all functions. But, some cells may become specialized to perform certain functions, such as reproduction.

Algae exist in a wide variety of colors because they contain many types of pigments. You may recall that pigments are chemicals that produce color. Depending on their pigments, algae can be green, yellow, red, brown, orange, or even black.

Diatoms Diatoms are unicellular protists with beautiful glasslike cell walls. Some float near the surface of lakes or oceans. Others attach to objects such as rocks in shallow water. Diatoms are a food source for heterotrophs in the water. Many diatoms can move by oozing chemicals out of slits in their cell walls. They then glide in the slime.

When diatoms die, their cell walls collect on the bottoms of oceans and lakes. Over time, they form layers of a coarse substance called diatomaceous (dy uh tuh MAY shus) earth. Diatomaceous earth makes a good polishing agent and is used in household scouring products. It is even used as an insecticide—the diatoms' sharp cell walls puncture the bodies of insects.

Dinoflagellates Dinoflagellates (dy noh FLAJ uh lits) are unicellular algae surrounded by stiff plates that look like a suit of armor. Because they have different amounts of green, orange, and other pigments, dinoflagellates exist in a variety of colors.

All dinoflagellates have two flagella held in grooves between their plates. When the flagella beat, the dinoflagellates twirl like toy tops as they move through the water. Many glow in the dark. They light up the ocean's surface when disturbed by a passing boat or swimmer.

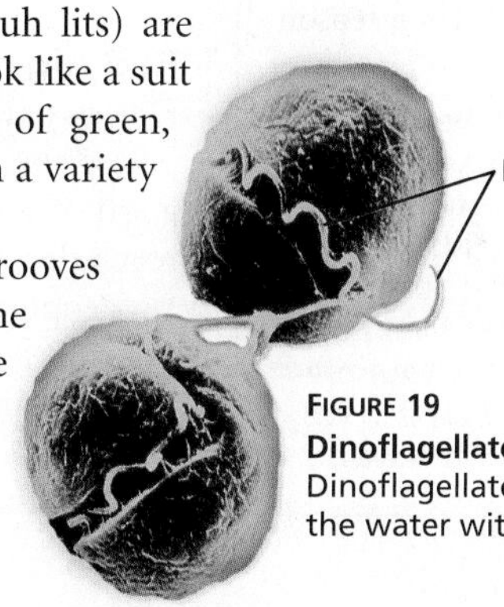

Try This Activity — Lab zone

Watching Protists

In this activity you will watch the interaction between paramecium, an animal-like protist, and *Chlorella*, a plantlike protist.

1. Use a plastic dropper to place 1 drop of paramecium culture on a microscope slide. Add some cotton fibers to slow down the paramecia.
2. Use the microscope's low-power objective to find some paramecia.
3. Add 1 drop of *Chlorella* to the paramecium culture on your slide.
4. Switch to high power and locate a paramecium. Observe what happens. Then wash your hands.

Inferring What evidence do you have that paramecia are heterotrophs? That *Chlorella* are autotrophs?

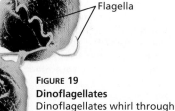

Flagella

FIGURE 19
Dinoflagellates
Dinoflagellates whirl through the water with their flagella.

Chapter 7 ◆ 231

Lab zone — Try This Activity

Skills Focus Inferring · **L2**

Materials paramecium culture, *Chlorella* culture, plastic dropper, microscope and slide, cotton fibers

Time 15 minutes

Tip Students can also slow down the paramecia by placing a coverslip over the drop of culture and absorbing water from the edge of the coverslip with lens paper, or by adding a drop of 2–3% clear gelatin solution to the drop of culture. Make sure students wash their hands after the activity.

Expected Outcome Green food vacuoles form inside the paramecia as they ingest the *Chlorella*. Students should conclude that paramecia are heterotrophs, while *Chlorella* are autotrophs. **learning modality: visual**

Plantlike Protists

Teach Key Concepts · **L2**
Describing Plantlike Protists

Focus Have students look at the pictures in this section of plantlike protists.

Teach Ask: **What is the name commonly used for plantlike protists?** *(Algae)* **How are algae similar to plants?** *(They are autotrophs—they can make their own food.)* **What traits of algae vary greatly?** *(Size—unicellular to colonies of thousands of cells; colors—green, red, brown, yellow, orange, or black)*

Apply Explain that algae can make their own food. Ask: **What important role do algae, like plants, play in the environment?** *(They produce oxygen and serve as an important food source for other organisms.)* **learning modality: logical/mathematical**

All in One Teaching Resources, Unit 2
• Transparencies LS66, LS67

Monitor Progress · **L2**

Oral Presentation Ask students to give the other names for animal-like protists and plantlike protists. *(Animal-like—protozoans; plantlike—algae)*

Answers
Figure 17 To remove disease-causing *Giardia* and other harmful organisms from the water

Reading Checkpoint A close relationship between two species in which at least one of the species benefits

231

Building Models of Algae

Materials none

Time 15 minutes

Focus Direct students to make a "living" model of how algae of various sizes take in food and eliminate waste.

Teach Divide the class into three groups: unicellular algae, multicellular algae, and a colony of algae. Have each student act out the role of an individual algae cell. Give each group a deck of cards to use as a food source, and encourage the "cells" to act out how each organism accomplishes food intake and waste elimination.

Apply Have students describe food intake and waste elimination in terms of whether they are individual or cooperative processes. *(Sample answers: unicellular: individual students pick up and put down cards without interacting; multicellular: cooperative model—one student picks up a card and passes it on, another puts it down; colony: both individual and cooperative.* **learning modality: kinesthetic**

Help Students Read

Summarizing Summarizing the information presented in the text will help students to focus on main ideas and remember what they read. Have students read the paragraphs describing the types of plantlike protists and summarize them by restating the main ideas in their own words.

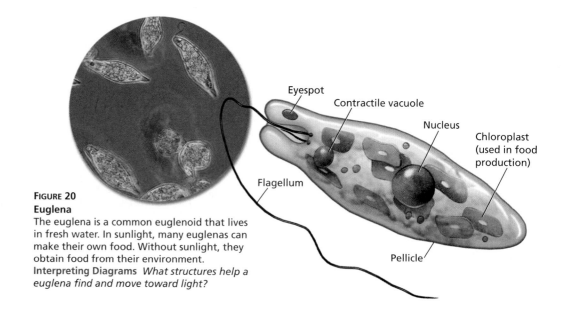

FIGURE 20
Euglena
The euglena is a common euglenoid that lives in fresh water. In sunlight, many euglenas can make their own food. Without sunlight, they obtain food from their environment.
Interpreting Diagrams *What structures help a euglena find and move toward light?*

Skills Activity

Predicting

Predict what will happen when you pour a culture of euglena into a petri dish, and then cover half the dish with aluminum foil. Give a reason for your prediction.

Then carry out the experiment with a culture of euglena in a plastic petri dish. Cover half the dish with aluminum foil. After 10 minutes, uncover the dish. What do you observe? Was your prediction correct? Explain why euglena behave this way.

Euglenoids Euglenoids (yoo GLEE noydz) are green, unicellular algae that are found mostly in fresh water. Unlike other algae, euglenoids have one animal-like characteristic—they can be heterotrophs under certain conditions. When sunlight is available, most euglenoids are autotrophs that produce their own food. However, when sunlight is not available, euglenoids will act like heterotrophs by obtaining food from their environment. Some euglenoids live entirely as heterotrophs.

In Figure 20, you see a euglena, which is a common euglenoid. Notice the long, whiplike flagellum that helps the organism move. Locate the eyespot near the flagellum. Although the eyespot is not really an eye, it contains pigments. These pigments are sensitive to light and help the euglena recognize the direction of a light source. You can imagine how important this response is to an organism that needs light to make food.

Red Algae Almost all red algae are multicellular seaweeds. Divers have found red algae growing more than 260 meters below the ocean's surface. Their red pigments are especially good at absorbing the small amount of light that is able to reach deep ocean waters.

People use red algae in a variety of ways. Carrageenan (ka ruh JEE nun) and agar, substances extracted from red algae, are used in products such as ice cream and hair conditioner. For people in many Asian cultures, red algae is a nutrient-rich food that is eaten fresh, dried, or toasted.

232 ◆

Skills Activity

Skills Focus Predicting

Materials euglena culture, plastic petri dish, aluminum foil, compound microscope

Time 20 minutes

Tips Tell students to record their predictions and the reasons for them. Make sure students wash their hands after handling the paramecium cultures.

Expected Outcome Students will probably predict that the euglena will move toward the light because it needs light to make food. The result of the experiment will confirm this prediction. The covered area will no longer be green, because the euglena have moved to the uncovered area and the light.

Extend Ask students to identify the source of the green tint of the euglena culture. *(Chloroplasts)* **learning modality: visual**

FIGURE 21
Green Algae
Green algae range in size from unicellular organisms to multicellular seaweeds. This multicellular sea lettuce, *Ulva*, lives in oceans.

Green Algae Green algae, which contain green pigments, are quite diverse. Most green algae are unicellular. Some, however, form colonies, and a few are multicellular. Most green algae live in either fresh water or salt water. The few that live on land are found on rocks, in the crevices of tree bark, or in moist soils.

Green algae are actually very closely related to plants that live on land. Green algae and plants contain the same type of chlorophyll and share other important similarities. In fact, some scientists think that green algae belong in the plant kingdom.

Brown Algae Many of the organisms that are commonly called seaweeds are brown algae. In addition to their brown pigment, brown algae also contain green, yellow, and orange pigments. As you can see in Figure 22, a typical brown alga has many plantlike structures. Holdfasts anchor the alga to rocks. Stalks support the blades, which are the leaflike structures of the alga. Many brown algae also have gas-filled sacs called bladders that allow the algae to float upright in the water.

Brown algae flourish in cool, rocky waters. Brown algae called rockweed live along the Atlantic coast of North America. Giant kelps, which can grow as long as 100 meters, live in some Pacific coastal waters. The giant kelps form large underwater "forests" where many organisms, including sea otters and abalone, live.

Some people eat brown algae. In addition, substances called algins are extracted from brown algae and used as thickeners in puddings and other foods.

 Reading Checkpoint What color pigments can brown algae contain?

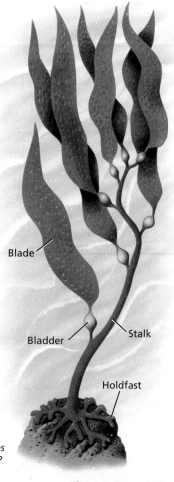

Blade

Bladder

Stalk

Holdfast

FIGURE 22 Brown Algae
Giant kelps are brown algae that have many plantlike structures.
Interpreting Diagrams *What plant structures do the kelp's holdfasts and blades resemble?*

Differentiated Instruction

Special Needs L1
Identifying Protists Display in stations around the room pictures of various protists, such as slime molds, paramecia, euglenoids, diatoms, and algae. Have small groups list on index cards the characteristics they observe in the pictures. Next display three headings on the board: animal-like protists, plantlike protists, and funguslike protists. Have students attach under the appropriate headings the index cards containing the protist traits observed in the pictures. Discuss any overlap of traits among the protist groups, and ask students if it is possible to create an operational definition of a protist. **learning modality: visual**

Use Visuals: Figure 20 L1
Euglena

Focus Emphasize that a unicellular organism can have functional structures.

Teach Ask: **How many cells does a euglena have?** *(One)* Point out that structures such as flagella, the eyespot, and the chloroplast are all part of the same cell. Some students may be confused that a unicellular organism has so many parts. Explain that a cell is the smallest structure capable of performing all the functions required for life.

Apply Ask: **Is the cell shown in the figure specialized to do certain tasks?** *(No, it performs all the functions necessary to maintain the euglena's life.)* **learning modality: visual**

Address Misconceptions
Not All Red Algae Are Red

Focus Explain that algae contain other pigments in addition to the dominant pigment. The combination of pigments creates a great variety of colors.

Teach Students may think that all red algae look red, all green algae look green, and all brown algae look brown. Inform them that although these algae contain the pigment in their names, they also contain other pigments, sometimes in such concentrations that, for example, a red alga may actually look pink or purple.

Apply Remind students that plant leaves also contain pigments. Ask: **What is the function of the pigments in algae and in plant leaves?** *(They absorb light needed for the algae and plants to make food.)* **learning modality: verbal**

Monitor Progress L2

Writing Ask students to describe the characteristics of diatoms, euglenoids, or red algae. Students can save their descriptions in their portfolios.

Answers
Figure 20 The eyespot helps the euglena find light, and the flagellum helps the euglena move toward light.
Figure 22 The holdfasts resemble roots and the blades resemble leaves.

 Reading Checkpoint Brown, green, yellow, and orange

Funguslike Protists

Teach Key Concepts

Exploring Funguslike Protists

Focus Review with students the characteristics of fungi: heterotrophs, have cell walls, use spores to reproduce.

Teach With students, prepare a chart or start a Venn diagram to show basic characteristics of plants, animals, and fungi. Illustrate your answers: **How are funguslike protists like animals?** (*They are heterotrophs.*) **How are they like plants?** (*Their cells have cell walls; they use spores to reproduce.*) **Which of these traits do fungi also exhibit?** (*They have cell walls, are heterotrophs, and, reproduce with spores*)

Apply Ask: **How have funguslike protists caused human deaths?** (*Water molds destroyed the Irish potato crops in 1845 and 1846, triggering starvation.*) **learning modality: visual**

Observing Slime Mold

Materials compound microscope, slime mold culture, plastic petri dish with cover, oatmeal

Time 15 minutes for setup, 10 minutes for observation after 24 hours

Focus Tell students that individual slime mold cells can join together and respond to stimuli as a giant mass.

Teach Pair students; give each pair a covered petri dish containing slime mold culture to observe under the microscope. Ask students to predict how slime molds will react when oatmeal is placed in the dish. Students can test predictions by uncovering the dish, putting a few flakes about 1 mm from a branch of the slime mold, and putting the cover back on. After 24 hours in a cool, dark place, the slime mold should increase in size, spread across, and engulf the oatmeal.

Apply Ask: **What did you observe that suggests the slime mold is alive?** (*It moved toward the oatmeal and engulfed it.*) **learning modality: visual**

Funguslike Protists

The third group of protists are the funguslike protists. You may recall that fungi include organisms such as mushrooms and yeast. Until you learn more about fungi, you can think of fungi as the "sort of like" organisms. Fungi are "sort of like" animals because they are heterotrophs. They are "sort of like" plants because their cells have cell walls. In addition, most fungi use spores to reproduce. A **spore** is a tiny cell that is able to grow into a new organism.

Like fungi, funguslike protists are heterotrophs, have cell walls, and use spores to reproduce. All funguslike protists are able to move at some point in their lives. The three types of funguslike protists are slime molds, water molds, and downy mildews.

Slime Molds Slime molds are often brilliantly colored. They live on forest floors and other moist, shady places. They ooze along the surfaces of decaying materials, feeding on bacteria and other microorganisms. Some slime molds are so small that you need a microscope to see them. Others may cover an area of several meters!

Slime molds begin their life cycle as tiny, individual amoeba-like cells. The cells use pseudopods to feed and creep around. Later, the cells grow bigger or join together to form a giant, jellylike mass. In some species, the giant mass is multi-cellular and forms when food is scarce. In others, the giant mass is actually a giant cell with many nuclei.

The mass oozes along as a single unit. When environmental conditions become harsh, spore-producing structures grow out of the mass and release spores. Eventually the spores develop into a new generation of slime molds.

FIGURE 23
Slime Molds
The chocolate tube slime mold first forms a tapioca-like mass (top). When conditions become harsh, the mass grows spore-producing stalks (right). The stalks, or "chocolate tubes," are covered with millions of brown spores.

Water Molds and Downy Mildews Most water molds and downy mildews live in water or moist places. These organisms often grow as tiny threads that look like fuzz. Figure 24 shows a fish attacked by a water mold and a leaf covered by downy mildew.

Water molds and downy mildews attack many food crops, such as potatoes, corn, and grapes. A water mold impacted history when it destroyed the Irish potato crops in 1845 and 1846. The loss of these crops led to a famine. More than one million people in Ireland died, and many others moved to the United States and other countries.

▲ Water mold on fish

Reading Checkpoint In what environments are water molds found?

▼ Downy mildew on grape leaf

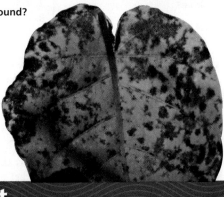

FIGURE 24
Water Molds and Downy Mildews
Many water molds are decomposers of dead aquatic organisms. Others are parasites of fish and other animals. Downy mildews are parasites of many food crops.

Section 3 Assessment

Target Reading Skill Outlining Use your outline about protists to help you answer the questions below.

Reviewing Key Concepts

1. **a. Listing** List the four types of animal-like protists. How does each type move or live?
   b. Comparing and Contrasting How are these four types of protists similar to animals? How are they different?
   c. Classifying You observe an animal-like protist under the microscope. It has no hairlike or whiplike structures. It moves by forming temporary bulges of cytoplasm. How would you classify this protist?
2. **a. Reviewing** In what way are diatoms, dinoflagellates, and other plantlike protists similar to plants?
   b. Making Generalizations Why is sunlight important to plantlike protists?
   c. Making Judgments Would you classify euglena as an animal-like protist or as a plantlike protist? Explain.
3. **a. Listing** What are the three types of funguslike protists?
   b. Describing In what ways are funguslike protists similar to fungi?

Lab zone At-Home Activity

Algae Scavenger Hunt Look around your house with a family member to find products that contain substances made from algae. Look at both food and nonfood items. Before you begin, tell your family member that substances such as diatomaceous earth, algin, and carrageenan are products that come from algae. Make a list of the products and the algae-based ingredient they contain. Share your list with the class.

Lab zone Chapter Project

Keep Students on Track By now, your teacher should have approved your plan, and you should have started growing your mushrooms. Make careful observations of growth daily, including appropriate sketches and measurements. Use a table to organize the data you collect. (*Hint:* As you make your observations, be careful not to disturb the experiment or introduce any new variables.)

Lab zone At-Home Activity

Algae Scavenger Hunt L1
Encourage students to explain to family members that algae can be found in many products such as ice cream, hair conditioners, toothpaste, and scouring products. Students may wish to see who can find the most products containing algae.

Objectives

After completing the lesson, students will be able to

7.4.1 Name the characteristics fungi share.

7.4.2 Explain how fungi reproduce.

7.4.3 Describe the roles fungi play in nature.

Target Reading Skill 🔄

Asking Questions Explain that changing a head into a question helps students anticipate the ideas, facts, and events they are about to read.

Answers

Possible questions and answers are:
What are fungi? *(Fungi are eukaryotes that have cell walls, are heterotrophs that feed by absorbing their food, and use spores to reproduce.)* **How do fungi reproduce?** *(Fungi usually reproduce by making spores.)* **What is the role of fungi in nature?** *(Fungi are important decomposers and recyclers.)*

All in One Teaching Resources, Unit 2

• Transparency LS68

Preteach

Build Background Knowledge L2

Considering Mushroom Habitat

Ask students to describe what they know about how mushrooms grow. Some students may have seen mushrooms growing in the woods, while others may have seen cultivated mushrooms. Encourage students to think about how mushrooms are similar to plants.

Skills Focus Observing L1

Reading Preview

Key Concepts
• What characteristics do fungi share?
• How do fungi reproduce?
• What roles do fungi play in nature?

Key Terms
• fungi • hyphae
• fruiting body • budding
• lichen

🔄 Target Reading Skill

Asking Questions Before you read, preview the red headings. In a graphic organizer like the one below, ask a *what* or *how* question for each heading. As you read, write answers to your questions.

Fungi

Question	Answer
What are fungi?	Fungi are . . .

Lab zone Discover **Activity**

Do All Molds Look Alike?

1. Your teacher will give you two sealed, clear plastic bags—one containing moldy bread and another containing moldy fruit. **CAUTION:** *Do not open the sealed bags at any time.*
2. In your notebook, describe what you see.
3. Next, use a hand lens to examine each mold. Sketch each mold in your notebook and list its characteristics.
4. Return the sealed bags to your teacher. Wash your hands.

Think It Over
Observing How are the molds similar? How are they different?

A speck of dust lands on a cricket's back. But this is no ordinary dust—it is alive! Tiny glistening threads emerge from the dust and begin to grow into the cricket's moist body. As they grow, the threads release chemicals that slowly dissolve the cricket's tissues. Soon, the cricket's body is little more than a hollow shell filled with a tangle of the threads. Then the threads begin to grow up and out of the dead cricket, producing long stalks with knobs at their tips. When a knob breaks open, it will release thousands of dustlike specks, which the wind can carry to new victims.

What Are Fungi?

The strange cricket-killing organism is a member of the fungi kingdom. Although you may not have heard of a cricket-killing fungus before, you are probably familiar with other kinds of fungi. For example, the molds that grow on stale bread and the mushrooms that sprout in yards are all fungi.

Most **fungi** share several important characteristics. **Fungi are eukaryotes that have cell walls, are heterotrophs that feed by absorbing their food, and use spores to reproduce.** In addition, fungi need moist, warm places in which to grow. They thrive on moist foods, damp tree barks, lawns coated with dew, and even wet bathroom tiles.

A killer fungus has attacked this bush cricket.

236 ◆

Lab zone Discover **Activity**

Materials Sealable bags, tape, hand lens, old bread, fruit

Time 15 minutes

Tips At least one week before the activity, place pieces of moist bread and fruit in separate self-seal bags. Seal the bags, then make an extra seal with tape. Keep bags in a dark place at room temperature. Make sure students do not open the bags. Dispose of the sealed bags and all other materials according to proper procedures; check your district's and state's guidelines for proper disposal.

Expected Outcome Observations will depend on the kinds of fungi that grow.

Think It Over The molds will probably have similar threadlike appearances and fruiting bodies but will probably be of different colors.

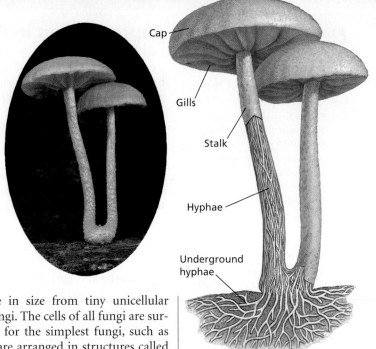

FIGURE 25
Structure of a Mushroom
The hyphae in the stalk and cap of a mushroom are packed tightly to form firm structures. Underground hyphae are arranged loosely.
Inferring What function might underground hyphae perform?

Cap

Gills

Stalk

Hyphae

Underground hyphae

Cell Structure Fungi range in size from tiny unicellular yeasts to large multicellular fungi. The cells of all fungi are surrounded by cell walls. Except for the simplest fungi, such as yeast, the cells of most fungi are arranged in structures called hyphae. **Hyphae** (HY fee) (singular hypha) are the branching, threadlike tubes that make up the bodies of multicellular fungi. The hyphae of some fungi are continuous threads of cytoplasm that contain many nuclei. Substances move quickly and freely through the hyphae.

What a fungus looks like depends on how its hyphae are arranged. In some fungi, the threadlike hyphae are loosely tangled. Fuzzy-looking molds that grow on old foods have loosely tangled hyphae. Other fungi have tightly packed hyphae. The stalks and caps of mushrooms are made of hyphae packed so tightly that they appear solid. Underground, however, a mushroom's hyphae form a loose, threadlike maze in the soil.

Obtaining Food Fungi absorb food through hyphae that grow into a food source. First, the fungus grows hyphae into the food source. Then digestive chemicals ooze from the hyphae into the food. The chemicals break down the food into small substances that can be absorbed by the hyphae. As an analogy, imagine yourself sinking your fingers down into a chocolate cake and dripping digestive chemicals out of your fingertips. Then imagine your fingers absorbing the digested particles of the cake!

✔ **Reading Checkpoint** What do the bodies of multicellular fungi consist of?

FIGURE 26
Mold Growing on Food Source
The mold *Penicillium* often grows on old fruits such as oranges. Some of its hyphae grow deep into the food source.

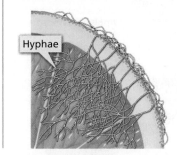

Hyphae

Chapter 7 ◆ 237

Instruct

What Are Fungi?

Teach Key Concepts L2
Identifying Fungi

Focus Ask students what bread mold has in common with the killer fungus shown attacking the bush cricket. *(Possible answer: Both grow on other organisms.)*

Teach Ask: **Which traits are shared by all fungi?** *(Eukaryotic, with cell walls; heterotrophs with similar means of feeding; spores for reproduction)* **Which fungi are unicellular?** *(Yeasts)* **What are hyphae?** *(Branching, threadlike tubes that form the body of multicellular fungi)*

Apply Explain that in most fungi, cytoplasm flows freely through the hyphae because the walls separating cells have a "hole" in them. Ask: **How do hyphae help a fungus in its life processes?** *(By allowing essential materials to move quickly throughout the fungus)* **learning modality: verbal**

All in One **Teaching Resources, Unit 2**
• Transparency LS69

Independent Practice L2

All in One **Teaching Resources, Unit 2**
• Guided Reading and Study Worksheet: *Fungi*

 Student Edition on Audio CD

**English Learners/Beginning L1
Vocabulary: Science Glossary**
Pronounce and define aloud for students the Key Terms for this section. Suggest that students start a personal glossary of vocabulary terms, with each term and its definition in English on one side of an index card and in the student's primary language on the other side. To help remember the meanings of the words, students might draw and label diagrams. **learning modality: verbal**

**Less Proficient Readers L1
Vocabulary: Science Glossary** Have students copy section Key Terms, then find and write the definitions as they read the section. Provide an unlabeled copy of Figure 25, and encourage students to add the labels. **learning modality: visual**

Monitor Progress L2

Answers
Figure 25 Anchoring; absorbing materials

✔ **Reading Checkpoint** Hyphae

Reproduction in Fungi

Teach Key Concepts   L2
Exploring How Fungi Reproduce

Focus Have students examine Figure 27.

Teach Ask: **What type of asexual reproduction occurs in yeasts?** *(Budding)* **What type of reproduction produces fungi that differ genetically from the parents?** *(Sexual reproduction)* **Under what conditions do most fungi reproduce asexually?** *(Adequate food and moisture)*

Apply Ask: **How are fungal spores similar to plant seeds?** *(They have protective coverings and are transported easily by air or water.)* **learning modality: logical/mathematical**

The Role of Fungi in Nature

Teach Key Concepts   L2
Examining the Diverse Roles of Fungi

Focus Tell students that fungi play many important roles in nature, both helpful and harmful.

Teach Ask: **How are fungi recyclers?** *(They are decomposers, breaking down chemicals in dead organisms and returning them to the soil.)* **How are they eaten as food?** *(Yeasts are used for making breads and wine, molds for making cheeses; many mushrooms are edible, truffles are delicacies.)* **Which types of fungi cause diseases?** *(Parasites in crop plants; athlete's foot and ringworm in humans)* **Which are disease fighters?** *(Those that produce antibiotics, such as* Penicillium*)* **How do fungi live associated with other organisms?** *(In mutualistic relationships with plant roots, or, in lichens, with an alga or bacterium)*

Apply Ask: **Fungi most often share their roles as decomposers, disease agents, and disease fighters with which organisms?** *(Bacteria)* **learning modality: logical/mathematical**

Help Students Read
Reciprocal Teaching Have students read the section with a partner. One partner reads a paragraph aloud. Then the other partner summarizes the paragraph's contents and explains the main concepts. The partners continue to switch roles with each new paragraph until they finish the section.

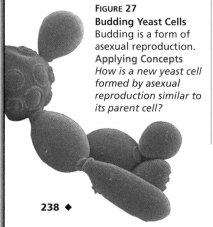

Lab zone Try This **Activity**

Spreading Spores
In this activity, you will make a model of a fruiting body.

1. Break a cotton ball into five equal pieces. Roll each piece into a tiny ball.
2. Insert the cotton balls into a balloon.
3. Repeat Steps 1 and 2 until the balloon is almost full.
4. Inflate the balloon. Tie a knot in its neck. Tape the knotted end of the balloon to a stick.
5. Stand the stick upright in a mound of modeling clay.
6. ✂ Pop the balloon with a pin. Observe what happens.

Making Models Draw a diagram of the model you made. Label the stalk, the spore case, and the spores. Use your model to explain why fungi are found just about everywhere.

FIGURE 27
Budding Yeast Cells
Budding is a form of asexual reproduction.
Applying Concepts
How is a new yeast cell formed by asexual reproduction similar to its parent cell?

238 ◆

Reproduction in Fungi

Like it or not, fungi are everywhere. The way they reproduce guarantees their survival and spread. **Fungi usually reproduce by making spores. The lightweight spores are surrounded by a protective covering and can be carried easily through air or water to new sites.** Fungi produce millions of spores, more than can ever survive. Only a few spores will fall where conditions are right for them to grow.

Fungi produce spores in reproductive structures called **fruiting bodies.** The appearances of fruiting bodies vary among different fungi. For some fungi, such as mushrooms, the part of the fungus that you see is the fruiting body. In other fungi, such as bread molds, the fruiting bodies are tiny, stalk-like hyphae that grow upward from the rest of the hyphae. A knoblike spore case at the tip of each stalk contains the spores.

Asexual Reproduction Most fungi reproduce both asexually and sexually. When there is adequate moisture and food, the fungi make spores asexually. Cells at the tips of their hyphae divide to form spores. The spores grow into fungi that are genetically identical to the parent.

Unicellular yeast cells undergo a form of asexual reproduction called **budding.** In budding, no spores are produced. Instead, a small yeast cell grows from the body of a parent cell in a way somewhat similar to the way a bud forms on a tree branch. The new cell then breaks away and lives on its own.

Sexual Reproduction Most fungi can also reproduce sexually, especially when growing conditions become unfavorable. In sexual reproduction, the hyphae of two fungi grow together and genetic material is exchanged. Eventually, a new reproductive structure grows from the joined hyphae and produces spores. The spores develop into fungi that differ genetically from either parent.

Classification of Fungi Figure 28 shows three major groups of fungi. The groups are named for the appearance of their reproductive structures. Additional groups include water species that produce spores with flagella and those that form tight associations with plant roots.

 Reading Checkpoint What is budding?

Lab zone Try This **Activity**

Skills Focus Making models   L2

Materials round balloon, cotton balls, tape, stick or ruler about 30 cm long, modeling clay, pin

Time 25 minutes

Tips ✂ If possible, blow up the balloons with a pump or compressed air so that the cotton balls do not get wet.

Suggest students make the cotton balls as small as possible.

Expected Outcome The "spores" should fly out from the balloons and land in many directions, fairly far from the balloons. Students should explain that, just as air scattered the cotton balls, air currents catch and carry spores far and wide.
learning modality: kinesthetic

238

The Role of Fungi in Nature

Fungi affect humans and other organisms in many ways. **Many fungi provide foods for people. Fungi play important roles as decomposers and recyclers on Earth. Some fungi cause disease while others fight disease. Still other fungi live in symbiosis with other organisms.**

Food and Fungi Yeasts, molds, and mushrooms are important food sources. Bakers add yeast to bread dough to make it rise. Yeast cells use the sugar in the dough for food and produce carbon dioxide gas as they feed. The gas forms bubbles, which cause the dough to rise. You see these bubbles as holes in a slice of bread. Molds are used to make foods such as some cheeses. The blue streaks in blue cheese, for example, are actually growths of *Penicillium roqueforti*. People enjoy eating mushrooms in salads and on pizza. You should never pick or eat wild mushrooms, however, because some mushrooms are extremely poisonous.

Discovery CHANNEL SCHOOL

Protists and Fungi

Video Preview
▶ Video Field Trip
Video Assessment

FIGURE 28
Classification of Fungi

Three major groups of fungi include sac fungi, club fungi, and zygote fungi.

Sac Fungi ▶
Sac fungi produce spores in structures that look like long sacs, such as these. The largest group of fungi, they include yeasts, morels, and truffles.

▲ **Club Fungi**
Club fungi produce spores in tiny clublike structures. This group includes mushrooms, rusts, and puffballs, such as these.

▲ **Zygote Fungi**
Zygote fungi produce very resistant spores. This group includes many common fruit and bread molds, like this *Rhizopus*.

Chapter 7 ◆ 239

Differentiated Instruction

Special Needs L1
Observing Fungi Group students to allow those with differing proficiencies to work together. Give groups a selection of mushrooms from the grocery store, and a hand lens to use to observe them. Challenge students to identify mushroom structures. Have students gently twist off the cap of one mushroom and break open the stalk from end to end. Ask: **Can you pull threadlike structures from the stalk?** (*Answers may vary depending on the mushroom.*) Tell students that these structures are hyphae. Make sure students wash their hands immediately after the activity. **learning modality: kinesthetic**

239

Considering Fungi as Decomposers

Materials components of a compost pile (leaves, manure, soil, weeds, grass clippings, vegetable and fruit wastes), small container, compost from a garden store or mature compost pile

Time 20 minutes

Focus Review the importance of decomposers to ecosystems.

Teach Ask: **Does anyone you know have a compost pile?** Explain that compost piles are made by alternating layers of soil, animal manure, and vegetable materials such as weeds, grass clippings, leaves, and food waste. Layer the sample components in the container. Explain further that after several months, the material in a compost pile becomes a rich mixture that can be used to supply nutrients necessary for garden plants to grow. Display for students the mature compost, allowing them a close view.

Apply Ask: **How do fungi help to produce compost?** (*Fungi are decomposers. They live in the soil in the compost pile and break down the chemicals in the dead plant matter.*)
learning modality: visual

Integrating Health   L1

Identifying a Fungal Disease

Encourage students to share what they know about athlete's foot. Ask: **How do you get athlete's foot?** (*Spores fall off infected feet and are picked up by your feet.*) **Where does this usually occur?** (*Public showers, gyms, etc.*) **What can you do to avoid getting athlete's foot?** (*Dry between toes; wear shoes in public areas.*) **How would you treat this fungus if you got it?** (*With a fungicide*) **learning modality: verbal**

Environmental Recycling Like bacteria, many fungi are decomposers. For example, many fungi live in the soil and break down the chemicals in dead plant matter. This process returns important nutrients to the soil. Without fungi and bacteria, Earth would be buried under dead plants and animals!

Disease-Fighting Fungi In 1928, a Scottish biologist named Alexander Fleming was examining petri dishes in which he was growing bacteria. To his surprise, Fleming noticed a spot of a bluish-green mold growing in one dish. Curiously, no bacteria were growing near the mold. Fleming hypothesized that the mold, a fungus named *Penicillium*, produced a substance that killed the bacteria near it.

Fleming's work contributed to the development of the first antibiotic, penicillin. Since the discovery of penicillin, many antibiotics have been isolated from both fungi and bacteria.

Disease-Causing Fungi Many fungi are parasites that cause serious diseases in plants. The sac fungus that causes Dutch elm disease is responsible for killing millions of elm trees in North America and Europe. Corn smut and wheat rust are two club fungi that cause diseases in important food crops. Fungal plant diseases also affect other crops, including rice, cotton, and soybeans, resulting in huge crop losses every year.

Some fungi cause diseases in humans. Athlete's foot fungus causes an itchy irritation in the damp places between toes. Ringworm, another fungal disease, causes an itchy, circular rash on the skin. Because the fungi that cause these diseases produce spores at the site of infection, the diseases can spread easily from person to person. Both diseases can be treated with antifungal medications.

Fungus-Plant Root Associations Some fungi help plants grow larger and healthier when their hyphae grow into, or on, the plant's roots. The hyphae spread out underground and absorb water and nutrients from the soil for the plant. With more water and nutrients, the plant grows larger than it would have grown without its fungal partner. The plant is not the only partner that benefits. The fungi get to feed on the extra food that the plant makes and stores.

Most plants have fungal partners. Many plants are so dependent on the fungi that they cannot survive without them. For example, orchid seeds cannot develop without their fungal partners.

FIGURE 29
Fungus–Plant Root Associations
An extensive system of fungal hyphae has grown in association with the roots of the pine seedling in the middle.
Classifying *What type of symbiosis do these two organisms exhibit?*

Roots of the pine seedling

Hyphae of fungus

240 ◆

Differentiated Instruction

Gifted and Talented   L3
Designing Experiments Challenge small groups of students to design experiments that show how yeast reacts with other ingredients to make bread. Suggest that students find simple bread recipes and vary the ingredients for their experiments. Students can make predictions about how different quantities of ingredients will affect the outcome of the baked bread.

Bring a bread machine into class so students can try out their recipes.
learning modality: logical/mathematical

Less Proficient Readers   L1
Identifying Roles Have students write down the various roles of fungi, as noted on the paragraph headings, then listen to the *Student Edition on Audio* CD and record notes on the importance of each role. **learning modality: verbal**

FIGURE 30
Lichens
The British soldier lichen consists of a fungus and an alga. The inset shows how entwined the alga is among the fungus's hyphae.

Alga

Fungus

Lichens A **lichen** (LY kun) consists of a fungus and either algae or autotrophic bacteria that live together in a mutualistic relationship. You have probably seen some familiar lichens—irregular, flat, crusty patches that grow on tree barks or rocks. The fungus benefits from the food produced by the algae or bacteria. The algae or bacteria, in turn, obtain shelter, water, and minerals from the fungus.

Lichens are often called "pioneer" organisms because they are the first organisms to appear on the bare rocks in an area after a volcanic eruption, fire, or rock slide has occurred. Over time, the lichens break down the rock into soil in which other organisms can grow. Lichens are also useful as indicators of air pollution. Many species of lichens are very sensitive to pollutants and die when pollution levels rise. By monitoring the growth of lichens, scientists can assess the air quality in an area.

 Reading Checkpoint What two organisms make up a lichen?

Go Online
SciLINKS
For: Links on fungi
Visit: www.SciLinks.org
Web Code: scn-0133

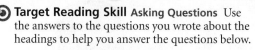

Section 4 Assessment

Target Reading Skill **Asking Questions** Use the answers to the questions you wrote about the headings to help you answer the questions below.

Reviewing Key Concepts

1. a. Listing List three characteristics that a bread mold shares with a mushroom.
   b. Comparing and Contrasting How are the cells of a bread mold arranged? How are the cells of a mushroom arranged?
   c. Summarizing How does the cell structure of a fungus help it obtain food?
2. a. Reviewing What role do spores play in the reproduction of fungi?
   b. Sequencing Outline the steps by which fungi produce spores by sexual reproduction.
   c. Inferring Why is it advantageous to a fungus to produce millions of spores?

3. a. Identifying Name six roles that fungi play in nature.
   b. Predicting Suppose all the fungi in a forest disappeared. What do you think the forest would be like without fungi?

Writing in Science

Wanted Poster Design a "Wanted" poster for a mold that has been ruining food in your kitchen. Present the mold as a "criminal of the kitchen." Include detailed descriptions of the mold's physical characteristics, what it needs to grow, how it grows, and any other details that will help your family identify this mold. Propose ways to prevent new molds from growing in your kitchen.

Chapter 7 ◆ 241

Lab zone Chapter **Project**

Keep Students on Track Students will need help drawing conclusions about their results. As you review students' sketches, point out questions that are not addressed by the poster. If necessary, list some ideas for information students should include on their posters before they make their sketches.

Writing in Science

Writing Mode Description
Scoring Rubric
4 Includes detailed, accurate descriptions; writing and art are engaging
3 Includes all criteria; writing and art not engaging
2 Minimally meets criteria
1 Includes inaccurate or incomplete information

241

Skills Lab

What's for Lunch?   L2

Prepare for Inquiry

Key Concept
The activity of yeast varies, depending on the amount of available food.

Skills Objectives
After this lab, students will be able to
- measure the circumference of balloons to determine the amount of carbon dioxide produced.
- make inferences about the factors that caused or failed to cause carbon dioxide production.
- draw conclusions about whether sugar and salt act as food sources for yeast.

 **Prep Time** 20 minutes
Class Time 45 minutes

Advance Planning
Before the lab, check a sample of yeast that is dissolved in warm water with sugar for 20 minutes, to make sure the yeasts are alive.

Safety
Students should wear safety goggles in case a balloon pops off a bottle or a bottle is accidentally dropped. Review the safety guidelines in Appendix A.

All in One Teaching Resources, Unit 2
- Lab Worksheet: *What's for Lunch?*

Guide Inquiry

Invitation
Tell students that yeasts produce carbon dioxide when they break down food. Carbon dioxide production can be measured to determine whether yeasts are feeding. Have students explain how carbon dioxide production will be measured in this lab.

Introduce the Procedure
Help students understand that when carbon dioxide gas forms in water, much of it will escape from the water's surface.

Skills Lab

What's for Lunch?

Problem
How does the presence of sugar or salt affect the activity of yeast?

Skills Focus
measuring, inferring, drawing conclusions

Materials
- 5 small plastic narrow-necked bottles
- 5 round balloons • 5 plastic straws
- dry powdered yeast • sugar • salt
- warm water (40°–45°C) • marking pen
- beaker • graduated cylinder • metric ruler
- string

Procedure

1. Copy the data table into your notebook. Then read over the entire procedure to see how you will test the activity of the yeast cells in bottles A through E. Write a prediction about what will happen in each bottle.

2. Gently stretch each of the balloons so that they will inflate easily.

3. Using the marking pen, label the bottles *A, B, C, D,* and *E.*

4. Use a beaker to fill each bottle with the same amount of warm water. **CAUTION:** *Glass is fragile. Handle the beaker gently to avoid breakage. Do not touch broken glass.*

5. Put 25 mL of salt into bottle B.

6. Put 25 mL of sugar into bottles C and E.

7. Put 50 mL of sugar into bottle D.

8. Put 6 mL of powdered yeast into bottle A, and stir the mixture with a clean straw. Remove the straw and discard it.

9. Immediately place a balloon over the opening of bottle A. Make sure that the balloon opening fits very tightly around the neck of the bottle.

10. Repeat Steps 8 and 9 for bottle B, bottle C, and bottle D.

242 ◆

Troubleshooting the Experiment
- Do not let students overfill the bottles.
- Balloons may pop off the bottles during the lab.
- Caution students to use a fresh straw for each mixing. This is particularly important when mixing bottle E, because students must not introduce yeast by accident.

Expected Outcome
Balloon D should inflate the most. Balloon C should also inflate but noticeably less than balloon D. Balloons A, B, and E should not inflate.

Data Table

Bottle	Prediction	Observations	Circumference			
			10 min	20 min	30 min	40 min
A (Yeast alone)						
B (Yeast and 25 mL of salt)						
C (Yeast and 25 mL of sugar)						
D (Yeast and 50 mL of sugar)						
E (No yeast and 25 mL of sugar)						

11. Place a balloon over bottle E without adding yeast to the bottle.

12. Place the five bottles in a warm spot away from drafts. Every ten minutes for 40 minutes, measure the circumference of each balloon by placing a string around the balloon at its widest point. Include your measurements in the data table.

Analyze and Conclude

1. **Measuring** Which balloons changed in size during this lab? How did they change?

2. **Inferring** Explain why the balloon changed size in some bottles and not in others. What caused that change in size?

3. **Interpreting Data** What did the results from bottle C show, compared with the results from bottle D? Why was it important to include bottle E in this investigation?

4. **Drawing Conclusions** Do yeast use salt or sugar as a food source? How do you know?

5. **Communicating** In a paragraph, summarize what you learned about yeast from this investigation. Be sure to support each of your conclusions with the evidence you gathered.

Design an Experiment

Develop a hypothesis about whether temperature affects the activity of yeast cells. Then design an experiment to test your hypothesis. *Obtain your teacher's permission before carrying out your investigation.*

For: Data sharing
Visit: PHSchool.com
Web Code: ced-1033

Chapter 7 ◆ 243

Analyze and Conclude

1. Balloons C and D changed during the lab. Balloon C filled up a little, and balloon D filled up a lot.

2. Some balloons were inflated by carbon dioxide gas. Other balloons remained unchanged because no carbon dioxide gas was produced by the yeast.

3. The balloon on bottle C did not inflate as much as the balloon on bottle D. When less sugar was available to the yeast (25 mL in bottle C versus 50 mL in bottle D), the yeast gave off less carbon dioxide. Without bottle E, there would be no way of knowing whether the gas was being produced by the sugar alone as it dissolved in the water.

4. They use sugar. Bottle B, which contained salt, produced no gas, indicating that the yeast was not active.

5. Student answers should explain that yeast cells use sugar as a food source, and they produce carbon dioxide as they break down food. Their feeding and production of carbon dioxide were proven by the inflation of balloons in bottles containing sugar, particularly in the bottle with the most sugar.

Extend Inquiry

Design an Experiment Students could prepare another bottle D and place it in a refrigerator. They would find that yeasts require warm environments to carry out their basic life processes.

For: Data sharing
Visit: PHSchool.com
Web Code: ced-1033

Students can go online to pool and analyze their data with students nationwide.

interactive
Textbook

- Complete student edition
- Section and chapter self-assessments
- Assessment reports for teachers

Help Students Read

Building Vocabulary

Vocabulary Rating Chart Have each student construct a chart with four columns labeled *Term, Can Define or Use It, Have Heard or Seen It,* and *Don't Know.* Tell students to copy the Key Terms from this chapter into the first column and rate their knowledge by putting a check in one of the other columns. Then have them reread the parts that pertain to Key Terms in question.

Words in Context Help students learn the meaning of new words or phrases by examining context. Tell students to look for familiar words or phrases around a new term for clues to the term's meaning.

Connecting Concepts

Concept Maps Help students develop one way to show how the information in the chapter is related. Viruses are nonliving particles that need to be inside a living cell in order to reproduce. Bacteria are prokaryotes. Protists are a diverse group of eukaryotic organisms that include traits shared with animals, plants, and fungi. Fungi, heterotrophs that reproduce with spores, vary in the role they play in nature. Have students brainstorm to identify the key concepts, key terms, details, and examples. Then write each one on a sticky note and attach it at random to chart paper or to the board.

Tell students that this concept map will be organized in hierarchical order and to begin at the top with the key concepts. Ask students these questions to guide them to categorize the information on the stickies: **What are some characteristics of viruses? Describe the basic structure of a virus. What structures can be found in a bacterial cell? What traits do protists share and how do they differ? How are fungi similar to protists? What are the traits and roles of fungi?**

1 Viruses

Key Concepts

- The only way in which viruses are like organisms is that they can multiply.
- All viruses have two basic parts: an outer coat that protects the virus and an inner core made of genetic material.
- Once inside a cell, a virus's genetic material takes over many of the cell's functions. The genetic material instructs the cell to produce the virus's proteins and genetic material. These proteins and genetic material then assemble into new viruses.
- Resting, drinking plenty of fluids, and eating well-balanced meals may be all you can do while you recover from a viral disease.

Key Terms
virus
host
parasite
bacteriophage

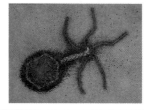

2 Bacteria

Key Concepts

- Bacteria are prokaryotes. The genetic material in their cells is not contained in a nucleus.
- Bacteria must have a source of food and a way of breaking down the food to release its energy.
- When bacteria have plenty of food, the right temperature, and other suitable conditions, they thrive and reproduce frequently.
- Bacteria are involved in oxygen and food production, environmental recycling and cleanup, and in health maintenance and medicine production.

Key Terms

bacteria	conjugation
flagellum	endospore
binary fission	pasteurization
asexual reproduction	decomposer
sexual reproduction	

244 ◆

3 Protists

Key Concepts

- Like animals, animal-like protists are heterotrophs, and most are able to move from place to place to obtain food.
- Like plants, algae are autotrophs.
- Like fungi, funguslike protists are heterotrophs, have cell walls, and use spores to reproduce.

Key Terms

protist	symbiosis
protozoan	mutualism
pseudopod	algae
contractile vacuole	spore
cilia	

4 Fungi

Key Concepts

- Fungi are eukaryotes that have cell walls, are heterotrophs that feed by absorbing their food, and use spores to reproduce.
- Fungi usually reproduce by making spores. The lightweight spores are surrounded by a protective covering and can be carried easily through air or water to new sites.
- Many fungi provide foods for people. Fungi play important roles as decomposers and recyclers on Earth. Some fungi cause disease while others fight disease. Still other fungi live in symbiosis with other organisms.

Key Terms

fungi	budding
hyphae	lichen
fruiting body	

Prompt students by using connecting words or phrases, such as "classified by," "is composed of," "reproduces by," and "can cause" to indicate the basis for the organization of the map. The phrases should form a sentence between or among a set of concepts.

Answer
Accept all logical presentations by students.

All in One Teaching Resources, Unit 2

- Key Terms Review: *Viruses, Bacteria, Protists, and Fungi*
- Connecting Concepts: *Viruses, Bacteria, Protists, and Fungi*

Review and Assessment

Go Online
PHSchool.com
For: Self-Assessment
Visit: PHSchool.com
Web Code: cha-2070

Organizing Information

Comparing and Contrasting Copy the Venn diagram comparing viruses and bacteria onto a separate sheet of paper. Then complete it and add a title. (For more information on Comparing and Contrasting, see the Skills Handbook.)

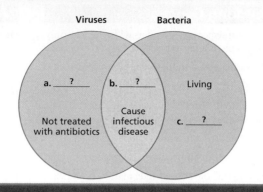

Viruses   Bacteria

a. ____?____   b. ____?____   Living

Not treated with antibiotics   Cause infectious disease   c. ____?____

Reviewing Key Terms

Choose the letter of the best answer.

1. Bacteriophages are viruses that attack and destroy
   a. other viruses.
   b. bacteria.
   c. plants.
   d. humans.

2. Which part of a virus determines which host cells it can infect?
   a. nucleus
   b. ribosomes
   c. flagellum
   d. surface proteins

3. Most bacteria are surrounded by a rigid protective structure called the
   a. cell wall.
   b. cell membrane.
   c. protein coat.
   d. flagellum.

4. Which of the following characteristics describes all protists?
   a. They are unicellular.
   b. They can be seen with the unaided eye.
   c. Their cells have nuclei.
   d. They are unable to move on their own.

5. A lichen is a symbiotic association between
   a. fungi and plant roots.
   b. algae and fungi.
   c. algae and bacteria.
   d. protozoans and algae.

If the statement is true, write *true*. If it is false, change the underlined word or words to make the statement true.

6. <u>Active viruses</u> enter a cell and immediately begin to multiply.

7. During <u>conjugation</u>, one bacterium transfers genetic material to another bacterial cell.

8. Plantlike protists are called <u>protozoans</u>.

9. Bacteria form <u>endospores</u> to survive unfavorable conditions in their surroundings.

10. Most fungi are made up of threadlike structures called <u>spores</u>.

Writing in Science

Informational Pamphlet Create a pamphlet to teach young children about fungi. Explain where fungi live, how they feed, and the roles they play. Include illustrations as well.

DISCOVERY CHANNEL SCHOOL

Protists and Fungi
Video Preview
Video Field Trip
▶ Video Assessment

Go Online
PHSchool.com
For: Self-Assessment
Visit: PHSchool.com
Web Code: cha-2070

Students can take a practice test online that is automatically scored.

All in One Teaching Resources, Unit 2
- Transparency LS70
- Chapter Test
- Performance Assessment Teacher Notes
- Performance Assessment Student Worksheet
- Performance Assessment Scoring Rubric

◉ *ExamView*® Computer Test Bank CD-ROM

Review and Assessment

Organizing Information
a. Nonliving
b. Can be useful
c. Treated with antibiotics
Possible title: Comparing Viruses and Bacteria

Reviewing Key Terms
1. b 2. d 3. a 4. c 5. b
6. True
7. True
8. False; algae
9. True
10. False; hyphae

Writing in Science

Writing Mode Description

Scoring Rubric
4 Includes detailed, accurate information for all criteria and illustrations; art is neat and supports text
3 Includes all criteria; art somewhat extraneous
2 Minimally meets all criteria
1 Includes inaccurate or incomplete information

DISCOVERY CHANNEL SCHOOL Video Assessment

Protists and Fungi

Show the Video Assessment to review chapter content and as a prompt for the writing assignment. Discussion questions: **Describe the relationship between fungi and algae in lichens.** (*In a lichen, the alga provides food for the fungus, while the fungus provides water and shelter for the alga; both organisms benefit.*) **What important role do fungi play in the ecosystem in which they live?** (*They act as decomposers and provide food.*)

Checking Concepts

11. The proteins in the coat of the virus will fit only with certain proteins on the surface of a cell.

12. After a hidden virus enters a host cell, its genetic material becomes part of the cell's genetic material. When the host cell divides, the virus's genetic material is copied along with the host's genetic material. When certain conditions cause the virus's genetic material to become active, it takes over the cell's functions.

13. Most bacteria reproduce asexually by binary fission, especially when conditions are favorable. Some bacteria can reproduce sexually by conjugation.

14. They help you digest food, make vitamins for you, and keep harmful bacteria from living in your tissues.

15. Antibiotics kill bacteria without harming body cells. For example, penicillin weakens the cell walls of some bacteria and causes them to burst.

16. An amoeba extends pseudopods around a food particle to engulf it.

17. Animal-like and funguslike protists are heterotrophs. Plantlike protists are autotrophs, but some can also be heterotrophs.

18. In sexual reproduction, two hyphae grow together, exchange genetic material, and produce a fruiting body.

Thinking Critically

19. Both invade the host cell and cause it to start producing new viruses. With an active virus, the takeover occurs immediately after entry into the cell. With hidden viruses, the genetic material of the virus is incorporated into the cell's genetic material, and it can be years before the virus actively takes over the cell.

20. A substance that includes living cells because viruses need to infect living cells in order to multiply

21. Organism A is an amoeba, which engulfs its food with pseudopods. Organism B is a paramecium, which uses cilia to push food-containing water into its oral groove.

22. Most other life forms would probably disappear also. Algae provide food and oxygen for water animals and help maintain the oxygen in the atmosphere.

23. Fungi play many beneficial roles, especially that of decomposer. Killing fungi could allow the buildup of dead organisms. Fungi also help many plants to survive.

Review and Assessment

Checking Concepts

11. Explain why a certain virus will attach to only one type or a few types of cells.

12. Describe how a hidden virus multiplies.

13. Describe how bacteria reproduce.

14. How do the bacteria that live in your intestines help you?

15. Explain how antibiotics kill bacteria.

16. How does an amoeba obtain food?

17. Compare how animal-like, plantlike, and funguslike protists obtain food.

18. How does sexual reproduction occur in fungi?

Thinking Critically

19. Comparing and Contrasting Describe the similarities and differences between active and hidden viruses.

20. Problem Solving Bacteria will grow in the laboratory on a gelatin-like substance called agar. Viruses will not grow on agar. If you needed to grow viruses in the laboratory, what kind of substance would you have to use? Explain your reasoning.

21. Comparing and Contrasting Identify the organisms below. Describe the method by which each obtains food.

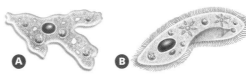

Ⓐ   **Ⓑ**

22. Predicting If all algae suddenly disappeared from Earth's waters, what would happen to living things on Earth? Explain your answer.

23. Making Judgments You see an advertisement for a new, powerful fungicide guaranteed to kill most fungi on contact. What should people take into consideration before choosing to buy this fungicide?

Applying Skills

Use the graph to answer Questions 24–27.

When yeast is added to bread dough, the yeast cells produce carbon dioxide, which causes the dough to rise. The graph below shows how temperature affects the amount of carbon dioxide that is produced.

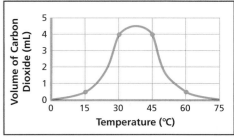

Temperature and Carbon Dioxide Production

Volume of Carbon Dioxide (mL) — *Temperature (°C)*

24. Interpreting Data Based on the graph, at what temperature does yeast produce the most carbon dioxide?

25. Inferring Use the graph to explain why yeast is dissolved in warm water, rather than in cold water, when it is used to make bread.

26. Predicting Based on the graph, would you expect bread dough to rise if it were placed in a refrigerator (which is kept at about 2°C to 5°C)? Explain.

27. Drawing Conclusions Explain how temperature affects the amount of carbon dioxide that the yeast cells produce.

Lab zone Chapter **Project**

Performance Assessment Create a poster that summarizes your experiment for the class. In your poster, include your hypothesis and describe the conditions that produced the best mushroom growth. Use diagrams and graphs to display your results. Did the project raise any new questions about mushrooms for you? If so, how could you answer those questions?

Lab zone Chapter **Project**   **L3**

Performance Assessment Provide students with materials for making the posters. Set aside time for them to work on posters during class, and allow them to look at each other's posters for ideas. Students should organize information on their posters in a clear manner.

Reflect and Record Some students may have found it difficult to organize their results because they changed the variables too often or were not confident of their results. Students may propose another experiment or talking to an expert as a way of answering their questions.

Standardized Test Prep

Choose the letter of the best answer.

1. Which of the following statements about a paramecium is correct?
  A It has two contractile vacuoles that remove excess water from the cytoplasm.
  B It uses cilia to move.
  C It has two nuclei.
  D all of the above

2. Which of the following statements about fungus reproduction is true?
  F Fungi reproduce sexually by budding.
  G Fungi reproduce by making spores.
  H Fungi reproduce asexually when two hyphae join together and exchange genetic material.
  J Fungi do not reproduce sexually.

3. What will most likely happen after the virus in the diagram attaches to the bacterial cell?

  A The virus will inject its proteins into the bacterial cell.
  B The virus will inject its genetic material into the bacterial cell.
  C The bacterial cell will inject its proteins into the virus.
  D The bacterial cell will inject its genetic material into the virus.

4. Which of the following statements about viruses is *not* true?
  F Viruses can multiply only inside a living cell.
  G Viruses have genetic material.
  H Virus particles are smaller than bacterial cells.
  J Diseases caused by viruses can be cured by antibiotics.

5. Paola grew a new culture of bacteria and measured the population's growth over time. The number of bacteria increased sharply over the first few hours but then tapered off. Which of the following statements about these observations is true?
  A The initial conditions for bacterial growth were favorable.
  B The number of bacteria increased as the bacteria reproduced asexually.
  C After a period of time, the bacteria started to run out of food, space, and other resources.
  D all of the above

Constructed Response

6. Compare and contrast viruses and bacteria with respect to their sizes, structures, and methods of reproduction.

Applying Skills

24. At about 38°C

25. Yeast must be active and produce carbon dioxide so the dough will rise, and it is more active in warm water.

26. No. For the most part the dough would not continue to rise because yeast are usually inactive at that temperature.

27. The optimal temperature range for yeast activity is between 30°C and 45°C. Above or below this range, the amount of carbon dioxide produced decreases sharply.

Standardized Test Prep

1. D **2.** G **3.** B **4.** J **5.** D
6. Size: Viruses are very small and are measured in nanometers. Bacteria vary in size, but are larger than viruses and can be seen by a light microscope.

Structure: Viruses have two parts, a protein coat that protects the virus, and an inner core made of genetic material. Bacteria have a cell wall, a cell membrane, cytoplasm with ribosomes in it and with genetic material, and may have a flagellum.

Methods of reproduction: Viruses enter a host cell and the virus's genetic material takes over many of the cell's functions. It instructs the cell to produce the virus's proteins and genetic material. Bacteria may reproduce by asexual or sexual reproduction, or the formation of endospores.

Chapter at a Glance

PRENTICE HALL
TeacherEXPRESS™
Plan • Teach • Assess

 Chapter Project *Design and Build an Interactive Exhibit*

Technology

Local Standards

All in One Teaching Resources, Unit 2
• Chapter Project Teacher Notes, pp. 88–89
• Chapter Project Student Overview , pp. 90–91
• Chapter Project Student Worksheets , pp. 92–93
• Chapter Project Scoring Rubric, p. 94

Video Preview

Section 1 The Plant Kingdom

2 periods
1 block

8.1.1 Identify the characteristics all plants share.
8.1.2 Name the things that a plant needs to live successfully on land.
8.1.3 Compare nonvascular and vascular plants.
8.1.4 Describe the stages of a plant's life cycle.

Section 2 Plants Without Seeds

2 periods
1 block

8.2.1 Name some nonvascular plants and list the characteristics they share.
8.2.2 Name some seedless vascular plants and list the characteristics they share.

Section 3 The Characteristics of Seed Plants

2 periods
1 block

8.3.1 Identify the characteristics that seed plants share.
8.3.2 Explain how seeds become new plants.
8.3.3 Describe the functions of roots, stems, and leaves.

Video Field Trip

Section 4 Gymnosperms and Angiosperms

3 periods
1 1/2 blocks

8.4.1 Identify the characteristics of gymnosperms and describe how they reproduce.
8.4.2 Describe the characteristics of angiosperms and their flowers.
8.4.3 Explain how angiosperms reproduce.
8.4.4 Describe the two types of angiosperms.
8.4.5 List products from seed plants.

Section 5 Plant Responses and Growth

1 period
1/2 block

8.5.1 Identify three stimuli that produce plant responses.
8.5.2 Describe how plants respond to seasonal changes.
8.5.3 State how long different angiosperms live.

Review and Assessment

Test Preparation

All in One Teaching Resources, Unit 2
• Key Terms Review, p. 138
• Transparency LS88
• Performance Assessment Teacher Notes, p. 145
• Performance Assessment Scoring Rubric, p. 146
• Performance Assessment Student Worksheet, p. 147
• Chapter Test, pp. 148–151

Video Assessment

PHSchool.com

Test Preparation
Blackline Masters

Chapter Activities Planner

Student Edition	Inquiry	Time	Materials	Skills	Resources
Chapter Project, p. 249	Open-Ended	3–4 weeks	**All in One** Teaching Resources, **Unit 2**, p. 88	Observing, making models, communicating	**Lab zone Easy Planner** **All in One** Teaching Resources, **Unit 2**, Support pp. 88–89
Section 1					
Discover Activity, p. 250	Guided	10 minutes	Hand lens, leaf from plant with thick, fleshy leaves, such as a jade, yucca, or aloe plant; leaf of a temperate climate plant, such as a maple, oak, or common garden plant	Inferring	**Lab zone Easy Planner**
Section 2					
Discover Activity, p. 256	Directed	15 minutes	3 plastic graduated cylinders, dropper, 20 mL peat moss, 20 mL sand, stopwatch, water	Predicting	**Lab zone Easy Planner**
Try This Activity, p. 259	Guided	20 minutes	Fern plant, hand lens, plastic dropper, water	Inferring	**Lab zone Easy Planner**
Skills Lab, p. 261	Guided	45 minutes	Clump of moss, hand lens, metric ruler, toothpicks, plastic dropper, water	Observing, measuring	**Lab zone Easy Planner** **All in One** Teaching Resources, **Unit 2**, Skills Lab: *Masses of Mosses*, pp. 110–111
Section 3					
Discover Activity, p. 262	Guided	10 minutes	Foods from flowerless seed plants, such as carrots, parsnips, broccoli, cabbage, lettuce, celery, parsley, potato, onion	Classifying	**Lab zone Easy Planner**
Try This Activity, p. 264	Guided	10 minutes	Hand lens; dried kidney, lima, or black beans; dried yellow or green peas; shelled peanuts	Observing	**Lab zone Easy Planner**
Skills Activity, p. 268	Directed	35 minutes (20 wait time); 2 hours to test prediction	Calculator, celery stalk, clock or stopwatch, dropper, food coloring, lab apron, plastic container, spoon, water	Calculating	**Lab zone Easy Planner**
Section 4					
Discover Activity, p. 272	Guided	10 minutes	Hand lens; metric ruler; 2 or 3 leaves from angiosperms, such as oak or maple tree, day lily, and rose; 2 or 3 leaves from gymnosperms, such as pine, yew, and spruce	Classifying	**Lab zone Easy Planner**
Try This Activity, p. 274	Guided	10 minutes	Mature female pine cone, hand lens, sheet of white paper	Inferring	**Lab zone Easy Planner**
Skills Lab, pp. 282–283	Directed	40 minutes	Paper towels, plastic dropper, hand lens, microscope, slide, large flower, coverslip, scalpel, tape, water, metric ruler, lens paper	Observing, inferring, measuring	**Lab zone Easy Planner** **Lab Activity Video** **All in One** Teaching Resources, **Unit 2**, Skills Lab: *A Close Look at Flowers*, pp. 128–130
Section 5					
Discover Activity, p. 284	Directed	10 minutes	Touch-sensitive plant, common houseplant	Inferring	**Lab zone Easy Planner**

Section 1 The Plant Kingdom

🕐 *2 periods, 1 block*

Objectives

8.1.1 Identify the characteristics all plants share.

8.1.2 Name the things that a plant needs to live successfully on land.

8.1.3 Compare nonvascular and vascular plants.

8.1.4 Describe the stages of a plant's life cycle.

Key Terms

• photosynthesis • tissue • chloroplast • vacuole • cuticle • vascular tissue
• fertilization • zygote • nonvascular plant • vascular plant • chlorophyll
• sporophyte • gametophyte

Local Standards

Preteach

Build Background Knowledge

Ask students to explain how plants and animals are different.

 **Discover Activity** *What Do Leaves Reveal About Plants?* **L1**

Targeted Print and Technology Resources

All in One Teaching Resources, Unit 2

L2 Reading Strategy: Building Vocabulary

 PresentationEXPRESS™ CD-ROM

Instruct

What Is a Plant? Use discussion to emphasize that all plants are autotrophs, that is, they produce their own food, and that all plants are eukaryotes that contain many cells.

Adaptations for Living on Land Help students understand that, to live on land, all plants need a way to get water and nutrients from their surroundings, transport water and nutrients within their bodies, support their bodies, and reproduce.

Classification of Plants Assist students in discerning two major categories of plants: plants with vascular tissue and plants without.

Complex Life Cycles Help students recognize that a plant's life cycle consists of two stages: the sporophyte stage and the gametophyte stage.

Targeted Print and Technology Resources

All in One Teaching Resources, Unit 2

L2 Guided Reading, pp. 97–100

L2 Transparencies LS71, LS72

PHSchool.com Web Code: cep-1041

⊙ **Student Edition on Audio CD**

Assess

Section Assessment Questions

🔄 Have students use their own definitions to help them answer questions.

Reteach

Direct students to make a chart listing the adaptations plants need to live on land and identify the adaptations as belonging to vascular plants.

Targeted Print and Technology Resources

All in One Teaching Resources, Unit 2

• Section Summary, p. 96

L1 Review and Assessment, p. 101

L3 Enrich, p. 102

Section 2 **Plants Without Seeds**

2 periods, 1 block

Objectives

8.2.1 Name some nonvascular plants and list the characteristics they share.

8.2.2 Name some seedless vascular plants and list the characteristics they share.

Key Terms

• rhizoid • frond

ABILITY LEVELS
L1 Basic to Average
L2 For All Students
L3 Average to Advanced

Local Standards

Preteach

Build Background Knowledge

Invite students to describe any mosses with which they are familiar.

 Discover Activity *Will Mosses Absorb Water?* **L1**

Targeted Print and Technology Resources

 **Teaching Resources, Unit 2**

L2 Reading Strategy Transparency LS73: Identifying Main Ideas

 PresentationEXPRESS™ CD-ROM

Instruct

Nonvascular Plants Help students understand that nonvascular plants may have leaflike, stemlike, and rootlike structures resembling those of other plants, but their lack of transport tissue limits their potential growth and distribution.

Seedless Vascular Plants Stress that plants with vascular tissue can grow taller than nonvascular plants but that, without seeds, the plants must still live in moist areas to complete reproduction.

 Skills Lab *Masses of Mosses* **L2**

Targeted Print and Technology Resources

 **Teaching Resources, Unit 2**

L2 Guided Reading, pp. 105–107
L2 Transparencies LS74, LS75
L2 Skills Lab: *Masses of Mosses*, pp. 110–111

www.SciLinks.org Web Code: scn-0143

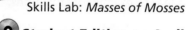 **Lab Activity Video/DVD**
Skills Lab: *Masses of Mosses*

 Student Edition on Audio CD

Assess

Section Assessment Questions

Have students use their Identifying Main Ideas graphic organizers to answer the questions.

Reteach

Ask students to describe the life cycle of moss, describing how the sporophyte is formed and its function.

Targeted Print and Technology Resources

 **Teaching Resources, Unit 2**

• Section Summary, p. 104
L1 Review and Assessment, p. 108
L3 Enrich, p. 109

Section 3 The Characteristics of Seed Plants

ABILITY LEVELS
- **L1** Basic to Average
- **L2** For All Students
- **L3** Average to Advanced

 2 periods, 1 block

Objectives

8.3.1 Identify the characteristics that seed plants share.

8.3.2 Explain how seeds become new plants.

8.3.3 Describe the functions of roots, stems, and leaves.

Local Standards

Key Terms

- phloem • xylem • pollen • seed • embryo • cotyledon • germination
- root cap • cambium • transpiration

Preteach

Build Background Knowledge

Ask students to generate a list of plants they see often and identify which have seeds and which do not.

Lab zone Discover Activity *Which Plant Part Is It?* **L1**

Targeted Print and Technology Resources

All in One Teaching Resources, Unit 2

L2 Reading Strategy Transparency
LS76: Outlining

○ **PresentationEXPRESS™ CD-ROM**

Instruct

What Is a Seed Plant? Discuss that all seed plants have vascular tissue and produce seeds.

How Seeds Become New Plants Ask questions and use an illustration to discuss the structures of seeds and how they germinate.

Roots Identify the functions, types, and structures of roots.

Stems Use illustrations to describe the functions of stems.

Leaves Use a cross-section of a leaf to examine its functions.

Targeted Print and Technology Resources

All in One Teaching Resources, Unit 2

L2 Guided Reading, pp. 114–118

L2 Transparencies LS77, LS78, LS79, LS80, LS81

DISCOVERY CHANNEL SCHOOL
Video Field Trip

PHSchool.com Web Code: ced-1051

○ **Student Edition on Audio CD**

Assess

Section Assessment Questions

Have students use their outlines to help them answer the questions.

Reteach

Use the section figures to summarize the functions of roots, stems, and leaves.

Targeted Print and Technology Resources

All in One Teaching Resources, Unit 2

- Section Summary, p. 113
- **L1** Review and Reinforce, p. 119
- **L3** Enrich, p. 120

Section 4 Gymnosperms and Angiosperms

ABILITY LEVELS
- **L1** Basic to Average
- **L2** For All Students
- **L3** Average to Advanced

🕐 *3 periods, 1 1/2 blocks*

Objectives

8.4.1 Identify the characteristics of gymnosperms and describe how they reproduce.

8.4.2 Describe the characteristics of angiosperms and their flowers.

8.4.3 Explain how angiosperms reproduce.

8.4.4 Describe the two types of angiosperms.

8.4.5 List products from seed plants.

Key Terms

- gymnosperm • cone • ovule • pollination • angiosperm • flower • sepal
- petal • stamen • pistil • ovary • fruit • monocot • dicot

Local Standards

Preteach

Build Background Knowledge

Prompt students to name trees that stay green all year and describe their features.

 **Discover Activity** *Are All Leaves Alike?* **L1**

Targeted Print and Technology Resources

All in One Teaching Resources, Unit 2

L2 Reading Strategy: Building Vocabulary

⊙ **PresentationEXPRESS™ CD-ROM**

Instruct

Gymnosperms Analyze the characteristics of gymnosperms.

Reproduction in Gymnosperms Use a cycle diagram to identify the steps in reproduction of gymnosperms.

Angiosperms Help students recognize the characteristics that have made angiosperms the dominant type of plant today.

The Structure of Flowers Use a diagram to examine the reproductive parts of a flower.

Reproduction in Angiosperms Ask questions to help students understand the steps in reproduction of angiosperms.

Types of Angiosperms Compare and contrast the structures of monocots and dicots.

Angiosperms in Everyday Life Identify commercial uses of gymnosperms and angiosperms.

 Skills Lab *A Close Look at Flowers* **L2**

Targeted Print and Technology Resources

All in One Teaching Resources, Unit 2

L2 Guided Reading, pp. 123–125

L2 Transparencies LS82, LS83, LS84, LS85

L2 Skills Lab: *A Close Look at Flowers*, pp. 128–130

📼 **Lab Activity Video/DVD**
Skills Lab: *A Close Look at Flowers*

www.SciLinks.org Web Code: scn-0152

PHSchool.com Web Code: cep-1053

⊙ **Student Edition on Audio CD**

Assess

Section Assessment Questions

🔄 Have students use their completed sentences to answer the questions.

Reteach

Review the life cycle of angiosperms.

Targeted Print and Technology Resources

All in One Teaching Resources, Unit 2

- Section Summary, p. 122
L1 Review and Reinforce, p. 126
L3 Enrich, p. 127

Section 5 **Plant Responses and Growth**

ABILITY LEVELS
L1 Basic to Average
L2 For All Students
L3 Average to Advanced

1 period, 1/2 block

Objectives

8.5.1 Identify three stimuli that produce plant responses.
8.5.2 Describe how plants respond to seasonal changes.
8.5.3 State how long different angiosperms live.

Local Standards

Key Terms

• tropism • hormone • auxin • photoperiodism • short-day plant
• long-day plant • day-neutral plant • dormancy • annual • biennial
• perennial

Preteach

Build Background Knowledge

Have students describe the usual direction of plant stem and root growth.

Lab zone Discover Activity *Can a Plant Respond to Touch?* **L1**

Targeted Print and Technology Resources

All in One Teaching Resources, Unit 2

L2 Reading Strategy Transparency
LS86: Relating Cause and Effect

PresentationEXPRESS™ CD-ROM

Instruct

Tropisms Identify plant responses to the stimuli of touch, light, and gravity.

Seasonal Changes Analyze the different ways plants respond to changing seasons.

Life Spans of Angiosperms Contrast the life spans of annuals, biennials, and perennials.

Targeted Print and Technology Resources

All in One Teaching Resources, Unit 2

L2 Guided Reading, pp. 133–135
L2 Transparency LS87

www.SciLinks.org Web Code: scn-0154

Student Edition on Audio CD

Assess

Section Assessment Questions

Have students use their cause and effect graphic organizers to answer the questions.

Reteach

Sketch examples of tropisms, photoperiodism, and dormancy, and have students describe them.

Targeted Print and Technology Resources

All in One Teaching Resources, Unit 2

• Section Summary, p. 132
L1 Review and Reinforce, p. 136
L3 Enrich, p. 137

Go Online

NSTA–*PD*LINKS

For: Professional development support
Visit: www.SciLinks.org/PDLinks
Web Code: scf-0150

Professional Development

Professional Development

Section 1 The Plant Kingdom

Plant Traits and Diversity Plants are defined by a combination of traits. Plants are multicellular eukaryotes, with cell walls that contain cellulose. The great majority of plants are autotrophs—they capture the sun's energy and photosynthesize, thus making their own food. However, some plant species are entirely or partly heterotrophic. For example, dodder is a nonphotosynthetic parasite. Dodder grows on its host plant (such as buckwheat and sage) and completely depends on it for food. Other plants, such as mistletoe, are only partially parasitic, with some photosynthetic parts. Some plants are "carnivorous"—they attract, trap, digest, and absorb insects to obtain an additional source of nutrients.

There is great diversity within the plant kingdom. Carnivorous plants represent only one example. Land plants in particular have developed successful adaptations that enable them to live in a wide variety of environments. One important adaptation of land plants is the production of lignin, a chemical that stiffens cell walls. Lignin provides strength and support, allowing a plant to grow large and tall.

Plants play critical roles in the ecosystems in which they are found. They are primary producers and form the foundation of many food webs. Plants also release oxygen gas, a product of photosynthesis essential for other organisms.

Section 2 Plants Without Seeds

Nonvascular Plants Mosses, liverworts, and hornworts are commonly referred to as nonvascular plants. Note, however, that some mosses do contain water-conducting tissues, though these tissues are not strong enough to provide efficient support or transport for the plant. Nonvascular plants have only their cell walls to provide support. (In vascular plants, the walls of the water-conducting tubes of true vascular plants contain a substance called lignin, which makes them stiff and strong.) Without efficient support and transport, nonvascular plants are small and restricted to moist environments.

Vascular Tissue and Water Transport Ferns, although more complex than mosses, are among the simplest of the vascular plants. Vascular tissue is responsible for delivering water and nutrients to parts of the plant distant from the roots. This allows plants to live at a distance from water and grow taller than their mossy relatives.

Dye travels up a plant stalk, such as celery, showing that vascular tissues accomplish their task. But how? How does a plant "suck up" water? Capillary action alone moves an insignificant amount of water upwards, especially in tall trees. The secret lies in the loss of water through a plant's leaves—transpiration.

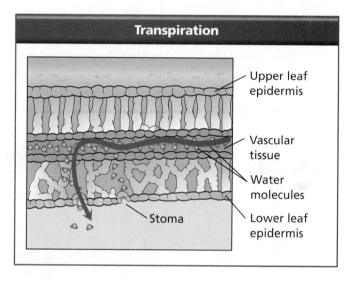

Transpiration

- Upper leaf epidermis
- Vascular tissue
- Water molecules
- Lower leaf epidermis
- Stoma

Transpiration subjects water in the xylem to tension, reaching from leaves to stems to roots. Water molecules are pulled upward, like links in a chain, partly due to capillary action but mostly due to the attraction of one water molecule to the next. The three-dimensional geometry of water's hydrogen bonds makes the bonds strong enough to link water molecules one to another in the xylem, but weak enough to allow molecules to escape from a leaf's surface. As one water molecule escapes from the leaf surface, another is pulled up to replace it. With this process, water can move at a rate of about 60 centimeters per minute in most plants. Of the water that moves through the leaf, 90 percent is lost by transpiration; only about 2 percent is used during photosynthesis.

Section 3 The Characteristics of Seed Plants

Vascular Tissue The vascular systems of seed plants include xylem and phloem tissues. In angiosperms, xylem has two components—tracheids and vessel elements (right and center, below). Both types of vessels are hollow and nonliving, but the vessel elements are larger and do not have transverse end walls. As a result they form a continuous, hollow tube for water and mineral transport.

A tracheid is a long, thick wall with ends that taper. Water moves from tracheid to tracheid through pores in the tracheid wall.

Phloem is made up of sieve-tube cells (left, below), which have cytoplasm but no nuclei. Their transverse walls contain channels through which sugars can pass. Lying next to each sieve tube cell is a companion cell that controls and maintains the life functions of both cells.

⚑ Address Misconceptions

Many students think that trees "grow up" much the same way that grasses grow. However, trees grow by adding layers to the outside of the stem, so that the outer rings are newer than the inner rings. For a strategy for overcoming this misconception, see **Address Misconceptions** *in the section The Characteristics of Seed Plants.*

Vascular Tissues

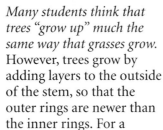

Sieve tube cell

Companion cell

Sieve tubes   Vessel elements   Tracheids

Section 4 Gymnosperms and Angiosperms

Types of Angiosperms Angiosperms, the flowering plants, are the most diverse and widespread of all plants. They make up more than 88 percent of all living plant species and can be found almost anywhere on Earth.

Angiosperms can be categorized in several ways. Traditionally, they have been subdivided into monocots and dicots. Monocots and dicots differ in the number of cotyledons, or seed leaves, that are present in the plant embryo, in the arrangement of vascular tissue, and in the number of petals per flower.

Another way to classify angiosperms is as woody or herbaceous, according to characteristics of their stems. Woody plants have stems that contain wood and are therefore hard and rigid. Their cells have thick cell walls that support the plant body. Woody plants include trees, shrubs, and woody vines. In contrast, herbaceous plants do not produce wood as they grow. Their stems are often soft and smooth. However, some herbaceous plants, such as corn, have stems that are rather hard.

Angiosperms can also be grouped as annuals, biennials, and perennials, based on their life cycle. Some plants have life spans that are genetically determined, and these plants will die at a certain point, even when they are grown under favorable conditions. Other plants have life spans that are environmentally determined. When these plants are grown in favorable conditions, they will typically live longer than they would in nature. A plant's life cycle includes germination, maturity, flowering, seed production, and death. Annuals complete their life cycle in a single year or less. Biennials complete their life cycle in two years, and perennials live for more than two years.

Though they can be classified in many ways, angiosperms have unique characteristics that unify the group—flowers and fruits. Flowers enclose the ovary in which seeds develop. Fruits are the mature ovaries, consisting of a thick wall of tissue that surrounds the seeds. Flowers and fruits play an important role in the reproductive success of angiosperms. The various colors, sizes, shapes, and scents of flowers attract pollinators and help ensure that fertilization occurs. Fruits protect the seeds and help the seeds disperse.

Section 5 Plant Responses and Growth

Rapid Responses Unlike animals, plants cannot move from one location to another. However, they do respond to some stimuli. All plants respond to light and gravity: plant shoots move upward toward light and away from gravity, while roots move downward away from light and toward gravity.

The response center for gravity appears to be in the root cap and may be governed by starch molecules. Response to light is governed by a plant hormone called auxin. Other plant hormones include gibberillins, cytokinins, and substances associated with the formation of flowers, tubers, bulbs, and buds.

Some plant responses do not involve growth. If the leaves of *Mimosa pudica,* appropriately called the "sensitive plant," are touched, its leaflets fold together completely within only two or three seconds. The secret to this movement is changes in osmotic pressure. Recall that osmotic pressure is caused by the diffusion of water into cells. The leaflets are held apart due to osmotic pressure at the base of the leaflets, where they join. When a leaf is touched, cells near the center of the leaflets pump out ions and lose water due to osmosis. Pressure from cells on the underside of the leaf, which do not lose water, force the leaflets together.

The carnivorous Venus' flytrap also demonstrates rapid responses. Each plant grows several kidney-shaped leaves with sensitive inner bristles. When a fly triggers sensory cells on the inside of the flytrap's leaf, electrical signals are sent from cell to cell. A combination of changes in osmotic pressure and cell wall expansion causes the leaf to snap shut, trapping the insect inside. Enzymes flood the inside of the trap and slowly digest the prey. Specialized glands absorb the nutrients. When the insect is fully digested, the trap opens again.

Venus' Flytrap

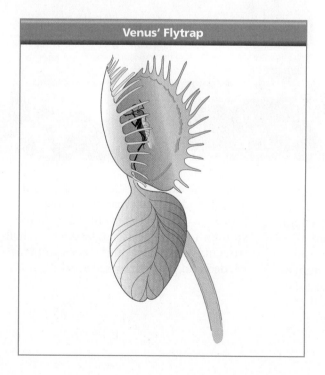

Chapter 8
Plants

The *Passiflora* plant produces delicate, highly scented flowers. ▶

248 ◆

Objectives

During this project, students will produce an interactive exhibit describing how a specific product is derived from plants. Students will choose a single item, find its plant origin, and build an exhibit to present or explain the production or manufacturing processes surrounding the chosen product. After this Chapter Project, students will be able to

- identify materials and other products made from plants
- describe, and if feasible model, the production process from plant to finished item
- create an interactive exhibit
- adjust or redesign the exhibit based on initial feedback

Skills Focus

Observing, making models, communicating

Project Time Line 3 to 4 weeks

All in One Teaching Resources, Unit 2

- Chapter Project Teacher Notes
- Chapter Project Overview
- Chapter Project Worksheet 1
- Chapter Project Worksheet 2
- Chapter Project Scoring Rubric

Developing a Plan

During the first week, students select a food-, clothing-, shelter-, or industry-related item, and begin researching where the plant needed to produce the item is grown and harvested. During the second week, students can research the processes used to turn the plant into the final product. In week three, students concentrate on designing an interactive exhibit to illustrate the plant growth and product manufacturing processes. Students show initial exhibit to young children and solicit feedback. Finally, students revise their interactive exhibit as needed and present revised exhibit to class.

Chapter **Project**

Design and Build an Interactive Exhibit

Cotton, medicines, and paper are just some of the products that come from plants. Which plants are the sources of these products, and how are the products made? In this project, you will build an exhibit to teach young children how a plant becomes a useful product.

Your Goal To build an interactive exhibit showing how a particular plant is transformed into a useful product

To complete this project successfully, you must

● choose one plant product and research where it comes from

● design an interactive exhibit that shows how the product is made

● build your exhibit and ask some children to critique it

● use the children's feedback to redesign your exhibit

● follow the safety guidelines in Appendix A

Plan It! Think of a creative way to teach children about the plant product you chose. Then sketch out your exhibit design and obtain your teacher's approval to build it. Also, identify a few children who can provide you with useful feedback.

Chapter 8 ◆ 249

Seed Plants

Show the Video Preview to introduce the Chapter Project and overview the chapter content. Discussion question: **Why do seeds have a better chance of survival if they are dispersed over a wide area?** (*Because they will have a better chance of landing in an environment where conditions are favorable for germination*)

Performance Assessment

The Chapter Project Scoring Rubric will help you evaluate how well students complete the Chapter Project. You may want to share the scoring rubric with your students so they know what will be expected of them. Students will be assessed on

● thoroughness of research of the plant cultivation, harvest, and processing as plant is made into final product

● completeness of interactive exhibit, inclusion of major harvesting and processing steps

● revision or redesign of exhibit to accommodate initial feedback

Portfolio

Possible Materials

● To begin research, students will need access to reference books, encyclopedias, and, if feasible, the Internet.

● Students will need art supplies to prepare their interactive exhibits. Access to a computer would be helpful if students wish to develop a virtual interactive exhibit.

Launching the Project

With the class, make a list of products that come from plants. Have students identify the plant that each product comes from.

Indicate to students they may choose one of these products for their chapter project, or research a product of their own choosing. If a number of students are interested in the same product, allow them to work together to design and present the exhibit.

249

Objectives

After this lesson, students will be able to

8.1.1 Identify the characteristics that all plants share.

8.1.2 Name the things that a plant needs to live successfully on land.

8.1.3 Compare nonvascular and vascular plants.

8.1.4 Describe the stages of a plant's life cycle.

Target Reading Skill

Building Vocabulary Explain that knowing the definitions of Key Terms helps students understand what they read.

Answers

Students' definitions will vary. Check to see that definitions are appropriate or call on volunteers to share their definitions.

Preteach

Build Background Knowledge   L2

How are Plants Different From Animals?

Present students with a potted plant and ask them to identify at least two ways in which the plant is different from an animal.
(*Sample answers: Plants cannot make noise; a plant does not move around.*)

Section 1

The Plant Kingdom

Reading Preview

Key Concepts

- What characteristics do all plants share?
- What do plants need to live successfully on land?
- How do nonvascular plants and vascular plants differ?
- What are the different stages of a plant's life cycle?

Key Terms

- cuticle
- vascular tissue
- zygote
- nonvascular plant
- vascular plant
- sporophyte
- gametophyte

Target Reading Skill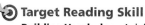

Building Vocabulary A definition states the meaning of a word or phrase by telling about its most important feature or function. After you read the section, reread the paragraphs that contain definitions of Key Terms. Use all the information you have learned to write a definition of each Key Term in your own words.

Lab zone Discover **Activity**

What Do Leaves Reveal About Plants?

1. Your teacher will give you two leaves from plants that grow in two very different environments: a desert and an area with average rainfall.
2. Carefully observe the color, size, shape, and texture of the leaves. Touch the surfaces of each leaf. Examine each leaf with a hand lens. Record your observations in your notebook.
3. When you have finished, wash your hands thoroughly with soap and water.

Think It Over

Inferring Use your observations to determine which plant lives in the desert and which does not. Explain.

There are some very strange plants in the world. There are plants that trap animals, plants that bloom only once every thirty years, and plants with flowers that smell like rotting meat. You probably don't see such unusual plants every day. But you probably do see plants every day. You encounter plants whenever you see moss on a tree trunk, run across a lawn, or pick ripe tomatoes from a garden. And all plants, both the unfamiliar and the familiar, have a lot in common.

What Is a Plant?

Members of the plant kingdom share several characteristics. **Nearly all plants are autotrophs, organisms that produce their own food. All plants are eukaryotes that contain many cells. In addition, all plant cells are surrounded by cell walls.**

Plants are autotrophs. You can think of a plant as a sun-powered, food-making factory. Sunlight provides the energy for this food-making process, photosynthesis.

You don't need a microscope to see plants because they are multicellular. Like many other multicellular organisms, plant cells are organized into tissues. Recall that tissues are groups of similar cells that perform a specific function. Plants vary greatly in size. Both the tiniest moss and the tallest redwood tree are plants.

Lab zone Discover **Activity**

Skills Focus Inferring   L1

Materials hand lens, leaf from plant with thick, fleshy leaves, such as a jade, yucca, or aloe plant; leaf of a temperate climate plant, such as a maple, oak, or common garden plant

Time 10 minutes

Tips Select leaves that display adaptations easily associated with protection from bright sun and dry weather. Both leaves should be green.

Expected Outcome Students should observe a difference in leaf thickness, texture, and size.

Think It Over Students should infer that the plant with the small, thick, fleshy leaf lives in the desert or other hot, sunny climate, and that the plant with the larger, thinner, flatter leaf lives in an area of sufficient rainfall. Students will probably say that the thick leaf looks as if it has water in it.

▼ Plant cells

Go Online
active art

For: Plant Cell Structures activity
Visit: PHSchool.com
Web Code: cep-1041

If you were to look at a plant's cells under a microscope, you would see that plants are eukaryotes. But unlike the cells of some other eukaryotes, a plant's cells are enclosed by a cell wall. Within a cell are chloroplasts and a vacuole, which is a large storage sac for water, wastes, food, and other substances.

Adaptations for Living on Land

Most plants live on land. How is living on land different from living in water? Imagine multicellular green algae floating in the ocean. The algae obtain water and other materials directly from the water around them. The water holds their bodies up toward sunlight. When algae reproduce, sperm cells can swim to egg cells.

Now imagine plants living on land. What adaptations must they have to meet their needs without water all around them? **For plants to survive on land, they must have ways to obtain water and other nutrients from their surroundings, retain water, transport materials in their bodies, support their bodies, and reproduce.**

Obtaining Water and Other Nutrients

Recall that all organisms need water to survive. Obtaining water is easy for algae because water surrounds them. To live on land, though, plants need adaptations for obtaining water from the soil. Plants must also have ways of obtaining other nutrients from the soil.

Chloroplast
Nucleus
Cell wall
Vacuole
Cell membrane
▲ Single plant cell

FIGURE 1
Plant Cell Structures
Like all plants, this maple tree is multicellular. Plants have eukaryotic cells that are enclosed by a cell wall. **Relating Diagrams and Photos** *Which cell structures can you see in the inset photograph of plant cells?*

Reading Checkpoint Why is obtaining water easy for algae?

Chapter 8 ◆ 251

Instruct

What Is a Plant?

Teach Key Concepts   L2
Autotrophs

Focus Ask students to explain why plants do not need to obtain food from other organisms.

Teach Point out that autotrophs convert energy from sunlight into the chemical energy of the food they make, which the plants use to live. Ask: **In what plant structures is food made?** *(Chloroplasts)*

Apply Ask: **Are animals autotrophs? How do you know?** *(No, they eat plants or other animals.)* **learning modality: verbal**

All in One Teaching Resources, Unit 2
• Transparency LS71

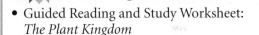

Go Online
active art

For: Plant Cell Structures activity
Visit: PHSchool.com
Web Code: cep-1041

Students investigate the structure of a plant cell.

Independent Practice   L2

All in One Teaching Resources, Unit 2
• Guided Reading and Study Worksheet:
  The Plant Kingdom

⊙ **Student Edition on Audio CD**

Adaptations for Living on Land

Teach Key Concepts   L2
Plants Need Water

Focus Remind students that, like all other organisms, plants need water to survive.

Teach Ask: **How is life on land challenging for plants?** *(Land plants aren't surrounded by water as algae are, and need a way to get water from the soil and transport it throughout its body.)*

Apply Ask: **What plant adaptation helps reduce water loss?** *(Cuticle)* **What plant adaptation transports water, minerals, and food throughout the plant?** *(Vascular tissue)* **learning modality: logical/mathematical**

Monitor Progress   L2

Answers
Figure 1 Cell walls and chloroplasts

Reading Checkpoint They are surrounded by water.

Transporting Materials

Materials clear container, blue food coloring, white carnation

Time 10 minutes for setup and observation, 24 hours waiting time

Focus Tell students that this demonstration will help them see a plant's vascular system at work.

Teach Fill the vase with water and add 10 drops of the food coloring. Trim the carnation stem and place the carnation in the vase. The next day, ask: **What changes have occurred in the carnation?** *(The carnation now has blue streaks on the leaves.)* Allow students to observe the carnation. Ask: **What do you notice about the flower's petals?** *(There are thin streaks of color in the white petals.)*

Apply Ask: **How did the coloring reach the flower?** *(The blue water must have moved up the stem of the flower, through the vascular system.)* **learning modality: visual**

Help Students Read L1

Active Comprehension Have students read the first paragraph of *Transporting Materials*. Then ask: **What would you like to know about the kinds of things plants need to transport water?** *(Sample: How do they get water? Why can they stand upright?)* Write student responses on the board and have students read the remainder of the selection. After students are finished reading, ask them to respond to each question on the board.

Math Analyzing Data

Math Skill Interpreting graphs

Focus Tell students that a line graph shows how two variables are related.

Teach Ask: **What is this graph showing?** *(The amount of water loss in a plant at different times of the day)* **How can you tell how much water the plant lost at 6 P.M.?** *(Find 6 P.M. on the horizontal axis. Follow the vertical line extending up from the 6 P.M. mark until it hits the graph line. Read across to the vertical axis value—210 g.)* Point out that the water loss is measured in grams.

Water and minerals

Food

252 ◆

Ask: **Why is water loss measured in grams rather than milliliters?** *(It is easier to measure the mass of a plant than the volume of water lost from a plant every hour. The mass of the plant is measured every hour; then the mass is subtracted from the measurement made an hour before.)*

Retaining Water Plants must have ways of holding onto the water they obtain. Otherwise, they could easily dry out due to evaporation. When there is more water in plant cells than in the air, the water leaves the plant and enters the air. One adaptation that helps a plant reduce water loss is a waxy, waterproof layer called the **cuticle** that covers the leaves of most plants.

Transporting Materials A plant needs to transport water, minerals, food, and other materials from one part of its body to another. In general, water and minerals are taken up by the bottom part of the plant, while food is made in the top part. But all of the plant's cells need water, minerals, and food.

In small plants, materials can simply move from one cell to the next. But larger plants need a more efficient way to transport materials farther, from one part of the plant to another. These plants have transport tissue called vascular tissue. **Vascular tissue** is a system of tubelike structures inside a plant through which water, minerals, and food move.

Support A plant on land must support its own body. It's easier for small, low-growing plants to support themselves. But for larger plants to survive, the plant's food-making parts must be exposed to as much sunlight as possible. Rigid cell walls and vascular tissue strengthen and support the large bodies of these plants.

Reproduction All plants undergo sexual reproduction that involves fertilization, the joining of a sperm cell with an egg cell. The fertilized egg is called a **zygote.** For algae and some plants, fertilization can only occur if there is water in the environment. This is because the sperm cells of these plants swim through the water to the egg cells. Other plants, however, have an adaptation that makes it possible for fertilization to occur in dry environments.

Reading Checkpoint Why do plants need adaptations to prevent water loss?

FIGURE 2
Transport and Support
For this tall coconut palm to survive, it must transport water, minerals, and food over long distances. It must also support its body so its leaves are exposed to sunlight.

Answers
1. Horizontal axis—time of day; vertical axis—water loss
2. Most—midday; least—in the evening.
3. The plant seemed to lose the most water during the sunniest or warmest parts of the day.
4. The line graph would descend during the night and then rise again in the morning hours, because the water loss is less during the night when there is no sun.

Water Loss in Plants

The graph shows how much water a certain plant loses during the hours shown.

1. **Reading Graphs** What variable is plotted along each axis?

2. **Interpreting Data** According to the graph, during what part of the day did the plant lose the most water? The least water?

3. **Drawing Conclusions** What could account for the pattern of water loss shown?

4. **Predicting** How would you expect the graph to look from 10 P.M. to 8 A.M.? Explain your reasoning.

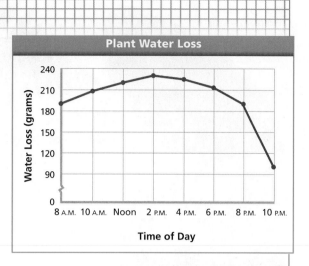

Plant Water Loss

(Graph: x-axis "Time of Day" from 8 A.M. to 10 P.M.; y-axis "Water Loss (grams)" from 0 to 240)

Classifying Plants

Hundreds of thousands of plant species exist in the world today. **Scientists informally group plants into two major groups—nonvascular plants and vascular plants.**

Nonvascular Plants Plants that lack a well-developed system of tubes for transporting water and other materials are known as **nonvascular plants.** Nonvascular plants are low-growing and do not have roots for absorbing water from the ground. Instead, they obtain water and materials directly from their surroundings. The materials then simply pass from cell to cell. This means that materials do not travel very far or very quickly. This slow method of transport helps explain why most nonvascular plants live in damp, shady places.

Most nonvascular plants have only thin cell walls to provide support. This is one reason why these plants cannot grow more than a few centimeters tall.

Vascular Plants Plants with true vascular tissue are called **vascular plants.** Vascular plants are better suited to life in dry areas than are nonvascular plants. Their well-developed vascular tissue solves the problem of transport, moving materials quickly and efficiently throughout the plant's body.

Vascular tissue also provides strength, stability, and support to a plant. Thus, vascular plants are able to grow quite tall.

Chapter 8 ◆ 253

Classifying Plants

Teach Key Concepts L2
Vascular and Nonvascular Plants

Focus Point out to students that scientists classify plants so that they are easier to study.

Teach Ask: **What are the two major groups of plants?** (*Vascular and nonvascular*) **Why are nonvascular plants short and low to the ground?** (*They have no tissue to provide support or to transport materials.*) **Why do nonvascular plants live in damp, shady places?** (*Materials must pass directly from the environment into cells, and then from one cell to the next.*)

Apply Ask: **Why can vascular plants survive in a greater variety of environments than nonvascular plants?** (*Because vascular plants have a system to transport materials to every part of the plant, they can live in dry as well as damp environments.*)

Lab zone Build Inquiry L2

Local Plant Diversity

Focus Ask students how many different kinds of plants they think they could find around the school in 15 minutes.

Teach Take students on a walk around the school and have them record a description of as many different plant species they can find in 15 minutes. Each description should include where the plant was found, the plant's estimated size, any distinguishing characteristics, and a quick sketch of the plant. Allow students to work in pairs. One student can sketch while the partner records the description.

Apply Have students use their descriptions and the information in this section to classify the plants they recorded. **learning modality: visual**

Monitor Progress _____ L2

Answer

 Reading Checkpoint They need water to survive; they could easily dry up.

L2

Algae and Plants

Materials microscope, samples of green algae, plant leaves, glass slides, tweezers, water, cover slips, dropper

Time 30 minutes

Focus Have students observe the algae and plant leaves without magnification. Ask: **How are the algae and plant leaves alike?** (*Both are green.*)

Teach Caution students that glass slides and cover slips are fragile. Have students place a drop of water containing the algae on a glass slide and cover it with a cover slip. Students should look at the algae slide and plant cross section under the microscope. Have students draw what they see and ask them to compare the cells in each. Ask: **What evidence did you see to support the idea that plants are descended from green algae?** (*Sample answer: Both types of cells contain chlorophyll.*) Encourage students to speculate on how scientists determined that the chlorophyll in the algae and the leaf was the same. (*Sample: They performed chemical tests to find the chemical structure.*) **learning modality: visual**

Complex Life Cycles

Teach Key Concepts
L2
Sporophyte and Gametophyte

Focus Have students study Figure 4 and note that the plant life cycle alternates between two phases.

Teach Have students follow the diagram as you explain what is happening at each stage.

Apply Ask: **Which stage involves sexual reproduction? How can you tell?** (*The gametophyte stage; because the plant produces sperm cells and egg cells that join to become a zygote*) **learning modality: logical/ mathematical**

All in One Teaching Resources, Unit 2
• Transparency LS72

Rock containing two plant fossils ▶

FIGURE 3
Ancient and Modern Plants
Fossils of ancient plants help scientists understand the origin of plants. These fossils are of two plants that lived about 300 million years ago. Notice the similarities between the fossils and modern-day horsetails (above) and ferns (top right).

Origin of Plants Which organisms were the ancestors of today's plants? In search of answers, biologists studied fossils, the traces of ancient life forms preserved in rock and other substances. The oldest plant fossils are about 400 million years old. The fossils show that even at that early date, plants already had many adaptations for life on land, including vascular tissue.

Better clues to the origin of plants came from comparing the chemicals in modern plants to those in other organisms. In particular, biologists studied the green pigment chlorophyll, found in the chloroplasts of plants, algae, and some bacteria. Land plants and green algae contain the same forms of chlorophyll. This evidence led biologists to infer that ancient green algae were the ancestors of today's land plants. Further comparisons of genetic material clearly showed that plants and green algae are very closely related. In fact, some scientists think that green algae should be classified in the plant kingdom.

 Reading Checkpoint What are the most likely ancestors of today's plants?

Complex Life Cycles

Plants have complex life cycles that include two different stages, the sporophyte stage and the gametophyte stage. In the **sporophyte** (SPOH ruh fyt) stage, the plant produces spores, tiny cells that can grow into new organisms. A spore develops into the plant's other stage, called the gametophyte. In the **gametophyte** (guh MEE tuh fyt) stage, the plant produces two kinds of sex cells: sperm cells and egg cells.

Figure 4 shows a typical plant life cycle. A sperm cell and egg cell join to form a zygote. The zygote then develops into a sporophyte. The sporophyte produces spores, which develop into the gametophyte. Then the gametophyte produces sperm cells and egg cells, and the cycle starts again. The sporophyte of a plant usually looks quite different from the gametophyte.

 Reading Checkpoint During which stage does a plant produce spores?

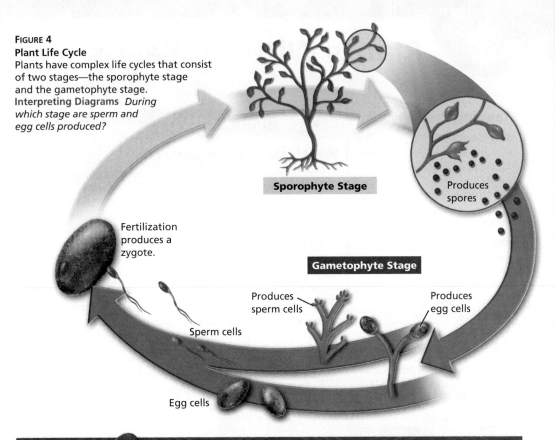

FIGURE 4
Plant Life Cycle
Plants have complex life cycles that consist of two stages—the sporophyte stage and the gametophyte stage.
Interpreting Diagrams *During which stage are sperm and egg cells produced?*

Sporophyte Stage

Produces spores

Gametophyte Stage

Fertilization produces a zygote.

Produces sperm cells

Produces egg cells

Sperm cells

Egg cells

Section 1 Assessment

Target Reading Skill Building Vocabulary
Use your sentences to help you answer the questions below.

Reviewing Key Concepts

1. **a. Listing** List three characteristics of plants.
   b. Comparing and Contrasting Describe three ways that plant cells differ from the cells of some other eukaryotes.
   c. Predicting How might a plant cell be affected if it lacked chloroplasts?
2. **a. Identifying** What are five adaptations that plants need to survive on land?
   b. Inferring Why is a cuticle a useful adaptation in plants but not in algae?
3. **a. Reviewing** How do vascular plants differ from nonvascular plants?

   b. Explaining Explain why vascular plants are better suited to life in dry areas.
   c. Classifying Would you expect a tall desert plant to be a vascular plant? Explain.
4. **a. Describing** What are the two major stages of a plant's life cycle?
   b. Sequencing Describe in order the major events in the life cycle of a plant, starting with a zygote.

Writing in Science

Video Script You are narrating a video called *Living on Land*, which is written from the perspective of a plant. Write a one-page script for your narration. Be sure to discuss the challenges that life on land poses for plants and how they meet their needs.

Chapter 8 ◆ 255

Objectives

After this lesson, students will be able to

8.2.1 Name some nonvascular plants and list the characteristics they share.

8.2.2 Name some seedless vascular plants and list the characteristics they share.

Target Reading Skill

Identifying Main Ideas Explain that identifying main ideas and details helps students sort the facts from the information into groups. Each group can have a main topic, subtopics, and details.

Answers

Details include: Mosses, liverworts, and hornworts

All in One **Teaching Resources, Unit 2**

• Transparency LS73

Preteach

Build Background Knowledge   L2

Moss Descriptions

Ask students to describe any mosses with which they are familiar. (*Some may know about peat moss, sphagnum moss, or have seen moss growing on rocks or in wooded areas. Most students will describe them as green, spongy, soft, and moist.*) Explain to students that not everything people identify as mosses are actually classified as mosses. Point out that in this section students will learn the characteristics of mosses.

Reading Preview

Key Concept

• What characteristics do the three groups of nonvascular plants share?

• What characteristics do the three groups of seedless vascular plants share?

Key Terms

• rhizoid

• frond

Target Reading Skill

Identifying Main Ideas As you read this section, write the main idea—the biggest or most important idea—in a graphic organizer like the one below. Then write three supporting details that give examples of the main idea.

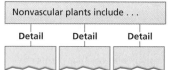

Main Idea

| Nonvascular plants include . . . |

| Detail | Detail | Detail |

Lab zone Discover Activity

Will Mosses Absorb Water?

1. Place 20 mL of sand into a plastic graduated cylinder. Place 20 mL of peat moss into a second plastic graduated cylinder.

2. Predict what would happen if you were to pour 10 mL of water slowly into each graduated cylinder and then wait five minutes.

3. To test your prediction, add 10 mL of water slowly to the sand. Then add 10 mL of water to the moss. After five minutes, record your observations.

Think It Over

Predicting How did your prediction compare with your results? What did you learn about moss from this investigation?

Imagine you are hiking in the forest. You see many ferns along the trail. You walk a little farther and stop to rest near a stream. Here, you see mosses everywhere—on the forest floor, on rocks, and along the banks of the stream. Although ferns and mosses look very different, they have something in common. They reproduce without forming seeds.

Nonvascular Plants

Mosses are a type of seedless plant that have no vascular tissue. **There are three major groups of nonvascular plants: mosses, liverworts, and hornworts. These low-growing plants live in moist areas where they can absorb water and other nutrients directly from their environment.** The watery surroundings also enable sperm cells to swim to egg cells.

Lab zone Discover Activity

Skills Focus Predicting   L1

Materials 3 plastic graduated cylinders, dropper, 20 mL peat moss, 20 mL sand, stopwatch, water

Time 15 minutes

Tips Suggest that students use a dropper to slowly add water to the sand and the peat moss. The peat moss absorbs water more readily if it is already damp.

Expected Outcome Students should find that the peat moss absorbs much more water than the sand.

Think It Over Some students will predict that the peat moss will absorb more water, others will predict that the sand will absorb more water. Students should observe that peat moss absorbs water well, and better than sand does.

Mosses With more than 10,000 species, mosses are the most diverse group of nonvascular plants. You have probably seen mosses growing in sidewalk cracks, on tree trunks, and in other damp, shady spots.

Figure 5 shows the structure of a moss plant. The familiar green, fuzzy moss is the gametophyte generation of the plant. Structures that look like tiny leaves grow off a small, stemlike structure. Thin, rootlike structures called **rhizoids** anchor the moss and absorb water and nutrients from the soil. The sporophyte generation grows out of the gametophyte. It consists of a slender stalk with a capsule at the end. The capsule contains spores.

Liverworts There are more than 8,000 species of liverworts. Liverworts are often found growing as a thick crust on moist rocks or soil along the sides of a stream. This group of plants is named for the shape of the plant's leaflike gametophyte, which looks somewhat like a human liver. *Wort* is an old English word for "plant." Liverworts have sporophytes that are too small to see.

Hornworts There are fewer than 100 species of hornworts. Unlike mosses or liverworts, hornworts are seldom found on rocks or tree trunks. Instead, hornworts usually live in moist soil, often mixed in with grass plants. Hornworts are named for the slender, curved structures that grow out of the gametophytes. These hornlike structures are the sporophytes.

Reading Checkpoint What does a hornwort sporophyte look like?

Go Online
SCi LINKS NSTA

For: Links on nonvascular plants
Visit: www.SciLinks.org
Web Code: scn-0143

FIGURE 5 A Moss Plant
A moss gametophyte has stemlike, leaflike, and rootlike structures.
Interpreting Diagrams *What structures anchor the gametophyte?*

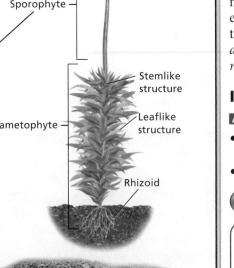

Capsule

Stalk

Sporophyte

Stemlike structure

Leaflike structure

Gametophyte

Rhizoid

Moss plants growing on rock ▶

◆ 257

Instruct

Nonvascular Plants

Teach Key Concepts L2

A Typical Nonvascular Plant

Focus Prompt students to name the three types of nonvascular plants, and to say which type is the most common. (*Mosses*)

Teach Show students samples of mosses or refer them to the photographs and diagram in the text. Ask: **Which parts of the plant look like roots?** (*The rhizoids*) **Which parts look like true stems and leaves?** (*The green stemlike and leaflike structures*) **Why don't scientists call these moss parts roots, stems, and leaves?** (*Because they do not have transport tissue, as true roots, stems, and leaves do.*) **How are mosses and other nonvascular plants limited by their lack of vascular tissue?** (*They do not grow very tall because they cannot transport water as far and as fast as is needed for a tall plant to survive.*)

Apply Prompt students to explain how a nonvascular structure is related to the environments where these plants typically thrive. (*The plants tend to thrive in moist areas that provide the water that the plants need.*) **learning modality: verbal**

Independent Practice L2

All in One Teaching Resources, Unit 2

• Guided Reading and Study Worksheet: *Plants Without Seeds*
• Transparency LS74

⊙ Student Edition on Audio CD

Go Online
SCi LINKS NSTA

For: Links on nonvascular plants
Visit: www.SciLinks.org
Web Code: scn-0143

Download a worksheet that will guide students' review of Internet resources on nonvascular plants.

Monitor Progress _____ L2

Writing Have students write one or two sentences to describe the function of rhizoids.

Answers
Figure 5 The rhizoids

Reading Checkpoint Like little horns

Differentiated Instruction

Special Needs L1
Moss Structure Students who are visually impaired might benefit by exploring the sporophyte and gametophyte of mosses by feeling a moss plant. Pair these students with sighted students, who can describe each part of the moss as visually impaired students feel it. **learning modality: logical/mathematical**

Seedless Vascular Plants

Teach Key Concepts [L2]

Vascular Tissue

Focus Have students study the plants in the illustration on this page. Ask: **How do these plants differ from mosses?** *(They are taller than mosses.)*

Teach Discuss with students how these plants differ from most larger plants today: They reproduce by spores, not seeds. Ask: **How are these plants similar to most larger plants today?** *(They have vascular tissue.)* **What structures give these seedless plants strength and stability?** *(Vascular tissue)* **Why is moisture important for reproduction in seedless vascular plants?** *(Sperm must swim through water to the eggs.)*

Apply Ask: **Why do you think seedless vascular plants are not as common today as in the past?** *(The environment is drier in most places than in the past.)* **learning modality: visual**

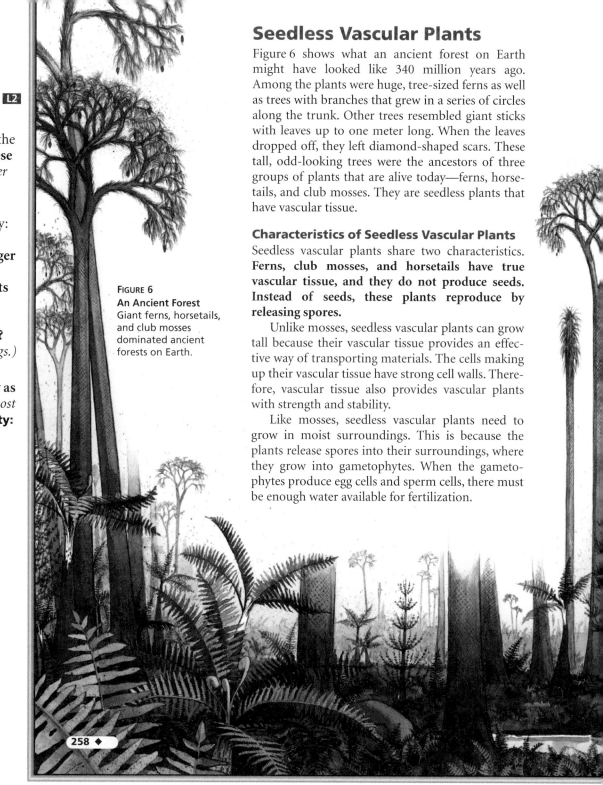

FIGURE 6
An Ancient Forest
Giant ferns, horsetails, and club mosses dominated ancient forests on Earth.

258 ◆

Seedless Vascular Plants

Figure 6 shows what an ancient forest on Earth might have looked like 340 million years ago. Among the plants were huge, tree-sized ferns as well as trees with branches that grew in a series of circles along the trunk. Other trees resembled giant sticks with leaves up to one meter long. When the leaves dropped off, they left diamond-shaped scars. These tall, odd-looking trees were the ancestors of three groups of plants that are alive today—ferns, horsetails, and club mosses. They are seedless plants that have vascular tissue.

Characteristics of Seedless Vascular Plants

Seedless vascular plants share two characteristics. **Ferns, club mosses, and horsetails have true vascular tissue, and they do not produce seeds. Instead of seeds, these plants reproduce by releasing spores.**

Unlike mosses, seedless vascular plants can grow tall because their vascular tissue provides an effective way of transporting materials. The cells making up their vascular tissue have strong cell walls. Therefore, vascular tissue also provides vascular plants with strength and stability.

Like mosses, seedless vascular plants need to grow in moist surroundings. This is because the plants release spores into their surroundings, where they grow into gametophytes. When the gametophytes produce egg cells and sperm cells, there must be enough water available for fertilization.

Differentiated Instruction

Special Needs Students [L1]
Vascular Tissue Students who are visually impaired or need extra help may benefit by exploring a celery stalk's vascular tissue. Ask: **What do you feel on the outside of the celery stalk?** *(Narrow ridges)* Explain that these ridges are bundles of vascular tissue. Have students hold the base of a celery stalk in one hand and apply pressure to the top of the stalks with the other. Ask: **Why couldn't you crush or push together the celery stalk?** *(The vascular tissue is strong enough to resist the force of a hand pressing on it.)* **learning modality: kinesthetic**

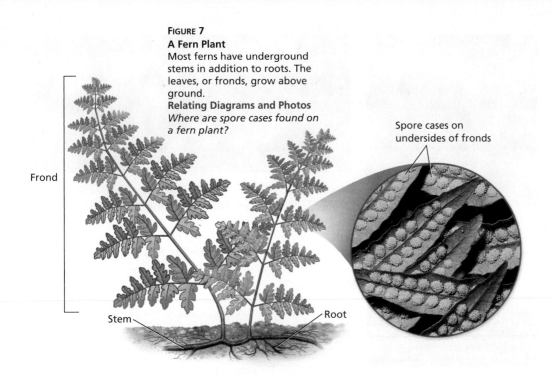

FIGURE 7
A Fern Plant
Most ferns have underground stems in addition to roots. The leaves, or fronds, grow above ground.
Relating Diagrams and Photos *Where are spore cases found on a fern plant?*

Frond

Spore cases on undersides of fronds

Stem

Root

Ferns There are more than 12,000 species of ferns alive today. Like other vascular plants, ferns have true stems, roots, and leaves. The stems of most ferns are underground. Leaves grow upward from the top side of the stems, while roots grow downward from the bottom of the stems. The roots anchor the fern to the ground and absorb water and nutrients from the soil. These substances enter the root's vascular tissue and travel through the tissue into the stems and leaves.

Figure 7 shows a fern's structure. Notice that the fern's leaves, or **fronds,** are divided into many smaller parts that look like small leaves. The upper surface of each frond is coated with a cuticle that helps the plant retain water.

The familiar fern, with its visible fronds, is the sporophyte stage of the plant. On the underside of mature fronds, spores develop in tiny spore cases. Wind and water can carry the spores great distances. If a spore lands in moist, shaded soil, it develops into a gametophyte. Fern gametophytes are tiny plants that grow low to the ground.

 Reading Checkpoint How are seedless vascular plants like mosses?

Lab zone Try This **Activity**

Examining a Fern
1. Your teacher will give you a fern plant to observe.
2. Draw a diagram of the plant and label the structures that you see.
3. Use a hand lens to observe the top and lower surfaces of the leaf. Run a finger over both surfaces.
4. With a plastic dropper, add a few drops of water to the top surface of the leaf. Note what happens.

Inferring Use your observations to explain how ferns are adapted to life on land.

Use Visuals: Figure 7 L2
Fern Structure and Reproduction

Focus Remind students that vascular plants have true stems, roots, and leaves. Ferns are the most common vascular plants that reproduce with spores instead of seeds.

Teach Have students study the parts of the fern shown in Figure 7. Point out the underground stem. Ask: **How does this stem differ from most stems you are familiar with?** (*It is underground.*) **Which part of the fern is its leaf?** (*The frond*) Tell students that the upper surface of the frond is covered by a waxlike coating called the cuticle. Ask: **What advantage is the cuticle to the plant?** (*It helps prevent water loss from the plant.*) Point out the spores on the under surface of the fronds. Ask: **What stage is the fern plant shown in the picture?** (*The sporophyte*)
learning modality: visual

All in One **Teaching Resources, Unit 2**
• Transparency LS75

Lab zone Try This **Activity**

Skills Focus Inferring L2
Materials fern plant, hand lens, plastic dropper, water
Time 20 minutes
Tips Students should observe the fronds, stems, and roots. They should notice that the upper surface of a frond is smooth and shiny compared to the lower surface. Spore cases may be visible on the underside of the blade. Water dropped onto the upper surface of the frond should run off.

Expected Outcome Students should note that the roots anchor the plant and absorb water. The cuticle on the upper surface reduces water loss.

Extend Students can release spores with a dissecting knife and examine them with a hand lens. **learning modality: visual**

Monitor Progress L2

Skills Check Have students list two functions of vascular tissue. (*Transports food and transports water through the plant's body, provides support*)

Answers
Figure 7 On the undersides of the fronds

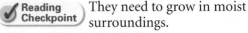 **Reading Checkpoint** They need to grow in moist surroundings.

Assess

Reviewing Key Concepts

1. a. They are low growing and live in moist environments where they can absorb water and nutrients directly from their environment. **b.** Nonvascular plants have no way to transport nutrients throughout a large plant body, so they remain small and low to the ground and live in moist surroundings that can quickly provide them what they need. **c.** They are all nonvascular plants. Moss grows in soil and on rocks and trees. Liverworts live in very moist areas near streams. Hornworts live in moist soil.

2. a. True vascular tissue and the use of spores to reproduce **b.** They differ from mosses because they have vascular tissue; mosses do not. They are similar in that they grow in moist places. **c.** So that the released spores can develop into gametophytes and that sperm can swim to the eggs

Reteach   L1

Use Figure 5 to describe the life cycle of a moss.

Performance Assessment   L2

Skills Check Have students make Venn diagrams to compare and contrast the three types of nonvascular plants.

All in One Teaching Resources, Unit 2

- Section Summary: *Plants Without Seeds*
- Review and Reinforce: *Plants Without Seeds*
- Enrich: *Plants Without Seeds*

Horsetails There are very few species of horsetails on Earth today. As you can see in Figure 8, the stems of horsetails are jointed. Long, coarse, needle-like branches grow in a circle around each joint. Small leaves grow flat against the stem just above each joint. The whorled pattern of growth somewhat resembles the appearance of a horse's tail. The stems contain silica, a gritty substance also found in sand. During colonial times, Americans used the plants to scrub their pots and pans. Another name for horsetails is scouring rushes.

Club Mosses Like ferns, club mosses have true stems, roots, and leaves. They also have a similar life cycle. However, there are only a few hundred species of club mosses alive today.

Do not be confused by the name *club mosses*. Unlike true mosses, club mosses have vascular tissue. The plant, which looks a little like the small branch of a pine tree, is sometimes called ground pine or princess pine. Club mosses usually grow in moist woodlands and near streams.

FIGURE 8
Horsetails and Club Mosses
Horsetails (left) have branches and leaves that grow in a circle around each joint. Club mosses (right) look like tiny pine trees.
Inferring *Which grow taller— true mosses or club mosses?*

Reading Checkpoint **Where do club mosses usually grow?**

Section 2 Assessment

 Target Reading Skill Identifying Main Ideas Use your graphic organizer to help you answer the questions below.

Reviewing Key Concepts

1. a. Describing What two characteristics do mosses, liverworts, and hornworts share?
   b. Relating Cause and Effect How are these two characteristics related?
   c. Comparing and Contrasting In what ways are mosses, liverworts, and hornworts similar? In what ways do they differ?
2. a. Listing What two characteristics do ferns, horsetails, and club mosses share?

b. Comparing and Contrasting In what ways do ferns, horsetails, and club mosses differ from true mosses? In what way are they similar to mosses?
c. Inferring Although ferns have vascular tissue, they still must live in moist, shady environments. Explain why.

Writing in Science

Product Label Create a product label to be attached to pots of fern plants for sale at a garden shop. Describe the structure of ferns and growing instructions. Include other helpful information or diagrams.

Lab zone Chapter Project

Keep Students on Track Students should be completing their research of the processes used to change a plant or plant materials into their chosen item. Inform students that they should be designing their exhibit using an outline, storyboards, or a flowchart to organize their ideas.

Writing in Science

Writing Mode Description
Scoring Rubric
4 Label includes detailed, accurate information about growth requirements; clearly presented
3 Includes all criteria; presentation somewhat unclear
2 Includes basic information; lacks details
1 Includes inaccurate information or is incomplete

Masses of Mosses

Problem

How is a moss plant adapted to carry out its life activities?

Skills Focus

observing, measuring

Materials

- clump of moss
- hand lens
- metric ruler
- toothpicks
- plastic dropper
- water

Procedure

1. Your teacher will give you a clump of moss. Examine the clump from all sides. Draw a diagram of what you see. Measure the size of the overall clump and the main parts of the clump. Record your observations.

2. Using toothpicks, gently separate five individual moss plants from the clump. Be sure to pull them totally apart so that you can observe each plant separately. If the moss plants start to dry out as you are working, moisten them with a few drops of water.

3. Measure the length of the leaflike, stemlike, and rootlike structures on each plant. If brown stalks and capsules are present, measure them. Find the average length of each structure.

4. Make a drawing of a single moss plant. Label the parts, give their sizes, and record the color of each part. When you are finished observing the moss, return it to your teacher. Wash your hands thoroughly.

5. Obtain class averages for the sizes of the structures you measured in Step 3. Also, if the moss that you observed had brown stalks and capsules, share your observations about those structures.

Analyze and Conclude

1. **Observing** Describe the overall appearance of the moss clump, including its color, size, and texture.

2. **Measuring** What was the typical size of the leaflike portion of the moss plants, the typical height of the stemlike portion, and the typical length of the rootlike portion?

3. **Inferring** In which part(s) of the moss does photosynthesis occur? How do you know?

4. **Communicating** Write a paragraph explaining what you learned about mosses from this investigation. Include explanations of why mosses cannot grow tall and why they live in moist environments.

More to Explore

Select a moss plant with stalks and capsules. Use toothpicks to release some of the spores, which can be as small as dust particles. Examine the spores under a microscope. Create a labeled drawing of what you see.

Analyze and Conclude

1. Sample answer: The moss clump is green and small but contains many individual plants, and has a leafy texture.

2. Leaflike: a few millimeters long by a fraction of a millimeter thick; stemlike: up to 15 cm high, usually much shorter; rootlike: very short.

3. In the green parts (leaflike and stemlike); only the green parts can carry out photosynthesis because only the green parts have chlorophyll.

4. Paragraphs should explain that mosses cannot transport water over long distances, so they cannot grow tall and they must live in moist environments.

Extend Inquiry

More to Explore Show students how to gently crush the moss capsules to release the spores. Students can then observe these structures with a microscope.

Masses of Mosses L2

Prepare for Inquiry

Key Concept

Students will observe a moss and describe its structures.

Skills Objectives

After this lab, students will be able to

- make detailed observations of a moss and communicate their observations
- measure the structures of a moss and calculate class averages

⏱ Class Time 45 minutes

Advance Planning

Provide a variety of species of mosses. If possible, obtain some moss clumps with sporophytes present.

Alternate Materials

If you have microscopes available, allow students to use them.

Safety

Students should wash their hands thoroughly after finishing the lab. If students use microscopes, review all relevant safety procedures. Review the safety guidelines in Appendix A.

All in One Teaching Resources, Unit 2

- Lab Worksheet: *Masses of Mosses*

Guide Inquiry

Troubleshooting the Experiment

Moss clumps from nature may contain more than one type. Have a field guide on hand for students to consult.

Expected Outcome

- Students should be able to identify all the parts of the moss plant.
- Measurements will vary, depending on the type of moss.

Objectives

After this lesson, students will be able to

8.3.1 Identify the characteristics that seed plants share.

8.3.2 Explain how seeds become new plants.

8.3.3 Describe the functions of roots, stems, and leaves.

Target Reading Skill

Outlining Explain that using an outline format helps students organize information by main topic, subtopic, and details.

Answer

The Characteristics of Seed Plants
  I. What Is a Seed Plant?
     A. Vascular Tissue
     B. Pollen and Seeds
  II. How Seeds Become New Plants
     A. Seed Structure
     B. Seed Dispersal
     C. Germination
  III. Roots
     A. Types of Roots
     B. The Structure of a Root
  IV. Stems
     A. The Structure of a Stem
     B. Annual Rings
  V. Leaves
     A. The Structure of a Leaf
     B. The Leaf and Photosynthesis
     C. Controlling Water Loss

All in One Teaching Resources, Unit 2

• Transparency LS76

Preteach

Build Background Knowledge L2

Plants With and Without Seeds

Have students generate a list of plants they see everyday. Have them write the name of each plant under one of the following headings: *Has Seeds* or *Does Not Have Seeds*. Tell students that not only are most of the plants they are familiar with seed plants but that seed plants make up the greater number of all plants.

262

Reading Preview

Key Concepts

• What characteristics do seed plants share?

• How do seeds become new plants?

• What are the main functions of roots, stems, and leaves?

Key Terms

• phloem • xylem • pollen
• seed • embryo • cotyledon
• germination • root cap
• cambium • transpiration

Target Reading Skill

Outlining As you read, make an outline about seed plants that you can use for review. Use the red headings for the main ideas and the blue headings for the supporting ideas.

The Characteristics of Seed Plants
I. What is a seed plant?
A. Vascular tissue
B.
II. How seeds become new plants
A.
B.

Lab zone Discover **Activity**

Which Plant Part Is It?

1. With a partner, carefully observe the items of food your teacher gives you.

2. Make a list of the food items.

3. For each food item, write the name of the plant part—root, stem, or leaf—from which you think it is obtained.

Think It Over

Classifying Classify the items into groups depending on the plant part from which the food is obtained. Compare your groupings with those of your classmates.

Have you ever planted seeds in a garden? If so, then you may remember how it seemed to take forever before those first green shoots emerged. Shortly afterwards, you saw one set of leaves, and then others. Then a flower may have appeared. Did you wonder where all those plant parts came from? How did they develop from one small seed? Read on to find out.

What Is a Seed Plant?

The plant growing in your garden was a seed plant. So are most of the other plants around you. In fact, seed plants outnumber seedless plants by more than ten to one. You eat many seed plants—rice, peas, and squash, for example. You wear clothes made from seed plants, such as cotton and flax. You may live in a home built from seed plants—oak, pine, or maple trees. In addition, seed plants produce much of the oxygen you breathe.

Seed plants share two important characteristics. They have vascular tissue, and they use pollen and seeds to reproduce. In addition, all seed plants have body plans that include roots, stems, and leaves. Like seedless plants, seed plants have complex life cycles that include the sporophyte and the gametophyte stages. In seed plants, the plants that you see are the sporophytes. The gametophytes are microscopic.

262 ◆

Lab zone Discover **Activity**

Skills Focus Classifying L1

Materials edible parts of seed plants such as carrots, parsnips, broccoli, cabbage, lettuce, celery, parsley, potato, onion (do not use fruits, the mature ovary of flowers)

Time 10 minutes

Tips Mention that underground plant parts are not necessarily roots. For

example, potatoes and onions are underground stems. Celery is not a true stem, but a leaf stalk.

Expected Outcome Carrots and parsnips are roots, lettuce and cabbage are leaves, and broccoli is a stem.

Think It Over The foods should be classified as roots, stems, or leaves.

Vascular Tissue Most seed plants live on land. Recall that land plants face many challenges, including standing upright and supplying all their cells with food and water. Like ferns, seed plants meet these two challenges with vascular tissue. The thick walls of the cells in the vascular tissue help support the plants. In addition, food, water, and nutrients are transported throughout the plants in vascular tissue.

There are two types of vascular tissue. **Phloem** (FLOH um) is the vascular tissue through which food moves. When food is made in the leaves, it enters the phloem and travels to other parts of the plant. Water and minerals, on the other hand, travel in the vascular tissue called **xylem** (ZY lum). The roots absorb water and minerals from the soil. These materials enter the root's xylem and move upward into the stems and leaves.

Pollen and Seeds Unlike seedless plants, seed plants can live in a wide variety of environments. Recall that seedless plants need water in their surroundings for fertilization to occur. Seed plants do not need water for sperm to swim to the eggs. Instead, seed plants produce **pollen,** tiny structures that contain the cells that will later become sperm cells. Pollen delivers sperm cells directly near the eggs. After sperm cells fertilize the eggs, seeds develop. A **seed** is a structure that contains a young plant inside a protective covering. Seeds protect the young plant from drying out.

 Reading Checkpoint What material travels in phloem? What materials travel in xylem?

FIGURE 9
Harvesting Wild Rice
Like all seed plants, wild rice plants have vascular tissue and use seeds to reproduce. The seeds develop in shallow bodies of water, and the plants grow up above the water's surface. These men are harvesting the mature rice grains.

What Is a Seed Plant?

Teach Key Concepts [L2]
Characteristics of Seed Plants

Focus Remind students that ferns have vascular tissue and reproduce using spores.

Teach Ask: **What two characteristics are common to all seed plants?** (*Vascular tissue and seeds to reproduce*) **Which is different from ferns?** (*Ferns reproduce using spores.*) **What is the body structure of seed plants?** (*Plant bodies include roots, stems, and leaves.*)

Apply Remind students that seed plants evolved after mosses and ferns. Ask: **How did the evolution of seeds allow plants to live in places where mosses and ferns could not?** (*Seeds provide protection for the young plant inside. With seeds, plants can reproduce in drier environments.*) **learning modality: verbal**

Independent Practice [L2]

 **Teaching Resources, Unit 2**

• Guided Reading and Study Worksheet: *The Characteristics of Seed Plants*

◉ Student Edition on Audio CD

Monitor Progress [L2]

Drawing Have students make flowcharts showing the movement of food, water, and nutrients through a vascular plant. (*Phloem—food moves from leaves to stems, roots, and other parts; xylem—water and minerals travel from roots into stems and leaves.*) Students can save their flowcharts in their portfolios.

Answer

Reading Checkpoint Food travels in phloem. Water and minerals travel in xylem.

⌐ Differentiated Instruction

English Learners/Beginning [L1]
Vocabulary: Science Glossary Pair students with English-proficient students. Have them work together to create a glossary that includes the phonetic English pronunciation and the definition for each key term. Students can draw and label their own diagrams of the structures. **learning modality: verbal**

English Learners/Intermediate [L1]
Vocabulary: Science Glossary Have students do the *Beginning* activity, and then write a sentence that uses each of these words. Call on students to read their sentences aloud to give them an opportunity to practice pronunciation. **learning modality: verbal**

How Seeds Become New Plants

Teach Key Concepts
What's Inside a Seed?

Focus Remind students that unlike seedless plants, seeds do not need water to be capable of surviving.

Teach Explain that one of the main parts of a seed is the seed coat, which keeps the seed from drying out. Ask: **What else is inside a seed?** (*A partially developed plant, or embryo*) **Why does the seed contain stored food?** (*The embryo uses the stored food until it can make its own food.*) **What is germination?** (*The early growth stage of the embryo*) Refer students to Figure 12 and ask them to describe the process of germination. (*The embryo uses its food, the roots grow downward, and the stem and leaves begin to grow upward.*)

Apply Ask: **Why is it an advantage for seeds to be able to remain inactive and not germinate immediately after the embryo forms?** (*This allows for them to be dispersed and to germinate under ideal growing conditions.*) **learning modality: verbal**

Use Visuals: Figure 10
Seed Structure

Focus Have students locate the main parts in each seed.

Teach Ask: **What structures are common to all the seeds?** (*Seed coat, embryo, stored food, cotyledon*) **What plant characteristics can you see in the embryos?** (*The beginnings of roots, stems, and leaves*)

Apply Tell students to note the areas of stored food. Explain that when seeds absorb water, the food-storing tissues swell, which cracks open the seed coat. **learning modality: visual**

All in One Teaching Resources, Unit 2
• Transparency LS77

FIGURE 10
Seed Structure
The structures of three different seeds are shown here. *Inferring* *How is the stored food used?*

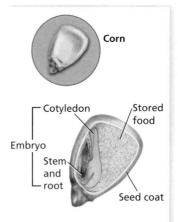
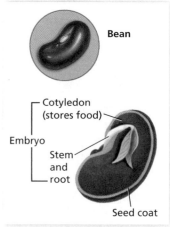
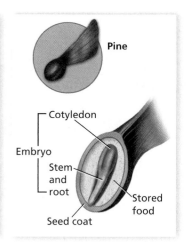

Corn — Cotyledon, Embryo, Stem and root, Stored food, Seed coat

Bean — Cotyledon (stores food), Embryo, Stem and root, Seed coat

Pine — Cotyledon, Embryo, Stem and root, Stored food, Seed coat

Lab zone Try This **Activity**

The In-Seed Story
1. Your teacher will give you a hand lens and two different seeds that have been soaked in water.
2. Carefully observe the outside of each seed. Draw what you see.
3. Gently remove the coverings of the seeds. Then carefully separate the parts of each seed. Use a hand lens to examine the inside of each seed. Draw what you see.

Observing Based on your observations, label the parts of each seed. Then describe the function of each part next to its label.

264 ◆

How Seeds Become New Plants

All seeds share important similarities. **Inside a seed is a partially developed plant. If a seed lands in an area where conditions are favorable, the plant sprouts out of the seed and begins to grow.**

Seed Structure A seed has three main parts—an embryo, stored food, and a seed coat. The young plant that develops from the zygote, or fertilized egg, is called the **embryo.** The embryo already has the beginnings of roots, stems, and leaves. In the seeds of most plants, the embryo stops growing when it is quite small. When the embryo begins to grow again, it uses the food stored in the seed until it can make its own food by photosynthesis. In all seeds, the embryo has one or more seed leaves, or **cotyledons** (kaht uh LEED unz). In some seeds, food is stored in the cotyledons. In others, food is stored outside the embryo. Figure 10 compares the structure of corn, bean, and pine seeds.

The outer covering of a seed is called the seed coat. Some familiar seed coats are the "skins" on lima beans and peanuts. The seed coat acts like plastic wrap, protecting the embryo and its food from drying out. This allows a seed to remain inactive for a long time. In many plants, the seeds are surrounded by a structure called a fruit.

Lab zone Try This **Activity**

Skills Focus Observing

Materials hand lens; dried kidney, lima, or black beans; dried yellow or green peas; shelled peanuts

⚠ **CAUTION:** *Some students have severe reactions to eating peanuts or inhaling peanut dust. Do not use peanuts if any student is allergic to them.*

Time 10 minutes

Tips Before the activity, soak the beans for 2 hours and the peas for 24 hours. Remove peanuts from their shells 3 or 4 days before the activity, and store them in a moist place so the cotyledons will open.

Expected Outcome Students will observe that each of the seeds is composed of two

sections that can easily be separated. They will see the tiny leaves and root (and possibly the miniature stem) of the embryo plant. Sketches should include the seed coat, the cotyledons, and the embryo.

Extend Invite students to repeat the activity with other kinds of seeds.
learning modality: kinesthetic

Seed Dispersal After seeds have formed, they are usually scattered, sometimes far from where they were produced. The scattering of seeds is called seed dispersal. Seeds are dispersed in many ways. One method involves other organisms. For example, some animals eat fruits, such as cherries or grapes. The seeds inside the fruits pass through the animal's digestive system and are deposited in new areas. Other seeds are enclosed in barblike structures that hook onto an animal's fur or a person's clothes. The structures then fall off the fur or clothes in a new area.

A second means of dispersal is water. Water can disperse seeds that fall into oceans and rivers. A third dispersal method involves wind. Wind disperses lightweight seeds that often have structures to catch the wind, such as those of dandelions and maple trees. Finally, some plants eject their seeds in a way that might remind you of popping popcorn. The force scatters the seeds in many directions.

FIGURE 11
Seed Dispersal
The seeds of these plants are enclosed in fruits with adaptations that help them disperse.

Dispersal by wind:
Dandelion fruits
with "parachutes" ▶

◀ Dispersal
by animals:
Barblike fruits

Dispersal by water:
Floating coconut
palm fruit ▶

Chapter 8 ◆ 265

265

Seed Plants

Show the Video Field Trip to help students understand seed dispersal and development. Discussion question: **What are some ways in which seeds can be dispersed?** *(By wind, water, or animal, or by being ejected)*

Roots

Teach Key Concepts L2
Functions of Roots

Focus Point out to students that unlike nonvascular plants, seed plants are vascular plants and they have true roots.

Teach Ask: **What do roots do for a plant?** *(Anchor the plant in soil and absorb water and nutrients)* **What types of roots are there?** *(Some plants have a taproot, a long thick main root reaching down into the soil. Other plants have thin fibrous roots that form a tangled mass and take soil with them when they are pulled.)* **What is the purpose of a root cap?** *(It protects the root from injury.)*

Apply Ask: **Which root type is likely to be more useful in preventing soil erosion?** *(The fibrous root system holds soil between the root fibers so it works better than a tap root in preventing erosion.)* **learning modality: verbal**

All in One Teaching Resources, Unit 2
• Transparency LS78

Seed Plants

Video Preview
▶Video Field Trip
Video Assessment

Germination After a seed is dispersed, it may remain inactive for a while before it germinates. **Germination** (jur muh NAY shun) occurs when the embryo begins to grow again and pushes out of the seed. Germination begins when the seed absorbs water from the environment. Then the embryo uses its stored food to begin to grow. As shown in Figure 12, the embryo's roots first grow downward; then its stem and leaves grow upward. Once you can see a plant's leaves, the plant is called a seedling.

A seed that is dispersed far from its parent plant has a better chance of survival. When a seed does not have to compete with its parent for light, water, and nutrients, it has a better chance of becoming a seedling.

 Reading Checkpoint **What must happen in order for germination to begin?**

Roots

Have you ever tried to pull a dandelion out of the soil? It's not easy, is it? That is because most roots are good anchors. Roots have three main functions. **Roots anchor a plant in the ground, absorb water and minerals from the soil, and sometimes store food.** The more root area a plant has, the more water and minerals it can absorb.

Types of Roots The two main types of root systems are shown in Figure 13. A fibrous root system consists of many similarly sized roots that form a dense, tangled mass. Plants with fibrous roots take much soil with them when you pull them out of the ground. Lawn grass, corn, and onions have fibrous root systems. In contrast, a taproot system has one long, thick main root. Many smaller roots branch off the main root. A plant with a taproot system is hard to pull out of the ground. Carrots, dandelions, and cacti have taproots.

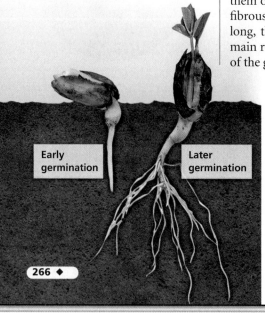

Early germination

Later germination

FIGURE 12
Germination
The embryo in this peanut seed uses its stored food to germinate. First, the embryo's roots grow downward. Then, its stem and leaves begin to grow upward.

266 ◆

The Structure of a Root In Figure 13, you can see the structure of a typical root. Notice that the tip of the root is rounded and is covered by a structure called the root cap. The **root cap** protects the root from injury from rocks as the root grows through the soil. Behind the root cap are the cells that divide to form new root cells.

Root hairs grow out of the root's surface. These tiny hairs can enter the spaces between soil particles, where they absorb water and minerals. By increasing the surface area of the root that touches the soil, root hairs help the plant absorb large amounts of substances. The root hairs also help to anchor the plant in the soil.

Locate the vascular tissue in the center of the root. The water and nutrients that are absorbed from the soil quickly move into the xylem. From there, these substances are transported upward to the plant's stems and leaves.

Phloem transports food manufactured in the leaves to the root. The root tissues may then use the food for growth or store it for future use by the plant.

 **Reading Checkpoint** What is a root cap?

FIGURE 13
Root Structure
Some plants have fibrous roots while others have taproots. A root's structure is adapted for absorbing water and minerals from the soil. **Relating Cause and Effect** *How do root hairs help absorb water and minerals?*

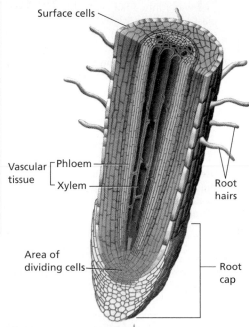

Surface cells

Vascular tissue — Phloem — Xylem

Root hairs

Area of dividing cells

Root cap

Fibrous root system: Onion

Taproot system: Dandelion

 267

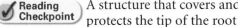

Stems

Help Students Read

Active Comprehension Have students read the first paragraph of *Stems*. Then ask: **What would you like to know about stems?** *(Possible answers: Are the stems of trees and flowers similar? How are substances transported through stems?)* Write student responses on the board and have students read the remainder of the selection. After students are finished reading, ask them to respond to each question.

Teach Key Concepts

The Functions of Stems

Focus Remind students that nonvascular plants grow very close to the ground so that they can obtain the water they need. Indicate that stems are unique to vascular plants.

Teach Ask students to name the functions of stems. *(Stems carry water and nutrients from roots to leaves and food from leaves to roots. Stems support plants and hold leaves so that they are exposed to sunlight. Some stems also store food.)* Point out the structures in Figures 14 and 15. Ask: **How can you distinguish between the two types of stems? What are their names?** *(Woody stems contain wood and are hard and rigid; herbaceous stems are often soft and flexible and do not contain wood.)*

Apply Ask: **What will happen to a tree if a wound encircling the tree cuts through to the inner bark?** *(Because the inner bark is the phloem, the tree will be unable to transport food from leaves to other parts of the tree. It will die.)* **learning modality: verbal**

All in One Teaching Resources, Unit 2
- Transparencies LS79, LS80

Lab zone Skills Activity

Calculating

In this activity, you will calculate the speed at which water moves up a celery stalk.

1. Pour about 1 cm of water into a tall plastic container. Stir in several drops of red food coloring.
2. Place the freshly cut end of a celery stalk in the water. Lean the stalk against the container's side.
3. After 20 minutes, remove the celery. Use a metric ruler to measure the height of the water in the stalk.
4. Use the measurement and the following formula to calculate how fast the water moved up the stalk.

$$\text{Speed} = \frac{\text{Height}}{\text{Time}}$$

Based on your calculation, predict how far the water would move in 2 hours. Then test your prediction.

Stems

The stem of a plant has two main functions. **The stem carries substances between the plant's roots and leaves. The stem also provides support for the plant and holds up the leaves so they are exposed to the sun.** In addition, some stems, such as those of asparagus, store food.

The Structure of a Stem Stems can be either herbaceous (hur BAY shus) or woody. Herbaceous stems contain no wood and are often soft. Coneflowers and pepper plants have herbaceous stems. In contrast, woody stems are hard and rigid. Maple trees and roses have woody stems.

Both herbaceous and woody stems consist of phloem and xylem tissue as well as many other supporting cells. Figure 14 shows the inner structure of one type of herbaceous stem.

As you can see in Figure 15, a woody stem contains several layers of tissue. The outermost layer is bark. Bark includes an outer protective layer and an inner layer of living phloem, which transports food through the stem. Next is a layer of cells called the **cambium** (KAM bee um), which divide to produce new phloem and xylem. It is xylem that makes up most of what you call "wood." Sapwood is active xylem that transports water and minerals through the stem. The older, darker, heartwood is inactive but provides support.

Reading Checkpoint What function does the bark of a woody stem perform?

FIGURE 14
A Herbaceous Stem
Herbaceous stems, like those on these coneflowers, are often soft. The inset shows the inner structure of one type of herbaceous stem.

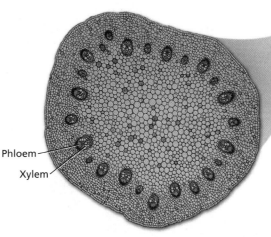

Phloem
Xylem

Lab zone Skills Activity

Skills Focus Calculating

Materials calculator, celery stalk, clock or stopwatch, dropper, food coloring, lab apron, plastic container (tall and narrow), spoon, water

Time 35 minutes (20 wait time); 2 hours wait time to test prediction

Tips Make sure students wear lab aprons. Choose stalks 15–30 cm long. Before the activity, cut the end of each stalk, and peel a thin layer off the back of each.

Expected Outcome The water moves about 1.5 mm/min (30 mm ÷ 20 min). After 2 hours, it should rise 180 mm (120 min × 1.5 mm/min).

Extend Have students repeat the activity with another plant, such as a green onion or a leek. **learning modality: logical/mathematical**

Annual Rings Have you ever looked at a tree stump and seen a pattern of circles that looks something like a target? These circles are called annual rings because they represent a tree's yearly growth. Annual rings are made of xylem. Xylem cells that form in the spring are large and have thin walls because they grow rapidly. They produce a wide, light brown ring. Xylem cells that form in the summer grow slowly and, therefore, are small and have thick walls. They produce a thin, dark ring. One pair of light and dark rings represents one year's growth. You can estimate a tree's age by counting its annual rings.

The width of a tree's annual rings can provide important clues about past weather conditions, such as rainfall. In rainy years, more xylem is produced, so the tree's annual rings are wide. In dry years, rings are narrow. By examining annual rings from some trees in the southwestern United States, scientists were able to infer that severe droughts occurred in the years 840, 1067, 1379, and 1632.

FIGURE 15

A Woody Stem

Trees like these maples have woody stems. A typical woody stem is made up of many layers. The layers of xylem form annual rings that can reveal the age of the tree and the growing conditions it has experienced.
Interpreting Diagrams *Where is the cambium located?*

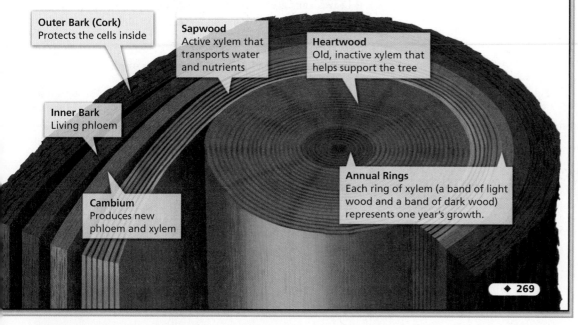

Outer Bark (Cork)
Protects the cells inside

Sapwood
Active xylem that transports water and nutrients

Heartwood
Old, inactive xylem that helps support the tree

Inner Bark
Living phloem

Cambium
Produces new phloem and xylem

Annual Rings
Each ring of xylem (a band of light wood and a band of dark wood) represents one year's growth.

◆ 269

Go Online
PHSchool.com

For: More on leaves
Visit: PHSchool.com
Web Code: ced-1051

Students can review leaves in an online activity.

Leaves

Teach Key Concepts L2

The Functions of Leaves

Focus Remind students that plants are autotrophs—they make their own food.

Teach Ask: **How do leaves provide food for a plant?** (*They capture energy from sunlight and use it to carry out photosynthesis.*) Have students examine Figure 16 as you ask questions such as **Where are the stomata mostly found?** (*On a leaf's underside*) **What do they do?** (*They open to let in carbon dioxide, and allow water vapor and oxygen to leave. They close to conserve water.*) **What happens to the sugars made in the leaf during photosynthesis?** (*They enter the phloem and travel to other parts of the plant.*)

Apply Ask: **If the temperature is not very hot, when would stomata generally be open and closed?** (*Open during the daytime when sunlight is available and photosynthesis is active; closed at night when open stomata would only lead to water loss*) **learning modality: verbal**

All in One Teaching Resources, Unit 2

• Transparency LS81

Use Visuals: Figure 16 L2

The Structure of a Leaf

Focus Ask student volunteers to read each caption in the figure.

Teach Ask: **Where is the leaf cuticle and what does it do?** (*It covers the leaf's surface and prevents water loss.*) **Where are the chloroplasts?** (*In the upper and lower leaf cells*) **What structure contains the xylem and phloem?** (*Vein*)

Apply Ask: **What is the benefit of upper leaf cells that are densely packed, rather than loosely packed?** (*Densely packed cells can collect more energy for photosynthesis.*) **learning modality: visual**

FIGURE 16
The Structure of a Leaf

A leaf is a well-adapted food factory. Each structure helps the leaf produce food.

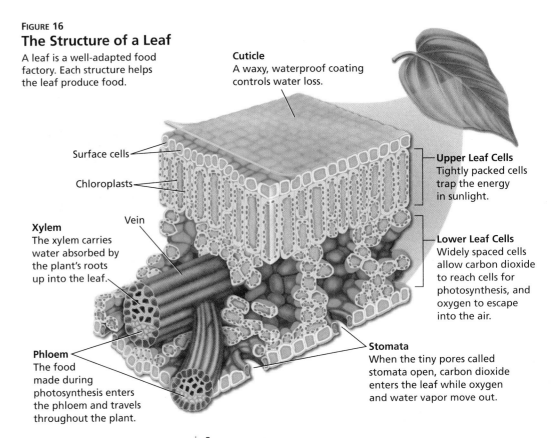

Cuticle
A waxy, waterproof coating controls water loss.

Surface cells

Chloroplasts

Upper Leaf Cells
Tightly packed cells trap the energy in sunlight.

Xylem
The xylem carries water absorbed by the plant's roots up into the leaf.

Vein

Lower Leaf Cells
Widely spaced cells allow carbon dioxide to reach cells for photosynthesis, and oxygen to escape into the air.

Phloem
The food made during photosynthesis enters the phloem and travels throughout the plant.

Stomata
When the tiny pores called stomata open, carbon dioxide enters the leaf while oxygen and water vapor move out.

Leaves

Leaves vary greatly in size and shape. Pine trees, for example, have needle-shaped leaves. Birch trees have small rounded leaves with jagged edges. Regardless of their shape, leaves play an important role in a plant. **Leaves capture the sun's energy and carry out the food-making process of photosynthesis.**

The Structure of a Leaf If you were to cut through a leaf and look at the edge under a microscope, you would see the structures in Figure 16. The leaf's top and bottom surface layers protect the cells inside. Between the layers of cells are veins that contain xylem and phloem.

The surface layers of the leaf have stomata, the pores that open and close to control when gases enter and leave the leaf. The Greek word *stoma* means "mouth"—and stomata do look like tiny mouths, as you can see in Figure 17. When the stomata are open, carbon dioxide enters the leaf, and oxygen and water vapor exit.

Go Online
PHSchool.com

For: More on leaves
Visit: PHSchool.com
Web Code: ced-1051

The Leaf and Photosynthesis The structure of a leaf is ideal for carrying out photosynthesis. The cells that contain the most chloroplasts are located near the leaf's upper surface, where they get the most light. Recall that the chlorophyll in the chloroplasts traps the sun's energy.

Carbon dioxide enters the leaf through open stomata. Water, which is absorbed by the plant's roots, travels up the stem to the leaf through the xylem. During photosynthesis, sugar and oxygen are produced from the carbon dioxide and water. Oxygen passes out of the leaf through the open stomata. The sugar enters the phloem and then travels throughout the plant.

Controlling Water Loss Because such a large area of a leaf is exposed to the air, water can quickly evaporate, or be lost, from a leaf into the air. The process by which water evaporates from a plant's leaves is called **transpiration.** A plant can lose a lot of water through transpiration. A corn plant, for example, can lose almost 4 liters of water on a hot summer day. Without a way to slow down the process of transpiration, a plant would shrivel up and die.

Fortunately, plants have ways to slow down transpiration. One way that plants retain water is by closing the stomata. The stomata often close when leaves start to dry out.

 Reading Checkpoint How does water get into a leaf?

FIGURE 17
Stomata
Stomata open (top) and close (bottom) to control when gases enter and exit the leaf.
Relating Cause and Effect What gases enter and exit when the stomata open?

Section 3 Assessment

 Target Reading Skill Outlining Use the information in your outline about seed plants to help you answer the questions below.

Reviewing Key Concepts

1. **a. Reviewing** What two characteristics do all seed plants share?
   b. Relating Cause and Effect What characteristics enable seed plants to live in a wide variety of environments? Explain.
2. **a. Listing** Name the three main parts of a seed.
   b. Sequencing List the steps in the sequence in which they must occur for a seed to grow into a new plant.
   c. Applying Concepts If a cherry seed were to take root right below its parent tree, what three challenges might the cherry seedling face?

3. **a. Identifying** What are the main functions of a plant's roots, stems, and leaves?
   b. Comparing and Contrasting What type of tissue carries water from the roots to the rest of the plant? What type of tissue carries food away from the leaves?
   c. Applying Concepts How are the structures of a tree's roots and leaves well-suited for their roles in supplying the tree with water and sugar?

Writing in Science

Product Label Write a "packaging label" for a seed. Include a name and description for each part of the seed. Be sure to describe the role of each part in producing a new plant.

Chapter 8 ◆ 271

Monitor Progress _____ L2

Answers
Figure 17 Carbon dioxide enters the leaf, and water vapor and oxygen exit.

Reading Checkpoint It is absorbed by the roots and travels up the stem to the leaf through the xylem.

Assess

Reviewing Key Concepts

1. **a.** They have vascular tissue and they use pollen and seeds to reproduce. **b.** They have structures to bring water and nutrients to all parts of the plant, and they do not need water for fertilization to occur.
2. **a.** Embryo, stored food, seed coat **b.** Dispersal, absorb water, germination, embryo begins to grow, plant leaves emerge **c.** It would compete with the parent tree for light, water, and minerals.
3. **a.** Roots—anchor plant, absorb water and nutrients from soil, some store food; stems—carry substances between roots and leaves, some store food; leaves—capture sun's energy and carry out photosynthesis **b.** Water moves from roots to leaves through the xylem; sugar moves from leaves to stems, roots, and other parts, through phloem. **c.** Tree roots have root hairs that help absorb water from the soil. Roots have xylem to carry water to leaves. Sugar made by the chloroplasts in the leaves moves to phloem and then travels to all parts of the plant.

Reteach L1

Use the section figures to summarize the functions of roots, stems, and leaves.

Performance Assessment L2

Oral Presentation Have groups of students make posters showing the functions of leaves, stems, or roots, then present their posters to the class.

All in One Teaching Resources, Unit 2

- Section Summary: *The Characteristics of Seed Plants*
- Review and Reinforce: *The Characteristics of Seed Plants*
- Enrich: *The Characteristics of Seed Plants*

Writing in Science

Writing Mode Description
Scoring Rubric
4 Includes the name, function, and description for each part of a seed; uses vivid descriptions that resemble a real label and engage the reader
3 Includes all criteria, but descriptions are uninteresting
2 Includes brief but accurate descriptions
1 Includes incomplete or inaccurate descriptions

Gymnosperms and Angiosperms

Objectives
After this lesson, students will be able to
8.4.1 Identify the characteristics of gymnosperms and describe how they reproduce.
8.4.2 Describe the characteristics of angiosperms and their flowers.
8.4.3 Explain how angiosperms reproduce.
8.4.4 Describe the two types of angiosperms.

Target Reading Skill

Building Vocabulary Explain that using a vocabulary strategy such as using the words in a sentence helps students define Key Terms.

Answers
Have students write what they know about each key term before reading the definitions in the section. Explain that connecting what they already know about key terms helps them to remember the terms. As they read each passage that contains key terms, remind them to write the definitions in their own words.

All in One Teaching Resources, Unit 2
• Guided Reading Study Worksheet: *Gymnosperms and Angiosperms, Use Target Reading Skills*

Preteach

Build Background Knowledge
L1

Green Trees in Winter
Ask students to name trees that stay green all winter and describe their features. (*Possible answers: Fir, pine; tall with needles for leaves, cones, needle-like leaves, sticky sap*)

Section
4

Gymnosperms and Angiosperms

Reading Preview

Key Concepts
• What are the characteristics of gymnosperms and how do they reproduce?
• What are the characteristics of angiosperms and their flowers?
• How do angiosperms reproduce?
• What are the two types of angiosperms?

Key Terms
• gymnosperm • cone • ovule
• pollination • angiosperm
• flower • sepal • petal
• stamen • pistil • ovary
• fruit • monocot • dicot

Target Reading Skill
Building Vocabulary Using a word in a sentence helps you think about how best to explain the word. After you read the section, reread the paragraphs that contain definitions of Key Terms. Use all the information you have learned to write a meaningful sentence using each Key Term.

Go Online
SciLINKS NSTA

For: Links on gymnosperms
Visit: www.SciLinks.org
Web Code: scn-0152

Discover Activity

Are All Leaves Alike?
1. Your teacher will give you a hand lens, a ruler, and the leaves from some seed plants.
2. Using the hand lens, examine each leaf. Sketch each leaf in your notebook.
3. Measure the length and width of each leaf. Record your measurements in your notebook.

Think It Over
Classifying Divide the leaves into two groups on the basis of your observations. Explain why you grouped the leaves as you did.

Here's a question for you: What do pine cones and apples have in common? The answer is that they are both the parts of plants that contain seeds. Plants that produce seeds are known as seed plants. Pine trees and apple trees are both seed plants but belong to two different groups—gymnosperms and angiosperms.

Gymnosperms
Pine trees belong to the group of seed plants known as gymnosperms. A **gymnosperm** (JIM nuh spurm) is a seed plant that produces naked seeds. The seeds of gymnosperms are referred to as "naked" because they are not enclosed by a protective fruit.

Every gymnosperm produces naked seeds. In addition, many gymnosperms have needle-like or scalelike leaves, and deep-growing root systems. Gymnosperms are the oldest type of seed plant. According to fossil evidence, gymnosperms first appeared on Earth about 360 million years ago. Fossils also indicate that there were many more species of gymnosperms on Earth in the past than there are today. Four groups of gymnosperms exist today.

Discover Activity

Skills Focus Classifying L1

Materials hand lens; metric ruler; 2 or 3 leaves from angiosperms, such as oak tree, maple tree, day lily, and rose; 2 or 3 leaves from gymnosperms, such as pine, yew, and spruce

Time 10 minutes

Tips Encourage students to include a detailed description of the leaf's features.

Direct students to wash their hands after handling the leaves.

Expected Outcome Students will observe differences in size, length, width, and thickness.

Think It Over Groups should be needle-like shapes and broad-shaped leaves. Students' reasons may include the difference in thickness and broadness of the leaves.

FIGURE 18
Types of Gymnosperms
Gymnosperms are the oldest seed plants. Cycads, conifers, ginkgoes, and gnetophytes are the only groups that exist today.

Ginkgo: ▲
Ginkgo biloba

Gnetophyte: ▲
Welwitschia

Cycad: ▲
Sago palm

Conifer: ▶
Giant sequoia

Cycads About 175 million years ago, the majority of plants were cycads. Today, cycads (SY kadz) grow mainly in tropical and subtropical areas. Cycads look like palm trees with cones. A cycad cone can grow as large as a football.

Conifers Conifers (KAHN uh furz), or cone-bearing plants, are the largest and most diverse group of gymnosperms today. Most conifers, such as pines, sequoias, and junipers, are evergreens—plants that keep their leaves, or needles, year-round. When needles drop off, they are replaced by new ones.

Ginkgoes Ginkgoes (GING kohz) also grew hundreds of millions of years ago, but today, only one species of ginkgo, *Ginkgo biloba*, exists. It probably survived only because the Chinese and Japanese cared for it in their gardens. Today, ginkgo trees are planted along city streets because they can tolerate air pollution.

Gnetophytes Gnetophytes (NEE tuh fyts) live in hot deserts and in tropical rain forests. Some gnetophytes are trees, some are shrubs, and others are vines. The *Welwitschia* shown in Figure 18 grows in the deserts of West Africa and can live for more than 1,000 years.

Reading Checkpoint What are the four types of gymnosperms?

◆ 273

Instruct

Go Online
SCI LINKS NSTA

For: Links on gymnosperms
Visit: www.SciLinks.org
Web Code: scn-0152

Download a worksheet to guide students' review of gymnosperms.

Gymnosperms

Teach Key Concepts L2
Characteristics of Gymnosperms

Focus Explain that *gymnosperm* comes from the Greek root *gymno*, meaning "naked," and *sperma*, meaning "seed."

Teach Ask: **What characteristic of a gymnosperm gives the plant its name?** (*Gymnosperms have naked seeds.*) **What other characteristics are common to most gymnosperms?** (*Needle-like leaves and deep-growing root systems*)

Apply Ask students to infer why the conifers are the largest group of gymnosperms. (*Possible answer: They have adaptations that allow them to live in a wide variety of places. For example, many conifers can live in dry conditions because their long, thin needles limit water loss.*)
learning modality: verbal

Independent Practice L2

All in One **Teaching Resources, Unit 2**
• Guided Reading and Study Worksheet: *Gymnosperms and Angiosperms*

 Student Edition on Audio CD

Monitor Progress _____ L2

Oral Presentation Have students state the characteristics common to gymnosperms.

Answer

Reading Checkpoint Cycads, conifers, ginkoes, and gnetophytes

---

Differentiated Instruction

Special Needs L1
Visual Science Glossary Have students draw a characteristic of a typical gymnosperm, as well as a characteristic of each group of gymnosperms, based on the text description. Drawings should include needle-like or scalelike leaves, deep-growing root systems, and seeds that are not enclosed in a fruit. Encourage students to add a mnemonic device or memory jogger to their drawings that will help them remember the characteristic shown. (*Examples: A sewing needle for needle-like leaves, a marble for unprotected seeds, a ladder for deep-growing root systems*) **learning modality: visual**

Interpreting Data on Gymnosperms

Materials references on gymnosperms, including Web sites; state map, map pins

Time 20 minutes

Focus Challenge students to create a map showing the distribution of gymnosperms in your state.

Teach Allow students to research gymnosperms, then place pins on the map (one color for each type of gymnosperm) as they locate an area where each type grows.

Apply Ask students to explain which type of gymnosperm is most common in your state and why. *(Answers should include climate conditions in your state.)* **learning modality: visual**

Reproduction in Gymnosperms

Teach Key Concepts　L2
Pollination and Fertilization

Focus Refer students to Figure 19.

Teach Ask: **What process occurs in the male cone?** *(Male cones produce pollen.)* **What processes occur in the female cone before fertilization?** *(First, an egg cell forms inside an ovule on a scale of a female cone. Next, pollination takes place on the scales. After pollen falls from a male cone onto a female cone, a sperm cell and an egg cell join in an ovule on the female cone.)* **What process follows fertilization but occurs before seeds mature and disperse?** *(The fertilized egg develops into an embryo.)* **Once the embryo develops, what else must happen for a seed to be ready to disperse?** *(The seed must mature—the seed coat and its stored food develops.)*

Apply Ask: **Is pollen more or less likely to be dispersed by wind during rainy weather?** *(Less, because the rain moistens the pollen; the pollen falls to the ground instead of being in the air.)* **learning modality: logical/ mathematical**

All in One Teaching Resources, Unit 2
• Transparency LS82

The Scoop on Cones
In this activity, you will observe the structure of a female cone.

1. Use a hand lens to look closely at the female cone. Gently shake the cone over a piece of white paper. Observe what happens.
2. Break off one scale from the cone. Examine its base. If the scale contains a seed, remove the seed.
3. With a hand lens, examine the seed from Step 2 or examine a seed that fell on the paper in Step 1.
4. Wash your hands.

Inferring How does the structure of the cone protect the seeds?

274 ◆

Reproduction in Gymnosperms

Most gymnosperms have reproductive structures called **cones.** Cones are covered with scales. Most gymnosperms produce two types of cones: male cones and female cones. Usually, a single plant produces both male and female cones. In some types of gymnosperms, however, individual trees produce either male cones or female cones. A few types of gymnosperms produce no cones at all.

In Figure 19, you can see the male and female cones of a Ponderosa pine. Male cones produce tiny grains of pollen—the male gametophyte. Pollen contains the cells that will later become sperm cells. Each scale on a male cone produces thousands of pollen grains.

The female gametophyte develops in structures called ovules. An **ovule** (OH vyool) is a structure that contains an egg cell. Female cones contain at least one ovule at the base of each scale. After fertilization occurs, the ovule develops into a seed.

You can follow the process of gymnosperm reproduction in Figure 19. **First, pollen falls from a male cone onto a female cone. In time, a sperm cell and an egg cell join together in an ovule on the female cone.** After fertilization occurs, the seed develops on the scale of the female cone.

Pollination The transfer of pollen from a male reproductive structure to a female reproductive structure is called **pollination.** In gymnosperms, wind often carries the pollen from the male cones to the female cones. The pollen collects in a sticky substance produced by each ovule.

Fertilization Once pollination has occurred, the ovule closes and seals in the pollen. The scales also close, and a sperm cell fertilizes an egg cell inside each ovule. The fertilized egg then develops into the embryo part of the seed.

Seed Development Female cones remain on the tree while the seeds mature. As the seeds develop, the female cone increases in size. It can take up to two years for the seeds of some gymnosperms to mature. Male cones, however, usually fall off the tree after they have shed their pollen.

Seed Dispersal When the seeds are mature, the scales open. The wind shakes the seeds out of the cone and carries them away. Only a few seeds will land in suitable places and grow into new plants.

Reading Checkpoint　What is pollen and where is it produced?

Skills Focus Inferring　L2

Materials mature female pine cone, hand lens, sheet of white paper

Time 10 minutes

Tips CAUTION: *Check for student allergies before this lab.* Make certain that cones have some seeds inside the scales. Remind students to wash their hands afterwards.

Expected Outcome The scales probably protect developing seeds from wind, rain, and very cold temperatures.

Extend Have students compare, then sketch, male and female pine cones. Sketches should indicate differences in size, shape, and structure of the scales. **learning modality: visual**

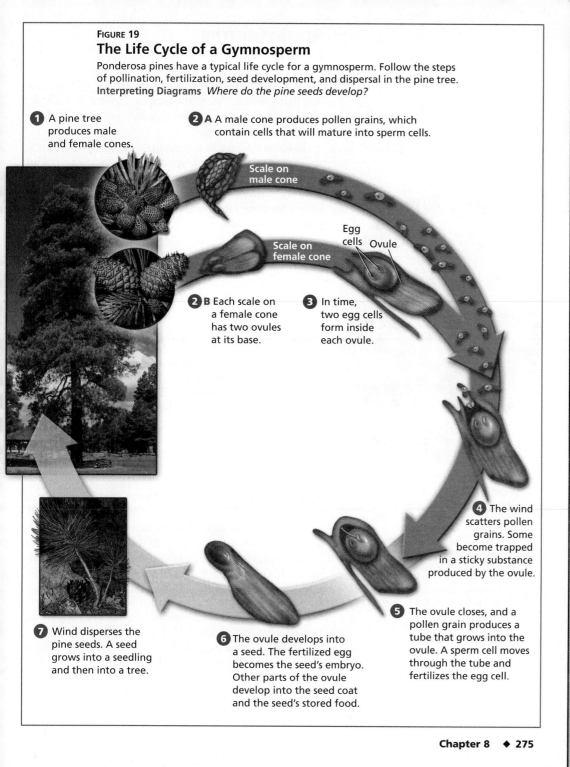

FIGURE 19

The Life Cycle of a Gymnosperm

Ponderosa pines have a typical life cycle for a gymnosperm. Follow the steps of pollination, fertilization, seed development, and dispersal in the pine tree.
Interpreting Diagrams *Where do the pine seeds develop?*

1 A pine tree produces male and female cones.

2 A A male cone produces pollen grains, which contain cells that will mature into sperm cells.

Scale on male cone

Egg cells   Ovule

Scale on female cone

2 B Each scale on a female cone has two ovules at its base.

3 In time, two egg cells form inside each ovule.

4 The wind scatters pollen grains. Some become trapped in a sticky substance produced by the ovule.

5 The ovule closes, and a pollen grain produces a tube that grows into the ovule. A sperm cell moves through the tube and fertilizes the egg cell.

6 The ovule develops into a seed. The fertilized egg becomes the seed's embryo. Other parts of the ovule develop into the seed coat and the seed's stored food.

7 Wind disperses the pine seeds. A seed grows into a seedling and then into a tree.

Chapter 8 ◆ 275

Help Students Read L1

Reciprocal Teaching Have students read *Reproduction in Gymnosperms* with a partner. One partner reads a paragraph out loud. Then, the other partner summarizes the paragraph's contents and explains the main concepts. The partners continue to switch roles with each new paragraph.

Use Visuals: Figure 19 L2

Life Cycle of a Gymnosperm

Focus Encourage students to study the photographs of the male and female cones in Figure 19.

Teach Ask: **How is pollen transferred from the male to the female cone?** *(Wind)* **Why are male cones at the tips of branches rather than closer to the trunk?** *(Branch tips allow more efficient pollen distribution.)* **What happens to male cones after they shed their pollen?** *(They fall from the tree.)* **What happens to female cones after fertilization?** *(They stay on the tree as the seed matures.)*

Apply Ask: **How does the shape of the seed affect its motion in the wind?** *(The shape of the seed allows the wind to carry the seed some distance away from the parent tree.)* **learning modality: logical/mathematical**

Differentiated Instruction

Less Proficient Readers L2
Understanding Reproduction in Gymnosperms Provide students with this section of the Student Edition on Audio CD and a copy of the passage *Reproduction in Gymnosperms*. Have them listen to this passage as they read along and highlight key phrases and sentences that explain the

sequence of events in pollination, fertilization, seed development, and dispersal. Then pair students with more proficient readers. Have them construct a flowchart in their own words with the steps in the life cycle of gymnosperms. **learning modality: verbal**

Monitor Progress L2

Writing Have students use the following words in paragraphs to describe gymnosperm reproduction: *ovule, pollen, male, female, fertilization, seed,* and *scales.*

Answers

Figure 19 On the female cones

Reading Checkpoint Pollen contains cells that mature into sperm cells. It is produced in male cones.

Angiosperms

Teach Key Concepts   L2

Angiosperms Are Flowering Plants

Focus Stress to students that angiosperms are plants that produce flowers and fruits.

Teach Explain to students that angiosperms are the largest group of plants, the most widely distributed, and an incredibly diverse group. Ask students to list some angiosperms they are familiar with.

Apply Direct students' attention to the photo of the Rafflesia, or "stinking corpse lily," in Figure 20. Explain to students that the foul odor of Rafflesia plants attracts their pollinators—carrion beetles and flies. **learning modality: verbal**

The Structure of Flowers

Teach Key Concepts   L2

Flowers Are Reproductive Organs

Focus Remind students that in gymnosperms, the cone is the reproductive structure.

Teach Explain that in angiosperms, a flower is the reproductive structure. Ask: **What is the function of flowers?** (*To reproduce*) **What kinds of structures do you expect to find in a flower?** (*Male and female reproductive structures of the plant*) Refer students to Figure 21. Ask them to examine each part as student volunteers read the captions and the sentences in the passage containing key terms. Ask: **What structures make up the male parts of a flower?** (*Stamens with their filaments and anthers*) **The female parts?** (*Pistils, which have stigmas, styles, and an ovary*) **What purpose do the color and shape of the petals serve?** (*To help ensure pollination*)

Apply Ask: **How is it an advantage for a plant to have many flowers together in a single structure?** (*More flowers might attract more pollinators, which increases the chance of pollination.*) **learning modality: visual**

Extend The Active Art will show students how the structures of flowers are specialized for reproduction.

All in One Teaching Resources, Unit 2
• Transparency LS83

FIGURE 20 Rafflesia
Rafflesia plants grow in the jungles of Southeast Asia. The giant flowers measure about 1 meter across and weigh about 7 kilograms!
Classifying *What kind of seeds do Rafflesia plants produce—uncovered seeds or seeds enclosed in fruits?*

Angiosperms

You probably associate the word *flower* with a sweet-smelling plant growing in a garden. You certainly wouldn't think of something that smells like rotting meat. But that's exactly what the corpse flower, or rafflesia, smells like. You won't be seeing rafflesia in your local florist shop any time soon.

Rafflesia belongs to the group of seed plants known as **angiosperms** (AN jee uh spurmz). **All angiosperms, or flowering plants, share two important traits. First, they produce flowers. Second, in contrast to gymnosperms, which produce uncovered seeds, angiosperms produce seeds that are enclosed in fruits.**

Angiosperms live almost everywhere on Earth. They grow in frozen areas in the Arctic, tropical jungles, barren deserts, and at the ocean's edge.

 Reading Checkpoint Where do angiosperms live?

The Structure of Flowers

Flowers come in all sorts of shapes, sizes, and colors. But, despite their differences, all flowers have the same function—reproduction. A **flower** is the reproductive structure of an angiosperm. Figure 21 shows the parts of a typical flower. As you read about the parts, keep in mind that some flowers lack one or more of the parts. For example, some flowers have only male reproductive parts, and some flowers lack petals.

Sepals and Petals When a flower is still a bud, it is enclosed by leaflike structures called **sepals** (SEE pulz). Sepals protect the developing flower and are often green in color. When the sepals fold back, they reveal the flower's colorful, leaflike **petals.** The petals are generally the most colorful parts of a flower. The shape, size, and number of petals vary greatly from flower to flower.

Stamens Within the petals are the flower's male and female reproductive parts. The **stamens** (STAY munz) are the male reproductive parts. Locate the stamens inside the flower in Figure 21. The thin stalk of the stamen is called the filament. Pollen is produced in the anther, at the top of the filament.

276 ◆

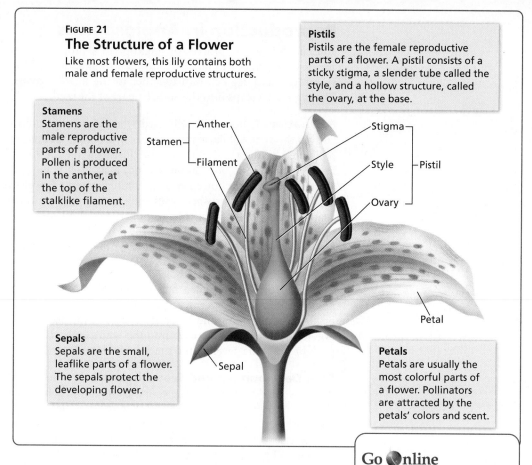

FIGURE 21
The Structure of a Flower
Like most flowers, this lily contains both male and female reproductive structures.

Stamens
Stamens are the male reproductive parts of a flower. Pollen is produced in the anther, at the top of the stalklike filament.

Pistils
Pistils are the female reproductive parts of a flower. A pistil consists of a sticky stigma, a slender tube called the style, and a hollow structure, called the ovary, at the base.

Stamen — Anther
— Filament

Stigma
Style — Pistil
Ovary

Sepals
Sepals are the small, leaflike parts of a flower. The sepals protect the developing flower.

Sepal

Petal

Petals
Petals are usually the most colorful parts of a flower. Pollinators are attracted by the petals' colors and scent.

Pistils The female parts, or **pistils** (PIS tulz), are found in the center of most flowers. Some flowers have two or more pistils; others have only one. The sticky tip of the pistil is called the stigma. A slender tube, called a style, connects the stigma to a hollow structure at the base of the flower. This hollow structure is the **ovary,** which protects the seeds as they develop. An ovary contains one or more ovules.

Pollinators The colors and shapes of most petals and the scents produced by most flowers attract insects and other animals. These organisms ensure that pollination occurs. Pollinators include birds, bats, and insects such as bees and flies. The rafflesia flower you read about at the beginning of the section is pollinated by flies. The flies are attracted by the strong smell of rotting meat.

 Reading Checkpoint What are the male and female parts of a flower?

Chapter 8 ◆ 277

Go Online
active art

For: The Structure of a Flower activity
Visit: PHSchool.com
Web Code: cep-1053

Students can interact with the art of the structure of a flower online.

Lab zone Build Inquiry L2

Modeling Flowers

Materials construction paper, markers, toothpicks, modeling clay, cornmeal, drinking straws, dry peas, glue, tape, other arts and crafts materials, botany references or Internet resources

Time 20 minutes

Focus Remind students that flowers vary widely in structure. Explain that while most flowers contain both male and female reproductive parts, some flowers contain only one or the other.

Teach Divide students into four groups. Assign each group one of the following flowers: corn, tulip, wild rose, and sunflowers. Have students use references to locate diagrams of the reproductive structures of their flower. If they cannot locate structures on their flower, they may choose another type. Try to make sure that flowers with different arrangements of reproductive structures are represented. Encourage students to create a model of a flower showing its reproductive structures. Then have them sketch their model and label the parts. Confirm that the models are correctly constructed and the sketches correctly labeled. Ask groups to present their models to the class, then leave the models on display for all students to use as study aids.

Apply After students have presented their models, ask the class to compare and contrast the differences in the structures.
learning modality: kinesthetic

Monitor Progress _____ L2

Skills Check Have students make a compare/contrast table listing the male and the female parts of a flower.

Answers
Figure 20 Seeds enclosed in fruits

 Reading Checkpoint Almost everywhere on Earth

 Reading Checkpoint Male: stamen—anther and filament; female: pistil—stigma, style, ovary

---

Differentiated Instruction

Less Proficient Readers L1
Organizing Information Suggest that students construct concept maps to organize the information about angiosperms. With student input, write the key terms and main concepts of the section on the board. Then help students start the map. **learning modality: visual**

Gifted and Talented L3
Researching Flowers in Art Encourage students who are artistically talented to compare paintings of flowers by artists such as O'Keeffe, Van Gogh, Monet, and Picasso. Ask students to analyze the differences. *(Possible answers: O'Keeffe included accurate details. Van Gogh used interpretative colors and limited detail.)* **learning modality: visual**

Reproduction in Angiosperms

Teach Key Concepts L2

Processes in Angiosperm Reproduction

Focus Ask: **What reproductive structures are unique to angiosperms?** *(Flowers and fruits)*

Teach Ask: **After a plant has produced a mature flower, what is the first step in reproduction?** *(Pollen falls on the stigma.)* **What is this process called?** *(Pollination)* **What happens next?** *(A sperm cell in the pollen joins with an egg cell inside the ovary.)* **What is the process called? What is the result of the process?** *(Fertilization, a zygote)* **What happens to the ovary as the seed develops?** *(The ovary changes into a fruit.)*

Apply Have students suppose they have discovered a new plant that has tiny green flowers against a background of green leaves. Ask: **How do you think this plant is pollinated?** *(Probably the wind because it does not have colorful flowers to attract animal pollinators)* **learning modality: visual**

All in One Teaching Resources, Unit 2

• Transparency LS84

Lab zone Build Inquiry

Comparing and Contrasting Fruit L2

Materials whole fruit and fruit slices, such as grapes, coconut, apples, bananas, tomatoes, and so on

Time 10 minutes

Focus Review the definition of a fruit.

Teach CAUTION: *Check for allergies before allowing students to handle fruit. Make certain students do not eat or taste the fruit.* Encourage students to feel the shape, weight, and texture of several fruits. Ask students to describe how the physical characteristics of each fruit and its seeds might be related to the way in which its seeds are dispersed.

Apply Ask: **What is the purpose of fruits being sweet and fleshy?** *(Animals are more likely to eat the fruit, which helps the plants disperse their seeds.)* **learning modality: kinesthetic**

Reproduction in Angiosperms

You can follow the process of angiosperm reproduction in Figure 23. **First, pollen falls on a flower's stigma. In time, the sperm cell and egg cell join together in the flower's ovule. The zygote develops into the embryo part of the seed.**

Pollination A flower is pollinated when a grain of pollen falls on the stigma. Like gymnosperms, some angiosperms are pollinated by the wind. But most angiosperms rely on birds, bats, or insects for pollination. Nectar, a sugar-rich food, is located deep inside a flower. When an animal enters a flower to obtain the nectar, it brushes against the anthers and becomes coated with pollen. Some of the pollen can drop onto the flower's stigma as the animal leaves the flower. The pollen can also be brushed onto the sticky stigma of the next flower the animal visits.

Fertilization If the pollen falls on the stigma of a similar plant, fertilization can occur. A sperm cell joins with an egg cell inside an ovule within the ovary at the base of the flower. The zygote then begins to develop into the seed's embryo. Other parts of the ovule develop into the rest of the seed.

Fruit Development and Seed Dispersal As the seed develops after fertilization, the ovary changes into a **fruit**—a ripened ovary and other structures that enclose one or more seeds. Apples and cherries are fruits. So are many foods you usually call vegetables, such as tomatoes and squash. Fruits are the means by which angiosperm seeds are dispersed. Animals that eat fruits help to disperse their seeds.

 **Reading Checkpoint** What flower part develops into a fruit?

FIGURE 22
Fruits
The seeds of angiosperms are enclosed in fruits, which protect and help disperse the seeds.

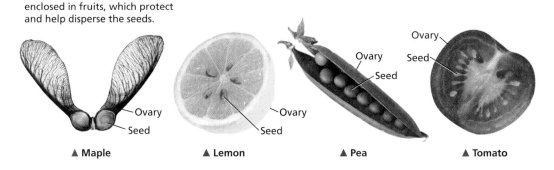

▲ Maple — Ovary, Seed

▲ Lemon — Ovary, Seed

▲ Pea — Ovary, Seed

▲ Tomato — Ovary, Seed

278 ◆

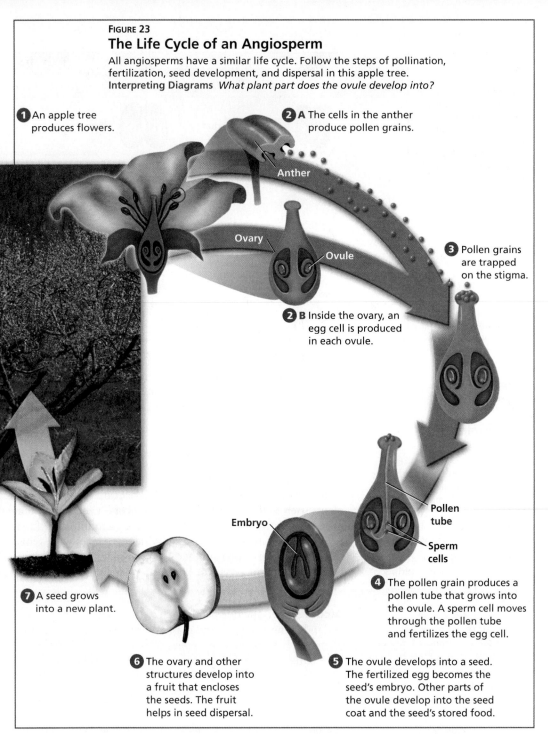

FIGURE 23
The Life Cycle of an Angiosperm

All angiosperms have a similar life cycle. Follow the steps of pollination, fertilization, seed development, and dispersal in this apple tree.
Interpreting Diagrams *What plant part does the ovule develop into?*

1 An apple tree produces flowers.

2 A The cells in the anther produce pollen grains.

Anther

Ovary

Ovule

3 Pollen grains are trapped on the stigma.

2 B Inside the ovary, an egg cell is produced in each ovule.

Embryo

Pollen tube

Sperm cells

4 The pollen grain produces a pollen tube that grows into the ovule. A sperm cell moves through the pollen tube and fertilizes the egg cell.

7 A seed grows into a new plant.

6 The ovary and other structures develop into a fruit that encloses the seeds. The fruit helps in seed dispersal.

5 The ovule develops into a seed. The fertilized egg becomes the seed's embryo. Other parts of the ovule develop into the seed coat and the seed's stored food.

Chapter 8 ◆ 279

Use Visuals: Figure 23 `L1`
The Life Cycle of an Angiosperm

Focus Encourage students to follow the reproductive process of flowering plants shown in Figure 23.

Teach Make sure students can identify the ovary and anther in Step 1. Ask: **Why are there Steps 2A and 2B?** *(One step is the male—cells in the anther produce pollen; the other step is the female—cells in each ovule produce egg cells.)* As students review the steps in the visual, have them record what each of these structures produces and its role in the life cycle: anther *(Pollen grains)*, ovule *(Egg cell, seed)*, pollen grain *(Pollen tube)*, ovule's wall *(Seed coat)*, and ovary *(Fruit)*. Ask: **What is the purpose of the stigma?** *(To trap pollen)* **What happens to the ovule parts that are not the embryo?** *(They develop into a seed coat and stored food.)* **What is the purpose of fruit?** *(Enclose seeds and aid in seed dispersal.)*

Apply Call students' attention to Step 6. Ask students to infer how animals that eat fruit help to ensure the germination of seeds. *(When animals eat fruits, the seeds pass through the animals' digestive system. When the animals travel, they disperse seeds away from the parent plant. Seeds may then have a better chance of germinating because they won't have to compete with the parent plant for resources.)* **learning modality: visual**

Differentiated Instruction

English Learners/Beginning `L1` Comprehension: Link to Visual Help students construct a table listing each reproductive structure, what it produces, and what role the structure plays in the plant's life cycle. Use the headings *Plant Part*, *Produces*, and *Role*. Entries in the *Plant Part* column should include *anther*, *ovule*, *ovary*, *sperm cells*, and so on.
learning modality: visual

English Learners/Intermediate `L2` Comprehension: Modified Cloze Have student pairs write sentences with blanks for key terms and concepts, then switch with another pair to fill in the blanks. Example: **The _anther_ produces _pollen grains_ that fertilize the _egg_. learning modality: verbal**

Monitor Progress _____ `L2`

Oral Presentation Have students describe the roles of an orange blossom and an orange in the reproduction of an orange tree.

Answers
Figure 23 A seed

 The ovary

Types of Angiosperms

Teach Key Concepts L2

Monocots and Dicots

Focus Remind students that a cotyledon is a seed leaf that sometimes stores food for the plant embryo.

Teach Ask: **How can you classify angiosperms by the number of cotyledons?** *(A monocot has one seed leaf; a dicot has two seed leaves.)* **How are the petals of each type different?** *(A monocot has petals in groups of three or multiples of three; a dicot has petals in groups of four or five or multiples of four or five.)*

Apply Ask: **What can you infer about a cross-section of a fossilized stem that has holes scattered randomly throughout?** *(It was vascular because it had a stem with vascular tissue. It was probably seed bearing and a monocot because the vascular tissue was scattered throughout the stem.)* **learning modality: verbal**

All in One Teaching Resources, Unit 2
• Transparency LS85

Math Skill Whole number operations

Focus Reinforce that monocots may have more than 3 petals.

Teach Ask: **How can you use the number of petals to determine if a flower is a monocot or a dicot?** *(Divide the number of petals by 3. It is a monocot if you get a whole number.)*

Answer 12 and 16

Seed Plants in Everyday Life

Teach Key Concepts L2

Uses of Seed Plants

Focus Tell students that angiosperms have greater commercial use than gymnosperms, except in forest products.

Teach Ask: **Besides for food, how do people use angiosperms?** *(Clothing, rubber, furniture, medications)*

Apply Ask students to name specific food crops that are angiosperms. *(Rice, wheat, corn, all types of fruits and vegetables)* **learning modality: verbal**

FIGURE 24
Monocots and Dicots
Monocots and dicots differ in the number of cotyledons, the pattern of veins and vascular tissue, and the number of petals.
Interpreting Tables
How do monocot and dicot leaves differ?

Plant Part	Monocots		Dicots	
Seed	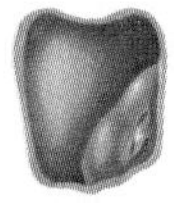	One cotyledon	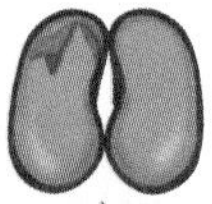	Two cotyledons
Leaf	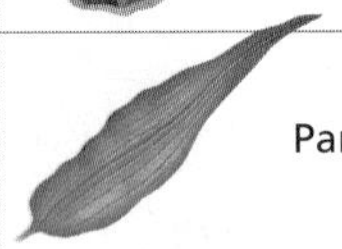	Parallel veins		Branching veins
Stem	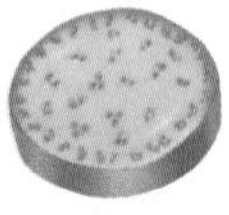	Bundles of vascular tissue scattered throughout stem		Bundles of vascular tissue arranged in a ring
Flower		Flower parts in threes		Flower parts in fours or fives

Comparing Monocots and Dicots

Multiples

Is a flower with 6 petals a monocot? To answer this question, you need to determine if 6 is a multiple of 3. A number is a multiple of 3 if there is a nonzero whole number that, when multiplied by 3, gives you that number.

In this case, 6 is a multiple of 3 because you can multiply 2 (a nonzero whole number) by 3 to get 6.

$$2 \times 3 = 6$$

Therefore, a flower with 6 petals is a monocot. Other multiples of 3 include 9 and 12.

Practice Problem Which of these numbers are multiples of 4?

6, 10, 12, 16

Types of Angiosperms

Angiosperms are divided into two major groups: monocots and dicots. "Cot" is short for *cotyledon*. Recall that in some seeds, the cotyledon, or seed leaf, provides food for the embryo. *Mono* means "one" and *di* means "two." **Monocots** are angiosperms that have only one seed leaf. **Dicots,** on the other hand, produce seeds with two seed leaves. In Figure 24, you can compare the characteristics of monocots and dicots.

Monocots Grasses, including corn, wheat, and rice, and plants such as lilies and tulips are monocots. The flowers of a monocot usually have either three petals or a multiple of three petals. Monocots usually have long, slender leaves with veins that run parallel to one another like train rails. The bundles of vascular tissue in monocot stems are usually scattered randomly throughout the stem.

Dicots Dicots include plants such as roses and violets, as well as dandelions. Both oak and maple trees are dicots, as are food plants such as beans and apples. The flowers of dicots often have either four or five petals or multiples of these numbers. The leaves are usually wide, with veins that branch many times. Dicot stems usually have bundles of vascular tissue arranged in a ring.

Reading Checkpoint How do the petals of monocots and dicots differ in number?

Seed Plants in Everyday Life

Products from seed plants are all around you. Gymnosperms, especially conifers, provide useful products such as paper and the lumber used to build homes. Conifers are also used to produce turpentine, the rayon fibers in clothes, and the rosin used by baseball pitchers, gymnasts, and musicians.

Angiosperms are an important source of food, clothing, and medicine for other organisms. Plant-eating animals eat various parts of flowering plants, including stems, leaves, and flowers. People eat vegetables, fruits, and cereals, all of which are angiosperms. People also make clothing and other products from angiosperms. For example, cotton fibers come from cotton plants. The sap of rubber trees is used to make rubber for tires and other products. The wood of maple, cherry, and oak trees is often used to make furniture.

FIGURE 25
Food From Seed Plants
The cucumbers, tomatoes, and spinach in this salad are all angiosperms.

✓ **Reading Checkpoint** What are two products made from gymnosperms?

Section 4 Assessment

 Target Reading Skill Building Vocabulary Use your sentences to help you answer the questions below.

Reviewing Key Concepts

1. **a. Listing** What characteristics do all gymnosperms share? What other characteristics do many gymnosperms have?
   b. Describing What is a cone? What role do cones play in gymnosperm reproduction?
   c. Sequencing Briefly describe the steps in the reproduction of a gymnosperm.
2. **a. Reviewing** What two characteristics do all angiosperms share?
   b. Identifying What is the function of an angiosperm's flowers?
3. **a. Reviewing** On what part of a flower must pollen land for pollination to occur?
   b. Sequencing Briefly describe the steps in the reproduction of an angiosperm, from pollination to seed dispersal.

4. **a. Listing** Name the two major groups of angiosperms.
   b. Comparing and Contrasting How do the seeds, leaves, stems, and flowers of these two groups differ?
   c. Classifying A plant's leaves have parallel veins, and each of its flowers has six petals. To which group does it belong? Explain.

Math ▶ **Practice**

5. **Multiples** Which of the following numbers are multiples of 3? Which of the numbers are multiples of 4?

   5, 6, 8, 10, 12, 15

6. **Multiples** Suppose you found a flower with 12 petals. Would you know from the number of petals whether the flower is a monocot or a dicot? Explain.

Lab zone **Chapter Project**

Keep Students on Track Students should show the design of their interactive exhibit so some younger children and ask them if they can think of ways to make the exhibit easier to use or easier to understand. They should also ask if it should answer some overlooked question. Students should then revise their exhibit to accommodate the comments.

Monitor Progress ___ L2

Answers

Figure 24 The leaves of monocots have parallel veins. The leaves of dicots have branching veins.

✓ **Reading Checkpoint** Monocots have petals in multiples of three; dicots have petals in multiples of four or five.

✓ **Reading Checkpoint** Any two: paper, lumber, turpentine, rayon, rosin

Assess

Reviewing Key Concepts

1. **a.** They produce unprotected seeds; many have needle-like or scalelike leaves and deep root systems. **b.** A cone is the reproductive structure of a gymnosperm. Male cones produce pollen; female cones contain ovules. **c.** Not likely; the seeds aren't enclosed in fruits that animals are attracted to.

2. **a.** They produce flowers and seeds encased in fruits. **b.** Reproduction

3. **a.** Stigma **b.** Pollen falls on a stigma. The sperm cell and egg cell join in the ovule and a zygote develops into the embryo part of the seed. The seed matures, a fruit develops around it, and the seed is dispersed, often with the help of animals.

4. **a.** Monocots and dicots **b.** Monocots: one cotyledon, leaves with parallel veins, stems show scattered bundles of vascular tissue, flower parts are three or multiples of three; dicots: two cotyledons, leaves with branching veins, stem contains a circle of vascular tissue, flower parts are four or five or multiples of four or five **c.** Monocot; its leaves have parallel veins, and six is a multiple of three.

Math Practice

5. 6, 12, 15; 8, 12
6. No; 12 is a multiple of 3 and 4.

Reteach L1

Review the life cycle of angiosperms.

All in One Teaching Resources, Unit 2

- Section Summary: *Gymnosperms and Angiosperms*
- Review and Reinforce: *Gymnosperms and Angiosperms*
- Enrich: *Gymnosperms and Angiosperms*

A Close Look at Flowers

Prepare for Inquiry

Key Concept
Flowers contain several distinct parts whose structures can be studied for a more complete understanding of their functions.

Skills Objectives
After this lab, students will be able to
- Observe the structures of flowers
- Infer the method of pollination and classify the plant as a monocot or a dicot
- Measure petal size, and the heights of pistil and stamen

 Class Time 40 minutes

All in One Teaching Resources, Unit 2
- Lab Worksheet: *A Close Look at Flowers*

Advance Planning
Provide a variety of flowers so that students can observe more than one type. Use large- or medium-sized flowers that have all the essential structures, such as tulips, lilies, gladiolas, daffodils, petunias, and others.

Safety
Before starting the lab, find out which students may be allergic to pollen. Provide a substitute activity for these students, or make other arrangements. Make sure all students wash their hands immediately after this activity. Teach scalpel safety. Substitute scissors for scalpels whenever possible. Advise students to take care not to drop the glass microscope slides. Review the safety guidelines in Appendix A.

Lab zone Skills Lab

A Close Look at Flowers

Problem
What is the function of a flower, and what roles do its different parts play?

Skills Focus
observing, inferring, measuring

Materials
- paper towels
- plastic dropper
- hand lens
- microscope
- slide
- large flower
- coverslip
- scalpel
- tape
- water
- metric ruler
- lens paper

Procedure

PART 1 The Outer Parts of the Flower

1. Tape four paper towel sheets on your work area. Obtain a flower from your teacher. While handling the flower gently, observe its shape and color. Use the ruler to measure it. Notice whether the petals have any spots or other markings. Does the flower have a scent? Record your observations with sketches and descriptions.

2. Observe the sepals. How many are there? How do they relate to the rest of the flower? (*Hint:* The sepals are often green, but not always.) Record your observations.

3. Use a scalpel to carefully cut off the sepals without damaging the structures beneath them. **CAUTION:** *Scalpels are sharp. Cut in a direction away from yourself and others.*

4. Observe the petals. How many are there? Are all the petals the same, or are they different? Record your observations.

PART 2 The Male Part of the Flower

5. Carefully pull off the petals to examine the male part of the flower. Try not to damage the structures beneath the petals.

6. Observe the stamens. How many are there? How are they shaped? How tall are they? Record your observations.

7. Use a scalpel to carefully cut the stamens away from the rest of the flower without damaging the structures beneath them. Lay the stamens on the paper towel.

8. Obtain a clean slide and coverslip. Hold a stamen over the slide, and gently tap some pollen grains from the anther onto the slide. Add a drop of water to the pollen. Then place the coverslip over the water and pollen.

9. Observe the pollen under both the low-power objective and the high-power objective of a microscope. Draw and label a pollen grain.

Guide Inquiry

Invitation
Ask: **What is the function of the flower?** (*Reproduction*) Ask students to think about how each structure of the flower relates to the two stages of reproduction in angiosperms—pollination and fertilization.

Introduce the Procedure
- Introduce or review the use of a microscope and how to make a wet mount.
- To obtain pollen samples, students can simply tap the stamen of the flower if sufficiently developed. If the flower has just opened, demonstrate how to crush the stamen against the slide.

PART 3 The Female Part of the Flower

10. Use a scalpel to cut the pistil away from the rest of the flower. Measure the height of the pistil. Examine its shape. Observe the top of the pistil. Determine if that surface will stick to and lift a tiny piece of lens paper. Record your observations.

11. Lay the pistil on the paper towel. Holding it firmly at its base, use a scalpel to cut the pistil in half at its widest point, as shown in the diagram below. **CAUTION:** *Cut away from your fingers.* How many compartments do you see? How many ovules do you see? Record your observations.

Analyze and Conclude

1. **Observing** Based on your observations, describe how the sepals, petals, stamens, and pistils of a flower are arranged.

2. **Inferring** How are the sepals, petals, stamens, and pistil involved in the function of this flower?

3. **Measuring** Based on your measurements of the heights of the pistil and stamens, how do you think the flower you examined is pollinated? Use additional observations to support your answer.

4. **Classifying** Did you find any patterns in the number of sepals, petals, stamens, or other structures in your flower? If so, describe that pattern. Is your flower a monocot or a dicot?

5. **Communicating** Write a paragraph explaining all you can learn about a plant by examining one of its flowers. Use your observations in this lab to support your conclusions.

More to Explore

Some kinds of flowers do not have all the parts found in the flower in this lab. Obtain a different flower. Find out which parts that flower has, and which parts are missing. *Obtain your teacher's permission before carrying out your investigation.*

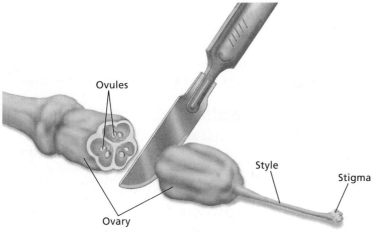

Ovules

Ovary

Style

Stigma

- If pollen begins to fall off as students handle the flowers, they can collect it on a sheet of paper and put it aside for Steps 8–9.
- Make sure students do not grip the test tubes too tightly. Remind students to tell you immediately if any glass is broken.

Expected Outcome

- The top of the pistil (the stigma) may be rough, smooth, sticky, branched, or feathery.
- The number of chambers in the ovary is equal to or is a multiple of the number of petals and stamens.

Analyze and Conclude

1. In circles, in this order: sepals on the outside, then petals, then stamens, the pistil at the center.

2. The sepals protect the flower as it develops and support the base of the flower. The petals may attract the attention of animals by color or scent. Stamens produce pollen, which releases sperm cells. Pistils hold the egg cells.

3. Answers will vary. Possible answers: Colorful petals suggest the flower is pollinated by organisms attracted to colors. A pistil that is taller than the stamens may suggest that the flower does not self-pollinate. A flower structure in which the anthers and stigma are located deep within the flower suggests pollination by small pollinators such as insects or hummingbirds.

4. Flower parts of monocots are usually in threes or multiples of threes. Flower parts of dicots are usually in fives or fours, or multiples of those numbers.

5. Answers will depend on students' observations. Paragraphs should indicate that examination of the flower parts can determine how the structures are arranged in a flower, how the flower parts function relative to one another, the most likely way the flower is pollinated, and whether the flower is a monocot or a dicot.

Extend Inquiry

More to Explore Make certain students' second flower is different from the first flower they examined. Upon comparing flowers, students will discover that flowers vary greatly in structure. For example, some plants have separate male and female flowers, whereas some have male and female parts in different relative positions.

Plant Responses and Growth

Objectives

After this lesson, students will be able to

8.5.1 Identify three stimuli that produce plant responses.

8.5.2 Describe how plants respond to seasonal changes.

8.5.3 State how long different angiosperms live.

Target Reading Skill

Relating Cause and Effect Explain that cause is the reason for what happens. The effect is what happens because of the cause. Relating cause and effect helps students relate the reason for what happens to what happens as a result.

Answers

Effects: Tropisms; Germination; Forming flowers, stems, leaves; Shedding leaves; Development and ripening of fruit

All in One Teaching Resources, Unit 2

• Transparency LS86

Preteach

Build Background Knowledge L2

Descriptions of Plant Growth

Ask students to describe the usual direction of root and stem growth for plants on Earth. *(Roots grow downward; stems grow upward.)* Tell students that researchers are studying how plants grow in low-gravity conditions. This knowledge could help them develop food crops for future space expeditions. Challenge students to speculate how low-gravity conditions might affect plant growth. *(Possible answer: Plants might not grow in the same orientation as they do on Earth.)*

For: Links on plant responses
Visit: www.SciLinks.org
Web Code: scn-0154

Download a worksheet to guide students' review of plant responses.

Plant Responses and Growth

Reading Preview

Key Concepts

• What are three stimuli that produce plant responses?

• How do plants respond to seasonal changes?

• How long do different angiosperms live?

Key Terms

• tropism • hormone
• auxin • photoperiodism
• short-day plant
• long-day plant
• critical night length
• day-neutral plant • dormancy
• annual • biennial • perennial

Target Reading Skill

Relating Cause and Effect As you read through the paragraphs under the heading Hormones and Tropisms, identify four effects of plant hormones. Write the information in a graphic organizer like the one below.

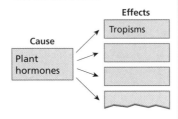

For: Links on plant responses
Visit: www.SciLinks.org
Web Code: scn-0154

284 ◆

Lab zone Discover **Activity**

Can a Plant Respond to Touch?

1.  Your teacher will give you two plants. Observe the first plant. Gently touch a leaf with the tip of a pencil. Observe what happens over the next three minutes. Record your observations.

2. Repeat Step 1 with the second plant. Record your observations.

3. Wash your hands with soap and water.

Think It Over
Inferring What advantage might a plant have if its leaves responded to touch?

The bladderwort is a freshwater plant with small yellow flowers. Attached to its floating stems are open structures called bladders. When a water flea touches a sensitive hair on a bladder, the bladder flicks open. Faster than you can blink, the water flea is sucked inside, and the bladder snaps shut. The plant then digests the trapped flea.

A bladderwort responds quickly—faster than many animals respond to a similar stimulus. You may be surprised to learn that some plants have lightning-quick responses. In fact, you might have thought that plants do not respond to stimuli at all. But plants do respond to some stimuli, although they usually do so more slowly than the bladderwort.

Tropisms

Animals usually respond to stimuli by moving. Unlike animals, plants commonly respond by growing either toward or away from a stimulus. A plant's growth response toward or away from a stimulus is called a **tropism** (TROH piz um). If a plant grows toward the stimulus, it is said to show a positive tropism. If a plant grows away from a stimulus, it shows a negative tropism. **Touch, light, and gravity are three important stimuli to which plants show growth responses, or tropisms.**

Lab zone Discover **Activity**

Skills Focus Inferring L1

Materials touch-sensitive plant such as a Venus' flytrap or mimosa; common houseplant such as a geranium or impatiens

Time 10 minutes

Tips If you have difficulty obtaining sensitive plants, contact a biological supply house or specialty gardening shop.

Remind students to wash their hands after touching the plants.

Expected Outcome The leaf of the sensitive plant closes when it is touched. The leaf of the houseplant does not respond.

Think It Over Students might infer that having sensitive leaves helps protect a plant from predators and environmental conditions.

Touch Some plants, such as bladderworts, show a response to touch called thigmotropism. The prefix *thigmo-* comes from a Greek word that means "touch." The stems of many vines, such as grapes and morning glories, show a positive thigmotropism. As the vines grow, they coil around any object that they touch.

Light Have you ever noticed plants on a windowsill with their leaves and stems facing the sun? All plants exhibit a response to light called phototropism. The leaves, stems, and flowers of plants grow toward light, showing a positive phototropism. By growing towards the light, a plant receives more energy for photosynthesis.

Gravity Plants also respond to gravity. This response is called gravitropism. Roots show positive gravitropism—they grow downward. Stems, on the other hand, show negative gravitropism—they grow upward.

Hormones and Tropisms Plants are able to respond to touch, light, and gravity because they produce hormones. A **hormone** produced by a plant is a chemical that affects how the plant grows and develops.

One important plant hormone is named **auxin** (AWK sin). Auxin speeds up the rate at which a plant's cells grow. Auxin controls a plant's response to light. When light shines on one side of a plant's stem, auxin builds up in the shaded side of the stem. The cells on the shaded side begin to grow faster. Eventually, the cells on the stem's shaded side are longer than those on its sunny side. So the stem bends toward the light.

In addition to tropisms, plant hormones also control many other plant activities. Some of these activities are germination, the formation of flowers, stems, and leaves, the shedding of leaves, and the development and ripening of fruit.

 Reading Checkpoint What is one role that the plant hormone auxin plays?

FIGURE 26
Tropisms

Touch, light, and gravity are three stimuli to which plants show growth responses, or tropisms.

▲ **Touch** A vine coiling around a wire shows positive thigmotropism.

▲ **Light** A plant's stems and flowers growing toward light show positive phototropism.

▲ **Gravity** A plant's stem growing upward, against the pull of gravity, shows negative gravitropism.

Chapter 8 ◆ 285

Seasonal Changes

Teach Key Concepts L2

The Factor of Darkness in Blooming

Focus Ask: **Why don't some plants bloom in winter in locations that have seasonal changes?** *(Temperatures are too low and days are too short.)*

Teach Ask: **What environmental factor triggers plants to flower?** *(The amount of darkness a plant receives)* **What is photoperiodism?** *(A plant's response to hours of light and darkness)* **When does a short-day plant flower?** *(When nights are longer than its critical night length)* **A long-day plant?** *(When nights are shorter than its critical night length)* **If a long-day plant has a critical night length of 10 hours, when will it flower?** *(When nights are shorter than 10 hours)* **What are plants that bloom no matter what the periods of darkness called?** *(Day-neutral plants)*

Apply Ask students to infer the advantage of different plants flowering at different times of the year. *(Possible answers: The plant's pollinators may pollinate only during certain times of the year. Plants have adapted to the climate—for example, a particular plant may not be able to flower during the summer.)* **learning modality: logical/ mathematical**

All in One Teaching Resources, Unit 2

• Transparency LS87

Help Students Read L1

Sequencing Refer to the Content Refresher for guidelines on sequencing. After students have read the passage *Winter Dormancy,* have them sketch the steps showing the changes a tree undergoes when winter approaches. Have them label each step and write in their own words what happens.

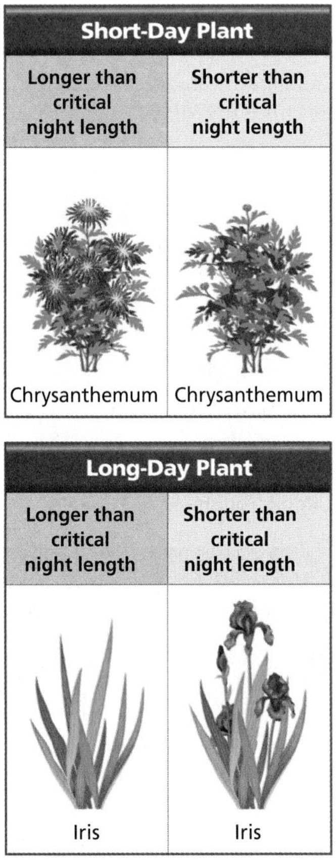

Short-Day Plant	
Longer than critical night length	Shorter than critical night length
Chrysanthemum	Chrysanthemum

Long-Day Plant	
Longer than critical night length	Shorter than critical night length
Iris	Iris

FIGURE 27
Short-Day and Long-Day Plants
A short-day plant flowers when nights are longer than the critical night length. A long-day plant flowers when nights are shorter than the critical night length.
Applying Concepts *Is an iris or chrysanthemum more likely to flower in early summer?*

Seasonal Changes

People have long observed that plants respond to the changing seasons. Some plants bloom in early spring, while others don't bloom until summer. The leaves on some trees change color in autumn and then fall off by winter. **Plant responses to seasonal changes include photoperiodism and dormancy.**

Photoperiodism What environmental factor triggers a plant to flower? The amount of darkness a plant receives determines the time of flowering in many plants. A plant's response to seasonal changes in length of night and day is called **photoperiodism.**

Plants differ in how they respond to the length of nights. **Short-day plants** flower when nights are *longer* than a critical length. **Long-day plants** flower when nights are *shorter* than a critical length. This critical length, called the **critical night length,** is the number of hours of darkness that determines whether or not a plant will flower. For example, if a short-day plant has a critical night length of 11 hours, it will flower only when nights are longer than 11 hours.

Short-day plants bloom in the fall or winter, when nights are growing longer. Chrysanthemums and poinsettias are short-day plants. In contrast, long-day plants flower in the spring or summer, when nights are getting shorter. Long-day plants include irises and lettuce.

Other plants, such as dandelions, rice, and tomatoes, are **day-neutral plants.** Their flowering cycle is not sensitive to periods of light and dark.

Dormancy As winter draws near, many plants prepare to go into a state of dormancy. **Dormancy** is a period when an organism's growth or activity stops. Dormancy helps plants survive freezing temperatures and the lack of liquid water.

With many trees, the first change is that the leaves begin to turn color. Cooler weather and shorter days cause the leaves to stop making chlorophyll. As chlorophyll breaks down, yellow and orange pigments become visible. In addition, the plant begins to produce new red pigments. The brilliant colors of autumn leaves result.

Over the next few weeks, all of the remaining sugar and water are transported out of the tree's leaves. The leaves then fall to the ground, and the tree is ready for winter.

 Reading Checkpoint What is dormancy?

Life Spans of Angiosperms

Angiosperms are classified as annuals, biennials, or perennials based on the length of their life cycles. Flowering plants that complete a life cycle within one growing season are called **annuals.** Most annuals have herbaceous stems. Annuals include marigolds, petunias, wheat, and cucumbers.

Angiosperms that complete their life cycle in two years are called **biennials** (by EN ee ulz). In the first year, biennials germinate and grow roots, very short stems, and leaves. During their second year, biennials lengthen their stems, grow new leaves, and then produce flowers and seeds. Once the flowers produce seeds, the plant dies. Parsley, celery, and foxglove are biennials.

Flowering plants that live for more than two years are called **perennials.** Most perennials flower every year. Some perennials, such as peonies, have herbaceous stems. The leaves and stems of these plants die each winter, and new ones are produced each spring. Most perennials, however, have woody stems that live through the winter. Maple trees are examples of woody perennials.

 Reading Checkpoint How long does a biennial live?

▲ **Annual:** Morning glory

◀ **Biennial:** Foxglove

Perennial: Peony ▶

FIGURE 28
Life Spans of Angiosperms
Annuals live for one year. Biennials live for two years, and perennials live for many years.

Section 5 Assessment

Target Reading Skill Relating Cause and Effect Refer to your graphic organizer about plant hormones to help you answer Question 1.

Reviewing Key Concepts

1. a. Describing Describe three tropisms that take place in plants.
b. Explaining How does auxin control a plant's response to light?
c. Developing Hypotheses The stems of your morning glory plants have wrapped around your garden fence. Explain why this has occurred.

2. a. Defining What is photoperiodism? What is winter dormancy?
b. Comparing and Contrasting How do short-day plants and long-day plants differ?
c. Sequencing List in order the changes that a tree undergoes as winter approaches.

3. a. Defining How do annuals, biennials, and perennials differ?
b. Applying Concepts Is the grass that grows on most lawns an annual, a biennial, or a perennial? Explain.

Lab zone At-Home **Activity**

Sun Seekers With a family member, soak some corn seeds or lima bean seeds in water overnight. Then push them gently into some soil in a paper cup until they are just covered. Keep the soil moist. When you see the stems break through the soil, place the cup in a sunny window. After a few days, explain to your family member why the plants grew in the direction they did.

Chapter 8 ◆ 287

All in One Teaching Resources, Unit 2

- Section Summary: *Plant Responses and Growth*
- Review and Reinforce: *Plant Responses and Growth*
- Enrich: *Plant Responses and Growth*

Lab zone At-Home **Activity**

Sun Seekers L2 Review the explanation with students: the plants respond with positive phototropism because they grow toward light. Ask students to identify what part of the seedling demonstrated positive gravitropism. *(Roots)*

Life Spans of Angiosperms

Teach Key Concepts L2

Annuals, Biennials, and Perennials

Focus Review the meanings of the terms *annual, biennial,* and *perennial.*

Teach Ask: **What are the life spans of angiosperms?** *(Annuals—one growing season, biennial—two years; perennials—many years)*

Apply Ask: **Why are trees sold as seedlings rather than seeds?** *(Trees are perennials and too slow-growing to start as seeds.)* **learning modality: verbal**

Monitor Progress L2

Answers
Figure 27 Iris

 Reading Checkpoint A period when an organism's growth or activity stops

Reading Checkpoint Two years

Assess

Reviewing Key Concepts

1. a. Thigmotropism—a plant's response to touch; phototropism—a plant's response to light; gravitropism—a plant's response to gravity **b.** It makes the cells on the shaded side grow longer than other cells. **c.** Possible answer: The plants display positive thigmotropism to cling to something for support.
2. a. A plant's response to seasonal changes in length of night and day; a period when an organism's growth or activity stops **b.** Short-day plants bloom when nights are longer than a critical length. Long-day plants bloom when nights are shorter than a critical length. **c.** Leaves stop making chlorophyll. Chlorophyll breaks down. Pigments masked by chlorophyll become visible. New red pigments are produced. Remaining sugar and water leave the leaves. Leaves fall to the ground.
3. a. Annuals complete a life cycle within one growing year, biennials within two years, and perennials more than two years. **b.** Perennial; it lives for many years.

Reteach L1

Sketch examples of tropisms, photoperiodism, and dormancy, and have students describe them.

287

Interactive Textbook

- Complete student edition
- Section and Chapter Self-Assessments
- Assessment reports for teachers

Help Students Read

Building Vocabulary

Word-Part Analysis Have students use a dictionary to find the meanings of the prefixes of *annual*, *biennial*, and *perennial* and relate them to their definitions. (*Annual comes from the Latin word* annus, *meaning "year." Annuals live for only one season. Biennial has the prefix* bi- *meaning "two." Biennials live for two years. Perennial has the prefix* per- *meaning "throughout." Perennials live for many years.*)

Vocabulary Knowledge Rating Chart

Have students construct a chart with four columns: Term, Can Define or Use It, Have Heard or Seen It, Don't Know. Students can copy the vocabulary terms for this chapter under column 1, then place a checkmark under one of the other columns for each term. If students did not check the Can Define or Use It column, have them re-read passages with those terms.

Connecting Concepts

Concept Maps Help students develop one way to show how information in this chapter is related. Have students brainstorm to identify the key concepts, key terms, details, and examples. Then write each one on a sticky note and attach it at random to chart paper or the board.

Tell students that this concept map can be organized in hierarchical order beginning at the top with the key concepts. Ask students these questions to guide them to categorize the information on the stickies. **What are characteristics of plants? How can plants be classified? What are the characteristics of seed plants? How are angiosperms classified into monocots and dicots?**

Prompt students by using connecting words or phrases such as "is made up of," "consists of," "may be," and "have," to

---

Chapter 8 Study Guide

① The Plant Kingdom

Key Concepts

- Nearly all plants are autotrophs. All plants are eukaryotes that contain many cells, all of which are surrounded by cell walls.
- Land plants must have ways to obtain water and other nutrients from their surroundings, retain water, transport materials in their bodies, support their bodies, and reproduce.
- Scientists informally group plants as nonvascular plants and vascular plants.
- Plants have complex life cycles that include the sporophyte stage and the gametophyte stage.

Key Terms

cuticle	vascular plant
vascular tissue	sporophyte
zygote	gametophyte
nonvascular plant	

② Plants Without Seeds

Key Concepts

- Mosses, liverworts, and hornworts are low-growing plants that live in moist environments where they can absorb water and other nutrients directly from their environment.
- Ferns, horsetails, and club mosses have vascular tissue and do not produce seeds. They reproduce by releasing spores.

Key Terms

rhizoid	frond

③ The Characteristics of Seed Plants

Key Concepts

- Seed plants have vascular tissue and use pollen and seeds to reproduce.
- If a seed lands in an area where conditions are favorable, it can begin to develop into a plant.
- Roots anchor a plant in the ground and absorb water and minerals. Stems carry substances between roots and leaves, provide support, and hold up the leaves. Leaves capture the sun's energy for photosynthesis.

Key Terms

phloem	embryo	cambium
xylem	cotyledon	transpiration
pollen	germination	
seed	root cap	

④ Gymnosperms and Angiosperms

Key Concepts

- Every gymnosperm produces naked seeds. In addition, many gymnosperms have needle-like or scalelike leaves, and deep-growing roots.
- During gymnosperm reproduction, pollen falls from a male cone onto a female cone. In time, sperm and egg cells join in an ovule on the female cone.
- All angiosperms produce flowers and fruits.
- All flowers function in reproduction.
- During angiosperm reproduction, pollen falls on a flower's stigma. In time, sperm and egg cells join in the flower's ovule.
- Angiosperms are divided into two major groups: monocots and dicots.

Key Terms

gymnosperm	flower	ovary
cone	sepal	fruit
ovule	petal	monocot
pollination	stamen	dicot
angiosperm	pistil	

⑤ Plant Responses and Growth

Key Concepts

- Plant tropisms include responses to touch, light, and gravity.
- Plant responses to seasonal changes include photoperiodism and dormancy.
- Angiosperms are classified as annuals, biennials, or perennials.

Key Terms

tropism	critical night length
hormone	day-neutral plant
auxin	dormancy
photoperiodism	annual
short-day plant	biennial
long-day plant	perennial

---

indicate the basis for the organization of the map. The phrases should form a sentence between or among a set of concepts.

Answers
Accept logical presentations by students.

All in One Teaching Resources, Unit 2

- Key Terms Review: *Plants*
- Connecting Concepts: *Plants*

Review and Assessment

For: Self-Assessment
Visit: PHSchool.com
Web Code: cha-2080

Organizing Information

Concept Mapping Copy the concept map about seed plants onto a sheet of paper. Then complete it and add a title. (For more on Concept Mapping, see the Skills Handbook.)

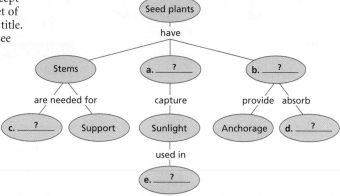

Reviewing Key Terms

Choose the letter of the best answer.

1. The familiar green, fuzzy moss is the
   a. frond.
   b. rhizoid.
   c. gametophyte.
   d. sporophyte.

2. The leaves of ferns are called
   a. rhizoids.
   b. sporophytes.
   c. fronds.
   d. cuticles.

3. The process by which a seed sprouts is called
   a. pollination.   b. fertilization.
   c. dispersal.   d. germination.

4. In woody stems, new xylem cells are produced by the
   a. bark.   b. cambium.
   c. phloem.   d. pith.

5. What kind of tropism do roots display when they grow downward into the soil?
   a. positive gravitropism
   b. negative gravitropism
   c. phototropism
   d. thigmotropism

If the statement is true, write _true_. If it is false, change the underlined word or words to make the statement true.

6. <u>Vascular tissue</u> is a system of tubelike structures through which water and food move.

7. <u>Stems</u> anchor plants in the soil.

8. The needles of a pine tree are actually its <u>leaves</u>.

9. <u>Gymnosperm</u> seeds are dispersed in fruits.

10. Flowering plants that live for more than two years are called <u>annuals</u>.

Writing in Science

Firsthand Account Write a story from the viewpoint of a seedling. Describe how you were dispersed as a seed and how you grew into a seedling.

Seed Plants
Video Preview
Video Field Trip
▶ Video Assessment

Chapter 8 ◆ 289

For: Self-Assessment
Visit: PHSchool.com
Web Code: cha-2080

Students can take a practice test online that is automatically scored.

All in One Teaching Resources, Unit 2
- Transparency LS88
- Chapter Test
- Performance Assessment Teacher Notes
- Performance Assessment Student Worksheet
- Performance Assessment Scoring Rubric

ExamView® Computer Test Bank CD-ROM

Review and Assessment

Organizing Information
   a. Leaves
   b. Roots
   c. Transport
   d. Water and minerals
   e. Photosynthesis
Possible title: Structures of Seed Plants

Reviewing Key Terms
   1. c 2. c 3. d 4. b 5. a
   6. true
   7. false; Roots
   8. true
   9. false; Angiosperm
   10. false; perennials

Writing in Science

Writing Mode Description
Scoring Rubric
4 Includes accurate information with many details; writing is clear and organized
3 Includes all criteria but few details
2 Includes most criteria
1 Includes inaccurate or incomplete information

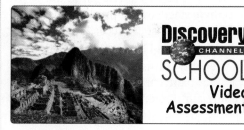

Seed Plants

Show the Video Assessment to review chapter content and as a prompt for the writing assignment. Discussion questions: **What are the three basic parts of a seed?** *(Embryo, stored food, seed coat)* **What conditions are necessary for seeds to germinate?** *(Favorable temperature, water, and oxygen conditions)*

Checking Concepts

11. Sample answer: a way to retain water; a way to obtain water and nutrients from soil; support for its body

12. Mosses are nonvascular plants; club mosses are vascular. Both need to grow in moist environments because they reproduce with spores.

13. Seeds can be dispersed by wind, water, or animals. Some plants shoot out their seeds.

14. Stomata open and allow carbon dioxide to enter the leaf and also allow the oxygen and water vapor produced during photosynthesis to escape into the air. Stomata close and retain water in leaf cells during warm temperatures.

15. Female cones are covered by scales that contain at least one ovule each.

16. Fruits attract and are eaten by animals that help to disperse the seeds, increasing the areas that the angiosperms inhabit.

17. The plant hormone auxin is involved in phototropism. Auxin speeds up the rate at which plant cells grow. It builds up on the shadier side of a plant, causing those cells to grow faster than the cells on the sunny side of the plant. With longer cells on one side than the other, the stem bends toward the light.

Thinking Critically

18. The sporophyte generation produces the spores. The spores develop into the gametophyte stage, which produces two kinds of gametes—sperm cells and egg cells.

19. Students should indicate that their friend probably is mistaken. Mosses are nonvascular plants and cannot grow more than a few centimeters tall.

20. The inner part of bark is phloem. If the bark is stripped around the entire base of a tree, all the phloem is removed in that space. Food made in the leaves can no longer reach the lower parts of the tree. These cells die, followed by the entire tree.

21. If helpful insects are killed by a pesticide, the plants that depend on these insects for pollination may not be pollinated.

22. Plant B is a monocot because it has parallel veins, and it has six petals—the petals of monocots are present in groups of three. Plant A is a dicot because it has branching veins and ten petals—the petals of dicots are present in groups of four or five.

Review and Assessment

Checking Concepts

11. Name one adaptation that distinguishes plants from algae.

12. In what ways do mosses and club mosses differ from each other? In what ways are they similar?

13. Describe four different ways that seeds can be dispersed.

14. Explain the role that stomata play in leaves.

15. Describe the structure of a female cone.

16. What role does a fruit play in an angiosperm's life cycle?

17. What role do plant hormones play in phototropism?

Thinking Critically

18. **Comparing and Contrasting** How does the sporophyte generation of a plant differ from the gametophyte generation?

19. **Applying Concepts** A friend tells you that he has seen moss plants that are about 2 meters tall. Is your friend correct? Explain.

20. **Relating Cause and Effect** When a strip of bark is removed all the way around the trunk of a tree, the tree dies. Explain why.

21. **Predicting** Pesticides are designed to kill harmful insects. Sometimes, however, pesticides kill helpful insects as well. What effect could this have on angiosperms?

22. **Comparing and Contrasting** Which of the plants below is a monocot? Which is a dicot? Explain your conclusions.

 **A**

 **B**

Math Practice

23. **Multiples** Use what you know about multiples to determine which flower is a monocot and which is a dicot: a flower with nine petals; a flower with ten petals. Explain.

Applying Skills

Use the data in the graph below to answer Questions 24–26.

A scientist measured transpiration in an ash tree over an 18-hour period. She also measured how much water the tree's roots took up in the same period.

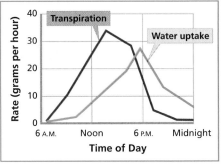

Transpiration and Water Uptake

24. **Interpreting Data** At what time is the rate of transpiration highest? At what time is the rate of water uptake highest?

25. **Inferring** Why do you think the transpiration rate increases and decreases as it does during the 18-hour period?

26. **Drawing Conclusions** Based on the graph, what is one conclusion you can reach about the pattern of water loss and gain in the ash tree?

Lab zone Chapter **Project**

Performance Assessment Present your exhibit to your classmates. Describe your original exhibit and how you changed it based on the feedback you received. Explain what you learned by doing this project. What factors are most important in creating a successful educational exhibit for children?

Lab zone Chapter **Project**   L3

Performance Assessment Students' exhibits should be well organized and should contain detailed pictures and/or drawings of the process used to make their product. As students view one another's exhibits, have them take brief notes. After all exhibits are viewed, discuss any questions or comments students might have.

Standardized Test Prep

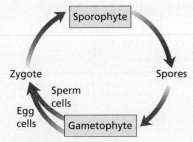

Sample Question
A spore develops into a
 A sporophyte.
 B gametophyte.
 C sperm cell.
 D egg cell.

Answer
Choice **B** is correct. The arrows in the diagram show that spores develop into gametophytes. Choice **A** is incorrect because it is the sporophyte that produces the spores. Choice **C** and **D** can be eliminated because sperm and egg cells are produced by the gametophyte.

Choose the letter of the best answer.

1. Based on the diagram above, which of these statements about a plant's life cycle is true?
 A Plants spend part of their lives producing spores.
 B Plants spend part of their lives producing sperm and egg cells.
 C A zygote develops into the spore-producing stage of the plant.
 D all of the above

2. Which statement below best explains why mosses and liverworts cannot grow tall?
 F They have no rootlike structures.
 G Taller plants in their surroundings release chemicals that slow down their growth.
 H They cannot take in enough oxygen from their surroundings.
 J They do not have true vascular tissue.

3. The diagram below shows the parts of a flower. In which flower part is pollen produced?

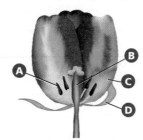

 A part A
 C part C
 B part B
 D part D

4. Which would a student expect to find when examining a dicot?
 F one cotyledon
 G flower parts in multiples of threes
 H stems with bundles of vascular tissue arranged in a ring
 J leaves with parallel veins

5. Which of the following statements is true about gymnosperms and angiosperms?
 A Both gymnosperms and angiosperms produce flowers.
 B Gymnosperms produce flowers, while angiosperms produce cones.
 C Most gymnosperms have broad leaves, while angiosperms do not.
 D Angiosperm seeds are enclosed within fruits, while gymnosperm seeds are not.

Constructed Response

6. Describe three adaptations that plants have for living on land. Explain why each adaptation is important for a plant to survive on land.

Math Practice

23. A flower with nine petals is a monocot because 9 can be divided by 3 to produce a whole number ($9 \div 3 = 3$). A flower with 10 petals is a dicot because 10 can be divided by 5 to produce a whole number ($10 \div 5 = 2$).

Applying Skills

24. Transpiration is at its highest at about 1:30 P.M. Water uptake is at its highest at about 5:30 P.M.

25. The transpiration rate increases throughout the morning until early afternoon, then starts to decrease because most evaporation occurs during the hot middle part of the day. Not much water evaporates in the cool evening.

26. The maximum amount of transpiration occurs about 5 hours before the peak in water uptake.

Standardized Test Prep

1. D 2. J 3. A 4. H 5. D
6. Sample answer: Land plants have roots that absorb water and minerals. A waxy cuticle helps prevent the loss of water from the plant. Vascular tissue transports materials throughout the plant.

Chapter at a Glance

PRENTICE HALL
TeacherEXPRESS™
Plan • Teach • Assess

Local Standards

 Chapter Project *Design and Build an Animal Habitat*

Technology

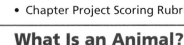 **Teaching Resources, Unit 2**
- Chapter Project Teacher Notes, pp. 160–161
- Chapter Project Student Overview, pp. 162–163
- Chapter Project Student Worksheets, pp. 164–165
- Chapter Project Scoring Rubric, p. 166

Discovery CHANNEL SCHOOL
Video Preview

Section 1 — What Is an Animal?

1 period
1/2 block

9.1.1 Describe levels of organization in animal bodies.
9.1.2 Identify four functions that enable animals to meet their basic needs.
9.1.3 Explain how animals are classified.

Go Online
SC*LINKS*™ NSTA

Section 2 — Animal Symmetry

2 periods
1 block

9.2.1 Define symmetry.
9.2.2 Infer general characteristics of an animal based on its symmetry.

Go Online
SC*LINKS*™ NSTA

Section 3 — Sponges and Cnidarians

2 periods
1 block

9.3.1 Identify the characteristics of sponges.
9.3.2 Describe the characteristics of cnidarians.
9.3.3 Explain the importance of coral reefs.

Go Online
active art

Discovery CHANNEL SCHOOL
Video Field Trip

Go Online
PHSchool.com

Section 4 — Worms

2 periods
1 block

9.4.1 Identify the three main phyla of worms.
9.4.2 Describe the characteristics of each worm phylum.

Go Online
PHSchool.com

Review and Assessment

Test Preparation

 Teaching Resources, Unit 2
- Key Terms Review, p. 201
- Transparency LS100
- Performance Assessment Teacher Notes, p. 210
- Performance Assessment Scoring Rubric, p. 211
- Performance Assessment Student Worksheet, p. 212
- Chapter Test, pp. 213–216

Go Online
PHSchool.com

Discovery CHANNEL SCHOOL
Video Assessment

Test Preparation
Blackline Masters

Lab zone Chapter Activities Planner

Student Edition	Inquiry	Time	Materials	Skills	Resources
Chapter Project, p. 293	Open-Ended	3–4 weeks	**All in One** **Teaching Resources, Unit 2,** p. 160	Observing, drawing conclusions, communicating	**Lab zone Easy Planner** **All in One** **Teaching Resources, Unit 2,** Support pp. 160–161
Section 1					
Discover Activity, p. 294	Guided	15 minutes	Crickets, earthworms, ferns, minnows, pill bugs, potted plants, or sponges	Forming operational definitions	**Lab zone Easy Planner**
Try This Activity, p. 297	Guided	15 minutes	Aluminum cans, drawing materials, modeling clay, paper, wire pipe cleaners	Making models	**Lab zone Easy Planner**
Section 2					
Discover Activity, p. 300	Guided	10 minutes	Circular object, pen or pencil, scissors, tracing paper	Classifying	**Lab zone Easy Planner**
Section 3					
Discover Activity, p. 303	Directed	20 minutes	Hand lens or microscope, natural sponges, scissors, synthetic kitchen sponges	Observing	**Lab zone Easy Planner**
Consumer Lab, p. 306	Directed	Prep: 20 minutes Class: 25 minutes	Piece of cellulose sponge, piece of natural sponge, piece of foam sponge, balance, bowl of tap water, graduated cylinder, beaker, paper towel	Observing, predicting, communicating	**Lab zone Easy Planner** **Lab Activity Video** **All in One** **Teaching Resources, Unit 2,** Consumer Lab: *Soak It Up!* pp. 188–189
Try This Activity, p. 307	Directed	25 minutes	Hand lens or microscope, live hydra, small glass bowl or petri dish, toothpick	Classifying	**Lab zone Easy Planner**
Section 4					
Discover Activity, p. 314	Directed	15 minutes	Bottled water, hand lens, live planarian, plastic dropper, small paintbrush, small transparent container or petri dish	Observing	**Lab zone Easy Planner**
Skills Lab, p. 321	Directed	Prep: 20 minutes Class: 30 minutes	Plastic dropper, clock or watch, 2 earthworms, water, paper towels, storage containers, cardboard, flashlight, tray	Observing, interpreting data	**Lab zone Easy Planner** **Lab Activity Video** **All in One** **Teaching Resources, Unit 2,** Skills Lab: *Earthworm Responses,* pp. 198–200

Section 1 What Is an Animal?

 1 period, 1/2 block

Objectives

9.1.1 Describe levels of organization in animal bodies.
9.1.2 Identify four functions that enable animals to meet their basic needs.
9.1.3 Explain how animals are classified.

Local Standards

Key Terms
• cell • tissue • organ • adaptation • sexual reproduction • fertilization
• asexual reproduction • phylum • vertebrate • invertebrate

Preteach

Build Background Knowledge
Use student sketches to help students identify characteristics of animals.

 Discover Activity *Is It an Animal?* **L1**

Targeted Print and Technology Resources

All in One Teaching Resources, Unit 2
L2 Reading Strategy Transparency
LS89: Asking Questions

○ **PresentationEXPRESS™ CD-ROM**

Instruct

Structure of Animals Define the levels of organization in animals and prompt students to cite examples of each.

Functions of Animals Ask leading questions for a discussion on how different kinds of animals meet their basic needs.

Classification of Animals Use diagrams to show how animals are classified and how different animals are related.

Targeted Print and Technology Resources

All in One Teaching Resources, Unit 2
L2 Guided Reading, pp. 169–172
L2 Transparencies LS90, LS91

www.SciLinks.org Web Code: scn-0211

○ **Student Edition on Audio CD**

Assess

Section Assessment Questions
Have students use their asking-questions graphic organizer to help answer the questions.

Reteach
Use photos of animals to review animals' features.

Targeted Print and Technology Resources

All in One Teaching Resources, Unit 2
• Section Summary, p. 168
L1 Review and Reinforce, p. 173
L3 Enrich, p. 174

Section 2 **Animal Symmetry**

 2 periods, 1 block

Objectives

9.2.1 Define symmetry.

9.2.2 Infer general characteristics of an animal based on its symmetry.

Key Terms

• bilateral symmetry • radial symmetry

Local Standards

Preteach

Build Background Knowledge

Separate objects into those that exhibit symmetry and those that do not.

 Discover Activity *How Many Ways Can You Fold It?* **L1**

Targeted Print and Technology Resources

All in One Teaching Resources, Unit 2

L2 Reading Strategy Transparency
LS92: Comparing and Contrasting

⊙ **PresentationEXPRESS™ CD-ROM**

Instruct

The Mathematics of Symmetry Contrast bilateral and radial symmetry.

Symmetry and Daily Life Describe how the kinds of symmetry relate to animals' general characteristics.

Targeted Print and Technology Resources

All in One Teaching Resources, Unit 2

L2 Guided Reading, pp. 177–178

www.SciLinks.org Web Code: scn-0212

⊙ **Student Edition on Audio CD**

Assess

Section Assessment Questions

 Have students use their Venn diagram on symmetry to help answer the questions.

Reteach

Ask leading questions to elicit from students examples of animals having radial, bilateral, and no symmetry.

Targeted Print and Technology Resources

All in One Teaching Resources, Unit 2

• Section Summary, p. 176

L1 Review and Reinforce, p. 179

L3 Enrich, p. 180

Section 3 Sponges and Cnidarians

🕐 *2 periods, 1 block*

Objectives

9.3.1 Identify the characteristics of sponges.

9.3.2 Describe the characteristics of cnidarians.

9.3.3 Explain the importance of coral reefs.

Local Standards

Key Terms

• larva • cnidarian • polyp • medusa • colony • coral reef

Preteach

Build Background Knowledge

Question students about the features of sponges.

 **Discover Activity** *How Do Natural and Synthetic Sponges Compare?* L1

Targeted Print and Technology Resources

All in One Teaching Resources, Unit 2

L2 Reading Strategy Transparency LS93: Comparing and Contrasting

⊙ **PresentationEXPRESS™ CD-ROM**

Instruct

Sponges Use diagrams to identify the parts of a sponge and the stages of sponge reproduction.

Cnidarians Use diagrams to show how body structure governs cnidarian movement and food gathering.

Life in a Colony Discuss the characteristics of animals that live in colonies.

Consumer Lab *Soak It Up!* L2

Targeted Print and Technology Resources

All in One Teaching Resources, Unit 2

L2 Guided Reading, pp. 183–185

L2 Transparencies LS94, LS95, LS96

L2 Consumer Lab: *Soak It Up!* pp. 188–189

📼 **Lab Activity Video/DVD** Consumer Lab: *Soak It Up!*

PHSchool.com Web Code: cep-2013

DISCOVERY CHANNEL SCHOOL Video Field Trip

PHSchool.com Web Code: ceh-2010

⊙ **Student Edition on Audio CD**

Assess

Section Assessment Questions

Have students use their table comparing sponges and cnidarians to answer the questions.

Reteach

Use figures to review structures involved in the reproduction of sponges.

Targeted Print and Technology Resources

All in One Teaching Resources, Unit 2

• Section Summary, p. 182

L1 Review and Reinforce, p. 186

L3 Enrich, p. 187

Section 4 Worms

2 periods, 1 block

ABILITY LEVELS
L1 Basic to Average
L2 For All Students
L3 Average to Advanced

Objectives
9.4.1 Identify the three main phyla of worms.
9.4.2 Describe the characteristics of each worm phylum.

Local Standards

Key Terms
• parasite • host • free-living organism • scavenger • anus • closed circulatory system

Preteach

Build Background Knowledge
Use examples of familiar experiences with worms to discuss the characteristics of worms.

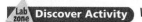 **Discover Activity** *What Does a Flatworm Look Like?* L1

Targeted Print and Technology Resources

 Teaching Resources, Unit 2
L2 Reading Strategy Transparency LS97: Using Prior Knowledge

 PresentationEXPRESS™ CD-ROM

Instruct

Characteristics of Worms Use photographs to identify body shapes of three worm phyla.

Flatworms Use a diagram to identify host and parasite in a tapeworm life cycle.

Roundworms Ask leading questions to discuss the importance of one-way digestion.

Segmented Worms Note where different organs are found in a segmented worm.

 Skills Lab *Earthworm Responses* L2

Targeted Print and Technology Resources

 Teaching Resources, Unit 2
L2 Guided Reading, pp. 192–195
L2 Transparencies LS98, LS99
L2 Skills Lab: *Earthworm Responses,* pp. 198–200

 Lab Activity Video/DVD
Skills Lab: *Earthworm Responses*

PHSchool.com Web Code: ced-2014

 Student Edition on Audio CD

Assess

Section Assessment Questions
Have students use their Using Prior Knowledge graphic organizers to answer the questions.

Reteach
Use pictures to compare and contrast the three worm phyla.

Targeted Print and Technology Resources

 Teaching Resources, Unit 2
• Section Summary, p. 191
L1 Review and Reinforce, p. 196
L3 Enrich, p. 197

Go Online

NSTA-PDi LINKS

For: Professional development support
Visit: www.SciLinks.org/PDLinks
Web Code: scf-0210

Professional Development

Section 1 What Is an Animal?

Movement A defining characteristic of animals is that they are heterotrophs, organisms that acquire nutrients by consuming other organisms. In order to feed, most animals must move, and to move, animals must overcome two forces—gravity and friction.

The particular adaptations for movement depend on which of the three media—air, land, or water—the animal is moving in. Animals encounter less friction in air than in water. However, water provides buoyancy and thereby reduces the effect of gravity. Animals that fly have adaptations, such as wings, for overcoming gravity. They also tend to be less massive than animals that run. Aquatic animals tend to be streamlined, which reduces friction.

Overall, swimming requires the least energy for those animals that are adapted to an aquatic lifestyle. The amount of energy used is also related to the animal's size. Larger animals expend less energy per unit of body mass than do smaller animals—for example, elephants use less energy per unit mass than do dogs. Overall, however, elephants use much more energy than dogs because they are so much bigger.

Section 2 Animal Symmetry

Types of Symmetry There are three basic kinds of symmetry among living things—spherical, radial, and bilateral. Animals that lack these basic symmetries, such as sponges, are said to be asymmetrical. Spherical symmetry (not mentioned in the student text) is rare but may be observed in free-floating organisms, such as some protozoans. Amoebas become spherical at rest.

Some animals exhibit both radial and bilateral symmetry but at different stages in their life cycles. For example, echinoderms are radially symmetrical as adults, but the larvae are bilaterally symmetrical. The presence of bilateral symmetry in the larval stage is one characteristic that shows the relation between echinoderms and chordates.

Section 3 Sponges and Cnidarians

Coral Reef Ecology Coral reefs are the most productive ecosystems, even more productive than tropical rain forests, in terms of the amount of organic matter available for consumption. More productive ecosystems typically support longer food chains and thereby more species diversity.

Another factor that contributes to the enormous species diversity of coral reefs is the large number of habitats the reef supports. The coral reef skeleton provides a structure that supports the corals themselves. In addition, the coral reef provides a substrate for sponges, anemones, and other sessile (nonmoving, attached) organisms. These organisms attract dozens of fish species, including predators such as sharks and rays.

Corals contain symbiotic photosynthetic algae from which the coral obtains some of its nutrients. Corals can survive without the algae, though the rate at which the corals lay down reef is diminished. An increase in water temperature can cause the corals to expel their symbiotic algae and die. This fact is behind the well-known concern that coral reefs may be at risk from global warming.

Section 4 Worms

Germ Layers and Body Cavities As the embryos of most animals develop, they form three layers called germ layers. Each germ layer gives rise to specific organs and tissues. The ectoderm, which is the outermost layer, is the source of sense organs, nerves, and the outermost layer of the skin. The middle layer, which is called the mesoderm, produces the muscles and parts of the excretory, circulatory, and reproductive systems. The innermost germ layer, or endoderm, gives rise to the lining of the digestive tract as well as much of the respiratory system. The illustration shows a simplified version of how these germ layers are arranged in flatworms, roundworms, and segmented worms.

Address Misconceptions

Students may think that the skin disease, ringworm, is caused by a worm. Ringworm is caused by a fungus, which is in a different kingdom altogether from roundworms. For more on this misconception, see **Address Misconceptions** in the section *Worms.*

Body cavities also form during embryonic development. Flatworms have no body cavity other than the digestive cavity. In addition to the digestive cavity, roundworms have a body cavity called a pseudocoelom that is partly lined with tissue derived from mesoderm. Segmented worms, like animals in most complex animal phyla, have a true coelom, which is a fluid-filled body cavity completely lined with mesoderm. Body cavities are important because they provide a space in which organs and organ systems can be located.

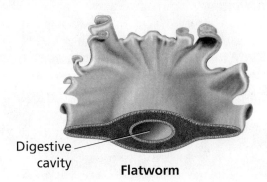

Digestive cavity

Flatworm

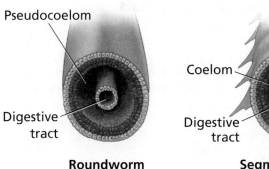

Pseudocoelom

Digestive tract

Roundworm

Coelom

Digestive tract

Segmented worm

Help Students Read

Previewing Visuals

Visualize Important Concepts While Reading

Strategy Help students understand and visualize the steps in a process, or the order in which events occur. Locate a figure showing a process that involves several steps, such as the diagrams of reproduction in sponges or cnidarians, or the tapeworm life cycle. Copy the figure and make blank cycle diagrams for students to fill in as they read the passage and study the diagram.

Example

1. First, have students read the passage and/or study the figure, thinking about what takes place first, second, third, and so on.

2. Point out that the text may sometimes use order words such as *next, then,* or *finally.*

3. Draw a cycle diagram on the board and have students tell the sequence while you write each part in a separate box.

4. Put students in groups and have them locate additional examples of sequential relationships in the chapter and depict them using graphic organizers.

292H

Interactive Textbook
- Complete student edition
- Video and audio
- Simulations and activities
- Section and chapter activities

Chapter Project
L3

Objectives

This project will give students an opportunity to pose questions about how to meet the needs of a particular animal by designing a suitable habitat for that animal. After completing this Chapter Project, students will be able to

- identify the important needs of an animal
- design and build a suitable habitat for the animal
- communicate their findings about the animal and its habitat requirements

Skills Focus

Observing, drawing conclusions, communicating

Project Time Line 3 to 4 weeks

All in One Teaching Resources, Unit 2

- Chapter Project Teacher Notes
- Chapter Project Overview
- Chapter Project Worksheet 1
- Chapter Project Worksheet 2
- Chapter Project Scoring Rubric

Safety

Review the Safety Guidelines in Appendix A. **CAUTION:** *Do not release animals used in this project outdoors after the conclusion of the project (unless they were obtained locally, in which case they can be returned to the location where they were collected). Otherwise, they should be returned to the pet store or supply house from which they were obtained, or kept as classroom pets. It is irresponsible to release animals into a new environment as it can disrupt the local flora and fauna or harm the released animal.*

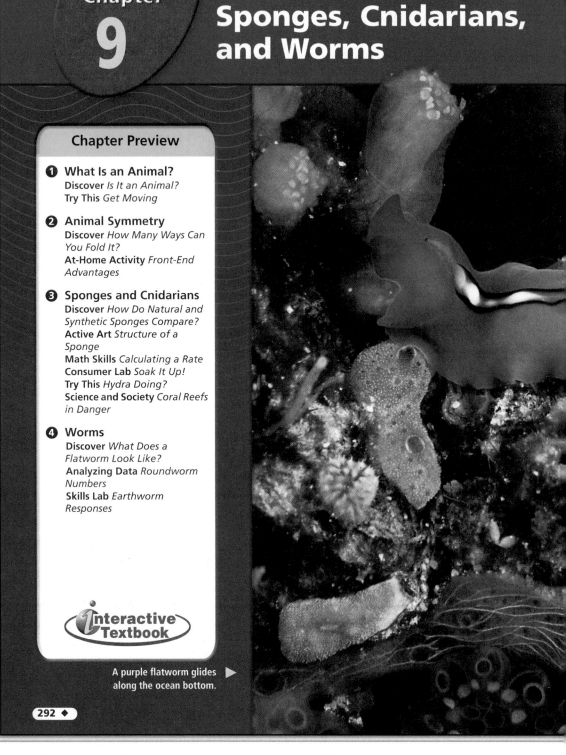

Chapter Preview

❶ **What Is an Animal?**
Discover *Is It an Animal?*
Try This *Get Moving*

❷ **Animal Symmetry**
Discover *How Many Ways Can You Fold It?*
At-Home Activity *Front-End Advantages*

❸ **Sponges and Cnidarians**
Discover *How Do Natural and Synthetic Sponges Compare?*
Active Art *Structure of a Sponge*
Math Skills *Calculating a Rate*
Consumer Lab *Soak It Up!*
Try This *Hydra Doing?*
Science and Society *Coral Reefs in Danger*

❹ **Worms**
Discover *What Does a Flatworm Look Like?*
Analyzing Data *Roundworm Numbers*
Skills Lab *Earthworm Responses*

Interactive Textbook

A purple flatworm glides along the ocean bottom.

292 ◆

Developing a Plan

Students choose their animals, design their habitats, and have their habitats ready for the animals to live in before obtaining their animals. Students can then place their animals in their habitats and observe the behaviors for one to two weeks.

Possible Materials

- Suitable project animals include snails, earthworms, pill bugs, spiders, millipedes, crickets, guppies, and anole lizards. Before students choose their animals, explain any school rules about live animals in the classroom, limitations on classroom storage space, and building conditions such as nighttime and weekend temperatures.

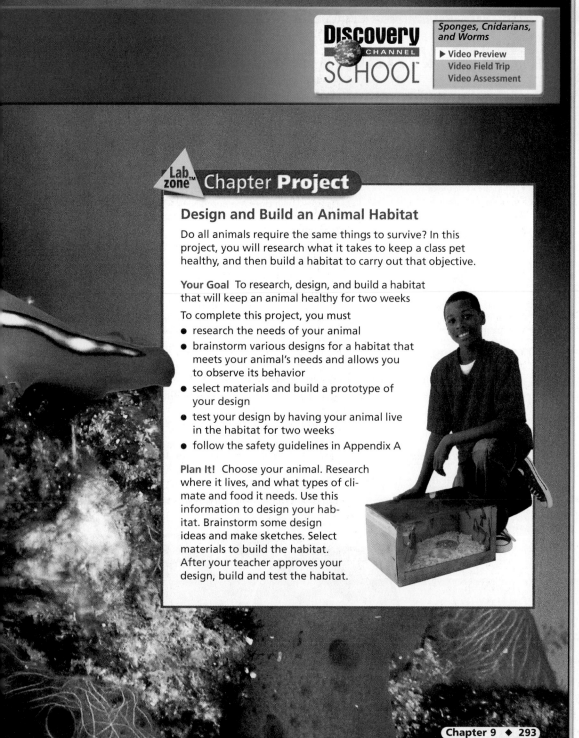

Lab zone™ Chapter Project

Design and Build an Animal Habitat

Do all animals require the same things to survive? In this project, you will research what it takes to keep a class pet healthy, and then build a habitat to carry out that objective.

Your Goal To research, design, and build a habitat that will keep an animal healthy for two weeks

To complete this project, you must
- research the needs of your animal
- brainstorm various designs for a habitat that meets your animal's needs and allows you to observe its behavior
- select materials and build a prototype of your design
- test your design by having your animal live in the habitat for two weeks
- follow the safety guidelines in Appendix A

Plan It! Choose your animal. Research where it lives, and what types of climate and food it needs. Use this information to design your habitat. Brainstorm some design ideas and make sketches. Select materials to build the habitat. After your teacher approves your design, build and test the habitat.

Chapter 9 ◆ 293

- Leaves, vegetable trimmings, and insects are possible food sources. All habitats must have an adequate supply of water.
- A two-liter soft-drink bottle could serve as a terrarium for an insect. Cut off the top of the bottle, fill it with soil, leaf litter, and plants; then, cover the bottle with plastic wrap and cut holes in the wrap for ventilation.

Possible Shortcuts

- You may wish to choose the animal for the students, or keep one animal for the entire class and have student groups care for and observe it on different days.
- Have students observe the animals for only one week.

Discovery CHANNEL **SCHOOL** Video Preview

Sponges, Cnidarians, and Worms

Show the Video Preview to introduce cnidarians and overview the chapter content. Discussion question: **What substances make up the protective shells of polyps?** (*Calcium carbonate*)

Launching the Project

Bring an animal into the classroom. Ask: **What does this animal need to live?** (*Food, water, a place to live, a certain range of temperatures*) **Where could you find this information?** (*Possible answers: In the library, on the Internet, or in a pet store*) **What kinds of things do you think you can learn by watching this animal's behavior?** (*What the animal eats, how it moves, when it is active, where it stays in its habitat*)

Performance Assessment

The Chapter Project Scoring Rubric will help you evaluate how well students complete the Chapter Project. You may want to share the rubric with your students so that they will know what is expected of them. Students will be assessed on
- how well they plan for their animal's care
- how well they observe and record their animal's behavior
- the thoroughness and organization of their presentation
- how well they participate in their groups

Portfolio

Objectives

After this lesson, students will be able to

9.1.1 Describe levels of organization in animal bodies.

9.1.2 Identify four functions that enable animals to meet their basic needs.

9.1.3 Explain how animals are classified.

Target Reading Skill

Asking Questions Explain that changing a head into a question helps students anticipate the ideas, facts, and events they are going to read about.

Answers

Possible student question and answers are these: **What is a cell?** (*A cell is the basic unit of structure and function in living things.*) **What is the structure of animals?** (*The cells of animals are organized into tissues, organs, and systems.*) **What are the functions of animals?** (*Animals must obtain food and oxygen, keep a stable environment within their bodies, reproduce, and move about to meet their needs.*) **How are animals classified?** (*Animals are classified according to how they are related to other organisms.*)

All in One Teaching Resources, Unit 2

• Transparency LS89

Preteach

Build Background Knowledge   L2

Defining an Animal

Ask: **What does an animal look like? How is it different from a flower or a tree?** (*Sample answer: An animal must eat other living things.*) Have students sketch an animal on a piece of paper and list three things that make it an animal. Lead students to realize that there is tremendous diversity among animals.

Section 1
What Is an Animal?

Reading Preview

Key Concepts
• How are animal bodies typically organized?
• What are four major functions of animals?
• How are animals classified?

Key Terms
• cell • tissue • organ
• adaptation
• sexual reproduction
• fertilization
• asexual reproduction
• phylum • vertebrate
• invertebrate

Target Reading Skill

Asking Questions Before you read, preview the red headings. In a graphic organizer like the one below, ask a *what* or *how* question for each heading. As you read, write the answers to your questions.

Structure of Animals

Question	Answer
What is a cell?	A cell is . . .

Lab zone Discover Activity

Is It an Animal?

1. Carefully examine each of the organisms that your teacher gives you.
2. Decide which ones are animals. For each organism, write down the reasons for your decision. Wash your hands after handling each of the organisms.

Think It Over
Forming Operational Definitions Use your notes about each organism to write a definition of "animal."

Your parents may have told you not to eat with your fingers, but they probably never worried that you'd eat with your feet! But animals called barnacles do just that.

A barnacle begins life as a many-legged speck that floats in the ocean. After a while, it settles its head down on a hard surface and fixes itself in place. Then it builds a hard cone around its body. To feed, the barnacle flicks its feathery feet in and out of the cone, as shown below. The feet trap tiny organisms, or living things, that float in the water.

A barnacle may look like a rock, but it is actually an animal. Animals are many-celled organisms that feed on other organisms.

A barnacle feeding (inset) ▲ **and many barnacles at rest (right)**

294 ◆

Lab zone Discover Activity

Skills Focus Forming operational definitions

Materials crickets, earthworms, ferns, minnows, pill bugs, potted plants, or sponges

Time 15 minutes

Tips Make sure students record their observations while looking at

L1 the specimen. Remind students to treat all living things with care.

Expected Outcome Earthworms and minnows will be recognizable as animals; sponges may not.

Think It Over Students may note behavioral characteristics, such as eating, or physical features, such as mouths, hair, or legs.

Structure of Animals

Animals are composed of many cells. A **cell** is the basic unit of structure and function in living things. **The cells of most animals are organized into higher levels of structure, including tissues, organs, and systems.** A group of similar cells that perform a specific function is called a **tissue.** One type of tissue is nerve tissue, which carries messages in the form of electrical signals from one part of the body to another. Another type of tissue is bone tissue, a hard tissue that gives bones strength.

Tissues may combine to form an **organ,** which is a group of several different tissues. For example, a frog's thigh bone is composed of bone tissue, nerve tissue, and blood. An organ performs a more complex function than each tissue could perform alone.

Groups of structures that perform the broadest functions of an animal are called systems. One example of a system is the skeletal system of a frog shown in Figure 1.

Reading Checkpoint What is an organ?

Go Online
SciLINKS NSTA

For: Links on the animal kingdom
Visit: www.SciLinks.org
Web Code: scn-0211

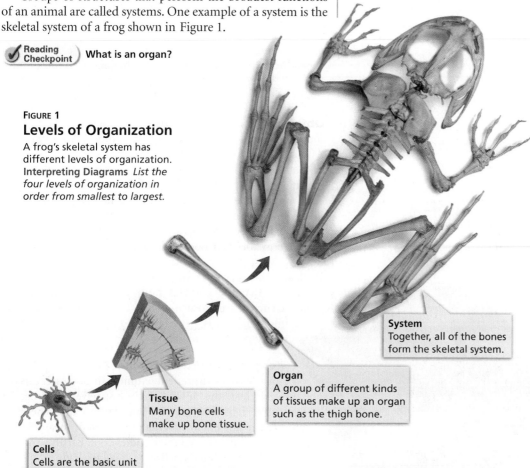

FIGURE 1
Levels of Organization
A frog's skeletal system has different levels of organization. **Interpreting Diagrams** *List the four levels of organization in order from smallest to largest.*

System
Together, all of the bones form the skeletal system.

Organ
A group of different kinds of tissues make up an organ such as the thigh bone.

Tissue
Many bone cells make up bone tissue.

Cells
Cells are the basic unit of animal structure.

◆ **295**

Instruct

Structure of Animals

Teach Key Concepts L1
Levels of Organization in Animals

Focus Tell students that the cells of most animals are organized into levels of structure, including tissues, organs, and systems.

Teach Point out the levels of organization in Figure 1. Ask: **What are cells?** *(Working units that carry out the basic activities of life)* **What are tissues made of?** *(Cells)* Stress that these levels of organization can be observed in nearly all animals with few exceptions (sponges and cnidarians, for example).

Apply Brainstorm with students examples of these levels of organization in different animals. Include as many animals and body systems as time allows. **learning modality: visual**

Independent Practice L2

All in One Teaching Resources, Unit 2

- Transparency LS90
- Guided Reading and Study Worksheet: *What Is an Animal?*

O Student Edition on Audio CD

Go Online
SciLINKS NSTA

For: Links on the animal kingdom
Visit: www.SciLinks.org
Web Code: scn-0211

Download a worksheet that will guide students' review of Internet sources on the animal kingdom.

Differentiated Instruction

Gifted and Talented ✂ 🧤 L3
Observing Tissues Give students a chicken drumstick with the thigh still attached, a dissection kit, and hand lens. **CAUTION:** *Beforehand, soak chicken overnight in diluted bleach solution, and then rinse and store in the refrigerator. Have students wear disposable gloves and use dissecting probes and scalpels carefully. Tell* *students not to taste the chicken, put their hands in their mouths, or touch the chicken with their bare hands.* Ask them to disassemble, sketch, and count the muscles of the thigh and lower leg. Have students carefully slice through one of the larger muscles to make a cross section and then observe it with a hand lens. **learning modality: logical/mathematical**

Monitor Progress L2

Answers
Figure 1 cell, tissue, organ, system

Reading Checkpoint A group of several different tissues

Functions of Animals

Teach Key Concepts `L2`
Classifying Animal Adaptations

Focus Tell students that all animals have the same basic needs.

Teach Review with students the major functions of animals: obtain food and oxygen, keep internal conditions stable, move, and reproduce. Ask: **What are adaptations?** (*Structures and behavior that enable an animal to perform basic functions in the environment*) **Why do animals need food?** (*To get energy for growth and body activities*) **Why must animals maintain a stable environment within their bodies?** (*If balance is lost, they will not survive long.*)

Apply Ask: **How do sexual and asexual reproduction differ?** (*Sexual reproduction involves two parents; asexual reproduction involves a singe organism.*) **learning modality: verbal**

Inferring What an Animal Eats `L2`

Materials Pictures of animal jawbones showing the shapes of teeth

Time 15 minutes

Focus Tell students that tooth shape helps to determine diet.

Teach Give students several pictures to study. Have students describe the tooth shapes in the pictures. Ask: **What are sharp, pointed teeth adapted to do?** (*Tear skin or flesh*) **What are broad, flat teeth adapted to do?** (*Grind or shred plants*)

Apply Have students compare their own teeth and jaws to those in the pictures. Have them describe the characteristics of their teeth. (*Sample answer: Some of my front teeth are sharp and pointed; some of my teeth are broad and flat.*) Explain that humans are adapted to eating both meat and plants. **learning modality: visual**

Help Students Read `L1`
Identifying Details As students read, have them make four index cards with one of the functions of animals on each card. While reading the section *Functions of Animals*, have students record on the back of each card characteristics that help animals to carry out each function.

Functions of Animals

From tiny worms to giant whales, animals are diverse. Animals vary not only in size but also in body structure, outward appearance, and the environments in which they live. Despite their diversity, however, all animals carry out the same basic functions. **The major functions of animals are to obtain food and oxygen, keep internal conditions stable, move, and reproduce.** Structures or behaviors that allow animals to perform these basic functions in their environments are called **adaptations.**

Obtaining Food and Oxygen An animal cannot make food for itself—it obtains food by eating other organisms. Animals may feed on plants, other animals, or a combination of plants and animals. They have adaptations that allow them to eat particular kinds of food. For example, the tarantula shown in Figure 2 has an adaptation called fangs—structures it uses to pierce other animals and suck up their juices.

Food provides animals with raw materials for growth and with energy for their bodies' activities, such as breathing and moving. Most animals take food into a cavity inside their bodies. Inside this cavity the food is digested, or broken down into substances that the animal's body can absorb and use. To release energy from food, the body's cells need oxygen. Some animals, like birds, get oxygen from air. Others, like fish, get oxygen from water.

FIGURE 3
Keeping Cool
This dog is keeping cool by getting wet and panting.

Keeping Conditions Stable Animals must maintain a stable environment within their bodies. If this balance is lost, the animal cannot survive for long. For example, cells that get too hot start to die. Therefore, animals in hot environments are adapted, meaning they have adaptations, to keep their bodies cool. Earthworms stay in moist soil during hot days, lizards crawl to shady places, and dogs pant.

296 ◆

Differentiated Instruction

English Learners/Beginning `L1`
Link to Visual Use the photographs to help students understand the boldface sentence. Read the boldface sentence aloud, slowly, pointing to the appropriate photo as you recite the relevant phrase. For example, when you say "obtain food," point to the spider and grasshopper. Then pair beginners with students who are more proficient in English. Have the pairs discuss the Key Concept. **learning modality: visual**

English Learners/Intermediate `L2`
Link to Visual Do the same exercise that you did for beginners. However, instead of pairing students, have each student write, in English, sentences that explain how animals perform the functions. **learning modality: visual**

Movement All animals move in some way at some point in their lives. Most animals move freely from place to place throughout their lives; for example, by swimming, walking, or hopping. Other animals, such as oysters and barnacles, move from place to place only during the earliest stage of their lives. After they find a good place to attach, these animals stay in one place.

Animal movement is usually related to meeting the basic needs of survival and reproduction. Barnacles wave feathery structures through the water and trap tiny food particles. Some geese fly thousands of miles each spring to the place where they lay eggs. And you've probably seen a cat claw its way up a tree trunk to escape from a barking dog.

Reproduction Because no individual animal lives forever, animals must reproduce. Most animals reproduce sexually. **Sexual reproduction** is the process by which a new organism develops from the joining of two sex cells—a male sperm cell and a female egg cell. The joining of an egg cell and a sperm cell is called **fertilization.** Sperm and egg cells carry information about the characteristics of the parents that produced them, such as size and color. New individuals resulting from sexual reproduction have a combination of characteristics from both parents.

Some animals can reproduce asexually as well as sexually. **Asexual reproduction** is the process by which a single organism produces a new organism identical to itself. For example, animals called sea anemones sometimes split down the middle, producing two identical organisms.

 Reading Checkpoint What is asexual reproduction?

FIGURE 4
Owl Family
Baby owls are produced by sexual reproduction. **Classifying** *Which kind of reproduction involves fertilization?*

Chapter 9 ◆ 297

Lab zone Try This Activity

Get Moving
Design an animal with a new and different way of moving. Your design should help your animal obtain food or get out of danger.

1. Make and label a drawing that shows how the animal would move.
2. Using clay, aluminum cans, construction paper, pipe cleaners, and whatever other materials are available, create a three-dimensional model of your animal.
3. Compare your animal to those of other classmates. What are some similarities? What are some differences?

Making Models What features of your design help your animal obtain food or escape danger?

Lab zone Try This Activity

Skills Focus Making models

Materials aluminum cans, drawing materials, modeling clay, paper, wire pipe cleaners

Time 15 minutes

Tips Encourage students to concentrate on the purposes of moving, such as obtaining food or avoiding danger.

L2 **Expected Outcome** Models may resemble familiar animals with adaptations such as long limbs.

Extend Challenge students to design an animal with a new way of moving underwater. **learning modality: kinesthetic**

Lab zone Build Inquiry L2

Modeling Feeding Adaptations

Materials birdseed, butter knife, cardboard tube (one-half of a paper towel tube or a toilet paper tube), chopsticks, masking tape, plastic dropper, plastic wrap, rubber band, tweezers

Time 15 minutes

Focus Identify some of the feeding adaptations of animals, for example, sticky structures, structures that spear or suck up food, jaws, and structures that filter nutrients from water.

Teach Seal one end of a cardboard tube with plastic wrap and the rubber band. Place about 2 centimeters of birdseed in the tube. Then, tape the sealed end of the tube to a table. Challenge students to find the best way to remove the birdseed using the remaining materials. Allow students to be creative, such as wrapping the knife in masking tape.

Apply Ask: **What real-life adaptations do students' solutions to the problem stand for?** *(Sample answer: The sticky masking tape is like a frog's tongue.)* **learning modality: kinesthetic**

Monitor Progress L2

Writing Have each student choose an animal and write a description of its adaptations for feeding, protection, or reproduction. Students can save their presentation materials in their portfolios.

Answers
Figure 4 Sexual reproduction

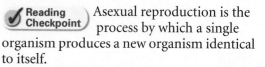 **Reading Checkpoint** Asexual reproduction is the process by which a single organism produces a new organism identical to itself.

Classification of Animals

Teach Key Concepts [L2]

Classification Systems

Focus Tell students that classification systems are ways of organizing information reasonably and realistically.

Teach Ask: **What characteristics do scientists use to classify an animal?** (*How it looks, how it develops, and the content of its DNA*) **What can scientists tell about different groups of animals based on their classification?** (*Their relationship to each other*)

Apply Ask: **If scientists discover a new animal, how would they go about classifying it?** (*They would look at its characteristics to see if they are similar to a particular group of animals.*) **learning modality: verbal**

All in One Teaching Resources, Unit 2

• Transparency LS91

Use Visuals: Figure 5 [L1]

Classifying Living Things

Focus Tell students that the figure shows one way to illustrate relationships among living things. The more closely related groups are, the closer together they will be in the diagram.

Teach Have students read aloud the names on the limbs of the tree. Some of the names will be unfamiliar to students. Tell students that they will learn more about these animals as they study this book.

Apply Ask: **Are insects more closely related to spiders or to mollusks?** (*Spiders*) **Which group probably arose earlier, crustaceans or echinoderms?** (*Echinoderms*) Continue in this fashion with other animal groups. **learning modality: visual**

FIGURE 5

Major Animal Groups

This branching tree shows one hypothesis of how the major animal groups are related. **Interpreting Diagrams** *Are flatworms more closely related to roundworms or mollusks?*

Classification of Animals

Biologists have already identified more than 1.5 million species, or distinct types, of animals. Each year they discover more. Classifying, or sorting animals into categories, helps biologists make sense of this diversity. Biologists have classified animals into about 35 major groups, each of which is called a **phylum** (FY lum) (plural *phyla*). In Figure 5 you can see some animals from the largest phyla. Notice that the phyla are arranged like branches on a tree.

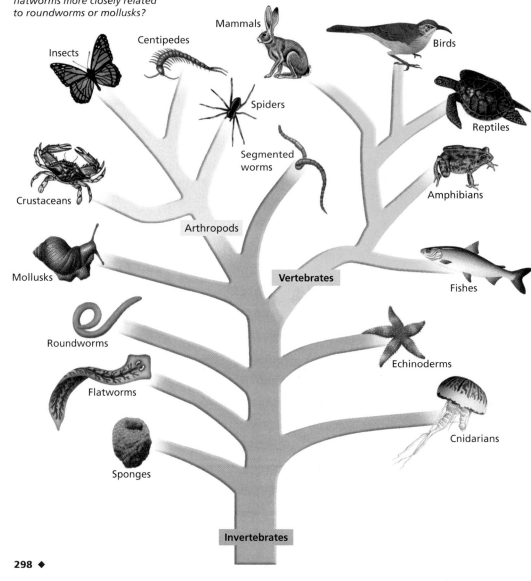

Insects · Centipedes · Mammals · Birds · Spiders · Reptiles · Segmented worms · Crustaceans · Amphibians · Arthropods · Mollusks · Vertebrates · Fishes · Roundworms · Echinoderms · Flatworms · Cnidarians · Sponges · Invertebrates

The branching pattern of the tree in Figure 5 shows how many biologists think the major groups of animals are related. For example, you can see that segmented worms are more closely related to arthropods than to sponges from their positions on the tree.

A branching tree can also show how biologists think animal life has evolved, or changed over time. This process has resulted in all the different phyla that exist today. Biologists do not know the exact way in which evolution took place. Instead, they can only make inferences on the basis of the best evidence available. Biologists hypothesize that all animals arose from single-celled ancestors.

Animals are classified according to how they are related to other animals. These relationships are determined by an animal's body structure, the way the animal develops, and its DNA. DNA is a chemical in cells that controls an organism's inherited characteristics. All **vertebrates,** or animals with a backbone, are classified in only one phylum. All the other animal phyla contain **invertebrates,** or animals without backbones. Of all the types of animals, about 97 percent are invertebrates!

 Reading Checkpoint What is a phylum?

Section 1 Assessment

Target Reading Skill Asking Questions Use the answers to the questions you wrote about the headings to help you answer the questions below.

Reviewing Key Concepts

1. **a. Defining** What is the basic unit of structure and function in an animal?
   b. Sequencing Arrange in order from simplest to most complex structure: tissue, system, cell, organ.
2. **a. Reviewing** What are four major functions of animals?
   b. Summarizing How do animals obtain food?
   c. Drawing Conclusions Why is movement important for animals?
3. **a. Defining** What is a vertebrate?
   b. Classifying How do biologists classify animals?
   c. Interpreting Diagrams According to the branching tree shown in Figure 5, are reptiles more closely related to mammals or to fishes? Explain your answer.

Writing in Science

Functional Description Write a few paragraphs about how your classroom pet or a pet at home performs the basic functions of an animal.

Chapter 9 ◆ 299

Lab zone Chapter Project

Keep Students on Track Group students who have researched and planned habitats for the same kind of animal. Have students discuss plans for acquiring, housing, and caring for the animal. Verify that all students meet the planning requirements of the project and will be able to care for the needs of their animals. Then allow students to prepare the habitats. Check habitats for safety before allowing students to obtain animals.

Writing in Science

Writing Mode Description
Scoring Rubric
4 Includes an accurate and detailed description of all the basic functions the student was able to observe
3 Includes an accurate description and some details
2 Includes sufficient information but lacks details
1 Includes incomplete or inaccurate descriptions

Objectives

After this lesson, students will be able to

9.2.1 Define symmetry.

9.2.2 Infer general characteristics of an animal based on its symmetry.

Target Reading Skill

Comparing and Contrasting Explain that comparing and contrasting information shows how ideas, facts, and events are similar and different. The results of the comparison can have importance.

Answers

Radial symmetry—many lines of symmetry, no distinct front end, live in water, move slowly

Bilateral symmetry—one line of symmetry, halves that are mirror images, front end with sense organs, quick movement

Both—balanced arrangement of parts, perform all the basic life functions

All in One Teaching Resources, Unit 2

• Transparency LS92

Preteach

Build Background Knowledge L1

Observing Symmetry

Bring to class several objects, such as leaves, shells, keys, gloves, and scissors. Sort them into two groups—symmetrical and asymmetrical. Ask: **What characteristics were used to group the objects?** (*Possible answers: round or long and thin; irregular or regular*) After you introduce the section, make sure students understand you sorted the objects based on symmetry.

Reading Preview

Key Concepts
• What is symmetry?
• What can you infer about an animal based on its symmetry?

Key Terms
• bilateral symmetry
• radial symmetry

Target Reading Skill

Comparing and Contrasting As you read, compare and contrast the characteristics of animals with bilateral symmetry and radial symmetry in a Venn diagram like the one below. Write the similarities where the circles overlap, and write the differences on the left and right sides.

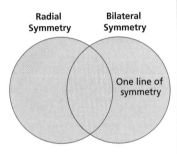

Radial Symmetry · Bilateral Symmetry

One line of symmetry

Lab zone Discover Activity

How Many Ways Can You Fold It?

1. Trace the triangle onto a sheet of paper and cut it out. Then draw a circle by tracing the rim of a glass or other round object. Cut out the circle.
2. Fold the triangle so that one half matches the other. Do the same with the circle.
3. See how many different ways you can fold each figure so that the two halves are identical.

Think It Over

Classifying Name an animal whose body shape can be folded in the same number of ways as the triangle.

Have you ever stopped to look at a butterfly perched on a flower? You probably noticed that bright colors and dark lines criss-cross its wings, making a pretty pattern. Did you also see that the pattern on the left side of the butterfly is a mirror image of the pattern on the right?

The Mathematics of Symmetry

As you can see from the photo of the butterfly in Figure 7, a butterfly's body has two halves. Each half looks like a reflection of the other. **This balanced arrangement of parts, called symmetry, is characteristic of many animals.** A butterfly's symmetry contributes to its pleasing appearance. But, more important, the balanced wings help the butterfly to fly easily.

FIGURE 7
Butterfly Halves
This butterfly's body has two mirror-image halves.
Applying Concepts *What is this balanced arrangement called?*

Lab zone Discover Activity

Skills Focus Classifying L1

Materials circular object, pen or pencil, scissors, tracing paper

Time 10 minutes

Tips Suggest that students first determine how many ways the triangle can be folded before they attempt to fold the circle.

Expected Outcome Students will conclude that the triangle can be folded one way into identical halves, and that the circle can be folded in an infinite number of ways.

Think It Over Students may say that the body shapes of butterflies, tigers, and dogs could be folded the same number of ways as a triangle. The body shapes of a sea urchin and jellyfish could be folded the same number of ways as a circle.

Bilateral Symmetry

Radial Symmetry

No Symmetry

FIGURE 8
Types of Symmetry
Animals have either bilateral or radial symmetry, except for most sponges, which usually have no symmetry.

Animals have different types of symmetry, as shown in Figure 8. In the case of a fish, you can draw a line lengthwise down the middle of its body. This line is called a line of symmetry. An object has **bilateral symmetry** if there is just one line that divides it into halves that are mirror images. In contrast, objects with **radial symmetry** have many lines of symmetry that all go through a central point. For example, the sea star is circular if you look at it from the top. Any line drawn through its center can divide the sea star into two symmetrical halves. A few animals, such as most sponges, have no symmetry.

Reading Checkpoint How many lines divide an animal with bilateral symmetry into halves?

Symmetry and Daily Life

Animals without symmetry tend to have simple body plans. In contrast, the bodies of animals with bilateral symmetry or radial symmetry are complex. **Depending on their symmetry, animals share some general characteristics.**

FIGURE 9
Radial Symmetry
The sea stars in this tide pool have radial symmetry.

Animals With Radial Symmetry The external body parts of animals with radial symmetry are equally spaced around a central point, like spokes on a bicycle wheel. Because of the circular arrangement of their parts, animals with radial symmetry, such as sea stars, jellyfishes, and sea urchins, do not have distinct front or back ends.

Animals with radial symmetry have several characteristics in common. All of them live in water. Most of them do not move very fast. They stay in one spot, are moved along by water currents, or creep along the bottom.

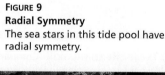

Chapter 9 ◆ 301

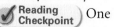

Monitor Progress ———— L2

Answer

✓ Reading Checkpoint   On their front ends

Assess

Reviewing Key Concepts

1. a. The balanced arrangement of parts in animals and other objects **b.** In both types of symmetry, there is a balanced arrangement of parts. In bilateral symmetry, there is only one line of symmetry. In radial symmetry, there are many. **c.** Bilateral symmetry. A grasshopper has a distinct front end and its body parts on one side (such as the legs) are a mirror image of those on the other side.

2. a. They have no distinct front end, live in water, and move slowly. **b.** They are larger and more complex, they have a front end, they move more quickly and efficiently than animals with radial symmetry, and they have sense organs in their front ends. **c.** Having sense organs in their front ends help bilaterally symmetrical animals obtain food and avoid predators.

Reteach   L1

Write the words *bilateral symmetry, radial symmetry,* and *no symmetry* on the board. Ask students to call out names of animals for each category as you write them under the appropriate heading.

All in One Teaching Resources, Unit 2

• Section Summary: *Animal Symmetry*
• Review and Reinforce: *Animal Symmetry*
• Enrich: *Animal Symmetry*

FIGURE 10
Bilateral Symmetry
Animals with bilateral symmetry, like this tiger, have a front end with sense organs that pick up information.

Animals With Bilateral Symmetry Most animals you know have bilateral symmetry, including yourself! In general, animals with bilateral symmetry are larger and more complex than those with radial symmetry. They have a front end that typically goes first as the animal moves along. These animals move more quickly and efficiently than most animals with radial symmetry. This is partly because bilateral symmetry allows for a streamlined body. In addition, most animals with bilateral symmetry have sense organs in their front ends that pick up information about what is in front of them. For example, a tiger has eyes, ears, a nose, and whiskers on its head. Swift movement and sense organs help animals with bilateral symmetry obtain food and avoid enemies.

✓ Reading Checkpoint   Where are the sense organs of an animal with bilateral symmetry typically found?

Section 2 Assessment

⟳ **Target Reading Skill** Comparing and Contrasting Use the information in your Venn diagram about symmetry to help you answer Question 1 below.

Reviewing Key Concepts

1. a. Reviewing What is symmetry?
  b. Comparing and Contrasting How are bilateral symmetry and radial symmetry alike? How are they different?
  c. Applying Concepts What kind of symmetry does a grasshopper have? Explain.
2. a. Identifying What general characteristics do animals with radial symmetry share?
  b. Summarizing What four body characteristics do animals with bilateral symmetry usually have?
  c. Making Generalizations How would having sense organs in front be helpful to an animal?

302 ◆

At-Home Activity

Front-End Advantages With a family member, observe as many different animals as possible in a yard or at a park. Look in lots of different places, such as in the grass, under rocks, and in the air. Explain the advantages an animal with a distinct front end has. Tell the person what this type of body arrangement is called.

Lab zone At-Home Activity

Front-End Advantages L1 Direct students' attention to the paragraph that explains the advantages of having a distinct front end. Ask students to list these advantages. *(Animals move more quickly because of streamlined, balanced bodies. Sense organs in the front end pick up* *information about what is in front of the animal, such as food or predators.)* Suggest students show their lists to a family member when explaining bilateral symmetry. When observing animals at home, students can sketch the animals they see.

Reading Preview

Key Concepts
- What are the main characteristics of sponges?
- What are the main characteristics of cnidarians?
- Why are coral reefs important?

Key Terms
- larva • cnidarian • polyp
- medusa • colony • coral reef

Target Reading Skill
Comparing and Contrasting
As you read, compare and contrast sponges and cnidarians by completing a table like this one.

Sponges and Cnidarians

Feature	Sponge	Cnidarian
Body structure	Hollow bag with pores	
Cell type that traps food		
Method(s) of repro-duction		

◄ Diver investigating a barrel sponge

Lab zone Discover Activity

How Do Natural and Synthetic Sponges Compare?

1. Examine a natural sponge, and then use a hand lens or a microscope to take a closer look. Look carefully at the holes in the sponge. Draw what you see through the lens.
2. ✂ Cut out a small piece of sponge and examine it with a hand lens. Draw what you see.
3. Repeat Steps 1 and 2 with a synthetic kitchen sponge.

Think It Over
Observing What are three ways a natural and a synthetic sponge are similar? What are three ways they are different?

Eagerly but carefully, you and the others in your group put on scuba gear as you prepare to dive into the ocean. Over the side of the boat you go. As you descend through the water, you see many kinds of fishes. When you get to the bottom, you notice other organisms, too. Some are as strange as creatures from a science fiction movie. A few of these unusual organisms may be invertebrate animals called sponges.

Sponges don't look or act like most animals you know. In fact, they are so different that for a long time, people thought that sponges were plants. Like plants, adult sponges stay in one place. But unlike most plants, sponges take food into their bodies.

Sponges

Sponges live all over the world—mostly in oceans, but also in freshwater rivers and lakes. Adult sponges are attached to hard surfaces underwater. Water currents carry food and oxygen to them and take away their waste products. Water currents also play a role in their reproduction and help transport their young to new places to live.

Chapter 9 ◆ 303

Section 3
Sponges and Cnidarians

Objectives
After this lesson, students will be able to
9.3.1 Identify the characteristics of sponges.
9.3.2 Describe the characteristics of cnidarians.
9.3.3 Explain the importance of coral reefs.

Target Reading Skill 🔄

Comparing and Contrasting Explain that comparing and contrasting information shows how ideas, facts, and events are similar and different. The results of the comparison can have importance.

Answers
Possible answers:
Sponge—hollow body with pores; collar cells; sexual and asexual
Cnidarian—polyp or medusa, central body cavity, tentacles; stinging cells; sexual and asexual

All in One Teaching Resources, Unit 2
- Transparency LS93

Preteach

Build Background Knowledge 　　　　L2

Features of Sponges
Ask: **How are sponges used around the house?** *(Mopping floors, wiping up spills, washing dishes)* **What feature of sponges makes them useful?** *(They soak up liquids.)* Tell students that natural sponges were once live animals, and that divers have harvested sponges for thousands of years.

Lab zone Discover Activity

Skills Focus Observing 　　L1

Materials hand lens or microscope, natural sponges, scissors, synthetic kitchen sponges

Time 20 minutes

Tips ✂ Provide students with sponge specimens. Direct students' attention to the pores on the sponge's

surface. Tell them that pores in a natural sponge are the openings of pathways. In a synthetic sponge, the openings are not connected by regular pathways. Students can diagram natural and synthetic sponges and compare their features.

Expected Outcome Students will observe similarities and differences between natural and synthetic sponges.

Think It Over Both have pores, hold liquid, and are soft. They are different in material, color, texture, and shape.

303

Instruct

Sponges

Teach Key Concepts L2

Sponge Structure and Function

Focus Have students study Figure 11.

Teach Ask: **How do pores help a sponge feed?** (*They allow water (food) into the sponge.*) **How do collar cells help a sponge feed?** (*They move water through the sponge and trap food.*)

Go Online
active art

For: Structure of a Sponge activity
Visit: PHSchool.com
Web Code: cep-2013

Students learn about a sponge and how it is dependent on water for survival.

All in One Teaching Resources, Unit 2

• Transparency LS94

Lab zone Teacher Demo L2

Observing Sponge Spikes

Materials 50% bleach solution, binocular microscope, large jar, natural dried sponge

Time 10 minutes for setup, 1–2 days to complete demonstration

Focus Tell students that spikes are made of calcium carbonate (like chalk or limestone) or silicon dioxide (glass).

Teach Prepare 600 mL of bleach solution by pouring bleach into an equal amount of water. **CAUTION:** *Wear goggles and an apron.* Fill the jar with solution and place the sponge in the jar. Seal and let stand overnight. Carefully pour out the liquid making sure not to pour out the gel and spikes on the bottom. Place some gel under a microscope for students to observe.

Apply Have students draw the shapes they see. **learning modality: visual**

Independent Practice L2

All in One Teaching Resources, Unit 2

• Guided Reading and Study Worksheet: *Sponges and Cnidarians*

 **Student Edition on Audio CD**

304

Go Online
active art

For: Structure of a Sponge activity
Visit: PHSchool.com
Web Code: cep-2013

FIGURE 11
Structure of a Sponge

Structures surrounding the central cavity of a sponge are adapted for different functions.
Interpreting Diagrams *Which kind of cell in the sponge digests and distributes food?*

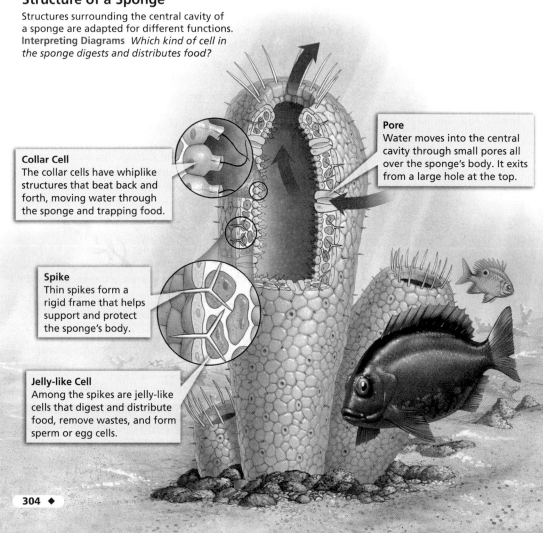

Collar Cell
The collar cells have whiplike structures that beat back and forth, moving water through the sponge and trapping food.

Pore
Water moves into the central cavity through small pores all over the sponge's body. It exits from a large hole at the top.

Spike
Thin spikes form a rigid frame that helps support and protect the sponge's body.

Jelly-like Cell
Among the spikes are jelly-like cells that digest and distribute food, remove wastes, and form sperm or egg cells.

Body Structure **Sponges are invertebrate animals that usually have no body symmetry and never have tissues or organs.** A sponge looks something like a hollow bag with a large opening at one end and many tiny pores covering its surface. In fact, the name of the phylum to which sponges belong—phylum Porifera—means "having pores."

Look at Figure 11. A sponge's body has different kinds of cells and structures for different functions. For example, most sponges have spikes. The network of spikes throughout the sponge supports its soft body, keeping it upright in the water. The spikes also help a sponge defend itself against an animal that might eat it, which is called a predator. The spikes can be as sharp as needles. Even so, some fish eat sponges.

Differentiated Instruction

Special Needs L1
Interpreting Visuals As students examine Figure 11, make sure they understand that the enlargement feature on the diagram helps them to better see the collar cells and spikes. Have students note the arrows and describe what they indicate. (*The path of water through a sponge*) **learning modality: visual**

FIGURE 12

Reproduction of a Sponge

The sexual reproduction of sponges involves a larval stage that moves. Adult sponges stay in one place.

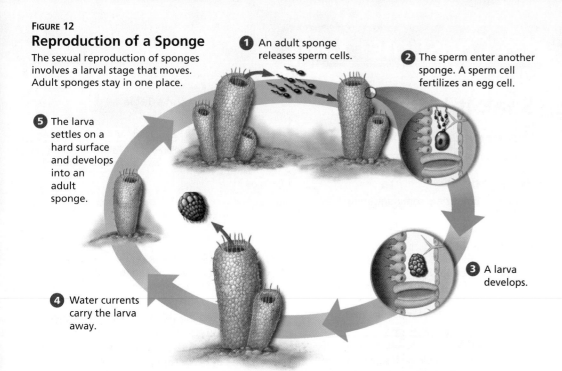

1 An adult sponge releases sperm cells.

2 The sperm enter another sponge. A sperm cell fertilizes an egg cell.

3 A larva develops.

4 Water currents carry the larva away.

5 The larva settles on a hard surface and develops into an adult sponge.

Obtaining Food and Oxygen A sponge eats tiny single-celled organisms. The sponge filters these organisms from the water moving through it. The collar cells that line the central cavity trap the tiny organisms. Jelly-like cells inside the sponge then digest, or break down, the food. Larger sponges can filter thousands of liters of water per day!

A sponge gets its oxygen from water, too. After the water moves through a sponge's pores, it passes over cells inside the sponge. Oxygen in the water then moves into the sponge's cells.

Reproduction Sponges reproduce both asexually and sexually. Budding is one form of asexual reproduction in sponges. In budding, small new sponges grow from the sides of an adult sponge. Eventually, the buds break free and begin life on their own.

Sponges reproduce sexually, too, but they do not have separate sexes. A sponge produces both sperm cells and egg cells. The sperm cells are released into the water. They enter another sponge and fertilize its eggs, as shown in Figure 12. After fertilization, a larva develops. A **larva** (plural *larvae*) is an immature form of an animal that looks very different from the adult.

 Reading Checkpoint What is a larva?

Math Skills

Calculating a Rate

To calculate the rate of water flow in a sponge, divide the volume of water that the sponge filters by the time it takes the water to pass through the sponge.

$$\text{Flow rate} = \frac{\text{Volume of water}}{\text{Time}}$$

For example, a marble-sized sponge filters 15.6 liters of water in a day. How many liters does it filter per hour?

$$\frac{15.6 \text{ L}}{24 \text{ h}} = 0.65 \text{ L/h}$$

Practice Problem In 4 days, a sponge filters 1,200 L. What is its rate of water flow per day?

Chapter 9 ◆ 305

 **Math Skills**

Math Skills Calculating a Rate

Focus Tell students they will divide volume by time to get a rate in liters per hour.

Teach Remind students that it is often necessary to use conversions to find rates. In the example, days must be converted to hours. Then, divide volume by time to get the rate.

Answers
300 L/day

 Build **Inquiry**

Diffusion in Sponges

Materials clock or watch, food coloring, large plastic beaker, plastic dropper, water

Time 20 minutes

Focus Explain to students that diffusion is movement of a material from an area of higher concentration to an area of lower concentration.

Teach Have student groups fill a beaker three-quarters full of water and allow the water to stand for 2 minutes. Then, put eight drops of food coloring into the water. Ask: **What does the food coloring look like as it enters the water?** (*It is dark and concentrated.*) Have students observe the water every 2 minutes over a 10-minute period. Ask: **What happened to the food coloring?** (*It spread evenly through the water.*)

Apply Tell students the way the food coloring spreads through the water is diffusion, and is similar to the way oxygen in water diffuses into a sponge's cells. **learning modality: kinesthetic**

All in One Teaching Resources, Unit 2
• Transparency LS95

Monitor Progress

Oral Presentation Ask students to compare and contrast the pores and large opening at the top of a sponge. (*Water enters the sponge through the pores and exits through the larger opening.*)

Answers
Figure 11 Jelly-like cells

 Reading Checkpoint An immature form of an animal that looks very different from the adult

Consumer Lab

Soak It Up! L2

Prepare for Inquiry

Key Concept
Natural and artificial sponges can be compared for their ability to absorb water.

Skills Objectives
After this lab, students will be able to
- observe which sponge absorbed the most water
- predict how a change in a sponge's mass would affect the absorption of water
- communicate a recommendation to consumers

Prep Time 20 minutes

Class Time 25 minutes

Advance Planning
Buy sponges and soak them in water. Just prior to the lab, squeeze all the excess water out of the sponges so that they are still damp, but so that no water drips from them.

Safety
Make sure students wipe up any spills.

 **Teaching Resources, Unit 2**
- Lab Worksheet: *Soak It Up!*

Guide Inquiry

Invitation
What type of sponge is best absorbing spilled liquids? Show several types of sponges.

Introduce the Procedure
Before students begin, have them carefully examine all three types of sponges to compare their structures.

Troubleshooting the Experiment
Make sure students do not squeeze sponges as they remove them from the bowls. Also make sure that when students remove each sponge from the water, they place it in the beaker as quickly as possible to minimize how much absorbed water drips back into the bowl.

Expected Outcome
The foam sponge will hold more water.

306

 Consumer Lab

Soak It Up!

Problem
Which sponge absorbs the most water?

Skills Focus
observing, predicting, communicating

Materials
- damp piece of cellulose sponge
- damp piece of natural sponge
- damp piece of foam sponge
- balance
- large bowl of tap water
- graduated cylinder
- beaker
- paper towel

Procedure

1. Copy the data table on a separate sheet.
2. Examine the size of the pores in each sponge. Record your observations.
3. Make a prediction about which sponge will absorb the most water. Record your prediction and give a reason.
4. Place a damp piece of cellulose sponge on a balance and measure its mass. Record the mass in the data table. Remove the sponge from the balance.
5. Repeat Step 4 with the natural sponge and then the foam sponge.
6. Submerge the cellulose sponge in a bowl of water. Squeeze it several times to remove all air bubbles. Release the sponge and let it absorb water. Then remove the sponge and place it in the beaker.
7. Squeeze out as much water as possible from the sponge into the beaker. (Hint: Squeeze and twist the sponge until no more drops of water come out.)
8. Pour the water from the beaker into the graduated cylinder. Measure the volume of water and record the volume in the data table. Pour the water from the graduated cylinder back into the bowl. Dry the graduated cylinder and beaker with a paper towel.

306 ◆

Data Table				
Type of Sponge	Mass of Damp Sponge	Size of Pores	Volume of Absorbed Water	
			Total (mL)	Per Gram (mL/g)
Cellulose				
Natural				
Foam				

9. Repeat Steps 6–8 using the natural sponge and then the foam sponge. When you are finished, squeeze all the water from your sponges, and return them to your teacher.
10. Calculate the volume of water absorbed per gram of sponge, using this formula:

$$\frac{\text{Volume of absorbed water}}{\text{Mass of damp sponge}} = \frac{\text{Volume absorbed}}{\text{per gram}}$$

Analyze and Conclude

1. **Observing** Which sponge absorbed the most water per gram of sponge? The least? Was your prediction confirmed?
2. **Drawing Conclusions** What can you conclude about the relationship between pore size and the ability of the sponge to absorb water?
3. **Predicting** How would the volume of absorbed water change if each of the sponges had twice the mass of the sponges you studied? Explain.
4. **Communicating** Natural sponges can cost more than cellulose and foam sponges. Consider that information and the results of your investigation. Which sponge would you recommend to consumers for absorbing water spills? Explain your choice.

Design an Experiment
Design an experiment to test the prediction you made in Question 3 above. Write your hypothesis as an "If … then …" statement. *Obtain your teacher's permission before carrying out your investigation.*

Analyze and Conclude

1. The foam sponge will absorb the most water per gram of sponge. The cellulose sponge will absorb the least. Answers about predictions will vary.

2. Student answers should show an understanding that sponges with smaller pore sizes generally absorb the most water.

3. Doubling the mass of the sponge pieces would increase the volume of water absorbed by each sponge.

4. Student recommendations should take into account the volume of absorbed water

per gram of sponge as well as the cost of each sponge. The foam sponge is the best deal.

Extend Inquiry

Design an Experiment
Students hypotheses might take the form of an "If …, then …" statement. For example, "If three sponges with different pore sizes are tested, then the sponge with the smallest pore size will absorb the most water." Student experimental designs should list the materials they will need and should include clear, logical procedure steps that will test the hypothesis.

Cnidarians

Some other animals you might notice on an underwater dive are jellyfishes, corals, and sea anemones. These animals are **cnidarians** (ny DEHR ee unz), invertebrates that have stinging cells and take food into a central body cavity. **Cnidarians use stinging cells to capture food and defend themselves.**

Body Structure Cnidarians have two different body plans, which you can see in Figure 13. Notice that one form looks something like a vase and the other form looks like an upside-down bowl. Both body plans have radial symmetry, a central hollow cavity, and tentacles that contain stinging cells.

The vase-shaped body plan is called a **polyp** (PAHL ip). The sea anemone you see in Figure 13 is a polyp. A polyp's mouth opens at the top and its tentacles spread out from around the mouth. Most polyps are adapted for a life attached to an underwater surface.

The bowl-shaped body plan is called a **medusa** (muh DOO suh). The jellyfish you see in Figure 13 is a medusa. A medusa, unlike a polyp, is adapted for a swimming life. Medusas have mouths that open downward and tentacles that trail down. Some cnidarians go through both a polyp stage and a medusa stage during their lives. Others are either polyps or medusas for their entire lives.

FIGURE 13
Cnidarian Body Plans

Cnidarians have two basic body forms, the vase-shaped polyp and the bowl-shaped medusa.
Comparing and Contrasting *Contrast the location of the mouth in the polyp and the medusa.*

▼ Sea anemone

Jellyfish ▶

Polyp — Mouth
Central cavity

Medusa
Central cavity
Mouth

◆ 307

> **Lab zone** Try This **Activity**

Skills Focus Classifying   **L2**

Materials hand lens or microscope, live hydra, small glass bowl or petri dish, toothpicks

Time 25 minutes

Tips You can order hydras from a biological supply house. Guide students to observe characteristics of a cnidarian.

Expected Outcome The hydras will respond by wrapping their tentacles around the toothpick. A hydra is a polyp. It moves from place to place by somersaulting.

Extend Ask if anyone sees a hydra with a bulb (bud) developing on its stalk. If so, explain that the hydra is reproducing asexually. **learning modality: visual**

Cnidarians

Teach Key Concepts   **L2**
Jellyfish Texture

Focus Ask: **How would you describe a bag full of gelatin?** *(Possible answer: solid but not hard)* Tell students that the body of a jellyfish has the texture of firm gelatin.

Teach Direct students' attention to the pictures of the cnidarian polyp and medusa. Ask: **How do they differ?** *(The opening to the central cavity is at the top of a polyp and on the bottom in the medusa.)* Point out that some cnidarians go through both stages during their life. **How do cnidarians reproduce?** *(Both sexually and asexually)*

Apply Ask: **How is the medusa body plan adapted to life in the water?** *(Possible answer: The shape enables the animal to float and be carried easily by the water.)* **learning modality: kinesthetic**

Help Students Read   **L1**
Previewing Visuals Refer to the Content Refresher, which provides guidelines for Previewing Visuals. Draw students' attention to Figure 13. Point out that a medusa may be thought of as a polyp turned upside down, or vice versa. Have students note that both have tentacles, a central cavity, and a mouth.

Monitor Progress   **L2**

Writing Ask students to write two diary entries, the first from the viewpoint of a sponge, and the second from the viewpoint of a cnidarian. Entries should include what and how the animals eat, and a description of the animals' physical features. Students can save their diary entries in their portfolios.

Portfolio

Answer
Figure 13 Polyps have mouths that face upward; medusas have mouths that face downward.

Modeling Movement in Cnidarians

Materials balloon, umbrella

Time 10 minutes

Focus Remind students that adult sponges do not move, as compared to cnidarians, which are highly mobile by comparison.

Teach Give each student group a balloon partially filled with water. (Note: You may wish to do this activity as a demonstration.) Tell students that the balloon represents a cnidarian gastrovascular cavity. Have students gently squeeze the balloon to make it change shape, with one part growing larger while the other shrinks. Next, have students take turns rapidly opening and closing the umbrella. Tell them that this action models the movement of a medusa.

Apply Explain that medusas have muscles that contract the bell in a similar way. Just as the umbrella pushes air backward, a medusa's bell pushes water backward, thus propelling the organism forward. **learning modality: kinesthetic**

FIGURE 14
Cnidarian Attack!
A stinging cell fires when its trigger brushes against prey, such as a fish.

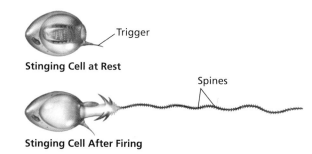

Trigger

Stinging Cell at Rest

Spines

Stinging Cell After Firing

Obtaining Food Both polyps and medusas obtain food in the same way. Cnidarians use stinging cells to catch the animals they eat, which are called prey. You can see a stinging cell in Figure 14. The cell contains a threadlike structure, which has many sharp spines. When the stinging cell touches prey, this threadlike structure explodes out of the cell and into the prey. Some stinging cells also release venom into the prey. When the prey becomes helpless, the cnidarian uses its tentacles to pull the prey into its mouth. From there, the prey passes into a hollow central body cavity, where it is digested. Undigested food is expelled through the mouth.

Movement Unlike adult sponges, many cnidarians can move to escape danger and to obtain food. Some cnidarians have muscle-like tissues that allow them to move in different ways. Jellyfishes swim through the water, and hydras turn slow somersaults. Sea anemones stretch out, shrink down, bend slowly from side to side, and often move slowly from place to place. A cnidarian's movements are directed by nerve cells that are spread out like a basketball net. This nerve net helps a cnidarian respond quickly to danger and to nearby food.

FIGURE 15
Movement of a Medusa
A medusa's nerve net signals the top part of the medusa's body to contract and relax. As the top of its body contracts, the medusa moves upward through the water.

308 ◆

Differentiated Instruction

Less Proficient Readers L1
Silent Consonants Students may have difficulty remembering that the *c* in *cnidarian* is silent. Write the word *cnidarian* on the board. Point out that the word begins with the letter *c*. Then say the word out loud. Call on volunteers to repeat the word. You might point out other words that begin with silent consonants, such as *pneumonia, knot, psalm, psychology, knuckle,* and *know*. **learning modality: verbal**

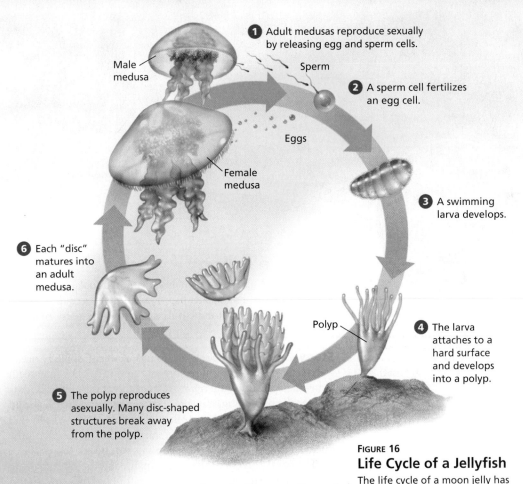

① Adult medusas reproduce sexually by releasing egg and sperm cells.

Male medusa

Sperm

② A sperm cell fertilizes an egg cell.

Eggs

Female medusa

③ A swimming larva develops.

⑥ Each "disc" matures into an adult medusa.

Polyp

④ The larva attaches to a hard surface and develops into a polyp.

⑤ The polyp reproduces asexually. Many disc-shaped structures break away from the polyp.

FIGURE 16

Life Cycle of a Jellyfish

The life cycle of a moon jelly has both a polyp and a medusa stage, and both asexual reproduction and sexual reproduction. **Interpreting Diagrams** *Which form of the moon jelly (polyp or medusa) shows a form of asexual reproduction? Explain.*

Reproduction Cnidarians reproduce both asexually and sexually. For polyps such as hydras, corals, and sea anemones, budding is the most common form of asexual reproduction. Amazingly, some polyps just pull apart, forming two new polyps. Both kinds of asexual reproduction allow the numbers of polyps to increase rapidly in a short time.

Sexual reproduction in cnidarians occurs in a variety of ways. Some species of cnidarians have both sexes within one individual. In others, the sexes are separate individuals. Many cnidarians have life cycles, or a sequence of different stages of development. In Figure 16, you can see the life cycle of a moon jelly, which involves both asexual and sexual reproduction.

 Reading Checkpoint What are two examples of asexual reproduction seen in polyps?

Focus Direct students' attention to Figure 16, the life cycle of a jellyfish.

Teach Pair students and have them read aloud the descriptions of the reproductive stages, starting with number one. Ask: **Which body form is reproducing sexually?** *(Medusa)* **Which is reproducing asexually?** *(Polyp)* **How are polyps produced?** *(Male medusas release sperm, which fertilize eggs of female medusas. The fertilized egg develops into a larva, which then develops into a polyp.)* Make sure students understand that polyps are produced sexually, but that they themselves reproduce asexually. The opposite is true for medusas, which are produced asexually but reproduce sexually.

Apply Compare reproduction in the moon jelly with reproduction in the hydra, which undergoes budding. Budding yields offspring that look like mini-adults projecting from the stalk of the parent. **learning modality: visual**

All in One Teaching Resources, Unit 2

• Transparency LS96

Differentiated Instruction

Gifted and Talented ⬛L3
Comb Jellies Students might be interested in learning about comb jellies, or ctenophores. These organisms, like cnidarians, have a jellylike body that exhibits radial symmetry, but they are in a phylum, Ctenophora, of their own. Students can do library or Internet research to find out the structures, habitats, and other characteristics of these animals. When they have finished their research, students might present their findings in the form of an oral or written report accompanied by illustrations or photographs. **learning modality: verbal**

Monitor Progress ⬛L2

Skills Check Have students compare and contrast how jellyfish, sea anemones, and hydras move.

Answers
Figure 16 Polyp; disc-shaped structures break away and form new individuals.

 Reading Checkpoint Budding, pulling apart

309

Life in a Colony

Teach Key Concepts
Formation of a Coral Reef

Focus Discuss with students that a colony of settlers is a group of individuals living together in one place.

Teach Ask: **How is a colony of cnidarians similar to a colony of settlers?** *(A colony of cnidarians is a group of many individuals living together.)* **How is a colony like a single unit?** *(It moves and functions as one unit.)* Explain how the polyps in a Portuguese man-of-war colony perform specialized functions. Some capture and digest prey; others produce reproductive cells; some are swimming organs that act as floats, or air-filled sacs.

Apply Ask: **Why do you think this colonial organization is rare in animals?** *(Sample answer: Colonial organization requires that individual animals coordinate their activities to become part of a whole organism.)* **learning modality: logical/mathematical**

Sponges, Cnidarians, and Worms
Show the Video Field Trip to let students experience the world of the jellyfish.

◄ **Coral polyps**   ▼ **Coral reef**

FIGURE 17
Coral Reef
The massive reef surrounding this tropical island is made from the skeletal remains of the tiny cnidarians called coral (inset).

Sponges, Cnidarians, and Worms
Video Preview
▶ Video Field Trip
Video Assessment

Life in a Colony

Many cnidarians spend their lives as individuals, but not all. Some species of cnidarians live in a **colony,** a group of many individual animals. Stony corals and the Portuguese man-of-war are two examples of colonies of cnidarians.

Stony Corals Coral reefs are found in warm, shallow ocean waters, mainly in tropical regions of the world. They may seem to be made of stone, but are not. A **coral reef** is built by cnidarians. At the beginning of its life, a coral polyp attaches to a solid surface. A broken shell, a sunken ship, or a rock will do just fine. After attaching to the solid surface, the coral polyp produces a hard, stony skeleton around its soft body.

The coral polyp reproduces asexually, and then its offspring reproduce asexually, too. Over time, that polyp may give rise to thousands more, each with a hard skeleton. When the polyps die, their skeletons remain behind. Over thousands of years, as live corals add their skeletons to those that have died, rocklike reefs grow up from the sea floor. The top layer of the reef is covered with hundreds of thousands of still-living coral polyps.

Coral reefs are home to more species of fishes and invertebrates than any other environment on Earth. Hundreds of sponge species live among the corals, constantly filtering water through their bodies. Worms burrow into the coral reef. Giant clams lie with their huge shells slightly open. Shrimp and crabs edge out of hiding places below the corals. At night, bright blue damselfish settle into pockets in the coral. At dawn and dusk, sea turtles, sea snakes, and sharks all visit the reef, hunting for prey. These living things interact in complex ways, creating a rich and beautiful environment.

FIGURE 18
Portuguese Man-of-War
The Portuguese man-of-war is a
tightly coordinated colony of polyps
and medusas.

Portuguese Man-of-War Sometimes the association of individual animals in a colony is so tight that the colony acts like a single animal. The Portuguese man-of-war contains as many as 1,000 individuals that function together as one unit.

At the top of the Portuguese man-of-war is a gas-filled chamber that allows the colony to float on the surface of the ocean. Various polyps with different functions drift below. Some polyps catch prey for the colony with stinging cells. Others digest the prey. Still other polyps are adapted for reproduction.

 Reading Checkpoint What are two examples of colonies of cnidarians?

Section 3 Assessment

 **Target Reading Skill** **Comparing and Contrasting** Use your table to quiz a partner about how sponges and cnidarians trap food. How do their methods for trapping food differ?

Reviewing Key Concepts

1. a. **Describing** What are the characteristics of a sponge?
   b. **Comparing and Contrasting** How are the cells of a sponge alike? How are they different?
2. a. **Identifying** What is one type of cell that all cnidarians have?
   b. **Sequencing** What steps are involved in how a cnidarian obtains food?
   c. **Inferring** How might a cnidarian protect itself?

3. a. **Identifying** What is a coral reef?
   b. **Summarizing** How is a coral reef built?
   c. **Making Judgments** Why is it important to protect coral reefs?

Math Practice

4. **Calculating a Rate** A very large sponge can filter 1,500 liters of water in a day. How much water can it filter per hour?

Chapter 9 ◆ 311

Coral Reefs in Danger

Key Concept
Coral reefs provide homes and food sources for a large variety of sea life and are in danger of being destroyed by natural disasters and humans.

Build Background Knowledge

Review Life on A Coral Reef

Help students recall how coral reefs are formed. Ask: **What is the first stage in the formation of a coral reef?** *(A free-swimming coral larva attaches itself to a solid surface underwater and then produces a stony skeleton around its soft body.)* Ask: **How do coral reefs, such as the Great Barrier Reef, reach such enormous sizes?** *(The living coral polyps reproduce asexually and over time they produce thousands more. As organisms die they leave behind their skeletons, which form the structure of the reef.)* Explain that it is in the shelter of the reef that a large variety of sea life finds food and shelter.

Introduce the Debate
Explain to students that they will be debating the proposition that "Diving near coral reefs should be banned to protect the reefs from ecological damage."

Facilitate the Debate
- Separate the class into two groups: one to support the proposition, the other to oppose it. Have groups review and investigate the issue from their respective points of view.
- Encourage students in the pro-diving group to explore such ideas as education and environmental awareness as an alternative to banning diving. Encourage students in the other group to think realistically and offer alternatives for those affected by the diving ban.

Science and Society

Coral Reefs in Danger

Coral reefs off the coasts of many nations are in danger. Although coral reefs are as hard as rocks, the coral animals themselves are quite delicate. Recreational divers can damage the fragile reefs. Is it possible to protect the reefs while still allowing divers to explore them?

Diving supports local businesses

The Issues

What's the Harm in Diving?

More than 1.5 million recreational divers live in the United States. With so many divers it is hard to guarantee that no harm will occur to coral reefs. Divers can cause significant damage by standing on or even touching these fragile reefs. Harm to the reefs is even more likely to occur when divers collect coral for their own enjoyment or to sell for profit. You can see brightly colored coral from the sea in jewelry and in decorations.

Should Reefs Be Further Protected?

The United States government has passed laws making it illegal, under most circumstances, to remove coral from the sea. Because a few divers break these laws, some people want to ban diving altogether. However, many divers say it's unfair to ban diving just because of a few lawbreakers.

Many divers consider coral reefs the most exciting and beautiful places in the ocean to explore. As divers and other people visit and learn more about these delicate coral reefs, they increase others' awareness of them. Public awareness may be the best way to ensure that these rich environments are protected.

More Than a Diving Issue

Coral reefs are major tourist attractions that bring money and jobs to people in local communities. If diving were banned, local businesses would suffer significantly. Also, although divers can harm coral reefs, other human activities that result in ocean pollution, oil spills, and illegal fishing can also cause harm. In addition, natural events, such as tropical storms, changes in sea level, and changes in sea temperature, can also damage the fragile reefs.

312 ◆

Reefs house and protect many species of sea animals, including sponges, shrimp, sea turtles, and fishes.

What Would You Do?

1. Identify the Problem
In your own words, explain the controversy surrounding diving near coral reefs.

2. Analyze the Options
List the arguments on each side of the issue. Note the pros and cons. How well would each position protect the reefs? Who might be harmed or inconvenienced?

3. Find a Solution
Write a newspaper editorial stating your position on whether diving should be allowed near coral reefs. State your position and reasons clearly.

Go Online
PHSchool.com
For: More on coral reefs
Visit: PHSchool.com
Web Code: ceh-2010

◆ 313

What Would You Do?

1. The problem is that many coral reefs, which house and protect many species of sea life and protect coastlines from flooding, are endangered, damaged, or threatened with destruction. Recreational divers can cause damage to the reefs.

2. Students' responses should include alternative solutions. The various consequences of banning access to the reefs should be acknowledged and considered when forming solutions.

3. Students should be responsible for providing verifiable documentation to justify their opinions.

Go Online
PHSchool.com
For: More on coral reefs
Visit: PHSchool.com
Web Code: ceh-2010

Students can research this issue online.

Background

Facts and Figures Coral reefs have extremely high levels of animal diversity—nowhere else in the ocean can you find so many kinds of fish and invertebrates. Like rain forests, coral reefs contain many plants and animals that produce potentially valuable chemicals. For this reason, it is important to protect the reefs.

Coral reefs are in danger from natural disasters and from humans. Natural forces, such as water that is too warm, can kill corals and produce a phenomenon called coral bleaching. Organisms that eat living corals, such as the crown-of-thorns sea star, can greatly damage reefs.

In addition to the destruction they cause when diving, people can harm reefs through ocean pollution, oil spills, fishing nets, and construction projects on islands near coral reefs.

313

Objectives

After this lesson, students will be able to

9.4.1 Identify the three main phyla of worms.

9.4.2 Describe the characteristics of each worm phylum.

Target Reading Skill ⟳

Using Prior Knowledge Explain that using prior knowledge helps students connect what they already know to what they are about to read.

Answers

Possible answers:

What You Know

1. Worms are long and skinny.
2. Live in the ground, digest soil
3. Are slimy and wriggly

What You Learned

1. Worms have bilateral symmetry.
2. May be flat
3. Some live in water
4. May be parasites
5. Have a nervous system

All in One Teaching Resources, Unit 2

• Transparency LS97

Preteach

Build Background Knowledge [L1]

Observations of Worms

Ask students if they have ever used worms as fishing bait or dug up worms in a garden. Encourage students to share any observations they have made about the appearance and behavior of worms. Then, ask: **What words would you use to describe worms?** (*Sample answer: Slimy, creepy, crawly*) Inform students that in this section, they will learn about the characteristics and nature of worms.

Section
4 Worms

Reading Preview

Key Concepts

• What are the three main phyla of worms?
• What are the main characteristics of each phylum of worms?

Key Terms

• parasite • host
• free-living organism
• scavenger • anus
• closed circulatory system

⟳ Target Reading Skill

Using Prior Knowledge Before you read, write what you know about worms in a graphic organizer like the one below. As you read, write what you learn.

What You Know
1. Worms are long and skinny.
2.

What You Learned
1.
2.

FIGURE 19
Giant Earthworm
A giant Gippsland earthworm can grow to be more than 1 meter long. It is one of approximately 1,000 earthworm species found in Australia.

314 ◆

Lab zone Discover **Activity**

What Does a Flatworm Look Like?

1. Your teacher will give you a planarian, a kind of flatworm. Pick the worm up with the tip of a small paintbrush. Place it carefully in a container. Use a dropper to cover the planarian with spring water.

2. Observe the planarian with a hand lens for a few minutes. Describe how the planarian moves. Draw a picture of the planarian.

3. Return the planarian to your teacher, and wash your hands.

Think It Over
Observing How does a planarian differ from a sponge?

You might think that all worms are small, slimy, and wriggly. But many worms do not fit that description. Some worms are almost three meters long and are as thick as your arm. Others look like glowing, furry blobs. Worms may glide through water or climb around with paddle-like bristles. Still others are very small and live underwater in tubes cemented to rocks.

Characteristics of Worms

There are many kinds of worms, all with their own characteristics. **Biologists classify worms into three major phyla—flatworms, roundworms, and segmented worms.** Flatworms belong to the phylum Platyhelminthes (plat ee HEL minth eez); roundworms belong to the phylum Nematoda; segmented worms belong to the phylum Annelida.

Lab zone Discover **Activity**

Skills Focus Observing [L1]

Materials bottled water, hand lens, live planarian, plastic dropper, small paintbrush, small transparent container or petri dish

Time 15 minutes

Tips Ask students to discuss how the planarians behave. Have them sketch the planarian and make notes of what they see. Verify that students note the bilateral symmetry of planarians.

Expected Outcome Planarians should react visibly to being touched.

Think It Over Suggest students refer to Section 3. Planarians have bilateral symmetry and distinct head and tail ends. Sponges are asymmetrical and do not have head and tail ends.

FIGURE 20
Three Phyla of Worms
The three major phyla of worms are flatworms, roundworms, and segmented worms. *Observing How are the body shapes of these three types of worms similar?*

Flatworm ▲
Long, flat body

Roundworm ▲
Long, round body

Segmented Worm ▲
Long, round body made up of linked segments

Body Structure All worms are invertebrates that have long, narrow bodies without legs. In Figure 20, you can compare the body shapes of three types of worms. Unlike sponges or cnidarians, worms have bilateral symmetry. Therefore, they have head and tail ends. In addition, they all have tissues, organs, and body systems.

Nervous System Worms are the simplest organisms with a brain, which is a knot of nerve tissue located in the head end. Because a worm's brain and some of its sense organs are located in its head end, the worm can detect objects, food, mates, and predators quickly. It can respond quickly, too. Sense organs that are sensitive to light, touch, and vibrations pick up information from the environment. The brain interprets that information and directs the animal's response. For example, if an earthworm on the surface of the ground senses the vibrations of a footstep, the worm will quickly return to its underground burrow.

Reproduction Both sexual and asexual reproduction are found in the worm phyla. In many species of worms, there are separate male and female animals, as in humans. In other species of worms, each individual has both male and female sex organs. A worm with both male and female sex organs does not usually fertilize its own eggs. Instead, two individuals mate and exchange sperm. Many worms reproduce asexually by methods such as breaking into pieces. In fact, if you cut some kinds of worms into several pieces, a whole new worm will grow from each piece.

 Reading Checkpoint What type of symmetry do worms have?

Characteristics of Worms

Teach Key Concepts L2
Shapes of Worms

Focus Have students note the shapes of the worms in Figure 20.

Teach Ask: **What distinguishes the three worms in the figure?** *(Shape and overall structure)* **What are the shapes and overall structure of the three worms?** *(Flat, round, segmented)* Point out that the terms *flatworm, roundworm,* and *segmented worm* describe major visible characteristics of the groups.

Apply Tell students that they may be familiar with the worm phyla, even though they may not realize it. Many students have observed planarians during school activities, or they may have a pet that has had worms (often tapeworms). Roundworms can often be seen in the soil as tiny, white objects. Finally, the familiar earthworm, which is segmented, is very common. **learning modality: visual**

Help Students Read L1
Outlining Have students outline the section using the red and blue heads. They can write supporting details below each head as they read.

Independent Practice L2
All in One Teaching Resources, Unit 2
• Guided Reading and Study Worksheet: *Worms*

 Student Edition on Audio CD

Monitor Progress ———— L2
Answer
Figure 20 Each worm has a long body without legs.

 Reading Checkpoint Bilateral symmetry

315

Flatworms

Teach Key Concepts L2
Tapeworm Life Cycle

Focus Tell students that flatworms can be as long as 12 meters or so small they are almost microscopic.

Teach Discuss each stage in the tapeworm life cycle shown in Figure 22. Remind students that eating a rabbit is only one way a dog can become infected. Ask: **What are the parasite and the hosts in this picture?** *(Parasite: tapeworm; hosts: dog and rabbit)* Ask: **Why are the pictures arranged in a cycle?** *(To emphasize that the sequence of events is continuous)*

Apply Ask: **Why do you think the tapeworm must attach itself to the dog's digestive system?** *(Its body is adapted to absorbing digested food.)* **learning modality: visual**

Go Online
PHSchool.com

For: More on worms
Visit: PHSchool.com
Web Code: ced-2014

Students can review worms in an online activity.

All in One Teaching Resources, Unit 2
• Transparency LS98

FIGURE 21
Planarian
Planarians are free-living flatworms that live in ponds, streams, and oceans.
Comparing and Contrasting
How does a free-living organism differ from a parasite?

Go Online
PHSchool.com

For: More on worms
Visit: PHSchool.com
Web Code: ced-2014

316 ◆

Flatworms

As you'd expect from their name, flatworms are flat. They include such organisms as tapeworms, planarians, and flukes. Although tapeworms can grow to be 10 to 12 meters long, some other flatworms are almost too small to be seen. All flatworms share certain characteristics. **Flatworms are flat and as soft as jelly.**

Many flatworms are parasites. A **parasite** is an organism that lives inside or on another organism. The parasite takes its food from its **host,** the organism in or on which it lives. Parasites may rob their hosts of food and make them weak. They may injure the host's tissues or organs, but they rarely kill their host. All tapeworms and flukes are parasites.

In contrast, some flatworms are free-living. A **free-living organism** does not live in or on other organisms. Free-living flatworms may glide over the rocks in ponds, slide over damp soil, or swim slowly through the ocean like ruffled, brightly patterned leaves.

Planarians Planarians are free-living flatworms. Planarians are **scavengers**—they feed on dead or decaying material. But they are also predators and will attack any animal smaller than they are. A planarian feeds like a vacuum cleaner. The planarian glides onto its food and inserts a feeding tube into it. Digestive juices flow out of the planarian and into the food. These juices begin to break down the food while it is still outside the worm's body. Then the planarian sucks up the partly digested bits. Digestion is completed within a cavity inside the planarian. Undigested food exits through the feeding tube.

Differentiated Instruction

Gifted and Talented L3
Reaction of Planarian to Light Provide students with planarians, flashlights, transparent plastic containers, bottled water, and dark paper or foil. Have them place a planarian in the dish and cover it with a few drops of water. Then, have them predict how the planarian will react to light and record their predictions. Have students cover half the container with paper or foil and shine the flashlight on the container. The planarians will probably move out of the light. **learning modality: visual**

If you look at the head of the planarian shown in Figure 21, you can see two dots. These dots are called eyespots. The eyespots can detect light but cannot see a detailed image as human eyes can. A planarian's head also has cells that pick up odors. Planarians rely mainly on smell, not light, to locate food.

Tapeworms Tapeworms are one kind of parasitic flatworm. A tapeworm's body is adapted to absorbing food from the host's digestive system. Some kinds of tapeworms can live in human hosts. Many tapeworms live in more than one host during their lifetime. You can see the life cycle of the dog tapeworm in Figure 22. Notice that this tapeworm has two different hosts—a dog and a rabbit.

 Reading Checkpoint How does a scavenger obtain food?

FIGURE 22
Life Cycle of a Dog Tapeworm
The tapeworm is a parasite that lives in more than one host during its life cycle.

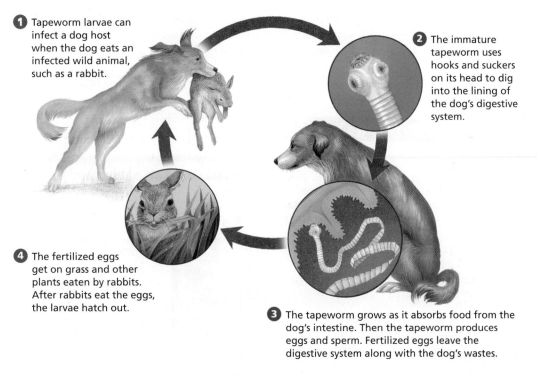

❶ Tapeworm larvae can infect a dog host when the dog eats an infected wild animal, such as a rabbit.

❷ The immature tapeworm uses hooks and suckers on its head to dig into the lining of the dog's digestive system.

❹ The fertilized eggs get on grass and other plants eaten by rabbits. After rabbits eat the eggs, the larvae hatch out.

❸ The tapeworm grows as it absorbs food from the dog's intestine. Then the tapeworm produces eggs and sperm. Fertilized eggs leave the digestive system along with the dog's wastes.

Chapter 9 ◆ 317

 **Lab zone** **Build Inquiry** ⬛L3

Planarian Feeding Behavior

Materials bottled water, ground meat, hand lens, lettuce, live planarian, small plastic dish, soft paintbrush

Time 45 minutes

Focus Tell students they will observe planarians to draw conclusions about their food preferences.

Teach Withhold feeding for a day before the activity to make sure the planarians are hungry at the start of the activity. Have students pour water into the dish until the bottom is completely covered. Then, have them place a small piece of ground meat and a piece of lettuce in one side of the dish about 3 centimeters apart. Students can then use the paintbrush to place the planarian at the other side of the dish. Have students observe how long it takes a planarian to start moving and whether it moves toward the lettuce or the meat. (*Planarians are mainly carnivorous.*) If the planarians are slow to respond, place a dark cover over the dish to reduce ambient light. Leave the cover on for about 10 minutes. Then, remove it and observe any movement. Have students wash their hands after the activity.

Apply Ask: **How did the planarian locate the food?** (*It detected chemicals from the food.*) **Where are its sense organs located?** (*At the front end of its body*) **Is having sense organs at the front end related to the type of symmetry the planarian has?** (*Yes. Planarians are bilaterally symmetrical. Most bilaterally symmetrical animals have their sense organs at the front ends of their bodies.*) **learning modality: visual**

Monitor Progress ⬛L2

Writing Ask students to list the distinguishing characteristics of flatworms. (*Bilateral symmetry; a brain; flat bodies; most are parasitic, but some are predators*)

Answers
Figure 21 A free-living organism does not live in or on other organisms and take food from these host organisms.

 Reading Checkpoint Scavengers feed on dead or decaying material.

317

Roundworms

Teach Key Concepts L2

Advancements in Roundworms

Focus Tell students that roundworms are different from flatworms in ways other than shape.

Teach Ask: **What feature do roundworms have that has not been observed in animals studied previously?** (*A complete digestive system, having both a mouth and an anus*)

Apply Ask: **What is the advantage of having a one-way digestive system?** (*It enables the animal's body to absorb a large amount of needed substances.*) **learning modality: verbal**

Math Analyzing Data

Skills Focus Interpreting graphs

Materials graph

Time 15 minutes

Tips Make sure students understand the relationship between the independent variable (soil depth) and dependent variable (number of worms).

Answers

1. in the first centimeter
2. about 87%
3. the deeper the soil, the fewer worms

Address Misconceptions L1

Ringworm Infection

Focus Tell students that ringworm infection is caused by a fungus, not a worm at all.

Teach Ringworm infection is a common skin infection in children. It is characterized by a round rash, often on the face. Make sure that students understand that fungi are in a different kingdom from roundworms.

Apply Pets, such as dogs and cats, may get ringworm, too. They will lose their fur at the site of the infection. **learning modality: verbal**

FIGURE 23
A Roundworm
The transparent body of this roundworm has been stained for better viewing under a microscope.

Roundworms

The next time you walk along a beach, consider that about a million roundworms live in each square meter of damp sand. Roundworms can live in nearly any moist environment—including forest soils, Antarctic sands, and pools of super-hot water. Most roundworms are tiny and difficult to see, but they may be the most abundant animals on Earth. Some species are free-living and some are parasites.

Unlike flatworms, roundworms have cylindrical bodies. They look like tiny strands of cooked spaghetti that are pointed at each end. **Unlike cnidarians or flatworms, roundworms have a digestive system that is like a tube, open at both ends.** Food travels in one direction through the roundworm's digestive system. Food enters at the animal's mouth, and wastes exit through an opening, called the **anus,** at the far end of the tube.

A one-way digestive system is efficient. It is something like an assembly line, with a different part of the digestive process happening at each place along the line. Digestion happens in orderly stages. First, food is broken down by digestive juices. Then the digested food is absorbed into the animal's body. Finally, wastes are eliminated. This type of digestive system enables the animal's body to absorb a large amount of the needed substances in foods.

 Reading Checkpoint What is each opening at opposite ends of a roundworm's digestive tube called?

Math Analyzing Data

Roundworm Numbers

Biologists counted all the roundworms living in a plot of soil. Then they calculated the percentage that lives in different centimeter depths of soil. Their results are graphed to the right.

1. **Reading Graphs** Where in the soil was the largest percentage of roundworms found?

2. **Calculating** What is the total percentage of roundworms found in the first 3-cm depth of soil?

3. **Drawing Conclusions** What is the relationship between the depth of the soil and the abundance of roundworms in the soil?

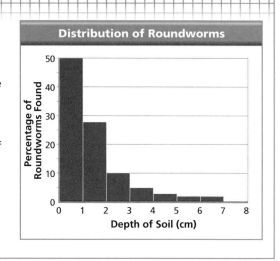

Distribution of Roundworms

(Graph: x-axis "Depth of Soil (cm)" from 0 to 8; y-axis "Percentage of Roundworms Found" from 0 to 50)

Differentiated Instruction

Special Needs L1

Digestive Systems Hold up two cardboard tubes, one open at both ends, the other sealed at one end. Ask: **Which digestive system(s) does each tube represent?** (*Closed—planarian; open—roundworm*) Fill the sealed tube with marbles. Pass marbles through the open tube. Stress that one advantage of two openings is that the animal can eat while digesting its food. **learning modality: kinesthetic**

Segmented Worms

If you have ever dug in a garden, you have probably seen earthworms wriggling through the moist soil. Earthworms are segmented worms. So are leeches and some sea-floor worms.

Body Structure When you look at an earthworm, you see a body made up of a series of rings separated by grooves, something like a vacuum cleaner hose. **Earthworms and other segmented worms have bodies made up of many linked sections called segments.** On the outside, the segments look nearly identical, as you can see in Figure 24. On the inside, some organs are repeated in most segments. For example, each segment has tubes that remove wastes. Other organs, however, such as the earthworm's reproductive organs, are found only in certain segments.

All segmented worms have a long string of nerve tissue called a nerve cord and a digestive tube that run the length of the worm's body. Like roundworms, segmented worms have a one-way digestive system with two openings.

Circulatory System Segmented worms have a closed circulatory system. In a **closed circulatory system,** blood moves only within a connected network of tubes called blood vessels. In contrast, some animals, such as snails and lobsters, have an open circulatory system in which blood leaves the blood vessels and sloshes around inside the body. In both cases the blood carries oxygen and food to cells. But a closed circulatory system can move blood around an animal's body much more quickly than an open circulatory system can.

FIGURE 24
Structure of an Earthworm
An earthworm's body is divided into more than 100 segments. Some organs are repeated in most of those segments. Other organs exist in only a few segments. *Interpreting Diagrams* *Name an example of a body system that runs through all of the worm's segments.*

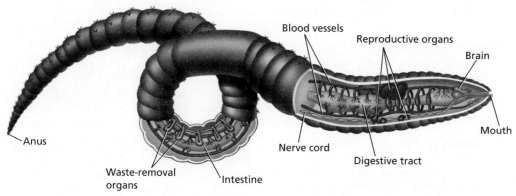

Blood vessels
Reproductive organs
Brain
Mouth
Nerve cord
Digestive tract
Intestine
Waste-removal organs
Anus

Chapter 9 ◆ 319

Segmented Worms

Teach Key Concepts · L2
Advancements in Segmented Worms

Focus Tell students that segmented worms show features not seen in roundworms.

Teach Ask: **What kind of circulatory system does an earthworm have?** *(Closed)* **Describe a closed circulatory system.** *(Blood moves within blood vessels.)*

Apply Ask: **What is the advantage of a closed circulatory system?** *(Blood can move throughout the body faster.)* **learning modality: verbal**

 **Teaching Resources, Unit 2**
• Transparency LS99

Lab zone **Build Inquiry** · L2

Earthworm Tunneling Behavior

Materials dark construction paper, earthworm, soil, transparent jar

Time 15 minutes per day for several days

Focus Tell students that earthworms break up and enrich the soil as they tunnel.

Teach Fill a jar with loose, moist soil and then add the earthworm. Wrap the jar with dark construction paper and keep the jar out of direct sunlight. That way the worms, which avoid light, may burrow along the outside wall of the jar. Have students note over several days the earthworm's location in the soil. Ask: **When the segments at the front end of the worm contract, do the segments at the back end contract at the same time?** *(No; segments contract independently.)*

Apply Raise earthworms in the classroom. Students will need to add a food source to the soil, such as vegetable waste or leaf litter. **learning modality: visual**

Monitor Progress _____ · L2

Drawing Ask students to draw a flatworm, a roundworm, and a segmented worm. Have them label the main characteristics. Students can save their drawings in their portfolios.

Answers
Figure 24 Sample answers: Nervous system, digestive system, circulatory system

 Reading Checkpoint Mouth and anus

319

Monitor Progress ————— L2

Answer

 Reading Checkpoint Earthworms obtain oxygen through moisture on their skin.

Assess

Reviewing Key Concepts

1. a. Flatworms (Platyhelminthes), roundworms (Nematoda), segmented worms (Annelida) **b.** The bodies of all worms have bilateral symmetry, tissues, organs, and body systems. They also have a brain. **c.** They use the sense organs of their nervous system to pick up information.
2. a. Flatworms are flat and have only one opening to their digestive system. Roundworms have cylindrical bodies with pointed ends and a digestive system with two openings. Segmented worms have segments, a digestive system with two openings, and a closed circulatory system. **b.** Sample answer: check to see if it's cylindrical with pointy ends and lacks segments. **c.** Free-living flatworms have a digestive system with one opening. Parasitic flatworms absorb their food from the host's digestive system. Roundworms and segmented worms have a digestive system with two openings. Food travels in one direction, and digestion happens in orderly stages along the way.

Reteach L1

Revisit Figure 20 as you quiz students on the main characteristics that differentiate the three worm phyla.

All in One Teaching Resources, Unit 2

- Section Summary: *Worms*
- Review and Reinforce: *Worms*
- Enrich: *Worms*

FIGURE 25
Earthworms and Garden Health
You are likely to find earthworms when you dig in garden soil.

Earthworms in the Environment Like many segmented worms, earthworms tunnel for a living. On damp nights or rainy days, they come up out of their burrows. They crawl on the surface of the ground, seeking leaves and other decaying matter that they will drag underground and eat. Staying in moist soil or damp air is important because this keeps the worm's skin moist. An earthworm obtains oxygen through moisture on its skin.

Did you know that earthworms are among the most helpful inhabitants of garden and farm soil? They benefit people by improving the soil in which plants grow. Earthworm tunnels loosen the soil, allowing air, water, and plant roots to move through it. Earthworm droppings make the soil more fertile.

Reading Checkpoint Why must earthworms stay moist?

Section 4 Assessment

Target Reading Skill **Using Prior Knowledge** Review your graphic organizer about worms and revise it based on what you just learned in the section.

Reviewing Key Concepts

1. a. Listing What are the three main phyla of worms?
b. Describing What are the common characteristics of the bodies of all worms?
c. Explaining How do worms get information about their environments?
2. a. Reviewing What are the main differences among the three main phyla of worms?
b. Classifying Suppose you use a microscope to look at a tiny worm. What characteristics would you look for to classify it?

c. Comparing and Contrasting Compare and contrast the types of digestive systems found in worms.

Writing in Science

Interview Suppose that worms can talk, and that you are an editor for *Worm* magazine. You have been assigned to interview a tapeworm about its feeding habits. Write a transcript of your interview—your questions and the worm's answers.

Lab zone Chapter Project

Keep Students on Track Students should begin to analyze what they have learned about their animal and its habitat. Tell students that they should summarize their observations and decide what their observations tell them about their animal.

Writing in Science

Writing Mode Description
Scoring Rubric
4 Includes complete questions and accurate answers
3 Includes complete questions and accurate but incomplete answers
2 Includes complete questions, but incomplete and inaccurate answers
1 Includes incomplete and inaccurate questions and answers

Earthworm Responses

Problem

Do earthworms prefer dry or moist conditions? Do they prefer light or dark conditions?

Skills Focus

observing, interpreting data

Materials

- plastic dropper   • water   • cardboard
- clock or watch   • paper towels   • flashlight
- 2 earthworms   • storage container   • tray

Procedure

1. Which environment do you think earthworms prefer—dry or moist? Record your hypothesis in your notebook.

2. Use the dropper to sprinkle water on the worms. Keep the worms moist at all times.

3. Fold a dry paper towel and place it on the bottom of one side of your tray. Fold a moistened paper towel and place it on the other side.

4. Moisten your hands. Then place the earthworms in the center of the tray. Make sure that half of each earthworm's body rests on the moist paper towel and half rests on the dry towel. Handle the worms gently.

5. Cover the tray with the piece of cardboard. After five minutes, remove the cardboard and observe whether the worms are on the moist or dry surface. Record your observations.

6. Repeat Steps 4 and 5.

7. Return the earthworms to their storage container. Moisten the earthworms with water.

8. Which do you think earthworms prefer—strong light or darkness? Record your hypothesis in your notebook.

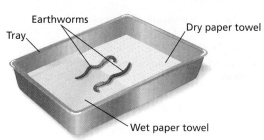

Earthworms

Tray

Dry paper towel

Wet paper towel

9. Cover the whole surface of the tray with a moistened paper towel.

10. Place the earthworms in the center of the tray. Cover half of the tray with cardboard. Shine a flashlight onto the other half.

11. After five minutes, note the locations of the worms. Record your observations.

12. Repeat Steps 10 and 11.

13. Moisten the earthworms and put them in the location designated by your teacher. Wash your hands after handling the worms.

Analyze and Conclude

1. **Observing** Which environment did the worms prefer—moist or dry? Bright or dark?

2. **Interpreting Data** Did the worms' behavior support your hypotheses?

3. **Communicating** Explain in a paragraph what knowledge or experiences helped you develop your hypotheses at the beginning of the experiments.

Design an Experiment

Do earthworms prefer a smooth or rough surface? Write your hypothesis. Then design an experiment to answer the question. *Obtain your teacher's permission before carrying out your investigation.*

Analyze and Conclude

1. Moist, dark

2. Sample answer: Yes, the worms preferred moist, dark environments as hypothesized.

3. Paragraphs might explain that earthworms are usually found in dark, moist places in nature.

Extend Inquiry

Design an Experiment To test the hypothesis that earthworms prefer a rough surface, students might suggest using sandpaper on one side of a tray and smooth ceramic tile on the other. Remind students that they must control other variables, such as temperature on each side of the tray.

 Skills **Lab**

Earthworm Responses 🄻2

Prepare for Inquiry

Key Concept

Students test hypotheses regarding earthworm preferences for soil and light conditions.

Skills Objectives

After this lab, students will be able to

- observe earthworm behavior to determine soil condition and light preferences
- interpret data regarding earthworm preferences

🕐 **Prep Time** 20 minutes
Class Time 30 minutes

Advance Planning

You can get worms from a biological supply company, a bait shop, or loose garden soil.

Alternative Materials

Cake pans can be used for trays. Do not substitute tissues for paper towels; they are too absorbent and will not last.

Safety

 Handle earthworms with care and keep them moist at all times. Return them to their container when finished.

All in One **Teaching Resources, Unit 2**
- Lab Worksheet: *Earthworm Responses*

Guide Inquiry

Invitation

Ask: **Think about the places you are likely to see an earthworm. Would these places be dry or moist?** *(Moist)* **Light or dark?** *(Dark)*

Introducing the Procedure

Have students review the diagram of the setup so they understand how to position the worms. Suggest that they conduct a trial one time before they collect data.

Troubleshooting the Experiment

Rough handling of worms can harm them and prevent them from moving. If a dry paper towel becomes damp, have students replace it.

Expected Outcome

The worms generally preferred the moist towel and the dark environment and moved toward them.

Interactive Textbook

- Complete student edition
- Section and chapter self-assessments
- Assessment reports for teachers

Help Students Read

Building Vocabulary

Word Forms Students may have seen several of the vocabulary terms for this chapter used in different contexts. Help them to relate these familiar meanings to chapter content. For example, ask: **What is a scavenger hunt?** (*A game in which participants must find specific items, usually junk items, within a certain time limit*) **What is a scavenger?** (*An animal that feeds on refuse—that is, dead or decaying material; also, a person who is a scavenger is a junk collector*)

Words in Context Select Key Terms from the chapter. Have students write a sentence for each term that places the term in the correct context. Provide them with one example before they begin: *Cell: Sponges, cnidarians, flatworms, roundworms, and segmented worms are all animals and therefore are composed of many cells.*

Connecting Concepts

Concept Maps Help students develop one way to show how the information in this chapter is related. Have students brainstorm to identify the key concepts, key terms, details, and examples. Then write each one on a sticky note and attach it at random on chart paper or on the board.

Tell students that this concept map will be organized in hierarchical order and to begin at the top with the key concepts. Ask students these questions to guide them to categorize the information on the stickies: **What characteristics of animals can you observe directly? Indirectly? How are animals classified?** Prompt students by using connecting words or phrases, such as "composed of," "arranged by," and "are identified by," to indicate the basis for the

---

① What Is an Animal?

Key Concepts

- The cells of most animals are organized into higher levels of structure, including tissues, organs, and systems.
- The major functions of animals are to obtain food and oxygen, keep internal conditions stable, move, and reproduce.
- Animals are classified according to how they are related to other animals. These relationships are determined by an animal's body structure, the way an animal develops, and its DNA.

Key Terms

cell
tissue
organ
adaptation
sexual reproduction
fertilization
asexual reproduction
phylum
vertebrate
invertebrate

② Animal Symmetry

Key Concepts

- The balanced arrangement of parts, called symmetry, is characteristic of many animals.
- Depending on their symmetry, animals share some general characteristics.

Key Terms

bilateral symmetry
radial symmetry

③ Sponges and Cnidarians

Key Concepts

- Sponges are invertebrate animals that usually have no body symmetry and never have tissues or organs.
- Cnidarians use stinging cells to capture food and defend themselves.
- Coral reefs are home to more species of fishes and invertebrates than any other environment on Earth.

Key Terms

larva
cnidarian
polyp
medusa
colony
coral reef

④ Worms

Key Concepts

- Biologists classify worms into three major phyla—flatworms, roundworms, and segmented worms.
- Flatworms are flat and soft as jelly.
- Unlike cnidarians or flatworms, roundworms have a digestive system that is like a tube, open at both ends.
- Earthworms and other segmented worms have bodies made up of many linked sections called segments.

Key Terms

parasite
host
free-living organism
scavenger
anus
closed circulatory system

---

organization of the map. The phrases should form a sentence between or among a set of concepts.

Answer
Accept logical presentations by students.

All in One Teaching Resources, Unit 2

- Key Terms Review: *Sponges, Cnidarians, and Worms*
- Connecting Concepts: *Sponges, Cnidarians, and Worms*

Review and Assessment

Organizing Information

Sequencing Copy the cycle diagram about the life of a sponge onto a sheet of paper. Then complete it and add a title.

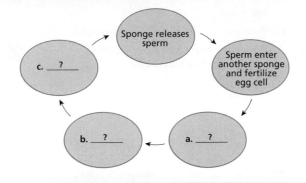

Sponge releases sperm

Sperm enter another sponge and fertilize egg cell

c. ___?___

b. ___?___

a. ___?___

Reviewing Key Terms

Choose the letter of the best answer.

1. The highest level of organization in an animal is a(n)
   a. cell.
   b. tissue.
   c. organ.
   d. system.

2. An animal without a backbone is called a(n)
   a. vertebrate.
   b. invertebrate.
   c. larva.
   d. parasite.

3. An animal with many lines of symmetry
   a. has bilateral symmetry.
   b. has radial symmetry.
   c. has no symmetry.
   d. has a distinct head and tail end.

4. Which animal is a medusa?
   a. coral
   b. moon jelly
   c. planarian
   d. sea anemone

5. An organism that does not live in or on another organism is called a
   a. scavenger.
   b. parasite.
   c. free-living organism.
   d. host.

If the statement is true, write *true*. If it is false, change the underlined word or words to make the statement true.

6. A tissue is a group of <u>organs</u> that work together to perform a job.

7. Fishes have <u>bilateral symmetry</u>.

8. Budding is a form of <u>sexual reproduction</u>.

9. A <u>polyp</u> is an immature form of an animal that looks very different from the adult form.

10. Some tapeworms are <u>parasites</u> of dogs.

Writing in Science

Letter Suppose that you have just come back from a trip to a coral reef. Write a letter to a friend that compares corals and jellyfish. Be sure to explain how the two animals are alike and how they are different.

Discovery CHANNEL SCHOOL™

Sponges, Cnidarians, and Worms
Video Preview
Video Field Trip
► Video Assessment

Chapter 9 ◆ 323

Go Online
PHSchool.com
For: Self-Assessment
Visit: PHSchool.com
Web Code: cea-2010

Students can take a practice test online that is automatically scored.

All in One Teaching Resources, Unit 2
- Transparency LS100
- Chapter Test
- Performance Assessment Teacher Notes
- Performance Assessment Student Worksheet
- Performance Assessment Scoring Rubric

ExamView® Computer Test Bank CD-ROM

Review and Assessment

Organizing Information
a. Larva develops.
b. Water currents carry away larva.
c. Larva settles on a surface and develops into adult sponge.
Sample title: Life Cycle of a Sponge

Reviewing Key Terms
1. d **2.** b **3.** b **4.** b **5.** c
6. false; A tissue is a group of cells
7. true
8. false; Budding is a form of asexual reproduction.
9. false; A larva is an immature form of an animal that looks very different from the adult form.
10. true

Writing in Science

Writing Mode Description
Scoring Rubric
4 Includes detailed descriptions of sights, dangers and other adventures; descriptions are lively and fun to read.
3 Includes all criteria
2 Includes one or two criteria or only brief descriptions
1 Includes only one description and inaccurate information

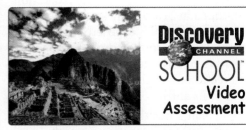
Discovery CHANNEL SCHOOL™
Video Assessment

Sponges, Cnidarians, and Worms

Show the Video Assessment to review chapter content and as a prompt for the writing assignment. Discussion question: **Describe two ways in which jellyfish move through the water.** (*They swim by expanding and contracting their bodies; they also float.*) **What is one possible function of bioluminescence in jellyfish?** (*To send signals to potential mates; to scare off predators*)

Checking Concepts

11. Tissues are made up of similar cells that work together to perform a specific job. Organs are made up of different types of tissues.

12. The functions of animals are obtaining food and oxygen, keeping internal conditions stable, moving, and reproducing.

13. Animals with bilateral symmetry have front ends and streamlined bodies. Thus, they can move quickly and efficiently. They have sense organs in their front ends that pick up information about what is in front of them, which helps them find food and avoid enemies.

14. A polyp is usually attached to a surface. Its mouth is at the top of its body. A medusa is free-swimming. Its mouth is at the bottom of its body. Both are radially symmetrical.

15. Humans are free-living organisms. They do not live in or on other organisms.

16. In a one-way digestive system, food enters at one end, is digested along the way, and wastes are expelled at the opposite end.

Thinking Critically

17. The title is misleading. The animals on Earth include both vertebrates and invertebrates; in fact 97% of Earth's animals are invertebrates.

18. Sea anemones have radial symmetry; sponges have no symmetry; fishes, humans, and butterflies have bilateral symmetry.

19. In a sponge, jellylike cells digest the food. In a planarian, digested juices that flow out onto the food begin digestion; digestion is continued in a cavity within the planarian; undigested material is expelled through the feeding tube. In a roundworm, digestion happens in orderly stages as food passes in one direction through the worm, from its mouth to its anus.

20. The plants' health might suffer because there will likely be less water, air, and nutrients available to the plants' roots. It might also be more difficult for plants' roots to move through the soil.

21. *B:* roundworm; *A:* sponge; *C:* cnidarian. Sponges have no symmetry and lack tissues and organs. Cnidarians have radial symmetry and stinging cells, and a mouth that opens into a central body cavity. Roundworms have bilateral symmetry, a digestive system with two openings, and long cylindrical bodies with pointed ends.

Checking Concepts

11. Explain the relationship among cells, tissues, and organs.

12. What are four key functions of animals?

13. What advantages does an animal with bilateral symmetry have over an animal with radial symmetry?

14. Compare and contrast a medusa and a polyp.

15. Are humans parasitic or free-living organisms? Explain.

16. Explain what a one-way digestive system is.

Thinking Critically

17. Making Judgments Suppose you check out a book from the library called *Earth's Animals*. You notice that all the animals in the book are vertebrates. Is this title a good one? Explain your reasoning.

18. Classifying Classify each of the following animals as having radial symmetry, bilateral symmetry, or no symmetry: sea anemones, sponges, fishes, humans, and butterflies.

19. Comparing and Contrasting Compare and contrast the ways in which a sponge, a planarian, and a roundworm digest their food.

20. Relating Cause and Effect If a disease killed off many of the earthworms in a garden, how might the plants growing in the soil be affected? Explain.

21. Classifying Which of the animals below is a roundworm? A sponge? A cnidarian? Describe the major characteristics of the members of these three phyla.

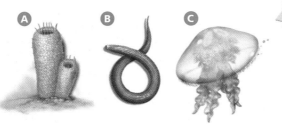

Ⓐ Ⓑ Ⓒ

Math Practice

22. Calculating a Rate In 24 hours, 110 L of water pass through a sponge. What is the rate of water flow?

Applying Skills

Use the tables to answer Questions 23–25.

A scientist used a pesticide on one field and left a nearby field untreated. Next, she marked off five plots of equal size in each field. Then she dug up a cubic meter of soil beneath each plot and counted the earthworms in the soil. The tables below show her data.

Field With Pesticide		Untreated Field	
Plot	Worms per Cubic Meter	Plot	Worms per Cubic Meter
A	730	F	901
B	254	G	620
C	319	H	811
D	428	I	576
E	451	J	704

23. Controlling Variables Identify the manipulated and responding variables in this experiment.

24. Calculating Calculate the average number of worms per cubic meter in the field treated with pesticide. Then do the same for the untreated field.

25. Drawing Conclusions How did this pesticide affect the number of worms?

Lab zone Chapter **Project**

Performance Assessment Write a summary explaining what you have learned about your animal. Describe its habitat, the food it eats, its behavior, and any surprising observations that you made. Then introduce your animal to your classmates and share what you have discovered.

Lab zone Chapter **Project** L3

Performance Assessment Ask the students to write down the major characteristics of each animal as other students present their projects.

After all presentations have been made, have students evaluate their projects.

Students should decide what animals were best for the projects and the best methods for taking care of the animals. Help students resettle their animals humanely after completing their projects.

Standardized Test Prep

Choose the letter of the best answer.

1. What is the correct sequence in which a stinging cell reacts to the touch of another organism?
   A trigger brushes against prey, stinging cell fires, barbs snare prey
   B barbs snare prey, stinging cell fires, barbs release prey
   C prey is paralyzed, venom enters prey, stinging cell fires
   D tentacles pull prey to mouth, prey is ingested, stinging cell fires

2. Which of the following is true of a one-way digestive system?
   F It is found in all parasites.
   G It has two openings.
   H It has one opening.
   J It is found in all parasites and has one opening.

3. Of the four animals shown below, which has the same symmetry as a jellyfish?

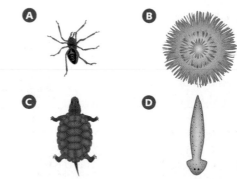

4. Imagine that the animals illustrated above are real and are resting on this page. Predict which of the animals would travel toward the top of the page if they began moving in a straight line.
   F animals A and D
   G animals A and B
   H animals B and D
   J animals A and C

5. The following terms can all be used to describe a tapeworm *except*
   A parasite
   B invertebrate
   C flatworm
   D medusa

Constructed Response

6. Compare and contrast the feeding process of a sponge with that of an earthworm. How are their feeding processes similar? How are they different?

Math Practice

22. 4.58 L/h

Applying Skills

23. The manipulated variable is whether the field is treated with the pesticide or not. The responding variable is the number of worms in the soil.

24. The average number of worms per cubic meter in the treated field is 436.4. The average number in the untreated field is 722.4.

25. The pesticide reduced the number of worms per cubic meter.

Standardized Test Prep

1. A **2.** G **3.** B **4.** J **5.** D

6. A sponge draws water in through its pores where collar cells strain tiny one-celled organisms from the water and jelly-like cells digest them. Wastes exit through the hole at its top. In contrast, food enters an earthworm's body through its mouth, enters its digestive system, and is digested along the way. Wastes leave the body through the anus.

The processes are similar in that there is a flow of food in one direction. For the sponge, the flow is from pores to central cavity, then out the large opening at the top; for the earthworm, it is from mouth to anus.

Chapter at a Glance

 Chapter Project *Going Through Changes*

All in One Teaching Resources, Unit 2
- Chapter Project Teacher Notes, pp. 226–227
- Chapter Project Student Overview, pp. 228–229
- Chapter Project Student Worksheets, pp. 230–231
- Chapter Project Scoring Rubric, p. 232

PRENTICE HALL
TeacherEXPRESS™
Plan • Teach • Assess

Technology

 Discovery CHANNEL SCHOOL
Video Preview

Local Standards

 Section 1 **Mollusks**
2 periods
1 block
- **10.1.1** Identify the main characteristics of mollusks.
- **10.1.2** Describe the major groups of mollusks and tell how they differ.

 Discovery CHANNEL SCHOOL
Video Field Trip

 Section 2 **Arthropods**
2 periods
1 block
- **10.2.1** Identify four major groups of arthropods and the main characteristics of arthropods.
- **10.2.2** Describe how crustaceans, arachnids, and centipedes and millipedes differ.

 Go Online
SCLINKS NSTA

 Section 3 **Insects**
2 periods
1 block
- **10.3.1** Identify the main characteristics of insects.
- **10.3.2** Explain how insects are adapted to obtain food.
- **10.3.3** Name the two types of metamorphosis found in insects.

 Go Online
PHSchool.com

 Section 4 **Insect Ecology**
1 period
1/2 block
- **10.4.1** Explain why insects are important in food chains.
- **10.4.2** Name two other ways insects interact with their environments.
- **10.4.3** Describe some methods used to control pest insects.

 Go Online
SCLINKS NSTA

 Section 5 **Echinoderms**
1 period
1/2 block
- **10.5.1** List the main characteristics of echinoderms.
- **10.5.2** Name the major groups of echinoderms.

Go Online
active art

Review and Assessment

All in One Teaching Resources, Unit 2
- Key Terms Review, p. 272
- Transparency LS111
- Performance Assessment Teacher Notes, p. 281
- Performance Assessment Scoring Rubric, p. 282
- Performance Assessment Student Worksheet, p. 283
- Chapter Test, pp. 284–287

 Discovery CHANNEL SCHOOL
Video Assessment

Go Online
PHSchool.com

Test Preparation

Test Preparation Blackline Masters

Lab zone Chapter Activities Planner

For more activities
LAB ZONE Easy Planner CD-ROM

Student Edition	Inquiry	Time	Materials	Skills	Resources
Chapter Project, p. 327	Open-Ended	2 to 3 weeks	**All in One Teaching Resources, Unit 2,** p. 226	Observing, designing, organizing data, drawing conclusions	**Lab zone Easy Planner** **All in One Teaching Resources, Unit 2,** Support pp. 226–227
Section 1					
Discover Activity, p. 328	Guided	20 minutes	Mollusk shells, such as those from clams, mussels, oysters, land and marine snails, and nautiluses	Inferring	**Lab zone Easy Planner**
Skills Activity, p. 331	Guided	10 minutes	None	Classifying	**Lab zone Easy Planner**
Skills Lab, p. 334	Guided	Prep: 30 minutes Class: 45 minutes	Freshwater snail, plastic petri dish, timer, spring water at three temperatures: cool (9–13°C); medium (18–22°C); warm (27–31°C), thermometer, 2 sheets graph paper, ruler	Interpreting data, predicting	**Lab zone Easy Planner** **All in One Teaching Resources, Unit 2,** Skills Lab: *A Snail's Pace,* pp. 241–242
Section 2					
Discover Activity, p. 335	Directed	Prep: 5 minutes Class: 15 minutes	Sheets of heavy cardboard, about 30 × 45 cm; tape	Inferring	**Lab zone Easy Planner**
Try This Activity, p. 339	Directed	20 minutes	Shoe box, aluminum foil, paper towels, masking tape, live pill bugs, water	Interpreting data	**Lab zone Easy Planner**
Section 3					
Discover Activity, p. 343	Directed	Prep: 5 minutes Class: 15 minutes	Insect collection, hand lenses	Inferring	**Lab zone Easy Planner**
Skills Activity, p. 344	Guided	15 minutes	None	Graphing	**Lab zone Easy Planner**
Skills Lab, pp. 348–349	Guided	Prep: 45 minutes Class: 15 minutes on the first day, 45 minutes on the second day	2-liter plastic bottle, trowel, cheesecloth, gooseneck lamp, large, wide-mouthed jar, coarse steel wool, large scissors, large rubber band, hand lens, small jar, fresh sample of soil and leaf litter	Observing, classifying	**Lab zone Easy Planner** **All in One Teaching Resources, Unit 2,** Skills Lab: *What's Living in the Soil?* pp. 257–259
Section 4					
Discover Activity, p. 350	Open-Ended	20 minutes	Flowers, cotton swab, pencil, other materials as selected	Inferring	**Lab zone Easy Planner**
Section 5					
Discover Activity, p. 358	Directed	5 minutes	Plastic dropper, water	Predicting	**Lab zone Easy Planner**

Section 1 Mollusks

🕐 *2 periods, 1 block*

ABILITY LEVELS
L1 Basic to Average
L2 For All Students
L3 Average to Advanced

Objectives

10.1.1 Identify the main characteristics of mollusks.
10.1.2 Describe the major groups of mollusks and tell how they differ.

Key Terms

• mollusk • open circulatory system • gill • gastropod • herbivore
• carnivore • radula • bivalve • omnivore • cephalopod

Local Standards

Preteach

Build Background Knowledge

Ask students who are familiar with mollusks to share their knowledge.

Lab zone Discover Activity *How Can You Classify Shells?* **L1**

Targeted Print and Technology Resources

All in One Teaching Resources, Unit 2

L2 Reading Strategy Transparency LS101: Comparing and Contrasting

◎ **PresentationEXPRESS™ CD-ROM**

Instruct

Characteristics of Mollusks Use pictures to show that all mollusks have the same basic body structures.

Snails and Slugs Use class discussion to help students identify the characteristics of gastropods.

Two-Shelled Mollusks Ask leading questions to identify the characteristics of bivalves.

Octopuses and Their Relatives Use photographs to teach the characteristics of cephalopods.

Lab zone Skills Lab *A Snail's Pace* **L2**

Targeted Print and Technology Resources

All in One Teaching Resources, Unit 2

L2 Guided Reading, pp. 235–238
L2 Transparency LS102
L2 Skills Lab: *A Snail's Pace,* pp. 241–242

📼 **Lab Activity Video/DVD**
Skills Lab: *A Snail's Pace*

DISCOVERY
CHANNEL
SCHOOL
Video Field Trip

◎ **Student Edition on Audio CD**

Assess

Section Assessment Questions

🎯 Have students use the information in their Comparing and Contrasting graphic organizers to help them answer the questions.

Reteach

Use a chart to compare different kinds of mollusks.

Targeted Print and Technology Resources

All in One Teaching Resources, Unit 2

• Section Summary, p. 234
L1 Review and Reinforce, p. 239
L3 Enrich, p. 240

Section 2 Arthropods

⏱ *2 periods, 1 block*

ABILITY LEVELS
L1 Basic to Average
L2 For All Students
L3 Average to Advanced

Objectives

10.2.1 Identify four major groups of arthropods and the main characteristics of arthropods.

10.2.2 Describe how crustaceans, arachnids, and centipedes and millipedes differ.

Local Standards

Key Terms

• arthropod • exoskeleton • molting • antenna • crustacean • metamorphosis
• arachnid • abdomen

Preteach

Build Background Knowledge

Question students about their experience with arthropods.

Lab zone **Discover Activity** *Will It Bend and Move?* **L1**

Targeted Print and Technology Resources

All in One Teaching Resources, Unit 2

L2 Reading Strategy Transparency LS103: Asking Questions

⊙ **PresentationEXPRESS™ CD-ROM**

Instruct

Characteristics of Arthropods Use Figure 10 to compare the differences among the four major groups.

Crustaceans Have students use illustration callouts to identify characteristics of crustaceans.

Arachnids Use leading questions to discuss the characteristics of arachnids.

Centipedes and Millipedes Use simple sketches to illustrate characteristics of centipedes and millipedes.

Targeted Print and Technology Resources

All in One Teaching Resources, Unit 2

L2 Guided Reading, pp. 245–248
L2 Transparencies LS104, LS105

www.SciLinks.org Web Code: scn-0222

⊙ **Student Edition on Audio CD**

Assess

Section Assessment Questions

🔄 Have students use their completed Asking Questions graphic organizers to answer the questions.

Reteach

Use a table to review characteristics of arthropod groups.

Targeted Print and Technology Resources

All in One Teaching Resources, Unit 2

• Section Summary, p. 244
L1 Review and Reinforce, p. 249
L3 Enrich, p. 250

Section 3 Insects

⏱ *2 periods, 1 block*

Objectives

10.3.1 Identify the main characteristics of insects.

10.3.2 Explain how insects are adapted to obtain food.

10.3.3 Name the two types of metamorphosis found in insects.

Key Terms

• insect • thorax • complete metamorphosis • pupa • gradual metamorphosis
• nymph

Local Standards

Preteach

Build Background Knowledge

Ask students to describe insects they have observed.

 **Discover Activity** *What Characteristics Do Insects Share?* L1

Targeted Print and Technology Resources

All in One Teaching Resources, Unit 2

L2 Reading Strategy Transparency LS106: Sequencing

⊙ **PresentationEXPRESS™ CD-ROM**

Instruct

Body Structure Use an illustration to discuss the three body sections of a grasshopper.

Obtaining Food Compare and contrast insects' mouthparts and discuss how they are adapted for a highly specific way of getting food.

Life Cycle Use illustrations to compare and contrast complete metamorphosis and gradual metamorphosis.

Skills Lab *What's Living in the Soil?* L2

Targeted Print and Technology Resources

All in One Teaching Resources, Unit 2

L2 Guided Reading, pp. 253–254
L2 Transparencies LS107, LS108
L2 Skills Lab: *What's Living in the Soil?* pp. 257–259

📼 **Lab Activity Video/DVD**
Skills Lab: *What's Living in the Soil?*

PHSchool.com Web Code: ced-2023

⊙ **Student Edition on Audio CD**

Assess

Section Assesment Questions

↻ Have students use their completed Sequencing graphic organizers to answer the questions.

Reteach

Use an illustration to review the events in insect metamorphosis.

Targeted Print and Technology Resources

All in One Teaching Resources, Unit 2

• Section Summary, p. 252
L1 Review and Reinforce, p. 255
L3 Enrich, p. 256

Section 4 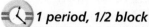 Insect Ecology

 *1 period, 1/2 block*

ABILITY LEVELS
L1 Basic to Average
L2 For All Students
L3 Average to Advanced

Objectives

10.4.1 Explain why insects are important in food chains.

10.4.2 Name two other ways insects interact with their environments.

10.4.3 Describe some methods used to control pest insects.

Key Terms

• food chain • ecology • producer • consumer • decomposer • pollinator
• pesticide • biological control

Local Standards

Preteach

Build Background Knowledge

Ask questions to find out what students know about the roles of insects.

Lab zone Discover Activity *What Materials Carry Pollen Best?* L1

Targeted Print and Technology Resources

All in One Teaching Resources, Unit 2
L2 Reading Strategy: Building Vocabulary

⊙ **PresentationEXPRESS™ CD-ROM**

Instruct

Insects and the Food Chain Describe the roles played by insects in food chains.

Other Interactions Use photographs to relate that some insects interact with their communities by carrying pollen or diseases.

Controlling Pests Discuss the benefits and costs of different types of insect pest control.

Targeted Print and Technology Resources

All in One Teaching Resources, Unit 2
L2 Guided Reading, pp. 262–263

www.SciLinks.org Web Code: scn-0224

PHSchool.com Web Code: ceh-2020

⊙ **Student Edition on Audio CD**

Assess

Section Assessment Questions

Have students use their completed sentences to answer the questions.

Reteach

List examples of beneficial insects and harmful insects.

Targeted Print and Technology Resources

All in One Teaching Resources
• Section Summary, p. 261
L1 Review and Reinforce, p. 264
L3 Enrich, p. 265

Section 5 Echinoderms

1 period, 1/2 block

Objectives

10.5.1 List the main characteristics of echinoderms.
10.5.2 Name the major groups of echinoderms.

Key Terms

• echinoderm • endoskeleton • water vascular system • tube feet

Local Standards

Preteach

Build Background Knowledge

Help students identify similarities among Echinoderms.

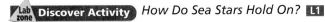 **Discover Activity** *How Do Sea Stars Hold On?* **L1**

Targeted Print and Technology Resources

All in One Teaching Resources, Unit 2

L2 Reading Strategy Transparency
LS109: Previewing Visuals

⊙ **PresentationEXPRESS™ CD-ROM**

Instruct

Characteristics of Echinoderms Use an illustration to discuss the distinctive characteristics of echinoderms.

Diversity of Echinoderms Compare photographs to identify the four major groups of echinoderms.

Targeted Print and Technology Resources

All in One Teaching Resources, Unit 2

L2 Guided Reading, pp. 268–269
L2 Transparency LS110

PHSchool.com Web Code: cep-2025

⊙ **Student Edition on Audio CD**

Assess

Section Assessment Questions

Have students use their Previewing Visuals graphic organizers to answer the questions.

Reteach

Create a table to summarize the body structure, movement, and reproduction of echinoderms.

Targeted Print and Technology Resources

All in One Teaching Resources, Unit 2

• Section Summary, p. 267
L1 Review and Reinforce, p. 270
L3 Enrich, p. 271

Go Online

NSTA-_PDi_LINKS

For: Professional development support
Visit: www.SciLinks.org/PDLinks
Web Code: scf-0220

Professional Development

Professional Development

Section 1 **Mollusks**

Open and Closed Circulatory Systems In open circulatory systems, a heart pumps blood into short blood vessels that empty into open spaces. In these low-pressure systems, the blood percolates along, delivering oxygen and nutrients and collecting wastes, until the cavities narrow into vessels that direct the blood back to the heart. In closed systems, blood remains within vessels, and all exchanges are carried out through the capillary walls. Blood pressure is generally much higher in closed systems.

The kind of system that an animal has relates generally to the oxygen demands of the animal. If the demands are low, the animal probably is sedentary or moves very slowly. For these animals, a low-pressure, more sluggish flow of blood is sufficient. If the oxygen demands are high, meaning that the animal is very active, the animal often has the oxygen-efficient, high-pressure, closed system. But there are important exceptions to these generalizations.

Most vertebrates are active animals. So, as you would expect, vertebrates have closed circulatory systems. There is no clear pattern in invertebrates. Many have open systems and are comparatively sluggish, but others with open systems, including insects, are quite active. Some slow-moving invertebrates, such as segmented worms, have closed systems.

Section 2 **Arthropods**

Lyme Disease Identified in 1975, the disease is named for the town of Lyme, Connecticut, where it was first observed. Lyme disease is caused by _Borrelia burgdorferi_, a spiral-shaped bacterium that is transmitted to the human bloodstream by the bite of a deer tick.

In humans, the disease begins with a circular rash in a bull's-eye pattern around the tick bite. If not treated in the early stage with antibiotics, the disease may go on to cause arthritic pain and neurological symptoms.

The disease cycle begins when a tick picks up the bacterium by biting an infected animal, often a white-tailed deer. Once infected, the adult tick lays eggs, which hatch and become larvae and then nymphs. Both the nymph stage and adult stage of the tick are likely to bite humans and transmit the disease, particularly during the summer months. Nymph stages of the deer tick are much smaller than the more familiar wood tick (commonly found on dogs and cats), making them difficult to spot.

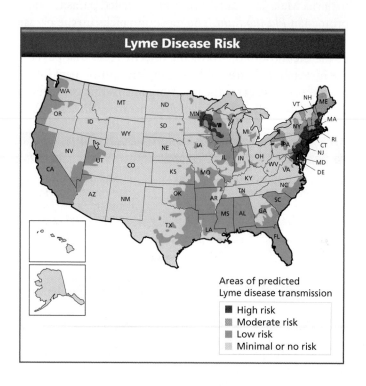

Lyme Disease Risk

Areas of predicted Lyme disease transmission

- High risk
- Moderate risk
- Low risk
- Minimal or no risk

To reduce the likelihood of Lyme disease, persons who live in high-risk areas should take precautions before spending time in yards or in wooded areas with overgrown brush. Long-sleeved shirts, long pants, and high socks reduce the chance of tick bites. Tucking pants into socks or boot tops will reduce the chances of ticks reaching your skin. The risk of tick attachment can be reduced by using appropriate insecticides. Check all over your body for ticks after being outdoors. Use fine-tipped tweezers to promptly remove any attached ticks.

Address Misconceptions

Students may think that all spiders catch their prey in webs. This is false. For a strategy for overcoming this misconception, see **Address Misconceptions** in the section _Arthropods_.

Section 3 Insects

Mosquito-Borne Diseases Of all of the world's disease-carriers, mosquitoes transmit more serious human diseases than any other. Because female mosquitoes require a blood meal before laying their eggs, mosquitoes are common transmitters of bloodborne diseases.

Mosquitoes in the genus *Anopheles* are the sole carriers of malaria. Malaria is caused by a single-celled parasite, the protozoan *Plasmodium*. The mosquito picks up the parasite when biting an infected person. The parasite reproduces inside the mosquito, producing infective cells that pass into the human bloodstream during the mosquito's next bite. Mosquitoes also carry the microorganisms that cause filariasis, encephalitis, yellow fever, dengue, and West Nile encephalitis.

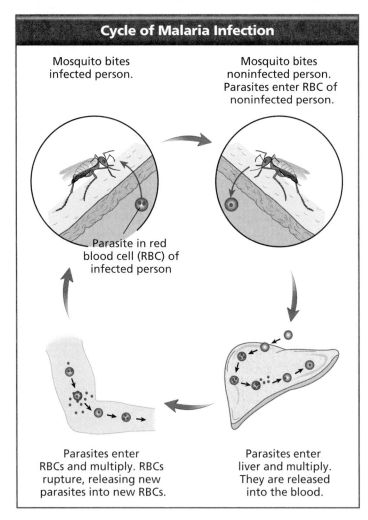

Cycle of Malaria Infection

Mosquito bites infected person.

Mosquito bites noninfected person. Parasites enter RBC of noninfected person.

Parasite in red blood cell (RBC) of infected person

Parasites enter RBCs and multiply. RBCs rupture, releasing new parasites into new RBCs.

Parasites enter liver and multiply. They are released into the blood.

Mosquito control efforts involve community-wide measures, such as draining swamps, marshes, and stagnant water where mosquitoes breed, and the use of insecticides. Window screens and mosquito netting are widely used to protect sleeping individuals from mosquitoes, which are active mainly at night.

Section 4 Insect Ecology

Food Chains and Food Webs A food chain is a series of events in which one organism eats another and obtains energy. Food chains are generally diagrammed as shown in the illustration, with an arrow running from each organism that is eaten to the organism that eats it. The sun is the source of energy in almost all food chains.

The first organism in a food chain is always a producer, such as a plant or photosynthetic microorganism. In the food chain in the illustration, algae are the producers. The other organisms in this particular food chain, such as the zooplankton that eat the algae and the small fish that eat the zooplankton, are consumers. Energy from the sun flows in one direction, indicated by the arrows, to the producer, to the first consumer, and so forth.

In most environments, feeding relationships are much more complex than those diagrammed in food chains. Different food chains usually intersect with one another. For example, the small fish, which in the illustration are eaten by squid, may also be eaten by larger fishes and birds. Scientists use the term *food web* to describe these complex feeding relationships.

One Food Chain

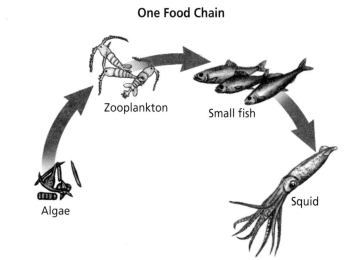

Zooplankton

Small fish

Algae

Squid

Section 5 Echinoderms

The Water Vascular System An echinoderm's water vascular system is involved in more than movement. The fluid in the water vascular system is the main medium through which needed materials and wastes travel throughout the echinoderm's body. Oxygen passes from water into the echinoderm's body through the tube feet, which have thin walls. The tube feet also pass nitrogenous wastes, mainly in the form of ammonia, into the water that surrounds the echinoderm.

Crown-of-Thorns Sea Star As one of the largest and most venomous sea stars, the crown-of-thorns sea star, *Acanthaster planci,* can reach 50 cm in diameter. It has 10 to 20 arms covered with toxic spines. At about six months of age, the crown-of-thorns sea star begins to eat coral. Although they don't look edible, coral reefs are actually the home of coral polyps, the living invertebrates that produce the colorful corals. After the coral polyps are eaten, the white coral skeleton is left behind.

A healthy coral reef can support small populations of crown-of-thorns sea stars for many years. But when sea stars are present in large numbers, they can kill most of the living coral within an entire section of the reef. When this occurs, a reef can take 10 years or more to recover its coral population.

Help Students Read

Outline

Understanding Text Structure

Strategy Help students focus on the text and not simply skim it. Outlining is a good strategy to apply to an entire section, if it is not excessively long, using the headings as major divisions. Outlining is best applied to sections in which the headings are parallel, and in which there are main headings and subheadings. Before you begin, choose a section for students to read and outline.

Example
1. Before students read, have them preview the section's title and headings. Demonstrate and display how to make a skeleton outline for the section. Have students list the section title at the top level, the main headings as major divisions, and the subheadings at the next level.
2. I. Section Title
    A. Main Heading
       1. Subheading
         a. detail
         b. detail
         c. detail
3. Have students copy the skeleton outline as they read, filling in details under each main heading and subheading of the outline.
4. Advise students not to outline sections that focus on the details of cycles or processes. Students can better represent these by diagrams and flowcharts rather than outlining.
5. After reading, have students review the entire section and their outlines to make sure they have included all vocabulary definitions and Key Concepts as main ideas or details under the appropriate levels of their outlines.

Interactive Textbook
- Complete student edition
- Video and audio
- Simulations and activities
- Section and chapter activities

Interactive Textbook

▶ This weevil from Southeast Asia uses its impressive front legs to court females.

326 ◆

Lab zone Chapter **Project** ⬛L3

Objectives
This project will give students an opportunity to investigate the metamorphosis of mealworms under a variety of different conditions (variables). After this Chapter Project, students will be able to
- observe how different conditions affect mealworm development
- design experiments to test the effect of an environmental variable on metamorphosis
- organize data in tables to record daily mealworm observations
- draw conclusions regarding the effect of the environmental change on metamorphosis

Skills Focus
Observing, designing, organizing data, drawing conclusions

Project Time Line 2 to 3 weeks

All in One Teaching Resources, Unit 2
- Chapter Project Teacher Notes
- Chapter Project Overview
- Chapter Project Worksheet 1
- Chapter Project Worksheet 2
- Chapter Project Scoring Rubric

326

Developing a Plan
Allow time for students to read the description of the project in their text. Then encourage discussions of the environmental factors that might affect metamorphosis, such as temperature, light, and type of food supplied. Students can work in small groups as a cooperative learning task. To ensure that every student will have ample opportunity to participate in designing an experiment, you may wish to limit groups to three students.

Possible Materials
- You can obtain mealworms from local pet stores. Make sure they are well fed and have a moisture source until the project launch day.
- Tell students to bring in plastic containers with lids, such as empty margarine tubs.
- Students can bring in corn meal, unprocessed bran, dry cereal or uncooked oatmeal for mealworm food. Slices of apple, potato, or carrot can be used as moisture sources. Students can use plastic spoons to transfer the cereal to the containers and to count the mealworms.

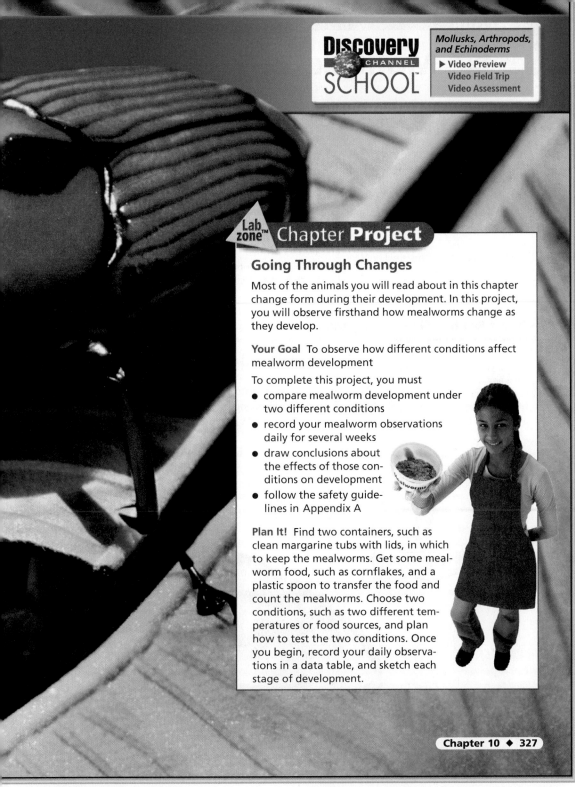

Lab zone™ Chapter Project

Going Through Changes

Most of the animals you will read about in this chapter change form during their development. In this project, you will observe firsthand how mealworms change as they develop.

Your Goal To observe how different conditions affect mealworm development

To complete this project, you must
- compare mealworm development under two different conditions
- record your mealworm observations daily for several weeks
- draw conclusions about the effects of those conditions on development
- follow the safety guidelines in Appendix A

Plan It! Find two containers, such as clean margarine tubs with lids, in which to keep the mealworms. Get some mealworm food, such as cornflakes, and a plastic spoon to transfer the food and count the mealworms. Choose two conditions, such as two different temperatures or food sources, and plan how to test the two conditions. Once you begin, record your daily observations in a data table, and sketch each stage of development.

Chapter 10 ◆ 327

Mollusks

Show the Video Preview to introduce the Chapter Project and overview the chapter content. Discussion question: **In what ways do squids use their tentacles?** (For movement and to capture prey)

Performance Assessment

The Chapter Project Scoring Rubric will help you evaluate how well students complete the Chapter Project. You may want to share the scoring rubric with your students so they are clear about what will be expected of them. Students will be assessed on
- how well they describe the two conditions that they are comparing
- how well they identify and observe the larval, pupal, and adult stages of mealworm development
- how clearly the data sheets show the number of larvae, pupae, and adults in their samples
- how correctly the graphs show the numbers of mealworm larvae, pupae, and adult beetles

Portfolio

Possible Shortcuts
- Acquire mealworms in advance of the project. The larval stage of mealworms lasts for 10 weeks. However, mealworms obtained from a pet store are probably partly through the larval period. Larger larvae are generally older.
- If necessary for scheduling purposes, keep the mealworms at a warm temperature to accelerate development or a cold temperature to delay development.

Launching the Project
To introduce the project, ask: **Have any of you seen a caterpillar turn into a butterfly?** (Answers may vary.) **What are the major differences and similarities between caterpillars and butterflies?** (Sample answer: differences—wings; similarities—legs) Tell students the mealworms will turn into beetles. Reassure them that the beetles will not fly out when the lid of the container is removed.

Objectives

After completing the lesson, students will be able to

10.1.1 Identify the main characteristics of mollusks.

10.1.2 Describe the major groups of mollusks and tell how they differ.

Target Reading Skill 🔄

Comparing and Contrasting Explain that comparing and contrasting information shows how ideas, facts, and events are similar and different. The results of the comparison can have importance.

Answer

Possible answers: Gastropods—use radula to tear through plant or animal tissues; creep along on a broad foot. Bivalves—filter feed; float or swim. Cephalopods—use tentacles to capture prey, crush prey in beaks, use radula to scrape and cut flesh; swim by jet propulsion.

All in One Teaching Resources, Unit 2

• Transparency LS101

Preteach

Build Background Knowledge   L2

Experience With Mollusks

Ask: **Have you ever eaten a mollusk?** If students don't know what a mollusk is, ask if they have eaten clams, squid, or snails. Then inform them that all of these animals are mollusks. **Where could you find mollusks in nature?** *(Answers will vary, but may include oceans, bays, ponds, rivers, streams, or moist areas in forests.)*

Reading Preview

Key Concepts
• What are the main characteristics of mollusks?
• What are the major groups of mollusks and how do they differ?

Key Terms
• mollusk
• open circulatory system • gill
• gastropod • herbivore
• carnivore • radula • bivalve
• omnivore • cephalopod

🔄 Target Reading Skill
Comparing and Contrasting When you compare and contrast things, you explain how they are alike and different. As you read, compare and contrast three groups of mollusks by completing a table like the one below.

Characteristics of Mollusks

Type of Mollusk	How They Obtain Food	How They Move
Gastropod		
Bivalve		
Cephalopod		

Lab zone Discover **Activity**

How Can You Classify Shells?

1. Your teacher will give you an assortment of shells.
2. Examine each shell carefully. Look at the shape and color of the shells and feel their inner and outer surfaces.
3. Classify the shells into groups based on the characteristics you observe.

Think It Over
Inferring How might it help an animal to have a shell? How might it be a disadvantage?

From the shells of clams, Native Americans in the Northeast once carved purple and white beads called wampum. They wove these beads into belts with complex designs that often had special, solemn significance. A wampum belt might record a group's history. When warring groups made peace, they exchanged weavings made of wampum. Iroquois women would honor a new chief with gifts of wampum strings.

The soft bodies inside the shells used to make wampum were a major source of food for Native Americans. Today, clams and similar animals, such as scallops and oysters, are still valuable sources of food for people in many parts of the world.

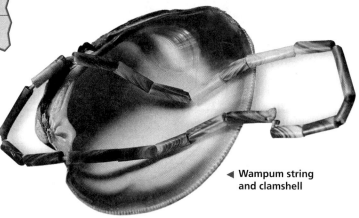

◄ Wampum string and clamshell

Lab zone Discover **Activity**

Skills Focus Inferring   L1

Materials mollusk shells, such as those from clams, mussels, oysters, land and marine snails, and nautiluses

Time 20 minutes

Tips Place the shells at the stations around the room. Group students at each station. Help students develop a set of characteristics to use for grouping the shells. Be sure that students write down the characteristics they used to group the shells.

Expected Outcome Students should become aware of the wide diversity of shells.

Think It Over The shell might help the animal by protecting the animal from predators and supporting its body; it also might be cumbersome and slow down the animal's movements.

Characteristics of Mollusks

Clams, oysters, and scallops are all mollusks (phylum Mollusca). Snails and squids are mollusks, too. **Mollusks** are invertebrates with soft, unsegmented bodies that are often protected by a hard outer shell. **In addition to a soft body often covered by a shell, a mollusk has a thin layer of tissue called a mantle that covers its internal organs, and an organ called a foot.** In many mollusks, the mantle produces the hard shell. Depending on the type of mollusk, the foot has different functions—crawling, digging, or catching prey.

Body Structure Like segmented worms, mollusks have bilateral symmetry and a digestive system with two openings. However, unlike segmented worms, the body parts of mollusks are not usually repeated. Instead, the internal organs are located together in one area, as shown in Figure 1.

Circulatory System Most groups of mollusks have an **open circulatory system,** in which the blood is not always inside blood vessels. The heart pumps blood into a short vessel that opens into the body spaces containing the internal organs. The blood sloshes over the organs and returns eventually to the heart.

Obtaining Oxygen Most mollusks that live in water have **gills,** organs that remove oxygen from the water. The gills have tiny, hairlike structures called cilia and a rich supply of blood vessels. The cilia move back and forth, making water flow over the gills. The gills remove the oxygen from the water and the oxygen moves into the blood. At the same time, carbon dioxide, a waste gas, moves out of the blood and into the water.

 Reading Checkpoint Which organs of a mollusk obtain oxygen from water?

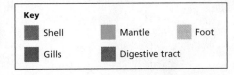
FIGURE 1
Comparing Mollusks
Although they don't look much alike at first, a snail, a clam, and a squid have the same basic body structures.

Key
- Shell
- Gills
- Mantle
- Digestive tract
- Foot

Snail

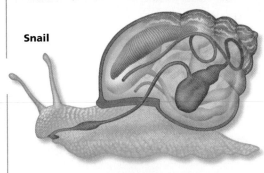

Clam

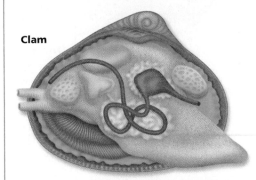

Squid

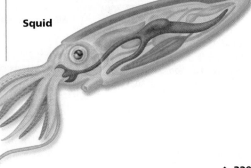

◆ 329

 Instruct

Characteristics of Mollusks

Teach Key Concepts L2
Definition of a Mollusk

Focus Remind students that all mollusks, no matter how different they look, share common features.

Teach Have students study the three illustrations in Figure 1. Ask: **What do these three mollusks have in common?** (*Each of them has a mantle, a foot, a digestive tract, a shell, and gills.*) **What is a mantle?** (*A thin layer of tissue that covers the internal organs of mollusks*) **What is a foot?** (*A muscular structure adapted for crawling, digging, or catching prey*) **What gas exchange takes place in the gills?** *Oxygen passes into the blood and carbon dioxide moves out of the blood.*) Discuss with students additional key characteristics of mollusks: internal organs located within the mantle cavity and an open circulatory system.

Apply Ask: **If you found a new animal in the ocean, what features would you look for to determine whether it is a mollusk?** (*Bilateral symmetry, soft body, mantle, foot, open circulatory system*) **Why don't you find mollusks in hot dry areas?** (*Soft bodies would dry out, gills only function in water or in damp environments.*) **learning modality: logical/mathematical**

All in One Teaching Resources, Unit 2
- Transparency LS102

Independent Practice L2

All in One Teaching Resources, Unit 2
- Guided Reading and Study Worksheet: *Mollusks*

 Student Edition on Audio CD

Monitor Progress L2

Drawing Have students make a simple drawing of a mollusk. Label the major characteristics. Have students place their drawings in their portfolios.

 Portfolio

Answer

Reading Checkpoint Gills obtain oxygen from water.

 ## Differentiated Instruction

English Learners/Beginning L1
Vocabulary: Science Glossary
Pronounce and define aloud the following Key Terms for students: *mollusk, open circulatory system, gill.* Suggest that they start a personal glossary of vocabulary terms, with each term and its definition in English on one side of an index card and in the student's primary language on the other side. **learning modality: verbal**

English Learners/Intermediate L2
Vocabulary: Science Glossary Students can expand on the activity for Beginning students by adding the other Key Terms in this section. Have students write sentences that use each of these words. Give students an opportunity to practice pronunciation by calling on individuals to read their sentences aloud. **learning modality: verbal**

329

Snails and Slugs

Teach Key Concepts L2
Characteristics of Gastropods

Focus Tell students that gastropods are mollusks that have a single external shell or no shell at all. Gastropods also have a unique feeding structure called a radula.

Teach Ask: **What characteristics do snails and slugs have that cause them to be classified as gastropods?** *(They have a radula; they creep along using their broad feet; those with shells have a single external shell)* **How does a gastropod eat?** *(A gastropod uses a radula, a flexible ribbon of tiny teeth, to scrape up food and move it into the digestive tract.)* **How do gastropods vary?** *(Presence and absence of shell, type of shell, type of foot, complexity of nervous system)*

Apply Ask: **How do the characteristics that enable the organism to obtain food differ between gastropods that are herbivores and gastropods that are carnivores?** *(The radulas of herbivores are designed to scrape off plant material. Some carnivores use their radulas to drill into the shells and then scrape the flesh.)* **learning modality: logical/mathematical**

Studying Snails

Materials aquarium, live snails

Time 20 minutes

Focus Tell students that people put snails in fish tanks to eat the algae.

Teach Ask students to study the snails but not touch them or bang the aquarium. Ask: **What features can you identify?** *(Students can probably identify the shell, foot, and mouth.)* Have students study the foot of snails crawling up the side of the tank. Help students observe the foot moving and the slime trails left behind.

Apply Ask: **How would you describe the way in which the snails feed on algae in the tank?** *(They use their radulas to scrape up algae growing on the side of the tank.)* **learning modality: visual**

FIGURE 2
Gastropods
Although the land snail has a shell and the sea slug does not, both are gastropods.

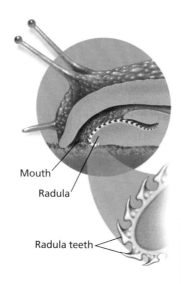

Mouth
Radula
Radula teeth

FIGURE 3
The Radula of a Snail
A snail has a food-gathering organ called a radula, which tears and scrapes up food.

Snails and Slugs

Biologists classify mollusks into groups based on their physical characteristics. These characteristics include the presence of a shell, the type of shell, the type of foot, and the type of nervous system. **The three major groups of mollusks are gastropods, bivalves, and cephalopods.**

The **gastropods** are the largest group of mollusks. They include snails and slugs, like the ones shown in Figure 2, and live nearly everywhere on Earth. They live in oceans, on rocky shores, in fresh water, and on land. **Gastropods have a single external shell or no shell at all.**

Obtaining Food Like all organisms, gastropods need food. Some gastropods are **herbivores,** animals that eat only plants. Some are scavengers that eat decaying material. Still others are **carnivores,** animals that eat only other animals.

But no matter what they eat, gastropods use an organ called a **radula** (RAJ oo luh), a flexible ribbon of tiny teeth, to obtain food. Herbivores use the radula like sandpaper to tear through plant tissues. Carnivores use their radulas in different ways. For example, a gastropod called an oyster drill uses its radula to bore a hole through an oyster's shell. Then it scrapes up the oyster's soft body tissues.

Movement A gastropod usually moves by creeping along on a broad foot. The foot may ooze a carpet of slippery mucus, which you may have seen if you've ever watched a snail move. The mucus makes it easier for the gastropod to move.

Reading Checkpoint What is the function of a radula?

Two-Shelled Mollusks

A second group of mollusks, **bivalves,** includes oysters, clams, scallops, and mussels. **Bivalves are mollusks that have two shells held together by hinges and strong muscles.** They are found in all kinds of watery environments.

Obtaining Food Like gastropods, bivalves need food. But unlike gastropods, bivalves do not have radulas. Instead, most are filter feeders that strain tiny organisms from water. Bivalves capture food as water flows over their gills. Food particles stick to mucus that covers the gills. The cilia on the gills then move the food particles into the bivalve's mouth. Most bivalves are **omnivores,** animals that eat both plants and animals.

Movement Like gastropods, bivalves don't move quickly. The larvae of most bivalves float or swim through the water. But the adults stay in one place or use their foot to move very slowly. For example, oysters and mussels attach themselves to rocks or other underwater surfaces. Clams, in contrast, move. Look at Figure 4 to see how a clam digs into mud.

Protection Sometimes an object such as a grain of sand gets stuck between a bivalve's mantle and shell. The object irritates the soft mantle. Just as you might put smooth tape around rough bicycle handlebars to protect your hands, the bivalve's mantle produces a smooth, pearly coat to cover the irritating object. Sometimes a pearl forms eventually around the object. Some oysters make beautiful pearls that are used in jewelry.

FIGURE 4
How a Clam Digs
A razor clam digs into the mud by changing the shape of its foot.
Predicting *How might the clam use its foot to move back up?*

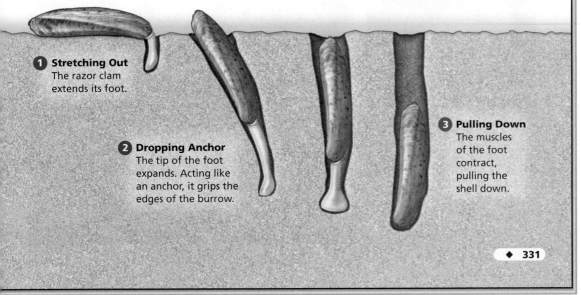

1 Stretching Out
The razor clam extends its foot.

2 Dropping Anchor
The tip of the foot expands. Acting like an anchor, it grips the edges of the burrow.

3 Pulling Down
The muscles of the foot contract, pulling the shell down.

◆ 331

Octopuses and Their Relatives

Teach Key Concepts `L2`
Characteristics of Cephalopods

Focus Have students look at Figure 5. Ask: **What is the first thing you notice when you look at the octopus?** *(Most students will answer that they notice the tentacles first.)*

Teach Ask: **Which characteristics enable cephalopods to catch prey?** *(Tentacles for snaring prey, suckers that sense food, large eyes, jet propulsion.)* **How does a complex nervous system enable cephalopods to capture prey?** *(It allows them to process information that they sense with their tentacles and see with their eyes; it may help them learn and remember strategies for catching prey.)*

Apply Give students this fictional scenario: A zoo octopus is given a glass screw-top jar containing a fish. The octopus opens the jar. Describe how the characteristics of cephalopods made this possible. *(Cephalopods have flexible tentacles that can grasp and manipulate objects. They have relatively large brains and can learn how to solve puzzles, such as opening the closed jar.)* **learning modality: logical/mathematical**

Teacher Demo `L2`

Jet Propulsion in Cephalopods

Materials aquarium or sink, balloon, water

Time 10 minutes

Focus Ask: **How is the ability to swim fast helpful to cephalopods?** *(It helps cephalopods pursue and capture prey. It also helps them escape from danger.)*

Teach To demonstrate how cephalopods move using jet propulsion, fill the balloon with water. Pinch the neck to keep water from squirting out. Immerse the balloon in an aquarium or sink. Ask: **What will happen when I release the balloon?** *(It will shoot through the water.)* Release the balloon. Students will observe the balloon shooting through the water.

Apply Ask students to compare the movement of the octopus with the movement of a balloon. *(Just as the balloon squeezes water out through the opening, cephalopods squeeze out water from their mantle.)* **learning modality: visual**

Discovery CHANNEL SCHOOL™

Mollusks, Arthropods, and Echinoderms

Video Preview
▶ Video Field Trip
Video Assessment

FIGURE 5
Three Cephalopods

A nautilus, an octopus, and a squid are all cephalopods. In cephalopods, the foot is adapted to form tentacles. **Drawing Conclusions** *Why is* cephalopod, *which is Greek for "head foot," a good name for members of this group?*

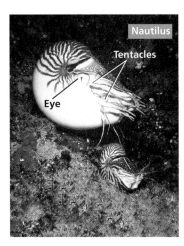

Octopuses and Their Relatives

Octopuses and squids are **cephalopods** (SEF uh luh pahdz). So are nautiluses and cuttlefishes. **A cephalopod is an ocean-dwelling mollusk whose foot is adapted to form tentacles around its mouth.** Unlike bivalves, not all cephalopods have shells. For example, nautiluses have an external shell, squids and cuttlefish have a small shell within the body, and octopuses have no shells. Cephalopods are the only mollusks with a closed circulatory system.

Obtaining Food Cephalopods are carnivores. A cephalopod captures prey using its muscular tentacles. Then it crushes the prey in a beak and scrapes and cuts the flesh with its radula.

A cephalopod's tentacles contain sensitive suckers, which you can see on the octopus in Figure 5. The suckers receive sensations of taste as well as touch. A cephalopod doesn't have to touch something to taste it because the suckers respond to chemicals in the water. For example, when an octopus feels beneath a rock, its tentacles may find a crab by taste before touching it.

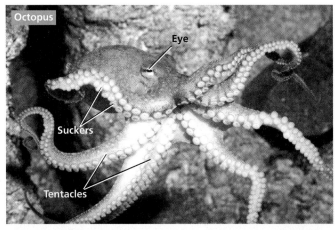

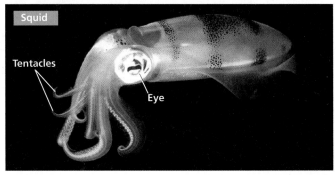

Nervous System Cephalopods have large eyes and excellent vision. They also have the most complex nervous system of any invertebrate. Cephalopods have large brains and can remember things they have learned. For example, in captivity, octopuses can learn when to expect deliveries of food. Some even figure out how to escape from their tanks.

Movement Cephalopods swim by jet propulsion. They squeeze a current of water out of the mantle cavity and through a tube. Then, like rockets, they shoot off in the opposite direction. By turning the tube around, they can reverse direction.

 Reading Checkpoint What does the foot of a cephalopod look like?

FIGURE 6
An Escaping Octopus
This octopus has figured out how to escape from a jar through a tiny hole in the lid.

Section 1 Assessment

Target Reading Skill **Comparing and Contrasting** Use the information in your table about mollusks to help you answer Question 2 below.

Reviewing Key Concepts

1. a. **Listing** List the characteristics of a mollusk.
   b. **Explaining** How is a mollusk's mantle related to its shell?
   c. **Predicting** What would happen to a mollusk if the cilia on its gills did not work? Explain.
2. a. **Identifying** What are three groups of mollusks?
   b. **Classifying** What are the characteristics of the three groups of mollusks?
   c. **Comparing and Contrasting** How are the foot structures of a snail, a clam, and an octopus similar? How are they different?

Lab zone **At-Home Activity**

Edible Mollusks Visit a local supermarket with a family member and identify any mollusks that are being sold as food. Be sure to look in places other than the fish counter, such as the canned-foods section. Discuss the parts of the mollusks that are used for food and the parts that are not edible.

Chapter 10 ◆ 333

Mollusks

Show students the Video Field Trip to help them understand the adaptations of octopuses that make octopuses well suited to their habitat. Discussion question: **How do octopuses move quickly through the water?** *(They are able to move about by jet propulsion.)*

Monitor Progress _____ L2

Answers
Figure 5 Because the tentacles (modified foot) extend from the head

 Reading Checkpoint The foot is adapted into tentacles.

Assess

Reviewing Key Concepts

1. a. A mollusk is an invertebrate with a soft unsegmented body usually protected by a shell. A mollusk has a mantle that covers its internal organs, and a mollusk has a foot.
b. The mantle produces the hard shell in mollusks that have a shell. **c.** Without working cilia, water would not flow over the gills, and the mollusk then might become oxygen-deprived.
2. a. The three groups of mollusks are gastropods, bivalves, and cephalopods.
b. Gastropods have no shell or one shell and use a radula to obtain food. Bivalves have two shells. Cephalopods have a foot adapted to form tentacles. **c.** In a snail and a clam the food is used for movement; in a cephalopod it is adapted as tentacles and used for capturing prey.

Reteach L1
Have student groups make a chart comparing the different kinds of mollusks.

Performance Assessment L2
Writing Have each student explain, in his or her own words, why snails, slugs, clams, and squids are all classified as mollusks.

All in One Teaching Resources, Unit 2
- Section Summary: *Mollusks*
- Review and Reinforce: *Mollusks*
- Enrich: *Mollusks*

Lab zone **At-Home Activity**

Edible Mollusks L2 Ask students which mollusks they expect to find. *(Snails, oysters, clams, squid, canned clams, smoked oysters)* Suggest students visit a seafood store with a larger variety of seafood.

Prepare for Inquiry

Key Concept
The activity of some animals can be affected by the temperature of their environment.

Skills Objectives
After this lab, students will be able to
- interpret data on how a snail's activity changes as temperature changes
- predict snail activity at higher temperatures

 Prep Time 30 minutes
Class Time 45 minutes

Advance Planning
Place the snails in a small aquarium of pond water. Aerate the aquarium if the snails will be kept more than a few days. For the lab, use the most active snails. For safety reasons, prepare the cool, medium, and warm water yourself.

Safety
- Students should be very careful with the thermometers. Make sure they do not let them roll off a table top.
- Remind students to treat snails gently and disturb them as little as possible.

 **Teaching Resources, Unit 2**
- Lab Worksheet: *A Snail's Pace*

Guide Inquiry

Introduce the Procedure
Have students read through the entire activity, and then ask: **What is the purpose of this activity?** (*To compare the distance a snail moves in water of different temperatures*) **Why do you draw four circles on the graph paper?** (*One is to place under the petri dish with the snail so that students can observe how the snail moves; each of the others is for recording the snail's movement in different temperatures.*)

Troubleshooting the Experiment
Do not allow students to tap the petri dish to get the snail moving. Remind students not to leave the snails out of the water for very long.

Expected Outcome
Snails usually move more slowly in colder water than in warmer water.

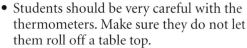

Problem
How do changes in the temperature of the environment affect the activity level of a snail?

Skills Focus
interpreting data, predicting

Materials
- freshwater snail
- thermometer
- ruler
- plastic petri dish
- graph paper, 2 sheets
- timer
- spring water at three temperatures: cool (9–13°C); medium (18–22°C); warm (27–31°C)

Procedure

1. Create a data table for recording the water temperatures and the distance the snail travels at each temperature.

2. On one sheet of graph paper labeled *Snail*, trace a circle using the base of an empty petri dish. Divide and label the circle as shown in the illustration. On a second sheet of graph paper labeled *Data*, draw three more circles like the one in the illustration.

3. Place the petri dish over the circle on the Snail page, fill it with cool water, and record the water temperature. Then place the snail in the water just above the "S" in the circle. Handle the snail gently.

4. For five minutes, observe the snail. Record its movements by drawing a line that shows its path in the first circle on the Data page.

5. Find the distance the snail moved by measuring the line you drew. You may need to measure all the parts of the line and add them together. Record the distance in your data table.

6. Repeat Steps 3 through 5, first with medium-temperature water and then with warm water. Record the snail's paths in the second circle and third circle on the Data page.

7. Return the snail to your teacher when you are done. Wash your hands thoroughly.

8. For each temperature, compute the class average for distance traveled.

Analyze and Conclude

1. **Graphing** Make a bar graph showing the class average for each temperature.

2. **Interpreting Data** How does a snail's activity level change as temperature increases?

3. **Predicting** Do you think the pattern you found would continue at higher temperatures? Explain.

4. **Communicating** Write an e-mail to a friend describing how you conducted your experiment, any problems you ran into, and your results. Did your results help answer the question posed at the beginning of the lab? Explain your results to your friend.

Design an Experiment
Design an experiment to measure how different kinds of natural surfaces beneath the snail affect its rate of movement. Obtain three surface materials, such as fine sand, medium-grain gravel, and coarse gravel. Explain how you would modify the procedure. *Obtain your teacher's permission before carrying out your investigation.*

Analyze and Conclude
1. Answers will vary. Plot temperature on the *x*-axis and the distance moved on the *y*-axis.

2. Snails move more in warmer water.

3. No. Although snails move more in warmer water, hot water will kill them.

4. Answers will vary. Student responses should accurately describe their experiment and whether or not its results answered the question posed at the beginning of the lab.

Extend the Inquiry

Design an Experiment Advise students to ensure that all surface materials are thoroughly rinsed with pond water and allowed to settle before beginning their experiments.

Reading Preview

Key Concepts
- What are the four major groups of arthropods and what are their characteristics?
- How do crustaceans, arachnids, and centipedes and millpedes differ?

Key Terms
- arthropod • exoskeleton
- molting • antenna
- crustacean • metamorphosis
- arachnid • abdomen

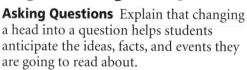 Target Reading Skill

Asking Questions Before you read, preview the red headings. In a graphic organizer like the one below, ask a *what* or a *how* question for each heading. As you read, write the answers to your questions.

Characteristics of Arthropods

Question	Answer
What is an arthropod?	

Lab zone Discover Activity

Will It Bend and Move?

1. Have a partner roll a piece of cardboard around your arm to form a tube that covers your elbow. Your partner should put three pieces of tape around the tube to hold it closed—one at each end and one in the middle.
2. With the tube in place, try to write your name on a piece of paper. Then try to scratch your head.
3. Keep the tube on your arm for 10 minutes. Observe how the tube affects your ability to do things.

Think It Over
Inferring Insects and many other animals have rigid skeletons on the outside of their bodies. Why do their skeletons need joints?

At dusk near the edge of a meadow, a grasshopper leaps through the grass. Nearby, a hungry spider waits in its web. The grasshopper leaps into the web. It's caught! As the grasshopper struggles to free itself, the spider rushes toward it. Quickly, the spider wraps the grasshopper in silk. The grasshopper cannot escape. Soon it will become a tasty meal for the spider.

The spider and grasshopper are both **arthropods,** or members of the arthropod phylum (phylum Arthropoda). Animals such as crabs, lobsters, centipedes, and scorpions are also arthropods.

FIGURE 7
A Spider at Work
This spider wraps its prey, a grasshopper, in silk. Both animals are arthropods.

◆ 335

Lab zone Discover Activity

Skills Focus Inferring

Materials sheets of heavy cardboard, about 30 × 45 cm, tape

Prep Time 5 minutes

Class Time 15 minutes

Tips Use cardboard that is flexible enough to roll into a tube and tape that is strong enough to stay attached when students attempt to bend their elbows. Students

L1 whose partners already have an arm wrapped in cardboard will need assistance when putting on their own tubes.

Expected Outcome Students will find that restricting their joints makes it impossible for them to bend their elbows.

Think It Over Joints in skeletons allow movement.

Objectives
After completing the lesson, students will be able to

10.2.1 Identify four major groups of arthropods and the main characteristics of arthropods.

10.2.2 Describe how crustaceans, arachnids, and centipedes and millipedes differ.

Target Reading Skill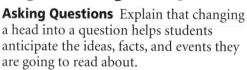

Asking Questions Explain that changing a head into a question helps students anticipate the ideas, facts, and events they are going to read about.

Answers
Possible questions and answers are these:
What is an arthropod? (*Invertebrate that has an external skeleton, a segmented body, and jointed appendages*) **What is a crustacean?** (*Arthropod with two or three body sections, five or more pairs of legs, and two pairs of antennae*) **What is an arachnid?** (*Arthropod with two body sections, four pairs of legs, and no antennae*) **What are centipedes and millipedes?** (*Arthropods with two body sections and numerous pairs of legs*)

All in One Teaching Resources, Unit 2
- Transparency LS103

Preteach

Build Background Knowledge **L2**

Experience with Arthropods
Ask students to name examples of insects and spiders they have seen. Ask: **Who has ever seen scorpions, crabs, crayfish, or lobsters?** (*Answers will vary depending on students' experiences.*) Ask volunteers to describe these animals. Use leading questions to prompt students to mention the external shells and jointed limbs of these animals. Tell students that the features they described are characteristics of arthropods.

335

Instruct

Characteristics of Arthropods

Teach Key Concepts   L2
Key Traits of Arthropods

Focus Tell students that arthropods share certain similarities with mollusks, but also have other different and unique characteristics.

Teach Ask: **What are three features of arthropods?** *(Exoskeleton, segmented body, jointed appendages)* **What are the advantages of having an exoskeleton?** *(It protects the body, prevents water loss, and provides support.)* **What are the disadvantages of having an exoskeleton?** *(Its rigidity limits movement and growth.)*

Apply Ask: **What features compensate for the limitations of the exoskeleton?** *(Segmented bodies and jointed appendages enable movement. Molting enables growth.)* Point out that despite the exoskeleton's limitations, arthropods are the most successful and diverse animals in the world. **learning modality: logical/mathematical**

Help Students Read   L1
Summarize Summarizing the information presented in the text will help students to focus on main ideas and remember what they read. Have students read about the main characteristics of arthropods. Ask them to summarize the information by restating the main ideas in their own words.

Independent Practice   L2

All in One Teaching Resources, Unit 2

• Guided Reading and Study Worksheet: *Arthropods*

⊙ Student Edition on Audio CD

Characteristics of Arthropods

Arthropods are classified into four major groups. **The major groups of arthropods are crustaceans, arachnids, centipedes and millipedes, and insects.** All arthropods share certain characteristics. **Arthropods are invertebrates that have an external skeleton, a segmented body, and jointed attachments called appendages.** Wings, mouthparts, and legs are all appendages. Jointed appendages are such a distinctive characteristic that arthropods are named for it. *Arthros* means "joint" in Greek, and *podos* means "foot" or "leg."

Arthropods share some characteristics with many other animals, too. They have bilateral symmetry, an open circulatory system, and a digestive system with two openings. In addition, most arthropods reproduce sexually.

Outer Skeleton If you were an arthropod, you would have a waterproof covering. This waxy covering is called an **exoskeleton,** or outer skeleton. It protects the animal and helps prevent evaporation of water. Water animals are surrounded by water, but land animals need a way to keep from drying out. Arthropods may have been the first animals to live on land. Their exoskeletons probably enabled them to do this because they keep the arthropods from drying out.

As an arthropod grows larger, its exoskeleton cannot expand. The growing arthropod is trapped within its exoskeleton, like a knight in armor that is too small. Arthropods solve this problem by occasionally shedding their exoskeletons and growing new ones that are larger. The process of shedding an outgrown exoskeleton is called **molting.** After an arthropod has molted, its new skeleton is soft for a time. During that time, the arthropod has less protection from danger than it does after its new skeleton has hardened.

FIGURE 9
A Molting Cicada
This cicada has just molted. You can see its old exoskeleton hanging on the leaf just below it.
Applying Concepts *Why must arthropods molt?*

336 ◆

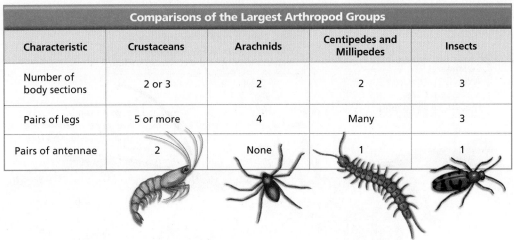

Comparisons of the Largest Arthropod Groups				
Characteristic	Crustaceans	Arachnids	Centipedes and Millipedes	Insects
Number of body sections	2 or 3	2	2	3
Pairs of legs	5 or more	4	Many	3
Pairs of antennae	2	None	1	1

FIGURE 10
Members of the largest arthropod groups differ in several characteristics. **Interpreting Tables** *Which group of arthropods has no antennae?*

Segmented Body The bodies of arthropods are segmented. A segmented body plan is easiest to see in centipedes and millipedes, which have bodies made up of many identical-looking segments. In fact, their bodies look something like the bodies of earthworms. You can also see segments on the tails of shrimp and lobsters. In some groups of arthropods, several body segments become joined into distinct sections. An arthropod may have up to three sections—a head, a midsection, and a hind section.

Jointed Appendages Just as your fingers are appendages attached to your palms, many arthropods have jointed appendages attached to their bodies. The joints in the appendages give the animal flexibility and enable it to move. If you did the Discover activity, you saw how important joints are for allowing movement. Arthropod appendages tend to be highly specialized tools used for moving, obtaining food, reproducing, and sensing the environment. For example, arthropods use legs to walk and wings to fly. In addition, most arthropods have appendages called antennae (singular *antenna*). An **antenna** is an appendage attached to the head that contains sense organs.

Diversity Scientists have identified more species of arthropods—over one million—than all other species of animals combined! There are probably many others that have not yet been discovered. Look at Figure 10 to compare some characteristics of the four major groups of arthropods.

 Reading Checkpoint What does an antenna do?

For: Links on arthropods
Visit: www.SciLinks.org
Web Code: scn-0222

Chapter 10 ◆ 337

Differentiated Instruction

Less Proficient Readers [L1]
Identifying Prefixes To help students remember the meaning of *exoskeleton*, point out that the words *external* and *exoskeleton* both begin with the prefix *ex-*.

Explain that *ex-* and *exo-* may mean "outside." Ask students to think of other words that start with these prefixes. *(Possible answers:* exit, expedition*)* **learning modality: verbal**

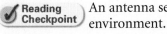

Crustaceans

Focus Tell students that a unique feature of crustaceans is the large number of specialized appendages.

Teach Have students observe Figure 11. Point out specific features such as the segmented abdomen, the different types of antennae, and the walking legs and chelipeds. Have volunteers read aloud the callouts. Ask: **How are the walking legs different from the chelipeds?** (*The chelipeds are larger and have pincers.*) **What are they used for?** (*Capturing food and defense*) **How do the many different specialized appendages help crustaceans?** (*The large number of specialized appendages enables crustaceans to carry out highly specific tasks, such as catching prey or manipulating food.*) **What are some ways crustaceans obtain food?** (*Many are scavengers; others are predators. Krill are herbivores.*)

Apply Remind students that most crustaceans are aquatic. Ask: **What characteristics enable crustaceans to live in the water?** (*Swimmerets, gills for obtaining oxygen, larvae that swim*) **learning modality: verbal**

All in One Teaching Resources, Unit 2

• Transparency LS105

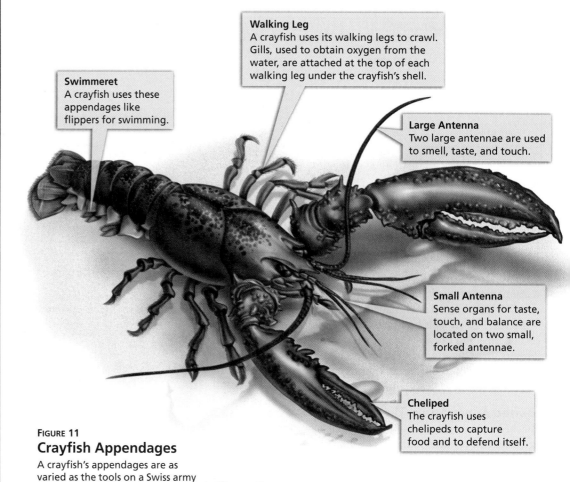

Swimmeret
A crayfish uses these appendages like flippers for swimming.

Walking Leg
A crayfish uses its walking legs to crawl. Gills, used to obtain oxygen from the water, are attached at the top of each walking leg under the crayfish's shell.

Large Antenna
Two large antennae are used to smell, taste, and touch.

Small Antenna
Sense organs for taste, touch, and balance are located on two small, forked antennae.

Cheliped
The crayfish uses chelipeds to capture food and to defend itself.

FIGURE 11
Crayfish Appendages
A crayfish's appendages are as varied as the tools on a Swiss army knife. The appendages are adapted for different functions. *Interpreting Diagrams What functions do the chelipeds serve?*

Crustaceans

If you've ever eaten shrimp cocktail or crab cakes, you've dined on **crustaceans** (krus TAY shunz). Crayfish and lobsters are other familiar crustaceans. Crustaceans thrive in freshwater lakes and rivers, and even in puddles that last a long time. You can find them in the deepest parts of oceans and along coastlines. A few, like the pill bug, live in damp places on land.

Body Structure Crustaceans share certain characteristics. **A crustacean is an arthropod that has two or three body sections, five or more pairs of legs, and two pairs of antennae.** Each crustacean body segment has a pair of legs or another type of appendage attached to it. The various types of appendages function differently, as you can see in Figure 11.

338 ◆

Differentiated Instruction

Less Proficient Readers   L1
Answering Questions Select a passage from the text, such as *Obtaining Oxygen and Food*. Read the passage aloud to students as they follow along in their books. After reading, ask some questions about the passage. If they don't know the answers, challenge them to find them in the passage. **learning modality: verbal**

Gifted and Talented   L3
Researching Specialized Appendages
Have students research and summarize the specialized appendages found in crayfish. (*One or more pairs of the following: antennules, antennae, mandibles, maxillae, maxillipeds, chelipeds, walking legs, swimmerets, and uropods*) **learning modality: verbal**

The appendages attached to the head of a crayfish include two pairs of antennae that are used for smelling, tasting, touching, and keeping balance. The crayfish uses most of its leg appendages for walking. However, it uses its first pair of legs, called chelipeds, for obtaining food and defending itself.

Obtaining Oxygen and Food Because crustaceans live in watery environments, most have gills to obtain oxygen. The gills are located beneath the shell of a crustacean. Water containing oxygen reaches the gills as a crustacean moves along in its environment.

Crustaceans obtain food in many ways. Some are scavengers that eat dead plants and animals. Others are predators, eating animals they have killed. The pistol shrimp is a predator with an appendage that moves with such force that it stuns its prey. Krill, which are shrimplike crustaceans that live in cold ocean waters, are herbivores that eat plantlike microorganisms. In turn, krill are eaten by predators such as fishes, penguins, seals, and even great blue whales, the world's largest animals.

Life Cycle Most crustaceans, such as crabs, barnacles, and shrimp, begin their lives as microscopic, swimming larvae. The bodies of these larvae do not resemble those of adults. Crustacean larvae develop into adults by **metamorphosis** (met uh MAWR fuh sis), a process in which an animal's body undergoes dramatic changes in form during its life cycle.

 Reading Checkpoint What organs does a crustacean use to obtain oxygen?

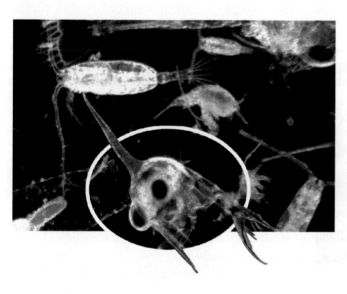

FIGURE 12
Crab Larva
This larva of a crab floats in the ocean with other microscopic animals.

Arachnids

Teach Key Concepts   L2

Recognizing Four Kinds of Arachnids

Focus Point out to students that arachnids are abundant everywhere we live and that most escape our notice.

Teach Ask: **What is an example of an arachnid?** (*Answers will vary, but most students will mention spiders first.*) **How does a spider differ from a mite?** (*Spiders are predators; mites are parasites.*) Have students study the picture of the deer tick, and then ask: **What disease is spread by deer ticks?** (*Lyme disease*) After students look at Figure 15, ask: **Where would you most likely find a scorpion during the day?** (*Hiding in a cool place, such as under a rock*)

Apply Ask: **What are some ways arachnids defend themselves?** (*A spider has fangs through which it injects venom into its prey. A scorpion has a spinelike stinger at the end of its abdomen.*) **learning modality: verbal**

Address Misconceptions   L1

Spiders

Focus Many students believe that all spiders catch their prey in webs and that all spiders' bites are extremely dangerous to people.

Teach Help students understand that many commonly held beliefs about spiders are false. Ask: **How do spiders catch their prey?** (*Some spiders use webs, but others chase or trap their prey.*) **Are most spiders' bites extremely dangerous to people?** (*Spiders rarely bite people, and most spider bites are uncomfortable but not dangerous.*)

Apply Tell students that two kinds of spiders that may inflict bites that require medical care are the brown recluse and the black widow. **learning modality: logical/ mathematical**

FIGURE 13
Red Knee Tarantula
This red knee tarantula lives in an underground burrow. The spider uses fangs to inject venom into its prey.

Arachnids

Spiders, mites, ticks, and scorpions are the **arachnids** (uh RAK nidz) that people most often meet. **Arachnids are arthropods with two body sections, four pairs of legs, and no antennae.** Their first body section is a combined head and midsection. The hind section, called the **abdomen,** is the other section. The abdomen contains the reproductive organs and part of the digestive system.

Spiders Spiders are probably the most familiar, most feared, and most fascinating kind of arachnid. All spiders are predators, and most of them eat insects. Some, such as tarantulas and wolf spiders, run down their prey. Others, such as golden garden spiders, spin sticky webs to trap their prey.

Spiders have hollow fangs through which they inject venom into their prey. Spider venom turns the tissues of the prey into mush. Later the spider uses its fangs like drinking straws, and sucks in the food. In spite of what some people might think, spiders rarely bite people. When spiders do bite, their bites are often painful but not life-threatening. However, the bite of a brown recluse or a black widow may require hospital care.

FIGURE 14
Dust Mite
This microscopic dust mite feeds on dead skin and hair shed by humans. **Classifying** *Would you describe the mite as a carnivore, scavenger, or filter feeder? Why?*

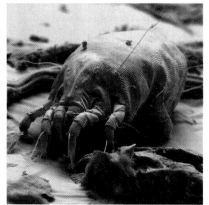

Mites If chiggers have ever given you an itchy rash, you've had an unpleasant encounter with tiny arachnids called mites. Chiggers and many other mites are parasites. Ear mites, for example, give dogs and cats itchy ears. Mites are everywhere. Even the cleanest houses have microscopic dust mites. If you are allergic to dust, you may actually be allergic to the exoskeletons of dust mites. In addition to living in dry areas, mites also live in fresh water and in the ocean.

 Reading Checkpoint   What kind of arachnid is a chigger?

340 ◆

FIGURE 15
Scorpion
A scorpion is a carnivore that injects venom from a stinger at the end of its abdomen.

Scorpions Scorpions live mainly in hot climates, and are usually active at night. During the day, scorpions hide in cool places—under rocks and logs, or in holes in the ground, for example. At the end of its abdomen, a scorpion has a spinelike stinger. The scorpion uses the stinger to inject venom into its prey, which is usually a spider or an insect.

Ticks Ticks are parasites that live on the outside of a host animal's body. Nearly every kind of land animal has a species of tick that sucks its blood. Some ticks that attack humans can carry diseases. Lyme disease, for example, is spread by the bite of an infected deer tick. You can see an enlarged deer tick to the right. In reality, a deer tick is just a few millimeters long.

◄ **Deer tick**

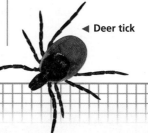

Math ► Analyzing Data

Lyme Disease Cases

The graph shows the numbers of cases of Lyme disease by age group reported by Connecticut during one year. Use the graph to answer the questions.

1. **Reading Graphs** What variable is plotted on the *y*-axis? What does the first bar tell you?

2. **Interpreting Data** Which age group is least at risk for Lyme disease? Explain.

3. **Interpreting Data** Which two age groups are most at risk?

4. **Calculating** Suppose a particular school in Connecticut has 1,000 students ranging in age from 10 to 19. About how many of these students would you expect to get Lyme disease per year?

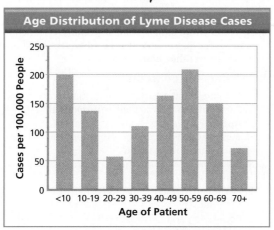

Age Distribution of Lyme Disease Cases

(bar graph: *y*-axis "Cases per 100,000 People" from 0 to 250; *x*-axis "Age of Patient" with groups <10, 10-19, 20-29, 30-39, 40-49, 50-59, 60-69, 70+)

Math Skills

Math Skill Interpreting Data

Focus Point out to students that a bar graph is used to compare data.

Teach Ask: **What does the *x*-axis show?** *(Age of the patients)* **What does the *y*-axis show?** *(Cases per 100,000 people)* **What do the bars represent?** *(Number of people in each category)*

Answers
1. Cases per 100,000 people; the first bar shows that for every 100,000 children under the age of ten, 200 had Lyme disease.
2. 20–29 year-olds; just over 50 per 100,000 people were infected
3. Children under 10 and people between the ages of 50 and 59
4. One or two students

Differentiated Instruction

English Learners/Beginning [L1] **Comprehension: Modified Cloze** Write some simple sentences on the board that require the terms *arthropod, arachnid,* and *abdomen.* For example: "A group of animals called _____ includes crustaceans, _____, centipedes and millipedes, and insects." "The second body section of an arachnid is called the _____." Complete one or two sentences as a model, then fill in the blanks together. **learning modality: verbal**

English Learners/Intermediate [L2] **Comprehension: Modified Cloze** Use the same sentences described for Beginning students, but fill in incorrect terms. Have students work in pairs to determine the correct answers. **learning modality: verbal**

Monitor Progress _____ [L2]

Writing Have each student choose a group of arachnids and list its characteristics.

Answers
Figure 14 The dust mite is a scavenger; it eats dead skin and hair from humans.

 Reading Checkpoint A mite

341

Centipedes and Millipedes

Teach Key Concepts   L2
Centipede and Millipede Characteristics

Focus Tell students that centipedes and millipedes search for food in dark, moist places, such as under logs and stones.

Teach Draw two lines of connected circles on the blackboard. Tell students that the circles represent body segments. Ask: **How many pairs of legs should I draw on each segment to make it a centipede?** *(One)* **How many for a millipede?** *(Two)*

Apply Ask: **How does the way millipedes get energy differ from that of a centipede?** *(Centipedes are carnivores that eat other animals; millipedes are scavengers that eat decayed leaves.)* **learning modality: visual**

Monitor Progress   L2
Answer
Figure 16 One pair

Assess

Reviewing Key Concepts

1. a. Crustaceans, arachnids, centipedes and millipedes, and insects **b.** All arthropods are invertebrates with an exoskeleton, segmented body, and jointed appendages. **c.** It had just molted.
2. a. Crustaceans are arthropods with two or three body sections, five or more pairs of legs, and two pairs of antennae. **b.** An arachnid has two body sections, four pairs of legs, and no antennae. **c.** Centipedes and millipedes both have two body sections and many pairs of legs. A centipede has one pair of legs on each segment of its abdomen, while a millipede has two legs per segment.

Reteach   L1
Use Figure 10 to review the characteristics of each arthropod group.

All in One Teaching Resources, Unit 2

- Section Summary: *Arthropods*
- Review and Reinforce: *Arthropods*
- Enrich: *Arthropods*

Centipede   Millipede

FIGURE 16
Centipede and Millipede
Both centipedes and millipedes have many pairs of legs.
Interpreting Photographs How many pairs of legs does each segment of the centipede have?

Centipedes and Millipedes

Centipedes and millipedes are arthropods with two body sections and many pairs of legs. The two body sections are a head with one pair of antennae, and a long abdomen with many segments. Centipedes have one pair of legs attached to each segment. Some centipedes have more than 100 segments. In fact, the word *centipede* means "hundred feet." Centipedes are swift predators that inject venom into their prey.

Millipedes, which may have more than 80 segments, have two pairs of legs on each segment—more legs than any other arthropod. Though *millipede* means "thousand feet," they don't have quite that many legs. Most millipedes are scavengers that graze on partly decayed leaves. When they are disturbed, millipedes can curl up into a ball, protected by their tough exoskeleton. Some will also squirt an awful-smelling liquid at a potential predator.

Section 2 Assessment

Target Reading Skill *Asking Questions* Use the answers to the questions you wrote about the headings to help you answer the questions below.

Reviewing Key Concepts

1. a. Naming What are the major groups of arthropods?
  b. Summarizing How are all arthropods alike?
  c. Applying Concepts Some restaurants serve soft-shelled crab. What do you think happened to the crab just before it was caught?
2. a. Identifying What are the characteristics of a crustacean?
  b. Reviewing Describe the body structure of an arachnid.
  c. Comparing and Contrasting How are centipedes and millipedes alike? How are they different?

342 ◆

Writing in Science

Observation Write about an arthropod that you have observed. Describe details about its physical appearance, its movements, and any other behaviors that you observed.

Lab zone Chapter Project

Keep Students on Track Ensure that students observe mealworms daily, recording how many mealworms in each group are wormlike larvae, how many have formed motionless pupae, and how many, if any, have become adult insects. Ensure each mealworm container has food and a source of moisture.

Writing in Science

Writing Mode Description
Scoring Rubric
4 Includes complete descriptions, and is written in an engaging tone
3 Includes complete, accurate description of the organism
2 Includes accurate but brief description
1 Includes incomplete or inaccurate descriptions

3 Insects

Section
3 Insects

Reading Preview

Key Concepts
- What are the main characteristics of insects?
- What is one way insects are adapted to obtain particular types of food?
- What are two types of metamorphosis that insects undergo?

Key Terms
- insect • thorax
- complete metamorphosis
- pupa
- gradual metamorphosis
- nymph

 **Target Reading Skill**
Sequencing A sequence is the order in which a series of events or steps in a process occurs. As you read, make a cycle diagram that shows the steps in the complete metamorphosis of an insect. Write each step in a separate circle.

Complete Metamorphosis

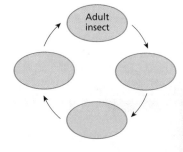
Adult insect

Lab zone Discover Activity

What Characteristics Do Insects Share?
1. Your teacher will give you a collection of insects. Observe the insects carefully.
2. Note the physical characteristics of each insect's body covering. Count the number of body sections.
3. Count the number of legs, wings, and antennae on each insect. Then return the insects to your teacher and wash your hands.

Think It Over
Inferring Compare the legs and the wings of two different species of insect. How is each insect adapted to move?

What do you do if you want to avoid being noticed? You keep perfectly quiet and you don't do anything that will attract attention. You might even wear clothes that help you to blend into the environment—a tactic called camouflage. The thorn insect is a master of camouflage. Not only does it look like a thorn, but it acts like one, too, staying quite still unless a predator like a bird comes too close. Then it springs away to safety.

Other kinds of insects have different camouflage tactics. For example, some caterpillars look like bird droppings, and others look and act like twigs. Plant hoppers may gather in clusters that look like yellow blossoms. And many kinds of moths resemble dead leaves.

Thorn insect ▶

◆ 343

Objectives
After completing the lesson, students will be able to

10.3.1 Identify the main characteristics of insects.

10.3.2 Explain how insects are adapted to obtain food.

10.3.3 Name the two types of metamorphosis found in insects.

Target Reading Skill

Sequencing Explain that sequencing shows the steps in a process. A process is easier to remember when you put each step in a separate box in the order in which it occurs.

Answers
Adult, egg, larva, pupa

All in One Teaching Resources, Unit 2
- Transparency LS106

Preteach

Build Background Knowledge L2

Insect Structure and Behavior
Ask students to describe insects they have observed. Ask: **What do they have in common?** *(Sample answers: Antennae, six legs, hard outer covering)* Tell students that they will learn the characteristics insects share in this section.

Lab zone Discover Activity

Skills Focus Inferring L1
Materials hand lenses, insect collection
Prep Time 5 minutes
Class Time 15 minutes
Tips Facilitate careful observation of the specimens by asking students to describe one or two insects that they find particularly interesting. Ask

students to point out several characteristics that the insects have in common.

Expected Outcome Students should observe that all the insects have the same number of legs *(six)* and body sections *(three)*.

Think It Over Encourage students to compare insects that are very different.

(Answers may vary. Sample: A grasshopper and a dragonfly both have six legs and two pairs of wings. The grasshopper has large hind legs that it uses to jump. The dragonfly has large flat wings that it uses to fly.)

343

Body Structure

Teach Key Concepts L2
Characteristics of Arthropod

Focus Direct students' attention to Figure 17. Have them read the callouts.

Teach Ask: **What structures are visible on the head of this grasshopper?** *(Simple eyes, compound eyes, antennae)* **How do the functions of the simple eye and compound eye differ?** *(Compound eyes are keen at seeing movement; simple eyes can distinguish between light and dark.)* **What important parts of an insect are attached to the thorax?** *(Legs and wings)*

Apply Ask: **Why are insects classified as arthropods?** *(They have body segments, jointed appendages, and an exoskeleton.)*
learning modality: verbal

All in One Teaching Resources, Unit 2
• Transparency LS107

Lab zone Build **Inquiry** L1

Identifying External Parts of the Grasshopper

Materials sealable plastic bags or small clear plastic container containing grasshoppers or crickets from a pet or bait shop; hand lenses

Time 10 minutes

Focus Review the parts of a grasshopper.

Teach Let students examine the insects, without opening the bags or containers, with and without a hand lens and note the varying structures, particularly the three distinct body sections. You may wish to use dead insects, or insects that have been refrigerated to slow activity. In either case, remind students to handle the bags containing the insects gently. Cricket structures will be similar to those found in a grasshopper. Have students compare what they see with the grasshopper shown in Figure 17.

Apply Ask: **How are jointed appendages essential for the grasshopper's survival?** *(Jointed appendages enable the grasshopper to move to seek food and to jump to evade predators.)* **learning modality: visual**

Lab zone Skills **Activity**

Graphing
Use the data to make a circle graph that shows the percentage of total insect species in each group. (See the Skills Handbook.)

Insect Groups

Group	Number of Species
Ants, bees, and wasps	115,000
Beetles and weevils	350,000
Butterflies and moths	178,000
Flies and mosquitoes	110,000
Other insect groups	147,000

Body Structure

Moths are **insects,** as are caterpillers, plant hoppers, dragonflies, cockroaches, and bees. You can identify insects, like other arthropods, by counting their body sections and legs. **Insects are arthropods with three body sections, six legs, one pair of antennae, and usually one or two pairs of wings.** The three body sections are the head, thorax, and abdomen, as you can see in Figure 17.

Head Most of an insect's sense organs, such as the eyes and antennae, are located on the head. Insects usually have two large compound eyes. These eyes contain many lenses, which are structures that focus light to form images. Compound eyes are especially keen at seeing movement. Most insects also have small simple eyes that can distinguish between light and darkness.

Thorax An insect's midsection, or **thorax,** is the section to which wings and legs are attached. Most species of insects can fly once they are adults. Insects are the only invertebrates that can fly. By flying, insects can travel long distances to find mates, food, and new places to live. Being able to fly also enables insects to escape from many predators.

Abdomen Inside the abdomen are many of the insect's internal organs. Small holes on the outside of the abdomen lead to a system of tubes inside the insect. These tubes allow air, which contains oxygen, to enter the body. The oxygen in the air travels directly to the insect's cells.

Reading Checkpoint What are the three sections of an insect's body?

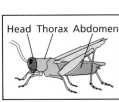
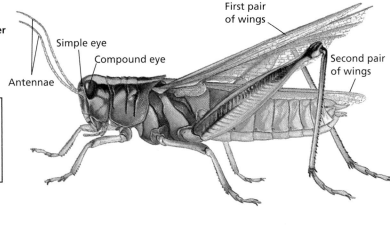

FIGURE 17
Structure of a Grasshopper
A grasshopper's body, like that of every insect, has three sections.

Head Thorax Abdomen

Antennae
Simple eye
Compound eye
First pair of wings
Second pair of wings

344 ◆

Lab zone Skills **Activity**

Skills Focus Graphing

Materials none

Time 15 minutes

Tips Review the method for constructing a circle graph by calculating one section of the graph with students. First, note the total number of insects *(900,000)*. Calculate the ratio of ants, bees, and wasps to the total number of insects:

L3 115,000/900,000 = 0.13, or 13%. Find the angle measure of the section: 360° × 0.13 = 47°. Sketch this section inside a circle using a protractor to measure the central angle.

Expected Outcome Ants, bees wasps: 13%; Beetles and weevils: 39%; Butterflies and moths: 20%; Flies and mosquitoes: 12%; Other: 16% **learning modality: logical/mathematical**

Lapping mouthparts of a fly

Sucking mouthparts of a butterfly

Chewing mouthparts of an ant

FIGURE 18
Diversity of Mouthparts
The mouthparts of this fly, butterfly, and wood ant are very different in their structure.
Inferring *Could a butterfly eat an ant's food? Explain.*

Obtaining Food

The rule seems to be this: If it is living, or if it once was living, some kind of insect will eat it. You probably know that many insects eat parts of plants, such as leaves or nectar. But insects also eat products that are made from plants, such as paper. If you open a very old book, watch for book lice. These tiny insects live in old books, chewing crooked tunnels through the pages.

Insects may feed on animals, too. Some, like fleas and mosquitoes, feed on the blood of living animals. Others, like dung beetles, feed on animal droppings. Still others, like burying beetles, feed on the decaying bodies of dead animals.

An insect's mouthparts are adapted for a highly specific way of getting food. You can see some of these adaptations in Figure 18. Some flies have a sponge-like mouthpart that they use to lap up decaying flesh. A butterfly's mouthparts are shaped like a coiled tube, which can be uncoiled and used like a drinking straw to suck up nectar from flowers. Most ants have sharp-edged mouthparts that can cut through seeds, wood, and other foods.

Reading Checkpoint How does a butterfly obtain food?

Life Cycle

Insects begin life as tiny, hard-shelled, fertilized eggs. After they hatch, insects begin a process of metamorphosis that eventually produces an adult insect. **Each insect species undergoes either complete metamorphosis or gradual metamorphosis.**

Go Online
PHSchool.com

For: More on insect metamorphosis
Visit: PHSchool.com
Web Code: ced-2023

Differentiated Instruction

Special Needs L1
Communicating Partner special needs students with more able students. Have them write the names of structures found on insects on separate index cards. On the other side of each card, tell them to write the function of each structure. Then have them separate the cards into three piles representing the body sections where they belong. **learning modality: kinesthetic**

Gifted and Talented L3
Researching Mosquitoes Have students research the biting apparatus of mosquitoes. Have students prepare a brief summary and drawing describing how mosquitoes are able to bite and withdraw blood without the victim's knowledge.
learning modality: logical/mathematical

Obtaining Food

Teach Key Concepts L2
Diet and Mouthpart Adaptations

Focus Tell students that one reason insects are so successful is that they have adapted to eating a huge variety of things.

Teach Explain that insect mouthparts are highly adapted to suit the diet of each species. Emphasize that insects eat many different kinds of materials, yet most insect species have fairly narrow food requirements. Ask: **What does a grasshopper eat?** *(leaves)* **What does a female mosquito eat?** *(blood)*

Apply Ask students to describe examples they have seen of insects eating different things. *(Possible answers: Aphids on house plants, hornets eating fruit, grasshoppers eating grass)* **learning modality: verbal**

Go Online
PHSchool.com

For: More on insect metamorphosis
Visit: PHSchool.com
Web Code: ced-2023

Students can review metamorphosis in an online activity.

Monitor Progress L3

Oral Presentation Call on individual students to name one insect body part and tell its function.

Answers
Figure 18 No; the butterfly's mouthparts are not adapted to cut through seeds, wood, and other foods.

 Head, thorax, abdomen

 A butterfly sucks up nectar from flowers using its tube-shaped mouthpart.

345

Life Cycle

Teach Key Concepts

Two Kinds of Metamorphosis

Focus Remind students that in order to grow, insects must shed their exoskeleton (molt) and grow a new one. Tell students that every insect species undergoes either complete metamorphosis or gradual metamorphosis.

Teach Have students study Figure 19 and read the description of each type of metamorphosis. Discuss each stage and its characteristics. Ask: **How do insects change when they undergo complete metamorphosis?** *(After hatching, they spend time as a larva, then become an immobile pupa, and then become an adult.)* **How does a firefly's metamorphosis differ from a grasshopper's metamorphosis?** *(A firefly goes through four distinct stages. A grasshopper changes form gradually.)* **When does a grasshopper acquire wings?** *(After the final molt.)* **At what stage do fireflies reproduce?** *(Adult)*

Apply Ask: **Which stage does a moth cocoon represent?** *(Pupa)* **learning modality: logical/mathematical**

All in One Teaching Resources, Unit 2

• Transparency LS108

Help Students Read

Outlining Refer to the Content Refresher, which provides guidelines for using an outline. Have students create an outline of the information in this section. Outlines should use the head structures used in the section. Major headings are shown in red, and subheads are shown in blue.

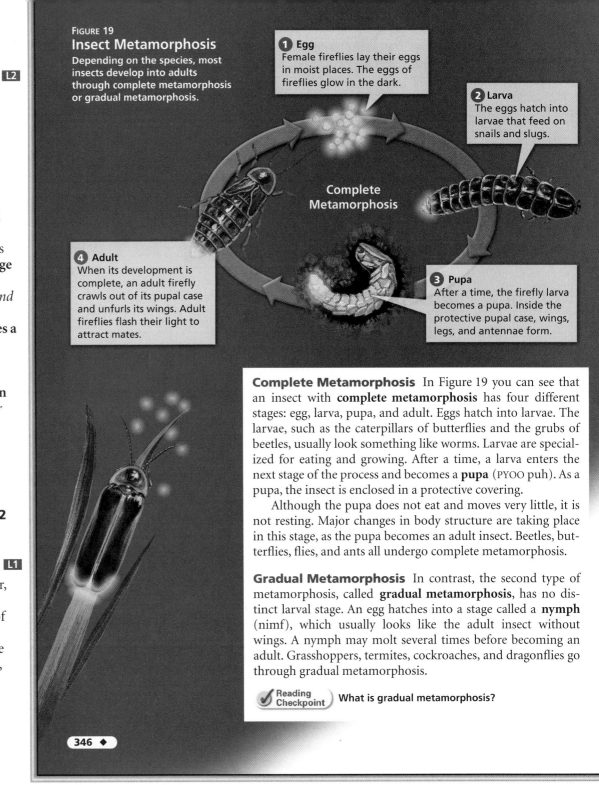

FIGURE 19
Insect Metamorphosis
Depending on the species, most insects develop into adults through complete metamorphosis or gradual metamorphosis.

Complete Metamorphosis

1 Egg
Female fireflies lay their eggs in moist places. The eggs of fireflies glow in the dark.

2 Larva
The eggs hatch into larvae that feed on snails and slugs.

3 Pupa
After a time, the firefly larva becomes a pupa. Inside the protective pupal case, wings, legs, and antennae form.

4 Adult
When its development is complete, an adult firefly crawls out of its pupal case and unfurls its wings. Adult fireflies flash their light to attract mates.

Complete Metamorphosis In Figure 19 you can see that an insect with **complete metamorphosis** has four different stages: egg, larva, pupa, and adult. Eggs hatch into larvae. The larvae, such as the caterpillars of butterflies and the grubs of beetles, usually look something like worms. Larvae are specialized for eating and growing. After a time, a larva enters the next stage of the process and becomes a **pupa** (PYOO puh). As a pupa, the insect is enclosed in a protective covering.

Although the pupa does not eat and moves very little, it is not resting. Major changes in body structure are taking place in this stage, as the pupa becomes an adult insect. Beetles, butterflies, flies, and ants all undergo complete metamorphosis.

Gradual Metamorphosis In contrast, the second type of metamorphosis, called **gradual metamorphosis**, has no distinct larval stage. An egg hatches into a stage called a **nymph** (nimf), which usually looks like the adult insect without wings. A nymph may molt several times before becoming an adult. Grasshoppers, termites, cockroaches, and dragonflies go through gradual metamorphosis.

Reading Checkpoint What is gradual metamorphosis?

346 ◆

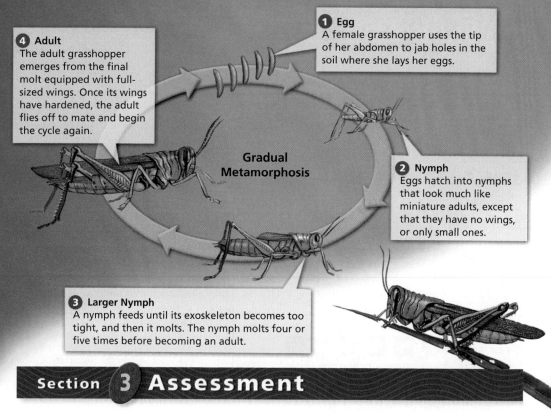

4 Adult
The adult grasshopper emerges from the final molt equipped with full-sized wings. Once its wings have hardened, the adult flies off to mate and begin the cycle again.

1 Egg
A female grasshopper uses the tip of her abdomen to jab holes in the soil where she lays her eggs.

Gradual Metamorphosis

2 Nymph
Eggs hatch into nymphs that look much like miniature adults, except that they have no wings, or only small ones.

3 Larger Nymph
A nymph feeds until its exoskeleton becomes too tight, and then it molts. The nymph molts four or five times before becoming an adult.

Section 3 Assessment

Target Reading Skill Sequencing Refer to your cycle diagram about complete metamorphosis as you answer Question 3.

Reviewing Key Concepts

1. a. **Identifying** What characteristics do insects share?
   b. **Interpreting Diagrams** Look at Figure 17. To which body section are a grasshopper's wings attached?
   c. **Making Generalizations** Suppose the adaptation of wings was suddenly lost in all insects. Predict what would happen to the number and diversity of insects.
2. a. **Naming** Name a type of insect that has chewing mouthparts.
   b. **Reviewing** What are three ways that the mouthparts of insects are adapted for obtaining food?

3. a. **Listing** List the stages of gradual metamorphosis and the stages of complete metamorphosis.
   b. **Interpreting Diagrams** Look at Figure 19. How are complete metamorphosis and gradual metamorphosis different?
   c. **Applying Concepts** Why is a nymph more likely than a larva to eat the same food as its parents?

Monitor Progress _____ L2

Answer

Reading Checkpoint A type of metamorphosis with no distinct larval stage

Assess

Reviewing Key Concepts

1. **a.** Three body sections; six legs; one pair of antennae; usually wings **b.** Thorax **c.** Their number and diversity would decline because wings enable insects to live in many unique habitats that would be otherwise inaccessible.
2. **a.** Answers may vary. Sample: ant, grasshopper. **b.** Some flies have sponge-like mouthparts that are used to lap up decaying flesh; most ants have mouthparts that can cut through seeds, wood, and other foods. Butterflies have a tubelike mouthpart that can be uncoiled and used to suck nectar.
3. **a.** Gradual: egg, nymph, adult; complete: egg, larva, pupa, adult **b.** Complete metamorphosis consists of four very different stages; in gradual metamorphosis, a nymph looks very much like an adult. **c.** A nymph resembles an adult insect, so it would have similar food preferences and the abilities to eat the same food.

Reteach L1
Use Figure 19 to review the events in insect metamorphosis. Ask students to work with a partner. Students explain one form of metamorphosis (complete or gradual) to their partners, and then switch roles.

Performance Assessment L2
Writing Have students explain how complete metamorphosis reduces competition for food among members of the same species. (Different stages—larva and adult—often eat different kinds of food, which reduces competition within the species.)

All in One Teaching Resources, Unit 2
- Section Summary: *Insects*
- Review and Reinforce: *Insects*
- Enrich: *Insects*

347

What's Living in the Soil?

L2

Prepare for Inquiry

Key Concept
Soil and leaf litter make up a miniature environment that contains a variety of organisms.

Skills Objectives
After this lab, students will be able to
- observe soil, leaf litter, and the organisms they contain
- classify organisms into phyla based on key distinguishing characteristics

Prep Time 45 minutes

Class Time 15 minutes on the first day, 45 minutes on the second day

Advance Planning
Try the lab in advance to ensure that there are enough organisms present. Three or four days before the lab, go to two different sites. Try to select sites that are moist but not too wet. Collect leaf litter and the first inch or so of soil in buckets. Keep the buckets covered to keep contents moist. Set up the lamp and jars, and test a soil sample from each site. If you do not obtain enough organisms, collect more material from another site.

Safety

Emphasize to students that no organisms should be handled, since animals may sting or bite. Students should wash their hands after handling soil or leaf litter. To avoid danger of fire, keep the light bulb at a safe distance from the leaf litter.

All in One Teaching Resources, Unit 2
- Lab Worksheet: *What's Living in the Soil?*

Guide Inquiry

Invitation
Have students think about how many animals might be present in soil. Ask: **What advantage do you think living in the soil gives some animals?** (*Moist environment, decaying organic matter for food, protection from predators*) Invite students to write predictions about the number and kind of organisms they will see in a few scoops of soil.

348

What's Living in the Soil?

Problem
What kinds of animals live in soil and leaf litter?

Skills Focus
observing, classifying

Materials
- 2-liter plastic bottle
- large scissors
- trowel
- cheesecloth
- large rubber band
- gooseneck lamp
- hand lens
- large, wide-mouthed jar
- small jar
- coarse steel wool
- fresh sample of soil and leaf litter

Procedure

1. Select a location where your equipment can be set up and remain undisturbed for about 24 hours. At that location, place the small jar inside the center of the large jar as shown in the photograph on page 61.

2. Use scissors to cut a large plastic bottle in half. **CAUTION:** *Cut in a direction away from yourself and others.* Turn the top half of the bottle upside down to serve as a funnel.

3. Insert a small amount of coarse steel wool into the mouth of the funnel to keep the soil from falling out. Do not pack the steel wool too tightly. Leave spaces for small organisms to crawl through. Place the funnel into the large jar as shown in the photograph.

4. Using the trowel, fill the funnel with soil and surface leaf litter. When you finish, wash your hands thoroughly.

5. Look closely to see whether the soil and litter are dry or wet. Record your observation.

6. Make a cover for your sample by placing a piece of cheesecloth over the top of the funnel. Hold the cheesecloth in place with a large rubber band. Immediately position a lamp about 15 cm above the funnel, and turn on the light. Allow this setup to remain undisturbed for about 24 hours. **CAUTION:** *Hot light bulbs can cause burns. Do not touch the bulb.*

7. When you are ready to make your observations, turn off the lamp. Leave the funnel and jar in place while making your observations. Use a hand lens to examine each organism in the jar. **CAUTION:** *Do not touch any of the organisms.*

8. Use a data table like the one shown to sketch each type of organism and to record other observations. Be sure to include evidence that will help you classify the organisms. (*Hint:* Remember that some animals may be at different stages of metamorphosis.)

9. Examine the soil and leaf litter, and record whether this material is dry or wet.

10. When you are finished, follow your teacher's directions about returning the organisms to the soil. Wash your hands with soap.

348 ◆

Data Table				
Sketch of Organism	Number Found	Size	Important Characteristics	Probable Phylum

Analyze and Conclude

1. **Observing** Describe the conditions of the soil environment at the beginning and end of the lab. What caused the change?

2. **Classifying** What types of animals did you collect in the small jar? What characteristics did you use to identify each type of animal? Which types of animals were the most common?

3. **Developing Hypotheses** Why do you think the animals moved down the funnel away from the soil?

4. **Inferring** Using what you have learned about arthropods and other animals, make an inference about the role that each animal you collected plays in the environment.

5. **Communicating** Develop a field guide that categorizes and describes the types of animals you found in your soil sample. Include sketches and brief descriptions of the animals.

Design an Experiment

What kinds of organisms might live in other soil types—for example, soil at the edge of a pond, dry sandy soil, or commercially prepared potting soil? Design an experiment to answer this question.

◆ 349

Extend Inquiry

Design an Experiment To find out which types of organisms live in other types of soil, students can repeat the lab with other soil types.

Introducing the Procedure

Tell students not to disturb the funnel once they have placed soil and leaf litter in it. If they do, soil may run into the collection jar. Warn students only to observe the animals, not to handle them, since some might bite or sting. Students should find that millipedes and other small animals are best viewed with a hand lens. The types and numbers of soil organisms found will vary in different regions of the country. Help students familiarize themselves with the animals they might find.

Troubleshooting the Experiment

If students have trouble classifying the organisms, have them list the features of worms and arthropods. Features include the presence or absence of legs and wings, and the number of pairs of legs. Certain times of the year are better than others for finding a greater variety and abundance of organisms. If students find only a few organisms, tell them not to be discouraged. The scarcity of organisms may be seasonal.

Expected Outcome

Several kinds of organisms may be present, and distinguishing among them may be difficult. Have students count the number of pairs of legs, number of body segments, and, if possible, observe how the organism moves.

Analyze and Conclude

1. At first, the soil was damp and clumped together. At the end of the lab, it was dry and loose. The heat from the lamp dried out the soil.

2. Answers will vary. Students should refer to the animals listed in their data tables. These will most likely be worms and arthropods.

3. The animals moved away from the heat and drying soil.

4. Answers will vary. Sample: Some animals, such as worms and insects, are important as decomposers. Some, such as pseudo-scorpions and spiders, are carnivores.

5. Answers will vary. Student field guides should accurately categorize and describe the types of animals that they found in their sample.

Objectives

After completing this lesson, students will be able to

10.4.1 Explain why insects are important in food chains.

10.4.2 Name two other ways insects interact with their environments.

10.4.3 Describe some methods used to control pest insects.

Target Reading Skill

Building Vocabulary Explain that using a new word in a sentence helps students understand its meaning.

Answer

Call on volunteers to read their sentences aloud. Make sure that students have come up with original sentences.

Preteach

Build Background Knowledge

L1

Insects—Good or Bad?

Help students to think about the many roles played by insects in their community. Ask: **What are some insects you see at least once a week?** *(Answers will vary depending on the season and your region. Examples: mosquitoes, bees, flies, cockroaches, spiders, moths, butterflies, ants, scorpions)* **Are these insects helpful or harmful?** *(Accept all responses without comment at this time.)* Encourage students to recognize that even insect pests, although annoying, play an important ecological role and should not necessarily be labeled as "bad."

350

Reading Preview

Key Concepts
- Why are insects important in food chains?
- What are two other ways insects interact with their environments?
- What are some ways used to control insect pests?

Key Terms
- food chain • ecology
- producer • consumer
- decomposer • pollinator
- pesticide
- biological control

Target Reading Skill

Building Vocabulary Using a word in a sentence helps you think about how best to explain the word. After you read the section, reread the paragraphs that contain definitions of Key Terms. Use all the information you have learned to write a meaningful sentence using the Key Term.

Lab zone · Discover **Activity**

What Materials Carry Pollen Best?

1. Use an eraser to transfer some pollen between two flowers your teacher gives you.
2. Next, use a cotton swab to do the same. Did the eraser or cotton swab transfer pollen better?

Think It Over

Inferring How might its ability to transfer pollen between flowers affect an insect's role in the environment?

In a meadow, a caterpillar munches the leaves of a plant. Later that day, a bird eats the caterpillar. Years later, after the bird has died, a beetle eats the dead bird. The plant, caterpillar, bird, and beetle are all part of one food chain. A **food chain** is a series of events in which one organism eats another and obtains energy. The study of food chains and other ways that organisms interact with their environment is called **ecology.**

Insects and the Food Chain

A food chain starts with a **producer**—an organism that makes its own food. Most producers, such as grass and other plants, use energy from sunlight to make their food. In a food chain, producers are food for consumers. A **consumer** is an organism that obtains energy by eating other organisms. Some consumers, like caterpillars, eat producers, and some eat other consumers. Decomposers, such as carrion beetles, also play a role in food chains. A **decomposer** breaks down the wastes and dead bodies of other organisms. In a food chain insects may play the roles of consumer and decomposer. In addition, some insects are prey for other consumers.

350 ◆

Lab zone · Discover **Activity**

Skills Focus Inferring **L2**

Materials flowers, cotton swabs, pencil, other materials as selected

Time 20 minutes

Tips Pre-select the test materials to save time. Use large flowers with plenty of pollen. Tell the students to handle the flowers gently. Advise students with strong allergies to pollen to observe a classmate transfer the pollen rather than do it themselves. Have all students wash their hands afterwards.

Expected Outcome Materials with a textured surface will hold pollen best.

Think It Over The insects will help plants reproduce. Many plants have adaptations to attract good pollinators.

Insects as Consumers of Plants The roles of insects in a food chain are shown in Figure 20. **Insects play key roles in food chains because of the many different ways that they obtain food and then become food for other animals.**

Many insects are consumers of plants. Perhaps you have tried growing tomato plants and seen how fat green caterpillars ate up the leaves. In fact, insects eat about 20 percent of the crops grown for humans. Insects eat most species of wild plants, too. Some insects eat the leaves of plants, while others eat the sap, bark, roots, and other parts of plants.

Insects as Prey Insects play another role in food chains—they are prey for many animals. That is, other consumers eat insects. Many fishes and birds eat insects to survive. For example, the main source of food for trout and bass is insects. Indeed, that's why people use lures called "flies" to catch fishes like these. The lures look like the mayflies and stoneflies these fishes normally eat. Some species of birds feed their young, called chicks, only insects. And the chicks are big eaters! A single swallow chick, for example, may consume about 200,000 insects before it leaves the nest.

Math Skills

Percentage

A percentage is a ratio that compares a number to 100. If 25 percent of 900,000 insect species eat other insects, how many insect-eating species are there? Set up a proportion and solve it.

$$\frac{\text{insect-eating species}}{900{,}000 \text{ insect species}} = \frac{25\%}{100\%}$$

insect-eating species = 225,000

Practice Problem A swallow chick eats 200,000 insects. If 12 percent of the insects are beetles, how many beetles does it eat?

FIGURE 20
Insects in a Food Chain

In a food chain, some insects are consumers of plants. Some insects are prey for other consumers. Other insects are decomposers.

Insects as Decomposers This carrion beetle feeds on the tissues of a dead bird.

Insects as Prey Caterpillars and other insects are consumed by other types of animals, such as birds.

Insects as Consumers This caterpillar is one of many types of insects that consume plant material.

◆ 351

Differentiated Instruction

Less Proficient Readers [L1]
Classifying Examples Have students use sketches, photographs, and short captions to create a poster for each of the three insect roles discussed in this section. Tell students to use ideas from the headings and illustrations in the chapter. **learning modality: visual**

Gifted and Talented [L3]
Researching Fishing Lures Have students do research to learn about fly-fishing lures that are made to mimic aquatic insects. Ask students to describe how anglers select lures to match the insect species that are currently hatching. **learning modality: logical/mathematical**

Insects and the Food Chain

Teach Key Concepts [L2]
Many Roles of Insects

Focus Remind students how insects fill many different roles.

Teach Make a different column on the chalkboard for each of the four roles discussed in this section. Ask: **What are the three roles that insects play in food chains?** *(They are consumers that eat plants and other insects. They are food for other animals. They are decomposers.)* **What insects are major consumers of plants?** *(Answers will vary. Examples: Caterpillars, grasshoppers)* **What kinds of animals eat insects?** *(Birds, fishes)* **How can insects serve as decomposers?** *(They eat wastes and dead organisms.)* **What kinds of insects are eaten by humans?** *(grasshoppers, beetles, ants, crickets, cicadas)*

Apply Ask: **What would happen if the insects that are decomposers vanished?** *(Wastes and dead organisms would accumulate; nutrients could not be recycled.)*
learning modality: logical/mathematical

Independent Practice

All in One Teaching Resources, Unit 2
• Guided Reading and Study Worksheet: *Insect Ecology*

⊙ Student Edition on Audio CD

Math Skills

Percentage Remind students that 25% is equal to 0.25.

Answer
Practice problem
p beetles/200,000 insects = 12%/100%
p = 24,000

Monitor Progress [L2]

Oral Presentation Ask students to define three important roles that insects play in food chains.

351

• Tech & Design in History •

Focus Tell students that people have been using products from insects for thousands of years.

Teach Ask: **What time span does the time line cover?** *(From 100 B.C. until 2000, or 2100 years)* **When did humans first spin silk from silkworms?** *(More than 4,000 years ago)* **How have scientists used the light-producing chemicals from fireflies?** *(To study genes and diseases)* **What is cochineal?** *(A red dye extracted from a tiny cactus-eating insect)*

Insects as Decomposers In a food chain some insects play the role of decomposers by breaking down the wastes and bodies of dead organisms. For example, in some tropical food chains, termites may break down up to one third of the dead wood, leaves, and grass produced there every year. In other food chains, flies and dung beetles break down animal droppings, called manure. By doing this, the buildup of manure from large animals is prevented.

The substances that insect decomposers break down enrich the soil. In addition, insect decomposers may burrow and nest in the ground. By doing so, these insects expose soil to oxygen from the air and mix up the nutrients in the soil.

• Tech & Design in History •

Products From Insects
Over the last few thousand years, insects have supplied humans with some important products.

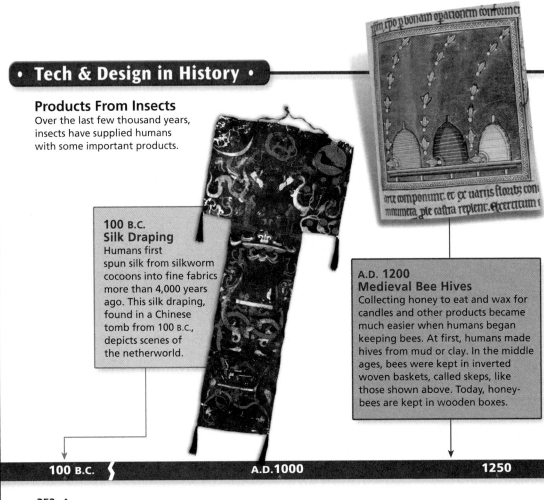

100 B.C.
Silk Draping
Humans first spun silk from silkworm cocoons into fine fabrics more than 4,000 years ago. This silk draping, found in a Chinese tomb from 100 B.C., depicts scenes of the netherworld.

A.D. 1200
Medieval Bee Hives
Collecting honey to eat and wax for candles and other products became much easier when humans began keeping bees. At first, humans made hives from mud or clay. In the middle ages, bees were kept in inverted woven baskets, called skeps, like those shown above. Today, honeybees are kept in wooden boxes.

| 100 B.C. | A.D.1000 | 1250 |

352 ◆

Insects as Food for Humans Did you know that insects were an important source of nutrition for prehistoric humans? Even today, insects are collected and eaten by people in many parts of the world. In some Mexican villages, dried grasshoppers are ground up and mixed with flour to make tortillas. In other parts of the world, the larvae of certain species of beetles are roasted over an open fire. Ants, crickets, and cicadas are just a few of the other types of insects eaten by humans.

Maybe you are thinking, "Yuck! I'd never eat an insect." Even if you'd never allow an insect on your dinner plate, you are likely to have used the products of insects in other aspects of your daily life. You can see some of the major uses of insect products through history in the timeline below.

 Reading Checkpoint What is an animal that breaks down wastes and dead organisms called?

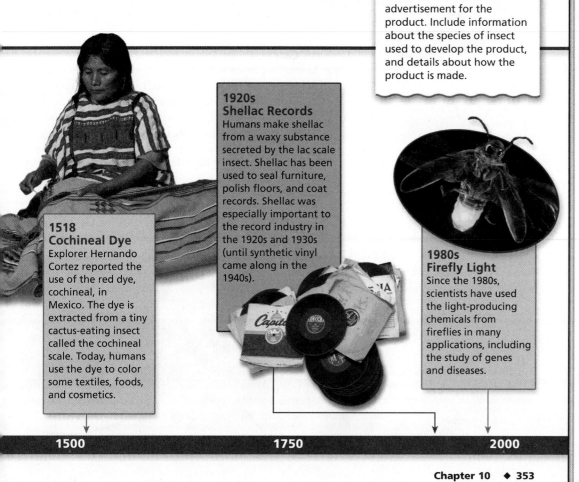

1920s
Shellac Records
Humans make shellac from a waxy substance secreted by the lac scale insect. Shellac has been used to seal furniture, polish floors, and coat records. Shellac was especially important to the record industry in the 1920s and 1930s (until synthetic vinyl came along in the 1940s).

1518
Cochineal Dye
Explorer Hernando Cortez reported the use of the red dye, cochineal, in Mexico. The dye is extracted from a tiny cactus-eating insect called the cochineal scale. Today, humans use the dye to color some textiles, foods, and cosmetics.

1980s
Firefly Light
Since the 1980s, scientists have used the light-producing chemicals from fireflies in many applications, including the study of genes and diseases.

1500   **1750**   **2000**

Chapter 10 ◆ 353

Helpful and Harmful Insect Roles

Focus Ask: **Do you think bees are helpful or harmful?** (*Students might respond that they are helpful because they carry pollen from one plant to another or that they are harmful because they can sting.*)

Teach Have students preview Figure 21. Ask: **What does a bee look like after it has visited a flower?** (*The bee looks like it is covered with dust.*) **What is the dust-like substance on the bee?** (*pollen*) **Why are pollinators critical to many plants?** (*By carrying pollen between plants, they enable plants to reproduce.*) Direct attention to Figure 22, and point out that the mosquito is piercing its host. Ask: **Why are some species of mosquitoes considered harmful?** (*Mosquitoes can spread disease since disease organisms may travel from a mosquito to its prey when the mosquito pierces its victim.*)

Apply Ask: **How do bees benefit by visiting flowers?** (*They take nectar and some pollen back to the hive.*) **How do flowers benefit from the visits of the bees?** (*They are able to produce fruits and seeds.*) **learning modality: visual**

Controlling Pests

Insect Pest Control

Focus Ask students if they are familiar with ways of controlling insect pests. Ask volunteers to describe their experiences.

Teach Ask: **What are some ways to kill pest insects other than using pesticides?** (*Traps, natural predators of the pest*)

Apply Ask: **What is the benefit of using biological control?** (*Biological control targets a specific pest.*) **learning modality: verbal**

FIGURE 21
A Bee as a Pollinator
This bee is getting dusted with yellow pollen as it drinks nectar from the flower. **Observing** *On which of the bee's structures can you observe pollen grains?*

Other Interactions

Besides eating and being eaten, insects interact in other ways with the living things in their environments. **Two ways insects interact with other living things are by moving pollen among plants and by spreading disease-causing organisms.**

Pollen Carriers Have you ever seen a bee crawling into a flower on a warm summer day? Have you wondered what it is doing? The bee is helping itself to the plant's nectar and pollen, which are food for bees. But plants also need to share their pollen with other plants. Pollen contains cells that become sperm cells, allowing plants to reproduce. When the bee crawls into a flower to obtain its food, it gets dusted with pollen, as shown in Figure 21. Then, as the bee enters the next flower, some of the pollen on its body is left in the second flower. An animal that carries pollen among plants is called a **pollinator.** Bees are pollinators, and so are many beetles and flies. Without pollinators, some plants cannot reproduce.

Disease Carriers Not all interactions between insects and other living things have happy endings. While some insects transfer pollen, others spread diseases to both plants and animals, including humans. Insects that spread diseases include some mosquitoes and fleas. These insects often have sucking mouthparts that pierce the skin of their prey, providing an opening for the disease-causing organisms to enter. Diseases that are carried by insects include malaria, which is spread by mosquitoes. Malaria causes high fevers and can be treated with medicines today.

 Reading Checkpoint What is a pollinator?

FIGURE 22
Disease-Causing Mosquito
A mosquito like the one shown here can spread disease-causing organisms such as malaria among humans.

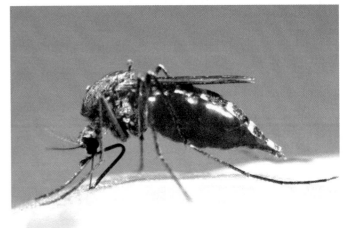

Controlling Pests

Some insects are harmful, even though they don't spread diseases. Harmful insects are called pests. **To try to control pests, people use chemicals, traps, and living things, including other insects.** Chemicals that kill pests are called **pesticides**. However, pesticides also kill pollinators, such as bees, and can harm other animals.

What are the alternatives to pesticides? Biologists are using their knowledge of insect ecology to develop new pest controls. One such control is a trap that attracts mosquitoes in a way similar to how humans attract mosquitoes. Another control is to surround crops with wild plants that are bad-tasting or even poisonous to the harmful insect.

People may prefer to use biological controls. A **biological control** is a natural predator or disease released into an area to fight a harmful insect. For example, ladybugs, which eat other insects, have been introduced to some areas where crops grow to control aphids. Aphids are tiny insects that damage plants by sucking plant sap.

 Reading Checkpoint What is a chemical intended to kill pest insects called?

FIGURE 23
Biological Control
Ladybugs are used as biological control agents against aphids. Here, one ladybug consumes its prey.

Section 4 Assessment

Target Reading Skill Building Vocabulary
Use your sentences to help answer the questions.

Reviewing Key Concepts

1. a. Defining What is a food chain?
  b. Interpreting Photographs What three roles do insects play in the food chain shown in Figure 20?
2. a. Reviewing Besides their role in food chains, what are two other ways insects interact with their environment?
  b. Summarizing What effect do pollinators have on their environment?
  c. Predicting What would a world without pollinators be like?

3. a. Reviewing How can insect pests be controlled?
  b. Comparing and Contrasting How are the effects of using biological controls similar to the effects of using pesticides? How are they different?
  c. Applying Concepts Some insect species are harmful only in areas of the world where they do not normally live but have been accidentally released. Why might this be?

 Math Practice

4. Percentage Suppose 33 percent of the 50 tons of wood produced in one year by a forest is consumed by termites and other insects. How many tons do the insects eat?

Answers
Figure 21 Legs, abdomen, thorax, head, antennae, and wings

Reading Checkpoint A pollinator is an insect or other animal that carries pollen among plants.

Reading Checkpoint A chemical that kills pest insects is called a pesticide.

Assess

Reviewing Key Concepts

1. a. A series of events in which one organism eats another and obtains energy
b. Consumers, prey, decomposers
2. a. Two other ways insects interact are as pollinators and disease-carriers.
b. Pollinators enable plants to reproduce.
c. There would be a sharp decline in the number of plants, which would cause a decline in the number of herbivores. That decline would result in fewer carnivores and decomposers.
3. a. Insect pests may be controlled with chemicals, traps, or living things (such as natural predators). **b.** Alike: Both can kill harmful insects. Different: Pesticides may kill or harm other types of animals, too. **c.** In their native countries, these insects have natural predators that control their population size.

Reteach L1
As a class, list examples of beneficial insects and harmful insects.

Performance Assessment L2
Oral Presentation Ask students to create brief oral presentations summarizing the roles of insects in food chains.

All in One Teaching Resources, Unit 2
• Section Summary: *Insect Ecology*
• Review and Reinforce: *Insect Ecology*
• Enrich: *Insect Ecology*

Lab zone Chapter Project

Keep Students on Track Verify that students' data are being collected on time and appear reasonable. Check students' sketches. Tell students they must be able to identify the stages of mealworm development from their sketches.

Math Practice

Math Skill Percentage
Answer
4. 16.5 tons

Technology and Society

Battling Pest Insects

Key Concepts
The use of pesticides has advantages and disadvantages.

Build Background Knowledge
Recalling Information About Insects
Review with students the concepts they learned in this chapter that apply to this feature content. Ask: **What is an exoskeleton?** *(A tough, waterproof, outer covering that protects the animal and helps prevent evaporation of water from the animal's body)* **What are the stages of an insect's life cycle?** *(Depending on the species, the insect can undergo complete metamorphosis—egg, larva, pupa, adult—or incomplete metamorphosis—egg, nymph, adult.)* *Point out that each year insects (not just adults, but larvae and nymphs, too) cause millions of dollars of damage to crops, buildings, and other materials. Ask:* **What are some examples of insect damage you are familiar with?** *(Sample answers: damage to lawns, shrubs, trees, fruit; holes in clothing)*

Introduce the Debate
Direct student's attention to the picture of the boll weevil. Point out that the boll weevil is the most serious cotton pest in North America. Tell students that it is estimated that between 3,000,000 and 5,000,000 bales of cotton are destroyed annually by this insect. Ask students what impact they think this damage has on cotton farmers and consumers. Lead students to understand the economic consequences of insect damage.

Battling Pest Insects

It's hard to believe that insects can cause much harm. But some species, such as the cotton boll weevil, can devastate crops. Boll weevils eat cotton bolls, the part of the plant that produces cotton fibers. Other insects, such as some mosquitoes, spread diseases. To control insect pests, people often use pesticides—chemicals or substances that kill insects or alter their life processes.

What Are Pesticides?

Since ancient times, people have used substances such as sulfur to kill pests. In the 1900s, people began developing new chemicals to battle harmful insects. Today, most pesticides used in the United States are synthetic—made by people in laboratories. On average, it takes about 15 years and about 20 million dollars to develop a new pesticide. That time includes obtaining approval from the Environmental Protection Agency, which oversees pesticide use. Once on the market, pesticides can work to kill insects in a variety of ways. They might attack the physical, chemical, or biological processes of the pests.

How Pesticides Work
Pesticides kill insects in a variety of ways. People may select one or more pesticides to attack a particular pest.

Attack the Gut
Pesticides that contain certain bacteria and viruses can attack the gut lining, killing the insect.

Paralyze the Nervous System
Pesticides that interfere with signals in the brain can cause convulsions, paralysis, and death.

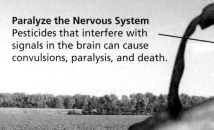

Boll weevil on a cotton boll

Background

Facts and Figures Adult boll weevils emerge in spring, and each female deposits between 100 and 300 eggs in cotton buds or fruit, called bolls. A female will not deposit eggs in cotton bolls that have already been visited by another female unless most of the cotton bolls are already infested.

Larvae live within the cotton boll, where they destroy the seeds and the surrounding cotton fibers. Because larvae do not leave the cotton boll, pesticides are useless at killing larvae. Because an egg develops into an adult in just two or three weeks, as many as ten generations can develop in a single year.

Programs to control boll weevil infestations include cleaning up areas where they hibernate, diversifying crops (mixing other crops in with the cotton crop), developing early maturing varieties of cotton, and early planting.

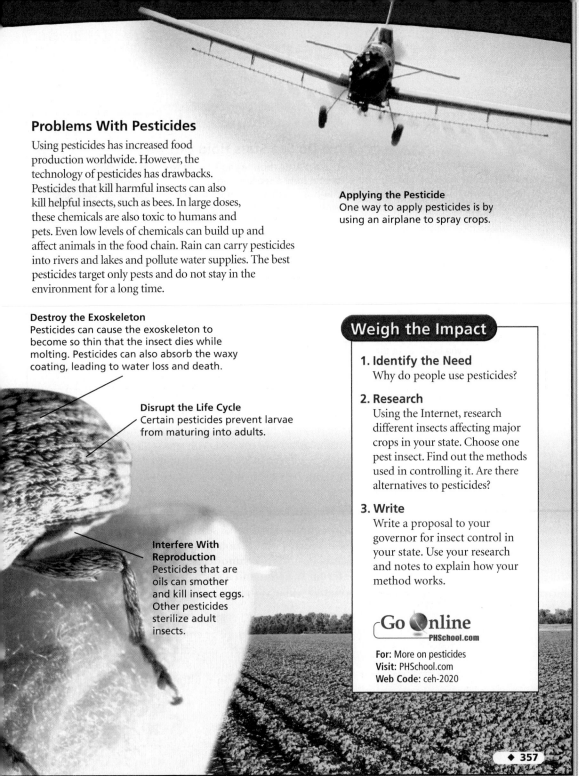

Problems With Pesticides

Using pesticides has increased food production worldwide. However, the technology of pesticides has drawbacks. Pesticides that kill harmful insects can also kill helpful insects, such as bees. In large doses, these chemicals are also toxic to humans and pets. Even low levels of chemicals can build up and affect animals in the food chain. Rain can carry pesticides into rivers and lakes and pollute water supplies. The best pesticides target only pests and do not stay in the environment for a long time.

Destroy the Exoskeleton
Pesticides can cause the exoskeleton to become so thin that the insect dies while molting. Pesticides can also absorb the waxy coating, leading to water loss and death.

Disrupt the Life Cycle
Certain pesticides prevent larvae from maturing into adults.

Interfere With Reproduction
Pesticides that are oils can smother and kill insect eggs. Other pesticides sterilize adult insects.

Applying the Pesticide
One way to apply pesticides is by using an airplane to spray crops.

Weigh the Impact

1. Identify the Need
Why do people use pesticides?

2. Research
Using the Internet, research different insects affecting major crops in your state. Choose one pest insect. Find out the methods used in controlling it. Are there alternatives to pesticides?

3. Write
Write a proposal to your governor for insect control in your state. Use your research and notes to explain how your method works.

Go Online
PHSchool.com

For: More on pesticides
Visit: PHSchool.com
Web Code: ceh-2020

Facilitate the Debate
• Have students read the feature and do the research in Weigh the Impact individually or in pairs as a homework assignment. The next day discuss these questions: What are the advantages of pesticides? What are the disadvantages? How might some of the disadvantages be reduced or eliminated? What other types of insect control might be used in place of the pesticides? What are the disadvantages of those methods?
• Organize the class into group according to the pest insects students have chosen. Have group members work together to write a proposal.
• Have one member of each groups present his or her group's proposal to the class. Allow time for students to respond to each proposal.

Weigh the Impact
1. People need pesticides to kill harmful insects and thereby reduce insect damage.
2. Students research will depend on individual state crops. If your state does not grow major crops, consider having students find information about several states in your area of the country.
3. Remind students to provide clear reasons for their proposals.

Go Online
PHSchool.com
For: More on pesticides
Visit: PHSchool.com
Web Code: ceh-2020

Students can research this issue online.

◆ 357

Section
5 Echinoderms

Objectives

After completing this lesson, students will be able to

10.5.1 List the main characteristics of echinoderms.

10.5.2 Name the major groups of echinoderms.

Target Reading Skill 🔄

Previewing Visuals Explain that previewing visuals helps students focus their thinking before reading by giving them something specific to look for as they read.

Answers

Possible student questions and answers are these: **What are tube feet?** (*Tiny structures that stick out from the underside of an echinoderm and act like suction cups*) **How does a sea star eat?** (*It captures food with tube feet and envelops it with its stomach.*) **How does a sea star reproduce?** (*By external fertilization*)

All in One Teaching Resources, Unit 2
• Transparency LS109

Preteach

Build Background Knowledge   L2

Echinoderm Symmetry

Have students examine the figures in this section. Ask: **What do the animals in these figures have in common?** (*Radial symmetry*)

Reading Preview

Key Concepts
• What are the main characteristics of echinoderms?
• What are the major groups of echinoderms?

Key Terms
• echinoderm • endoskeleton
• water vascular system
• tube feet

🔄 Target Reading Skill

Previewing Visuals When you preview, you look ahead at the material to be read. Preview Figure 24. Then write two questions that you have about the diagram in a graphic organizer like the one below. As you read, answer your questions.

Water Vascular System

Q. What are tube feet?
A.
Q.

Lab zone Discover Activity

How Do Sea Stars Hold On?

1. Use a plastic dropper and water to model how a sea star moves and clings to surfaces. Fill the dropper with water, and then squeeze out most of the water.

2. Squeeze the last drop of water onto the inside of your arm. Then, while squeezing the bulb, touch the tip of the dropper into the water drop. With the dropper tip against your skin, release the bulb.

3. Hold the dropper by the tube and lift it slowly, paying attention to what happens to your skin.

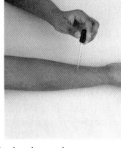

Think It Over

Predicting Besides moving and clinging to surfaces, what might sea stars use their suction structures for?

While exploring a rocky beach one day, you see what looks like a dill pickle at the bottom of a tide pool. You think it might be a plant or a rock covered with green slime. But as you look more closely, the pickle begins to crawl very slowly. This amazing creature is a sea cucumber, a relative of sea stars.

Characteristics of Echinoderms

Sea cucumbers, sea stars, sea urchins, and sand dollars are all **echinoderms** (ee KY noh durmz), members of the phylum Echinodermata. **Echinoderms are invertebrates with an internal skeleton and a system of fluid-filled tubes called a water vascular system.** All echinoderms live in salt water.

Body Structure The skin of most echinoderms is stretched over an internal skeleton, or **endoskeleton,** made of hardened plates. These plates give the animal a bumpy texture. Adult echinoderms have a unique kind of radial symmetry in which the body parts, usually in multiples of five, are arranged like spokes on a wheel.

Lab zone Discover Activity

Skills Focus Predicting

Materials plastic dropper, water

Time 5 minutes

Tips If students have trouble creating suction against their arm, have them practice the activity without using water. Tell them to squeeze the bulb, press the dropper tip against their skin, and then

L1 release the bulb. After a few tries, have them try the activity again with a drop of water.

Expected Outcome The droppers will briefly attach to the students' skins.

Think It Over Sea stars might use their suction structures to pry open mollusk shells.

Movement The internal system of fluid-filled tubes in echinoderms is called the **water vascular system.** You can see a sea star's water vascular system in Figure 24. Portions of the tubes in this system can contract, or squeeze together, forcing water into structures called **tube feet.** This process is something like how you move water around in a water balloon by squeezing different parts of the balloon.

The tube feet stick out from the echinoderm's sides or underside. The ends of tube feet are sticky. When filled with water, they act like small, sticky suction cups. The stickiness and suction enable the tube feet to grip the surface beneath the echinoderm. Most echinoderms use their tube feet to move along slowly and to capture food.

Reproduction and Life Cycle Almost all echinoderms are either male or female. Eggs are usually fertilized in the water, after a female releases her eggs and a male releases his sperm. The fertilized eggs develop into tiny, swimming larvae that look very different from the adults. The larvae eventually undergo metamorphosis and become adult echinoderms.

Reading Checkpoint What are the functions of an echinoderm's tube feet?

Go Online
active art

For: Water Vascular System activity
Visit: PHSchool.com
Web Code: cep-2025

FIGURE 24
A Water Vascular System
Echinoderms, such as this sea star, have a water vascular system that helps them move and catch food.
Interpreting Diagrams *Where does water enter the water vascular system?*

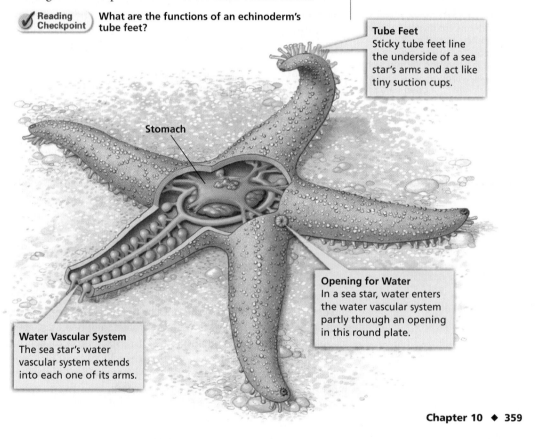

Tube Feet
Sticky tube feet line the underside of a sea star's arms and act like tiny suction cups.

Stomach

Opening for Water
In a sea star, water enters the water vascular system partly through an opening in this round plate.

Water Vascular System
The sea star's water vascular system extends into each one of its arms.

Chapter 10 ◆ 359

Characteristics of Echinoderms

Teach Key Concepts L2
Radially Symmetrical Invertebrates
Focus Tell students that echinoderms live on the sea floor at all depths throughout the ocean.

Teach Have students study Figure 24. Point out the animal's bumpy surface. **What forms these bumps?** (*The internal skeleton*) **Which structures enable the sea star to move?** (*The water vascular system and tube feet*) **Do sea stars ever swim?** (*Only during the larval phase*)

Apply Why do you think there are no echinoderms that live on land? (*The water vascular system would not function on land.*)
learning modality: logical/mathematical

All in One Teaching Resources, Unit 2
• Transparency LS110

Help Students Read L1
Build Vocabulary: Word-Part Analysis
Tell students that the prefix *exo-* means "out" and the prefix *endo-* means "in." Have students relate this to the meanings of the terms *exoskeleton* and *endoskeleton*. Ask: **What is an exoskeleton?** (*An outer skeleton*) **What is an endoskeleton?** (*An internal skeleton*)

Go Online
active art

For: Water Vascular System activity
Visit: PHSchool.com
Web Code: cep-2025

Students explore the water vascular system of a sea star.

Monitor Progress ————— L2

Answers
Figure 24 Through an opening in a round plate near the center of the body

Reading Checkpoint An echinoderm's tube feet grip the surface beneath the echinoderm and enable it to move and to capture food.

Differentiated Instruction

English Learners/Beginning L1
Vocabulary: Science Glossary
Pronounce and define the following terms for students: echinoderm, endoskeleton, water vascular system, tube feet. Give students the opportunity to practice the pronunciation, and then have them locate the water vascular system and tube feet in Figure 24. Have students write their own

definitions of the terms in their science glossaries. **learning modality: visual**

English Learners/Intermediate L2
Vocabulary: Science Glossary Students can expand on the Beginning activity by adding other vocabulary or unfamiliar terms in this section. Students can write a sentence that uses each term. **learning modality: visual**

Diversity of Echinoderms

Major Groups of Echinoderms

Focus Ask: **Have you ever observed echinoderms while visiting a zoo or a marine aquarium or while scuba diving?** *(Have student volunteers describe the characteristics of the animals they observed.)*

Teach Have students study the four major groups of echinoderms shown in Figure 25. Point out that the animals look very different. Ask: **Why are these animals grouped together?** *(They share similar internal features.)* **What common feature do these echinoderms have for movement?** *(Tube feet)*

Apply Ask students to compare how the four groups of echinoderms acquire their food. *(Sea stars pry open their prey using their tube feet. Brittle stars use their arms to catch food. Sea urchins scrape algae with teeth-like structures. Sea cucumbers use tentacles to sweep food into their mouths.)* **learning modality: logical/mathematical**

◀ Sea star eating a clam

▲ Brittle stars slithering on the ocean floor

FIGURE 25
Diversity of Echinoderms

Echinoderms are diverse in their appearance, but all have radial symmetry and are found in the ocean. **Interpreting Photographs** *Why is echinoderm, which means "spiny skinned," a good name for this group?*

Diversity of Echinoderms

There are four major groups of echinoderms: **sea stars, brittle stars, sea urchins, and sea cucumbers.** The members of these groups share many characteristics, but look quite different. They also have different ways of feeding and moving.

Sea Stars Sea stars are predators that eat mollusks, crabs, and even other echinoderms. Sea stars use their tube feet to move across the ocean bottom. They also use their tube feet to capture prey. A sea star will grasp a clam with all five arms. Then it pulls on the tightly closed shells with its tube feet. When the shells open, the sea star forces its stomach out through its mouth and into the opening between the clam's shells. Digestive chemicals break down the clam's tissues, and the sea star sucks in the partially digested body of its prey.

Brittle Stars Unlike a sea star's arms, a brittle star's arms are long and slender, with flexible joints. The tube feet, which have no suction cups, are used for catching food but not for moving. Instead, brittle stars slither along the ocean bottom by waving their long arms in a snakelike motion against the ocean floor.

Sea Urchins Unlike sea stars and brittle stars, sea urchins have no arms. Moveable spines cover and protect their bodies, so they look something like a pincushion. These spines cover a central shell that is made of plates joined together. To move, sea urchins use bands of tube feet that extend out between the spines. They scrape and cut their food, such as seaweed, with five teethlike structures that they project from their mouths.

▲ Sea urchins eating seaweed

▲ Sea cucumber crawling on the ocean floor

Sea Cucumbers As you might expect from their name, sea cucumbers look a little bit like the cucumbers you eat. These animals can be red, brown, blue, or green. Underneath their leather-like skin, their bodies are soft, flexible, and muscular. Sea cucumbers have rows of tube feet on their underside, enabling them to crawl slowly along the ocean floor where they live. At one end of a sea cucumber is a mouth surrounded by tentacles. The sea cucumber, which is a filter feeder, can lengthen its tentacles to sweep food toward its mouth.

 Reading Checkpoint How does a sea cucumber move?

Section 5 Assessment

Target Reading Skill Previewing Visuals Refer to your questions and answers about Figure 24 to help you answer Question 1 below.

Reviewing Key Concepts

1. a. **Reviewing** What characteristics do echinoderms have?
   b. **Summarizing** How does an echinoderm use its tube feet to grip a surface?
   c. **Inferring** Why is movement using tube feet slow?

2. a. **Identifying** Identify the four major groups of echinoderms.
   b. **Comparing and Contrasting** Compare and contrast how sea stars and sea urchins feed.
   c. **Predicting** Would a sea star be able to eat clams without using its tube feet? Explain.

Writing in Science

Comparison Paragraph In a paragraph, compare and contrast how sea stars, brittle stars, and sea urchins move.

Chapter 10 ◆ 361

Monitor Progress _____ L2

Answers
Figure 25 The surface of the skin of an echinoderm is bumpy or spiny.

Reading Checkpoint Sea cucumbers move by crawling slowly along the ocean floor using their tube feet.

Assess

Reviewing Key Concepts

1. a. Echinoderms are invertebrates that have an internal skeleton and a water vascular system. **b.** Tube feet are sticky at the ends; when filled with water, they act like suction cups. **c.** Tube feet operate by suction. Each time the animal moves, it must pull its feet up by releasing the suction, and then put them down again. Because this process is slow, tube feet are adapted to slow movement.
2. a. Sea stars, brittle stars, sea urchins, sea cucumbers **b.** Sea stars use their tube feet to open mollusks and then insert their stomach into the mollusk and digest the mollusk tissues; sea urchins scrape and cut food, using teeth-like structures. **c.** Without tube feet, sea stars would not be able to pry open animals protected by hard shells.

Reteach L1

As a class, describe the four major groups of echinoderms.

Performance Assessment L2

Skills Check Ask students to create a table summarizing the body structure, movement, and reproduction of echinoderms.

All in One Teaching Resources, Unit 2
- Section Summary: *Echinoderms*
- Review and Reinforce: *Echinoderms*
- Enrich: *Echinoderms*

Lab zone Chapter Project

Keep Students on Track When one half of a student's mealworms have reached the adult stage, have the student write a simple summary of his or her observations. To draw conclusions, students can make a bar graph comparing the numbers of mealworms in different stages of development under the two conditions. Tell students their conclusions must be based on data they have collected.

Writing in Science

Writing Mode Comparison
Scoring Rubric
4 Includes complete, accurate comparisons and many details
3 Includes complete, accurate comparisons but few details
2 Includes accurate comparisons; no details
1 Includes inaccurate or incomplete comparisons

Interactive Textbook

- Complete student edition
- Section and chapter self-assessments
- Assessment reports for teachers

Help Students Read

Developing Vocabulary

Definition Mapping Explain that using vocabulary strategies such as definition mapping and vocabulary quick-write help students define Key Concept words. Ask students to make definition maps for the Key Terms in this chapter. The Key Term is used in the center of the map. Branches include a definition of the Key Term, adjectives that describe it, and examples.

Vocabulary Quick-Write Write a group of related vocabulary terms on the board. Discuss the definitions of the terms. Ask students to write a paragraph that includes each of the terms.

Connecting Concepts

Concept Maps Help students develop one way to show how the information in this chapter is related. Mollusks, arthropods, and echinoderms are major groups of invertebrate animals. Have students brainstorm to identify the Key Concepts, Key Terms, details, and examples. Then write each one on a sticky note and attach it at random on chart paper on the board. Tell students that this concept map will be organized in hierarchical order and to begin at the top with the Key Concepts. Ask students these questions to guide them to categorize the information on the stickies: **What are three groups of invertebrates? What are some characteristics of each group?** Prompt students by using connecting words or phrases, such as "move by," "have bodies with," and "include" to indicate the basis for the organization of the map. The phrases should form a sentence between or among a set of concepts.

Answer Accept logical presentations by students.

① Mollusks

Key Concepts

- In addition to a soft body often covered by a shell, a mollusk has a thin layer of tissue called a mantle that covers its internal organs, and an organ called a foot.
- The three major groups of mollusks are gastropods, bivalves, and cephalopods.
- Gastropods are mollusks that have a single external shell or no shell at all.
- Bivalves are mollusks that have two shells held together by hinges and strong muscles.
- A cephalopod is an ocean-dwelling mollusk whose foot is adapted to form tentacles around its mouth.

Key Terms

mollusk	gill	radula
open circulatory system	gastropod	bivalve
	herbivore	omnivore
	carnivore	cephalopod

② Arthropods

Key Concepts

- The major groups of arthropods are crustaceans, arachnids, centipedes and millipedes, and insects.
- Arthropods are invertebrates that have an external skeleton, a segmented body, and jointed attachments called appendages.
- A crustacean is an arthropod that has two or three body sections, five or more pairs of legs, and two pairs of antennae.
- Arachnids are arthropods with two body sections, four pairs of legs, and no antennae.
- Centipedes and millipedes are arthropods with two body sections and many pairs of legs.

Key Terms

arthropod	antenna	arachnid
exoskeleton	crustacean	abdomen
molting	metamorphosis	

③ Insects

Key Concepts

- Insects are arthropods with three body sections, six legs, one pair of antennae, and usually one or two pairs of wings.
- An insect's mouthparts are adapted for a highly specific way of getting food.
- Each insect species undergoes either complete metamorphosis or gradual metamorphosis.

Key Terms

insect	pupa
thorax	gradual
complete	metamorphosis
metamorphosis	nymph

④ Insect Ecology

Key Concepts

- Insects play key roles in food chains because of the many different ways that they obtain food and then become food for other animals.
- Two ways insects interact with other living things are by moving pollen among plants and by spreading disease-causing organisms.
- To try to control pests, people use chemicals, traps, and living things, including other insects.

Key Terms

food chain	
ecology	pollinator
producer	pesticide
consumer	biological control
decomposer	

⑤ Echinoderms

Key Concepts

- Echinoderms are invertebrates with an internal skeleton and a system of fluid-filled tubes called a water vascular system.
- There are four major groups of echinoderms: sea stars, brittle stars, sea urchins, and sea cucumbers.

Key Terms

echinoderm	water vascular system
endoskeleton	tube feet

All in One Teaching Resources, Unit 2

- Key Terms Review: *Mollusks, Arthropods, and Echinoderms*
- Connecting Concepts: *Mollusks, Arthropods, and Echinoderms*

Review and Assessment

Go Online
PHSchool.com
For: Self-Assessment
Visit: PHSchool.com
Web Code: cea-2020

Organizing Information

Concept Mapping Copy the concept map about the classification of arthropods onto a sheet of paper. Then complete it and add a title. (For more on Concept Mapping, see the Skills Handbook.)

Arthropods

include

a. ___?___   Arachnids   Centipedes and millipedes   b. ___?___

have   have   have   have

Four antennae   c. ___?___   d. ___?___   Six legs, three body sections

Reviewing Key Terms

Choose the letter of the best answer.

1. An animal that eats other animals is a(n)
   a. carnivore.
   b. omnivore.
   c. filter feeder.
   d. herbivore.

2. Mollusks with two shells are known as
   a. cephalopods.
   b. gastropods.
   c. bivalves.
   d. sea stars.

3. An arthropod's antennae are located on its
   a. head.
   b. thorax.
   c. abdomen.
   d. mantle.

4. To obtain oxygen from their environments, mollusks and crustaceans use which organ?
   a. radula
   b. lungs
   c. gills
   d. legs

5. The shedding of an outgrown exoskeleton is called
   a. complete metamorphosis.
   b. incomplete metamorphosis.
   c. molting.
   d. reproduction.

6. At which stage of development would an insect be enclosed in a cocoon?
   a. egg
   b. larva
   c. pupa
   d. adult

7. One example of a biological control is
   a. catching pest insects in traps.
   b. making and selling honey by raising bees in hives.
   c. killing pest insects with pesticides.
   d. introducing a pest insect's natural predator.

8. An echinoderm has
   a. a radula.
   b. tube feet.
   c. antennae.
   d. an exoskeleton.

Writing in Science

News Report As a television reporter, you are covering a story about a giant squid that has washed up on the local beach. Write a short news story describing the discovery. Be sure to describe how scientists classified the animal as a squid.

 **Discovery CHANNEL SCHOOL**

Mollusks, Arthropods, and Echinoderms
Video Preview
Video Field Trip
▶ Video Assessment

 **Go Online**
PHSchool.com
For: Self-Assessment
Visit: PHSchool.com
Web Code: cea-2020

Students can take an online practice test that is automatically scored.

 **All in One Teaching Resources, Unit 2**
• Transparency LS111
• Chapter Test
• Performance Assessment Teacher Notes
• Performance Assessment Student Worksheet
• Performance Assessment Scoring Rubric

ExamView® Computer Test Bank CD-ROM

Review and Assessment

Organizing Information

a. Crustaceans
b. Insects
c. Eight legs, two body segments, no antennae
d. Highly segmented body, one or two pairs of legs on each segment, two antennae
Sample title: Arthropod Groups

Reviewing Key Terms

1. a **2.** c **3.** a **4.** c **5.** c **6.** c
7. d **8.** b

Writing in Science

Writing Mode Description
Scoring Rubric
4 Includes a description of the discovery of the squid and details of how it was identified in an interesting and engaging manner
3 Includes a description of the discovery of the squid and details of how it was identified
2 Includes a description of the discovery of the squid but few details of how it was identified
1 Includes a description of the discovery of the squid but lacks accurate details of how it was identified

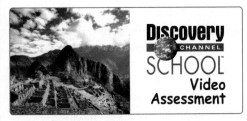 **Discovery CHANNEL SCHOOL Video Assessment**

Mollusks

Show the Video Assessment to review chapter content and as a prompt for the writing assignment. Discussion questions: **List two differences between squids and octopuses.** *(Squids have an internal shell; octopuses do not; squids have ten tentacles, but octopuses have only eight.)* **What is one advantage of octopuses not having hard shells?** *(They can squeeze into small places to hide from predators.)*

Checking Concepts

9. A snail uses its radula like a tongue to scrape up food and in some cases to bore holes in hard-shelled prey.

10. Cephalopods have a complex nervous system; they have large brains and they can learn and remember things.

11. Antennae can smell, taste, touch, and balance; legs walk; swimmerets function in swimming; chelipeds catch food and defend crayfish.

12. Centipedes have one pair of legs on each segment behind their head, while millipedes have two. Centipedes are carnivores, while millipedes are scavengers.

13. Unlike other arthropods, all insects have three body sections, six legs, and one pair of antennae. In addition, most have wings.

14. Answers may vary. Sample: Some insects destroy the food supply of humans (crops); some spread serious diseases, such as malaria.

15. An echinoderm's radial symmetry is a five-part symmetry, while a jellyfish's symmetry is not five-part.

Thinking Critically

16. Alike: Bivalves and cephalopods have a mantle covering internal organs; have soft bodies; live in water. Different: Bivalves have two outer shells, but many cephalopods have an internal shell or no shell; a cephalopod's foot is adapted to form tentacles; cephalopods move by jet propulsion, while bivalves move slowly using a foot; cephalopods have complex nervous systems, but bivalves do not.

17. Arthropods; A-crustacean, B-arachnid; number of antennae and legs

18. The cub looks similar to the adult lion from the time it is born. It grows larger, but does not change its form.

19. He might conclude that the dung beetles, which are decomposers, are improving the quality of the soil the grass is growing in by recycling the nutrients in the dung back into the soil.

20. Any argument presented by students is acceptable as long as it is supported by facts.

21. Both animals secrete juices that begin to digest the food before it enters the body.

Math Practice

22. 40,500

Review and Assessment

Checking Concepts

9. Explain how a snail uses its radula.

10. How is a cephalopod's nervous system different from that of other mollusks?

11. Describe four things that a crayfish can do with its appendages.

12. How are centipedes different from millipedes?

13. How are insects different from other arthropods?

14. Identify two reasons why insects sometimes must be controlled.

15. How is an echinoderm's radial symmetry different from that of a jellyfish?

Thinking Critically

16. Comparing and Contrasting Compare and contrast bivalves and cephalopods.

17. Classifying Which phylum does each of the animals below belong to? Explain your answer.

18. Applying Concepts Explain why the development of a lion, which grows larger as it changes from a tiny cub to a 90 kg adult, is not metamorphosis.

19. Drawing Conclusions A rancher imports dung beetles from Africa to help control manure build-up from cattle. Later, he observes that the pastures are producing more grass for the cattle to eat. What conclusion could the rancher draw about the dung beetles?

20. Making Judgments Do you think pesticides should be used to kill insect pests? Explain.

21. Comparing and Contrasting How is a spider's method of obtaining food similar to that of a sea star? How is it different?

Math Practice

22. Percentage Of approximately 150,000 species of mollusks, 27 percent are gastropods. About how many species of gastropods are there?

Applying Skills

Use the data table to answer Questions 23–25.
The following data appeared in a book on insects.

Flight Characteristics

Type of Insect	Wing Beats (per second)	Flight Speed (kilometers per hour)
Hummingbird moth	85	17.8
Bumblebee	250	10.3
Housefly	190	7.1

23. Graphing Use the data to make two bar graphs: one showing the three insect wing-beat rates and another showing the flight speeds.

24. Interpreting Data Which of the three insects has the highest wing-beat rate? Which insect flies the fastest?

25. Drawing Conclusions Based on the data, is there a relationship between the rate at which an insect beats its wings and the speed at which it flies? Explain. What factors besides wing-beat rate might affect flight speed?

Lab zone Chapter **Project**

Performance Assessment Prepare a display to show how you set up your experiment and what your results were. Construct and display graphs to show the data you collected. Include pictures of the mealworms in each stage of development. Write your conclusion of how the experimental conditions affected the growth and development of the mealworms. Also suggest some possible explanations for your results.

Lab zone Chapter **Project** L3

Performance Assessment Remind students to include illustrations of their setup, data, graph, and results. They must also include diagrams of the larvae, pupae, and adults, with arrows between these diagrams to illustrate the sequence of complete metamorphosis. Consider grouping students according to the variable they tested. Direct each group to discuss their results. Have them combine their data, create a graph to display the data, and then summarize their results. Instruct each group to present its graph and results to the rest of the class.

Reflect and Record Ask students to discuss their conclusions. Encourage discussion of why metamorphosis was or was not affected by the variables they tested.

Standardized Test Prep

Test-Taking Tip
Interpreting Graphs
Before you answer a question about a line graph, read all of its labels. The labels on the axes tell you what variables are being compared. On the graph below, the variables are temperature and the number of cricket chirps (sounds).

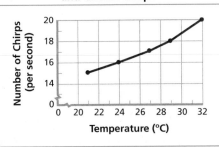

Relationship of Temperature and Cricket Chirps

Sample Question
How is the number of cricket chirps related to temperature?
- A The number of chirps increases as the temperature decreases.
- B The number of chirps stays the same as the temperature increases.
- C The number of chirps increases as the temperature increases.
- D The graph does not show a relationship.

Answer
The correct answer is **C**. The plotted line reveals that as the temperature increases, the number of chirps also increases. Therefore, **A**, **B**, and **D** can not be correct.

Choose the letter of the best answer.

1. An animal that has a soft, unsegmented body surrounded by a hard outer shell is most likely
   - A an earthworm.
   - B a cnidarian.
   - C a mollusk.
   - D an arthropod.

2. Which animal feature most likely evolved as an adaptation to provide direct protection from a predator's attack?
   - F a snail's radula
   - G a sea urchin's spines
   - H a crayfish's antennae
   - J an insect's thorax

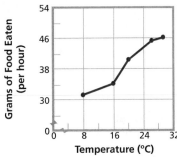
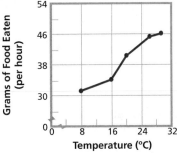

3. Examine the information in the graph above. Which is the best title for the graph?
   - A Effect of Caterpillar Feeding Rate on Temperature
   - B Caterpillar Behavior and Temperature
   - C Respiration Rate and Temperature
   - D Relationship of Temperature and Caterpillar Feeding Rate

4. What is the most reasonable prediction for what the feeding rate would be at 32°C?
   - F 60 g/hr
   - G 46 g/hr
   - H 40 g/hr
   - J 0 g/hr

Constructed Response

5. In a certain small country, mosquitoes are very common. The mosquitoes spread a disease that is deadly to humans. The government decides to spray the entire country with a pesticide that will kill all mosquitoes and other flying insects as well. How is this action likely to affect the food chain?

Applying Skills
23.

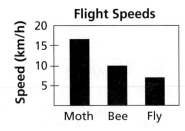

24. The bumblebee has the highest wing-beat rate. The hummingbird moth flies the fastest.

25. There is no trend in the data to support any relationship between wing-beat rate and flight speed. Other factors that affect flight speed might include mass and shape of the insect and the shape of the insect's wings.

Standardized Test Prep

1. C **2.** G **3.** D **4.** G

5. The action will disrupt the food chain by eliminating flying insects that act as consumers, decomposers, and prey for other animals.

Chapter at a Glance

PRENTICE HALL
TeacherEXPRESS™
Plan • Teach • Assess

 Chapter Project *Animal Adaptations*

Technology

Local Standards

All in One Teaching Resources, Unit 2
- Chapter Project Teacher Notes, pp. 296–297
- Chapter Project Student Overview, pp. 298–299
- Chapter Project Student Worksheets, pp. 300–301
- Chapter Project Scoring Rubric, p. 302

Video Preview

Section 1
What Is a Vertebrate?

2 periods
1 block

11.1.1 Name the characteristics that chordates share.

11.1.2 Describe the main characteristic shared by all vertebrates.

11.1.3 Describe how vertebrates differ in the way they control body temperature.

Go Online
SCiLINKS NSTA

Section 2
Fishes

3 periods
1 1/2 blocks

11.2.1 Name the main characteristics of fishes.

11.2.2 Name the major groups of fishes and describe how they differ.

Section 3
Amphibians

1 period
1/2 block

11.3.1 Describe amphibian characteristics.

11.3.2 Examine how adult amphibians are adapted for life on land.

Go Online
PHSchool.com

Go Online
active art

Section 4
Reptiles

2 periods
1 block

11.4.1 Identify adaptations that allow reptiles to live on land.

11.4.2 Contrast the characteristics of each of the three main groups of reptiles.

11.4.3 Describe one adaptation that helped dinosaurs survive before they became extinct.

Go Online
PHSchool.com

Video Field Trip

Section 5
Vertebrate History in Rocks

1 period
1/2 block

11.5.1 Identify the kind of rock in which fossils are frequently found.

11.5.2 Describe what scientists can learn from studying fossils.

Go Online
SCiLINKS NSTA

Review and Assessment

All in One Teaching Resources, Unit 2
- Key Terms Review, p. 342
- Transparency LS122
- Performance Assessment Teacher Notes, p. 351
- Performance Assessment Scoring Rubric, p. 352
- Performance Assessment Student Worksheet, p. 353
- Chapter Test, pp. 354–357

Video Assessment

Go Online
PHSchool.com

Test Preparation

Test Preparation Blackline Masters

Chapter Activities Planner

Student Edition	Inquiry	Time	Materials	Skills	Resources
Chapter Project, p. 367	Open-Ended	3–4 weeks	All in One Teaching Resources, Unit 2, p. 296	Making models, comparing and contrasting, communicating	Lab zone Easy Planner All in One Teaching Resources, Unit 2, Support pp. 296–297
Section 1					
Discover Activity, p. 368	Directed	15 minutes	Umbrella	Inferring	Lab zone Easy Planner
Skills Lab, pp. 372–373	Directed	Class: 30 minutes	Paper, pencil	Interpreting data, predicting	Lab zone Easy Planner Lab Activity Video All in One Teaching Resources, Unit 2, Skills Lab: *Soaking Up Those Rays*, pp. 310–311
Section 2					
Discover Activity, p. 374	Guided	10 minutes	Several live fish, each one in an aquarium or fishbowl	Observing	Lab zone Easy Planner
Skills Activity, p. 379	Guided	50 minutes	Preserved fish, goggles, dissecting tray, blunt probe, hand lens, rubber glove	Observing	Lab zone Easy Planner
Skills Lab, p. 381	Directed	Prep: 30 minutes Class: 10 minutes per day for two weeks	Gravel, guppy food, thermometer, aquarium filter, rectangular aquarium tank (15 to 20 liters) with cover, metric ruler, dip net, water plants, aquarium heater, guppies, tap water, snails	Observing, making models	Lab zone Easy Planner Lab Activity Video All in One Teaching Resources, Unit 2, Skills Lab: *Home Sweet Home*, pp. 319–320
Section 3					
Discover Activity, p. 382	Guided	10 minutes	Dried yellow and green peas; paper cup; green construction paper, approximately 1 m × 1 m; clock or watch with second hand	Inferring	Lab zone Easy Planner
Try This Activity, p. 385	Guided	15 minutes	Plastic bags, heavy rubber bands, pail of water or sink	Making models	Lab zone Easy Planner
Section 4					
Discover Activity, p. 387	Directed	10 minutes	sock with ribbed cuff, grapefruit, strong rubber band	Inferring	Lab zone Easy Planner
Section 5					
Discover Activity, p. 395	Directed	15 minutes	Modeling clay; paper; small objects of various textures and degrees of rigidity	Observing	Lab zone Easy Planner

Section 1 What Is a Vertebrate?

2 periods, 1 block

Objectives

11.1.1 Name the characteristics that chordates share.

11.1.2 Describe the main characteristic shared by all vertebrates.

11.1.3 Explain how vertebrates differ in the way they control body temperature.

Key Terms

• chordate • notochord • vertebra • ectotherm • endotherm

Local Standards

Preteach

Build Background Knowledge

Ask leading questions to discuss what students know about vertebrates and invertebrates.

 **Discover Activity** *How Is an Umbrella Like a Skeleton?* **L1**

Targeted Print and Technology Resources

All in One Teaching Resources, Unit 2

L2 Reading Strategy: Building Vocabulary

PresentationEXPRESS™ CD-ROM

Instruct

Characteristics of Chordates Identify characteristics of animals in the phylum Chordata.

Characteristics of Vertebrates Use a photograph to illustrate the function of the backbone and other features of vertebrate endoskeletons.

Keeping Conditions Stable Contrast the two groups of vertebrates, ectotherms and endotherms, by how they control body temperature.

Skills Lab *Soaking Up Those Rays* **L2**

Targeted Print and Technology Resources

All in One Teaching Resources, Unit 2

L2 Guided Reading, pp. 305–307
L2 Skills Lab: *Soaking Up Those Rays*, pp. 310–311

Lab Activity Video/DVD
Skills Lab: *Soaking Up Those Rays*

www.SciLinks.org Web Code: scn-0231

Student Edition on Audio CD

Assess

Section Assessment Questions

Have students use their list of definitions to help answer the questions.

Reteach

List characteristics of vertebrates.

Targeted Print and Technology Resources

All in One Teaching Resources, Unit 2

• Section Summary, p. 304
L1 Review and Reinforce, p. 308
L3 Enrich, p. 309

Section 2 Fishes

🕐 *3 periods, 1 1/2 blocks*

Objectives

11.2.1 Name the main characteristics of fishes.

11.2.2 Name the major groups of fishes and describe how they differ.

Key Terms

• fish • cartilage • swim bladder

Local Standards

Preteach

Build Background Knowledge

Draw on students' experiences with fishes to discuss fish characteristics they have observed.

 **Discover Activity** *How Does Water Flow Over a Fish's Gills?* **L1**

Targeted Print and Technology Resources

 Teaching Resources, Unit 2

L2 Reading Strategy Transparency
LS112: Previewing Visuals

⊙ **PresentationEXPRESS™ CD-ROM**

Instruct

Characteristics of Fishes Define *fish* and discuss body systems of fishes.

Jawless Fishes Identify traits that distinguish jawless fishes from other fish groups.

Cartilaginous Fishes Describe how cartilaginous fishes obtain food and oxygen.

Bony Fishes Use a diagram to identify features of bony fishes and explain the functions of those features.

 Skills Lab *Home Sweet Home* **L2**

Targeted Print and Technology Resources

Teaching Resources, Unit 2

L2 Guided Reading, pp. 314–316
L2 Transparencies LS113, LS114
L2 Skills Lab: *Home Sweet Home*, pp. 319–320

📼 **Lab Activity Video/DVD**
Skills Lab: *Home Sweet Home*

⊙ **Student Edition on Audio CD**

Assess

Section Assessment Questions

🔄 Have students use their Previewing Visuals graphic organizer to help answer the questions.

Reteach

Draw a table on the board to direct a class discussion comparing and contrasting the three groups of fishes.

Targeted Print and Technology Resources

Teaching Resources, Unit 2

• Section Summary, p. 313
L1 Review and Reinforce, p. 317
L3 Enrich, p. 318

Section 3 Amphibians

 *1 period, 1/2 block*

Objectives

11.3.1 Describe amphibian characteristics.

11.3.2 Examine how adult amphibians are adapted for life on land.

Key Terms

• amphibian • tadpole • lung • atrium • ventricle • habitat

Local Standards

Preteach

Build Background Knowledge

Students share any knowledge they have of characteristics of animals that live part of their life on land and part in the water.

Lab zone Discover Activity *What's the Advantage of Being Green?* L1

Targeted Print and Technology Resources

All in One Teaching Resources, Unit 2

L2 Reading Strategy Transparency LS115: Sequencing

⊙ **PresentationEXPRESS™ CD-ROM**

Instruct

What Is an Amphibian? Identify traits shared by amphibians and use a diagram to trace the life cycle of a frog.

Living on Land Compare and contrast the adaptations of amphibians for life in water and on land.

Targeted Print and Technology Resources

All in One Teaching Resources, Unit 2

L2 Guided Reading, pp. 323–325

L2 Transparencies LS116, LS117

PHSchool.com Web Code: ced-2033

PHSchool.com Web Code: cep-2032

⊙ **Student Edition on Audio CD**

Assess

Section Assessment Questions

Have students use their cycle diagram to help answer the questions.

Reteach

Call on students to give one characteristic of amphibians and tell how the characteristic helps the species survive in its environment.

Targeted Print and Technology Resources

All in One Teaching Resources, Unit 2

• Section Summary, p. 322

L1 Review and Reinforce, p. 326

L3 Enrich, p. 327

Section 4 **Reptiles**

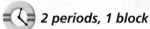 *2 periods, 1 block*

Objectives

11.4.1 Identify adaptations that allow reptiles to live on land.

11.4.2 Contrast the characteristics of each of the three main groups of reptiles.

11.4.3 Describe one adaptation that helped dinosaurs survive before they became extinct.

Local Standards

Key Terms

• reptile • kidney • urine • amniotic egg

Preteach

Build Background Knowledge

Brainstorm characteristics of snakes.

Lab zone Discover Activity *How Do Snakes Feed?* **L1**

Targeted Print and Technology Resources

All in One Teaching Resources, Unit 2

L2 Reading Strategy Transparency LS118: Identifying Main Ideas

 PresentationEXPRESS™ CD-ROM

Instruct

Adaptations for Life on Land Identify and describe adaptations that help reptiles survive on land.

Lizards and Snakes Compare and contrast characteristics and adaptations of lizards and snakes.

Alligators and Crocodiles Discuss traits that make crocodiles and alligators successful predators.

Turtles Describe physical features and feeding habits of land and aquatic turtles.

Extinct Reptiles—The Dinosaurs Contrast characteristics of dinosaurs and modern reptiles.

Targeted Print and Technology Resources

All in One Teaching Resources, Unit 2

L2 Guided Reading, pp. 330–333
L2 Transparency LS119

PHSchool.com Web Code: ced-2034

 Discovery CHANNEL SCHOOL Video Field Trip

Student Edition on Audio CD

Assess

Section Assessment Questions

Have students use their Identifying Main Ideas graphic organizer to help answer the questions.

Reteach

Call on students to describe the features of one of the three groups of reptiles.

Targeted Print and Technology Resources

All in One Teaching Resources, Unit 2

• Section Summary, p. 329
L1 Review and Reinforce, p. 334
L3 Enrich, p. 335

Section Lesson Plans

Section 5 **Vertebrate History in Rocks**

 *1 period, 1/2 block*

Objectives

11.5.1 Identify the kind of rock in which fossils are frequently found.

11.5.2 Describe what scientists can learn from studying fossils.

Key Terms

• fossil • sedimentary rock • paleontologist

Local Standards

Preteach

Build Background Knowledge

Use fossil-bearing rocks to elicit student observations and inferences about fossilized organisms.

Lab zone Discover Activity *What Can You Tell From an Imprint?* **L1**

Targeted Print and Technology Resources

All in One Teaching Resources, Unit 2

L2 Reading Strategy Transparency LS120: Asking Questions

○ **PresentationEXPRESS™ CD-ROM**

Instruct

What Are Fossils? Describe how fossils form in sedimentary rock.

Interpretation of Fossils Use diagrams to show how paleontologists use fossils to understand how animals are related.

Targeted Print and Technology Resources

All in One Teaching Resources, Unit 2

L2 Guided Reading, pp. 338–339

L2 Transparency LS121

www.SciLinks.org Web Code: scn-0235

Assess

Section Assessment Questions

Have students use their Asking Questions graphic organizers to answer the questions.

Reteach

Use a sketch of layers of sedimentary rock to place vertebrate fossils in their correct order.

Targeted Print and Technology Resources

All in One Teaching Resources, Unit 2

• Section Summary, p. 337

L1 Review and Reinforce, p. 340

L3 Enrich, p. 341

Chapter 11 **Content Refresher**

Go **Online**

NSTA-PD LINKS

For: Professional development support
Visit: www.SciLinks.org/PDLinks
Web Code: scf–0230

Professional Development

Section 1 **What Is a Vertebrate?**

Keeping the Heat Endotherms are vertebrates—birds and mammals—that maintain steady body temperatures regardless of the environmental temperatures. This adaptation allows these animals to take advantage of many different habitats and to function throughout the seasons. In contrast, the body temperatures of ectotherms—reptiles, amphibians, and fishes—are greatly affected by the temperature of their surroundings. Both the reptile and the human (represented by a hand) shown in the diagram below are in an environment with a temperature around 85°F. Notice that the human maintains its temperature.

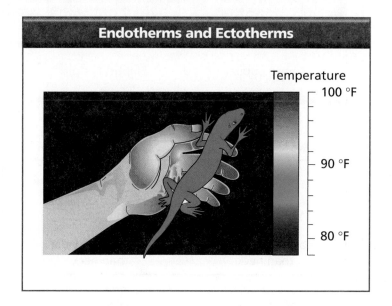

Endotherms and Ectotherms

Temperature
- 100 °F
- 90 °F
- 80 °F

Endotherms use a lot of energy to maintain their body temperatures. The energy allows them to cool themselves in hot environments and to generate heat in cold environments. The metabolic rate—the rate by which an animal generates energy—for a resting endotherm is about six times greater than the metabolic rate of a resting ectotherm that is the same size. Endotherms must eat more food than ectotherms to generate energy. For example, a snake might eat a small mammal only once every several days, yet a shrew—a tiny, insect-eating mammal—eats constantly when it is awake.

Endotherms do not depend entirely on generating energy to maintain internal temperatures, and ectotherms are not completely at the mercy of environmental temperatures. Endotherms and ectotherms both move between warm and cool areas to regulate body temperatures; some lizards that alternate basking in the sun with moving to shade have been shown to maintain nearly constant body temperatures with this behavior. Endotherms also have skin, fur, and feathers that prevent heat loss; some, particularly birds and whales, migrate when environmental conditions become too demanding.

All vertebrates, whether they are ectotherms or endotherms, need to maintain their body temperatures within a relatively narrow range. One reason is that an animal's enzymes function only within a narrow temperature range. Enzymes are proteins that speed up chemical reactions within cells. For example, enzymes help break food molecules into simpler substances, releasing energy in the process. Without the enzymes, such reactions could take a long time or not happen at all. With the enzymes, they take place in seconds. However, because enzymes are delicate chemicals, a substantial change in body temperature inactivates or destroys them. If an animal's body temperature is too high or too low, enzyme activity stops and the body will not function properly.

Section 2 **Fishes**

Hunting and Avoiding Being Eaten Fishes have adaptations for hunting prey and for avoiding predators. The lateral line system of fishes, a sensory organ uniquely suited to aquatic habitats, is an example. The lateral line system detects both vibrations in the water and changes in the water pressure. This information is then converted into nerve impulses. Scientists believe that fishes use the sensory information provided by the lateral line to determine the threat of an approaching predator as well as to locate prey.

Sharks and some bony fishes possess a modified version of the pressure-sensitive lateral line system, called the ampullae of Lorenzini, which allows the fish to detect electrical charges and fields in the water. Humans and most other animals emit an electrical field when in seawater. This field is altered if an organism is wounded or injured. This change in the electrical field can be detected by fishes with this sensory adaptation, thus targeting the injured organism as potential prey.

Lateral Line System

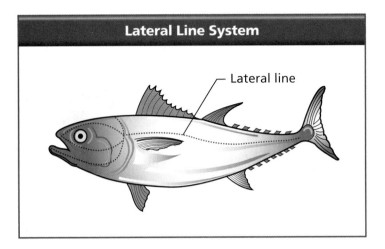

Lateral line

Beyond physiological adaptations, some fishes exhibit behaviors that reduce their vulnerability to predators. One such behavior is schooling. Scientists think that an individual fish that lives within a group of fishes has a better chance of survival than a lone fish when a predator approaches. Predators are believed to be confused by the fish school, and less likely to single out any particular individual prey.

Section 3   Amphibians

Mysterious Declines   Declines of frog populations in the United States are particularly dramatic in the Rocky Mountains, California, the Southwest, and Puerto Rico. But these areas are not the only ones with populations in trouble, as physical deformities have been documented for almost 60 species across 44 states. In some areas, as much as 60 percent of the local frog species show deformities. Common deformities include extra eyes or limbs, missing eyes, missing or malformed limbs, and malformed faces.

Scientists have been unable to isolate a single source of harm to the world's frogs. Many researchers suspect that there is more than one destructive process at work, and that this combination is especially damaging. In addition to environmental contamination and loss of habitat, other suspected culprits are UV radiation, parasites, and disease. Populations affected are found in urban, crowded areas where habitat has been recently destroyed, as well as in areas seemingly unaffected by humans, such as national parks.

Address Misconceptions

Students may think that someone who touches a toad will get warts. Anyone who has held a toad knows that this is not true, although toads can secrete irritating substances through their skin. For more explanation of this misconception, see the section entitled *Amphibians*.

Section 4   Reptiles

The Pain and Danger of Venom   Of the 2,300 snake species found on Earth, only 300 species are venomous. Although this is a small percentage of the total snake population, about 30,000 to 40,000 people worldwide die each year from snake bites. The greatest number of deaths occurs in Southeast Asia. Fewer than 100 people in the United States die each year from snake bites.

Snake venom is actually toxic saliva. Venom, which immobilizes a snake's prey, can be one of two types. Neurotoxic venoms attack a victim's central nervous system, and hemotoxic venoms attack the circulatory system and the muscle tissue.

Poisonous snakes can sometimes be distinguished from nonpoisonous snakes by differences in physical characteristics. Poisonous snakes usually have pupils that are vertically elliptical, like a cat's, and facial pits between the nostril and the eye, whereas nonpoisonous snakes generally have round pupils and no facial pits.

Nonvenomous Snakes	Venomous Snakes
Round pupils	Elliptical pupils
No sensing pit	Sensing pit
Head slightly wider than neck	Head much wider than neck
Double row of scales on the underside of the tail	Single scales on the underside of the tail

Section 5 Vertebrate History in Rocks

Preserved Animal History Some animal fossils are fossilized body parts or structures, such as bones, claws, teeth, and eggs. Other fossils are traces of animals—footprints, toothmarks, nests, dung, burrows, and so on. There are different forms of fossils: mold fossils preserve impressions, or negative images of an organism; cast fossils occur when a mold fossil is filled in; true-form fossils are the actual animals or parts of the animals; and trace fossils preserve evidence of animals' movements and behaviors, such as walking.

Animals or plants are turned into fossils by several very different processes. Sometimes animals are preserved unaltered, such as an intact insect trapped in amber, which is fossilized tree sap. Most bone and wood fossils are petrified, which means that original tissues were slowly replaced with rocklike minerals. Another means of fossilization is carbonization, which leaves only carbon behind.

Fossils in History Aristotle realized that fossils were evidence of past life, but he thought the organisms had grown in the rocks. During medieval times, from about A.D. 500 to 1500, people dismissed fossils as simply odd mineral formations that resembled living things by chance.

Leonardo da Vinci was one of the first scholars to understand how fossils were formed. He noticed that certain fossils not only looked like the live animal but were also buried in the rock in lifelike positions.

It was not until the late eighteenth century, when the English engineer William Smith recognized that certain fossils are limited to particular layers in Earth's crust, that paleontology became the study of the development of organisms over time.

Help Students Read

Previewing Visuals

Setting a Purpose Before Reading Through Visual Images

Strategy To show students why graphics and tables should be previewed prior to reading, explain that the preview helps a reader anticipate what the text will be about. Have students examine all the section graphics. Ask students to predict what the material in that section will be about, based on their observations.

Example

Select a section of the chapter, such as the section on fishes, or a single topic, such as *Characteristics of Fishes*. Instruct students to preview the material presented in the graphics. Discuss the ideas displayed in the graphics and ask students to predict what the text will be about.

Interactive Textbook
- Complete student edition
- Video and audio
- Simulations and activities
- Section and chapter activities

Chapter

11

Fishes, Amphibians, and Reptiles

Chapter Preview

Interactive Textbook

The fishes in this school are named "sweetlips." ▶

366 ◆

Chapter Project

L3

Objectives
This project will allow students to investigate and model how adaptations enable animals to survive in their environments. Students will select one adaptation to model in a reptile, an amphibian, and a fish. After this Chapter Project, students will be able to
- make models of adaptations that perform similar functions in three different kinds of organisms
- compare and contrast the adaptations of the three organisms
- communicate their findings about the adaptations that they model to their classmates

Skills Focus
Making models, comparing and contrasting, communicating

Project Time Line 3 to 4 weeks

All in One Teaching Resources, Unit 2
- Chapter Project Teacher Notes
- Chapter Project Overview
- Chapter Project Worksheet 1
- Chapter Project Worksheet 2
- Chapter Project Scoring Rubric

Developing a Plan
Each pair or group of students will review the chapter and other references. Then select an adaptation to model. As students complete each chapter section, they should begin to construct a model of one type of organism they studied in the section. Students can work on projects at home as well as at school.

Possible Materials
Provide a wide variety of materials from which students can choose. Have students bring any extra materials they might have at home for others in the class to use. Some possibilities are listed below. Encourage students to suggest and use other materials as well.
- For model building, include toothpicks, pipe cleaners, Styrofoam®, cardboard, construction paper, chicken wire, balsa wood, balloons, modeling clay, papier

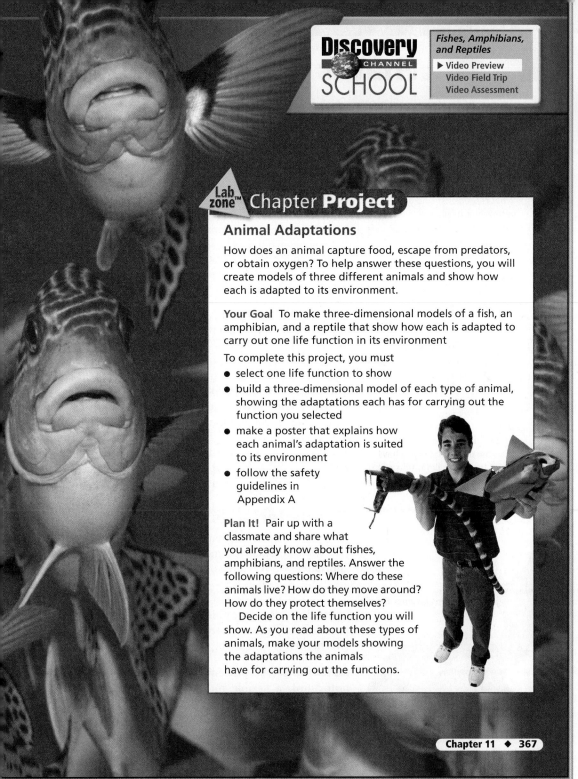

Fishes, Amphibians, and Reptiles

Show the Video Preview to introduce the Chapter Project and overview the chapter content. Discussion question: **List three functions of reptile scales.** (*Three functions are preventing evaporation of water, helping forward motion, and camouflage.*)

Lab zone™ Chapter Project

Animal Adaptations

How does an animal capture food, escape from predators, or obtain oxygen? To help answer these questions, you will create models of three different animals and show how each is adapted to its environment.

Your Goal To make three-dimensional models of a fish, an amphibian, and a reptile that show how each is adapted to carry out one life function in its environment

To complete this project, you must
● select one life function to show
● build a three-dimensional model of each type of animal, showing the adaptations each has for carrying out the function you selected
● make a poster that explains how each animal's adaptation is suited to its environment
● follow the safety guidelines in Appendix A

Plan It! Pair up with a classmate and share what you already know about fishes, amphibians, and reptiles. Answer the following questions: Where do these animals live? How do they move around? How do they protect themselves?

Decide on the life function you will show. As you read about these types of animals, make your models showing the adaptations the animals have for carrying out the functions.

Chapter 11 ◆ 367

---

of the three organisms. Before they construct each of their models, students should sketch the design and plan for needed materials. Where appropriate, suggest that students model only a part of the organisms, such as the mouths if they are modeling feeding behaviors. Pass out copies of the Chapter Project Worksheets in Teaching Resources for students to review.

Performance Assessment

The Chapter Project Scoring Rubric will help you evaluate how well students complete the Chapter Project. You may wish to share the scoring rubric with your students so they are clear about what will be expected of them. Students will be assessed on
● the thoroughness of their research into the adaptation that they model, and the appropriateness and accuracy of their sketches
● the size, proportion, and accuracy of their models
● the clarity and thoroughness of their posters
● the thoroughness and organization of their presentations

---

maché, glue, tape, scissors, paints, markers, and other decorating materials.
● For information about organisms, students can consult magazines and picture books.

Launching the Project

Students should read the project description and the Chapter Project Overview in Teaching Resources. Allow students to work in groups of three or four. Encourage them to skim through the chapter, books, and magazines to consider the ways fishes, amphibians, and reptiles are different, and then discuss characteristics that allow the three types of vertebrates to move, feed, and protect themselves. Suggest that students choose adaptations that differ in at least two

What Is a Vertebrate?

Objectives

After completing the lesson, students will be able to

11.1.1 Name the characteristics that chordates share.

11.1.2 Describe the main characteristic shared by all vertebrates.

11.1.3 Describe how vertebrates differ in the way they control body temperature.

Target Reading Skill

Building Vocabulary Explain that knowing the definitions of Key Concept words helps students understand what they read.

Answer

Call on volunteers to read their definitions aloud. Make sure that students have explained the definitions in their own words.

Preteach

Build Background Knowledge
L2

Comparing Vertebrates and Invertebrates

Help students recall what they know about vertebrates and invertebrates. Then ask a volunteer to list on the board all the kinds of vertebrates and invertebrates the students see in a single day. Once the lists are completed, have students compare and contrast several obvious ways vertebrates and invertebrates are similar and ways they are different.

Section

1

What Is a Vertebrate?

Reading Preview

Key Concepts
- What characterisics do chordates share?
- What characteristic do all vertebrates have?
- How do vertebrates differ in the way they control body temperature?

Key Terms
- chordate • notochord
- vertebra • ectotherm
- endotherm

Target Reading Skill

Building Vocabulary A definition states the meaning of a word or phrase by telling about its most important feature or function. After you read the section, reread the paragraphs that contain definitions of Key Terms. Use all the information you have learned to write a definition of each Key Term in your own words.

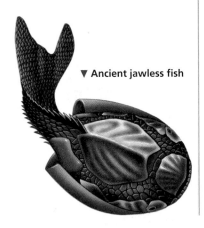

▼ Ancient jawless fish

368 ◆

Lab zone Discover **Activity**

How Is an Umbrella Like a Skeleton?

1. Open an umbrella. Turn it upside down and examine how it is made.
2. Now close the umbrella and watch how the braces and ribs collapse.
3. Think of what would happen if you removed the ribs from the umbrella and then tried to use it during a rainstorm.

Think It Over

Inferring What is the function of the ribs of an umbrella? How are the ribs of the umbrella similar to the bones in your skeleton? How are they different?

Look backward in time, into an ocean 530 million years ago. There you see a strange-looking creature—a jawless fish—that is about as long as your index finger. The creature is swimming with a side-to-side motion, like a flag flapping in the wind. Its tail fin is broad and flat. Tiny armorlike plates cover its small body. Its eyes are set wide apart. If you could see inside the animal, you would notice that it has a backbone. You are looking at one of the earliest vertebrates at home in an ancient sea.

Characteristics of Chordates

Vertebrates like the ancient jawless fish are a subgroup in the phylum Chordata. All members of this phylum are called **chordates** (KAWR dayts). Most chordates, including fishes, amphibians, such as frogs, and reptiles, such as snakes, are vertebrates. So are birds and mammals. But a few chordates are invertebrates. **At some point in their lives, chordates will have a notochord, a nerve cord that runs down their back, and slits in their throat area.**

Notochord The phylum name Chordata comes from the **notochord,** a flexible rod that supports a chordate's back. Some chordates, like the lancelet shown in Figure 1, have notochords all their lives. In contrast, in vertebrates, part or all of the notochord is replaced by a backbone.

Lab zone Discover **Activity**

Skills Focus Inferring

Materials umbrella

Time 15 minutes

Tips To avoid injuries, make sure students are standing in an open area away from others when they open the umbrellas.

L1 **Expected Outcome** An umbrella without its ribs loses its support and cannot function.

Think It Over The umbrella's ribs provide support to the umbrella and give it shape, just as human bones support and give shape to the body. The ribs of an umbrella are different from human bones in that they are near the surface, rather than deep within the body and covered by soft tissue.

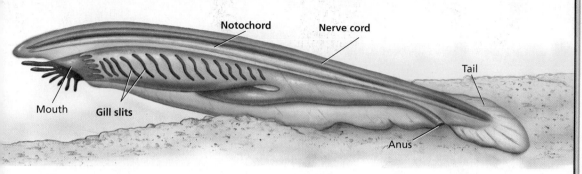

Notochord   Nerve cord

Tail

Mouth   Gill slits

Anus

Nerve Cord in Back In addition to having a notochord, all chordates have a nerve cord that runs down their back. Your spinal cord is such a nerve cord. The nerve cord is the connection between the brain and the nerves, on which messages travel back and forth. Many other groups of animals—arthropods and segmented worms, for example—have nerve cords, but their nerve cords do not run down their backs.

Slits in Throat Area At some point in their lives, chordates have slits in their throat area called pharyngeal (fuh RIN jee ul) slits, or gill slits. Some chordates, including fishes, keep these slits as part of their gills for their entire lives. But in many vertebrates, including humans, pharyngeal slits disappear before birth.

 Reading Checkpoint What is a notochord?

FIGURE 1
Characteristics of a Lancelet
This lancelet shows the characteristics of a chordate: a notochord that helps support its body, a nerve cord down its back, and gill slits.

Characteristics of Vertebrates

Most chordates are vertebrates. In addition to the characteristics shared by all chordates, vertebrates share certain other characteristics. **A vertebrate has a backbone that is part of an internal skeleton.** This endoskeleton supports the body and allows it to move.

Backbone A vertebrate's backbone, which is also called a spine, runs down the center of its back. You can see in Figure 2 that the backbone is formed by many similar bones called **vertebrae** (singular *vertebra*). The vertebrae are lined up in a row like beads on a string. Joints, or movable connections between the vertebrae, give the spine flexibility. You can bend over and tie your shoes because your backbone has flexibility. Each vertebra has a hole in it that allows the spinal cord to pass through it. The spinal cord fits into the vertebrae like fingers fit into rings.

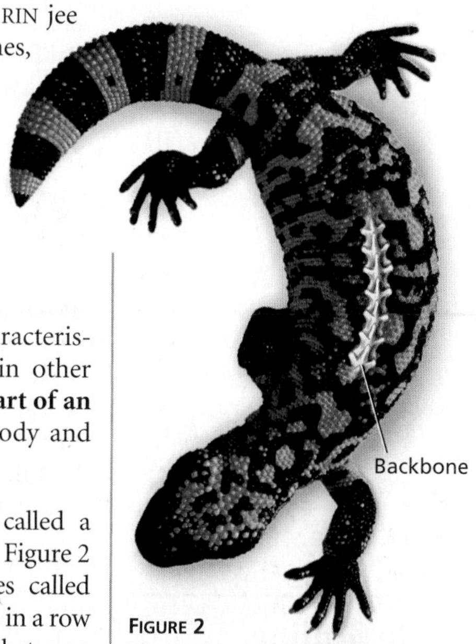

Backbone

FIGURE 2
The Backbone of a Lizard
The backbone of this gila monster has flexibility. **Predicting** *Could the backbone bend if the vertebrae did not have joints?*

Chapter 11 ◆ 369

Keeping Conditions Stable

Teach Key Concepts

Comparing Endotherms and Ectotherms

Focus Tell students that vertebrates differ in the way they control body temperature.

Teach Write two headings on the board, *Endotherms* and *Ectotherms*. Read aloud facts about each and ask students to assign each fact to its correct heading. (*Endotherms: birds and mammals; produces internal heat; stable body temperatures; have fur or feathers, sweat glands. Ectotherms: fishes, reptiles, and amphibians; do not produce internal heat; body temperatures change with environmental temperatures.*)

Apply Ask: **How can an ectotherm change its body temperature?** (*It can seek sun or shade.*) **learning modality: logical/mathematical**

Go Online SciLINKS NSTA

For: Links on vertebrates
Visit: www.SciLinks.org
Web Code: scn-0231

Download a worksheet that will guide students' review of Internet resources on vertebrates.

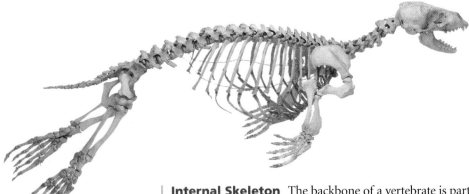

FIGURE 3
The Skeleton of a Seal
This seal's skeleton has adaptations for swimming. Long, flat bones support the flippers. The flat skull helps the seal move smoothly through the water.

Internal Skeleton The backbone of a vertebrate is part of its endoskeleton. This endoskeleton protects the internal organs of the body, helps give the body shape, and gives muscles a place to attach. In addition to the backbone, a vertebrate's endoskeleton includes the skull and ribs. The skull protects the brain. The ribs attach to the vertebrae and protect the heart, lungs, and other internal organs. Many vertebrates, like the seal shown in Figure 3, also have arm and leg bones adapted for movement.

A vertebrate's endoskeleton has several characteristics. Unlike an arthropod's exoskeleton, an endoskeleton doesn't need to be replaced as the animal grows. It also forms an internal frame that supports the body against the downward pull of gravity, while allowing easy movement. Because of these characteristics, vertebrates can grow bigger than animals with exoskeletons or no skeletons at all.

 Reading Checkpoint What does an endoskeleton protect?

Keeping Conditions Stable

One characteristic that differs among the major groups of vertebrates is the way they control their body temperature. **The body temperature of most fishes, amphibians, and reptiles is close to the temperature of their environment. In contrast, birds and mammals have a stable body temperature that is often warmer than their environment.**

Ectotherms Fishes, amphibians, and reptiles are ectotherms. An **ectotherm** is an animal whose body does not produce much internal heat. Its body temperature changes depending on the temperature of its environment. For example, when a turtle is lying on a sunny riverbank, it has a higher body temperature than when it is swimming in a cool river. Ectotherms are sometimes called "coldblooded." This term is misleading because their blood is often quite warm.

Go Online SciLINKS NSTA

For: Links on vertebrates
Visit: www.SciLinks.org
Web Code: scn-0231

Woma python ►

▼ Emperor penguins

Endotherms In contrast to a turtle, a beaver would have the same body temperature whether it is in cool water or on warm land. The beaver is an example of an **endotherm**—an animal whose body regulates its own temperature by controlling the internal heat it produces. An endotherm's body temperature usually does not change much, even when the temperature of its environment changes. Birds and mammals, such as beavers, are endotherms.

Endotherms also have other adaptations, such as sweat glands and fur or feathers, for maintaining their body temperature. On hot days, some endotherms sweat. As the sweat evaporates, the animal is cooled. On cool days, fur or feathers keep endotherms warm. Because endotherms can keep their body temperatures stable, they can live in a greater variety of environments than ectotherms can.

FIGURE 4
Temperature Regulation
On a cool, sunny morning, a woma python raises its body temperature by basking in the sun. In contrast, an emperor penguin stays warm by producing internal heat.
Inferring Which animal is an endotherm?

Section 1 Assessment

◐ **Target Reading Skill** Building Vocabulary Use your definitions to help answer the questions.

Reviewing Key Concepts

1. **a. Listing** List three characteristics of chordates.
   b. Comparing and Contrasting In chordates, how does the notochord of a vertebrate differ from that of an invertebrate?
   c. Explaining An earthworm has a nerve cord that runs along its body. Is an earthworm a chordate? Explain.
2. **a. Identifying** What characteristic do only vertebrates have?
   b. Describing Describe a backbone.
   c. Relating Cause and Effect What gives a backbone flexibility?

3. **a. Summarizing** What is the difference between an ectotherm and an endotherm?
   b. Making Generalizations Would an ectotherm or an endotherm be more active on a cold night? Explain your answer.

Lab zone At-Home **Activity**

Bumpy Back Rub Have members of your family feel the tops of the vertebrae running down the center of their backs. Then have them feel the hard skull beneath the skin on their foreheads. Tell them about the functions of the backbone and skull.

Chapter 11 ◆ 371

Monitor Progress _____ L2
Oral Presentation Call on students to explain the differences between ectotherms and endotherms.

Answers
Figure 4 The penguin

✓ Reading Checkpoint — The endoskeleton protects the brain, heart, lungs, and other internal organs.

Assess

Reviewing Key Concepts

1. **a.** notochord, nerve cord down their back, gill slits **b.** In a vertebrate, the notochord is replaced by a backbone, whereas invertebrate chordates have notochords their whole lives. **c.** No. An earthworm's nerve cord does not run down its back, and an earthworm does not have a notochord or gill slits.
2. **a.** Backbone **b.** A backbone runs down the center of the back and is made of many similar bones called vertebrae. **c.** The joints between the vertebrae give the backbone flexibility.
3. **a.** An ectotherm does not produce much internal heat and its body temperature changes with that of the environment. An endotherm regulates its body temperature by controlling the internal heat it produces. **b.** Endotherms; their constantly high body temperatures allow them to remain active when environmental temperatures are cool. Ectotherms would slow down because their body temperatures would drop.

Reteach L1
As a class, list characteristics of vertebrates.

Performance Assessment L2
Drawing Have students sketch simple human skeletons and label the skull, ribs, backbone, vertebrae, and spinal cord. Then ask them to title their sketches "An Endotherm" or "An Ectotherm." Students can save their drawings in their portfolios.

Portfolio

All in One Teaching Resources, Unit 2
• Section Summary: *What Is a Vertebrate?*
• Review and Reinforce: *What Is a Vertebrate?*
• Enrich: *What Is a Vertebrate?*

Lab zone At-Home **Activity**

Bumpy Back Rub L1 Review the various benefits of the backbone and skull for the students to share with family members: protection of the brain and the spinal cord, flexibility, support, muscle attachment, and growth. Remind them that joints between vertebrae give the spine flexibility, and that the ribs attach to the vertebrae and protect the heart, lungs, and other organs.

Soaking Up Those Rays

Prepare for Inquiry

Key Concept
The temperature of ectotherms changes as the animals approach or avoid heat sources in their environment.

Skills Objectives
After this lab, students will be able to
- interpret data associated with an ectotherm
- make predictions for endotherms

 Class Time 30 minutes

All in One Teaching Resources, Unit 2
- Lab Worksheet: *Soaking Up Those Rays*

Guide Inquiry

Invitation
Heat flows from a warmer object to a cooler object. Challenge students to consider whether this rule applies to living organisms. Ask: **What do you notice if you lean against a car parked in the sun?** (*The part of my body touching the car starts to get warm.*)

Introducing the Procedure
As needed, help individual students understand the significance of each type of information in the illustration.

Troubleshooting the Experiment
Students may have trouble relating to Celsius temperatures. Students can convert a few key temperatures in the diagram into degrees Fahrenheit. This may make it easier for them to understand the lizard's behavior. Students can check each other's work.

Expected Outcome
Through their behavior, lizards can maintain their body temperature within a range that is more limited than the temperature range in the environment.

Soaking Up Those Rays

Problem
How do some lizards control their body temperatures in the extreme heat of a desert?

Skills Focus
interpreting data, predicting

Materials
- paper • pencil

Procedure
1. The data below were collected by scientists studying how lizards control their body temperature. Examine the data.
2. Copy the data table into your notebook.
3. Organize the data in the diagrams by filling in the table, putting the appropriate information in each column. Begin by writing a brief description of each type of lizard behavior.
4. Complete the data table using the information in the diagrams.

Analyze and Conclude
1. **Interpreting Data** Describe how the lizard's body temperature changed between 6 A.M. and 9 P.M.
2. **Inferring** What are three sources of heat that caused the lizard's body temperature to rise during the day?
3. **Interpreting Data** During the hottest part of the day, what were the air and ground temperatures? Why do you think the lizard's temperature remained below 40°C?
4. **Predicting** Predict what the lizard's body temperature would have been from 9 P.M. to 6 A.M. Explain your prediction.
5. **Predicting** Predict what would happen to your own body temperature if you spent a brief period outdoors in the desert at noon. Predict what your temperature would be if you spent time in a burrow at 7 P.M. Explain your predictions.

6 A.M.–7 A.M.
Emerging from burrow
Air temperature **20°C**
Ground temperature **28°C**
Body temperature **25°C**

7 A.M.–9 A.M.
Basking (lying on ground in sun)
Air temperature **27°C**
Ground temperature **29°C**
Body temperature **32.6°C**

9 A.M.–12 NOON
Active (moving about)
Air temperature **27°C**
Ground temperature **30.8°C**
Body temperature **36.6°C**

Data Table

Activity	Description of Activity	Time of Day	Air Temperature (°C)	Ground Temperature (°C)	Body Temperature (°C)
1. Emerging					
2. Basking					
3. Active					
4. Retreat					
5. Stilting					
6. Retreat					

6. **Drawing Conclusions** Based on what you learned from the data, explain why it is misleading to say that an ectotherm is a "cold-blooded" animal.

7. **Communicating** Write a paragraph explaining why it is helpful to organize data in a data table before you try to interpret the data.

More to Explore

Make a bar graph of the temperature data. Explain what the graph shows you. How does this graph help you interpret the data about how lizards control their body temperature in the extreme heat of a desert?

.

12 NOON–2:30 P.M.
Retreat to burrow
Air temperature 40.3°C
Ground temperature 53.8°C
Body temperature 39.5°C

2:30 P.M.–6 P.M.
Stilting (belly off ground)
Air temperature 34.2°C
Ground temperature 47.4°C
Body temperature 39.5°C

6 P.M.–9 P.M.
Retreat to burrow
Air temperature 25°C
Ground temperature 26°C
Body temperature 25°C

Analyze and Conclude

1. The lizard's body temperature varied from a low of 25°C to a high of 39.5°C. By 9 P.M. it had dropped back down to 25°C.

2. The sun's rays, the surrounding air, and surface rocks. Note: In some periods, the air was cooler than the lizard's body temperature and so served to cool it.

3. Air temperature = 40.3°C, ground temperature = 53.8°C. The lizard remained cooler by staying in its burrow, which was in the shade and cooler than the ground temperature.

4. Accept all reasonable answers. Students may say that the body temperature will probably remain about 25°C, since the burrow tends to have a stable temperature.

5. Our body temperatures at both times would remain relatively constant, since human body temperature is controlled by its own internal controls.

6. "Coldblooded" implies that an animal's body temperature is cold. The lizard's temperature gets as high as 39°C, which is hotter than 100°F.

7. Sample answer: Organizing data in a table allows us to list all the data in the same place and makes data easier to compare. In this lab, the data table lets us quickly see temperature changes that happened over the course of the day. The table also makes comparing the temperatures at different times of the day easier.

Extend Inquiry

More to Explore On the bar graph, the temperature is plotted on the y-axis; the time of the day on the x-axis. The graph of ground temperature shows that the rocks are cool in the morning, become hot at noon, and remain hot until evening. Lizards keep their bodies off the rocks after the rocks become hot. They either retreat, as they did from 12–2:30 P.M., or show stilting behavior. Stilting keeps their bodies away from the heat of the rocks.

Sample Data Table

Description of Activity	Time	Air Temp. °C	Ground Temp. °C	Body Temp. °C
Leaves burrow	6–7 A.M.	20	28	25
Rests on surface	7–9	27	29	32.6
Moves around	9–12	27	30.8	36.6
Enters burrow	12–12:30 P.M.	40.3	53.8	39.5
Belly away from surface, tail over head	2:30–6	34.2	47.4	39.5
Enters burrow	6	25	26	25

Objectives
After completing the lesson, students will be able to

11.2.1 Name the main characteristics of fishes.

11.2.2 Name the major groups of fishes and describe how they differ.

Target Reading Skill ↻

Previewing Visuals Explain that looking at the visuals before they read helps students activate prior knowledge and predict what they are about to read.

Answers
Possible student questions and answers include: **What is a swim bladder?** (*A swim bladder is an internal, gas-filled sac that helps stabilize the fish at different depths in the water.*) **What is the function of the tail fin?** (*It helps provide the power for swimming.*)

All in One Teaching Resources, Unit 2
• Transparency LS112

Preteach

Build Background Knowledge   L2
Recalling Fish Characteristics
Ask students to describe characteristics of fishes they have observed. Ask questions such as: **What did the skin look like? What did the scales feel like? Where were the fins located?**

Reading Preview

Key Concepts
• What are the characteristics of most fishes?
• What are the major groups of fishes and how do they differ?

Key Terms
• fish • cartilage • swim bladder

↻ Target Reading Skill
Previewing Visuals Before you read, preview Figure 12. Then write two questions that you have about the diagram in a graphic organizer like the one below. As you read, answer your questions.

Structure of a Fish

Q. What is a swim bladder?
A.
Q.

Lab zone Discover **Activity**

How Does Water Flow Over a Fish's Gills?
1. Closely observe a fish in an aquarium for a few minutes. Note how frequently the fish opens its mouth.
2. Notice the flaps on each side of the fish's head behind its eyes. Observe how the flaps open and close.
3. Observe the movements of the mouth and the flaps at the same time. Note any relationship between the movements of these two structures.

Think It Over
Observing What do the flaps on the sides of the fish do when the fish opens its mouth? What role do you think these two structures play in a fish's life?

In the warm waters of a coral reef, a large spotted fish called a graysby hovers in the water, barely moving. A smaller striped fish called a goby swims up to the graysby. Then, like a vacuum cleaner moving over a rug, the goby swims slowly over the larger fish, eating dead skin and tiny parasites. The goby even cleans inside the graysby's mouth and gills. Both fishes benefit from this cleaning. The graysby gets rid of unwanted materials, and the goby gets a meal.

Gobies cleaning a ▶ graysby

Lab zone Discover **Activity**

Skills Focus Observing   L1

Materials several live fish, each one in an aquarium or fishbowl

Time 10 minutes

Tips Use a larger fish, such as a goldfish, whose gill movements can be easily observed.

Expected Outcome Students should observe that when the fish opens its mouth, its gill flaps also open.

Think It Over The mouth and the gill flaps open at the same time. The mouth enables water to enter the fish and pass over the gills, which take in oxygen from the water. The flaps open to enable the water to leave.

Extend Ask students to count the number of times the gill flaps open per minute. Direct them to work in pairs and compare their results with those of the other groups.

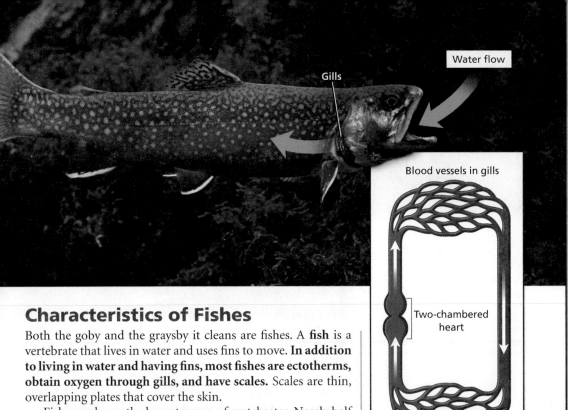

Gills

Water flow

Characteristics of Fishes

Both the goby and the graysby it cleans are fishes. A **fish** is a vertebrate that lives in water and uses fins to move. **In addition to living in water and having fins, most fishes are ectotherms, obtain oxygen through gills, and have scales.** Scales are thin, overlapping plates that cover the skin.

Fishes make up the largest group of vertebrates. Nearly half of all vertebrate species are fishes. In addition, fishes have been on Earth longer than any other kind of vertebrate.

Obtaining Oxygen Fishes get their oxygen from water. As a fish swims, it opens its mouth and takes a gulp of water, as you observed if you did the Discover Activity. The water, which contains oxygen, moves through openings in the fish's throat region that lead to the gills. Gills, which look like tiny feathers, have many blood vessels within them. As water flows over the gills, oxygen moves from the water into the fish's blood. At the same time, carbon dioxide, a waste product, moves out of the blood and into the water. After flowing over the gills, the water flows out of the fish through slits beneath the gills.

Circulatory System From the gills, the blood travels throughout the fish's body, supplying the body cells with oxygen. Like all vertebrates, fishes have a closed circulatory system. The heart of a fish has two chambers, or inner spaces. The heart of a fish pumps blood in one loop—from the heart to the gills, from the gills to the rest of the body, and back to the heart. You can trace this path in Figure 5.

Blood vessels in gills

Two-chambered heart

Blood vessels in body

Key
- ■ Oxygen-rich blood
- ■ Oxygen-poor blood

FIGURE 5
Respiration and Circulation
Water flows into the mouth of this fish and then over its gills. Oxygen moves into the blood and is delivered to the cells of the fish.
Interpreting Diagrams *Where does oxygen get into the blood of a fish?*

375

Teach Key Concepts

L2

Evaluating Reproduction Strategies

Focus Challenge students to make inferences about the advantages and disadvantages of external and internal fertilization in fishes.

Teach List on the chalkboard the advantages and disadvantages of each kind of fertilization. *(External fertilization: advantage—less energy expended by parent(s); disadvantage—lower survival rate. Internal fertilization: advantage—higher survival rate; disadvantage—more energy expended by parent(s))*

Apply Ask: **Why do you think more eggs are fertilized with external fertilization?** *(Because the survival rate is low; predators eat eggs and young receive no care.)* **learning modality: logical/mathematical**

Help Students Read

L1

Previewing Visuals Before students read, have them study Figures 5 and 6 and read the captions. Call on student volunteers to predict topics that the text will cover. *(How fishes obtain and use oxygen, details of the fish circulatory system, how fish swim)* Have students read the text, and then together discuss how accurately students predicted the text topics using only the figures.

▲ Skeleton

FIGURE 6
Fins of an Angelfish
The skeleton of a fish shows that the fins have bony support. The fins of this angelfish act like paddles as the fish moves through the water.

Movement Fins help fishes swim. Look at the fins on the angelfish in Figure 6. Each fin has a thin membrane stretched across bony supports. Like a canoe paddle, a fin provides a large surface to push against the water. The push allows for faster movement through the water. If you have ever swum wearing a pair of swim fins, you probably noticed how fast you moved through the water. Most of the movements of fishes are related to obtaining food, but some are related to reproduction.

Reproduction Most fishes have external fertilization. In external fertilization, the eggs are fertilized outside the female's body. The male hovers close to the female and spreads a cloud of sperm cells over the eggs she releases. The young develop outside the female's body.

In contrast, some fishes, such as sharks and guppies, have internal fertilization. In internal fertilization, eggs are fertilized inside the female's body. The young develop inside her body. When they are mature enough to live on their own, she gives birth to them.

Reading Checkpoint What is the structure of a fin?

FIGURE 7
Trout Eggs
Young brook trout fish are developing in these eggs on the bottom of a stream.

376 ◆

Nervous System The nervous system and sense organs of fishes help them find food and avoid predators. Most fishes can see much better in water than you can. Keen senses of touch, smell, and taste also help fishes capture food. Some fishes have taste organs in unusual places. For example, the catfish shown in Figure 8 tastes with its whiskers.

Jawless Fishes

Fishes have lived on Earth longer than any other kind of vertebrate. Fishes are organized into three main groups based on the structures of their mouths and the types of skeletons they have. **The major groups of fishes are jawless fishes, cartilaginous fishes, and bony fishes.**

Jawless fishes are unlike other fishes in that they have no jaws and no scales. Jaws are hinged bony structures that allow animals to open and close their mouths. Instead of jaws, jawless fishes have mouths containing structures for scraping, stabbing, and sucking their food. Their skeletons are made of **cartilage,** a tissue that is more flexible than bone.

Hagfishes and lampreys are the only kinds of jawless fishes that exist today. Hagfishes look like large, slimy worms. They crawl into the bodies of dead or dying fishes and use their rough tongues to scrape decaying tissues. Many lampreys are parasites of other fishes. They attach their mouths to healthy fishes and then suck in the tissues and blood of their victims. If you look at the lamprey's mouth in Figure 9, you can probably imagine the damage it can do.

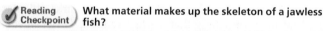
Reading Checkpoint What material makes up the skeleton of a jawless fish?

FIGURE 8
A Catfish
The whiskers of a catfish have many taste buds. To find food, the catfish drags its whiskers along muddy lake or river bottoms.

FIGURE 9
A Lamprey
Lampreys have eel-shaped bodies. They use sharp teeth and suction-cup mouths to feed on other fishes. *Classifying To which group of fishes do lampreys belong?*

▲ Mouth

Chapter 11 ◆ 377

Jawless Fishes

Teach Key Concepts L2
Examining a Jawless Mouth

Focus Review with students the location of the jaw on a fish.

Teach Direct students to locate the mouth of the jawless fish in Figure 9. Have them describe the mouth. *(Round, filled with many sharp teeth, and so on.)* Ask: **Does the lamprey's mouth look like the mouths of fishes that you are familiar with?** *(Students will probably say no.)* Inform students that the lamprey feeds by attaching to a living fish, gnawing a hole in the fish's side, and eating the fluids that leak out. Ask: **What do the teethlike structures do?** *(Help the lamprey stay attached to its host)*

Apply Ask: **What is the feeding classification if an animal gains its nutrients by attaching itself to and feeding on the tissues of another organism?** *(A parasite)* **learning modality: visual**

Help Students Read L1
Comparing and Contrasting As students read the section, have them compare and contrast photos and captions for Figures 9 and 11. Ask students to describe the differences in how lampreys and sharks feed.

Monitor Progress L2

Writing Ask students to write a few paragraphs that describe an hour in a fish's life. Paragraphs should include how a fish hunts for food and eludes predators. Encourage students to focus on how the fish uses its highly developed sense organs. Students can save their paragraphs in their portfolios.

Portfolio

Answers
Figure 9 The jawless fishes

Reading Checkpoint A fin has a thin membrane stretched over bony supports.

Reading Checkpoint Cartilage

Cartilaginous Fishes

Teach Key Concepts `L2`
Describing Cartilaginous Fishes

Focus Review the meaning of *cartilage*.

Teach Ask: **Name the cartilaginous fishes.**
(Sharks, skates, and rays) **Which of their
body parts are made of cartilage?** *(Jaws,
scales, and skeletons)*

Apply Ask: **Do most cartilaginous fishes
obtain the same types of food?** *(Yes, they are
carnivores.)* **Do they all have the same
patterns of moving and feeding?** *(No; sharks
swim constantly and eat almost anything;
skates and rays are less active and hunt small
animals on the ocean floor.)* **learning
modality: verbal**

 **Build Inquiry** `L2`

Comparing Bone and Cartilage

Materials partial skeleton from a whole,
cooked chicken breast

Time 15 minutes

Focus Have students directly compare the
properties of bone and cartilage.

Teach Allow students to work in small
groups. Before removing the skeleton from
the breast, cut the cartilage away from the
meat to be sure it remains with the skeleton.
Give a skeleton to each group and direct
students to distinguish between the bones
and the cartilage. Tell them that the cartilage
in the chicken breast is bluish-white and the
bone is brown. Urge students to attempt to
bend and twist both cartilage and bone.
Circulate among groups to be sure students
can distinguish between bone and cartilage.
Have students wash their hands afterwards.
Ask: **Which is more flexible, bone or
cartilage?** *(Cartilage)* **Which is more likely
to break than to bend?** *(Bone)*

Extend Ask: **Why is it beneficial to have a
skeleton made out of both bone and
cartilage?** *(Bone is stronger and provides
support; cartilage gives flexibility.)* **learning
modality: kinesthetic**

FIGURE 10
Blue-Spotted Ray
This ray is a cartilaginous fish
that lives on the ocean floor.

Cartilaginous Fishes

Sharks, rays, and skates are cartilaginous (kahr tuh LAJ uh
nuhs) fishes. **The cartilaginous fishes have jaws and scales,
and skeletons made of cartilage.** The pointed, toothlike scales
that cover their bodies give their skin a texture that is rougher
than sandpaper.

Obtaining Oxygen Most sharks cannot pump water over their
gills. Instead, they rely on swimming or currents to keep water
moving across their gills. For example, when sharks sleep, they
position themselves in currents that send water over their gills.

Rays and skates are not as active as sharks. They spend a lot of
time partially buried in the sand of the ocean floor. During this
time, they take in water through small holes located behind their
eyes. Water leaves through gill openings on their undersides.

Obtaining Food Cartilaginous fishes are usually carnivores.
Rays and skates hunt on the ocean floor, crushing mollusks,
crustaceans, and small fishes with their teeth. Sharks will attack
and eat nearly anything that smells like food. They can smell
and taste even a tiny amount of blood—as little as one drop in
115 liters of water! Although sharks have a keen sense of smell
their eyesight is poor. Because they see poorly, sometimes they
swallow strange objects. Indeed, one shark was found to have a
raincoat and an automobile license plate in its stomach.

The mouth of a shark contains jagged teeth arranged in
rows. Most sharks use only the first couple of rows for feeding.
The remaining rows are replacements. If a shark loses a front-
row tooth, a tooth behind it moves up to replace it.

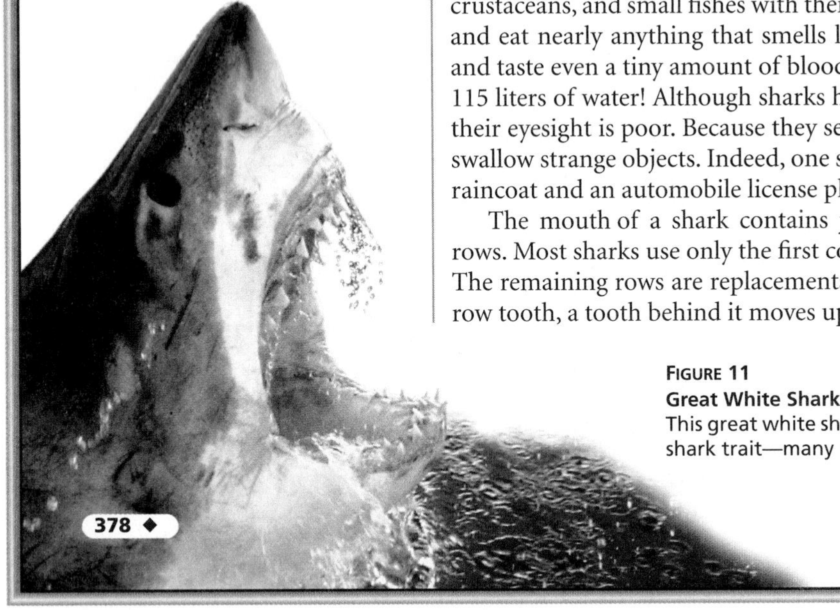

FIGURE 11
Great White Shark
This great white shark has a familiar
shark trait—many sharp teeth.

378 ◆

Differentiated Instruction

English Learners/Intermediate `L2`
Vocabulary: Word Analysis Write the
word *cartilaginous* on the board. Explain
that the word is an adjective formed from
the noun *cartilage*, and that English has
many words formed in this way. Find other
examples in the text of an adjective and
noun sharing the same root. *(symmetry—
symmetrical; parasite—parasitic; nerve—
nervous)* **learning modality: verbal**

English Learners/Beginning `L1`
Vocabulary: Use Visuals Use Figure 12
to help beginning students understand
section concepts. Point to each structure in
the diagram and say its name. Then have
beginning students work with those who
are more fluent in English to understand
the function of each structure. **learning
modality: visual**

FIGURE 12
Structure of a Bony Fish

This yellow perch has the characteristics of a bony fish. **Interpreting Diagrams** *What are the functions of fins?*

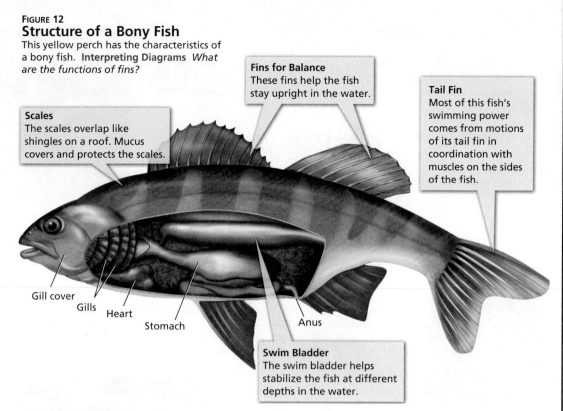

Scales
The scales overlap like shingles on a roof. Mucus covers and protects the scales.

Fins for Balance
These fins help the fish stay upright in the water.

Tail Fin
Most of this fish's swimming power comes from motions of its tail fin in coordination with muscles on the sides of the fish.

Gill cover

Gills

Heart

Stomach

Anus

Swim Bladder
The swim bladder helps stabilize the fish at different depths in the water.

Bony Fishes

Most familiar kinds of fishes, such as trout, tuna, and goldfishes, are bony fishes. **A bony fish has jaws, scales, a pocket on each side of the head that holds the gills, and a skeleton made of hard bones.** Each gill pocket is covered by a flap that opens to release water.

The major structures of a bony fish are shown in Figure 12. Notice that a bony fish has an organ called a **swim bladder,** which is an internal, gas-filled sac that helps the fish stay stable at different depths in the water. Gas levels in the swim bladder are adjusted after the fish reaches its desired depth. By adjusting these levels, the fish can stay at a depth without using a lot of energy.

Bony fishes make up about 95 percent of all fish species. They live in both salt water and fresh water. Some live in the dark depths of the ocean. Others thrive in light-filled waters, such as those around coral reefs. Figure 13 on the next page shows some of the great variety of bony fishes.

 Reading Checkpoint Which organ helps a bony fish maintain its position in the water?

Lab zone **Skills Activity**

Observing

Put on your goggles and disposable gloves. Place a preserved fish on newspaper on your desk and examine it closely. Note its size and shape, and the number and locations of its fins. Lift the gill cover and observe the gills with a hand lens. Use your observations to make a diagram of the fish. Wash your hands when you are finished.

Lab zone **Skills Activity**

Skills Focus Observing

Materials preserved fish, goggles, dissecting tray, blunt probe, hand lens, rubber gloves

Time 50 minutes

Tips CAUTION: *Provide gloves to all students. Students should wash their hands after handling the fish.* Help students see the connection between the mouth and gill slits by letting them pass the end of the probe into the fish's mouth and out through the gill openings.

Extend Have students closely examine the feathery structure of the gills. Ask: **How is the structure of the gills related to their function?** (*The feathery structure provides more surface area for absorbing oxygen.*)

Bony Fishes

Teach Key Concepts L2

Evaluating Bony Fish Characteristics

Focus Tell students that bony fishes have skeletons made of bone.

Teach Direct students to Figure 12. Discuss as a class the function of each structure shown. Ask students to think of how the structures described in the figure accomplish that function. For example, ask: **How does the tail fin help the perch move through the water?** (*The tail fin provides a large surface to push against the water, propelling the fish.*)

Apply Assign students to work in pairs to continue discussing the means by which structures carry out their functions. Have students describe for the class how they think each structure works. (*Descriptions will vary but should relate directly to Figure 12 descriptions.*) **learning modality: visual**

 **All in One Teaching Resources, Unit 2**

• Transparency LS114

Monitor Progress L2

Skills Check Have students infer what would happen to a shark in still water if the shark could not move. (*The shark would die, because it could not obtain oxygen.*)

Answers

Figure 12 Fins help a fish maintain its balance and power its swimming.

 Reading Checkpoint The swim bladder

Reviewing Key Concepts

1. a. Vertebrates; live in water; move using fins; most are ectotherms; obtain oxygen through gills, and have scales **b.** Fishes have gills for obtaining oxygen. As water is moved across the gills, oxygen in the water moves into the gills' many blood cells. **c.** The goldfish would not be able to obtain oxygen from water because water enters through the mouth before passing over the gills.

2. a. Jawless, cartilaginous, and bony fishes **b.** Cartilaginous fishes. **c.** Hagfishes use their rough tongues to scrape away decaying tissues from the bodies of dead or dying fishes; sharks directly attack their living prey, using mouths with many rows of jagged teeth.

Reteach   L1

Draw a table on the board to direct a class discussion comparing and contrasting the three groups of fishes.

Performance Assessment   L2

Concept Mapping Have each student draw a concept map to show the three main types of fishes described in this section, their characteristics, and examples.

All in One Teaching Resources, Unit 2

- Section Summary: *Fishes*
- Review and Reinforce: *Fishes*
- Enrich: *Fishes*

FIGURE 13
Diversity of Bony Fishes
These photographs show just a few species of bony fishes.

Balloonfish ▶
When threatened, a balloonfish swallows large amounts of water or air to make itself into a spiny ball.

Anemone Fish ▶
A sea anemone's tentacles can be deadly to other fishes, but they don't harm the anemone fish.

▼ Sockeye Salmon
Sockeye salmon are Pacific Ocean fishes that migrate from ocean to inland lakes to reproduce.

◀ Sea Dragon The leafy sea dragon is well camouflaged in weedy bays and lagoons.

Section 2 Assessment

Target Reading Skill **Previewing Visuals** Use the information in your graphic organizer about the structure of a fish to quiz a partner.

Reviewing Key Concepts

1. **a. Reviewing** What are the main characteristics of fishes?
   b. Explaining Why do fishes have gills?
   c. Applying Concepts What would happen to a goldfish that could not open its mouth? Explain.
2. **a. Identifying** What are three major groups of fishes?
   b. Classifying Into which group of fishes would you classify a fish with jaws and a skeleton made of cartilage?
   c. Comparing and Contrasting How do sharks and hagfishes obtain food?

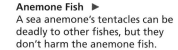

Writing in Science

Wanted Poster Design a "Wanted" poster for a lamprey. Present the lamprey as a "criminal of the ocean." Include the lamprey's physical characteristics, feeding habits, and any other details that will allow people to track down this fish.

Lab zone Chapter **Project**

Keep Students on Track Review and approve students' adaptation and fish choices. Make sure that the adaptation they have chosen is easily modeled for the fish and for an amphibian and a reptile. Help students locate reference sources and materials.

Writing in Science

Writing Mode Description
Scoring Rubric
4 Includes an exceptional number of details in a neat, creative format
3 Includes an acceptable number of details; appealing display
2 Lacks some important details; adequate display
1 Includes few details; disorganized and inadequate display

Home Sweet Home

Problem

What features does an aquarium need for fish to survive in it?

Skills Focus

observing, making models

Materials

- gravel • metric ruler • guppies • snails
- guppy food • dip net
- tap water • thermometer • water plants
- aquarium filter • aquarium heater
- rectangular aquarium tank (15 to 20 liters) with cover

Procedure

1. Wash the aquarium tank with lukewarm water—do not use soap. Then place it on a flat surface in indirect sunlight.

2. Rinse the gravel and spread it over the bottom of the tank to a depth of about 3 cm.

3. Fill the tank about two-thirds full with tap water. Position several water plants in the tank by gently pushing their roots into the gravel. Wash your hands after handling the plants.

4. Add more water until the level is about 5 cm from the top.

5. Place the filter in the water and turn it on. Insert an aquarium heater into the tank and turn it on. Set the temperature to 25°C. **CAUTION:** *Do not touch electrical equipment with wet hands.*

6. Allow the water to "age" by letting it stand for two days. Aging allows the chlorine to evaporate.

7. When the water has aged and is at the proper temperature, add guppies and snails to the tank. Include one guppy and one snail for each 4 liters of water. Cover the aquarium. Wash your hands after handling the animals.

8. Observe the aquarium every day for two weeks. Feed the guppies a small amount of food daily. Look for evidence that the fishes and snails have adapted to their new environment. Also look for the ways they carry out their life activities, such as feeding and respiration. Record your observations.

9. Use a dip net to keep the gravel layer clean and to remove any dead plants or animals.

Analyze and Conclude

1. **Observing** How does the aquarium meet the following needs of the organisms living in it: (a) oxygen supply, (b) proper temperature, and (c) food?

2. **Inferring** What happens to the oxygen that the fishes take in from the water in this aquarium? How is that oxygen replaced?

3. **Making Models** How is an aquarium like a guppy's natural environment? How is it different?

4. **Communicating** Write an e-mail to a friend or relative in which you summarize the record you made during the two weeks you observed the aquarium.

Design an Experiment

Write a one-page procedure for adding a second kind of fish to the aquarium. Include a list of questions that you would need to have answered before you could carry out your plan successfully. (Success would be marked by both types of fishes surviving together in the tank.) *Obtain your teacher's permission before carrying out your investigation.*

Expected Outcome

After a day or two, if the animals have adapted, the snails should be moving about the tank feeding. The fish should be swimming normally and feeding.

Analyze and Conclude

1. **a.** By air entering through the filter and oxygen from plants **b.** From the heater or sunlight **c.** By the plants and by the students.
2. The oxygen is used by the fish. Plants release oxygen.
3. In an aquarium, ideal conditions are maintained artificially. In nature, animals have to locate their own food and avoid predators.
4. E-mails should summarize observations and conclusions.

Extend Inquiry

Design an Experiment Questions might include: *Will the new fish prey on or be eaten by the guppies? Is there enough space?*

Home Sweet Home   L2

Prepare for Inquiry

Key Concept

Organisms need habitats that meet certain requirements in order to survive.

Skills Objectives

After this lab, students will be able to
- make a model habitat
- observe organisms in the model habitat

Prep Time 30 minutes

Class Time 10 minutes per day for two weeks

Advance Planning

- Provide sufficient clean water for all the groups. Chlorine may be removed by letting the water stand for 2–3 days or by treating it with a special chemical available at pet stores.
- Make sure other supplies are thoroughly clean. Do not use soap.

Safety

Students should be careful carrying the glass aquariums and should not move the aquarium once it is filled with water. **CAUTION:** *Students should make sure the area around the tank is dry and that their hands are dry before they plug in the electrical equipment.* Review the safety guidelines in Appendix A.

All in One Teaching Resources, Unit 2

- Lab Worksheet: *Home Sweet Home*

Guide the Inquiry

Invitation

Help students focus on the Key Concept by asking: **What is a key factor in an organism's survival?** (*An organism's habitat must meet its requirements for survival.*)

Introducing the Procedure

- Invite students to observe a functioning aquarium and to read over the procedure and materials list for this lab. Ask: **What habitat conditions will you establish for an aquarium?** (*Water temperature, food availability, plant cover*)

Objectives
After completing the lesson, students will be able to

11.3.1 Describe amphibian characteristics.
11.3.2 Examine how adult amphibians are adapted for life on land.

Target Reading Skill 🔄

Sequencing Explain that organizing information from beginning to end helps students understand a step-by-step process.

Answers
Adult frog; Fertilized eggs; Tadpole hatches; Hind legs develop; Front legs develop; Tail is absorbed.

All in One Teaching Resources, Unit 2

• Transparency LS115

Preteach

Build Background Knowledge   L2

Identifying Amphibian Characteristics
Have students describe any animals they know of that live part of their life on land and part in the water (*Frogs, salamanders*). Then ask: **What characteristics allow these animals to live on land and in water?** (*Ability to change/undergo metamorphosis; body structures that allow movement, feeding, and breathing on land or in water*).

Reading Preview

Key Concepts
• What are the main characteristics of amphibians?
• What are some adaptations of adult amphibians for living on land?

Key Terms
• amphibian • tadpole • lung
• atrium • ventricle • habitat

🔄 Target Reading Skill
Sequencing As you read, make a cycle diagram like the one below that shows the different stages of a frog's metamorphosis during its life cycle. Write each step of the process in a separate circle.

Frog Metamorphosis

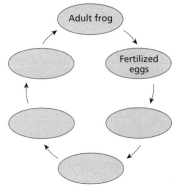

Spring peeper ▶

382 ◆

Lab zone Discover **Activity**

What's the Advantage of Being Green?

1. Count out 20 dried yellow peas and 20 green ones. Mix them up in a paper cup.
2. Cover your eyes. Have your partner gently scatter the peas onto a large sheet of green paper.
3. Uncover your eyes. Have your partner keep time while you pick up as many peas, one at a time, as you can find in 15 seconds.
4. When 15 seconds are up, count how many peas of each color you picked up.
5. Repeat Steps 2 through 4, but this time you scatter the peas and keep time while your partner picks up the peas.
6. Compare your results with those of your partner and your classmates.

Think It Over
Inferring Many frogs are green, as are their environments. What advantage does a frog have in being green?

What's that sound coming from the pond? Even 1 kilometer away you can hear the shrill calls of frogs called spring peepers on this damp spring night. By the time you reach the pond, the calls are ear-splitting. You might think that the frogs must be huge to make such a loud sound. But each frog is smaller than the first joint of your thumb! In the beam of your flashlight, you see the puffed-up throats of the males, vibrating with each call. Female peepers bound across roads and swim across streams to mate with the noisy males.

What Is an Amphibian?

A frog is one kind of amphibian; toads and salamanders are other kinds. An **amphibian** is a vertebrate that is ectothermic and spends its early life in water. Indeed, the word *amphibian* means "double life," and amphibians have exactly that. **After beginning their lives in water, most amphibians spend their adulthood on land, returning to water to reproduce.**

Lab zone Discover **Activity**

Skills Focus Inferring   L1

Materials dried yellow and green peas; paper cup; green construction paper, approximately 1 m × 1 m; clock or watch with second hand

Time 10 minutes

Tips To intensify the camouflage effect, make sure that the green background closely matches the color of the green peas.

Expected Outcome Students should pick up more yellow peas than green peas from the green background.

Think It Over Being a color that blends in with the environment makes frogs harder for predators to see and thus more likely to survive and reproduce. **learning modality: visual**

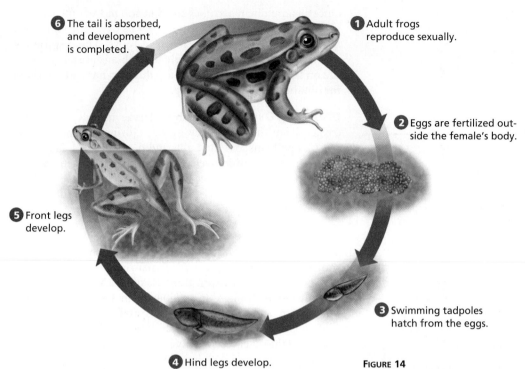

6 The tail is absorbed, and development is completed.

1 Adult frogs reproduce sexually.

2 Eggs are fertilized outside the female's body.

3 Swimming tadpoles hatch from the eggs.

4 Hind legs develop.

5 Front legs develop.

FIGURE 14
Life Cycle of a Frog
During its metamorphosis from tadpole to adult, a frog's body undergoes a series of dramatic changes. Applying Concepts *How do these changes prepare a frog for living on land?*

Groups of Amphibians The two major groups of amphibians are salamanders and frogs and toads. You can distinguish between the groups by the presence of a tail in the adults. Salamanders keep their tails in adulthood, while almost all frogs and toads do not.

Reproduction and Development Amphibians have a life cycle that suits the "double lives" they lead. Eggs are fertilized internally in most salamanders and externally in most frogs and toads. Fertilized eggs develop in water. After a few days, larvae wriggle out of a jelly that coats the eggs and begin a free-swimming, fishlike life.

The larvae of most amphibians grow and eventually undergo metamorphosis. You can trace the process of frog metamorphosis in Figure 14. The larva of a frog or a toad is called a **tadpole.**

Unlike tadpoles, the larvae of salamanders look like adults. Most salamander larvae undergo a metamorphosis in which they lose their gills. However, the changes are not as dramatic as those that happen during a frog or toad's metamorphosis.

 Reading Checkpoint What is a frog larva called?

Go Online
PHSchool.com
For: More on the frog life cycle
Visit: PHSchool.com
Web Code: ced-2033

English Learners/Beginning **L1**
Use Visuals Point to each part of the cycle in Figure 14, saying the most important terms, e.g., *adult frog, eggs*. Help students understand that the diagram shows a sequence. Then have students write, in their first language, a description of what happens in each part of the cycle. **learning modality: visual**

English Learners/Intermediate **L2**
Use Visuals Have students extend the beginning activity. After they have written the descriptions in their first language, students can write words and phrases in English that describe each stage. **learning modality: visual**

Instruct

What Is an Amphibian?

Teach Key Concepts **L2**
Exploring Amphibian Development

Focus Tell students that, during their life cycles, amphibians live both on land and in water.

Teach Direct students to Figure 14. Have students trace the stages of development, stating at least one difference between each stage (*Front legs develop, tail disappears, and so on*).

Apply Ask: **Why is water essential for amphibian life?** (*Amphibian eggs are laid and hatched in water; larvae live in water; adults must stay moist to absorb oxygen through their skin.*) **learning modality: visual**

 **Teaching Resources, Unit 2**
• Transparency LS116

Independent Practice **L2**
 **Teaching Resources, Unit 2**
• Guided Reading and Study Worksheet: *Amphibians*

Student Edition on Audio CD

Go Online
PHSchool.com
For: More on the frog life cycle
Visit: PHSchool.com
Web Code: ced-2033

Students can review the frog life cycle in an online activity.

Monitor Progress _____ **L2**

Answers
Figure 14 Developing legs and losing the tail allows frogs to move on land.

 Reading Checkpoint A tadpole

383

Living on Land

Teach Key Concepts   L2
Comparing Amphibian Adaptations

Focus Ask students to describe some differences between adult frogs and tadpoles.

Teach Write two headings on the board, *Larvae* and *Adults*. Then read characteristics of each aloud. Have students discuss which heading is appropriate for each characteristic. (*Example: Larvae—herbivores, swim, obtain oxygen through gills, have one-loop circulatory system; adults—carnivores, crawl/leap, breathe through lungs, have two-loop circulatory system*)

Apply Ask: **How does acquiring lungs change the life of amphibians?** (*They are able to leave the water, breathe air, and live on land.*) **learning modality: logical/ mathematical**

All in One **Teaching Resources, Unit 2**

• Transparency LS117

Address Misconceptions   L1
Toads Do Not Cause Warts

Focus Explain that the belief that someone who touches a toad will get warts is merely a superstition.

Teach Ask: **Can you think of any reason why this superstition came about?** (*Toads' skin is bumpy and looks "warty." People assumed that toads' "warts" were contagious.*)

Apply Explain further that although toad skin will not cause warts, it does sometimes secrete substances that can severely irritate skin. Ask: **What adaptation would these secretions offer?** (*Irritation would discourage predators.*) **learning modality: logical/ mathematical**

Go **O**nline
active art
For: Respiration and Circulation activity
Visit: PHSchool.com
Web Code: cep-2032

Students compare and contrast the circulatory systems found in fishes, typical adult amphibians, and birds.

Go **O**nline
active art

For: Respiration and Circulation activity
Visit: PHSchool.com
Web Code: cep-2032

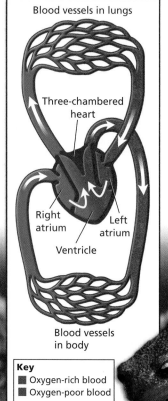
Blood vessels in lungs

Three-chambered heart

Right atrium

Left atrium

Ventricle

Blood vessels in body

Key
- Oxygen-rich blood
- Oxygen-poor blood

384 ◆

Living on Land

Once an amphibian becomes an adult and moves onto land, its survival needs change. It must now get its oxygen from the air, not the water. Fins no longer help it move. **The respiratory and circulatory systems of adult amphibians are adapted for life on land. In addition, adult amphibians have adaptations for obtaining food and moving.**

Obtaining Oxygen Amphibian larvae use gills to obtain oxygen from the water they live in. During metamorphosis, most amphibians lose their gills and develop lungs. **Lungs** are organs of air-breathing vertebrates in which oxygen gas and carbon dioxide gas are exchanged between the air and the blood. Oxygen and carbon dioxide are also exchanged through the thin, moist skins of adult amphibians.

Circulatory System A tadpole's circulatory system has a single loop and a heart with two chambers, like that of a fish. In contrast, the circulatory system of many adult amphibians has two loops and a heart with three chambers. You can trace the path of blood through an amphibian in Figure 15. The two upper chambers of the heart, called **atria** (singular *atrium*), receive blood. One atrium receives oxygen-rich blood from the lungs, and the other receives oxygen-poor blood from the rest of the body. From the atria, blood moves into the lower chamber, the **ventricle,** which pumps blood out to the lungs and body. Oxygen-rich and oxygen-poor blood mix in the ventricle.

FIGURE 15
Respiration and Circulation
This adult salamander has lungs and a double-loop circulatory system. **Interpreting Diagrams**
What kind of blood is in the ventricle?

FIGURE 16
Adaptations for Movement
Some frogs have sticky pads on their toes for climbing. Others have webbed feet for swimming.

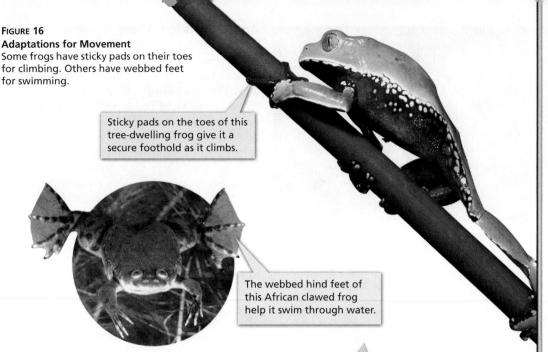

Sticky pads on the toes of this tree-dwelling frog give it a secure foothold as it climbs.

The webbed hind feet of this African clawed frog help it swim through water.

Obtaining Food Although most tadpoles are herbivores, most adult salamanders, frogs, and toads are carnivores that feed on small animals. Frogs and toads usually wait for their prey to come close. But salamanders, unlike frogs and toads, actively stalk and ambush their prey.

Frogs and toads have camouflage that helps them obtain food. Most frogs and toads are brownish-green, making them hard to see in their environment. In the Discover Activity, you learned that it is hard to see something green against a green background.

Movement A vertebrate that lives on land needs a strong skeleton to support its body against the pull of gravity. In addition, a land animal needs some way of moving. Fins work in water, but they don't work on land. Most adult amphibians have strong skeletons and muscular limbs adapted for moving on land.

Salamanders usually crawl in their environments, but frogs and toads have adaptations for other kinds of movements. Perhaps you've tried to catch a frog or a toad only to have it leap away from you. The legs of frogs and toads have adaptations for leaping. Leaping requires powerful hind-leg muscles and a skeleton that can absorb the shock of landing. The feet of frogs and toads have adaptations, too, as you can see in Figure 16.

Lab zone Try This **Activity**

Webbing Along
1. Fill a sink or pail with water.
2. Spread your fingers and put your hand into the water just far enough so that only your fingers are under water. Drag your fingers back and forth through the water.
3. Now dry your hand and cover it with a small plastic bag. Secure the bag around your wrist with a rubber band.
4. Repeat Step 2. Note any difference in the way in which your fingers push the water.

Making Models Use your model to explain how a frog's webbed feet help it move through water.

◆ 385

Lab zone Try This **Activity**

Skills Focus Making models **L1**
Materials plastic bags, heavy rubber bands, pail of water or sink
Time 15 minutes
Tips Make sure that students insert only their fingers into the water. No part of their palm should be under water as it will provide too much resistance. Encourage students to experiment with moving their bagged hands through the water with their fingers spread as wide as possible and with their hands balled into a fist.

Extend Ask: **How do some kinds of birds benefit from webbed feet?** (*Because these birds spend some part of their lives in water*) **learning modality: kinesthetic**

 Build **Inquiry** **L2**

Modeling Amphibian Circulation

Materials 25 red balloons
Time 15 minutes

Focus Have students trace the path of blood in Figure 15.

Teach Position students at five stations, representing parts of the circulatory system—lungs, body, right atrium, left atrium, ventricle. Place 25 balloons, representing oxygen, at the lungs station. Slowly clap your hands to indicate heartbeats. At each heartbeat, students change stations in the direction of blood flow. For example, students at the body station will move to the right atrium. Students at the ventricle move to the lungs or back to the body. As students pass the lungs station, they pick up a balloon. At the body station they drop a balloon. A student holding a balloon represents oxygen-rich blood. A student without a balloon represents oxygen-poor blood. Continue for about 4 minutes.

Apply Ask: **Where in an adult amphibian's circulatory system is oxygen acquired?** (*In the lungs and skin*)**Where does the mixing of oxygen-rich and oxygen-poor blood occur?** (*In the ventricle*) **learning modality: kinesthetic**

Monitor Progress _____ **L2**

Writing Have students write a brief paragraph comparing and contrasting the characteristics of fishes and adult amphibians. (*Compare: Both lay eggs in water and have internal skeletons, a backbone, and a closed circulatory system. Contrast: Fishes have gills, most adult amphibians have lungs; amphibians have a two-loop circulatory system and fish have one loop.*) Students can save their paragraphs in their portfolios.

Portfolio

Answer
Figure 15 A mixture of oxygen-rich blood and oxygen-poor blood

385

Monitor Progress L2

Answers

Figure 17 Destruction of habitat and chemicals in the environment

 Reading Checkpoint The specific environment in which the animal lives

Assess

Reviewing Key Concepts

1. a. An amphibian is an ectothermic vertebrate that spends its early life in water . **b.** Vertebrate, ectotherm, has double life (in water and on land). **c.** Salamander larvae resemble salamander adults. Larvae lose their gills during metamorphosis, but they do not undergo the dramatic physical changes seen in frog and toad metamorphosis.

2. a. Lungs, two-loop circulatory system and three-chambered heart, camouflage for stalking prey on land, strong skeletons and muscular limbs for movement on land **b.** Crawling, leaping, climbing; each adaptation helps amphibian get around on land **c.** Sample answer: Blood leaves the ventricle and travels to the lungs, where it picks up oxygen. Then blood returns to the ventricle via the left atrium. Then it goes to the body and drops off oxygen to the body's cells. Finally, it returns to the ventricle via the right atrium and begins the cycle again.

Reteach L1

Call on students to give one characteristic of amphibians and tell how the characteristic helps the species survive in its environment.

Performance Assessment L2

Organizing Information Have students create a cycle diagram of the life cycle of a frog.

All in One Teaching Resources, Unit 2

- Section Summary: *Amphibians*
- Review and Reinforce: *Amphibians*
- Enrich: *Amphibians*

FIGURE 17
Golden Frog
Golden frogs, like the one shown here, are rarely seen anymore in their native habitat—the rain forests of Panama. **Relating Cause and Effect** *What are two possible causes for the decrease in the number of golden frogs?*

Amphibians in Danger Worldwide, amphibian populations are decreasing. One reason for the decrease is the destruction of amphibian habitats. An animal's **habitat** is the specific environment in which it lives. When a swamp is filled in or a forest is cut, an area that was moist becomes drier. Few amphibians can survive for long in dry, sunny areas. But habitat destruction does not account for the whole problem of population decrease. Amphibians are declining even in areas where their habitats have not been damaged. Because their skins are delicate and their eggs lack shells, amphibians are especially sensitive to changes in their environment. Poisons in the environment, such as pesticides and other chemicals, can pollute the waters that amphibians need to live and reproduce. Even small amounts of these chemicals can weaken adult amphibians, kill amphibian eggs, or cause tadpoles to become deformed.

Reading Checkpoint What is a habitat?

Section 3 Assessment

Target Reading Skill Sequencing Review your cycle diagram about frog metamorphosis with a partner. Add any necessary information.

Reviewing Key Concepts

1. a. Defining What is an amphibian?
  b. Summarizing What are three main characteristics of amphibians?
  c. Comparing and Contrasting How is the metamorphosis of a salamander different from the metamorphosis of a frog?

2. a. Reviewing What are four adaptations of adult amphibians for living on land?
  b. Describing What are three adaptations frogs and toads have for moving? How does each adaptation help the amphibian survive in its environment?
  c. Sequencing How does blood move in the circulatory system of an amphibian? (*Hint:* Start with blood leaving the ventricle of the heart.)

Writing in Science

Web Site Design the home page of a Web site that introduces people to amphibians. First, come up with a catchy title for your Web site. Then, design your home page, the first page people will see. Consider these questions as you come up with your design: What information will you include? What will the illustrations or photos show? What links to specific topics relating to amphibians will you have?

Lab zone Chapter Project

Keep Students on Track Review students' amphibian choices for appropriateness. Before students begin work on their amphibian models, review their fish models. Discuss with students ways in which amphibians differ from fish and how these differences will be reflected in their amphibian model.

Writing in Science

Design a Web Site Before students create their Web sites, choose good examples of professional Web sites for them to view. Have them discuss what makes the Web sites interesting to look at and easy to use.

Reading Preview

Key Concepts
- What are some adaptations that allow reptiles to live on land?
- What are the characteristics of each of the three main groups of reptiles?
- What adaptation helped dinosaurs survive before they became extinct?

Key Terms
- reptile
- kidney
- urine
- amniotic egg

Target Reading Skill
Identifying Main Ideas As you read the information under the heading titled Adaptations for Life on Land, write the main idea in a graphic organizer like the one below. Then write three supporting details that give examples of the main idea.

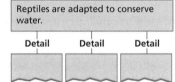

Main Idea

| Reptiles are adapted to conserve water. |

Detail	Detail	Detail

Lab zone Discover **Activity**

How Do Snakes Feed?

1. To model how a snake feeds, stretch a sock cuff over a grapefruit "prey" by first pulling on one side and then on the other. Work the grapefruit down into the "stomach." A snake's jawbones can spread apart like the sock cuff.

2. Remove the grapefruit and put a rubber band around the sock about 8 centimeters below the opening. The rubber band represents the firmly joined jawbones of a lizard. Now try to repeat Step 1.

Think It Over
Inferring What is the advantage of having jawbones like a snake's?

The king cobra of Southeast Asia is the world's longest venomous snake. It can grow to more than 4 meters long. When it encounters a predator, a king cobra flattens its neck and rears up. Its ropelike body sways back and forth, and its tongue flicks in and out.

A king cobra's fearsome behavior in response to a predator contrasts with the gentle way it treats its eggs. King cobras are one of the few snakes that build nests. The female builds a nest of grass and leaves on the forest floor. She lays her eggs inside the nest and guards them until they hatch.

King cobra ▶

◆ 387

Lab zone Discover **Activity**

Skills Focus Inferring

Materials sock with ribbed cuff, grapefruit, strong rubber band

Time 10 minutes

Tips Students can compare estimated diameters of the unstretched sock and the grapefruit. During Step 2, use a rubber band that is too small to fit around the

L1 grapefruit. Reinforce the lesson by showing students a picture of a snake skull, pointing out the lack of large regions of solid bone.

Think It Over Students should infer that the spreading jawbones of the snake allow it to eat larger prey than would be possible with firmly joined jawbones.

Objectives
After completing the lesson, students will be able to

11.4.1 Identify adaptations that allow reptiles to live on land.

11.4.2 Contrast the characteristics of each of the three main groups of reptiles.

11.4.3 Describe one adaptation that helped dinosaurs survive before they became extinct.

Target Reading Skill

Identifying Main Ideas Explain that identifying main ideas and details helps students sort the facts from the information into groups. Each group can have a main topic, subtopics, and details.

Answers
Possible answers:
Main idea—Reptiles are adapted to conserve water.
Details—Reptiles have a thick, scaly skin that prevents water loss; reptile eggs have a shell and membranes that keep them from drying out; reptile's kidneys concentrate wastes before excreting them so that little water is lost.

All in One Teaching Resources, Unit 2
- Transparency LS118

Preteach

Build Background Knowledge **L2**

Considering Snake Characteristics
Ask: **What are some characteristics of snakes?** (*Students may say no legs, poisonous, or fangs*) List students' answers on the board. After students have become familiar with the information in the section, revisit this list. Help students to decide which of the characteristics are facts, which are true of some snakes, and which are myths.

Adaptations for Life on Land

Teach Key Concepts L2

Investigating Reptilian Adaptations

Focus Tell students that land animals are adapted to environmental conditions that differ from those of aquatic animals.

Teach Call on student volunteers to discuss how reptilian adaptations differ from those of amphibians. Ask: **How do the two groups differ in egg laying?** (*Reptiles lay eggs on land that are protected from drying out; amphibians lay eggs in water.*) **How and why are their skins different?** (*Amphibian skins are moist, because amphibians obtain oxygen through the skin; reptilian skins are dry and scaly—reptiles breathe solely with lungs—and are able to prevent water loss.*)

Apply Ask: **Do sea turtles have amphibian or reptilian adaptations?** (*Reptilian: sea turtles breathe with lungs and lay eggs out of water.*) **learning modality: verbal**

 **Teaching Resources, Unit 2**
• Transparency LS119

Independent Practice L2

 **Teaching Resources, Unit 2**
• Guided Reading and Study Worksheet: *Reptiles*

For: More on reptiles
Visit: PHSchool.com
Web Code: ced-2034

Students can review reptiles in an online activity.

FIGURE 18
A Desert Tortoise
The tough, scaly skin of this desert tortoise helps it survive in a dry environment.

Adaptations for Life on Land

Like other reptiles, king cobras lay their eggs on land rather than in water. A **reptile** is an ectothermic vertebrate that has lungs and scaly skin. In addition to snakes such as the king cobra, lizards, turtles, and alligators are also reptiles. Unlike amphibians, reptiles can spend their entire lives on dry land.

The ancestors of modern reptiles were the first vertebrates adapted to life completely out of water. Reptiles get their oxygen from air and breathe entirely with lungs. Reptiles that live in water, such as sea turtles, evolved from reptiles that lived on land. So, even though they live in water, they still breathe with lungs and come ashore to lay eggs.

You can think of a land animal as a pocket of water held within a bag of skin. To thrive on land, an animal must have adaptations that keep the water within the "bag" from evaporating in the dry air. **The skin, kidneys, and eggs of reptiles are adapted to conserve water.**

Skin and Kidneys Unlike amphibians, which have thin, moist skin, reptiles have dry, tough skins covered with scales. This scaly skin protects reptiles and helps keep water in their bodies. Another adaptation that helps keep water inside a reptile's body is its **kidneys,** which are organs that filter wastes from the blood. The wastes are then excreted in a watery fluid called **urine.** The kidneys of reptiles concentrate the urine so that the reptiles lose very little water.

Reading Checkpoint What are two functions of a reptile's skin?

For: More on reptiles
Visit: PHSchool.com
Web Code: ced-2034

An Egg With a Shell Reptiles have internal fertilization and lay their eggs on land. While still inside a female's body, fertilized eggs are covered with membranes and a leathery shell. Unlike an amphibian's egg, a reptile's egg has a shell and membranes that protect the developing embryo and help keep it from drying out. An egg with a shell and internal membranes that keep the embryo moist is called an **amniotic egg.** Pores in the shell let oxygen gas in and carbon dioxide gas out.

Look at Figure 19 to see the membranes of a reptile's egg. One membrane holds a liquid that surrounds the embryo. The liquid protects the embryo and keeps it moist. A second membrane holds the yolk, or food for the embryo. A third membrane holds the embryo's wastes. Oxygen and carbon dioxide are exchanged across the fourth membrane.

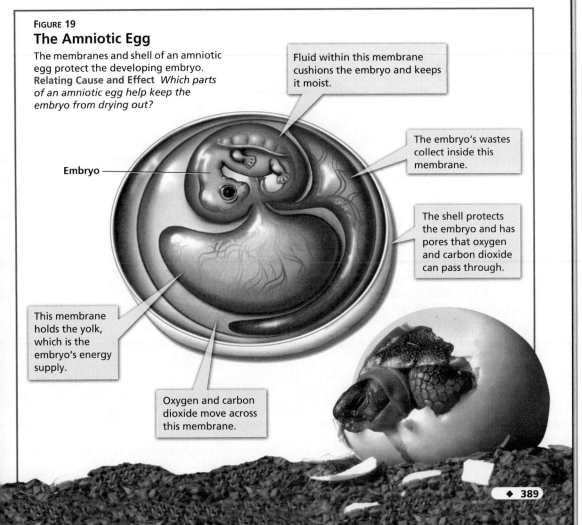

FIGURE 19
The Amniotic Egg
The membranes and shell of an amniotic egg protect the developing embryo.
Relating Cause and Effect *Which parts of an amniotic egg help keep the embryo from drying out?*

Fluid within this membrane cushions the embryo and keeps it moist.

The embryo's wastes collect inside this membrane.

The shell protects the embryo and has pores that oxygen and carbon dioxide can pass through.

Embryo

This membrane holds the yolk, which is the embryo's energy supply.

Oxygen and carbon dioxide move across this membrane.

◆ 389

 **Build Inquiry** L1

Making Inferences About Eggshells

Materials small, cut pieces of a sponge; plastic bag; water

Time 10 minutes over two class periods

Focus Challenge students to make inferences about how eggshells and membranes prevent fluid loss.

Teach Have students work in small groups; provide each group with two pieces of sponge and one resealable plastic bag that will model an egg's shell and membranes. Have students wet both sponge pieces thoroughly. Then put one piece in the plastic bag. They should place the other piece of sponge on top of the sealed bag and leave it overnight. The next day, ask students to describe the condition of their sponges. (*The sponge outside the bag is much drier and more rigid.*)

Apply Lead students to infer that the condition of the sponges left outside the bag is similar to what would happen to a developing embryo if the egg did not have a shell and membranes that retain moisture.
learning modality: visual

 Student Edition on Audio CD

Address Misconceptions
Investigating Snake Skin

Focus Snake skins are dry, not slimy.

Teach Some students may think snake skins are slimy. A snake's skin is actually quite dry, especially compared to that of a fish or amphibian. Under supervision, you may allow students to touch the scales of a molted snake skin. They should wash their hands afterward.

Monitor Progress L2

Skills Check Using Figure 19, point out the membranes of a tortoise egg and call on students to tell the function of each.

Answers
Figure 19 Shell; fluid within the membrane surrounding the embryo

 The scaly skin protects the reptile and prevents water loss.

Lizards and Snakes

Teach Key Concepts L2

Characteristics of Lizards and Snakes

Focus Direct students to Figure 20.

Teach Ask: **What are the chameleon's adaptations that make it a successful predator?** (*Sticky tongue that moves rapidly, claws that allow movement up trees, tail that grips, eyes that swivel, skin that changes color to match background*) **How is the chameleon's skin like that of all reptiles? Why is it like this?** (*Dry and scaly, to prevent water loss*) **Name two ways lizards differ from snakes.** (*Lizards have four legs, moveable eyelids, and two lungs; snakes have no legs or eyelids and only one lung.*)

Apply Ask: **What is the term for animals with a diet similar to most reptiles?** (*Carnivores*) **Besides assisting in obtaining food, what other benefit does the ability to blend into its surroundings offer a chameleon?** (*Makes it easier for chameleons to hide from their own predators*) **learning modality: visual**

Address Misconceptions L1

Investigating Venomous Snakes

Focus Tell students that venomous snakes are not necessarily aggressive.

Teach Students may mistakenly believe that venomous snakes are vicious and aggressive. Point out that although people rightly fear being bitten by venomous snakes, the most venomous snakes are not aggressive toward humans. Normally, they will bite a person only when cornered or startled. Snake venom is primarily an adaptation for capturing prey, not for defense.

Apply Ask: **If you do not know whether a snake you see is venomous, what should you do when you come upon it?** (*Possible answer: Move away in a nonthreatening manner.*) **learning modality: verbal**

390

Lizards and Snakes

Most reptiles alive today are either lizards or snakes. These two groups of reptiles share some important characteristics. **Both lizards and snakes are reptiles that have skin covered with overlapping scales.** As they grow, they shed their skin and scales, replacing the worn ones with new ones. Most lizards and snakes live in warm areas.

Lizards differ from snakes in an obvious way. Lizards have four legs, usually with claws on the toes, and snakes have no legs. In addition, lizards have long tails, external ears, movable eyelids, and two lungs. In contrast, snakes have streamlined bodies, no external ears, and no eyelids, and most have only one lung. You can see the characteristics of a lizard in Figure 20.

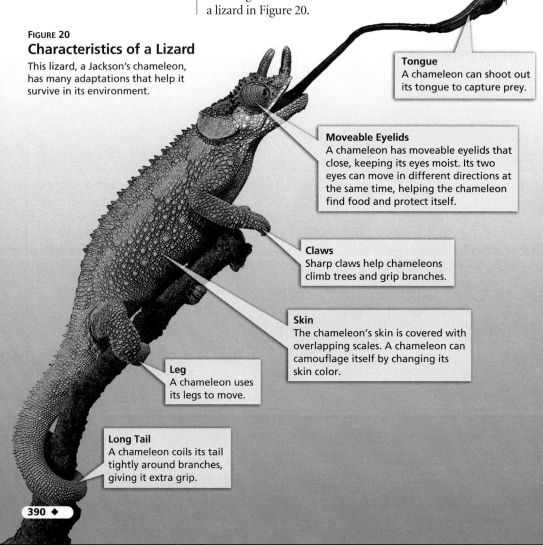

FIGURE 20
Characteristics of a Lizard
This lizard, a Jackson's chameleon, has many adaptations that help it survive in its environment.

Tongue
A chameleon can shoot out its tongue to capture prey.

Moveable Eyelids
A chameleon has moveable eyelids that close, keeping its eyes moist. Its two eyes can move in different directions at the same time, helping the chameleon find food and protect itself.

Claws
Sharp claws help chameleons climb trees and grip branches.

Skin
The chameleon's skin is covered with overlapping scales. A chameleon can camouflage itself by changing its skin color.

Leg
A chameleon uses its legs to move.

Long Tail
A chameleon coils its tail tightly around branches, giving it extra grip.

390 ◆

Obtaining Food A few lizards are herbivores that eat leaves. Most lizards, however, are carnivores that capture their prey by jumping at it. While some large lizards will eat frogs and birds, most smaller lizards are adapted to hunt insects. For example, chameleons have sticky tongues adapted for snaring insects.

All snakes are carnivores. Most snakes feed on small animals, such as mice, but some eat large prey. If you did the Discover Activity, you learned that a snake's jawbones can spread wide apart. In addition, the bones of a snake's skull can move to let the snake swallow an animal larger in diameter than itself. Snakes capture their prey in different ways. For example, some snakes have long, curved front teeth for hooking slippery prey. Other snakes, such as rattlesnakes and copperheads, have venom glands attached to hollow teeth called fangs. When these snakes bite their prey, venom flows down through the fangs and enters the prey.

Movement While lizards walk and run using their legs, snakes cannot move in this way. If you've ever seen a snake slither across the ground, you know that when it moves, its long, thin body bends into curves. Snakes move by contracting, or shortening, bands of muscles that are connected to their ribs and their backbones. Alternate contractions of muscles on the right and left sides produce a slithering side-to-side motion. Instead of slithering, sidewinder snakes, like the one shown in Figure 22, lift up their bodies as they move.

 Reading Checkpoint How do lizards move?

FIGURE 21
An Egg-Eating Snake
The jawbones of this snake's skull have moved to let the snake swallow an egg. **Making Generalizations** *How are snakes different from lizards?*

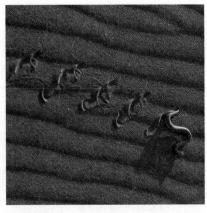

FIGURE 22
A Sidewinder Snake
This sidewinder snake lifts loops of its body off the desert sand as it moves along. Only a small part of its body touches the sand at one time.

Chapter 11 ◆ 391

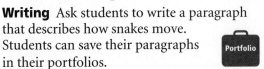

391

Alligators and Crocodiles

Teach Key Concepts

Investigating Large Reptilian Predators

Focus Tell students that alligators and crocodiles are known for their size, predator skills, and care of their young.

Teach Pace off 5 meters in your classroom to demonstrate to students the size of the largest alligators and crocodiles. Ask: **What traits make these animals successful predators?** (*Hunting at night when they are concealed, strong tail for rapid swimming, muscular jaws, many sharp teeth*)

Apply Ask: **Can you think of other vertebrate predators that share some of the alligator's and crocodile's traits?** (*Sharks are strong, fast, and large, have pointed teeth, and eat large prey; frogs and lizards sneak up on prey.*) **learning modality: verbal**

Turtles

Teach Key Concepts

Exploring Adaptations of Turtles

Focus Remind students that a turtle is a reptile.

Teach Ask: **Where do turtles live?** (*On land [tortoises] and in salt and fresh water*) **Do sea turtles have gills?** (*No, all turtles breathe with lungs.*) **What is a turtle shell made from?** (*The ribs and backbone*) **Without teeth, how do turtles feed?** (*Their sharp beaks tear food.*)

Apply Ask: **Do you think land turtles move quickly?** (*No*) **Then how do they escape predators?** (*By drawing into their protective shells*) **learning modality: verbal**

FIGURE 23
Alligator and Crocodile
Alligators and crocodiles are the largest reptiles still living on earth. They are similar in many ways, including appearance.
Comparing and Contrasting *How can you tell the difference between an alligator and a crocodile?*

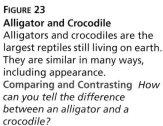

Fishes, Amphibians, and Reptiles

Video Preview
▶ Video Field Trip
Video Assessment

Alligators and Crocodiles

If you walk along a lake in Florida, you just might see an alligator swimming silently in the water. Most of its body lies beneath the surface, but you can see its large, bulging eyes above the surface. Alligators, crocodiles, and their relatives are the largest living reptiles. **Both alligators and crocodiles are large, carnivorous reptiles that care for their young.** So, how do you tell an alligator from a crocodile? Alligators have broad, rounded snouts, with only a few teeth visible when their mouths are shut. In contrast, crocodiles have pointed snouts, with most of their teeth visible when their mouths are shut.

Obtaining Food Alligators and crocodiles are carnivores that often hunt at night. They have several adaptations for capturing prey. They use their strong, muscular tails to swim rapidly. Their jaws are equipped with many large, sharp, and pointed teeth. Their jaw muscles are extremely strong when biting down. Although alligators will eat dogs, raccoons, and deer, they usually do not attack humans.

Reproduction Unlike most other reptiles, crocodiles and alligators care for their eggs and newly hatched young. After laying eggs, the female stays near the nest. From time to time, she comes out of the water and crawls over the nest to keep it moist. After the tiny alligators or crocodiles hatch, the female scoops them up in her huge mouth. She carries them from the nest to a nursery area in the water where they will be safer. For as long as a year, she will stay near her young until they can feed and protect themselves.

 When do alligators and crocodiles hunt?

Video Field Trip

Fishes, Amphibians, and Reptiles

Show the Video Field Trip to help students understand reptile adaptations. Discussion question: **Describe two adaptations that allow crocodiles to remain underwater for long periods of time.** (*Their heart rates slow down; some of the valves that control blood flow close. This diverts blood away from the lungs, where it isn't needed and sends it to the brain and other organs where the blood is essential.*)

The Sex Ratio of Newly Hatched Alligators

The temperature of the developing eggs of the American alligator affects the sex ratio of the young. (Sex ratio is the number of females compared with the number of males.) The graph on the right shows the numbers of young of each sex that hatched from eggs in which the young developed at different temperatures.

Sex Ratio of Newly Hatched Alligators

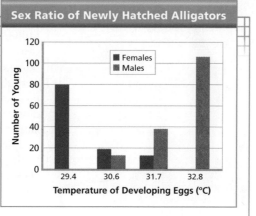

1. **Reading Graphs** At which temperature(s) did only females hatch?
2. **Drawing Conclusions** What effect does the temperature of developing eggs have on the sex of the baby alligators?
3. **Calculating** If 100 eggs developed at 31.7°C, about how many of the young would be male?

Turtles

Turtles live in the ocean, in fresh water, and on land. Turtles that live on land are commonly called "tortoises." **A turtle is a reptile whose body is covered by a protective shell that includes the ribs and the backbone.** The bony plates of the shell are covered by large scales made from the same material as the skin's scales. Some turtles have shells that can cover the whole body. Most turtles can draw the head, legs, and tail inside the shell for protection. Turtle shells may be hard or as soft as pancakes.

Turtles feed in a variety of ways, but all have a sharp-edged beak instead of teeth for tearing food. Some turtles are carnivores, such as the largest turtles, the leatherbacks. Leatherbacks feed mainly on jellyfishes. Their tough skin protects them from the effects of the stinging cells. Other turtles, such as the Galápagos tortoise, are herbivores. They feed mainly on cacti, using their beaks to scrape off the prickly spines before swallowing the cactus.

 Reading Checkpoint What are turtles that live on land called?

FIGURE 24
A Galápagos Tortoise
The Galápagos tortoise lives on land, where it eats mainly cacti.

Math Skill Making and interpreting graphs

Focus Compare bar graphs to determine the effect of incubation temperature on the sex of baby alligators.

Teach Make sure students understand that the answer to Question 2 is based on the ratio of males to females in the groups of eggs, not the absolute number.

Answers
1. 29.4°C
2. The warmer the incubation temperature, the greater the proportion of males.
3. According to the graph, out of the 50 alligators that were incubated at 31.7°C, 38 (or 76%) were males. So, I would expect about 76% of 100 eggs (76) to be males.

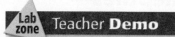
Turtle Breathing

Materials live turtle, such as a box turtle
Time 5 minutes

Focus Challenge students to consider adaptations turtles have for breathing within the confines of a shell.

Teach Ask: **How does your chest move when you breathe?** (*In and out*) **If the turtle's chest moves like yours does, does its shell get in the way?** (*Yes*) Allow students to carefully observe the turtle as it breathes. Students should notice that the exposed soft tissue around the turtle's forelimbs and hind limbs moves.

Apply Ask: **What replaces the in-and-out motion of chests of vertebrates without shells?** (*The front-and-back motion of tissue around limbs*) **learning modality: visual**

Monitor Progress ————— L2

Writing Have students compare the beaks of leatherback sea turtles with the teeth of alligators and crocodiles. Have them tell how each adaptation contributes to the animals' ability to successfully acquire food. Students can save their paragraphs in their portfolios.

Portfolio

Answers
Figure 23 An alligator has a broad rounded snout, and few of its teeth are visible when its mouth is shut. A crocodile has a pointed snout, and most of its teeth are visible when its mouth is shut.

 Reading Checkpoint They hunt at night.

 Reading Checkpoint Tortoises

Extinct Reptiles—The Dinosaurs

Teach Key Concepts

Investigating Dinosaurs

Focus Review with students the meaning of the term *extinct*.

Teach Explain that before dinosaurs died out 65 million years ago, they occupied many of the habitats and played many of the roles of modern vertebrates. Ask: **What type of vertebrates are dinosaurs?** *(Reptiles)*

Apply Ask: **How were dinosaurs unlike modern reptiles?** *(Some were much larger; they might have been endothermic)* **learning modality: verbal**

Monitor Progress

Answers
Figure 25 Sample answer: The long neck may have allowed *Brachiosaurus,* which was a herbivore, to reach the leaves on tall trees.

 Tyrannosaurus rex

Assess

Reviewing Key Concepts

1. a. Reptiles are ectothermic vertebrates with scaly skin that lay their eggs on land.
b. Dry, scaly skin; amniotic egg; kidneys that concentrate urine **c.** It would dry out.
2. a. Lizards and snakes, alligators and crocodiles, turtles **b.** Lizards **c.** Alligators are carnivores that hunt at night, swimming rapidly towards prey and clamping down on prey with their huge, muscular jaws. Turtles are either herbivores or carnivores that use their beaks to scrape and tear their food.
3. a. 65 million years ago **b.** *Brachiosaurus,* like other dinosaurs, had legs positioned directly under its body, which allowed it to move more easily than other reptiles.
c. Sample answer: It could have been more active at night and in colder climates.

Reteach

Call on students to describe the features of one of the three main groups of reptiles.

All in One Teaching Resources, Unit 2

• Section Summary: *Reptiles*
• Review and Reinforce: *Reptiles*
• Enrich: *Reptiles*

FIGURE 25
Brachiosaurus
Brachiosaurus grew to be more than 22.5 meters long—longer than two school buses put together end to end. **Inferring** *What advantage did a long neck give* Brachiosaurus?

Extinct Reptiles—The Dinosaurs

Millions of years ago, huge turtles and fish-eating reptiles swam in the oceans. Flying reptiles soared through the skies. Snakes and lizards basked on warm rocks. And there were dinosaurs of every description. Unlike today's reptiles, some dinosaurs may have been endothermic. Some dinosaurs, such as *Brachiosaurus* in Figure 25, were the largest land animals that ever lived.

Dinosaurs were the earliest vertebrates that had legs positioned directly beneath their bodies. This adaptation allowed them to move more easily than animals such as salamanders and lizards, whose legs stick out from the sides of their bodies. Most herbivorous dinosaurs, such as *Brachiosaurus,* walked on four legs. Most carnivores, such as the huge *Tyrannosaurus rex,* ran on two legs.

Dinosaurs became extinct, or disappeared from Earth, about 65 million years ago. No one is certain why. Today, it's only in movies that dinosaurs shake the ground with their footsteps. But the descendants of dinosaurs may still exist. Some biologists think that birds descended from certain small dinosaurs.

 Give an example of a dinosaur that ran on two legs.

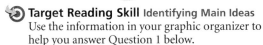

Section 4 Assessment

Target Reading Skill Identifying Main Ideas Use the information in your graphic organizer to help you answer Question 1 below.

Reviewing Key Concepts

1. a. Defining What is a reptile?
  b. Explaining What are three adaptations that allow reptiles to survive on land?
  c. Predicting What might happen to a reptile egg if part of its shell were removed?
2. a. Identifying What are the three main groups of reptiles?
  b. Classifying A gecko is a small reptile that has no shell protecting its body. It uses its legs to climb trees. Into which reptile group would you classify the gecko?
  c. Comparing and Contrasting Compare and contrast how alligators and turtles obtain food.

3. a. Reviewing When did the dinosaurs become extinct?
  b. Interpreting Diagrams What adaptation did the dinosaur in Figure 25 have that helped it survive?
  c. Inferring What advantage might a dinosaur that was an endotherm have had over other reptiles?

Writing in Science

Product Label Write a "packaging label" that will be pasted onto the eggshell of a reptile. Include on your label a list of the contents of the shell and a one-paragraph description of the egg's ability to survive in a dry environment.

Lab zone Chapter **Project**

Keep Students on Track Check that students have chosen appropriate and safe materials for building their reptile model. Be sure that students are modeling the same adaptation in all three models.

Writing in Science

Writing Mode Exposition How-To
Scoring Rubric
4 Includes an accurate, detailed description; writing is clear
3 Includes accurate description; clear writing
2 Includes accurate description; unclear writing
1 Description is inaccurate and unclear

Vertebrate History in Rocks

Reading Preview

Key Concepts
- Where are fossils most frequently found?
- What can scientists learn from studying fossils?

Key Terms
- fossil • sedimentary rock
- paleontologist

Target Reading Skill
Asking Questions Before you read, preview the red headings. In a graphic organizer like the one below, ask *what* and *how* questions for each heading. As you read, write the answers to your questions.

Vertebrate History in Rocks

Question	Answer
How do fossils form?	Fossils form by . . .

Lab zone Discover **Activity**

What Can You Tell From an Imprint?

1. Flatten some modeling clay into a thin sheet on a piece of paper.
2. Firmly press two or three small objects into different areas of the clay. The objects might include such things as a key, a feather, a postage stamp, or a flower. Don't let anyone see the objects you are using.
3. Carefully remove the objects from the clay, leaving only the objects' imprints.
4. Exchange your imprints with a partner. Try to identify the objects that made the imprints.

Think It Over
Observing What types of objects made the clearest imprints? If those imprints were fossils, what could you learn about the objects by looking at their "fossils"? What couldn't you learn?

Millions of years ago, in an ancient pond, some fishes died and their bodies settled into the mud on the bottom. Soon heavy rains fell, and more mud washed into the pond, covering the fishes. The soft tissues of the fishes decayed, but their bones remained. After many thousands of years, the mud hardened into rock, and the bones became the fossils shown here.

Fossilized fishes ▶

◆ 395

Objectives
After completing the lesson, students will be able to

11.5.1 Identify the kind of rock in which fossils are frequently found.

11.5.2 Describe what scientists can learn from studying fossils.

Target Reading Skill 🏷

Asking Questions Explain that changing a head into a question helps students anticipate the ideas, facts, and events they are going to read about.

Answers
Students' questions and answers might include: **How do fossils form?** *(Fossils form from imprints or the remains of organisms.)* **How are fossils interpreted?** *(Scientists examine fossil structure and make comparisons to present-day organisms.)*

All in One Teaching Resources, Unit 2
- Transparency LS120

Preteach

Build Background Knowledge L2
Identifying Fossils
Distribute some fossils. Ask: **What do you think made the patterns you see in the rocks?** *(Students may infer that the patterns are the remains or traces of dead animals or plants that lived long ago.)* **What can you infer about the organism that made the imprint and where it lived? Does it resemble any living organism that you know?** *(Answers will vary.)* Have students write brief descriptions of the fossils.

Lab zone Discover **Activity**

Skills Focus Observing

Materials modeling clay; paper; small objects of various textures and degrees of rigidity

Time 15 minutes

Tips Each student should use some objects that will make a clear impression, such as coins, and some that will not, such as feathers.

L1 **Expected Outcome** Harder objects, such as a key, will be easiest to identify. Imprints of soft objects with recognizable outlines, such as a leaf, will also be easy to recognize.

Think It Over The objects that made the clearest imprints were firm and had distinct borders. If the imprints were fossils, you could learn the size and shape of the object that made them. You could not learn what was inside the object or organism, what it ate, or why it died.

What Are Fossils?

Teach Key Concepts **L2**

Describing Types of Fossils

Focus Ask students to describe any fossils or pictures of fossils they have seen.

Teach Ask: **What chemical process is involved in forming fossils?** *(Tissues are replaced by minerals.)* **What is sedimentary rock?** *(Rock made from layers of sediment)*

Apply Ask: **Why aren't more organisms found as fossils?** *(Tissues of organisms decay rapidly, so they must be trapped quickly in appropriate conditions to be fossilized.)*
learning modality: verbal

Independent Practice **L2**

 Teaching Resources, Unit 2

• Guided Reading and Study Worksheet: *Vertebrate History in Rocks*

⊙ **Student Edition on Audio CD**

 **Build Inquiry** **L2**

Calculating Sedimentary Rock Depths

Materials calculator

Time 10 minutes

Focus Explain that sedimentary rock is deposited slowly but can eventually be thousands of meters thick.

Teach Give an example of a thick sedimentary deposit: Part of the Florida peninsula consists of limestone deposits more than 4,000 meters thick. Ask: **Suppose this limestone accumulated at a rate of 1 cm every 50 years. How many years did it take for 4,000 meters of limestone to accumulate?** *(4,000 m × 100 cm/m × 50 yr/ cm = 20 million years)*

Apply Ask: **Would dinosaur fossils be in this deposit?** *(No, dinosaurs became extinct 65 million years ago.)* **learning modality: logical/mathematical**

Go Online SCI LINKS NSTA

For: Links on fossils
Visit: www.SciLinks.org
Web Code: scn-0235

Download a worksheet that will guide students' review of Internet resources on fossils.

396

Go Online SCI LINKS NSTA

For: Links on fossils
Visit: www.SciLinks.org
Web Code: scn-0235

What Are Fossils?

A **fossil** is the hardened remains or other evidence of a living thing that existed a long time ago. Sometimes a fossil is an imprint in rock, such as an animal's footprint or the outline of a leaf. Other fossils are the remains of bones, shells, skeletons, or other parts of living things. Fossils are made when a chemical process takes place over time, during which an organism's tissues are replaced by hard minerals. Because most living tissues decay rapidly, only a very few organisms are preserved as fossils.

Fossils are found most frequently in sedimentary rock. Hardened layers of sediments make up **sedimentary rock.** Sediments contain particles of clay, sand, mud, or silt.

Science and **History**

Discovering Vertebrate Fossils

People have been discovering fossils since ancient times. Here are some especially important fossil discoveries.

1822
Dinosaur Tooth
In a quarry near Lewes, England, Mary Ann Mantell discovered a strange-looking tooth embedded in stone. Her husband Gideon drew the picture of the tooth shown here. The tooth belonged to the dinosaur *Iguanodon*.

1677
Dinosaur-Bone Illustration
Robert Plot, the head of a museum in England, published a book that had an illustration of a huge fossilized thighbone. Plot thought that the bone belonged to a giant human, but it probably was the thighbone of a dinosaur.

1811 Sea Reptile
Along the cliffs near Lyme Regis, England, 12-year-old Mary Anning discovered the fossilized remains of the giant sea reptile now called *Ichthyosaurus*. Mary became one of England's first professional fossil collectors.

| 1670 | 1760 | 1820 |

396 ◆

How do sediments build up into layers? Have you ever washed a dirty soccer ball and seen sand and mud settle in the sink? If you washed a dozen soccer balls, the sink bottom would be covered with layers of sediments. Sediments build up in many ways. For example, wind can blow a thick layer of sand onto dunes. Sediments can also form when muddy water stands in an area for a long time. Muddy sediment in the water eventually settles to the bottom and builds up.

Over a very long time, layers of sediments can be pressed and cemented together to form rock. As sedimentary rock forms, traces of living things that have been trapped in the sediments are sometimes preserved as fossils.

 Reading Checkpoint How does sedimentary rock form?

Writing in Science

Research and Write If you could interview the person who discovered one of the fossils, what questions would you ask about the fossil and how it was found? Write a list of those questions. Then use reference materials to try to find the answers to some of them.

1861 Bird Bones
A worker in a stone quarry in Germany found *Archaeopteryx*, a feathered, birdlike animal that also had many reptile characteristics.

1902 *Tyrannosaurus*
A tip from a local rancher sent Barnum Brown, a fossil hunter, to a barren, rocky area near Jordan, Montana. There Brown found the first relatively complete skeleton of *Tyrannosaurus rex*.

1964 *Deinonychus*
In Montana, paleontologist John Ostrom discovered the remains of a small dinosaur, *Deinonychus*. This dinosaur was probably a predator that could move rapidly. This fossil led scientists to hypothesize that dinosaurs may have been endotherms.

1991 Dinosaur Eggs in China
Digging beneath the ground, a farmer on Green Dragon Mountain in China uncovered what may be the largest nest of fossil dinosaur eggs ever found. A paleontologist chips carefully to remove one of the eggs from the rock.

1880   1940   2000

Chapter 11 ◆ 397

Science and **History**

Focus Help students relate these major events in vertebrate paleontology to other events in world history.

Teach Have students reproduce the timeline without the descriptive paragraphs, and then add the following major events in world history:
- The signing of the Declaration of Independence (1776)
- The end of the Civil War (1865)
- The end of World War II (1945)
- The first moon landing (1969)
- The breakup of the Soviet Union (1991)

Extend News of paleontological discoveries is often reported in newspapers. Ask students if they have read of recent discoveries that they might include on the timeline. Suggest discoveries made in China since 1996 of feathered dinosaurs that might represent an intermediate form between dinosaurs and birds.

Writing in Science

Writing Mode Research

Scoring Rubric

4 Includes at least four questions that show an understanding of lesson content; answers are correct, detailed, and complete

3 Includes two or three questions; answers are correct and complete

2 Includes two questions; most answers are correct and complete

1 Includes only one question or answers are incorrect and incomplete

---

Differentiated Instruction

Less Proficient Readers L1
Following the Time Line Have students needing a review of the text to write down the dates on the timeline, leaving room for notes. Then have students listen to the *Student Edition on Audio* CD and record events occurring in each year noted.
learning modality: verbal

Monitor Progress L2

Writing Have students write paragraphs describing how sedimentary rock is formed. Students can save their paragraphs in their portfolios.

Answer

Reading Checkpoint Particles of clay, sand, mud, or silt settle from the action of wind or water. The layers are pressed and cemented together over a long time.

397

Interpretation of Fossils

Teach Key Concepts
Examining the Fossil Record

Focus Tell students that scientists learn about how organisms change over time and how they are related to one another by studying fossils.

Teach Direct students to Figure 27. Ask: **Are mammals more closely related to fishes or to amphibians?** (*Amphibians*) **Which groups of vertebrates arose from reptiles?** (*Mammals and birds*)

Apply Ask: **What vertebrate fossils would be found in sediments 350 million years old but not in sediments 450 million years old?** (*Remains of amphibians*) **learning modality: visual**

 **Teaching Resources, Unit 2**

• Transparency LS121

Understanding Sedimentary Rock Formation

Materials plastic jar with lid, marbles, pea gravel, sand, powdered clay

Time 10 minutes

Focus Help students understand how sedimentary rock forms and traps fossils.

Teach Students will simulate the effect of moving water on different sizes of rocks. Have students half-fill the jar with the pebbles, gravel, sand, and clay, which represent different-sized rocks. Have them then fill the jar, fasten its lid securely, and shake it until the solid contents are suspended. Then they should quickly set the jar down and record the order in which the materials settle to the bottom. (*Pebbles first, then the gravel, then the sand, then much later, the clay*)

Apply Ask: **What is the relationship between the size of the rock and the length of time it takes to settle?** (*The larger the rock, the faster it settles.*) **learning modality: kinesthetic**

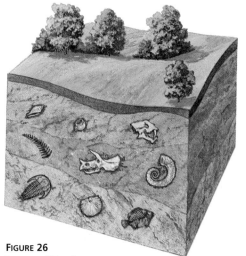

FIGURE 26
Layers of Fossils
Fossils most often form in layers of sedimentary rock.
Interpreting Diagrams *Which rock layer probably contains the oldest fossils?*

Interpretation of Fossils

What information can scientists learn from fossils? **Paleontologists** (pay lee un TAHL uh jists), the scientists who study extinct organisms, examine fossil structure and make comparisons to present-day organisms. **By studying fossils, paleontologists can infer how animals changed over time.** One important piece of information that paleontologists can learn from a fossil is its approximate age.

A Fossil's Age One method for estimating a fossil's age takes advantage of the process in which sediments form. Think about sediments settling out of water—the lowest layers are deposited first, and newer sediments settle on top of the older layers. Therefore, fossils in higher layers of rock are often younger than fossils in lower layers.

However, rock layers can become tilted or even turned upside down by events such as earthquakes. So, a fossil's position in rock is not always a good indication of its age. Scientists usually rely on other methods to help determine a fossil's age. For example, fossils—and the rocks in which they are found—contain some radioactive chemical elements. These radioactive elements decay, or change into other chemical elements, over a known period of time. The more there is of the decayed form of the element, the older the fossil.

Using Fossils Paleontologists have used fossils to determine a likely pattern of how vertebrates changed over time. You can see in Figure 27 that this pattern of vertebrate evolution looks something like a branching tree. Fossils show that the first vertebrates to live on Earth were fishes. Fishes first appeared on Earth about 530 million years ago. Amphibians, which appeared on Earth about 380 million years ago, are descended from fishes. Then, about 320 million years ago, amphibians gave rise to reptiles. Both mammals and birds, which you will learn about in the next chapter, are descended from reptiles. Based on the age of the oldest mammal fossils, mammals first lived on Earth about 220 million years ago. Birds were the latest group of vertebrates to arise. Their oldest fossils show that birds first appeared on Earth 150 million years ago.

Reading Checkpoint What is a paleontologist?

Differentiated Instruction

Gifted and Talented
Identifying Fossil Ages Challenge students to use library and Internet resources to investigate the actual processes that go into determining the ages of fossils, either by interpreting layers of sedimentary rock or carrying out radioactive dating. Students investigating fossil dating through examining sedimentary rock layers should prepare a visual display of the types and ages of fossils that could be found in rock layers in their area. Students exploring the details of radioactive dating should choose an example of a "famous" fossil whose age has been determined this way—such as an important dinosaur find—and provide a display presenting the steps involved in the technique. **learning modality: visual**

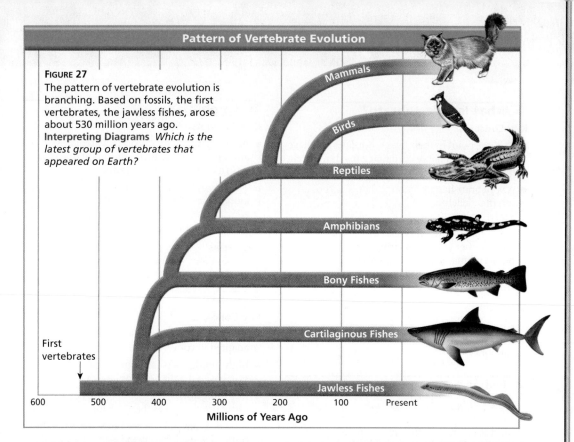

Pattern of Vertebrate Evolution

FIGURE 27
The pattern of vertebrate evolution is branching. Based on fossils, the first vertebrates, the jawless fishes, arose about 530 million years ago.
Interpreting Diagrams *Which is the latest group of vertebrates that appeared on Earth?*

Mammals
Birds
Reptiles
Amphibians
Bony Fishes
Cartilaginous Fishes
First vertebrates
Jawless Fishes

| 600 | 500 | 400 | 300 | 200 | 100 | Present |

Millions of Years Ago

Section 5 Assessment

Target Reading Skill Asking Questions Use your graphic organizer to answer the questions below.

Reviewing Key Concepts

1. a. **Identifying** Where are fossils most often found?
   b. **Describing** What are some types of fossils?
   c. **Inferring** How might a small fish that dies in a muddy pool become a fossil?
2. a. **Reviewing** What can be learned from studying fossils?
   b. **Summarizing** How does the measurement of radioactive elements help scientists calculate a fossil's age?
   c. **Interpreting Diagrams** Look at Figure 27. About how much time passed between the first appearance of vertebrates and the time birds appeared?

Lab zone At-Home Activity

Sedimentary Newspaper? If your family keeps newspapers in a stack, check the dates of the newspapers in the stack with a family member. Are the newspapers in any kind of order? If the oldest ones are on the bottom and the newest are on the top, you can relate this to the way in which sediments are laid down. Ask family members to imagine that two fossils were trapped in different newspapers. Explain which fossil would probably be older.

Chapter 11 ◆ 399

Lab zone At-Home Activity

Sedimentary Newspaper? L2
Ask: **What could you conclude if the newspapers in the top layer were older than those in the bottom layer?** *(Something must have disturbed the stack.)* **How is this similar to what can happen to rock layers?** *(Rock layers can be disturbed by natural events so that their original order is altered.)* **learning modality: verbal**

Interactive Textbook
- Complete student edition
- Section and chapter self-assessments
- Assessment reports for teachers

Help Students Read

Building Vocabulary
Word-Part Analysis Tell students that the prefix *ecto* means *outside* or *external*, *endo* means *inside* or *within*, and the root word *thermo* means *heat*. Thus an *ectotherm* uses heat from outside the body, and an *endotherm* generates heat from within.

Vocabulary Knowledge Rating Chart

Have students construct a chart with four columns: *Term, Can Define or Use It, Have Heard or Seen It, Don't Know*. Students should copy the Key Terms for the chapter under column 1. They should then check the appropriate column for each term, and use the chart to determine which terms to review.

Connecting Concepts

Concept Maps Help students develop one way to show how the information in this chapter is related. Fishes, amphibians, and reptiles are all adapted to their particular environments. The fossil record shows how these vertebrate groups are related. Have students brainstorm to identify the Key Concepts, Key Terms, details, and examples from this chapter. Then write each one on a sticky note and attach it at random on chart paper or on the board. Tell students that this concept map will be organized in hierarchical order and to begin at the top with the Key Concepts. Ask students these questions to guide them to categorize the information on the sticky notes: **What traits did these groups develop as they adapted to life on land? According to fossils, how are the groups related?** Prompt students by using connecting words or phrases, such as "led to," and "resulted in" to indicate the basis for the organization of the map. The

---

① What Is a Vertebrate?
Key Concepts
- At some point in their lives, chordates will have a notochord, a nerve cord that runs down their back, and slits in their throat area.
- A vertebrate has a backbone that is part of an internal skeleton.
- The body temperature of most fishes, amphibians, and reptiles is close to the temperature of their environment. In contrast, birds and mammals have a stable body temperature that is often warmer than their environment.

Key Terms

chordate   ectotherm
notochord   endotherm
vertebra

② Fishes
Key Concepts
- In addition to living in water and having fins, most fishes are ectotherms, obtain oxygen through gills, and have scales.
- The major groups of fishes are jawless fishes, cartilaginous fishes, and bony fishes.
- Jawless fishes are unlike other fishes in that they have no jaws and no scales.
- Cartilaginous fishes have jaws and scales, and skeletons made of cartilage.
- A bony fish has jaws, scales, a pocket on each side of the head that holds the gills, and a skeleton made of hard bone.

Key Terms
fish
cartilage
swim bladder

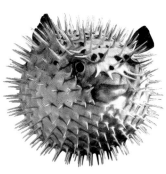

400 ◆

③ Amphibians
Key Concepts
- After beginning their lives in water, most amphibians spend their adulthood on land, returning to water to reproduce.
- The respiratory and circulatory systems of adult amphibians are adapted for life on land. In addition, adult amphibians have adaptations for obtaining food and moving.

Key Terms

amphibian   lung   ventricle
tadpole   atrium   habitat

④ Reptiles
Key Concepts
- The skin, kidneys, and eggs of reptiles are adapted to conserve water.
- Both lizards and snakes are reptiles that have skin covered with overlapping scales.
- Both alligators and crocodiles are large, carnivorous reptiles that care for their young.
- A turtle is a reptile whose body is covered by a protective shell that includes the ribs and the backbone.
- Dinosaurs were the earliest vertebrates that had legs positioned directly beneath their bodies.

Key Terms

reptile   kidney
urine   amniotic egg

⑤ Vertebrate History in Rocks
Key Concepts
- Fossils are found most frequently in sedimentary rock.
- By studying fossils, paleontologists can infer how a species changed over time.

Key Terms

fossil   sedimentary rock
paleontologist

---

phrases should form a sentence between or among a set of concepts.

Answer
Accept logical presentations by students.

All in One Teaching Resources, Unit 2
- Key Terms Review: *Fishes, Amphibians, and Reptiles*
- Connecting Concepts: *Fishes, Amphibians, and Reptiles*

Review and Assessment

Go Online
PHSchool.com
For: Self-Assessment
Visit: PHSchool.com
Web Code: cea-2030

Organizing Information

Identifying Main Ideas Copy the graphic organizer about amphibians onto a sheet of paper. Then complete it.

Main Idea

The larvae of amphibians are adapted for life in water, and adult amphibians are adapted for life on land.

Detail

a. _____?_____

Detail

b. _____?_____

Detail

c. _____?_____

Reviewing Key Terms

Choose the letter of the best answer.

1. Vertebrates are a subgroup of
   a. chordates.
   b. fishes.
   c. amphibians.
   d. reptiles.

2. A fish
   a. is an endotherm.
   b. has fins.
   c. has lungs.
   d. has a three-chambered heart.

3. A tadpole is the larva of a
   a. fish.
   b. salamander.
   c. frog or toad.
   d. lizard or snake.

4. A reptile
   a. is an endotherm.
   b. lays eggs.
   c. has a swim bladder.
   d. has a thin skin.

5. Layers of clay, sand, mud, or silt harden and become
   a. radioactive chemicals.
   b. sedimentary rock.
   c. fossils.
   d. dinosaur bones.

If the statement is true, write *true.* **If it is false, change the underlined word or words to make the statement true.**

6. A <u>notochord</u> is replaced by a backbone in many vertebrates.

7. A bony fish uses its <u>gills</u> to stabilize its position in the water.

8. <u>Amphibians</u> obtain oxygen through gills and have scales.

9. An <u>amniotic egg</u> is a characteristic of reptiles.

10. <u>Paleontologists</u> are scientists who study fossils.

Writing in Science

Description Suppose you are a journalist for a nature magazine and you have spent a week observing crocodiles. Write a paragraph describing how crocodiles obtain their food.

Discovery CHANNEL SCHOOL

Fishes, Amphibians, and Reptiles
Video Preview
Video Field Trip
▶ Video Assessment

Chapter 11 ◆ 401

Go Online
PHSchool.com
For: Self-Assessment
Visit: PHSchool.com
Web Code: cea-2030

Students can take a practice test online that is automatically scored.

All in One Teaching Resources, Unit 2
• Transparency LS122
• Chapter Test
• Performance Assessment Teacher Notes
• Performance Assessment Student Worksheet
• Performance Assessment Scoring Rubric

ExamView® Computer Test Bank CD-ROM

Review and Assessment

Organizing Information
a. Larvae have tails for swimming; adults have legs for walking.
b. Larvae have gills; adults have lungs.
c. Larvae have one-loop circulatory system and two-chambered heart; adults have two-loop circulatory system and three-chambered heart.

Reviewing Key Terms
1. a **2.** b **3.** c **4.** b **5.** b
6. true
7. swim bladder
8. Fishes
9. true
10. true

Writing in Science

Writing Mode Description
Scoring Rubric
4 Description includes many events placed in proper context and accurately reflecting crocodile adaptations
3 Includes adequate number of events, accurately presented
2 Includes inadequate number of events or some inaccuracies
1 Includes inadequate and inaccurate description

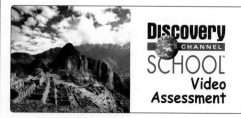
Discovery CHANNEL SCHOOL
Video Assessment

Fishes, Amphibians, and Reptiles

Show the Video Assessment to review chapter content and as a prompt for the writing assignment. Discussion questions: **Describe two adaptations of crocodiles that make them good predators.** *(Their muscular tail enables them to move very quickly in water and for short distances on land, and their strong jaw and long, sharp teeth help them eat their prey.)* **Describe how temperature is regulated in crocodile bodies.** *(Crocodiles rely on their environment to warm their bodies because they produce very little body heat of their own.)*

401

Checking Concepts

11. Chordates have a notochord, a nerve cord running down their back, and slits in their throat area.

12. Fish reproduce sexually. Most have external fertilization.

13. A frog begins life as an egg laid in water or a moist environment. The egg hatches into a fishlike tadpole, which gradually develops into an adult frog. Hind legs appear, then front legs; lungs replace gills; tadpole loses its tail. The adult frog returns to the water to mate and lay eggs, completing the cycle.

14. A fish has a circulatory system with one loop and a simple, two-chambered heart. An adult amphibian has a circulatory system with two loops and a three-chambered heart.

15. An adult amphibian obtains oxygen with its internal lungs and through its thin, moist skin.

16. A snake alternates contractions of muscles on opposite sides of its body to produce a slithering motion.

17. A reptile's egg has a tough, leathery shell and membranes inside that protect, nourish, and allow gas exchange to and from the embryo.

18. Scientists consider the layer of sediment in which a fossil is found, knowing the relative ages of different layers; and scientists measure decay of radioactive elements found in fossils.

Thinking Critically

19. The endoskeleton grows as the animal grows. Also, its strength supports the animal against the pull of gravity.

20. The heart pumps blood in one continuous loop from the heart to the gills, from the gills to the rest of the body, and back to the heart; oxygen enters the blood at the gills.

21. Sample answer: Wrap the towel in a material such as foil or plastic wrap that will keep water from escaping.

22. Sharp, pointed teeth indicate that the fish was a predator and a carnivore; body and fin shape suggest that the fish chased its prey.

Review and Assessment

Checking Concepts

11. Describe the main characteristics of chordates.

12. How do fishes reproduce?

13. Describe the life cycle of a frog.

14. How is the circulatory system of an adult amphibian different from that of a fish?

15. Describe the adaptations of an adult amphibian for obtaining oxygen from the air.

16. How does a snake move?

17. Explain how the structure of a reptile's egg protects the embryo inside.

18. Describe two methods that scientists use to determine the age of a fossil.

Thinking Critically

19. Relating Cause and Effect Explain why an endoskeleton allows vertebrates to grow larger than animals without endoskeletons.

20. Interpreting Diagrams How does blood move in the circulatory system shown below?

Key
■ Oxygen-rich blood
■ Oxygen-poor blood

21. Applying Concepts Imagine that you are in a hot desert with a wet paper towel. You must keep the towel from drying out. What strategy can you copy from reptiles to keep the towel from drying out?

22. Inferring A scientist discovers a fossilized fish with a body streamlined for fast movement, a large tail fin, and sharp, pointed teeth. What could the scientist infer about the type of food that this fish ate and how it obtained its food? On what evidence is the inference based?

Applying Skills

Use the graph to answer Questions 23–25.

A scientist performed an experiment on five goldfishes to test the effect of water temperature on "breathing rate"—the rate at which the fishes open and close their gill covers. The graph shows the data that the scientist obtained at four different temperatures.

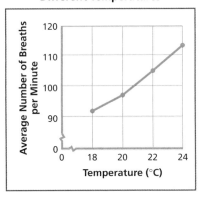

Fish Breathing Rate at Different Temperatures

23. Controlling Variables Identify the manipulated variable and the responding variable in this experiment.

24. Interpreting Data How does the breathing rate at 18°C compare to the breathing rate at 22°C?

25. Drawing Conclusions Based on the data shown, what is the relationship between water temperature and fish breathing rate?

Lab zone Chapter **Project**

Performance Assessment Display your models in a creative and interesting way—for example, show the models in action and show details of the animals' habitats. Also display your poster. List all the adaptations you learned from your classmates' presentations. How did constructing a three-dimensional model help you understand the characteristics of these groups?

Lab zone Chapter **Project** L3

Project Wrap-Up When students demonstrate their models for the class, some models may not perform the intended function as smoothly as they are designed to do. Locomotion can be a difficult adaptation to demonstrate successfully, but three-dimensional models should more accurately depict locomotion than would drawings. Look for realistic and thoughtful ideas.

Remind students that the poster, which can be a flowchart, can support their ideas. Guide students to record the adaptations that prompted their model choices. Also, have them record other adaptations modeled by classmates. After all students have presented their projects, you may wish to note which adaptations were modeled most often.

Standardized Test Prep

Choose the letter of the best answer.

1. If you monitored the body temperature of a snake in four different air temperatures, what would you notice about its body temperature?
A It rises or falls with the air temperature.
B It always stays at about 37°C.
C It is higher than the air temperature.
D It is lower than the air temperature.

Characteristics of Observed Animals

Animal	Skeleton	Scales	Outer Covering of Egg
1	Bone	None	Clear jelly
2	Bone	Yes	Leathery shell
3	Bone	Yes	Thin, moist membrane
4	Cartilage	Yes	No eggs observed

2. A scientist observed four different animals and recorded her data in the table shown above. Which of the animals is most likely a reptile?
F Animals 1 and 3
G Animal 2
H Animal 3
J Animal 4

3. Based on the data in the table above, what kind of animal can you infer Animal 3 might be?
A amphibian
B bony fish
C cartilaginous fish
D reptile

4. Suppose you are conducting an experiment that requires you to handle live bullfrogs. Which laboratory safety procedure should you carry out at the conclusion of each work session?
F Carefully clean the bullfrog's container.
G Put on gloves.
H Wash your hands thoroughly.
J Turn the heat on.

Constructed Response

5. Explain why amphibians can be said to have a "double life." Be sure to include details describing the two different phases in the life of a typical amphibian.

Applying Skills

23. The manipulated variable is the water temperature. The responding variable is the breathing rate of the fish.

24. The breathing rate at 18°C is lower than the breathing rate at 22°C.

25. The goldfish breathing rate is directly related to water temperature. The higher the water temperature, the faster the breathing rate.

Standardized Test Prep

1. A   **2.** G   **3.** B   **4.** H

5. Amphibians can be said to have a "double life" because an amphibian typically spends its larval stage in water and its adult life on land. Eggs are coated with a jelly and the larvae wriggle out of the jelly after a few days and begin to swim. They undergo metamorphosis, causing them to lose their gills and develop lungs. They move onto land to live.

Chapter at a Glance

PRENTICE HALL
TeacherEXPRESS™
Plan · Teach · Assess

 Chapter Project *Bird Watch*

Technology

Local Standards

 Teaching Resources, Unit 2
- Chapter Project Teacher Notes, pp. 366–367
- Chapter Project Student Overview, pp. 368–369
- Chapter Project Student Worksheets, pp. 370–371
- Chapter Project Scoring Rubric, p. 372

DISCOVERY
CHANNEL
SCHOOL
Video Preview

Section 1
2 periods
1 block

Birds

12.1.1 Identify the common characteristics of birds.

12.1.2 Explain how birds are adapted to their environments.

Go **Online**
active art

Section 2
1 period
1/2 block

The Physics of Bird Flight

12.2.1 Explain how a bird is able to fly.

12.2.2 Identify three types of flight birds use.

DISCOVERY
CHANNEL
SCHOOL
Video Field Trip

Go **Online**
PHSchool.com

Section 3
3 periods
1 1/2 blocks

Mammals

12.3.1 Describe the characteristics common to all mammals.

12.3.2 List the three main groups of mammals.

Go **Online**
SC*LINKS*™ NSTA

Review and Assessment

Go **Online**
PHSchool.com

Test Preparation

Test Preparation Blackline Masters

 Teaching Resources, Unit 2
- Key Terms Review, p. 398
- Transparency LS130
- Performance Assessment Teacher Notes, p. 409
- Performance Assessment Scoring Rubric, p. 410
- Performance Assessment Student Worksheet, p. 411
- Chapter Test, pp. 412–415

DISCOVERY
CHANNEL
SCHOOL
Video Assessment

404A

Lab zone — Chapter Activities Planner

For more activities

LAB ZONE Easy Planner CD-ROM

Student Edition	Inquiry	Time	Materials	Skills	Resources
Chapter Project, p. 405	Open-Ended	2–3 weeks	**All in One** Teaching Resources, **Unit 2**, p. 366	Observing, classifying, recording and interpreting data	**Lab zone Easy Planner** **All in One** Teaching Resources, **Unit 2**, Support, pp. 366–367
Section 1					
Discover Activity, p. 406	Directed	15 minutes	Feathers, hand lens	Observing	**Lab zone Easy Planner**
Try This, p. 411	Directed	20 minutes	Bowl, hand lens, uncooked egg, water	Observing	**Lab zone Easy Planner**
Skills Lab, pp. 414–415	Guided	Prep: 20 minutes Class: 50 minutes	Owl pellet, land lens, dissecting needle, metric ruler, forceps	Observing, drawing conclusions	**Lab zone Easy Planner** **Lab Activity Video** **All in One** Teaching Resources, **Unit 2**, Skills Lab: *Looking at an Owl's Leftovers*, pp. 380–382
Section 2					
Discover Activity, p. 416	Directed	10 minutes	Notebook paper, scissors, metric ruler, book	Predicting	**Lab zone Easy Planner**
Try This, p. 418	Open-Ended	30 minutes	Sheets of different kinds of paper (letter, construction, foil-covered), tape, glue, paper clips, string, rubber bands, staples	Making models	**Lab zone Easy Planner**
Section 3					
Discover Activity, p. 420	Guided	15 minutes	Cracker, hand mirror	Inferring	**Lab zone Easy Planner**
Try This, p. 422	Directed	15 minutes	Bucket or sink full of cold water, paper towels, rubber gloves, shortening (from animal fat)	Inferring	**Lab zone Easy Planner**
Consumer Lab, p. 429	Directed	Prep: 15 minutes Class: 35 minutes	Hot tap water, scissors, 1-L beaker, 3 thermometers, clock or watch, graph paper, pair of wool socks, room-temperature tap water, 3 250-mL containers with lids	Graphing, interpreting data	**Lab zone Easy Planner** **Lab Activity Video** **All in One** Teaching Resources, **Unit 2**, Consumer Lab: *Keeping Warm*, pp. 396–397

Section 1 Birds

 2 periods, 1 block

Objectives

12.1.1 Identify the common characteristics of birds.

12.1.2 Explain how birds are adapted to their environments.

Key Terms

• bird • contour feather • down feather • crop • gizzard

Local Standards

Preteach

Targeted Print and Technology Resources

Build Background Knowledge

Students investigate the shape, structure, and texture of feathers.

Lab zone Discover Activity *What Are Feathers Like?* L1

All in One Teaching Resources, Unit 2

L2 Reading Strategy Transparency LS123: Previewing Visuals

○ **PresentationEXPRESS™ CD-ROM**

Instruct

Targeted Print and Technology Resources

Characteristics of Birds Use pictures to teach characteristics of birds.

Birds in the Environment Use pictures to lead a discussion of the diversity of birds.

Lab zone Skills Lab *Looking at an Owl's Leftovers* L2

All in One Teaching Resources, Unit 2

L2 Guided Reading, pp. 375–377

L2 Transparencies LS124, LS125, LS126, LS127

L2 Skills Lab: *Looking at an Owl's Leftovers*, pp. 380–382

📼 **Lab Activity Video/DVD**
Skills Lab: *Looking at an Owl's Leftovers*

PHSchool.com Web Code: cep-2041

○ **Student Edition on Audio CD**

Assess

Targeted Print and Technology Resources

Section Assesment Questions

 Students can use their Previewing Visuals graphic organizers to answer the questions.

Reteach

Direct students to describe the kind of feathers that are used for flight.

All in One Teaching Resources, Unit 2

• Section Summary, p. 374

L1 Review and Reinforce, p. 378

L3 Enrich, p. 379

Section 2 The Physics of Bird Flight

 1 period, 1/2 block

ABILITY LEVELS
L1 Basic to Average
L2 For All Students
L3 Average to Advanced

Objectives

12.2.1 Explain how a bird is able to fly.
12.2.2 Identify three types of flight birds use.

Local Standards

Key Term

• lift

Preteach

Build Background Knowledge

Have students investigate flight by imitating flapping wings or gliding.

 **Discover Activity** *What Lifts Airplanes and Birds Into the Air?* **L1**

Targeted Print and Technology Resources

 **Teaching Resources, Unit 2**

L2 Reading Strategy Transparency LS128: Relating Cause and Effect

PresentationEXPRESS™ CD-ROM

Instruct

Staying in the Air Draw labeled sketches to use as prompts for students to answer questions about how bird stay in the air.

Birds in Flight Ask leading questions for a discussion on ways birds fly.

Targeted Print and Technology Resources

 **Teaching Resources, Unit 2**

L2 Guided Reading, pp. 385–386
L2 Transparency LS129

PHSchool.com Web Code: ced-2042

 DISCOVERY
SCHOOL
Video Field Trip

 Student Edition on Audio CD

Assess

Section Assessment Questions

Students can use their Relating Cause and Effects graphic organizers to answer the questions.

Reteach

Use the figure *Wing Shape and Lift* to explain how wing shape enables a bird to fly.

Targeted Print and Technology Resources

Teaching Resources, Unit 2

• Section Summary, p. 384
L1 Review and Reinforce, p. 387
L3 Enrich, p. 388

Section Lesson Plans

Section 3 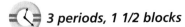 **Mammals**

3 periods, 1 1/2 blocks

ABILITY LEVELS
L1 Basic to Average
L2 For All Students
L3 Average to Advanced

Objectives

12.3.1 Describe the characteristics common to all mammals.

12.3.2 List the three main groups of mammals.

Key Terms

• mammal • mammary gland • diaphragm • monotreme • marsupial
• gestation period • placental mammal • placenta

Local Standards

Preteach

Build Background Knowledge

Record students' generalizations about the characteristics of pet mammals.

 **Discover Activity** *What Are Mammals' Teeth Like?* L1

Targeted Print and Technology Resources

All in One Teaching Resources, Unit 2

L2 Reading Strategy: Building Vocabulary

⊙ **PresentationEXPRESS™ CD-ROM**

Instruct

Characteristics of Mammals Relate characteristics of mammals to common organisms.

Diversity of Mammals Use pictures to discuss ways that mammals differ.

 **Consumer Lab** *Keeping Warm* L2

Targeted Print and Technology Resources

All in One Teaching Resources, Unit 2

L2 Guided Reading, pp. 391–393

L2 Consumer Lab: *Keeping Warm*, pp. 396–397

📼 **Lab Activity Video/DVD**
Consumer Lab: *Keeping Warm*

www.SciLinks.org Web Code: scn-0243

⊙ **Student Edition on Audio CD**

Assess

Section Assessment Questions

🔄 Students can use their definitions to answer the questions.

Reteach

Create a chart listing five characteristics common to all three groups of mammals.

Targeted Print and Technology Resources

All in One Teaching Resources, Unit 2

• Section Summary, p. 390

L1 Review and Reinforce, p. 394

L3 Enrich, p. 395

Chapter 12 Content Refresher

Go Online

NSTA-PDi LINKS

For: Professional development support
Visit: www.SciLinks.org/PDLinks
Web Code: scf-0240

Professional Development

Section 1 Birds

Feathers   The textbook identifies two main types of feathers—down and contour—but there are subcategories within those types. Down feathers, which are generally fluffy and provide insulation, include the down feathers found on adult birds as well as those that cover the bodies of many kinds of newly hatched birds. In addition, some kinds of birds, including parrots, hawks, and herons, have powder-down feathers. Powder-down feathers have tips that disintegrate, forming a powder that provides waterproofing.

Contour feathers have a central shaft with barbs attached. Many contour feathers are symmetrical. Flight feathers are often asymmetrical. This asymmetrical design contributes to the aerodynamics of the bird's wing during wing beats.

>
> ### Address Misconceptions
>
> *Some students may think that any animal that flies is a bird.* An animal is a bird if and only if it has feathers. For a strategy for overcoming this misconception, see **Address Misconceptions** in the section *Birds*.

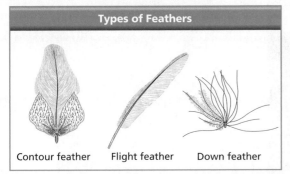

Types of Feathers

Contour feather   Flight feather   Down feather

Section 2 The Physics of Bird Flight

Aerodynamics of Bird Flight   Winged flight basically involves two forces: thrust, which pushes the object forward, and lift, which makes the object rise. In birds, thrust is provided by the movement of the wings. Lift is provided by the shape and angle of the wings.

The leading edge of the wing is thicker than the trailing edge, and in its natural position the trailing edge curves downward. So, the wing shape is convex on its upper side and concave on its lower. The airfoil shape causes air to move faster over the wing than it does under, providing an area of lower pressure above and greater pressure below. Combined with forward thrust, this creates the lift.

In soaring, birds increase lift by tilting the wing upward. But in so doing, some thrust is lost, and the bird slows. But what happens if birds fly too slow? As airplane pilots know, slowing too much can produce turbulence above the wing, causing a complete loss of lift, or "stall," which can lead to a crash. One way in which soaring birds overcome the problem is by occasionally flapping the wings, which increases thrust.

Section 3 Mammals

Adaptations of Mammals' Digestive Tracts   The digestive tract is similarly organized in all mammals. There's the mouth, esophagus, stomach, small intestine, and large intestine. The simplest versions are seen in omnivores and carnivores. The food they eat, consisting mostly of starches, proteins, and fats, is readily digested by enzymes released by the digestive glands. These mammals also digest a small amount of cellulose-laden plant fiber, but most cellulose passes through the gut unchanged. Herbivorous grazing mammals have more complex, very long digestive tracts, an adaptation to the slow and difficult task of breaking down cellulose, the main part of their diets.

These mammals cannot digest cellulose, however. They rely entirely on vast numbers of microorganisms that live in specialized chambers in the digestive tract. Herbivorous mammals fall into two categories: ruminants and nonruminants. The ruminants include cows, bison, goats, giraffes, and others, and are all named for the rumen, the first and largest chamber in their four-chambered stomachs. The rumen is a huge fermentation vat containing great numbers of microorganisms. It breaks down the tough cellulose material, yielding fatty acids, sugars, and starches. In nonruminants, including horses, rabbits, elephants, koalas, and others, cellulose digestion takes place in the cecum, a saclike organ found at the junction of the small and large intestine.

Help Students Read

Relate Text and Visuals

Strategy   Show students how to use the text's illustrations to help clarify difficult concepts or to understand information.

Example

1. Choose a section in the chapter. Read the paragraphs aloud before students open their texts.

2. Have students open their books, reread the passage you read, and study the figure. Ask what parts of the passage now make more sense.

Interactive Textbook

- Complete student edition
- Video and audio
- Simulations and activities
- Section and chapter activities

Interactive Textbook

► A three-toed sloth hangs from a tree branch in Costa Rica.

404 ◆

Lab zone Chapter **Project**   L3

Objectives
In this project, students will model the skills and observations required for the careful study of any group of animals. They will observe interactions between birds, and record feeding behavior and food preference of different birds. After this Chapter Project, students will be able to
- observe and identify birds at a feeder
- classify behaviors
- create data tables
- interpret data from their project

Skills Focus
Observing, classifying, recording and interpreting data

Project Time Line 2 to 3 weeks

All in One Teaching Resources, Unit 2
- Chapter Project Teacher Notes
- Chapter Project Overview
- Chapter Project Worksheet 1
- Chapter Project Worksheet 2
- Chapter Project Scoring Rubric

Developing a Plan
During the first week, students select a feeder location and begin observing and identifying visiting bird species. During the second week, students can list bird species observed and record common behaviors. In week three, students concentrate on feeding behaviors. Finally, students devise a way to present information they have collected.

Possible Materials
- To begin observations, each group will need a commercial bird feeder or materials to build a feeder. Students will need also string or wire to hang feeder.
- To attract the greatest variety of species, students may use an all-purpose bird feed mix, including hulled sunflower seeds, white millet, cracked corn, red millet, sunflower chips, peanut pieces, milo, thistle, and hulled millet.

Video Preview

Birds and Mammals

Show the Video Preview to introduce the Chapter Project and overview the chapter content. Discussion question: **What is the function of flight feathers?** *They help control flight, allowing the birds to steer and even brake before landing.*

Lab zone™ Chapter Project

Bird Watch

One of the best ways to learn about animals is to watch them in action. In this project, you'll watch birds and other animals that visit a bird feeder. You will discover how they eat and interact. What you observe may raise new questions for you to answer.

Your Goal To make detailed observations of the birds and other animals that appear at a bird feeder

To complete this project, you must
- observe the feeder regularly for at least two weeks and use a field guide to identify the kinds of birds that visit the feeder
- make detailed observations of how the birds at your feeder eat
- describe the most common kinds of bird behavior
- follow the safety guidelines in Appendix A

Plan It! Begin by sharing knowledge about the birds in your area with some classmates. What kinds of birds can you expect to see? What types of foods do birds eat? Then, using this knowledge, start observing your feeder. Record all your observations in detail in your notebook. After completing your observations, you will interpret your data and observations and make graphs and charts for your display.

Chapter 12 ◆ 405

- Students will need a field guide specific to your region of the country as well as guide to bird behaviors.
- Students will need art supplies to prepare their presentations. Cameras and videocassette recorders would be helpful, if available.

Launching the Project

To introduce the project, Ask: **How many different kinds of birds have you seen in your neighborhood?** (*Accept all responses at this time and encourage creative thinking.*) Encourage discussion of the different kinds of birds students have seen. Students could name source materials they found helpful for identifying unfamiliar species. Answer any initial questions that students may have. Discuss placement of the bird feeders so that they are easily refilled and observed while at the same time offering proximity to cover so birds can retreat if startled or threatened.

Performance Assessment

The Chapter Project Scoring Rubric will help you evaluate how well students complete the Chapter Project. You may want to share the scoring rubric with your students so they know what will be expected of them. Students will be assessed on
- thoroughness of research of the area's birds leading to the use of appropriate feeders, food, and location
- completeness of observation entries including: (1) what birds appeared, (2) their interactions, and (3) foods eaten
- application of chapter concepts to their observations
- thoroughness and organization of their presentations

Portfolio

Objectives

After this lesson, students will be able to

12.1.1 Identify the common characteristics of birds.

12.1.2 Explain how birds are adapted to their environments.

Target Reading Skill 🔄

Previewing Visuals Explain that looking at the visuals before they read can help students activate prior knowledge and predict what subject they are beginning to read about.

Answers

Possible questions and answers include: **How are birds adapted for flight?** (*They have lightweight bones, wings, and contour feathers.*) **What is the function of contour feathers?** (*They give shape to the body and help the bird balance and steer during flight.*)

All in One Teaching Resources, Unit 2

- Transparency LS123

Preteach

Build Background Knowledge L2

Birds in Language

Invite students to generate a list of verbal expressions about birds; record each expression on the chalkboard. (*Samples: Birds of a feather flock together, eats like a bird, proud as a peacock*) Ask students if they think any of these have any basis in science. Again, record students' ideas. After students have read the section, have them reconsider the expressions, evaluating each on the basis of what they have learned.

406

Section 1
Birds

Reading Preview

Key Concepts
- What are the main characteristics of birds?
- How are birds adapted to their environments?

Key Terms
- bird • contour feather
- down feather • crop • gizzard

🔄 Target Reading Skill

Previewing Visuals When you preview, you look ahead at the material to be read. Preview Figure 1. Then write two questions that you have about the diagram in a graphic organizer like the one below. As you read, answer your questions.

Adaptations for Flight

Q.	How are birds adapted for flight?
A.	
Q.	

406 ◆

Lab zone Discover **Activity**

What Are Feathers Like?

1. Observe the overall shape and structure of a feather. Then use a hand lens to examine the many hairlike barbs that project out from the feather's central shaft.
2. Gently separate two barbs in the middle of the feather. Rub the separated edges with your fingertip. How do they feel?
3. Use the hand lens to examine the edges of the two separated barbs. Draw a diagram of what you observe.
4. Rejoin the two separated barbs by gently pulling outward from the shaft. Then wash your hands.

Think It Over
Observing Once the barbs have been separated, is it easy to rejoin them? How might this be an advantage to the bird?

One day in 1861, in a limestone quarry in what is now Germany, Hermann von Meyer was inspecting rocks. Meyer, a fossil hunter, spotted something dark in a rock. It was the blackened imprint of a feather! Excited, he began searching for a fossil of an entire bird. He eventually found it—a skeleton surrounded by the imprint of many feathers. The fossil was given the scientific name *Archaeopteryx* (ahr kee AHP tur iks), meaning "ancient winged thing."

Paleontologists think that *Archaeopteryx* lived about 145 million years ago. *Archaeopteryx* didn't look much like the birds you know. It looked more like a reptile with wings. Unlike any modern bird, *Archaeopteryx* had a long, bony tail and a mouth full of teeth. But, unlike a reptile, it had feathers and wings. Paleontologists think that *Archaeopteryx* and modern birds descended from some kind of reptile, possibly a dinosaur.

◄ **A model of *Archaeopteryx***

Lab zone Discover **Activity**

Skills Focus Observing

Materials feathers, hand lens

Time 15 minutes

Tips Try to have a variety of contour feathers. Good sources of feathers include pet stores and biological supply houses. Any fresh feathers should be frozen for 72 hours to kill any microorganisms. Point out the shaft and barbs of a feather.

L1 **Expected Outcome** Students should observe that feathers have a central shaft with a vane made up of flexible barbs that link together but that can be pulled apart. The vanes of a flight feather are different widths.

Think It Over The barbs rejoin again, easily. This helps a bird quickly smooth its feathers in order to fly or swim.

No Teeth
Instead of heavy teeth, birds have a lightweight bill.

Air spaces

Lightweight Bones
Nearly hollow bones keep birds light in the air.

Wings
Bones of the forelimb are adapted as wings.

Hook   Barb

Contour Feathers
A series of hooks links the barbs of a feather together, keeping the feather smooth.

FIGURE 1
Adaptations for Flight
The bodies of most birds have adaptations for flight.
Interpreting Diagrams *Which of these adaptations make birds light?*

Characteristics of Birds

Modern **birds** all have certain characteristics in common. **A bird is an endothermic vertebrate that has feathers and a four-chambered heart. A bird also lays eggs.**

Adaptations for Flight The bodies of most birds are adapted for flight, as you can see in Figure 1. Many of a bird's bones are nearly hollow, making the bird lightweight. In addition, the bones of a bird's forelimbs form wings. Flying birds have large chest muscles that move the wings. Finally, feathers help birds fly. Birds are the only animals with feathers.

Feathers are not all the same. If you have ever picked up a feather, it was probably a contour feather. A **contour feather** is one of the large feathers that give shape to a bird's body. The long contour feathers that extend beyond the body on the wings and tail are called flight feathers. When a bird flies, these feathers help it balance and steer. You can see in Figure 1 that a contour feather consists of a central shaft and many small hairlike projections, called barbs. Hooks hold the barbs together. When birds fly, their barbs may pull apart, "unzipping" their feathers. Birds often pull the feathers through their bills to "zip" the barbs back together again.

In addition to contour feathers, birds have short, fluffy **down feathers** that are specialized to trap heat and keep the bird warm. Down feathers are found right next to the bird's skin, at the base of the contour feathers. Down feathers are soft and flexible, unlike contour feathers.

Differentiated Instruction

English Learners/Beginning **L1**
Vocabulary: Science Glossary Pair English learners with students proficient in English. Direct each pair to list terms such as *endothermic, vertebrate, feathers,* and *four-chambered heart.* Student pairs can compose a definition of each term and list two animals that share the characteristic.
learning modality: verbal

English Learners/Intermediate **L2**
Vocabulary: Science Glossary After students write definitions for unfamiliar terms, direct them to write sentences in which they use each term. Have them rewrite the sentences on a separate sheet of paper, replacing key terms with a blank line. Partners can exchange papers and fill in the missing terms. **learning modality: verbal**

Characteristics of Birds

Teach Key Concepts   L2
Feather Facts

Focus Tell students that feathers distinguish birds from all other organisms.

Teach Point out that birds have different kinds of feathers. Ask: **Which feathers help shape a bird?** (*Contour feathers*) **Which feathers does a bird use for flight?** (*Contour*) **Describe down and explain its use.** (*Down feathers are short and fluffy and keep a bird warm.*)

Apply Some birds, such as ptarmigan and snowy owls, live within the Arctic and Antarctic circles. **What characteristic allows them to survive in such a cold environment?** (*Down feathers*) **learning modality: verbal**

All in One Teaching Resources, Unit 2
• Transparency LS124

Address Misconceptions
Defining Characteristic

Focus Some students may think that "if it flies, it's a bird" or "if it lays eggs, it's a bird."

Teach Ask: **Give an example of an animal that can fly that is not a bird.** (*Bees and bats can fly.*) **Give an example of an animal that lays eggs but is not a bird.** (*Fishes, frogs, alligators, snakes*)

Apply Ask: **Why are egg-laying and flight not defining characteristics of birds?** (*Other animals can have these characteristics.*) **Why are feathers a defining characteristic of birds?** (*Only birds have feathers.*) **learning modality: logical/mathematical**

Independent Practice   L2

All in One Teaching Resources, Unit 2
• Guided Reading and Study Worksheet: *Birds*

 Student Edition on Audio CD

Monitor Progress _____   L2

Oral Presentation Ask students to name at least four characteristics all birds share. (*Endothermic, vertebrates, feathers, four-chambered heart, lay eggs.*)

Answer
Figure 1 No teeth and nearly hollow bones

407

Oxygen Delivery

Materials none

Time 10 minutes

Focus Tell students that birds need an efficient way to bring the additional oxygen they need for flying to their body cells.

Teach Have students find their resting pulse rates and count how many times they breathe in one minute. Suggest they record each of these figures. Next, have able students run in place for one minute. (**CAUTION:** *Students with medical problems that preclude running should be excused.*) Have students retake their pulse and breathing rates, record this information, and compare it to the "before run" data.

Apply Ask: **What happened to your heartbeat as you completed the physical activity?** *(The rate increased.)* **What do you think happens to a bird's heart and breathing rates when it flies?** *(They increase.)* **What features help birds get more oxygen to their muscles?** *(Air sacs and four-chambered heart)* **learning modality: kinesthetic**

For: Respiration and Circulation activity
Visit: PHSchool.com
Web Code: cep-2041

Compare and contrast the circulatory systems found in fishes, typical adult amphibians, and birds.

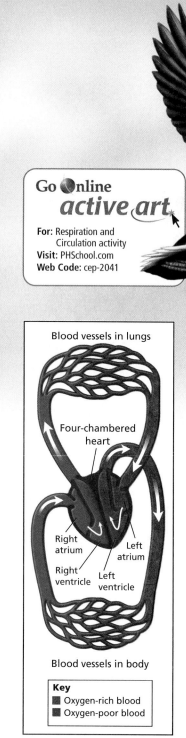

Go Online
active art

For: Respiration and Circulation activity
Visit: PHSchool.com
Web Code: cep-2041

Lungs
Air sacs
Air sacs

Air Sacs
Multiple air sacs connect to the lungs.

Heart
The four-chambered heart keeps oxygen-rich blood separate from oxygen-poor blood.

Blood vessels in lungs

Four-chambered heart

Right atrium
Left atrium

Right ventricle
Left ventricle

Blood vessels in body

Key
■ Oxygen-rich blood
■ Oxygen-poor blood

FIGURE 2
Respiration and Circulation
Air sacs and a four-chambered heart help birds obtain oxygen and move it to their cells.
Applying Concepts *Why is a four-chambered heart efficient?*

Obtaining Oxygen Flying uses a lot of energy. Therefore, cells must receive plenty of oxygen to release the energy contained in food. Birds have a highly efficient way to get oxygen into their bodies and to their cells. Birds have a system of air sacs in their bodies. This system connects to the lungs. The air sacs enable birds to obtain more oxygen from each breath of air than other animals can.

The circulatory systems of birds are also efficient at getting oxygen to the cells. Birds have hearts with four chambers—two atria and two ventricles. Trace the path of blood through a bird's two-loop circulatory system in Figure 2. The right side of a bird's heart pumps oxygen-poor blood to the lungs, where oxygen is picked up. Oxygen-rich blood returns to the left side of the heart, which pumps it to the cells.

The advantage of a four-chambered heart over a three-chambered heart is that oxygen-rich blood does not mix with oxygen-poor blood. Therefore, blood carried to the cells of the body has plenty of oxygen.

408 ◆

Obtaining Food Birds must obtain a lot of food to provide the energy needed for flight. To capture, grip, and handle food, birds mainly use their bills. Bills are shaped to help birds feed quickly and efficiently. For example, the pointy, curved bill of a hawk acts like a meat hook to pull off bits of its prey. In contrast, a duck's bill acts like a kitchen strainer, separating out seeds and tiny animals from muddy pond water.

After a bird eats its food, digestion begins. Each organ in a bird's digestive system is adapted to process food. Many birds have an internal storage tank, or **crop,** for storing food inside the body after swallowing it. Find the crop in Figure 3. The crop is connected to the stomach.

The stomach has two parts. In the first part, food is bathed in chemicals that begin to break it down. Then the food moves to a thick-walled, muscular part of the stomach called the **gizzard.** The gizzard squeezes and grinds the partially digested food. Remember that birds do not have teeth. The gizzard does the same grinding function for birds that your teeth do for you. The gizzard may contain small stones that the bird has swallowed. These stones help grind the food by rubbing against it and crushing it.

 **Reading Checkpoint** What is a gizzard?

FIGURE 3
Digestive System of a Hawk
Some birds like this hawk have a crop and a gizzard. The crop stores food, and the gizzard crushes food. **Interpreting Diagrams** *Does food reach the crop or the gizzard first?*

Crop
The crop stores food before it enters the stomach.

Gizzard
The gizzard is a thick-walled muscular part of the stomach that squeezes and grinds the food.

Chapter 12 ◆ 409

Keeping Warm L2

Materials 3 ice cubes, 3 plastic containers, aluminum foil, clock, cosmetic balls, down feathers, insulating materials such as shredded paper, plastic wrap, scrap of wool fabric

Time 35 minutes

Focus Show students the selection of insulators and ask them to rank the materials from least effective to most effective. Record the ranking so that students may check it when the activity is complete.

Teach Have students work in groups of four to test three different insulation materials. Each group should wrap an ice cube in one of the insulators, place it in a plastic container, and observe the container every 5 minutes for 30 minutes. Containers placed near a heat source or in sunlight may provide more dramatic results. Ask: **What variables must remain the same in order to test these materials properly?** *(Sample answer: The size and temperature of the ice cube and the container must be the same for all tested materials.)* Have groups describe and record their observations, for example: 10 minutes—beginning to melt; 20 minutes—nearly half melted; 25 minutes—all melted.

Apply Groups can compare data and draw conclusions about which materials are better insulators. Have students create a ranking according to their observations and compare it to the ranking they made at the beginning of the activity. Ask: **What can you conclude about down and its ability to insulate birds?** *(Down works well as an insulator.)*
learning modality: kinesthetic

FIGURE 4
Keeping Warm
A pine grosbeak puffs out its feathers to trap air in the layer of down feathers next to its skin.

Keeping Conditions Stable Like all animals, birds use their food for energy. You know that birds need energy for flight. Because birds are endotherms, they also need a lot of energy to maintain their body temperature. Each day, an average bird eats food equal to about a quarter of its body weight. When people say, "You're eating like a bird," they usually mean that you're eating very little. But if you were actually eating as much as a bird does, you would be eating huge meals. You might be eating as many as 100 hamburger patties in one day!

To maintain their body temperature, birds use feathers as well as energy from food. As you read earlier, down feathers are specialized to trap heat. They are found right next to a bird's skin. In Figure 4, you can see what a down feather looks like. Unlike contour feathers, down feathers are soft and flexible. So, they mingle and overlap, trapping air. Air is a good insulator—a material that does not conduct heat well and therefore helps prevent heat from escaping. By trapping a blanket of warm air next to the bird's skin, down feathers slow the rate at which the skin loses heat. In effect, down feathers cover a bird in lightweight long underwear. Humans use down feathers from the eider duck to insulate jackets, sleeping bags, and bedding.

FIGURE 5
A Down-Filled Jacket
Wearing a jacket stuffed with down feathers helps this boy stay warm.
Applying Concepts *Why is his down jacket so puffy?*

Reproduction and Caring for Young Like reptiles, birds have internal fertilization and lay eggs. Bird eggs are similar to reptile eggs except that their shells are harder. In most bird species, the female lays the eggs in a nest that has been prepared by one or both parents.

Bird eggs will only develop at a temperature close to the body temperature of the parent bird. Thus, a parent bird usually incubates the eggs by sitting on them to keep them warm. In some species, incubating the eggs is the job of just one parent. For example, female robins incubate their eggs. In other species, such as pigeons, the parents take turns incubating the eggs. Chicks may take from 12 to 80 days to develop, depending on the species.

When it is ready to hatch, a chick pecks its way out of the eggshell. Some newly hatched chicks, such as ducks, chickens, and partridges are covered with down and can run about soon after they have hatched. Other chicks, such as baby blue jays and robins, are featherless, blind, and so weak they can barely lift their heads to beg for food. Most parent birds feed and protect their young at least until they are able to fly.

Reading Checkpoint **How is a bird egg different from a reptile egg?**

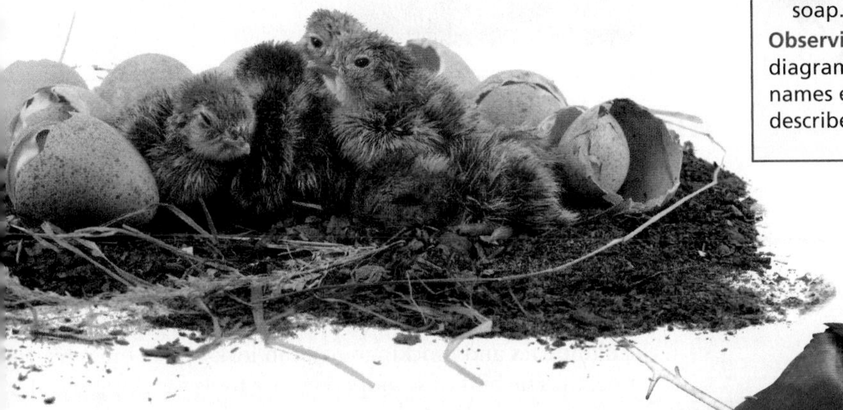

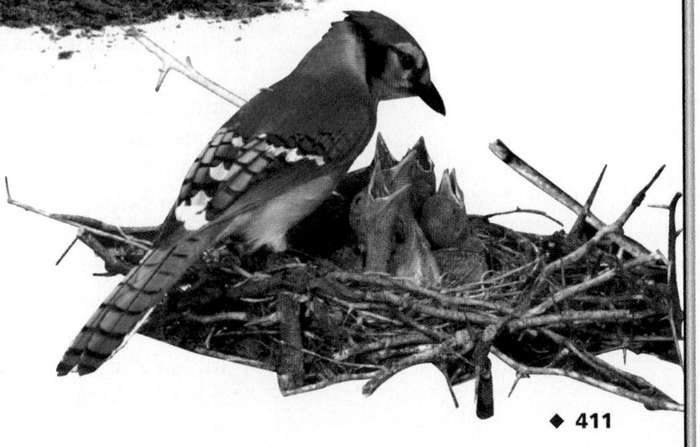

FIGURE 6
Parental Care
The partridge chicks (above) find their own food from the day they hatch. In contrast, the blue jay chicks (right) are featherless, blind, and totally dependent on their parents for food for several weeks.

Lab zone Try This Activity

"Eggs-amination"

1. Observe the surface of a chicken egg with a hand lens. Then gently crack the egg into a bowl. Do not break the yolk.
2. Note the membrane attached to the inside of the shell. Then look at the blunt end of the egg. What do you see?
3. Fill one part of the egg–shell with water. What do you observe?
4. Find the egg yolk. What is its function?
5. Look for a small white spot on the yolk. This marks the spot where the embryo would have developed if the egg had been fertilized.
6. Wash your hands with soap.

Observing Draw a labeled diagram of the egg that names each structure and describes its function.

Lab zone Teacher Demo L1

Eggs' Shape and Strength

Materials 4 uncooked chicken eggs, clay, cosmetic balls, heavy book

Time 10 minutes

Focus Ask students to describe some characteristics an egg should have in order to decrease the risk of breaking. List students' suggestions on the chalkboard.

Teach Place the eggs in a triangular pattern, securing them with clay supports and placing the small end up. Place the cosmetic balls between the eggs so their sides do not touch. Ask: **What will happen when I place a book on the eggs?** *(Tally break/will not break on the chalkboard.)* Carefully place the book on the eggs to confirm students' observations.

Apply Ask: **How does the eggshell's strength benefit birds?** *(They will not break if they roll or when a bird sits on them.)* **learning modality: visual**

Lab zone Try This Activity

Skills Focus Observing L2

Materials bowl, hand lens, uncooked egg, water

Time 20 minutes

Tips Uncooked eggs can carry bacteria. Direct students not to put the eggs in their mouths.

Expected Outcome Step 2, air pocket between the shell and the membrane; Step 3, shell holds water; Step 4, yolk provides food. Diagrams should identify the white spot, shell, yolk, egg white, and membrane. Egg and shell keep the water inside, protect the embryo, and provide nourishment. **learning modality: visual**

Monitor Progress L2

Oral Presentation Have students briefly describe activities related to parental care of unhatched and hatched young.

Answers

Figure 5 Down jackets are stuffed with down feathers. These feathers are good insulators because they are naturally fluffy so there can be many warm air pockets in the down. These pockets make the jacket puffy.

Reading Checkpoint The eggshells of birds are harder than reptile shells.

Birds in the Environment

L2

Teach Key Concepts
Significant Adaptations

Focus Tell students that there are several characteristics they can use to group or classify birds.

Teach Indicate further that each characteristic is an adaptation so that the bird might feed, fly, build nests, or reproduce more easily. Ask: **How are long legs and toes helpful to birds that wade in water?** *(They allow birds to wade into waters as deep as their legs are long.)* **How is a duck's bill useful for feeding?** *(It filters many tiny plants and animals from the water.)* **How do sharp talons help hawks and eagles eat?** *(The talons allow the bird to grasp their prey firmly so that they can carry it to a nest and so that they can hold it while they tear the flesh.)*

Apply Invite students to think of another way they could use observable characteristics to group birds. *(Sample criteria: How and where they nest, how they communicate with one another, how they mark their territory)*
learning modality: logical/mathematical

Help Students Read
L1

Summarize Summarizing the information presented in the text will help students focus on main ideas and remember what they read. Have students read the text related to the diversity of birds. Ask students to summarize the ways in which birds may be different from one another. **learning modality: verbal**

FIGURE 7
Diversity of Birds
Every bird has adaptations that help it live in its natural environment.

Owls ▲
Sharp vision and keen hearing help owls hunt at night. Razor-sharp claws and great strength allow larger owls, like this eagle owl, to prey on animals as large as deer.

Bee-Eaters ▲
This rainbow bee-eater feeds on bees and other insects, which it catches as it flies. Bee-eaters are found in Africa, Europe, Australia, and Asia.

◀ Game Birds
Wild turkeys are found in North America. When courting females, the male fans his tail feathers, holds his head high, and gobbles.

Birds in the Environment

With almost 10,000 species, birds are the most diverse land-dwelling vertebrates. **Birds are adapted for living in diverse environments. You can see some of these adaptations in the shapes of their legs, claws, and bills.** For example, the long legs and toes of wading birds, such as herons, cranes, and spoonbills, make wading easy. The claws of perching birds, such as goldfinches and mockingbirds, can lock onto a branch or other perch. The bills of woodpeckers are tools for chipping into the wood of trees. Birds also have adaptations for finding mates and caring for their young.

Birds play an important role in the environment. Nectar-eating birds, like hummingbirds, are pollinators. Seed-eating birds, like sparrows, carry the seeds of plants to new places. This happens when the birds eat the fruits or seeds of a plant, fly to a new location, and then eliminate some of the seeds in digestive wastes. In addition, birds are some of the chief predators of animals that may be pests. Hawks and owls eat rats and mice, while many perching birds feed on insect pests.

Ostriches ▼
The ostrich, found in Africa, is the largest living bird. It cannot fly, but it can run at speeds greater than 60 kilometers per hour. Its speed helps it escape from predators.

◄ Long-Legged Waders
The roseate spoonbill is found in the southern United States and throughout much of South America. The spoonbill catches small animals by sweeping its long, flattened bill back and forth under water.

Perching Birds ▶
Perching birds represent more than half of all the bird species in the world. The painted bunting, a seed-eating bird, lives in the southern United States and northern Mexico.

Section 1 Assessment

Target Reading Skill Previewing Visuals Refer to your questions and answers about Figure 1 to help you answer Question 1 below.

Reviewing Key Concepts

1. a. **Identifying** What characteristics do birds share?
   b. **Explaining** How is a bird's body adapted for flight?
   c. **Relating Cause and Effect** Why do birds need so much oxygen? What adaptation helps them obtain oxygen?
2. a. **Listing** What are three types of adaptations that allow birds to survive in diverse environments?
   b. **Summarizing** What are three roles birds play in the environment?
   c. **Comparing and Contrasting** Look at Figure 7. Compare and contrast the adaptations of an eagle owl and a roseate spoonbill for obtaining food.

Lab zone At-Home **Activity**

Count Down With the help of a family member, look for products in your home that contain down feathers. (*Hint:* Don't forget to check closets!) What kinds of items contain down feathers? What common purpose do these items have? Explain to your family member what down feathers look like and where they are found on a bird.

Reviewing Key Concepts

1. a. All birds are endothermic vertebrates with feathers and a four-chambered heart, and all lay eggs. b. Adaptations for flight include bones in the forelimbs modified as wings, lightweight bones, lack of teeth, large chest muscles, and feathers. c. Birds need a lot of oxygen to release the energy from food required for flying. Air sacs enable birds to obtain more oxygen per breath than other animals can. A four-chambered heart keeps oxygen-rich blood and oxygen-poor blood separate, so blood carried to the cells has more oxygen than if the blood were mixed.
2. a. Legs, claws, and bills b. Pollinators, seed-carriers, and predators of pests. c. The eagle owl has sharp vision and keen hearing for hunting at night. It also has sharp claws and great strength for killing large prey. The spoonbill has long legs so that it can wade in water; its bill is shaped to catch prey in water.

Reteach   L1
Have students describe the kind of feathers used for flight.

Performance Assessment   L2
Writing Have each student list and describe at least five adaptations of birds. Students should describe feathers, the four-chambered heart, feeding and digestive system adaptations, and reproductive adaptations. Students can save their descriptions in their portfolios.

Portfolio

All in One Teaching Resources, Unit 2
• Section Summary: *Birds*
• Review and Reinforce: *Birds*
• Enrich: *Birds*

Lab zone Chapter **Project**

Keep Students on Track Provide field guides to help students identify visiting species. Suggest observing the feeders at different times of day. Cardinals, for instance, are early eaters while sparrows feed later. Check to see that students are recording appropriate observations. As students proceed with their observations, meet with them regularly to discuss their progress.

Lab zone At-Home **Activity**

Count Down L2 Tell students that all clothing and bedding materials must be labeled with the materials that they are made from. Students may find down in items such as bed pillows, comforters, furniture cushions, and winter coats.

413

Looking at an Owl's Leftovers L2

Prepare for Inquiry

Key Concept
Students draw conclusions about an animal's diet by examining the parts of the diet not digested.

Skills Objectives
During this lab, students will be able to
- observe and analyze the components of an owl pellet
- draw conclusions about an owl's diet by studying the pellets it coughs up

 Prep Time 20 minutes
Class Time 50 minutes

Advance Planning
Order owl pellets from a biological supply company. If possible, obtain one for each student and a few extras.

Safety
  Students should wear safety goggles and handle the sharp dissecting needles carefully. Remind students to wash their hands thoroughly after completing the dissection. Review the safety guidelines in Appendix A.

All in One Teaching Resources, Unit 2
- Lab Worksheet: *Looking at an Owl's Leftovers*

Guide Inquiry

Invitation
Have students think about what they discard when they eat. Ask: **What do you have left over when you eat a chicken wing? When you eat an apple?** (Bones, apple core) Tell students that other animals also leave behind parts of their food and these leftovers can be studied to determine the animal's diet.

Introduce the Procedure
Allow students time to practice with dissecting needles by examining a cookie with nuts, chips, or raisins. (**CAUTION:** *Tell students not to eat the cookies.*)

Encourage students to examine the outside of the pellet before making their predictions. Provide pictures of lizard, rat, and snake bones to help students identify them.

  Skills Lab

Looking at an Owl's Leftovers

Problem
What can you learn about owls' diets from studying the pellets that they cough up?

Skills Focus
observing, drawing conclusions

Materials
- owl pellet • hand lens • dissecting needle
- metric ruler • forceps

Procedure

1. An owl pellet is a collection of undigested materials that an owl coughs up after a meal. Write a hypothesis describing what items you expect an owl pellet to contain. List the reasons for your hypothesis.

2. Use a hand lens to observe the outside of an owl pellet. Record your observations.

3. Use one hand to grasp the owl pellet with forceps. Hold a dissecting needle in your other hand, and use it to gently separate the pellet into pieces. **CAUTION:** *Dissecting needles are sharp. Never cut material toward you; always cut away from your body.*

4. Using the forceps and dissecting needle, carefully separate the bones from the rest of the pellet. Remove any fur that might be attached to bones.

5. Group similar bones together in separate piles. Observe the skulls, and draw them. Record the number of skulls, their length, and the number, shape, and color of the teeth.

6. Use the chart on the right to determine what kinds of skulls you found. If any skulls do not match the chart exactly, record which animal skulls they resemble most.

Skull Identification Key	
Shrew 	Upper jaw has at least 18 teeth; tips of the teeth are reddish brown. Skull length is 23 mm or less.
House mouse 	Upper jaw has two biting teeth and extends past lower jaw. Skull length is 22 mm or less.
Meadow vole 	Upper jaw has two biting teeth that are smooth, not grooved. Skull length is 23 mm or more.
Mole 	Upper jaw has at least 18 teeth. Skull length is 23 mm or more.
Rat 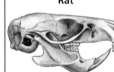	Upper jaw has two biting teeth. Upper jaw extends past lower jaw. Skull length is 22 mm or more.

7. Try to fit together any of the remaining bones to form complete or partial skeletons. Sketch your results.

8. Wash your hands thoroughly with soap when you are finished.

Analyze and Conclude

1. **Observing** How many animals' remains were in the pellet? What observations led you to that conclusion?

2. **Drawing Conclusions** Combine your results with the results of your classmates. Based on your class's data, which three animals were eaten most frequently? How do these results compare to your hypothesis?

3. **Calculating** Owls cough up about two pellets a day. Based on your class's data, what can you conclude about the number of animals an owl might eat in one month?

4. **Communicating** In this lab, you were able to examine only the part of the owl's diet that it did not digest. In a paragraph, explain how this fact might affect your confidence in the conclusions you reached.

Design an Experiment

Design an experiment to determine how an owl's diet varies at different times of the year. Give an example of a hypothesis you could test with such an experiment. What variables would you control? Before carrying out your experiment, obtain your teacher's approval of your plan.

Troubleshooting the Experiment

Explain that the pellets have been decontaminated. Reluctant students can work with a partner and perform data collection and record keeping. Break pellets into pieces and soak them in water to loosen materials before beginning the dissection.

Expected Outcome

Students should find varying numbers of identifiable animal remains in the pellets.

Analyze and Conclude

1. Answers will vary. Students should explain that the number of each type of bone could help determine the number of animals eaten. For example, each skull or each pair of femurs represents one animal.

2. Combined data should give an estimate of the total number and type of animals in the pellets.

3. The estimated total of animals found in all pellets divided by the number of pellets gives an average number of animals per pellet. Students can multiply this number by 2 to find the number of animals eaten per day. Then, multiplying the average number by 30 gives the average number of animals eaten in a month.

4. Students may explain that they are less confident in their results because they will probably underestimate the number of animals eaten each month.

Extend Inquiry

Design an Experiment A sample study might analyze pellets collected on the last two days of each month for a year. From this study, students would expect to conclude that an owl's diet varies during the year. In winter, hibernating animals will be absent. Animals such as house mice, which are always active, may be common in the diet all year.

Objectives
After this lesson, students will be able to
12.2.1 Explain how a bird is able to fly.
12.2.2 Identify three types of flight birds use.

Target Reading Skill
Relating Cause and Effect Explain that *cause* is the reason why something happens. The *effect* is what happens as a result of the cause. Relating cause and effect helps students make a connection between the reason for what happens and the result.

Answers
Possible causes include: Air flows around wing; the shape of wing causes differences in air pressure that produces an upward force; contour feathers give wings a smooth shape.

All in One Teaching Resources, Unit 2
• Transparency LS128

Preteach

Build Background Knowledge **L1**
Imitating Bird Flight
Ask students to demonstrate and describe birds in flight. *(Some students will flap their arms up and down, while others will glide with their arms outstretched.)* Call students' attention to this difference. Ask students to speculate about how some birds fly without seeming to put forth any effort.

Reading Preview
Key Concepts
• What causes a bird to rise in the air?
• How may birds fly?

Key Term
• lift

Target Reading Skill
Relating Cause and Effect A cause makes something happen. An effect is what happens. As you read, identify the physical properties of a bird's wing that cause lift. Write them in a graphic organizer like the one below.

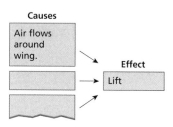

Causes

Air flows around wing.

Effect

Lift

FIGURE 8
Bird Feather
Contour feathers give a smooth shape to a bird's body and wings. This smooth shape is helpful for flight.

416 ◆

Lab zone Discover **Activity**

What Lifts Airplanes and Birds Into the Air?
1. Cut a strip of notebook paper 5 centimeters wide and 28 centimeters long. Insert about 5 centimeters of the paper strip into the middle of a book. The rest of the paper strip should hang over the edge.
2. Hold the book up so that the paper is below your mouth.
3. Blow gently across the top of the paper and watch what happens to the paper. Then blow harder.

Think It Over
Predicting If a strong current of air flowed across the top of a bird's outstretched wing, what might happen to the bird?

From ancient times, people have dreamed of soaring into the air like birds. When people first started experimenting with flying machines, they tried to glue feathers to their arms or to strap on feathered wings. Many failures, crash-landings, and broken bones later, these people had learned that feathers by themselves weren't the secret of flight.

Staying in the Air
All objects on land are surrounded by an invisible ocean of air. Air is a mixture of gas molecules that exert pressure on the objects they surround. Although you cannot see air pressure, you can see the results of air pressure. For example, when you blow into a balloon, it gets larger. The pressure of the air molecules pushing on the sides of the balloon makes it expand.

Lab zone Discover **Activity**

Skills Focus Predicting **L1**

Materials notebook paper, scissors, metric ruler, book

Time 10 minutes

Tips The paper should be curled so that the free edge of the strip faces away from the student. Make certain students hold the book so that their breath flows across the top of the paper strip—not down on the paper. Before students complete Step 3, ask them to predict what will happen. Then have them complete Step 3 and determine if their predictions were accurate.

Expected Outcome When students blow gently across the paper, the paper lifts slightly. Blowing harder lifts the strip higher and it remains in a horizontal position.

Think It Over The air flowing over the bird's wing might lift the bird up into the air.

Faster-moving air above wing exerts less pressure.

Air flow

Slower-moving air below wing exerts more pressure.

Lift

FIGURE 9
Wing Shape and Lift
The air pressure pushing up on the lower surface of this pelican's wing is greater than the pressure pushing down on its upper surface.
Relating Cause and Effect
How does the difference in pressure help a bird fly?

Movement and Air Pressure Air does not have to be inside a balloon to exert pressure. Moving air exerts pressure, too. The faster air moves, the less pressure it exerts. You saw this in the Discover Activity. The air blowing across the top of the paper was in motion. This moving air exerted less pressure on the paper than the air beneath it, so the paper rose.

Air Movement Around a Wing Like the paper, a flying bird's wing is surrounded by air molecules that exert pressure on the wing's surfaces. The wing allows air to flow smoothly over and under it. When a bird is between wing beats, the angle and shape of the wing cause the air to move faster above the wing than below it, as shown in Figure 9. The faster-moving air above the bird's wing exerts less pressure than the slower-moving air below it. **The difference in pressure above and below the wings as a bird moves through the air produces an upward force that causes the bird to rise.** That upward force is called **lift.**

 Reading Checkpoint As air moves faster, what happens to the pressure it exerts?

Discovery SCHOOL

Birds and Mammals

Video Preview
▶ Video Field Trip
Video Assessment

Instruct

Staying in the Air

Use Visuals: Figure 9   **L2**
Airfoils

Focus Direct students' attention to Figure 9.

Teach Point out that the angle and shape of a bird's wing allows air to flow around it in a specific manner. Ask: **Which exerts greater air pressure—moving air or air that is not moving?** (*Air that is not moving*) **How is air pressure affected when air moves faster?** (*Faster air produces less air pressure.*) **What is the result of faster-moving air above a bird's wing?** (*The pressure is less above the wing.*) **How does a difference in air pressure help a bird to fly?** (*It creates an upward force that lifts the bird.*) **learning modality: visual**

All in One Teaching Resources, Unit 2
• Transparency LS129

All in One Teaching Resources, Unit 2
• Guided Reading and Study Worksheet: *The Physics of Bird Flight*

 Student Edition on Audio CD

Discovery SCHOOL
Video Field Trip

Birds and Mammals
Show the Video Field Trip to help students understand the adaptations of birds that enable them to fly. Discussion question: **Describe three adaptations for flight found in most birds.** (*Wing shape; strong chest muscles; nearly hollow bones; four-chambered hearts; two distinct pathways in the circulatory system.*)

Monitor Progress _____ **L2**
Answers
Figure 9 The difference in pressure creates lift.

 Reading Checkpoint As air moves faster, it exerts less pressure.

Birds in Flight

Teach Key Concepts L2
Flying Is More Than Flapping

Focus Review the wing motions of a bird in flight. (Many students may indicate that a bird flaps its wings.)

Teach Indicate to students that some birds can cover great distances without flapping their wings. Ask: **How do some birds fly without flapping their wings?** (*They extend their wings and allow warm air currents to carry them upwards.*) **How can a bird fly without using lift?** (*By diving*) **What does a bird do with its wings when it dives?** (*Tucks them in*)

Apply Tell students that an albatross travels hundreds of miles over the ocean with no place to land. Ask: **Why is it useful for an albatross to be able to soar and glide?** (*Saves energy; the bird does not have to continuously flap its wings.*) Have students model the actual wing motions a bird uses while it flies. **learning modality: verbal**

FIGURE 10
Types of Flight
Flapping, soaring and gliding, and diving are three types of flight. **Applying Concepts** *Which type of flight requires the most energy? Explain.*

Flapping allows these macaws to lift off and move forward through the air.

Birds in Flight

Before a bird can use lift to fly, it must have some way of getting off the ground. To get into the air, a bird pushes off with its legs and moves forward at the same time. The bird must move forward to make air move over its wings. Sharply pulling down its wings provides the power that pushes the bird forward. The forward motion creates lift. When birds are in the air, they fly in a variety of ways. **Three types of bird flight are flapping, soaring and gliding, and diving.**

Flapping Once in flight, all birds continue to flap their wings at least part of the time. To flap, a bird must sharply pull down its wings as it did when it pushed off the ground. Most small birds, such as sparrows, depend heavily on flapping flight. Canada geese and many other birds that travel long distances also use flapping flight. Flapping requires a lot of energy.

Soaring and Gliding Unlike flapping flight, soaring and gliding flight involve little wing movement. Birds soar and glide with their wings extended. When soaring, birds use rising currents of warm air to move upward. In contrast, when gliding, birds use falling currents of cool air to move downward. Soaring and gliding use less energy than flapping because they require less wing movement.

Sometimes birds fly using a combination of soaring and gliding. They "take the elevator up" by flying into a current of warm, rising air. The birds stretch their wings out and circle round and round, moving upward within the current of rising air. As the warm air rises it starts to cool. Finally, the air stops rising. At this point the bird begins gliding downward until it reaches another "up elevator" of rising air.

Lab zone · Try This Activity

It's Plane to See

1. Work with a partner to design a paper airplane with wings shaped like those of a bird. You can use any of these materials: paper, tape, glue, paper clips, string, rubber bands, and staples. Draw a sketch of your design.

2. Construct your "birdplane" and make one or two trial flights. If necessary, modify your design and try again.

3. Compare your design with those of other groups. Which designs were most successful?

Making Models In what ways was the flight of your airplane like the flight of a bird? In what ways was it different?

418 ◆

Go Online
PHSchool.com

For: More on bird adaptations
Visit: PHSchool.com
Web Code: ced-2042

Students can review bird adaptations in an online activity.

Lab zone · Try This Activity

Skills Focus Making models L3

Materials Sheets of different kinds of paper (letter, construction, foil-covered), tape, glue, paper clips, string, rubber bands, staples

Time 30 minutes

Tips Discuss with students their ideas for an airplane design that allows air to flow rapidly over the nose and wing.

Expected Outcome Both flights are the result of lift. However, a bird moves its wings, the airplane glides.

Extend Have students select a factor such as distance or time and compute the average for all their flights. **learning modality: kinesthetic**

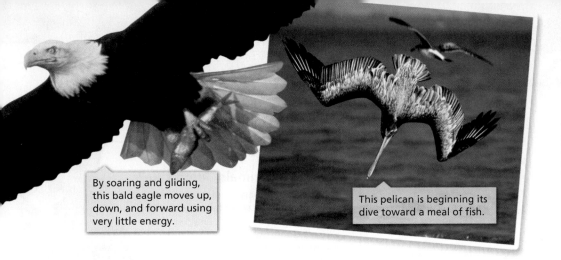

By soaring and gliding, this bald eagle moves up, down, and forward using very little energy.

This pelican is beginning its dive toward a meal of fish.

Diving A type of flight that doesn't use lift is diving. Birds that hunt their prey from the sky may use diving flight. For example, a brown pelican flies above the ocean, looking for schools of fish under the water's surface. Once it spots the fish, the pelican dives with great speed. As it dives, the pelican pulls its wings in close to its body. Pulling in the wings changes the pelican's body shape. The new body shape produces no lift at all. Without lift, the pelican falls from the sky headfirst into the ocean and hits the fish with enough force to stun them.

Some hawks and falcons dive from high in the sky towards their prey, too. Peregrine falcons can clock speeds up to 300 kilometers per hour while diving for pigeons or other prey.

 Reading Checkpoint Which type of bird flight is the fastest?

Go Online
PHSchool.com

For: More on bird adaptations
Visit: PHSchool.com
Web Code: ced-2042

Section 2 Assessment

Target Reading Skill **Relating Cause and Effect** Refer to your graphic organizer about lift to help you answer Question 1 below.

Reviewing Key Concepts

1. a. **Defining** What is lift?
   b. **Explaining** What effect does lift have on a flying bird?
   c. **Applying Concepts** What causes lift in an airplane?
2. a. **Identifying** What are three types of bird flight?
   b. **Summarizing** How does a bird take off from the ground to fly?
   c. **Comparing and Contrasting** How are soaring and gliding alike? How are they different?

Writing in Science

Advertisement You have been hired by an outdoor adventure company to write an exciting ad for one of their birdwatching hikes. In the ad, describe several interesting birds and types of bird flight that people will see on the hike.

Chapter 12 ◆ 419

Chapter Project

Keep Students on Track At this point, students should have a list of the various species of birds that visit their feeders. While students continue general observations, they should also concentrate on observing specific feeding behaviors. Feeding behavior includes how birds perch while eating, how birds use their beaks, and rituals such as head bobbing. Review students' notebooks and monitor their progress.

Writing in Science

Writing Mode Persuasion

Scoring Rubric

4 Includes accurate, detailed descriptions of at least four birds

3 Includes accurate descriptions of two or three birds

2 Includes brief descriptions of two birds

1 Includes inaccurate or incomplete descriptions

Students can save their advertisements in their portfolios.

 Portfolio

Objectives
After this lesson, students will be able to
12.3.1 Describe the characteristics common to all mammals.
12.3.2 List the three main groups of mammals.

Target Reading Skill
Building Vocabulary Explain that using vocabulary strategies, such as defining words by their context, helps students define Key Concept words.

Answers
Students' definitions will vary but should convey an accurate meaning for the context.

Preteach

Build Background Knowledge
L2

Survey of Pet Mammals
Ask students who have mammals as pets to describe their pets' physical characteristics and behavior. Students can use their descriptions as a foundation for making generalizations about the characteristics of mammals. Record their generalizations on the chalkboard. After students complete the section, return to the generalizations and have students correct any incorrect statements.

Section 3 Mammals

Reading Preview

Key Concepts
• What characteristics do all mammals share?
• What are the main groups of mammals and how do they differ?

Key Terms
• mammal   • mammary gland
• diaphragm   • monotreme
• marsupial   • gestation period
• placental mammal   • placenta

Target Reading Skill
Building Vocabulary A definition states the meaning of a word or phrase by telling about its most important feature or function. After you read the section, reread the paragraphs that contain definitions of Key Terms. Use all the information you have learned to write a definition of each Key Term in your own words.

Lab zone Discover Activity

What Are Mammals' Teeth Like?
1. Wash your hands before you begin. Then, with a small mirror, examine the shapes of your teeth. Observe the incisors (the front teeth); the pointed canine teeth; the premolars behind the canine teeth; and the molars, which are the large teeth in the very back.
2. Compare and contrast the structures of the different kinds of teeth.
3. Use your tongue to feel the cutting surfaces of the different kinds of teeth in your mouth.
4. Bite off a piece of cracker and chew it. Observe the teeth that you use to bite and chew. Wash your hands when you are finished.

Think It Over
Inferring What is the advantage of having teeth with different shapes?

▲ Himalayan yak

High in the Himalaya Mountains of Tibet, several yaks inch their way, single file, along a narrow cliff path. The cliff plunges thousands of meters to the valley below, so one false step can mean disaster. But the sure-footed yaks, carrying heavy loads of grain, slowly but steadily cross the cliff and make their way through the mountains.

People who live in the mountains of central Asia have depended on yaks for thousands of years. Not only do yaks carry materials for trade, they also pull plows and provide milk. Mountain villagers weave blankets from yak hair and make shoes and ropes from yak hides.

The yak is a member of the group of vertebrates called **mammals.** Today about 4,000 different species of mammals exist. Some, like the yak and wildebeest, you may never have seen. But others, such as dogs, cats, and mice are very familiar to you. What characteristics do mammals share?

420 ◆

Lab zone Discover Activity

Skills Focus Inferring

Materials cracker, hand mirror

Time 15 minutes

Tips Tell students that the tooth arrangement from the middle of the row to the back is 2 incisors, 1 canine, 2 premolars, and 3 molars.

L1

Direct students to wash their hands before they feel their teeth with their fingers.

Think It Over Teeth with different shapes are adapted for different functions. A variety of teeth means that a variety of foods can be eaten.

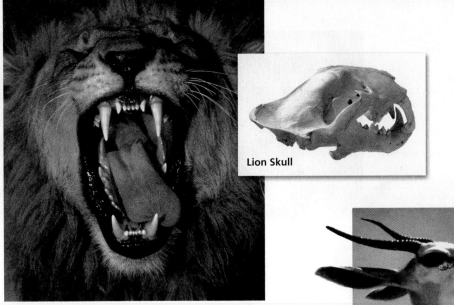
Lion Skull

Characteristics of Mammals

All mammals are endothermic vertebrates that have a four-chambered heart and skin covered with fur or hair. Most mammals are born alive, and every young mammal is fed with milk produced by organs in its mother's body. These organs are called **mammary glands.** The word *mammal,* in fact, comes from the term *mammary.*

Obtaining Food In addition to their other characteristics, most mammals have teeth. Their teeth are adapted to chew their food, breaking it into small bits that make digestion easier. Most mammals have teeth with four different shapes. If you did the Discover Activity, you observed these shapes. Incisors are flat-edged teeth used to bite off and cut food. Canines are pointed teeth that stab food and tear into it. Premolars and molars have broad, flat upper surfaces for grinding and shredding food.

The size, shape, and hardness of a mammal's teeth reflect its diet. For example, the canines of carnivores are especially large and sharp. Large carnivores, such as the lion in Figure 11, use their canines to hold their prey while they kill it. In contrast, herbivores, such as a springbok, have molars for grinding and mashing plants.

 Reading Checkpoint Which teeth stab and tear into food?

Springbok Skull

FIGURE 11
Teeth of Different Shapes
Lions have sharp, pointed canines. Springboks have broad molars.
Inferring *What kind of diet does each of these mammals eat?*

Chapter 12 ◆ 421

Instruct

Characteristics of Mammals

Teach Key Concepts   **L2**
Size as an Advantage

Focus Remind students that size can play a role in an animal's survival.

Teach Tell students that small, early mammals lived at the same time as the dinosaurs. Ask: **What might be the advantage of being small at the time of the dinosaurs?** *(Sample answer: Small animals could hide in small spaces to avoid the dinosaurs. Small animals might be hard to see as they run along the ground.)*

Apply Ask: **If dinosaurs were active mostly during the day, what other characteristic might help a small mammal survive?** *(Sample answer: To be active at night)*
learning modality: logical/mathematical

Independent Practice   **L2**

All in One **Teaching Resources, Unit 2**

- Guided Reading and Study Worksheet: *Mammals*

 Student Edition on Audio CD

Differentiated Instruction

Less Proficient Readers   **L1**
Some students may need extra help remembering names for the types of teeth. Obtain a model or preserved jaw of an herbivore, such as a cow, and one of a carnivore, such as a cat. Label the four types of teeth present in each model. Have students identify each tooth as they touch it. Also, have students describe the shape of the tooth—long and sharp, broad and flat—and tell whether the tooth is best for tearing, chewing, or grinding.

Ask students how they can determine which jaw belongs to an herbivore and which to a carnivore. *(The herbivore will have broad and flat teeth for grinding up leaves. The carnivore will have sharp pointed teeth so it can tear pieces of flesh.)* **learning modality: visual**

Monitor Progress   **L2**

Writing Have each student develop a chart that lists the four different shapes of teeth and the diet associated with each shape. Students can save their charts in their portfolios. **Portfolio**

Answers
Figure 11 Lions are carnivores; springboks are herbivores.

 Reading Checkpoint   Canines

Focus Direct students to look at the mammals in Figures 12 and 14 and compare the hair and fur they see.

Teach Ask: **Are there some kinds of hair common to all mammals?** (*Students should recognize that all the mammals shown have whiskers around the eyes, lips, and muzzle.*) Have students reexamine the wolf in Figure 12. Point out that some of the wolf's fur is long, some short. Ask: **What do you think is the function of the short, wooly hairs?** (*Insulation*) **What is the likely function of the longer, smooth hairs?** (*Protects the undercoat from water.*) **learning modality: visual**

FIGURE 12
Fur and Hair
A hippo has hardly any hair. In contrast, a wolf has a thick coat of fur.
Inferring What can you infer about the environment each animal lives in?

Lab zone Try This **Activity**

Insulated Mammals
Discover whether or not fat is an effective insulator.

1. Put on a pair of rubber gloves.
2. Spread a thick coating of solid white shortening on the outside of one of the gloves. Leave the other glove uncoated.
3. Put both hands in a bucket or sink filled with cold water.

Inferring Which hand got cold faster? Explain how this activity relates to mammalian adaptations.

422 ◆

Obtaining Oxygen To release energy, food must combine with oxygen inside cells. Therefore, a mammal must have an efficient way to get oxygen into the body and to the cells that need it. Like reptiles and birds, all mammals breathe with lungs. Mammals breathe in and out because of the combined action of rib muscles and a large muscle called the **diaphragm** (DY uh fram). The diaphragm is located at the bottom of the ribs. The lungs have a huge, moist surface area where oxygen can move into the blood.

Like birds, mammals have a four-chambered heart and a two-loop circulatory system. This efficient system takes oxygen to the cells.

Keeping Conditions Stable Like birds, mammals are endotherms. They need the energy in food to keep a steady internal temperature. In addition, all mammals have fur or hair at some point in their lives that helps them keep their internal temperature stable. The amount of fur or hair that covers a mammal's skin varies greatly. Each strand of fur or hair is composed of dead cells strengthened with the same tough material that strengthens feathers. In general, animals that live in cold regions, like the wolf shown in Figure 12, have more fur than animals from warmer environments.

Fur is not the only adaptation that allows mammals to live in cold climates. Mammals also have a layer of fat beneath their skin. Like fur and feathers, fat is an insulator.

Lab zone Try This **Activity**

Skills Focus Inferring $\boxed{\text{L2}}$

Materials bucket or sink full of cold water, paper towels, rubber gloves, shortening (from animal fat)

Time 15 minutes

Tips Explain to students that shortening is a form of animal fat that has been processed for cooking. Have students work in pairs to coat one another's gloves. When students are experimenting with reactions to temperature, be sure they do not use water that is dangerously cold.

Expected Outcome The hand in the glove without the shortening will feel the cold first. The glove with the shortening, which acts as an insulator, keeps heat in the hand just as animal fat keeps heat in the body of an animal.

Extend Have students coat the second glove with twice as much shortening as the first. Ask students to test whether more fat makes the hand less sensitive to cold.
learning modality: kinesthetic

Movement In addition to adaptations for living in cold environments, mammals have adaptations that allow them to move in more ways than members of any other group of vertebrates. Most mammals walk or run on four limbs, but some have specialized ways of moving. For example, kangaroos hop, orangutans swing by their arms from branch to branch, and "flying" squirrels can spread their limbs and glide down from high perches. Bats have wings adapted from their front limbs. Whales, dolphins, and other sea mammals lack hind limbs, but their front limbs are adapted as flippers for swimming in water. These specialized ways of moving allow mammals to survive in many habitats.

Nervous System A mammal's nervous system coordinates its movements. In addition, the nervous system receives information about the environment. The brains of mammals enable them to learn, remember, and behave in complex ways. For example, in order for squirrels to eat nuts, they must crack the nutshell to get to the meat inside. Squirrels learn to use different methods to crack different kinds of nuts, depending on where the weak point in each kind of shell is located.

The senses of mammals are highly developed and adapted for the ways a species lives. Tarsiers, which are active at night, have huge eyes that enable them to see in the dark. Bats use a keen sense of hearing to navigate in the dark and catch prey. Dogs, cats, and bears often use smell to track their prey. Other mammals, such as antelopes, can smell approaching predators in time to flee.

 Reading Checkpoint What are three ways that mammals can move?

FIGURE 13
A Swinging Orangutan
This young orangutan can grasp branches with its limbs and swing from place to place.

FIGURE 14
The Senses of Seals
Seals can see under water in near darkness. Their long whiskers help them obtain food by detecting the movements of their prey.

◆ 423

 **Lab zone Build Inquiry** **L2**

Compare and Contrast Movement

Materials photographs of porpoise, rabbit, gazelle, bat, and other mammals with interesting styles of movement

Time 10 minutes

Focus Remind students that movement is another defining characteristic of mammals; each mammal has a unique way of moving.

Teach Allow students time to study the photographs. Ask: **What adaptations does each animal have that helps or affects it movement?** (*The porpoise is streamlined for swimming in the sea. The rabbit has strong hind legs for hopping. The gazelle has long slender legs so that it can run fast. Bats have actual wings adapted from their front limbs.*)
learning modality: logical/mathematical

Monitor Progress _____ **L2**

Skills Check Ask students to predict how the fur or hair of a mammal living in the Arctic tundra would differ from the fur or hair of a mammal living in the tropical rain forest.

Answers
Figure 12 The heavy fur of the wolf indicates that it lives in a cold environment; the hippo has little hair so it most likely lives in a warm environment.

Reading Checkpoint Accept any three of the following: Run, hop, swing, swim, fly, or glide.

Diversity of Mammals

Teach Key Concepts
L2

Unusual Mammals

Focus Tell students that comparing physical characteristics is one way to observe diversity and commonality among mammals.

Teach Ask: **What characteristics can you see that make the mammals in Figures 16 and 17 different?** *(Possible answers: Kangaroo—long, strong rear legs, very short front legs, carrying young in pouch, short thick neck; Giraffe—all four legs are long, young stands beside parent; long neck)* Ask: **What do these animals have in common that makes them mammals?** *(They are endothermic vertebrates with four-chambered hearts, skin with fur or hair and they produce milk.)* **learning modality: visual**

Help Students Read
L1

Identifying Main Ideas Have students read the main topic sentence in bold type under *Diversity of Mammals.* Ask: **Given this topic sentence, what are the main ideas that you should look for in this selection?** *(The characteristics of each type of mammal)* Have students work in groups to create index cards with the characteristics of each type of mammal. **learning modality: visual**

FIGURE 15
A Spiny Anteater
The young of this spiny anteater, a monotreme, hatch from eggs.

Diversity of Mammals

Mammals are a very diverse group. Look at the spiny ant-eater and the kangaroo shown on this page. Both are mammals that feed their young milk. But, in other ways, they are different. **There are three main groups of mammals—monotremes, marsupials, and placental mammals. The groups differ in how their young develop.**

Monotremes Egg-laying mammals are called **monotremes.** There are just three species of monotremes—two species of spiny anteaters and the duck-billed platypus. A female spiny anteater lays one to three leathery-shelled eggs directly into a pouch on her belly. After the young hatch, they stay in the pouch for six to eight weeks. There they drink milk that seeps out of pores on the mother's skin. In contrast, the duck-billed platypus lays her eggs in an underground nest. The tiny young feed by lapping at the milk that oozes from slits onto the fur of their mother's belly.

Marsupials Koalas, kangaroos, and opossums are some of the better-known marsupials. **Marsupials** are mammals whose young are born at an early stage of development, and they usually continue to develop in a pouch on their mother's body.

Marsupials have a very short **gestation period,** the length of time between fertilization and birth. For example, opossums have a gestation period of about 13 days. Newborn marsupials are tiny—some opossums are less than 1 centimeter long at birth! When they are born, marsupials are blind, hairless, and pink. They crawl along the wet fur of their mother's belly until they reach her pouch. Once inside, they find one of her nipples and attach to it. They remain in the pouch until they have grown enough to peer out of the pouch opening.

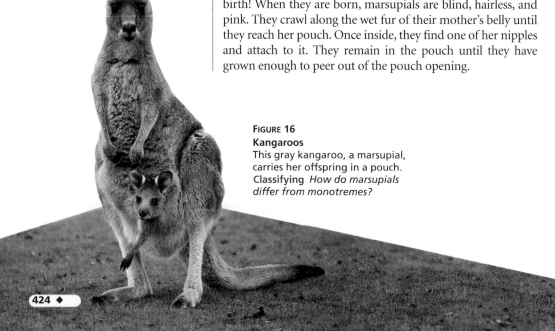

FIGURE 16
Kangaroos
This gray kangaroo, a marsupial, carries her offspring in a pouch.
Classifying *How do marsupials differ from monotremes?*

424 ◆

Placental Mammals Unlike a monotreme or a marsupial, a **placental mammal** develops inside its mother's body until its body systems can function independently. The name of this group comes from the **placenta,** an organ in pregnant female mammals that passes materials between the mother and the developing embryo. Food and oxygen pass from the mother to her young. Wastes pass from the young to the mother, who eliminates them. An umbilical cord connects the young to the mother's placenta. Most mammals, including humans, are placental mammals. Gestation periods of placental mammals are generally longer than those of marsupials. Usually, the larger the placental mammal, the longer the gestation period. The gestation period for an elephant, for example, averages about 21 months, but for a mouse, it's only about 20 days.

Placental mammals are classified into groups on the basis of characteristics such as how they eat and how their bodies move. You can see the diversity of placental mammals in Figure 18 on the next page.

 Reading Checkpoint What is a placenta?

FIGURE 17 Mother and Baby Giraffe
This baby giraffe, a placental mammal, feeds on milk produced by its mother.

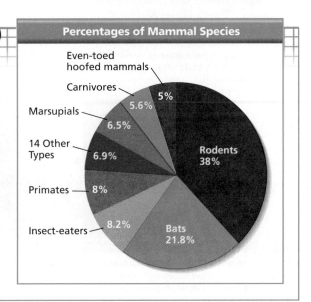

Math → **Analyzing Data**

Mammal Diversity

This circle graph shows the percentage of species of some types of mammals.

1. **Reading Graphs** What percentage of species are bats?
2. **Calculating** What percentage of species are not bats?
3. **Graphing** Suppose you used the data shown in the circle graph to make a bar graph. Which bar would be tallest?
4. **Predicting** What total should all the percentages in the pie chart add up to? Why?

Percentages of Mammal Species

- Even-toed hoofed mammals — 5%
- Carnivores — 5.6%
- Marsupials — 6.5%
- 14 Other Types — 6.9%
- Primates — 8%
- Insect-eaters — 8.2%
- Rodents — 38%
- Bats — 21.8%

Math → **Analyzing Data**

Math Skill Interpreting graphs

Focus For classification, mammals can be classed as: monotreme, marsupial, or placental. It is interesting to look at the number of species for each. Monotromes represent one tenth of one percent of all mammals, so do not have their own pie piece. They are lumped in the "14 Other Orders."

Teach Remind students that a circle graph shows how much of what kind goes to make up a whole class, group, or other entity. This circle graph, like most, is characterized by percents. Remind students that percentage means "per one hundred" Ask: **What information does each slice of the graph tell you?** (*What percentage of the whole is made up of each species*)

Answers

1. 21.8 percent
2. 78.2 percent
3. The group with the greatest number of species, the rodents, would be the tallest.
4. 100; In an accurate circle chart, the entire chart presents 100 percent of the items counted, in this case, mammal species.

Monitor Progress _____ L2

Skills Check Ask students to identify three characteristics common to all mammals and one distinguishing characteristic for each group of mammals.

Answer

Figure 16 Monotremes lay eggs. Marsupials are born, not hatched, and then find their way to their mother's pouch to continue their development.

Reading Checkpoint An organ in pregnant female mammals that passes materials between the mother and the developing embryo.

425

Use Visuals: Figure 18

Comparing Placental Mammals

Focus Review the definition of the term *placental mammal.*

Teach Explain that each of the animals pictured is a representative of a specific group of placental mammals that share several unique characteristics in addition to the characteristics shared by all placental mammals. Allow groups of four students to look at and discuss the photos. Encourage them to make comparisons using the photos and their accompanying captions. Then, have them list their observations about the characteristics of the mammals on these pages such as: ocean dweller, able to fly.

Extend Have students write the name of each mammal on the front of an index card and list several observable characteristics—including those common to all mammals—on the back of the card. Students may exchange cards and quiz one another.
learning modality: visual

FIGURE 18
Diversity of Placental Mammals
From tiny moles to huge elephants, placental mammals are diverse. They are grouped on the basis of how they eat and move as well as other characteristics.

Rabbits and Hares ▶
Leaping mammals like this black-tailed jack rabbit have long hind legs specialized for spectacular jumps. Rabbits and hares have long, curved incisors for gnawing.

Carnivores ▶
This river otter belongs to the group known as carnivores. Dogs, raccoons, and seals are other members of this group. Most carnivores have large canine teeth and clawed toes that help them catch and eat their prey.

Marine Mammals ▲
Whales, manatees, and these Atlantic spotted dolphins are ocean-dwelling mammals with a body shape adapted for swimming.

Rodents ▶
Rodents are gnawing mammals such as mice, rats, beavers, and the capybaras shown here. The incisor teeth of most rodents keep growing throughout their lives but are constantly worn down by gnawing.

Mammals With Trunks ▲
Elephants' noses are long trunks that they use for collecting food and water.

426 ◆

426

Insect-Eaters ▲
Moles and their relatives have sharp cutting surfaces on all of their teeth. This star-nosed mole spends much of its time searching for prey with its sensitive, tentacled snout.

◀ **Flying Mammals**
The wings of bats are made of a thin skin that stretches from their wrists to the tips of their long finger bones.

◀ **Toothless Mammals**
Armadillos, such as the one shown here, are toothless mammals. So are sloths. Although a few members of this group have small teeth, most have none.

Primates ▼
This group of mammals with large brains and eyes that face forward includes humans, monkeys, and apes such as this chimpanzee.

Hoofed Mammals ▲
Some mammals with hooves have an even number of toes and some have an odd number of toes. Cows, deer, and pigs all have an even number of toes. Horses and zebras have an odd number of toes.

◆ 427

Mammal Classification

Materials colored markers, glue, magazines, poster board, scissors; magazines that contain pictures of animals

Time 20 minutes

Focus Tell students that the great diversity of placental mammals offers interesting challenges for classification.

Teach Direct groups of three students to look through the magazines and cut out as many pictures of mammals as they can find. Challenge students to observe and list as many traits—eating, moving, caring for young, and so on—about each mammal as they can. Next, have them use the traits to classify the mammal. Provide a place for students to post their work.

Apply Allow student groups to display their work and critique the work of others. Allow students to query one another's work. Discuss questions regarding the validity of any of the classifications. Work toward a class consensus. **learning modality: logical/mathematical**

Monitor Progress _____ L2

Oral Presentation Ask students to name five mammals and state the group to which each belongs. Have them describe characteristics of the animal that place it in that group.

427

Answer

✓ Reading Checkpoint   The young are helpless—they may be furless, unable to open their eyes, or unable to feed themselves.

Assess

Reviewing Key Concepts

1. a. Four of the following: endothermic, vertebrates, four-chambered hearts, skin with fur or hair, produce milk, internal fertilization **b.** Mammals have teeth that are shaped to allow them to obtain food in particular ways. **c.** Fur or hair and fat help mammals live in colder environments than reptiles. Mammals are endotherms; reptiles are ectotherms.

2. a. Monotremes, marsupials, and placental mammals **b.** Monotremes lay eggs; marsupials are very immature when born and develop in a pouch; placental mammals develop inside the mother to a further extent than marsupials, with the aid of a placenta. **c.** Marine mammals have streamlined bodies for swimming, and flying mammals have wings made from thin skin that stretches from their wrists to the tips of their long finger bones.

Reteach   L1

On the board create a chart listing five characteristics common to all three groups of mammals

Performance Assessment   L2

Drawing Invite students to sketch a mammal or describe it in writing. They should then list the characteristics it has that are unique to mammals. Students can save their sketches in their portfolios.

Portfolio

All in One Teaching Resources, Unit 2

- Section Summary: *Mammals*
- Review and Reinforce: *Mammals*
- Enrich: *Mammals*

FIGURE 19
Parental Care by Dall's Sheep
Young mammals usually require much parental care. On a rocky slope in Alaska, this Dall's sheep, a placental mammal, keeps a close watch on her lamb.

Caring for Young Whether a monotreme, a marsupial, or a placental mammal, young mammals are usually quite helpless for a long time after being born. Many are born without a coat of insulating fur. Their eyes are often sealed and may not open for weeks. For example, black bear cubs are surprisingly tiny when they are born. The blind, nearly hairless cubs have a mass of only 240 to 330 grams—about the same mass as a grapefruit. The mass of an adult black bear, in contrast, ranges from about 120 to 150 kilograms—about 500 times as much as a newborn cub!

Young mammals usually stay with their mother or both parents for an extended time. After black bear cubs learn to walk, they follow their mother about for the next year, learning how to be a bear. They learn things that are important to their survival, such as which mushrooms and berries are good to eat and how to rip apart a rotten log and find good-tasting grubs within it. During the winter, when black bears go through a period of inactivity, the young bears stay with their mother. The following spring, she will usually force them to live independently.

✓ Reading Checkpoint   Why are most young mammals dependent on one or both parents after they are born?

Section 3 Assessment

↻ **Target Reading Skill** **Building Vocabulary** Use your definitions to help answer the questions below.

Reviewing Key Concepts

1. a. Defining What characteristics do mammals share?
   b. Describing Describe the adaptation that most mammals have for obtaining food.
   c. Relating Cause and Effect What enables mammals to live in colder environments than reptiles? Explain.

2. a. Reviewing What are the three main groups of mammals?
   b. Explaining How do monotremes, marsupials, and placental mammals differ?
   c. Interpreting Photographs Look at Figure 18. Describe the adaptations for movement of marine mammals and flying mammals.

Lab zone **At-Home Activity**

Mammals' Milk With a family member, examine the nutrition label on a container of whole milk. What types of nutrients does whole milk contain? Discuss why milk is an ideal source of food for young, growing mammals.

Lab zone Chapter **Project**

Keep Students on Track While students continue to observe, they should begin to plan how their observations will be analyzed and presented. Review graphing techniques for the benefit of students who are unfamiliar with this method of organizing mathematical data. Suggest students group their observations to establish the habits of specific birds of related species.

Lab zone At-Home **Activity**

Mammals' Milk L2 Show students the nutrition facts listed on a milk label so that they will know where to look for the information.

Keeping Warm

Problem

Do wool products provide insulation from the cold? How well does wool insulate when it is wet?

Skills Focus

graphing, interpreting data

Materials

- tap water, hot • scissors • beaker, 1-L
- 3 thermometers • clock or watch
- graph paper • a pair of wool socks
- tap water, room temperature
- 3 containers, 250-mL, with lids

Procedure

1. Put one container into a dry woolen sock. Soak a second sock with water at room temperature, wring it out so it's not dripping, and then slide the second container into the wet sock. Both containers should stand upright. Leave the third container uncovered.

2. Create a data table in your notebook, listing the containers in the first column. Provide four more columns in which to record the water temperatures during the experiment.

3. Use scissors to carefully cut a small "X" in the center of each lid. Make the X just large enough for a thermometer to pass through.

4. Fill a beaker with about 800 mL of hot tap water. Then pour hot water nearly to the top of each of the three containers. **CAUTION:** *Avoid spilling hot water on yourself or others.*

5. Place a lid on each of the containers, and insert a thermometer into the water through the hole in each lid. Gather the socks around the thermometers above the first two containers so that the containers are completely covered.

6. Immediately measure the temperature of the water in each container, and record it in your data table. Take temperature readings every 5 minutes for at least 15 minutes.

Analyze and Conclude

1. **Graphing** Graph your results using a different color to represent each container. Graph time in minutes on the horizontal axis and temperature on the vertical axis.

2. **Interpreting Data** Compare the temperature changes in the three containers. Relate your findings to the insulation characteristics of mammal skin coverings.

3. **Communicating** Suppose a company claims that its wool socks keep you warm even if they get wet. Do your findings support this claim? Write a letter to the company explaining why or why not.

Design an Experiment

Design an experiment to compare how wool's insulating properties compare with those of other natural materials (such as cotton) or manufactured materials (such as acrylic). Obtain your teacher's permission before carrying out your investigation.

For: Data sharing
Visit: PHSchool.com
Web Code: ced-2043

Analyze and Conclude

1. Students should graph data with time along the *x*-axis, temperature along the *y*-axis.

2. The temperature changed the most in the container without a sock, then the wet sock, and then the dry sock. Wool keeps animals warm even when it is wet.

3. Sample answer: No. Wet socks will keep you warmer than no socks, but not as warm as dry socks.

Extend Inquiry

Design an Experiment Remind students to use materials of the same thickness.

For: Data sharing
Visit: PHSchool.com
Web Code: ced-2043

Keeping Warm

Prepare for Inquiry

Key Concept

Wool is an insulator that helps conserve heat.

Skills Objectives

After this lab, students will be able to
- graph data
- interpret data to determine the insulation characteristics of various materials

Prep Time 15 minutes
Class Time 35 minutes

Advance Planning

Make sure groups use identical containers, such as plastic yogurt cups.

 **Teaching Resources, Unit 2**
- Lab Worksheet: *Keeping Warm*

Safety

Students should walk slowly when carrying glass containers or hot water to avoid breakage or spills. Students should be cautious when putting holes in lids with scissors. Students should be careful when handling glass thermometers and not force thermometers through the holes in the lids. They can make a larger hole if the thermometer does not fit. Review the safety guidelines in Appendix A.

Guide Inquiry

Invitation

Ask: **Name some ways we use insulation to conserve heat or keep heat in.** *(Sample answers: Wear warm clothes; use insulation to keep cold air out of houses)*

Introduce the Procedure

Before students begin, tell them that they will compare changes in temperature to find out which insulates better—dry wool or wet wool.

Troubleshooting the Experiment

Supply a large container of hot water so all groups will start with water around 40–45°C.

Expected Outcome

The containers should cool in this order: no sock, wet sock, dry sock.

Interactive Textbook

- Complete student edition
- Section and chapter self-assessments
- Assessment reports for teachers

Help Students Read

Building Reading Literacy

Have students read the passage about the characteristics of birds. As they reach the bottom of a page, have them stop and write down the main ideas in the passage. Have them ask themselves: **Did I have any trouble reading this passage? If so, why?** Then, have them devise their own strategies to improve their understanding. Suggest they use the strategy as they continue reading.

Build Vocabulary

Word Forms Before students read the chapter, have them look up the words *circulate, digest,* and *adapt.* Then, have students write a prediction for the meanings of the terms *circulation, digestion,* and *adaptation.* After students study the section, have them look at their predictions and discuss any differences between their predictions and the way in which the term is used in the text.

Connecting Concepts

Concept Maps Help students develop one way to show how the information in this chapter is related. Birds and mammals each have their own set of common characteristics. Have students brainstorm to identify the key concepts, key terms, details, and examples. Then write each one on a sticky note and attach it at random to chart paper on to the board.

Tell students that this concept map will be organized in hierarchical order and to begin at the top with the key concepts. Ask students these questions to guide them to categorize the information on the stickies: **What are some characteristcs shared by all mammals? What are three main groups of mammals?**

Chapter 12 Study Guide

① Birds

Key Concepts

- A bird is an endothermic vertebrate that has feathers and a four-chambered heart. A bird also lays eggs.
- Birds are adapted for living in diverse environments. You can see some of these adaptations in the shapes of their legs, claws, and bills.

Key Terms
bird
contour feather
down feather
crop
gizzard

② The Physics of Bird Flight

Key Concepts

- The difference in pressure above and below the wings as the bird moves through the air produces an upward force that causes the bird to rise.
- Three types of bird flight are flapping, soaring and gliding, and diving.

Key Term
lift

430 ◆

③ Mammals

Key Concepts

- All mammals are endothermic vertebrates that have a four-chambered heart and skin covered with fur or hair. Most mammals are born alive, and every young mammal is fed with milk produced by organs in its mother's body.
- There are three main groups of mammals—monotremes, marsupials, and placental mammals. The groups differ in how their young develop.

Key Terms
mammal
mammary gland
diaphragm
monotreme
marsupial
gestation period
placental mammal
placenta

Prompt students by using connecting words or phrases, such as "all have" and "can be divided into" to indicate the basis for the organization of the map. The phrases should form a sentence between or among a set of concepts.

Answers
Accept logical presentations by students.

All in One Teaching Resources, Unit 2

- Key Terms Review: *Birds and Mammals*
- Connecting Concepts: *Birds and Mammals*

Go Online
PHSchool.com
For: Self-Assessment
Visit: PHSchool.com
Web Code: cea-2040

Organizing Information

Comparing and Contrasting Copy the table comparing mammal groups onto a sheet of paper. Then fill in the empty spaces and add a title.

Characteristic	Monotremes	Marsupials	Placental Mammals
How Young Begin Life	a. ___?___	b. ___?___	c. ___?___
How Young Are Fed	milk from pores or slits on mother's skin	d. ___?___	e. ___?___
Example	f. ___?___	g. ___?___	h. ___?___

Reviewing Key Terms

Choose the letter of the best answer.

1. Birds are the only animals with
   a. scales.
   b. wings.
   c. feathers.
   d. a four-chambered heart.

2. The gizzard of a bird
   a. stores air.
   b. removes oxygen from air.
   c. helps a bird fly.
   d. grinds food.

3. An organ that produces milk to feed the young is called a
   a. mammary gland.
   b. placenta.
   c. pouch.
   d. egg.

4. Which muscle helps mammals move air into and out of their lungs?
   a. air muscle
   b. diaphragm
   c. placenta
   d. gestation

5. A monotreme differs from a placental mammal because it
   a. has fur.
   b. has a placenta.
   c. lays eggs.
   d. feeds its young milk.

If the statement is true, write *true*. If it is false, change the underlined word or words to make the statement true.

6. <u>Down feathers</u> give shape to a bird's body.

7. A bird's <u>crop</u> stores food.

8. The upward force on a bird's moving wing is called <u>lift</u>.

9. The function of <u>contour feathers</u> is similar to the function of fur.

10. A <u>diaphragm</u> is the length of time between fertilization and birth.

Writing in Science

Cause and Effect Paragraph Which adaptations improve a bird's ability to fly? Write a paragraph in which you describe the effects of adaptations you learned about on the ability of a bird to fly. Be sure to include a topic sentence.

Discovery CHANNEL SCHOOL

Birds and Mammals

Video Preview
Video Field Trip
▶ Video Assessment

Go Online
PHSchool.com
For: Self-Assessment
Visit: PHSchool.com
Web Code: cea-2040

Students can take a practice test online that is automatically scored.

All in One Teaching Resources, Unit 2
- Transparency LS130
- Chapter Test
- Performance Assessment Teacher Notes
- Performance Assessment Student Worksheet
- Performance Assessment Scoring Rubric

ExamView® Computer Test Bank CD-ROM

Organizing Information

a. hatch from egg
b. born live; crawl into mother's pouch
c. born live
d. feeds on milk produced by mother in her pouch
e. feeds on milk produced by mother
f. spiny anteater or duck-billed platypus
g. koala, kangaroo, or opossum
h. human, giraffe, bear, rabbit, whale, etc.
Sample title: Mammals

Reviewing Key Terms

1. c **2.** d **3.** a **4.** b **5.** c
6. Contour feathers
7. True
8. True
9. Down feathers
10. Gestation period

Writing in Science

Writing Mode Exposition: Cause and Effect

Scoring Rubric
4 Includes complete, accurate, detailed cause-and-effect relationships
3 Includes complete, accurate relationships
2 Includes incomplete but accurate relationships
1 Includes incomplete and inaccurate relationships

Discovery CHANNEL SCHOOL
Video Assessment

Birds and Mammals

Show the Video Assessment to review chapter content and as a prompt for the writing assignment. Discussion question: **What is one adaptation of birds that helps provide the extra energy needed for flight?** *(Air sacs in the lungs extract extra oxygen; the two-loop circulatory system and four-chambered heart enable birds to pump oxygen-rich blood very efficiently.)*

Checking Concepts

11. The bones are lightweight, and the forelimb bones are modified into wings.

12. Air sacs allow birds to obtain more oxygen from each breath than other animals can.

13. A bird's four-chambered heart includes separate ventricles for the oxygen-rich blood and the oxygen-poor blood. By not allowing them to mix, a bird's circulatory system thus delivers oxygen more efficiently to the body's cells.

14. Lift is caused by the difference in pressure above and below a bird's wings (with greater pressure pushing up on the wing from below).

15. Warm air rises, and soaring birds are carried upward by the rising air. When the air cools, the birds glide downward until they find another column of rising air.

16. An incisor has a flat edge that makes it good for biting off and cutting food.

17. Accept any two: They are endotherms; their fur insulates them; they have a layer of insulating fat.

18. Mammals have complex nervous systems and senses that are capable of directing and coordinating complicated movements.

Thinking Critically

19. Endothermic animals have four-chambered hearts. In a four-chambered heart, oxygenated blood does not mix with deoxygenated blood, and therefore the blood that reaches the body tissues is carrying a large amount of oxygen. Oxygen is needed to release the energy that enables endothermy.

20. The faster-moving air above the wing exerts less pressure than the slow-moving air beneath the wing. The difference in pressure produces an upward force called lift.

21. These three mammals live in cold water and need a thick, insulating layer of fat to protect them from the cold.

22. Since rodents' front teeth grow constantly, they might continue to grow and become very long.

Checking Concepts

11. Explain how the skeleton of a bird is adapted for flight.

12. What adaptations help a bird obtain enough oxygen for flight? Explain.

13. Why is a bird's circulatory system efficient? Explain.

14. What causes lift?

15. Explain how soaring and gliding birds such as vultures use air currents in their flight.

16. How does the structure of an incisor relate to its function?

17. Identify and explain two ways in which mammals are adapted to live in climates that are very cold.

18. What is the function of a mammal's nervous system?

Thinking Critically

19. Making Generalizations What is the general relationship between whether an animal is an endotherm and whether it has a four-chambered heart? Relate this to the animal's need for energy.

20. Relating Cause and Effect Look at the diagram below. Explain how lift occurs and what effect it has on the bird.

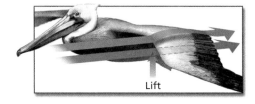

Lift

21. Applying Concepts Why do whales, polar bears, and seals have a thick layer of fat?

22. Predicting If a rodent were fed a diet consisting only of soft food that it did not need to gnaw, what might its front teeth look like after several months? Explain.

Applying Skills

Use the information in the table to answer Questions 23–25.

The data table below shows the approximate gestation period of several mammals and the approximate length of time that those mammals care for their young after birth.

Mammal	Gestation Period	Time Spent Caring for Young After Birth
Deer mouse	0.75 month	1 month
Chimpanzee	8 months	24 months
Harp seal	11 months	0.75 month
Elephant	21 months	24 months
Bobcat	2 months	8 months

23. Graphing Decide which kind of graph would be best for showing the data in the table. Then construct two graphs—one for gestation period and the other for time spent caring for young.

24. Interpreting Data Which mammals listed in the table care for their young for the longest time? The shortest time?

25. Drawing Conclusions How are the size of the mammal and the length of time it cares for its young related? Which animal is the exception to this pattern?

Lab zone Chapter **Project**

Performance Assessment When you present your bird-watch project, display your graphs, charts, and pictures. Describe the ways in which birds eat and the interesting examples of bird behavior you observed. Then, analyze how successful the project was. Was the bird feeder located in a good place for attracting and observing birds? Did many birds come to the feeder? If not, why might this have happened? What are the advantages and limitations of using field guides for identifying birds?

Lab zone Chapter **Project** L3

Project Wrap Up Students can present their projects in a number of ways. They can turn in a written report with sketches and graphs, make posters that show the different birds that visited their feeders and their behaviors, or give an oral presentation that focuses on their observations or on the behavior of a single type of bird. Encourage students to be creative in the way they report their data. On their graphs, students could add illustrations of the different types of birds rather than just their names.

Reflect and Record Students should explain why they think the bird feeder was or was not placed in a good location.

Standardized Test Prep

Choose the letter of the best answer.

1. Of the following structures found in a bird, which one's main function is to store food?
   A stomach
   B gizzard
   C crop
   D bill

2. Which characteristics do birds and mammals share?
   F Both are endothermic vertebrates.
   G Both have fur or hair.
   H Both have a three-chambered heart.
   J Both are vertebrates that produce milk.

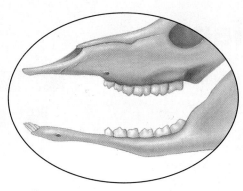

3. The diagram above shows the jawbone and teeth of an animal. The front of the mouth faces left. Which of the following best describes the teeth?
   A many sharp canines
   B broad molars at the back of the mouth
   C molars at the front of the mouth
   D flat incisors at the back of the mouth

4. Based on the kinds of teeth you observe in the diagram above, make your best inference about what this animal might be.
   F bird
   G cow
   H rabbit
   J bear

5. Which of the following best describes the function of the placenta?
   A to deliver oxygen to the body's cells
   B to store food inside the body before swallowing and digesting it
   C to direct and coordinate a mammal's complex movements
   D to pass materials between a mother and her offspring before it is born

Constructed Response

6. Describe how birds care for their eggs and newly hatched young. Your answer should include information about why this care is necessary.

Applying Skills

23. A bar graph would be best for showing this kind of data. Students' graphs should accurately reflect the data.

24. Longest — elephant and chimpanzee; Shortest — harp seal

25. In general, the larger the mammal, the more time it spends caring for its young. The harp seal is the exception.

Standardized Test Prep

1. C **2.** F **3.** B **4.** G **5.** D

6. Birds care for their eggs by sitting on them to keep the temperature close to that of the parent bird. The eggs need this warm temperature in order to develop. Bird parents feed and protect young birds until they are able to leave the nest and fly. This gives the birds time to develop feathers, sight, and strength.

Chapter at a Glance

 Chapter Project *Learning New Tricks*

Technology

Local Standards

All in One Teaching Resources, Unit 2
- Chapter Project Teacher Notes, pp. 424–425
- Chapter Project Student Overview, pp. 426–427
- Chapter Project Student Worksheets, pp. 428–429
- Chapter Project Scoring Rubric, p. 430

Video Preview

Section 1

2 periods
1 block

What Is Behavior?

13.1.1 Explain what causes animal behavior.
13.1.2 Describe what instincts are.
13.1.3 Describe four types of learned behavior.

Go Online
SCiLINKS NSTA

Video Field Trip

Section 2

2 periods
1 block

Patterns of Behavior

13.2.1 List the three main ways animals communicate.
13.2.2 Give examples of competitive and cooperative behaviors.
13.2.3 Describe cyclic behavior.

Go Online
active art

Section 3

1 period
1/2 block

Tracking Migrations

13.3.1 Explain how two electronic technologies help scientists track animals.
13.3.2 Explain the benefits of tracking animal migrations.

Go Online
SCiLINKS NSTA

Review and Assessment

All in One Teaching Resources, Unit 2
- Key Terms Review, p. 455
- Transparency LS136
- Performance Assessment Teacher Notes, p. 464
- Performance Assessment Scoring Rubric p. 465
- Performance Assessment Student Worksheet, p. 466
- Chapter Test, pp. 467–469

Video Assessment

Go Online
PHSchool.com

Test Preparation

**Test Preparation
Blackline Masters**

Lab zone Chapter Activities Planner

For more activities

LAB ZONE
Easy Planner
CD-ROM

Student Edition	Inquiry	Time	Materials	Skills	Resources
Chapter Project, p. 435	Open-ended	2 to 3 weeks	**All in One Teaching Resources, Unit 2,** p. 424	Observing, drawing conclusions, communicating	**Lab zone Easy Planner** **All in One Teaching Resources, Unit 2,** Support pp. 424–425
Section 1					
Discover Activity, p. 436	Guided	15 minutes	Small vertebrates, a cage or aquarium, food	Predicting	**Lab zone Easy Planner**
Skills Activity, p. 438	Guided	5 minutes	None	Predicting	**Lab zone Easy Planner**
Design Your Own Lab, p. 443	Open-Ended	40 minutes	None	Posing questions, designing experiments, calculating	**Lab zone Easy Planner** **Lab Activity Video** **All in One Teaching Resources, Unit 2,** Design Your Own Lab: *Become a Learning Detective, pp. 438–449*
Section 2					
Discover Activity, p. 444	Guided	15 minutes	None	Forming operational definitions	**Lab zone Easy Planner**
Skills Activity, p. 159	Open-ended	10 minutes	None	Developing hypotheses	**Lab zone Easy Planner**
Try This Activity, p. 449	Guided	15 minutes	22 × 28 cm sheets of paper, glue, stapler, or paste; scissors; timer	Calculating	**Lab zone Easy Planner**
Skills Lab, pp. 452–453	Directed	Prep: 30 minutes Class: 45 minutes plus a few minutes each day for two weeks	Large glass jar, water, hand lens, black paper, forceps, sandy soil, wire screen, bread crumbs, tape, large, thick rubber band, shallow pan, sponge, sugar, glass-marking pencil, 20–30 ants	Observing, inferring, posing questions	**Lab zone Easy Planner** **Lab Activity Video** **All in One Teaching Resources, Unit 2,** Skills Lab: *One for All, pp. 447–449*
Section 3					
Discover Activity, p. 454	Directed	20 minutes	graph paper, clicker	Inferring	**Lab zone Easy Planner**

Section 1  What Is Behavior?

 *2 periods, 1 block*

ABILITY LEVELS
L1 Basic to Average
L2 For All Students
L3 Average to Advanced

Objectives

13.1.1 Explain what causes animal behavior.
13.1.2 Describe what instincts are.
13.1.3 Describe four types of learned behavior.

Key Terms

• behavior • stimulus • response • instinct • learning • imprinting
• conditioning • trial-and-error learning • insight learning

Local Standards

Preteach

Build Background Knowledge

Use a chart to identify animal stimuli and responses.

Lab zone **Discover Activity** *What Behaviors Can You Observe?* **L1**

Targeted Print and Technology Resources

All in One Teaching Resources, Unit 2
L2 Reading Strategy Transparency
LS131: Outlining

● **PresentationEXPRESS™ CD-ROM**

Instruct

The Behavior of Animals Define *stimulus* and *response* and apply the terms to animal behavior.

Behavior by Instinct Use examples to teach about instinctive behavior.

Learned Behavior Use pictures to explain different kinds of learned behavior.

Lab zone **Design Your Own Lab** *Become a Learning Detective* **L2**

Targeted Print and Technology Resources

All in One Teaching Resources, Unit 2
L2 Guided Reading, pp. 433–435
L2 Transparency LS132
L2 Design Your Own Lab: *Become a Learning Detective*, pp. 438–439

▭ Lab Activity Video/DVD
Design Your Own Lab: *Become a Learning Detective*

www.SciLinks.org Web Code: scn-0251

DISCOVERY CHANNEL
SCHOOL
Video Field Trip

● **Student Edition on Audio CD**

Assess

Section Assessment Questions

Have students use their completed outlines about behavior to help answer the questions.

Reteach

Help students define and provide examples of the four types of learning.

Targeted Print and Technology Resources

All in One Teaching Resources, Unit 2
• Section Summary, p. 432
L1 Review and Reinforce, p. 436
L3 Enrich, p. 437

Section 2 Patterns of Behavior

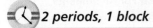 *2 periods, 1 block*

Objectives

Local Standards

13.2.1 List the three main ways animals communicate.

13.2.2 Give examples of competitive and cooperative behaviors.

13.2.3 Describe cyclic behavior.

Key Terms

• pheromone • aggression • territory • courtship behavior • society • circadian rhythm • hibernation • migration

Preteach

Build Background Knowledge

Use question to explore student behavior.

Lab zone Discover Activity *What Can You Express Without Words?* **L1**

Targeted Print and Technology Resources

All in One Teaching Resources, Unit 2

L2 Reading Strategy Transparency LS133: Using Prior Knowledge

⊙ **PresentationEXPRESS™ CD-ROM**

Instruct

Communication Ask leading questions to discuss animal communication.

Competitive Behavior Use comparisons to help students understand competitive behavior.

Group Behavior Use an illustration to discuss animal societies.

Behavior Cycles Define cyclic behavior and have students give examples of each type.

Lab zone Skills Lab *One for All* **L2**

Targeted Print and Technology Resources

All in One Teaching Resources, Unit 2

L2 Guided Reading, pp. 442–444
L2 Transparency LS134
L2 Skills Lab: *One for All*, pp. 447–449

📼 **Lab Activity Video/DVD**
Skills Lab: *One for All*

PHSchool.com Web Code: cep-2052

⊙ **Student Edition on Audio CD**

Assess

Section Assessment Questions

🔄 Have students use their graphic organizers on what they know and learned about patterns of animal behavior as they answer the questions.

Reteach

Use a concept map to organize information about cyclic behavior.

Targeted Print and Technology Resources

All in One Teaching Resources, Unit 2

• Section Summary, p. 441
L1 Review and Reinforce, p. 445
L3 Enrich, p. 446

Section 3 Tracking Migrations

 1 period, 1 block

Objectives

13.3.1 Describe how two electronic technologies help scientists track animals.

13.3.2 Explain the benefits of tracking animal migrations.

Key Terms

• transmitter • receiver • satellite

Local Standards

Preteach

Build Background Knowledge

Ask students to give examples of animals that migrate.

 **Discover Activity** *What Can More Data Points Tell You?* **L2**

Targeted Print and Technology Resources

All in One **Teaching Resources, Unit 2**

L2 Reading Strategy Transparency LS135: Comparing and Contrasting

PresentationEXPRESS™ CD-ROM

Instruct

Technologies for Tracking Students review a brief history of tracking technologies.

Why Tracking Is Important Students discuss the benefits — for people, animals, the environment — of tracking animal migrations.

Targeted Print and Technology Resources

All in One **Teaching Resources, Unit 2**

L2 Guided Reading, p. 452

www.SciLinks.org Web Code: scn-0253

Student Edition on Audio CD

Assess

Section Assessment Questions

Have students use their Comparing and Contrasting tables to answer the questions.

Reteach

List the advantages and disadvantages of electronic tagging to track migration.

Targeted Print and Technology Resources

All in One **Teaching Resources, Unit 2**

• Section Summary, p. 451

L1 Review and Reinforce, p. 453

L3 Enrich, p. 454

Chapter 13 Content Refresher

Go Online

NSTA-PDLINKS

For: Professional development support
Visit: www.SciLinks.org/PDLinks
Web Code: scf-0250

Professional Development

Section 1 What Is Behavior?

Different Stimuli Animals respond to a variety of stimuli. The most familiar are visible and ultraviolet light, infrared radiation (heat), magnetic fields, vibrating air, physical touch, pressure, gravity, and chemicals. All are detected by sensory receptors. Sensory receptors can be as complex as the eye, which perceives light, and the inner ear, which senses air waves (sounds) and gravity. Receptors may also occur in organized clusters, such as those of taste, and smell, which perceive chemicals in the environment. The simplest receptors are plain nerve endings in the skin that perceive heat, touch, and pain. Stimulation of the receptors initiates nerve impulses that pass along neurons to the brain. There, they terminate in specific centers, where they are analyzed, and reactions initiated.

Address Misconceptions

Some students may think that only simple behaviors are instinctive. For a strategy for overcoming this misconception, see **Address Misconceptions** in the section *What Is Behavior?*

Section 2 Patterns of Behavior

Circadian Rhythms The cues for circadian rhythms can be both internal and external. Many circadian rhythms are determined by an internal biological clock that "keeps time." Experiments have shown that certain behaviors will continue on a regular cycle in the absence of any external cues. Even when kept in total darkness, almost all fruit fly larvae will hatch in the early morning. A single gene acts as the internal clock. Light is the most common external cue that influences daily rhythms. Under controlled conditions with no external cues, most human biological clocks run on a 25-hour daily schedule. The internal clocks can be easily reset to 24 hours with exposure to natural light.

Section 3 Tracking Migrations

Tagging Devices Improvements to the tags used to track monarch butterfly migration have led to better tracking with less impact on the butterflies. The old tagging method involved removing the scales on a portion of the forewing and placing an oblong or rectangular adhesive tag on that area. The new tagging method, which uses new, all-weather polypropylene tags, involves placing the adhesive tag on the underside of the butterfly's hind wing. No scales need to be removed to attach the tag. The new tags are round and only 9 millimeters in diameter. The recapture rate is two to three times higher with the new tags compared to rates with the older tags.

Tagging Methods

Old method

New method

Help Students Read

Monitoring Your Understanding
Self-Questioning and Self-Adjusting

This strategy enables students to understand difficult material by focusing on their thought processes as they actively question and apply fix-up strategies to improve comprehension.

Example
1. Self-Question As students read, have them stop often to ask themselves questions such as "Do I understand this?"
2. Apply Fix-Up Strategies Have students use one of the following strategies when they do not understand a paragraph.

• Slowly reread what they do not understand, making sure they understand each sentence before continuing.

• Clarify by stating what they do not understand, talk through confusing points, or relate new information to concepts they are familiar with.

• Read ahead and use visuals and captions.

3. Self-Check After they read, have students summarize or restate the main idea of a paragraph or section.

interactive Textbook
- Complete student edition
- Video and audio
- Simulations and activities
- Section and chapter activities

Chapter 13
Animal Behavior

Chapter Preview

1 What Is Behavior?
Discover *What Behaviors Can You Observe?*
Skills Activity *Predicting*
Analyzing Data *"A-maze-ing" Mice*
Design Your Own Lab *Become a Learning Detective*

2 Patterns of Behavior
Discover *What Can You Express Without Words?*
Active Art *Pheromones*
Skills Activity *Developing Hypotheses*
Try This *Worker Bees*
At-Home Activity *Animal Signs*
Skills Lab *One for All*

3 Tracking Migrations
Discover *How Can You Track Animals?*

interactive Textbook

This pair of Sarus cranes is engaged in an elaborate courtship dance. ▶

434 ◆

Lab zone Chapter **Project** L3

Objectives
This project will enhance students' understanding of animal behavior, helping them differentiate between instinctive and learned behavior. After this project, students will be able to
- observe natural behavior patterns in an animal
- observe the animal's learning over a period of time
- draw conclusions about the animal's ability to learn new behaviors
- communicate their findings

Skills Focus
Observing, drawing conclusions, communicating

Project Time Line 2 to 3 weeks

All in One Teaching Resources, Unit 2
- Chapter Project Teacher Notes
- Chapter Project Overview
- Chapter Project Worksheet 1
- Chapter Project Worksheet 2
- Chapter Project Scoring Rubric

Safety
Be sure that students are not allergic to any animals with which they may be working. The animal's owner and, if the owner is a child, an adult should be present during the handling and training of the animal.

434

Developing a Plan
During the first week, students should familiarize themselves with their animal's natural behaviors. They should also decide what behavior they plan to teach the animal and what method (trial and error or conditioning) they will use to train the animal. Students should allot about two weeks' time for training.

Possible Materials
Students will need animals. In addition, they may need:
- materials to construct a maze
- food to use as a reward
- glue or tape
- timer or stopwatch
- sketchbook, camera, or video camera to record behavior
- poster board and markers for their presentation

Video Preview

Lab zone™ Chapter **Project**

Learning New Tricks

As you learn about animal behavior in this chapter, you will have a chance to study an animal on your own. Your challenge will be to teach the animal a new behavior.

Your Goal To monitor an animal's learning process as you teach it a new skill

To complete this project, you must

- observe an animal to learn about its behavior patterns
- choose a new skill for the animal to learn, and develop a plan that uses rewards to teach it the skill
- monitor the animal's learning over a specific period of time
- follow the safety guidelines in Appendix A

Plan It! Choose an animal to train. The animal could be a family pet, a neighbor's pet, or another animal approved by your teacher. Begin by observing the animal carefully to learn about its natural behaviors. Then think about an appropriate new skill to teach the animal. Write up a training plan to teach it the new skill. Be sure to have your teacher approve your training plan before you begin.

Animal Behavior

Show the Video Preview to introduce the Chapter Project and overview the chapter content. Discussion question: **What rewards do dogs receive that condition their behavior?** (*Praise*)

Launching the Project

To introduce the project, bring an animal into the classroom and show students a behavior it has learned. Talk about who trained the animal, how it was trained, and any difficulties that were encountered during the training process.

Performance Assessment

The Chapter Project Scoring Rubric will help you evaluate how well students complete the Chapter Project. You might want to share the rubric with your students so they will know what is expected. Students will be assessed on

- how well they choose an appropriate behavior for the animal to learn, a stimulus, and a reward; how thoroughly they plan a workable regimen
- the completeness of their observation entries, including what their animals do during training and descriptions of external factors that may affect progress
- the thoroughness and organization of their presentation

Portfolio

Objectives

After completing this lesson, students will be able to

13.1.1 Explain what causes animal behavior.
13.1.2 Describe what instincts are.
13.1.3 Describe four types of learned behavior.

Target Reading Skill

Outlining Explain that using an outline format helps students organize information by main topic, subtopic, and details.

Answers

Possible answers:

I. The behavior of animals
   A. Behavior as response
   B. The functions of behavior
II. Behavior by instinct
III. Learned behavior
   A. Imprinting
   B. Conditioning
   C. Trial-and-error learning
   D. Insight learning

All in One Teaching Resources, Unit 2

• Transparency LS131

Preteach

Build Background Knowledge L2

Animal Behavior

Make a two-column table on the board with the labels *Stimulus* and *Animal's Response*. List events in the first column that may produce a response in an animal. For example, a dog hears a doorbell, a cat or dog sees another animal, a cat sees a ball of yarn, or a fish sees food. Have students describe how the animal might respond in each case and list the responses in the second column.

What Is Behavior?

Reading Preview

Key Concepts

• What causes animal behavior?
• What are instincts?
• What are four types of learned behaviors?

Key Terms

• behavior • stimulus
• response • instinct
• learning • imprinting
• conditioning
• trial-and-error learning
• insight learning

Target Reading Skill

Outlining As you read, make an outline about behavior. Use the red headings for the main topics and the blue headings for the subtopics.

Understanding Behavior
I. Behavior of animals
A. Behavior as response
B.
II. Behavior by instinct
III.
A.
B.
C.
D.

Lab zone Discover **Activity**

What Behaviors Can You Observe?

1. Observe the behavior of a small vertebrate, such as a gerbil or a goldfish, for a few minutes. Write down your observations.
2. Place some food near the animal and observe the animal's behavior.
3. If there are other animals in the cage or aquarium, observe how the animals interact—for example, do they groom each other or ignore each other?
4. Note any other events that seem to make the animal change its behavior.

Think It Over
Predicting What are some circumstances under which you would expect an animal's behavior to change suddenly?

A male anole—a kind of lizard—stands in a patch of sun. As another male approaches, the first anole begins to lower and raise its head and chest in a series of quick push-ups. From beneath its neck a dewlap, a bright red flap of skin, flares out and then collapses, over and over. The anoles stare at one another, looking like miniature dinosaurs about to do battle. The first anole seems to be saying, "This area belongs to me. You'll have to leave or fight!"

FIGURE 1
Dewlap Display
These two anoles are displaying their dewlaps in a dispute over space.

Lab zone Discover **Activity**

Skills Focus Predicting **L1**

Materials cage or aquarium, food, small vertebrates

Time 15 minutes

Tips Students should not handle the animals. Students must wash their hands afterwards. Remind students that tapping on the glass of a cage or aquarium may cause an animal stress.

Expected Outcome Animals will respond to different stimuli such as food, another animal, or disturbing sounds. Responses may include feeding, social interaction, hiding, or escape attempts.

Think It Over Possible answers include the addition of another animal, a loud noise, or the addition of food.

The Behavior of Animals

The dewlap display by anole lizards is one example of behavior. An animal's **behavior** consists of all the actions it performs. For example, behaviors include actions an animal takes to obtain food, avoid predators, and find a mate. Like body structures, the behaviors of animals are adaptations that have evolved over long periods of time.

Most behavior is a complex process in which different parts of an animal's body work together. Consider what happens when a water current carries a small animal to a hydra's tentacles. After stinging cells on the tentacles catch the prey, the tentacles bend toward the hydra's mouth. At the same time, the hydra's mouth opens to receive the food.

Behavior as Response In the previous situation, the touch of the prey on the tentacles acts as a stimulus to the hydra. A **stimulus** (plural *stimuli*) is a signal that causes an organism to react in some way. The organism's reaction to the stimulus is called a **response.** The hydra's response to the prey is to sting it. **All animal behaviors are caused by stimuli.**

Some stimuli, such as prey brushing a hydra's tentacles, are outside the animal. Other stimuli, such as hunger, come from inside. An animal's response may include external actions or internal changes (such as a faster heartbeat), or both.

The Functions of Behavior Most behaviors help an animal survive or reproduce. When an animal looks for food or hides to avoid a predator, it is doing something that helps it stay alive. When animals search for mates and build nests for their young, they are behaving in ways that help them reproduce.

 Reading Checkpoint What is a stimulus?

FIGURE 2
A Moth's Startling "Eyes"
Certain moths have markings on their underwings that resemble eyes. When the moth is poked by a predator, it raises its forewings to reveal the "eyes." *Predicting How is this behavior important to the moth's survival?*

Go Online
SciLINKS
For: Links on animal behavior
Visit: www.SciLinks.org
Web Code: scn-0251

437

Behavior by Instinct

Teach Key Concepts   L2

Behavior That Isn't Learned

Focus Remind students that behavior occurs in response to a stimulus.

Teach Explain that instinctive behavior is behavior that is inborn; the animal can perform the behavior correctly the first time a certain stimulus occurs. Instincts can occur in response to a certain stimulus without an animal having seen another animal of its species perform the behavior; an animal does not have to be taught instinctive behavior. Ask: **What are some examples of instincts?** (*A newborn kangaroo crawling into its mother's pouch; a spider spinning a web, a bird building a nest*)

Apply Ask: **How does instinctive behavior help an animal survive?** (*Possible answers: Instinctive behaviors may occur in response to a food stimulus or in response to predators or other threats.*) **learning modality: logical/mathematical**

◼ Address Misconceptions   L2

Instinctive Behavior

Focus Some students may think that only simple behaviors are instinctive.

Teach Explain to students that many instinctive behaviors are complex. Spiders that spin an orb-web do so using different types of silk secreted by spinning glands. Some of the threads are non-adhesive, while others in the center of the web are sticky. When prey is trapped in the web, the spider responds to the vibrations it feels along the threads. The spider moves along the non-adhesive threads to inject venom into the prey. Other examples of complex behavior that is at least partly instinctive are seasonal migration and some elaborate courtship behaviors, such as cranes "dancing" for potential mates.

Apply When exposed to the stimulus of ultrasonic signals emitted by predatory bats, some moth species will automatically and instantly fold their wings and drop to the ground in response. Ask: **How is this instinctive behavior helpful to the moths?** (*Possible answer: The moths are less likely to be eaten the first time they encounter a predatory bat.*) **learning modality: logical/mathematical**

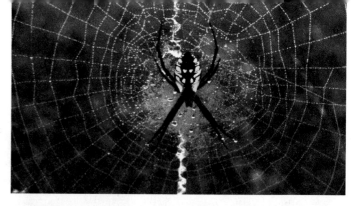

FIGURE 3
A Web Built by Instinct
Most spiders know by instinct how to build elaborate webs.

Lab zone | Skills **Activity**

Predicting

Hawks, which have short necks, prey on gull chicks. Geese, which have long necks, do not prey on the chicks. When newly hatched gull chicks see any bird's shadow, they instinctively crouch down. As the chicks become older, they continue to crouch when they see the shadow of a hawk, but they learn not to crouch when they see a goose's shadow. Predict how older gull chicks will behave when they see bird shadows shaped like A, B, and C. Explain your prediction.

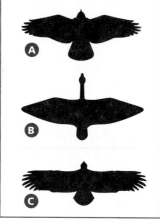

438 ◆

Behavior by Instinct

Animals perform some behaviors by **instinct,** without being taught. **An instinct is a response to a stimulus that is inborn and that an animal performs correctly the first time.** For example, a newborn kangaroo instinctively crawls into its mother's pouch and attaches itself to a nipple. Without this instinct, baby kangaroos could not obtain the milk they need to survive.

Some instincts are fairly simple. Earthworms, for example, crawl away from bright light. Other instincts are complex. Spiders spin complicated webs on their first try without making mistakes in the pattern. Most birds build their nests without ever being taught how.

 Reading Checkpoint   What is an instinct?

Learned Behavior

Recall the first time you rode a bicycle. It probably took a few tries before you did it well—you had to learn how. **Learning** is the process that leads to changes in behavior based on practice or experience. In general, the larger an animal's brain, the more the animal can learn. **Learned behaviors include imprinting, conditioning, trial-and-error learning, and insight learning.** Because learned behaviors result from an animal's experience, they are not usually done perfectly the first time.

All learned behaviors depend in part on inherited traits that have passed from parents to offspring. For example, lion cubs inherit physical features and instincts that are necessary for hunting. They are born with claws that help them capture prey. They also are born with the instinct to pounce on any object that attracts their attention. However, only through experience can they learn how to master hunting skills.

Lab zone | Skills **Activity**

Skills Focus Predicting

Time 10 minutes

Tips Prepare students to predict the chicks' responses by asking them to compare the shadow shapes. Suggest they note similarities and differences that a chick might use as clues for distinguishing between the shadows.

L1 **Expected Outcome** An older chick would learn not to crouch when it sees a shadow shaped like B, while shadows A and C would continue to elicit crouching behavior. This learning is a form of conditioning that modifies instinctive behavior. **learning modality: visual**

Imprinting Imprinting is a learned behavior. In **imprinting**, certain newly hatched birds and newborn mammals recognize and follow the first moving object they see. This object is usually the mother of the young animals. Imprinting involves a combination of instinct and learning. The young animal has an instinct to follow a moving object, but is not born knowing what its parent looks like. The young animal learns from experience what object to follow.

Once imprinting takes place, it cannot be changed. That is true even if the young animal has imprinted on something other than its mother. Young animals have imprinted on moving toys and even humans. Konrad Lorenz, an Austrian scientist, conducted experiments in which he, rather than the mother, was the first moving object that newly hatched birds saw. Figure 4 shows the result of one such experiment. Even as adults, the ducks followed Lorenz around.

Imprinting is valuable for two reasons. First, it keeps young animals close to their mothers, who know where to find food and how to avoid predators. Second, imprinting allows young animals to learn what other animals of their own species look like. This ability protects the animals while they are young. In later life, this ability is important when the animals search for mates.

FIGURE 4
Imprinting
Konrad Lorenz got these ducks to imprint on him by making himself the first moving object they ever saw.
Relating Cause and Effect *Why are the ducks following the swimmer?*

Chapter 13 ◆ 439

Learned Behavior

Teach Key Concepts **L2**

Learning

Focus Ask students to tell something they learned in the last week. *(Possible answers: examples from sporting activities, improving skills at computer or video games.)*

Teach Ask: **What is learning?** *(The process that leads to changes in behavior based on practice or experience.)* **What are some examples of learned behaviors?** *(Imprinting, conditioning, trial-and-error learning, insight learning)*

Apply Ask: **How does learning increase an animal's chance of survival?** *(Possible answer: An animal may learn to avoid predators and hunt for food more effectively.)*
learning modality: verbal

Lab zone Teacher **Demo** **L1**

Automatic Responses

Materials clear plastic sheet, foam ball
Time 10 minutes

Focus Explain to students that some responses to stimuli are automatic or reflexive. The automatic "blink" response is common among most mammals.

Teach Have several volunteers come to the front of the classroom. Each volunteer should hold the clear plastic sheet in front of his or her face while another volunteer gently tosses the soft foam ball at the sheet. Most students will involuntarily blink, even though they know the ball can't hit them.

Apply Ask: **How does this automatic response aid a mammal's survival?** *(Possible answer: It helps avoid injury to the eye.)*
learning modality: kinesthetic

Monitor Progress **L2**

Skills Check Have students compare instinctive and learned behavior.

Answers
Figure 4 The ducks had imprinted on the swimmer when they were newly hatched ducklings.

Reading Checkpoint Behavior that is inborn and that an animal performs correctly the first time

Designing a Behavior Experiment

Materials none

Time 15 minutes

Focus Remind students of the important steps in experimental design, such as posing a question, developing a hypothesis, controlling variables, and forming operational definitions before they begin the activity.

Teach Divide the class into cooperative groups. Instruct each group to design an experiment to investigate a particular animal's response to a stimulus, such as a dog's response to the ringing of a doorbell. Groups can assign the tasks of the designing process to specific students. Inform students that they must write a description of the procedure and remind them to think of ethical considerations, such as animal treatment and safety, as they outline the experiment.

Apply Have groups present their experimental designs to the rest of the class. Have the class review the experiments and ask questions. If possible allow students to do their experiments. **learning modality: logical/mathematical**

All in One Teaching Resources, Unit 2

• Transparency LS132

Animal Behavior

Show the Video Field Trip to introduce students to rescue and independence dogs and their training. Discussion question: **How do rescue and independence dogs learn to overcome their instincts?** (*By building up a dog's confidence in doing things it would normally avoid*)

FIGURE 5
Conditioning

Pavlov followed specific steps to condition a dog to salivate at the sound of a bell.
Predicting *Predict what the dog would do if it heard a bell ringing in another part of the house.*

Normal Stimulus Alone   **Two Stimuli Together**   **New Stimulus Only**

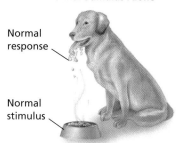  

Normal response

Normal stimulus

❶ When a hungry dog sees or smells food, it produces saliva. Dogs do not usually salivate in response to other stimuli, such as the sound of a ringing bell.

❷ For many days, Pavlov rang a bell every time that he fed the dog. The dog learned to associate the ringing of the bell with the sight and smell of food.

❸ Thus, when Pavlov rang a bell but did not give the dog food, the dog still produced saliva. The new stimulus produced the response that normally only food would produce.

Conditioning When a dog sees its owner approaching with a leash, the dog may jump up, eager to go for a walk. The dog has learned to associate the leash with a pleasant event—a brisk walk. Learning that a particular stimulus or response leads to a good or a bad outcome is called **conditioning.**

Pets are often trained using a form of conditioning. Suppose you want to train a puppy to come when you call it. The desired response is the puppy coming to you when it hears your call. The good outcome you will use is a food reward: a dog biscuit.

Here is how the conditioning works. At first, the puppy rarely comes when you call. But every now and then, the puppy runs to you in response to your call. Each time the puppy comes when you call, you give it a dog biscuit. Your puppy will soon learn to associate the desired response—coming when called—with the good outcome of a food reward. To get the reward, the puppy learns to come every time you call. After a while, the puppy will come to you even if you don't give it a dog biscuit.

During the early 1900s, the Russian scientist Ivan Pavlov performed experiments involving one kind of conditioning. Figure 5 shows the steps that Pavlov followed in his experiments.

"A-maze-ing" Mice

A scientist conducted an experiment to find out whether mice would learn to run a maze more quickly if they were given rewards. She set up two identical mazes. In one maze, cheese was placed at the end of the correct route through the maze. No cheese was placed in the second maze. Use the graph below to answer the questions.

1. **Reading Graphs** On Day 1, what was the average time it took mice with a cheese reward to complete the maze?

2. **Calculating** On Day 6, how much faster did mice with a reward complete the maze than mice without a reward?

3. **Interpreting Data** What was the manipulated variable in this experiment? Explain.

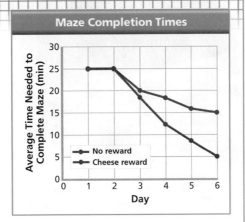

Maze Completion Times

y-axis: Average Time Needed to Complete Maze (min)
x-axis: Day

Legend:
- No reward
- Cheese reward

4. **Drawing Conclusions** Was the rate of learning faster for mice with the cheese reward or without the cheese reward? Explain.

Trial-and-Error Learning One form of conditioning is trial-and-error learning. In **trial-and-error learning,** an animal learns to perform a behavior more and more skillfully. Through repeated practice, an animal learns to repeat behaviors that result in rewards and avoid behaviors that result in punishment. When you learned to ride a bicycle, you did it by trial-and-error. You may have wobbled at first, but eventually you got better. You learned to move in ways that adjusted your balance and kept you from falling over.

Many animals learn by trial-and-error which methods are best for obtaining food. They also learn which methods to avoid. Think of what happens when a predator tries to attack a skunk. The skunk sprays the predator with a substance that stings and smells awful. In the future, the predator is likely to avoid skunks. The predator has learned to associate the sight of a skunk with its terrible spray.

FIGURE 6
Trial-and-Error Learning
After several failed attempts, this squirrel has finally figured out how to jump onto a hummingbird feeder, balance itself, and drink the water.

Chapter 13 ◆ 441

Math ▸ Analyzing Data

Math Skill Interpreting data

Focus Have students study the graph. Ask: **What does the graph show?** (*The differences in time for two groups of mice learning to run a maze*)

Teach Have students familiarize themselves with the line graph. Ask: **What does the x-axis show?** (*The number of days in the testing period*) **The y-axis?** (*The time it took the mice to complete each run*)

Answers

1. 25 minutes
2. 10 minutes
3. Whether a reward of cheese was given; the amount and kind of cheese for the reward should stay the same in repetitions.
4. After the second day, the rate of learning was faster with a reward given as positive reinforcement; rats learned to run the maze through trial and error; conditioning helped the rats learn that using the correct route through the maze would result in a reward, reinforcing and probably speeding up their response. **learning modality: logical/ mathematical**

Help Students Read L1

Comparing and Contrasting Have students read about trial-and-error and insight learning. Then have students construct a chart that compares and contrasts trial-and-error learning with insight learning. (*Possible answer: Both are types of learning that result in a particular behavior. In trial-and-error learning an animal learns to perform a behavior more skillfully through repeated practice. Insight learning involves solving a problem by applying prior knowledge, without a trial-and-error period.*)

Monitor Progress L2

Oral Presentation Ask students to describe an example of conditioning they have witnessed in themselves, another person, or in animals.

Answer
Figure 5 The dog would begin to salivate; it has been conditioned to salivate when it hears the bell.

Monitor Progress

Answer

✓ **Reading Checkpoint** Chimpanzees use twigs to probe into insect nests; a raven can figure out how to bring a piece of meat dangling from a string close enough to eat.

Assess

Reviewing Key Concepts

1. a. Stimuli **b.** A response is an organism's reaction to a stimulus; example: hydra firing stinging cells in response to prey brushing against it. **c.** The functions of behavior are to help an animal survive or reproduce. The hydra's response helped it to stay alive by obtaining food.

2. a. An instinct is a response to a stimulus that is inborn and performed correctly the first time. Any two: Newborn kangaroo crawls into mother's pouch and attaches itself to a nipple, earthworms crawl away from bright light, spiders spin webs, birds build nests. **b.** No, instinctive behaviors are inborn and performed correctly the first time. **c.** Instinctive behaviors often have to do with basic survival such as finding food or avoiding predators. For animals capable of learning, instinct has to get them through the earliest stages of life so that they can become old enough to learn.

3. a. Imprinting, conditioning, trial-and-error learning, and insight learning. **b.** During imprinting, an animal learns to recognize and follow the first moving object that it sees. **c.** The duckling will probably try to follow the child on the tricycle, because ducklings follow the first moving object they see after hatching. This behavior is called imprinting.

Reteach

Review the definitions of the four types of learning: imprinting, conditioning, trial-and-error, and insight. Have students provide an example for each type.

All in One Teaching Resources, Unit 2

- Section Summary: *What Is Behavior?*
- Review and Reinforce: *What Is Behavior?*
- Enrich: *What Is Behavior?*

FIGURE 7
Insight Learning
Using insight, this raven has figured out how to bring meat hanging from a string close enough to eat.

Insight Learning The first time you try out a new video game, you may not need someone to explain how to play it. Instead, you may use what you already know about other video games to figure out how the new one works. When you solve a problem or learn how to do something new by applying what you already know, without a period of trial-and-error, you are using **insight learning.**

Insight learning is most common in primates, such as gorillas, chimpanzees, and humans. For example, chimpanzees use twigs to probe into the nests of termites and other insects that they eat. The chimps use insight to bend or chew their twig "tools" into a shape that will best fit the holes.

In addition to primates, other kinds of animals have also shown insight learning. For example, you may be surprised to learn that the raven shown in Figure 7 is using insight learning to obtain food. The raven uses its beak to draw up a loop of string. Then, it holds the loop under its foot and draws up a second loop, and so on. Soon the food is within reach.

 Reading Checkpoint Give two examples of animals showing insight learning.

Section 1 Assessment

🔄 **Target Reading Skill Outlining** Use the information in your outline about behavior to help you answer the questions below.

Reviewing Key Concepts

1. a. Defining What are signals that cause behavior called?
b. Describing What is meant by *response*? Describe an example of a response.
c. Relating Cause and Effect What are the functions of behavior? Think about the response you described. What function did that response serve?

2. a. Listing What are instincts? List two examples.
b. Inferring Would instincts get better with practice? Explain.
c. Developing Hypotheses Why do you think instincts are particularly important for newborn animals?

3. a. Identifying Identify the types of learned behaviors.
b. Reviewing Describe what happens during imprinting.
c. Predicting Right after hatching, before seeing anything else, a duckling sees a child riding a tricycle. What will probably happen the next time the child rides the tricycle in front of the duckling? Explain.

Writing in Science

List of Questions Suppose you could travel back in time and interview Dr. Pavlov and Dr. Lorenz. Formulate a list of five questions you would ask each scientist about his research on animal learning.

Lab zone Chapter Project

Keep Students on Track Review students' training plans. Check to make sure students have obtained permission from the owners of the animals. Also make sure that the skills students are planning to teach their animals are reasonable. Ensure that students have chosen appropriate rewards for the animals, and that the animals will not be harmed during the training process.

Writing in Science

List of Questions
Scoring Rubric

4 Questions are well thought out and probe key points about each scientist's work.
3 Questions are logical but not probing.
2 Questions are formulaic.
1 Questions reflect minimal preparation.

Become a Learning Detective

Problem

What are some factors that make it easier for people to learn new things?

Skills Focus

calculating, posing questions, designing experiments

Materials

- paper
- pencil

Design a Plan

1. Look over the two lists of words shown in the diagram on this page. Researchers use groups of words like these to investigate how people learn. Notice the way the two groups differ. The words in List A have no meanings in ordinary English. List B contains familiar but unrelated words.

2. What do you think will happen if people try to learn the words in each list? Write a hypothesis about which list will be easier to learn. How much easier will it be to learn that list?

3. With a partner, design an experiment to test your hypothesis. Brainstorm a list of the variables you will need to control in order to make the results of your experiment reliable. Then write out your plan and present it to your teacher.

4. If necessary, revise your plan according to your teacher's instructions. Then perform your experiment using people your teacher has approved as test subjects. Keep careful records of your results.

List A	List B
zop	bug
rud	rag
tig	den
wab	hot
hev	fur
paf	wax
mel	beg
kib	cut
col	sip
nug	job

Analyze and Conclude

1. **Calculating** Find the average (mean) number of words people learned from each list. How do the results compare with your hypothesis?

2. **Posing Questions** What factors may have made one list easier to learn than the other? What other questions can you ask about your data?

3. **Designing Experiments** Look back at your experimental plan. Think about how well you were able to carry it out in the actual experiment. What difficulties did you encounter? What improvements could you make, either in your plan or in the way you carried it out?

4. **Communicating** Share your results with the rest of the class. How do the results of the different experiments in your class compare? What factors might explain the similarities or differences?

More to Explore

Plan an experiment to investigate how long people remember what they learn. Develop a hypothesis, and design an experiment to test your hypothesis.

Chapter 13 ◆ 443

Expected Outcome

Familiar words are easier to learn than unfamiliar ones.

Analyze and Conclude

1. Most test subjects should learn more from list B than list A.
2. It is easier to remember meaningful words than nonsense words; additional questions might include: How does the age of the test subject affect the results? Does the order in which the lists are learned affect results?
3. Results will depend on student plans.

4. Possible answers: The number of words learned depends on the time allowed to learn.

Extend Inquiry

More to Explore Students might hypothesize that familiar concepts are remembered longer. Have several test subjects learn concepts that include familiar and unfamiliar words. Test the subjects after 1, 2, and 4 hours.

Become a Learning Detective L2

Prepare for Inquiry

Key Concept

Various factors can make learning easier or harder.

Skills Objectives

After this lab, students will be able to
- pose questions about human learning
- design an experiment to answer their questions
- calculate the mean number of words learned

Prep Time none
Class Time 40 minutes

Advance Planning

To save class time, decide in advance who the test subjects will be.

Alternative Materials

If students conduct this experiment on classmates, they must generate new lists that are unfamiliar to the test subjects.

All in One Teaching Resources, Unit 2
- Lab Worksheet: *Become a Learning Detective*

Guide Inquiry

Invitation

Ask students to consider how the following factors may affect how easy it is to learn: It is a subject you enjoy; you are motivated by rewards; you are already familiar with the subject; there is much repetition.

Introduce the Procedure

Have students decide on a way to quantitatively measure learning. For example, each subject can examine the list of words for a given time. The subject then has a limited amount of time to write down all of the words he or she can remember. The subject will remember more words from the list that was easier to learn.

Troubleshooting the Experiment

Suggest that students have test subjects write down rather than speak words so that other groups will not overhear.

Objectives

After completing this lesson, students will be able to

13.2.1 List the three main ways animals communicate.

13.2.2 Give examples of competitive and cooperative behaviors.

13.2.3 Describe cyclic behavior.

Target Reading Skill

Using Prior Knowledge Explain that using prior knowledge helps students connect what they already know to what they are about to read.

Answers

Possible answers:

What You Know

1. Dogs bark at intruders.
2. Different sounds an animal makes mean different things.
3. Animals communicate without words.

What You Learned

1. Animals use sounds to communicate warnings about predators, establish territories, or find a mate.
2. Animals communicate with chemicals called pheromones to mark territory and find mates.
3. Animals communicate through body movements to show aggression and courtship behavior.

All in One Teaching Resources, Unit 2

• Transparency LS133

Preteach

Build Background Knowledge L2

Purpose of Behavior

Instruct students to immediately stop what they are doing. Choose students at random and ask them what they were doing when you asked them to stop. Explain that whatever each student was doing was a part of his or her behavior. Ask: **What do you think was the purpose of your behavior?** (*Student answers will depend on what they were doing at the time of the exercise.*)

Reading Preview

Key Concepts

• What are three main ways animals communicate?

• What are some examples of competitive behaviors and cooperative behaviors?

• What is a cyclic behavior?

Key Terms

• pheromone • aggression
• territory • courtship behavior
• society • circadian rhythm
• hibernation • migration

Target Reading Skill

Using Prior Knowledge Your prior knowledge is what you already know before you read about a topic. Before you read, write what you know about the different ways animals communicate in a graphic organizer like the one below. As you read, write what you learn.

What You Know
1. Dogs bark at intruders.
2.

What You Learned
1.
2.

Lab zone — Discover **Activity**

What Can You Express Without Words?

1. Use facial expressions and body movements, but no words, to show surprise or another emotion to your partner.

2. By observing your behavior, your partner should infer what you are communicating. Your partner should also note the behavior clues that led to this inference.

3. Now your partner should try to communicate a feeling or situation to you without words. Infer what your partner is trying to communicate, and note the behavior clues that led to your inference.

Think It Over
Forming Operational Definitions Write your own definition of *communication*. How did this activity change your idea of communication?

Oh no—ants have gotten into the sugar! As you watch in dismay, a stream of ants moves along the kitchen counter. They are heading right for the sugar bowl. Using their sense of smell, the ants follow a chemical trail that was first laid down by the ant that discovered the sugar. Each ant adds to the trail by depositing a tiny droplet of scent onto the counter. The droplet quickly evaporates, making an invisible cloud of scent above the path of the ants. The ants hold their antennae forward and use them to sniff their way to the sugar bowl. Then they turn around and follow the same chemical signal back to their nest.

Lab zone — Discover **Activity**

Skills Focus Forming operational definitions

Materials none

Time 15 minutes

Tips Have students write the feeling or situation they are trying to convey. After their partner guesses what is being communicated, students can check their

L1 notebooks. Students should use natural facial expressions and simple movements.

Expected Outcome Emotions should be able to be communicated. Abstract ideas may be difficult to communicate nonverbally.

Think It Over Most students will include gestures and expressions in the definition of communication.

Communication

You've just read that ants can communicate the location of foods using scent. Animal communication comes in many forms. Perhaps you've seen a cat hissing and arching its back. It is using sound and body posture to communicate a message that seems to say, "Back off!" **Animals use mostly sounds, scents, and body movements to communicate with one another.** An animal's ability to communicate helps it interact with other animals.

Animals communicate many kinds of messages using sound. Some animals use sound to attract mates. Female crickets, for example, are attracted to the sound of a male's chirping. Animals may also communicate warnings with sound. When it sees a coyote or other predator approaching, a prairie dog makes a yipping sound that warns other prairie dogs to take cover in their burrows. The wolf in Figure 8 is warning wolves outside its pack to keep away.

Animals also communicate with chemical scents. A chemical released by one animal that affects the behavior of another animal of the same species is called a **pheromone** (FEHR uh mohn). For example, perhaps you have seen a male house cat spraying a tree. The musky scent he leaves contains pheromones that advertise his presence to other cats in the neighborhood. The scent trail that leads the ants to the sugar bowl in Figure 9 is also made of pheromones.

 Reading Checkpoint What is a pheromone?

FIGURE 8
Howling Wolf
Wolves in a pack may howl all together to warn other packs to stay away.

Go **Online**
active art

For: Pheromones activity
Visit: PHSchool.com
Web Code: cep-2052

FIGURE 9
Follow the Pheromone Trail
These ants are finding their way to the sugar by following a pheromone trail. The first ant to find the sugar began the trail, and each ant added to its strength.
Applying Concepts *What form of communication is a pheromone trail?*

◆ 445

Competitive Behavior

Teach Key Concepts `L2`
Animals Compete for Resources

Focus Explain that animals compete within a species and between species.

Teach Ask: **What resources might animals compete for?** *(Food, water, space, shelter, and mates)* **Why do animals show aggression?** *(To gain control over another animal)* **Why do animals have to compete for resources?** *(In most habitats resources are limited.)* **How does establishing a territory help an animal to survive and reproduce?** *(Within the territory, the animal has access to the resources, which include food, water and shelter. In many animal species a male cannot attract a female unless he holds a territory.)*

Apply Tell students that red-winged blackbirds display their red "epaulets" (red patches on the shoulder area of their wings) to defend a territory. Ask: **What would happen if a male blackbird's red patches were dyed black?** *(The male would probably lose its territory.)* **learning modality: logical/mathematical**

Teacher **Demo** `L2`

Competition and Aggression

Materials 2 glass jars, 2 male bettas (Siamese fighting fish), opaque card, water

Time 15 minutes

Focus Explain to students that the males of this species are very aggressive toward other males.

Teach Place each fish in its own glass jar filled with water. Place the jars next to each other with the opaque card between them. Begin by allowing students to observe the behavior of the two fish for a few minutes with the card in place. Then, remove the card. Be sure each fish can clearly see the other. Have students record and observe the behaviors of the fish.

Apply Have students write short paragraphs to explain how they think these behaviors would benefit the bettas. *(The strongest and most aggressive males are those that survive and find mates.)* **learning modality: visual**

FIGURE 10
Boxing Hares
These Arctic hares are resolving their conflict by boxing. *Inferring What event might have led to this behavior?*

FIGURE 11
Aggressive Gorilla
This lowland gorilla needs no words to say, "Stay away!"

Competitive Behavior

Have you ever fed ducks in the park or pigeons on the street? Then you have probably seen how they fight over every crumb. These animals compete because there usually isn't enough food to go around. **Animals compete with one another for limited resources, such as food, water, space, shelter, and mates.**

Competition can occur among different species of animals. For example, a pride of lions may try to steal a prey from a troop of hyenas that has just killed the prey. Competition can also occur between members of the same species. A female aphid, a type of insect, kicks and shoves another female aphid while competing for the best leaf on which to lay eggs.

Showing Aggression When they compete, animals may display aggression. **Aggression** is a threatening behavior that one animal uses to gain control over another. Before a pride of lions settles down to eat its prey, individual lions show aggression by snapping, clawing, and snarling. First, the most aggressive members of the pride eat their fill. Then, the less aggressive and younger members of the pride get a chance to feed on the leftovers.

Aggression between members of the same species hardly ever results in the injury or death of any of the competitors. Typically, the loser communicates, "I give up" with its behavior. For example, to protect themselves from the aggressive attacks of older dogs, puppies often roll over on their backs, showing their bellies. This signal calms the older dog. The puppy can then creep away.

446 ◆

Differentiated Instruction

Less Proficient Readers `L1`
Using Visuals Have students use Figures 10, 11, and 12 to help them define and understand the concepts of competitive behavior, aggression, and courtship behavior, respectively. For each figure, have students write a description that tells what each animal is doing and identify the type of behavior being demonstrated.
learning modality: visual

Gifted and Talented `L3`
Establishing a Territory Have students research how an animal of their choice establishes and defends its territory. What is the size of its territory? What factors may influence how the animal chooses its territory? Have students share the results of their research with the rest of the class in the form of a multimedia presentation.
learning modality: logical/mathematical

Establishing a Territory On an early spring day, a male oriole fills the warm air with song. You may think the bird is singing just because it is a nice day. But in fact, he is alerting other orioles that he is the "owner" of a particular territory. A **territory** is an area that is occupied and defended by an animal or group of animals. If another animal of the same species enters the territory, the owner will attack the newcomer and try to drive it away. Birds use songs and aggressive behaviors to maintain their territories. Other animals may use calls, scratches, droppings, or pheromones.

By establishing a territory, an animal protects its access to resources such as food and possible mates. A territory also provides a safe area. Within it, animals can raise their young without competition from other members of their species. In most songbird species, and in many other animal species, a male cannot attract a mate unless he has a territory.

Attracting a Mate A male and female salamander swim gracefully in the water, moving around one another. They are engaging in **courtship behavior,** which is behavior in which males and females of the same species prepare for mating. Courtship behavior ensures that the males and females of the same species recognize one another, so that mating and reproduction can take place. Courtship behavior is typically also competitive. For example, in some species, several males may perform courtship behaviors for a single female. She then chooses one of them to mate with.

 Reading Checkpoint How does having a territory help an animal survive?

FIGURE 12
Kingfisher Courtship
These common kingfishers are engaged in courtship. The male on the left is offering the female a gift of food—a freshly caught fish.

447

Group Behavior

Teach Key Concepts L2

Living in a Group

Focus Tell students that animals such as fish, insects, and hoofed mammals often live in groups.

Teach Ask: **What are some advantages to living in a group?** *(Group members protect one another and work together to find food.)* **What are some examples of animal societies?** *(Honeybees, ants, termites, naked mole rats, pistol shrimp)*

Apply Ask: **What disadvantage might there be for animals living in a group?** *(Possible answers: The group members must share resources; some groups have a leader that everyone must follow.)* **learning modality: logical/mathematical**

All in One Teaching Resources, Unit 2

• Transparency LS134

Group Safety

Materials Photos of groups of animals including large schools of fishes, a herd of zebra, and a herd of antelope

Time 10 minutes

Focus Tell students that when many individuals of the same species are in a large group, it may be confusing for a predator to see and select a single individual.

Teach Allow students to examine the photos of the groups of animals. Have them describe the markings or coloration of the animals in the group. Ask: **When a large group of individuals are together, what happens to individual markings? How might this confuse a predator?** *(The markings of an individual animal would blend in with the rest of the group. It may be difficult for a predator to pick out an individual in the group.)*

Apply Ask: **If you wanted to be inconspicuous in a large group of people all dressed in dark suits, what would you do? Explain.** *(Dress in a dark suit to blend in and not be noticeable.)* **learning modality: visual**

FIGURE 13
Safety in Groups
When a predator threatens, musk oxen form a horn-rimmed circle with their young sheltered in the center. **Predicting** *Would a potential predator be more or less likely to attack a group arranged in this way? Explain.*

Group Behavior

Not all animal behaviors are competitive. **Living in groups enables animals to cooperate.** Although many animals live alone and only rarely meet one of their own kind, other animals live in groups. Some fishes form schools, and some insects live in large groups. Hoofed mammals, such as bison and wild horses, often form herds. Living in a group usually helps animals survive. For example, group members may protect one another or work together to find food.

How can group members help one another? If an elephant gets stuck in a mudhole, for example, other members of its herd will dig it out. When animals such as lions hunt in a group, they usually can kill larger prey than a single hunter can.

Safety in Groups Living in groups often protects animals against predators. Fishes that swim in schools are often safer than fishes that swim alone. It is harder for predators to see and select an individual fish in a group. In a herd, some animals may watch for danger while others feed.

Animals in a group sometimes cooperate in fighting off a predator. For example, the North American musk oxen shown in Figure 13 make a defensive circle against a predator, such as a wolf. Their young calves are sheltered in the middle of the circle. The adult musk oxen stand with their horns lowered, ready to charge. The predator often gives up rather than face a whole herd of angry musk oxen.

Animal Societies Some animals, including ants, termites, honeybees, naked mole rats, and pistol shrimp, live in groups called societies. A **society** is a group of closely related animals of the same species that work together in a highly organized way. In a society, there is a division of labor—different individuals perform different tasks. In a honeybee society, for example, there are thousands of worker bees that take on different tasks in the beehive. Some workers feed larvae. Some bring back nectar and pollen from flowers as food for the hive. Other worker bees guard the entrance to the hive.

 Reading Checkpoint What is a society?

Worker Bee Worker bees are females that do not lay eggs. They build, maintain, and defend the hive. They also search for flower nectar, and make honey from that nectar.

Queen Bee The queen bee's function is to lay eggs. A queen bee can lay up to 2,000 eggs a day during the summer.

Drone The only function of the male drones is to mate with queen bees from other colonies.

Cell With Larva The hive is made of six-sided compartments called cells. Some cells, like those shown here, hold eggs that hatch into larvae.

Cell With Honey This cell contains honey, which worker bees make from the flower nectar they collect. Honey is used to feed all the bees in the hive.

FIGURE 14
A Honeybee Society
A honeybee hive usually consists of one queen bee, thousands of female worker bees, and a few hundred male drones.

Chapter 13 ◆ 449

Lab zone **Try This Activity**

Worker Bees

1. Make a paper chain by cutting paper strips for loops and gluing or taping the loops together. After 5 minutes, count the loops in the chain.

2. Now work in a small group to make a paper chain. Decide how to divide up the work before beginning. After 5 minutes, count the loops in the chain.

Calculating Find the difference between the number of loops in your individual and group chains. For Step 2, calculate the number of loops made per person by dividing the total number of loops by the number of people in your group. Was it more productive to work individually or as a group?

Lab zone **Try This Activity**

Skills Focus Calculating L2

Materials 22 × 28 cm sheets of paper; glue, stapler, or paste; scissors; timer

Time 15 minutes

Tips When students work in groups, part of the planning should involve assigning tasks to each group member.

Expected Outcome By working cooperatively, students should have been able to make more paper-chain links. Group members can divide the work so that no one has to perform the whole task.

Extend Have students think about what kinds of tasks are probably performed more efficiently by one person than by a group. **learning modality: kinesthetic**

Use Visuals: Figure 14 L2

A Honeybee Society

Focus Tell students that different types of honeybees perform different tasks.

Teach After students read the description of the individuals in the honeybee society shown in Figure 14, ask: **Is any member of the honeybee society unimportant? Why?** (*None is unimportant. All members have their special tasks to perform.*)

Apply Have a volunteer list on the board the three types of honeybees and their duties. After reviewing the list, ask: **Why is it advantageous that there are more worker bees than other bees in the hive?** (*Worker bees have many different tasks to perform, such as caring for the hive, the queen, and the larvae, and finding and making food. The queens and the drones each have only one task.*) **learning modality: visual**

Address Misconceptions L2

Animal Societies

Focus Students may confuse human societies and animal societies.

Teach Explain to students that human societies may consist of associations of unrelated individuals. In animal societies such as those of ants, termites, honeybees, naked mole rats, and pistol shrimp, all individuals are close relatives, usually siblings. In addition, while roles in animal societies are usually rigid, roles in human societies are much more flexible.

Apply Ask: **What aspects of human society differ from those of an insect society?** (*Possible answers: In human society each individual can define his or her own role in society and complete an array of tasks related to survival.*) **learning modality: verbal**

Monitor Progress L2

Writing Have students form groups to make a list of the advantages of aggression, establishing a territory, and living in groups. Students can save their lists in their portfolios. Portfolio

Answers

Figure 13 A predator would be less likely to attack a group arranged this way because the predator's chance of success is limited.

Reading Checkpoint A society is a group of closely related animals of the same species that work together in a highly organized way.

Behavior Cycles

Teach Key Concepts L2
Circadian Rhythms

Focus Tell students that some animals have behaviors that change over time in regular patterns—usually over the course of a day or a season. Ask: **Give examples of regular changes in behavior in your own life.** *(Possible answers: Awake during the day, sleep at night; get hungry at same time each day)*

Teach Explain that circadian rhythms are behavior cycles that occur over a period of approximately one day. Explain to students that almost all animals display obvious circadian rhythms. Ask: **What are some behaviors that are related to seasons?** *(Hibernation and migration)*

Apply Ask: **How do migration and hibernation help animals survive?** *(Migration enables animals to move to favorable conditions as the seasons change; hibernation slows down an animal's processes, reducing the need for food when less is available.)* **learning modality: verbal**

Integrating Social Studies L2
Interpreting Maps Display several maps that show the migratory paths of different animals, such as monarch butterflies, golden plovers, starlings, humpback whales, or sea turtles. Allow students to examine the maps and the migratory routes. Have students describe the routes taken by the animals, including the names and areas of any relevant continents, countries, or islands. **learning modality: visual**

FIGURE 15
Hibernation
This common dormouse is hibernating for the winter.
Inferring Why is hibernation during the winter a useful adaptation for animals?

Behavior Cycles

Some animal behaviors, called cyclic behaviors, occur in regular, predictable patterns. **Cyclic behaviors usually change over the course of a day or a season.**

Daily Cycles Behavior cycles that occur over a period of approximately one day are called **circadian rhythms** (sur KAY dee un). For example, blowflies search for food during the day and rest at night. In contrast, field mice are active during the night and rest by day. Animals that are active during the day can take advantage of sunlight, which makes food easy to see. On the other hand, animals that are active at night do not encounter predators that are active during the day.

Hibernation Other behavior cycles are related to seasons. For example, some animals, such as woodchucks and chipmunks, are active during warm seasons but hibernate during the cold winter. **Hibernation** is a state of greatly reduced body activity that occurs during the winter when food is scarce. During hibernation, all of an animal's body processes, such as breathing and heartbeat, slow down. This slowdown reduces the animal's need for food. In fact, hibernating animals do not eat. Their bodies use stored fat to meet their reduced nutrition needs.

Migration While many animals live their lives in one area, others migrate. **Migration** is the regular, seasonal journey of an animal from one place to another and back again. Some animals migrate short distances. Dall's sheep, for example, spend summers near the tops of mountains and move lower down for the winters. Other animals migrate thousands of kilometers. The record-holder for distance migrated is the Arctic tern. This bird flies more than 17,000 kilometers between the North and South poles.

Animals usually migrate to an area that provides a lot of food or a good environment for reproduction. Most migrations are related to the changing seasons and take place twice a year, in the spring and in the fall. American redstarts, for example, are insect-eating birds that spend the summer in North America. There, they mate and raise young. In the fall, insects become scarce. Then the redstarts migrate south to areas where they can again find plenty of food.

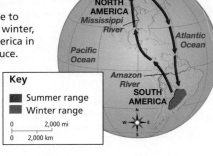

FIGURE 16
Migration
Golden plovers migrate to South America for the winter, and back to North America in the summer to reproduce.

Key

■	Summer range
■	Winter range

0   2,000 mi
0   2,000 km

Scientists are still learning about how migrating animals find their way. But they have discovered that animals use sight, taste, and other senses, including some that humans do not have. Some birds and sea turtles, for example, have a magnetic sense that acts something like a compass needle. Migrating birds also seem to navigate by using the positions of the sun, moon, and stars, as sailors have always done. Salmon use scent and taste to locate the streams where they were born, and return there to mate.

 Reading Checkpoint What happens to an animal during hibernation?

Section 2 Assessment

Target Reading Skill Using Prior Knowledge Review your graphic organizer and revise it based on what you just learned in the section.

Reviewing Key Concepts

1. a. Reviewing What are three main ways animals communicate?
   b. Explaining When house cats spray a tree with their scent, are they communicating? Explain.
   c. Developing Hypotheses What are some advantages of using pheromones to communicate instead of using sound?
2. a. Listing List examples of competitive behavior and cooperative behavior.
   b. Explaining Explain how competition is involved in establishing a territory.
   c. Predicting What might happen when a male mockingbird flies into the territory of another male mockingbird?

3. a. Reviewing What are behaviors that change over the course of a day or a season called?
   b. Comparing and Contrasting How are circadian rhythm and hibernation the same? How are they different?

Lab zone **At-Home Activity**

Animal Signs With a family member, spend some time making detailed observations of the behavior of an animal—a pet, an insect, a bird, or another animal. Watch the animal for signs of aggressive behavior or other communication. Try to figure out why the animal is behaving aggressively or what it is trying to communicate.

Lab zone **At Home Activity**

Animal Signs **L2** Encourage students to observe active animals in a location where they are likely to interact with other animals. Caution students not to approach wild animals.

Answers
Figure 15 It reduces the animal's need for food when food is scarce.

Reading Checkpoint All of the animal's processes slow down.

Assess

Reviewing Key Concepts

1. a. Animals communicate through sounds, scents, and body movements.
b. Yes, they are marking territory and making other cats aware of their presence.
c. Communicating through pheromones rather than sounds is less likely to alert a predator to an animal's immediate location. Also, the animal does not have to be physically present to communicate.
2. a. Animals may compete for food, territory, or mates. Examples of cooperative behavior include hunting in groups and living in groups to help reduce the chance of an attack by a predator. Animals such as honeybees and ants that live in societies also exhibit cooperative behavior. **b.** An animal would compete with other animals; for example, by singing, calling, or leaving droppings, during establishment of its territory. **c.** The resident mockingbird may attack the second bird until it flies away.
3. a. Cyclic behaviors **b.** Both are cyclic behaviors, but hibernation is a cyclic behavior that is on an annual cycle, while a circadian rhythm is on a daily cycle.

Reteach L1

Ask students to make a concept map to organize the information about cyclic behavior. Branches may include *Daily cycle*, *Seasonal cycle*, *Journey*, and *Examples*.

Performance Assessment L2

Have students write a short paragraph explaining the advantages to animals living in a group. Students should include examples of group behavior in their explanations.

Portfolio

All in One Teaching Resources, Unit 2

- Section Summary: *Patterns of Behavior*
- Review and Reinforce: *Patterns of Behavior*
- Enrich: *Patterns of Behavior*

Lab zone Skills Lab

One for All L2

Prepare for Inquiry

Key Concept
In ant colonies, individual members perform different tasks.

Skills Objectives
After this lab, students will be able to
- observe, infer, and pose questions to gather data about an assigned query.

Prep Time 30 minutes

Class Time 45 minutes plus a few minutes each day for two weeks

Advance Planning
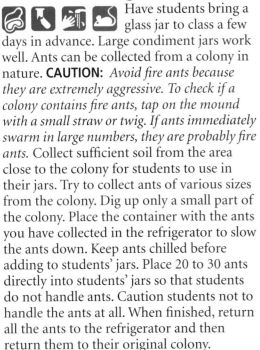 Have students bring a glass jar to class a few days in advance. Large condiment jars work well. Ants can be collected from a colony in nature. **CAUTION:** *Avoid fire ants because they are extremely aggressive. To check if a colony contains fire ants, tap on the mound with a small straw or twig. If ants immediately swarm in large numbers, they are probably fire ants.* Collect sufficient soil from the area close to the colony for students to use in their jars. Try to collect ants of various sizes from the colony. Dig up only a small part of the colony. Place the container with the ants you have collected in the refrigerator to slow the ants down. Keep ants chilled before adding to students' jars. Place 20 to 30 ants directly into students' jars so that students do not handle ants. Caution students not to handle the ants at all. When finished, return all the ants to the refrigerator and then return them to their original colony.

Alternative Materials
Nylon screen can be substituted for the wire screen as it is easier to cut with scissors. You may prefer to purchase an "ant farm" from a scientific supply house.

All in One Teaching Resources, Unit 2
- Lab Worksheet: *One for All*

Guide Inquiry

Invitation
Review with students the information on animal societies. Have students study Figure 14 about honeybee societies. Have students predict how tasks such as getting food and building nests are accomplished in an ant society.

Introduce the Procedure
Tell students they may not observe some tasks. For example, there may be no eggs, larvae, or pupae for adult ants to care for.

Students should think about how they will describe various behaviors. For example, ants may carry dirt grains (from digging), carry food, or interact with each other. Students should observe the tasks that ants of different sizes perform.

Lab zone Skills Lab

One for All

Problem
How does an ant society show organization and cooperative behavior?

Skills Focus
observing, inferring

Materials
- large glass jar • sandy soil • shallow pan
- water • wire screen • sponge • 20–30 ants
- hand lens • bread crumbs • sugar
- black paper • tape • glass-marking pencil
- forceps • large, thick rubber band

Procedure

1. Read over the entire lab to preview the kinds of observations you will be making. Copy the data table into your notebook. You may also want to leave space for sketches.

2. Mark the outside of a large jar with four evenly spaced vertical lines, as shown in the photograph on the next page. Label the sections with the letters A, B, C, and D. You can use these labels to identify the sections of soil on and below the surface.

3. Fill the jar about three-fourths full with soil. Place the jar in a shallow pan of water to prevent any ants from escaping. Place a wet sponge on the surface of the soil as a water source for the ants.

4. Observe the condition of the soil, both on the surface and along the sides of the jar. Record your observations.

5. Add the ants to the jar. Immediately cover the jar with the wire screen, using the rubber band to hold the screen firmly in place.

6. Observe the ants for at least 10 minutes. Look for differences in the appearance of adult ants, and look for eggs, larvae, and pupae. Examine both individual behavior and interactions between the ants.

7. Remove the screen cover and add small amounts of bread crumbs and sugar to the soil surface. Close the cover. Observe the ants for at least 10 more minutes.

8. Create dark conditions for the ants by covering the jar with black paper above the water line. Remove the paper only when you are making your observations.

9. Observe the ant colony every day for two weeks. Remove the dark paper, and make and record your observations. Look at the soil as well as the ants, and always examine the food. If any food has started to mold, use forceps to remove it. Place the moldy food in a plastic bag, seal the bag, and throw it away. Add more food as necessary, and keep the sponge moist. When you finish your observations, replace the dark paper.

10. At the end of the lab, follow your teacher's directions for returning the ants.

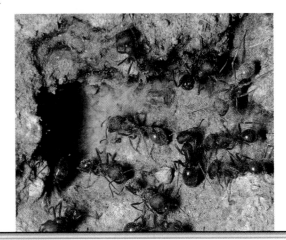

Data Table				
Date	Section A	Section B	Section C	Section D

Analyze and Conclude

1. **Observing** Describe the various types of ants you observed. What differences, if any, did you observe in their behavior? What evidence did you see of different kinds of ants performing different tasks?

2. **Inferring** How do the different behaviors you observed contribute to the survival of the colony?

3. **Inferring** How did the soil change over the period of your observations? What caused those changes? How do you know?

4. **Communicating** What kinds of environmental conditions do you think ant colonies need to thrive outdoors? Use the evidence you obtained in this lab to write a paragraph that supports your answer.

Design an Experiment

Design an experiment to investigate how an ant colony responds when there is a change in the ants' environment, such as the introduction of a new type of food. *Obtain your teacher's permission before carrying out your investigation.*

Objectives

After completing this lesson, students will be able to

13.3.1 Describe how two electronic technologies help scientists track animals.

13.3.2 Explain the benefits of tracking animal migrations.

Target Reading Skill 🔄

Comparing and Contrasting Explain that comparing and contrasting information shows how ideas, facts, and events are similar and different. The results of the comparison can have importance.

Answers

Possible answers:
Simple Banding—no signal, inexpensive, lightweight; radio—radio signal, costly, prohibitive for small animals; satellite—electronic signal, costly, prohibitive for small animals

All in One Teaching Resources, Unit 2

• Transparency LS135

Preteach

Build Background Knowledge L2

Animal Migrations

Ask students to give examples of animals that migrate. (*Birds, mammals such as caribou, whales, and manatees, sea turtles, some fishes such as salmon*) Ask: **Why do animals migrate?** (*To find food sources during winter months, to reproduce*)

Tracking Migrations

Reading Preview

Key Concepts
• How do electronic technologies help scientists track animals?
• What are the benefits of tracking animal migrations?

Key Terms
• transmitter • receiver
• satellite

🔄 Target Reading Skill
Comparing and Contrasting As you read, compare and contrast three types of animal tags by completing a table like the one below.

Animal Tags

Feature	Simple Banding	Radio	Satellite
Kind of Signal	None		
Cost			
Weight			

Lab zone — Discover **Activity**

How Can You Track Animals?
1. On a sheet of graph paper, sketch a map of your classroom.
2. Your teacher will produce a set of "signals" from a tracking device on an animal. Record the location of each signal on your map. Sketch the path of the animal you just tracked.
3. Your teacher will produce a second set of tracking signals. Record the location of each signal, then draw the animal's path. Compare the two pathways.

Think It Over
Inferring What does this activity show about actual animal tracking?

Have you ever changed your mind because of new information? Scientists who study manatees have done just that. The information came from a signaling device on a manatee.

Florida manatees are marine mammals that spend their winters in Florida and migrate north for the summer. Scientists once thought that the manatees didn't go any farther north than Virginia. Then they attached signaling devices to manatees to track their migration. They were quite surprised when they picked up a signal from a manatee swimming off the coast of Rhode Island, which is far north of Virginia.

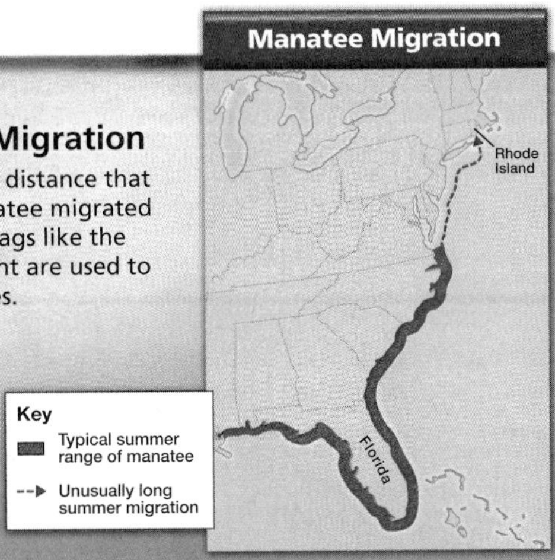

FIGURE 17
Florida Manatee Migration
This map shows the long distance that at least one Florida manatee migrated one summer. Electronic tags like the one shown at the far right are used to track migrating manatees.

Manatee Migration

Key
■ Typical summer range of manatee
--▶ Unusually long summer migration

Lab zone — Discover **Activity**

Skills Focus Inferring L2

Materials graph paper, clicker

Time 20 minutes

Tips For your first set of signals, move in a distinct path across the classroom, including several twists and turns. Move slowly so students have a chance to record their data. Click infrequently, only three times or so. Tell the students to note your location only when they hear a click, not what they see in between clicks, to graph the migratory path of the "animal" you represent. Then give students a second set of signals. Move along the exact path you took before, but click the clicker at least three times as often as before.

Think It Over Students should conclude that with more data points, they can draw better conclusions about the path traveled.

Technologies for Tracking

In the fall of 1803, American naturalist John James Audubon wondered whether migrating birds returned to the same place each year. So he tied a string around the leg of a bird before it flew south. The following spring, Audubon saw the bird with the string. He learned that the bird had indeed come back.

Scientists today still attach tags, such as metal bands, to track the movement of animals. But metal bands are not always useful tags. That is because the tagged animals have to be caught again for the scientists to get any data. Unfortunately, most tagged animals are never seen again.

Recent technologies have helped solve this problem. **Electronic tags give off repeating signals that are picked up by radio devices or satellites. Scientists can track the locations and movements of the tagged animals without recapturing them.** These electronic tags can provide a great deal of data. However, they are much more expensive than the "low-tech" tags that aren't electronic. Also, because of their weight, electronic tags may harm some animals by slowing them down.

Radio Tracking Tracking an animal by radio involves two devices. A **transmitter** attached to the animal sends out a signal in the form of radio waves, just as a radio station does. A scientist might place the transmitter around an animal's ankle, neck, wing, or fin. A **receiver** picks up the signal, just like your radio at home picks up a station's signal. The receiver is usually in a truck or an airplane. To keep track of the signal, the scientist follows the animal in the truck or plane.

FIGURE 18
Banded Puffin
Bands like the ones around the ankles of this Atlantic puffin are low-tech tags. **Inferring** *Why is a metal band tag useful?*

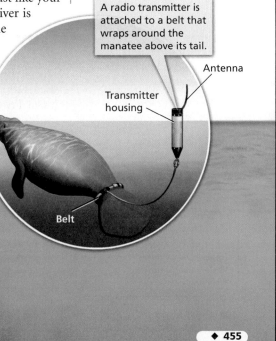

A radio transmitter is attached to a belt that wraps around the manatee above its tail.

Antenna

Transmitter housing

Belt

◆ 455

455

Why Tracking Is Important

Teach Key Concepts L3

Tracking Migrations

Focus Tell students that electronic tracking is helping biologists learn more about animal migration.

Teach Ask: **Why is it important to track animal migrations?** (*Scientists can learn more about species and how to protect them.*) **How can tracking technologies benefit people?** (*It helps people whose work or recreation depends on the use of animal habitats.*)

Apply Ask: **Why is it important to know where animals migrate?** (*Scientists can then work to protect the habitats that animals depend on.*) **learning modality: logical/ mathematical**

 **Build Inquiry** L3

Modeling Tagging Devices

Materials aluminum foil, cardboard, glue, letter and number crimper, mesh screen, photos of tagging devices to show as examples, wire

Time 20 minutes

Focus Tell students that they are going to design a tag for tracking the migration of an animal of their choice.

Teach Explain to students that the aluminum foil and cardboard are substitutes for other, more durable, materials they would use to make their tagging devices, such as plastic or metal. Show students photos of sample tags. Remind students that the tags should be safe for the animal and that they have to be durable for all kinds of environmental conditions.

Apply Have students present their devices to the rest of the class. They should explain what type of animal it will be used to track, whether it will be electronic, how they identify each animal, and how it will stay intact as the animal travels. **learning modality: kinesthetic**

FIGURE 19
Tracking Caribou
Scientists are fitting this caribou with a collar containing a satellite transmitter. *Inferring Why would it be difficult to track caribou without a satellite receiver?*

Satellite Tracking Receivers can be placed in satellites as well as in airplanes and trucks. A **satellite** is an instrument in orbit thousands of kilometers above Earth. Networks, or groups, of satellites are used to track animals. Each satellite in a network picks up electronic signals from a transmitter on an animal. Together, the signals from all the satellites determine the precise location of the animal. The satellites also track the animal's path as it moves. Satellite tracking is especially useful because the scientists do not have to follow after the animal. Satellite networks have tracked the migrations of many types of animals, including caribou, sea turtles, whales, seals, elephants, bald eagles, and ospreys.

Why Tracking Is Important

Electronic tracking tags are giving scientists a complete, accurate picture of migration patterns. For example, when scientists used radio transmitters to track one herd of caribou, they learned two important things. First, they learned that the herd moves over a larger area than previously thought. Second, they learned that each year the herd returns to about the same place to give birth to its young. This information would have been difficult to obtain with "low tech" tags.

Tracking migrations is an important tool to better understand and protect species. For example, Florida manatees are an endangered species, and therefore they need protection. Radio tracking showed that Florida manatees may travel as far north as Rhode Island when they migrate. This information suggests that the manatees may need protection along much of the Atlantic Coast of the United States. Previously, protection efforts focused mainly in the Florida area.

Go Online
SciLINKS NSTA

For: Links on migration
Visit: www.SciLinks.com
Web Code: scn-0253

Technologies for tracking animals may also help people whose work or recreation affects animals. For example, suppose officials at a state park want to protect a group of migrating animals during the spring. The officials plan to ban fishing or boating for the entire spring season. Detailed migration information, however, might give the officials a better choice. They might be able to decrease the length of time the ban is in effect, or ban fishing and boating only in those few areas visited by the animals.

 Reading Checkpoint What information did tracking provide biologists about a caribou herd?

FIGURE 20
Caribou Migration
These caribou are migrating across Alaska on the same path used by caribou for thousands of years.

Section 3 Assessment

🎯 **Target Reading Skill**
Comparing and Contrasting Use the information in your table about animal tags to help you answer Question 1 below.

Reviewing Key Concepts
1. a. **Identifying** What are two methods of electronic animal tracking?
   b. **Comparing and Contrasting** How are electronic tracking methods similar? How are they different?
   c. **Making Judgments** Are electronic tags better than traditional tags?
2. a. **Reviewing** What are the benefits of tracking migrations?

   b. **Applying Concepts** Migrating birds are sometimes killed by crashing into cellular telephone towers. How could tracking bird migrations help people protect the birds?
   c. **Making Judgments** Should governments spend more money tracking migrations? Defend your position.

Writing in Science

Persuasive Letter Suppose you are a scientist who needs money to study the migrations of an endangered sea turtle species. Write a letter justifying why you need money for electronic tags.

Chapter 13 ◆ 457

Writing in Science

Writing Mode Persuasion
Scoring Rubric
4 Includes two or three reasons for the grant and gives information to support the reasons
3 Includes one or two reasons and some supporting information
2 Includes only one reason and little supporting information
1 Includes only one reason and no supporting information

For: Links on migration
Visit: www.SciLinks.com
Web Code: scn-0253

Download a worksheet that will guide students' review of Internet resources on migration.

Monitor Progress _____ L2
Answers
Figure 19 Caribou travel through harsh weather and over difficult terrain.
✓ **Reading Checkpoint** The herd migrates over a larger area than previously thought and returns to the same place to give birth.

Assess

Reviewing Key Concepts
a. Radio tagging and satellite tagging
b. Both radio and satellite tags emit a signal. Both allow scientists to continuously track the positions of tagged animals without needing to recapture them. A radio tag sends out radio waves that are picked up by a receiver. In satellite tagging the receiver is a network of satellites that work together to determine the exact location of the animal.
c. Sample answer: It depends on the situation and the type of animal being studied. Advantages include being able to continuously track an animal without having to recapture it. Disadvantages include greater cost and weight of tags.
5. a. By tracking animal migration, scientists can better understand and protect a species. Recreational officials can coordinate when areas in the path of a migration will be opened and closed. **b.** By knowing the path of migration, people could avoid building cell phone towers in those locations. **c.** Accept all well-defended arguments.

Reteach
As a class, list the advantages and disadvantages of electronic tagging to track animal migration.

All in One **Teaching Resources, Unit 2**
• Section Summary: *Tracking Migrations*
• Review and Reinforce: *Tracking Migrations*
• Enrich: *Tracking Migrations*

Interactive Textbook

- Complete student edition
- Section and chapter self-assessments
- Assessment reports for teachers

Help Students Read

Building Vocabulary

Word Origins Point out to students that many science terms have Latin or Greek origins that give them their meaning. The word *aggression* is derived from the Latin *aggredi,* which means "to attack." The word *migrate* is derived from the Latin *migrare,* which means "to change." Have students explain how the Latin origins of these words relate to their modern meanings.

Vocabulary Rating Chart Have each student construct a chart with four columns labeled *Term, Can Define or Use It, Have Heard or Seen It,* and *Don't Know.* Have students copy the key terms from this chapter into the first column and rate their knowledge by putting a check in one of the other columns. Then have them reread the parts that pertain to the key terms in question.

Connecting Concepts

Concept Maps Help students develop one way to show how the information in this chapter is related. Most animal behaviors are complicated processes that help animals survive and reproduce. Have students brainstorm to identify the key concepts, key terms, details, and examples, and then write each one on a sticky note and attach it at random on chart paper or on the chalkboard.

Tell students that this concept map will be organized in a hierarchical order and to begin at the top with the key concepts. Ask students these questions to guide them to categorize the information in the stickers: **What causes behavior? How can animals learn new behavior? How do animals communicate?**

---

① What Is Behavior?

Key Concepts

- All animal behaviors are caused by stimuli.
- An instinct is a response to a stimulus that is inborn and that an animal performs correctly the first time.
- Learned behaviors include imprinting, conditioning, trial-and-error learning, and insight learning.

Key Terms
behavior
stimulus
response
instinct
learning
imprinting
conditioning
trial-and-error learning
insight learning

② Patterns of Behavior

Key Concepts

- Animals use mostly sounds, scents, and body movements to communicate with one another.
- Animals compete with one another for limited resources, such as food, water, space, shelter, and mates.
- Living in groups enables animals to cooperate.
- Cyclic behaviors usually change over the course of a day or a season.

Key Terms
pheromone
aggression
territory
courtship behavior
society
circadian rhythm
hibernation
migration

③ Tracking Migrations

Key Concepts

- Electronic tags give off repeating signals that are picked up by radio devices or satellites. Scientists can track the locations and movements of the tagged animals without recapturing them.
- Tracking migrations is an important tool to better understand and protect species.

Key Terms
transmitter
receiver
satellite

Prompt students by using such connecting words or phrases such as "caused by" and "through" to indicate the basis for the organization of the map. The phrases should form a sentence between or among a set of concepts.

Answer

Accept logical presentations by students.

All in One Teaching Resources, Unit 2

- Key Terms Review: *Animal Behavior*
- Connecting Concepts: *Animal Behavior*

Review and Assessment

Go Online
PHSchool.com
For: Self-Assessment
Visit: PHSchool.com
Web Code: cea-2050

Organizing Information

Concept Mapping Copy the concept map about behavior onto a separate sheet of paper. Then complete the map and add a title. (For more on Concept Mapping, see the Skills Handbook.)

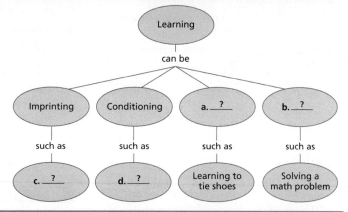

Reviewing Key Terms

Choose the letter of the best answer.

1. An organism's reaction to a signal is called
   a. a response.   **b.** a stimulus.
   c. aggression.   **d.** learning.

2. A process that leads to a change in behavior based on practice is called
   a. instinct.   **b.** response.
   c. learning.   **d.** behavior.

3. Learning that a particular stimulus or response leads to a good or a bad outcome is called
   a. instinct.
   b. imprinting.
   c. conditioning.
   d. insight learning.

4. A chemical released by one animal that affects the behavior of another animal of the same species is called a(n)
   a. stimulus.
   b. instinct.
   c. pheromone.
   d. circadian rhythm.

5. A threatening behavior that one animal uses to gain control over another is called
   a. courtship behavior.
   b. aggression.
   c. conditioning.
   d. cyclic behavior.

6. When a bird travels from its winter home in South America to its nesting area in New York, this is called
   a. learning.
   b. conditioning.
   c. migration.
   d. territorial behavior.

7. An instrument in orbit thousands of kilometers above Earth is called a
   a. pheromone.   **b.** transmitter.
   c. receiver.   **d.** satellite.

Writing in Science

Health Article Write a magazine article describing how dogs can be trained. Explain how trained dogs might assist people with special needs.

Animal Behavior
Video Preview
Video Field Trip
▶ Video Assessment

Chapter 13 ◆ 459

Review and Assessment

Review and Assessment

Organizing Information
 a. Trial-and-Error
 b. Insight Learning
 c. Ducklings swimming by following their mother
 d. A dog going to its master when called
Sample title: Types of Learning

Reviewing Key Terms
1. a **2.** c **3.** c **4.** c **5.** b **6.** c **7.** d

Writing in Science

Writing Skill Health Article
Scoring Rubric
4 Includes an engaging title and in-depth information about trained animal helpers
3 Includes the required information about the topic
2 Includes very general information, and specific and/or interesting examples are missing
1 Reflects minimal preparation

Animal Behavior

Show the Video Assessment to review chapter content and as a prompt for the writing assignment.

Go Online
PHSchool.com
For: Self-Assessment
Visit: PHSchool.com
Web Code: cea-2050

Students can take a practice test online that is automatically scored.

All in One Teaching Resources, Unit 2
- Transparency LS136
- Chapter Test
- Performance Assessment Teacher Notes
- Performance Assessment Teacher Worksheet
- Performance Assessment Scoring Rubric

ExamView® **Computer Test Bank CD-ROM**

Checking Concepts

8. The functions of behavior are to help an animal survive or reproduce.

9. Imprinting involves a combination of instinct and learning because the young animal has an instinct to follow a moving object, but it must learn from experience which object to follow.

10. In trial-and-error learning, an animal learns to perform a behavior more and more skillfully through repeated practice. An example is when a human learns to ride a bicycle.

11. Pheromones are chemicals released by an animal that affects the behavior of another animal of the same species. They may be used to signal the location of food, to attract mates, or to mark a territory, for example.

12. An animal may need to maintain a territory in order to attract mates. For example, if a male fights off other males that enter his territory, he can court females in his territory without much competition from other males.

13. Living in a group can help animals protect one another from predators, or to cooperate in finding food. For example, fishes that swim in schools are often safer than fishes that swim alone. When lions hunt in a group, they can kill larger prey than a single hunter can.

14. When tracking with a radio collar, the scientist must follow the animal with the receiver, usually in a vehicle or an airplane.

Thinking Critically

15. The behavior is an instinct because the bird did not have to learn how to build the nest, but did it correctly on the first try.

16. A racehorse's ability to win races is based on a combination of the traits it inherits, such as strong limbs and lungs, and the training it receives. It may learn through conditioning to associate the event of the race with a stimulus such as a special treat. It may learn the stages of a successful race through trial and error.

17. Sample answer: The owner might use conditioning to train the dog. When the dog jumps on the couch, the owner would use a stimulus to get him off. A stimulus could be a command or an unpleasant sound.

18. Sample answer: I learned how to operate a friend's DVD player because it was similar to the one my family has.

19. By hibernating, an animal reduces its need for food when food is scarce in its environment.

Checking Concepts

8. What are the functions of behavior?

9. Explain how both instinct and learning are involved in imprinting.

10. Explain what trial-and-error learning is. Describe an example.

11. What are pheromones? Explain how they are used in communication.

12. Explain how territorial behavior and courtship behavior are related.

13. Describe two examples of how living in a group can benefit an animal.

14. What is one disadvantage of tracking an animal by radio rather than by satellite?

Thinking Critically

15. Inferring Look at the photograph below. On its first try, this weaver bird is building a nest of grass with a hole at the bottom just the right size for the bird to enter. What kind of behavior is this? Explain.

16. Applying Concepts Explain how a racehorse's ability to win races is a combination of inherited and learned characteristics.

17. Problem Solving A dog keeps jumping onto a sofa. Describe how the owner might train the dog not to do this. The procedure must not involve any pain or harm to the dog.

18. Applying Concepts Give an example of something that you have learned by insight learning. Explain how you made use of your past knowledge and experience in learning it.

19. Drawing Conclusions How can hibernation help an animal survive the winter?

20. Applying Concepts Because a highway has been constructed through a forest, many animals have had to move to a different wooded area. Is their move an example of migration? Explain.

21. Making Judgments Is satellite tracking a good way to track the migration of monarch butterflies? Explain.

Applying Skills

Use the diagrams below, showing (A) a toad catching a bee and (B) the toad's reaction, to answer Questions 22–24.

22. Inferring Explain why the toad probably behaves as it does in diagram B.

23. Predicting If another bee flies by, how will the toad probably behave? Explain.

24. Classifying What type of learning might result from the toad's experience? Explain.

Lab zone Chapter **Project**

Performance Assessment Obtain your teacher's permission before bringing an animal to class. You can also show photographs or illustrations of the animal's training. Describe your training plan. What did you discover about the animal's learning process? How could you have improved your plan?

Lab zone Chapter **Project**   L3

Project Wrap-Up Encourage each student to demonstrate how well his or her animal learned its trick. Students should explain how they trained their animals. Encourage students to use appropriate vocabulary from the text.

Reflect and Record It is likely that some, perhaps many, students will have been unable to train their animals. It is important that every student who made an honest attempt feel successful. Whether the animal was trained or not, students can still write about their experiences and think about ways of improving training.

Standardized Test Prep

Choose the letter of the best answer.

1. An enclosed cage at a university laboratory holds dozens of birds. When a biologist adjusts the light schedule and temperature in the cage to match fall conditions, she observes that the birds spend most of their time at the south end of the cage. What is the most likely explanation for the behavior?

  A The birds are forming a society.
  B There is more food at the south end of the cage.
  C The birds are exhibiting migratory behavior.
  D The scientist has conditioned the birds to prefer the south end of the cage.

2. The chimpanzee in the diagram below has learned a way to reach the bananas. What type of learning most likely applies to this situation?

  F instinct
  G conditioning
  H insight
  J imprinting

3. Ants have laid a pheromone trail to a food source. While the ants are in their nest at night, a researcher pours gasoline over the entire trail. Which of the following will probably happen the next morning?

  A The gasoline will have no effect on the ants.
  B The ants will find the food more rapidly.
  C The ants will eat the gasoline.
  D The ants will be unable to find the food.

4. You are awake during the day and asleep at night. This behavior is an example of

  F circadian rhythm.
  G aggression.
  H trail-and-error learning.
  J hibernation.

Constructed Response

5. Describe the organization of a honeybee society, including daily tasks.

20. This is not an example of migration because it is not a regular behavior that the animals would repeat each season. The animals are moving because of a disturbance, not to seek food or mates elsewhere.

21. Satellite tags would be a good choice because monarch butterflies migrate long distances, however, the tags may not be practical because they may be too big and heavy for the butterflies.

Applying Skills

22. The bee probably stung the toad, and the toad spat it out in an effort to get rid of it.

23. The toad will probably not try to catch the insect, because the toad will associate the bee with the sting.

24. Conditioning, because the toad has learned to connect a stimulus, the bee, with a bad event, being stung.

Standardized Test Prep

1. C   **2.** H   **3.** D   **4.** F

5. Sample response: A honeybee society is highly organized. It is composed of a queen, whose function it is to mate and lay eggs for her lifetime; worker bees, females who do not reproduce but maintain the hive, search for nectar, and make honey; drones, males whose sole function it is to mate with queens.

Through the Lens of an Ocean Scientist

Inquiry and Ocean Science

Marine biologist Norbert Wu photographs marine life all over the world. This article shows how he uses inquiry skills such as observing, inferring, and communicating in his work. Although ocean life is discussed elsewhere in this book, students need not have previous knowledge of this topic to understand this real-world application of scientific inquiry.

Build Background Knowledge
Recalling experiences with cold water

Remind students that swimming in cold water can be uncomfortable. Ask: **How did you feel when you entered the water?** (*Cold, shocked*) **Why?** (*Heat was transferred from my body to the water.*) **How can divers swim in the frigid water near Antarctica?** (*Polar divers wear diving suits that keep them dry; warm clothing worn under the suits retain body heat.*)

Introduce the Career

Before students read the feature, let them read the title, examine the pictures, and read the captions on their own. Then ask: **What questions came into your mind as you looked at these pictures?** (*Students might suggest questions like these: "What types of animals live in ocean waters near Antarctica?" "Why do so many fish swim near seamounts?" and "Why do angelfish clean manta rays?"*) Point out to students that just as they have questions about what they are seeing, scientists too have questions about what they observe.

Through the Lens of an Ocean Scientist

In Antarctica, a diver glides toward a jellyfish.

Norbert Wu dives for his photographs. (He took all the photographs in this feature.) A trained marine biologist, he roams the underwater world looking for the perfect shot. "Photography has become a way of life for me," Norbert says. "At my best, I am both a scientist and an artist. Photographing new life forms and learning about the connections between different species makes my work a blend of science and art. Taking an in-depth look at the habits and behavior of marine life has become my specialty."

Norbert has followed the trail of manta rays slowly circling the top of an undersea mountain off the Mexican coast. He's photographed octopuses and snails on coral reefs. He's swum with jellyfish in the Antarctic Ocean.

"I went as far south as you can go and still have ocean," Norbert says. "And I fell in love with Antarctica. When you first get there at the beginning of the Antarctic spring, the water is clearer than anywhere in the world. It's really the last untouched place on Earth. That's what draws me back.

462 ◆

Talking With **Norbert Wu**

? **What protects divers from the cold?**

Underwater photography in polar seas is a challenge. For one thing, it's very cold. In Antarctica, scientists used to wear wet suits— suits that allow a thin layer of water to touch the skin. Now divers use dry suits, which are waterproof and sealed at the neck and wrists. You can wear long underwear or polyester fleece underneath. Dry suits make polar diving bearable, but it's never very pleasant.

Background

History of Science In 1902, Willy Heinrich became the first person to dive in Antarctica and the first person to dive beneath Antarctic ice. Heinrich served on a German research vessel named the *Gauss,* which was commanded by Erich von Drygalski. After the ship became temporarily frozen in pack ice, Heinrich dove several times to make repairs. He also made observations about the underside of the pack ice. Diving in the Antarctic for solely scientific purposes did not occur until more than 50 years later.

Norbert is shown below with his dogs Ange, a labrador, and Sam, a golden retriever.

Career Path

Norbert Wu attended Stanford University in California, where he received a bachelor's degree and master's degree in electrical and mechanical engineering. He then returned to the subject he loved in high school—marine biology. He attended graduate school at Scripps Institution of Oceanography in San Diego. In 1999, Norbert received a Pew Marine Conservation Fellowship to photograph threatened underwater habitats.

? How did you become an underwater photographer?

After college, I decided to pursue a career in marine biology. I got a job with a scientist working off the San Blas Islands near Panama. I counted sea urchins and measured coral growth. Before the trip, I'd never had any interest in photography. But I brought along books on photography, as well as an underwater flash and camera system.

My career didn't happen overnight. I returned to California to continue graduate school in marine biology. I sold some photographs taken at San Blas and gradually my career in photography just took over.

? How do you locate ocean organisms?

You learn the places in the world where particular ocean organisms are found. In the waters of Antarctica, you find seals, penguins, and jellyfish. Squid come up in the waters off California at certain times of the year. Local guides can also put you exactly on the right site to locate ocean organisms.

If you dive a reef every day, you get to know the organisms that live there. During the months I spent on the San Blas Islands, I was able to return again and again to photograph an octopus or a flamingo tongue snail. Being able to spend weeks, rather than a few weekends, makes a big difference in the photographs.

◆ 463

Explore the Career

Choose from among the teaching strategies on these pages as you help your students explore the practical application of inquiry skills in the real world.

Help Students Read

Preview Before students read the feature, ask them to preview the headings. Make certain that students understand that the headings are questions and that what follows each heading is an answer. Ask: **Who answered the questions?** *(Norbert Wu)*

Use Maps Have students identify Antarctica on a map. Explain that the continent is almost entirely covered by glaciers. Show students the shelves of glacier ice that extend over the sea at some places. Also indicate areas where open water exists, especially during the Antarctic summer. Ask: **Why might Norbert Wu and other ocean scientists enjoy diving here?** *(The region is pristine and beautiful. The oceans are not well explored, and many organisms have yet to be described and photographed.)*

Build Inquiry Skills Tell students that they have been hired as scientists on a marine research vessel. Their job is to describe marine life and understand how marine organisms interact with their environment. Challenge each student to develop a research plan that is designed to accomplish these goals. After students have finished their plans, work as a class to summarize their ideas.

Background

Facts and Figures Coral reefs are the most diverse habitat in the oceans. In addition to the coral, soft coral, algae, and other organisms that are anchored to the reef, a variety of swimming organisms, such as fish and turtles, feed around the reef. The warm, shallow water in which reefs grow is ideal for diving and studying animals. Although most reefs are well explored, much remains to be learned about these complex ecosystems.

Research Have students research mutualism, the mutually beneficial relationship between two species. Ask: **How do manta rays benefit from the activities of the clarion angelfish?** *(The fish remove parasites from the manta rays.)* **How do the angelfish benefit?** *(The parasites on the manta rays are a source of food for the angelfish.)* Have students identify other examples of mutualism.

Show Examples Gather a collection of photographs of marine organisms in their natural habitats, or ask students to collect the photos. Have students examine each photograph and speculate about how it was taken. Ask: **Why are these photographs important?** *(People can observe organisms that they otherwise might never see; scientists can study organisms and habitats in still photos; the photos provide a visual record of marine life.)*

Use Maps On a map, show students the location of Cocos Island. Tell them that this region is a protected marine park and has been designated a UNESCO (United Nations Educational, Scientific and Cultural Organization) World Natural Heritage Site.

Schooling snappers and blue-striped snappers swim around a seamount off the Cocos Island in the Pacific Ocean.

? How is your science background useful?

You need to know how ocean animals behave and how different animals interact with each other. I've taken pictures of manta rays coming to a seamount to be cleaned of parasites by bright orange clarion angelfish. Parasites are small organisms that live on and can harm another organism like a manta ray. As the manta rays swoop past the seamount, the angelfish come out from their shelter, dance about, and flash their bright orange bodies as if signaling their arrival. The manta rays may pause and allow the angelfish to go all about their bodies, picking off parasites.

? Why are you interested in an animal's behavior?

Understanding an ocean animal's behavior and its reactions is essential just to get near enough for a picture. Because of the limited visibility underwater, I am usually close to my subjects—often no more than a meter away. As a diver, the noise of your bubbles tells animals you're there. So an underwater photographer must move slowly and act in ways that won't threaten or frighten animals.

? What do you do on a typical diving trip?

Most of my diving trips last two to three weeks. Once I'm there, almost all my time is on a boat or getting ready to go underwater. My next trip is to Cocos Island, in Costa Rica, where I will photograph seamounts. Seamounts are undersea mountain tops that serve as gathering places for marine life. They attract some of the ocean's largest and most exciting animals.

Seamounts form in areas of volcanic action, where the ocean floor abruptly rises to the surface. These volcanic hot spots can be close to the coast or hundreds of miles offshore. In the Cocos, there are a lot of sharks to photograph—hammerheads and white-tipped reef sharks as well as manta rays and snappers.

464 ◆

Background

Facts and Figures Seamounts are mountains on the ocean floor that do not extend above water level. Most seamounts form at hot spots, regions within a tectonic plate where magma melts through the crust above it. Because of seafloor spreading, seamounts can be carried away from a hot spot after they form. If a volcanic island is carried away from a hot spot, it might sink below sea level to form a flat-topped, wave-cut seamount called a guyot.

Clarion angelfish clean manta rays near a seamount off the coast of Mexico.

? What new technology do you use in your work?

Two new technologies have made a big difference—closed-circuit rebreathers and digital cameras. A rebreather recycles your exhaled breath in a closed loop, so you can breathe the unused oxygen you took in during earlier breaths. You can get up to twelve hours on one tank of oxygen. If you can breathe an oxygen-rich mixture in the ocean, you can stay deeper, longer.

With digital cameras, I can also stay down a long time without running out of film. I can put a memory card in the camera and take 300 or 500 exposures. (A large roll of film takes just 36 exposures.)

? What would you tell students?

I've talked to young people a good deal. I'm amazed at how much they know about the world and the environment. I'd tell students that any subject you're passionate about is going to lead to good things. I'm very lucky. I've been able to combine a lot of things I love into my career—biology and diving and photography.

◀ Norbert on Antarctic ice

Writing in Science

Career Link For Norbert, one key to taking great scientific photographs is being at the right place at the right time. To do that, he says you need "an understanding of your subject's behavior." Choose an animal you know. In a paragraph, describe the right time and place to take a good photograph of that animal. Explain your choice.

Go Online
PHSchool.com
For: More on this career
Visit: PHSchool.com
Web Code: cfb-3000

◆ 465

Chapter at a Glance

PRENTICE HALL
TeacherEXPRESS™
Plan • Teach • Assess

 Chapter Project *Design and Build a Hand Prosthesis*

Technology

Local Standards

Teaching Resources, Unit 3
- Chapter Project Teacher Notes, pp. 24–25
- Chapter Project Student Overview, pp. 26–27
- Chapter Project Student Worksheets 1–2, pp. 28–29
- Chapter Project Scoring Rubric, p. 30

DISCOVERY CHANNEL SCHOOL
Video Preview

Section 1 — Body Organization and Homeostasis

1 period
1/2 block

14.1.1 Identify the levels of organization in the body.
14.1.2 Define homeostasis.

Go Online
SCLINKS NSTA

Section 2 — The Skeletal System

2 periods
1 block

14.2.1 Identify the functions of the skeleton.
14.2.2 Explain the role that joints play in the body.
14.2.3 Describe the characteristics of bone and how to keep bones strong and healthy.

Go Online
active art

DISCOVERY CHANNEL SCHOOL
Video Field Trip

Section 3 — The Muscular System

1 period
1/2 block

14.3.1 Identify the types of muscles found in the body.
14.3.2 Explain why skeletal muscles work in pairs.

Go Online
PHSchool.com

Section 4 — The Skin

2 periods
1 block

14.4.1 Describe the functions and the structures of skin.
14.4.2 Identify habits that can help keep skin healthy.

Go Online
SCLINKS NSTA

Review and Assessment

Teaching Resources, Unit 3
- Key Terms Review, p. 64
- Transparency LS146
- Performance Assessment Teacher Notes, p. 71
- Performance Assessment Scoring Rubric, p. 72
- Performance Assessment Student Worksheet, p. 73
- Chapter Test, pp. 74–77

DISCOVERY CHANNEL SCHOOL
Video Assessment

Go Online
PHSchool.com

Test Preparation

Test Preparation Blackline Masters

Lab zone Chapter Activities Planner

For more activities
LAB ZONE
Easy Planner
CD-ROM

Student Edition	Inquiry	Time	Materials	Skills	Resources
Chapter Project, p. 467	Open-ended	3 weeks	**All in One** Teaching Resources, **Unit 3**, p. 38	Making models, observing, problem solving	**Lab zone Easy Planner** **All in One** Teaching Resources, **Unit 3**, Support pp. 38–39
Section 1					
Discover Activity, p. 468	Guided	10 minutes	2 medium-sized books, clock or watch with second hand	Inferring	**Lab zone Easy Planner**
Try This Activity, p. 469	Guided	15 minutes	No special materials are required.	Making models	**Lab zone Easy Planner**
Section 2					
Discover Activity, p. 474	Open-ended	10 minutes	Leg bone from a cooked chicken or turkey, rock of similar size, hand lens	Observing	**Lab zone Easy Planner**
Skills Activity, p. 477	Guided	15 minutes	None	Classifying	**Lab zone Easy Planner**
Try This Activity, p. 478	Guided	Setup 15 minutes; Observation 15 minutes	2 plastic jars or other containers, vinegar, water, 2 clean chicken bones, gloves	Drawing conclusions	**Lab zone Easy Planner**
Section 3					
Discover Activity, p. 482	Guided	15 minutes	Spring-type clothespin	Predicting	**Lab zone Easy Planner**
Try This Activity, p. 484	Directed	10 minutes	Wooden stirrer, hairpin	Inferring	**Lab zone Easy Planner**
Skills Lab, p. 487	Guided	Prep 60 minutes; Class 30 minutes	Apron, goggles, water, paper towels, scissors, protective gloves, dissecting tray, uncooked chicken wing (treated with bleach)	Observing, drawing conclusions, classifying, communicating	**Lab zone Easy Planner** **Lab Activity Video** **All in One** Teaching Resources, **Unit 3**, Skills Lab: *A Look Beneath the Skin*, pp. 74–75
Section 4					
Discover Activity, p. 488	Open-ended	15 minutes	Hand lens, plastic gloves	Inferring	**Lab zone Easy Planner**
Try This Activity, p. 491	Directed	15 minutes	2 thermometers, wet cotton ball, piece of cardboard, safety goggles	Measuring	**Lab zone Easy Planner**
Design Your Own Lab, pp. 494–495	Part 1: Guided; Part 2: Open-ended	Prep 20 minutes; Class 45 minutes plus 20 minutes follow-up	Scissors, 3 different fabrics, photosensitive paper, white construction paper, resealable plastic bag, pencil, plastic knife, metric ruler, stapler, staple remover, 2 sunscreens with SPF ratings of 4 and 30	Observing, predicting, interpreting data, drawing conclusions, communicating	**Lab zone Easy Planner** **Lab Activity Video** **All in One** Teaching Resources, **Unit 3**, Design Your Own Lab: *Sun Safety*, pp. 82–84

Body Organization and
Section 1 Homeostasis

🕐 *1 period, 1/2 block*

ABILITY LEVELS KEY
L1 Basic to Average
L2 For All Students
L3 Average to Advanced

Objectives

14.1.1 Identify the levels of organization in the body.
14.1.2 Define homeostasis.

Local Standards

Key Terms

• cell • cell membrane • nucleus • cytoplasm • tissue • muscle tissue
• nervous tissue • connective tissue • epithelial tissue • organ • organ system
• homeostasis • stress

Preteach

Build Background Knowledge

Have students identify the similarities in organization between a marching band and the human body.

 **Discover Activity** *How Does Your Body Respond?* L1

Targeted Print and Technology Resources

 **Teaching Resources, Unit 3**

L2 Reading Strategy Transparency
LS137: Outlining

⊙ **PresentationEXPRESS™ CD-ROM**

Instruct

Cells Use an analogy to explain how a cell fits into the level of organization of the body. Use an illustration to discuss cell structures and functions.

Tissues Use illustrations to compare and contrast the different types of tissues.

Organs and Organ Systems Use illustrations to describe the different body systems and the organs that compose them.

Homeostasis Discuss homeostasis and apply it to examples within the human body.

Targeted Print and Technology Resources

Teaching Resources, Unit 3

L2 Guided Reading, pp. 33–36

www.SciLinks.org Web Code: scn-0411

⊙ **Student Edition on Audio CD**

Assess

Section Assessment Questions

Have students use their outlines of the section to help answer the questions.

Reteach

Use illustrations to identify different body systems.

Targeted Print and Technology Resources

Teaching Resources, Unit 3

• Section Summary, p. 32
L1 Review and Reinforce, p. 37
L3 Enrich, p. 38

Section 2 The Skeletal System

 2 periods, 1 block

Objectives

14.2.1 Identify the functions of the skeleton.

14.2.2 Explain the role that joints play in the body.

14.2.3 Describe the characteristics of bone and how to keep bones strong and healthy.

Key Terms

• skeleton • vertebra • joint • ligament • cartilage • compact bone
• spongy bone • marrow • osteoporosis

Local Standards

Preteach

Build Background Knowledge

Have students feel the bones in their hands and brainstorm what they know about bones.

 **Discover Activity** *Hard as a Rock?* L1

Targeted Print and Technology Resources

 **Teaching Resources, Unit 3**

L2 Reading Strategy Transparency LS138: Asking Questions

 PresentationEXPRESS™ CD-ROM

Instruct

What the Skeletal System Does Use an illustration to identify the functions of the skeleton.

Joints of the Skeleton Use illustrations to examine the role of different joints.

Bones—Strong and Living Use an illustration of a cross-section of a bone to relate characteristics of bone to its functions.

Taking Care of Your Bones Ask leading questions to help students identify ways to keep bones strong and healthy.

Targeted Print and Technology Resources

Teaching Resources, Unit 3

L2 Guided Reading, pp. 41–44
L2 Transparencies LS139, LS140, LS141

PHSchool.com Web Code: cep-4012

DISCOVERY CHANNEL SCHOOL
Video Field Trip

Student Edition on Audio CD

Assess

Section Assessment Questions

Have students use their graphic organizers with their questions and answers to help answer the questions.

Reteach

Have students define Key Terms and relate them to the Key Concepts in this section.

Targeted Print and Technology Resources

Teaching Resources, Unit 3

• Section Summary, p. 40
L1 Review and Reinforce, p. 45
L3 Enrich, p. 46

Section 3 The Muscular System

 1 period, 1/2 block

Objectives

14.3.1 Identify the types of muscles found in the body.

14.3.2 Explain why skeletal muscles work in pairs.

Key Terms

- involuntary muscle • voluntary muscle • skeletal muscle • tendon
- striated muscle • smooth muscle • cardiac muscle

Local Standards

Preteach

Build Background Knowledge

Have students hold a book and feel the muscles in their arms.

Lab zone Discover Activity *How Do Muscles Work?* L1

Targeted Print and Technology Resources

All in One Teaching Resources, Unit 3

L2 Reading Strategy Transparency
LS142: Previewing Visuals

⊙ **PresentationEXPRESS™ CD-ROM**

Instruct

Types of Muscle Use an illustration to compare and contrast the types of muscles.

Muscles at Work Use an illustration to help students model and understand how muscles work in pairs.

Lab zone Skills Lab *A Look Beneath the Skin* L2

Targeted Print and Technology Resources

All in One Teaching Resources, Unit 3

L2 Guided Reading, pp. 49–50
L2 Skills Lab: *A Look Beneath the Skin*, pp. 53–54
L2 Transparency LS143

📼 **Lab Activity Video/DVD**
Skills Lab: A *Look Beneath the Skin*

PHSchool.com Web Code: ced-4014

⊙ **Student Edition on Audio CD**

Assess

Section Assessment Questions

🔄 Have students use their graphic organizers with their questions and answers from previewing visuals to help answer the questions.

Reteach

Ask students to identify the type and function of the muscles in different body parts.

Targeted Print and Technology Resources

All in One Teaching Resources, Unit 3

- Section Summary, p. 48
L1 Review and Reinforce, p. 51
L3 Enrich, p. 52

Section 4 The Skin

2 periods, 1 block

ABILITY LEVELS KEY
L1 Basic to Average
L2 For All Students
L3 Average to Advanced

Objectives

14.4.1 Describe the functions and the structures of skin.

14.4.2 Identify habits that can help keep skin healthy.

Key Terms

• epidermis • melanin • dermis • pore • follicle • cancer

Local Standards

Preteach

Build Background Knowledge

Have students look at their skin and speculate about what they think it does.

 **Discover Activity** *What Can You Observe About Skin?* L1

Targeted Print and Technology Resources

 **Teaching Resources, Unit 3**

L2 Reading Strategy Transparency LS144: Identifying Main Ideas

⊙ **PresentationEXPRESS™ CD-ROM**

Instruct

The Body's Tough Covering Ask leading questions to help students identify the functions of the skin.

The Epidermis Describe the structure and function of the first layer of skin.

The Dermis Compare and contrast the epidermis and the dermis, and explain the structures and functions of the dermis.

Caring for Your Skin Discuss habits to keep skin healthy.

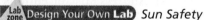 Design Your Own **Lab** *Sun Safety* L2

Targeted Print and Technology Resources

Teaching Resources, Unit 3

L2 Guided Reading, pp. 57–58
L2 Transparency LS145
L2 Design Your Own Lab: *Sun Safety*, pp. 61–63

📼 **Lab Activity Video/DVD**
Design Your Own Lab: *Sun Safety*

www.SciLinks.org Web Code: scn-0415

⊙ **Student Edition on Audio CD**

Assess

Section Assessment Questions

 Have students use their graphic organizers with main ideas and details to help answer the questions.

Reteach

Use an illustration of a cross-section of skin to review how the structures relate to the functions.

Targeted Print and Technology Resources

Teaching Resources, Unit 3

• Section Summary, p. 56
L1 Review and Reinforce, p. 59
L3 Enrich, p. 60

Chapter 14 **Content Refresher**

Go Online

NSTA-PD LINKS

For: Professional development support
Visit: www.SciLinks.org/PDLinks
Web Code: scf-0410

Professional Development

Section 1 **Body Organization and Homeostasis**

Epithelial Tissues Epithelial tissues cover the body and internal organs. They form the lining of cavities and passageways, and secrete mucus that lubricates these surfaces. Glands, which are clusters of epithelial cells, synthesize and secrete substances such as perspiration, saliva, and hormones.

Epithelial tissues that provide protection, such as the epidermis, are strengthened and reinforced by cell junctions that bind cells together. Tight junctions form seals around individual cells in internal organs to prevent leakage between cells.

Epithelial tissues are classified by cell shape. Squamous, or flat, cells are found in the outer layer of skin, the lining of the mouth, and in mucous membranes. Cuboidal and columnar cells are found in glands and the lining of passageways.

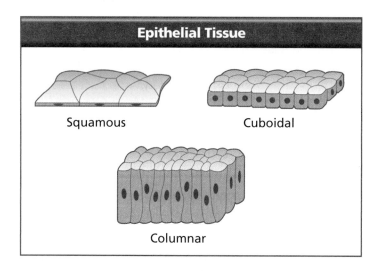

Epithelial Tissue

Squamous

Cuboidal

Columnar

Eliminating Excess Body Heat Temperature homeostasis often depends on the ability to transfer excess heat to the outside environment. This can challenge the body's abilities when the outside environment is hot. Specialized nerve cells in the brain (in the temperature-regulating center of the hypothalamus) detect excess heat in the blood flowing past them and respond by sending messages to cells in the skin. In response to these messages, blood vessels in the skin dilate, increasing the amount of blood that is flowing just under the surface. This increase in blood flow allows heat to be exchanged from blood vessel to skin surface to air. The same nerve messages trigger sweat glands to produce sweat. Heat is lost to the air as sweat evaporates. In very hot environments, almost all heat loss occurs through sweating.

Section 2 **The Skeletal System**

Building and Rebuilding Bone Bones do not become inactive after a person stops growing. Bone is constantly being remodeled—that is, cells called osteoblasts form new bone tissue. Bones stop getting larger because some bone tissue is continually being broken down by cells called osteoclasts.

The ability of bone cells to respond to environmental stress is important both in wellness and illness. When a person participates in weight-bearing activities such as soccer or tennis, cells called osteoblasts respond by forming new bone tissue. The ability to build stronger, denser bones in response to exercise may help prevent the bone disorder called osteoporosis. It is important to have a good calcium intake throughout life because calcium is necessary to form the mineral salts that give bone tissue its strength.

Bone cells also go into action when a person breaks, or fractures, a bone. All of the osteoblasts in the neighborhood of the break begin to form new bone tissue. In addition, a number of immature bone cells are stimulated to mature into osteoblasts and help the bone-building process. Doctors have learned how to harness the normal response of osteoblasts to build new tissue in response to stress as an aid in helping fractured bones heal. Suppose someone falls from a bike and breaks several bones in the wrist and forearm. Orthopedic surgeons can apply metal pins and other pieces of apparatus to build a frame that holds the broken ends of bones together. Because the bones are held together, the patient can immediately have some use of the arm and hand. Stress on the bone ends caused by the apparatus speeds up the osteoblasts' task of building new tissue to heal the fractures.

Address Misconceptions

Some students think that bone is dead. However, bone is composed of living tissue. For a strategy to overcome this misconception, see **Address Misconceptions** in *The Skeletal System.*

Section 3 The Muscular System

Structure of a Skeletal Muscle As you can see in the illustration, skeletal muscles are composed of bundles of muscle fibers. Each muscle fiber is actually one muscle cell. Some muscle fibers are only 1 millimeter long, while others can be as long as about 30 centimeters.

Muscle fibers contain individual units called myofibrils. Each skeletal muscle cell (fiber) contains hundreds to thousands of myofibrils. Each myofibril, in turn, is made up of threadlike filaments. Some filaments, which are thick, contain a protein called myosin. Other filaments, which are thin, are composed mainly of another protein, called actin. Myosin and actin filaments cause muscle fibers to contract. When the thin filaments slide over the thick filaments, a muscle fiber contracts.

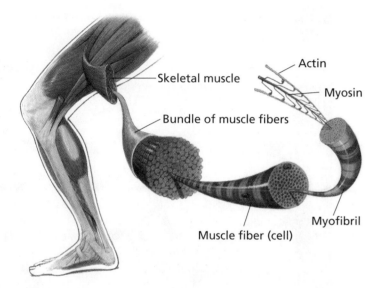

Actin
Skeletal muscle
Myosin
Bundle of muscle fibers
Myofibril
Muscle fiber (cell)

Section 5 The Skin

Keratin The layer of dead skin cells on the surface of skin forms the barrier between the inside and outside of the body. It is critical to water and temperature homeostasis and protection from infectious organisms and toxic substances. But what is in those important dead cells? Keratin.

Made by cells in the epidermis, keratin is a sturdy protein that forms sheets of fibers inside the cell. As epidermal cells move upward toward the skin surface, they make increasing amounts of keratin. By the time the cells die, they are essentially flat bags of keratin. Keratin, along with the pigment melanin, protects the skin from the cancer-causing effects of ultraviolet radiation in sunlight.

Keratin is also vital to two specialized skin structures, hair and nails. Cells in each hair bulb (the slightly rounded hair root that you can see when you look at hairs from your head) produce keratin. The visible hair strand we see is made up of hard, flat cells full of keratin wrapped around a small, central space. Nails are made of translucent sheets of keratin produced and released by the cells of the nail bed. As a nail grows, keratin is added at the edge of the nail bed and to the underside of the nail, thickening the nail as it lengthens and keeping the nail connected to the living cells of the nail bed. The bonds between the underside of the nail and the cells of the nail bed help to keep nails from becoming loose or falling off.

Help Students Read

SQ3R

Survey, Question, Read, Recite, and Review

Strategy Help students read material that contains technical information, diagrams, and figures. This SQ3R strategy helps students focus on the main points in a section, making it easier for them to remember what they have read. Before students begin, assign a section in the textbook for them to read.

Example

1. S Have students **survey** the entire assignment and look at the headings and material in boldface. Have them write a short explanation of what they see in each diagram.

2. Q Have students write **questions** they will answer when they complete their survey. They should turn each heading into a question and leave room below it for the answer.

3. R Have students **read** the section and look for the answers to their questions.

4. R When students finish reading, tell them to think about what they read. They should **recite** the questions they wrote and—using their own words—give the answers they found. If students can't answer a question, have them reread the material for the related heading, looking more carefully to find the answer. If necessary, help students answer questions that are not directly answered in the text.

5. R Have students **review** the section by writing the answers they recited. Finally, refer students to the Key Concepts questions on the first page of the section. Have students answer each of these questions.

Interactive Textbook
- Complete student edition
- Video and audio
- Simulations and activities
- Section and chapter reviews

Bones, Muscles, and Skin

Chapter Preview

❶ Body Organization and Homeostasis
Discover *How Does Your Body Respond?*
Try This *How Is a Book Organized?*

❷ The Skeletal System
Discover *Hard as a Rock?*
Active Art *Movable Joints*
Skills Activity *Classifying*
Try This *Soft Bones?*

❸ The Muscular System
Discover *How Do Muscles Work?*
Try This *Get a Grip*
Skills Lab *A Look Beneath the Skin*

❹ The Skin
Discover *What Can You Observe About Skin?*
Try This *Sweaty Skin*
Analyzing Data *SPF Ratings*
Design Your Own Lab *Sun Safety*

Interactive Textbook

No matter your age or ability level, ▶ playing sports is fun and healthful.

466 ◆

Lab zone **Chapter Project**   L3

Objectives

This project will give students an opportunity to make a model of a hand prosthesis. By doing this project, students will gain a better understanding of the complexity of the human hand, the problems people with disabilities face, and the role that technology and design play in the process. After this Chapter Project, students will be able to

- make a model of a human hand
- observe how the hand functions to carry out tasks
- compare and contrast the function of the hand to other devices that share some abilities of the hand
- solve problems in the design of their model
- communicate the features of their model to the class

Skills Focus

Making models, observing, comparing and contrasting, problem solving, communicating

Project Time Line   3 weeks

All in One Teaching Resources, Unit 3

- Chapter Project Teacher Notes
- Chapter Project Overview
- Chapter Project Worksheet 1
- Chapter Project Worksheet 2
- Chapter Project Scoring Rubric

Developing a Plan

Students will use the first week to experiment with various objects and develop ideas for construction. Devote the second week to building the device. Allow the third week for students to test and revise their models, and present their models to the class.

Possible Materials

- Provide wire coat hangers, craft sticks, binder clips, rubber bands, string, thin wire, thin plastic sheet (1/8 inch), plywood (1/4 inch), duct tape, heavy cardboard, and transparent tape.
- Provide tools such as several types of pliers, a vice, wire cutters, files, and saws.

Chapter **Project**

Design and Build a Hand Prosthesis

A prosthesis is an artificial device that replaces a human body part. Designing artificial replacements, such as prosthetic hands, can be a challenging task. This is because even a simple act, such as picking up a pen, involves a complex interaction of body parts.

Your Goal To design, build, and test a replacement for a human hand

Your prosthesis must

● grasp and lift a variety of objects
● be activated by pulling a cord or string
● spring back when the cord is released
● be built following the safety guidelines in Appendix A

Plan It! Before you design your prosthetic hand, study the human hand. Watch how the fingers move to pick up objects. Make a list of devices that mimic the ability of the hand to pick up objects. Examples include tongs, tweezers, pliers, and chopsticks. Then, choose materials for your hand and sketch your design. When your teacher has approved your design, build and test your prosthetic hand.

Chapter 14 ◆ 467

Video Preview

Bones, Muscles, and Skin

Show the Video Preview to introduce the Chapter Project and overview the chapter content. Discussion question: **What do osteoclasts and osteoblasts do?** (*Osteoclasts dissolve broken bone; osteoblasts cover the area with minerals, which harden into bone.*)

Launching the Project

Explain that an assistive device helps people with physical disorders to perform activities of daily living. Provide the example that glasses are an assistive device. Ask: **What are some other assistive devices?** (*Sample answers: Hearing aids, wheelchairs, leg braces, dentures, implanted joints*) Ask student

volunteers to try to perform the following tasks with one hand: lifting a book, buttoning a coat, and tying a shoe. Discuss the difficulty in carrying out these tasks. Tell students that in this project, they will design and construct an assistive device that can grasp and lift objects.

Performance Assessment

The Chapter Project Scoring Rubric will help you evaluate how well students complete the Chapter Project. You may want to share the scoring rubric with your students so they are clear about what will be expected of them. Students will be assessed on

● how well constructed their models are
● how effectively the model can perform the functions of the hand
● how easy the hand is to operate
● how effectively they present their models to the class

Portfolio

Section

1

Integrating Health

Body Organization
and Homeostasis

Objectives
After this lesson, students will be able to
14.1.1 Identify the levels of organization in the body.
14.1.2 Define homeostasis.

Target Reading Skill
Outlining Explain that using an outline format helps students organize information by main topic, subtopic, and details.

Answers
Body Organization and Homeostasis
I. Cells
   A. Structures of Cells
   B. Functions of Cells
II. Tissues
III. Organs and Organ Systems
IV. Homeostasis
   A. Homeostasis in Action
   B. Maintaining Homeostasis
   C. Stress and Homeostasis

All in One Teaching Resources, Unit 3
• Transparency LS137

Preteach

Build Background Knowledge
L2
Body Parts Work Together
Pose to students that a marching band is organized on several levels from bandleader to individual members to sections, and that each part at each level performs a different function in the band. Ask: **How is the organization of the human body similar to that of a marching band?** *(Different parts, such as the heart or the muscles, perform different functions.)* Tell students that in this section they will learn how the organization of the human body on different levels helps the body to work together as a whole.

Reading Preview
Key Concepts
• What are the levels of organization in the body?
• What is homeostasis?

Key Terms
• cell • cell membrane
• nucleus • cytoplasm
• tissue • muscle tissue
• nervous tissue
• connective tissue
• epithelial tissue
• organ • organ system
• homeostasis • stress

Target Reading Skill
Outlining An outline shows the relationship between main ideas and supporting ideas. As you read, make an outline about body organization and homeostasis. Use the red headings for the main ideas and the blue headings for the supporting ideas.

Body Organization and Homeostasis
I. Cells
A. Structures of cells
B.
II. Tissues

Lab zone Discover Activity

How Does Your Body Respond?
1. Stack one book on top of another one.
2. Lift the two stacked books in front of you so the lowest book is about level with your shoulders. Hold the books in this position for 30 seconds. While you are performing this activity, note how your body responds. For example, how do your arms feel at the beginning and toward the end of the 30 seconds?
3. Balance one book on the top of your head. Walk a few steps with the book on your head.

Think It Over
Inferring List all the parts of your body that worked together as you performed the activities in Steps 1 through 3.

The bell rings—lunchtime! You hurry down the noisy halls to the cafeteria. The unmistakable aroma of hot pizza makes your mouth water. At last, you balance your tray of pizza and salad while you pay the cashier. You look around the cafeteria for your friends. Then, you walk to the table, sit down, and begin to eat.

Think about how many parts of your body were involved in the simple act of getting and eating your lunch. Every minute of the day, whether you are eating, studying, walking, or even sleeping, your body is busily at work. Each part of the body has a specific job to do. And all the different parts of your body usually work together so smoothly that you don't even notice them.

This smooth functioning is due partly to the way in which the body is organized. **The levels of organization in the human body consist of cells, tissues, organs, and organ systems.** The smallest unit of organization is the cell. The next largest unit is tissue; then, organs. Finally, the organ system is the largest unit of organization.

Lab zone Discover Activity

Skills Focus Inferring   **L1**

Materials two medium-sized books, clock or watch with second hand

Time 10 minutes

Tips Make sure the books are heavy enough so that students will tire holding them, but not so heavy that students will

not be able to hold them level with their shoulders.

Expected Outcome Most students' arms will feel tired after 30 seconds.

Think It Over Most students will include arms, shoulders, hands, brain, heart, head, and muscles.

Cells

A **cell** is the basic unit of structure and function in a living thing. Complex organisms are composed of many cells in the same way a brick building is composed of many bricks. The human body contains about 100 trillion cells. Cells are quite tiny, and most cannot be seen without a microscope.

Structures of Cells Most animal cells, including those in the human body, have a structure similar to the cell in Figure 1. The **cell membrane** forms the outside boundary of the cell. Inside the cell membrane is a large structure called the nucleus. The **nucleus** is the control center that directs the cell's activities and contains the information that determines the cell's form and function. When the cell divides, or reproduces, this information is passed along to the newly formed cells. The material within a cell apart from the nucleus is called the **cytoplasm** (SYT uh plaz um). The cytoplasm is made of a clear, jellylike substance containing many cell structures called organelles.

Functions of Cells Cells carry on the processes that keep organisms alive. Inside cells, for example, molecules from digested food undergo chemical reactions that release energy for the body's activities. Cells also grow and reproduce. And they get rid of waste products that result from these activities.

 Reading Checkpoint What is the function of the nucleus?

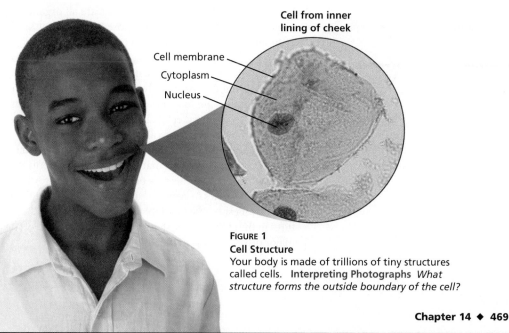

Cell from inner lining of cheek

Cell membrane
Cytoplasm
Nucleus

FIGURE 1
Cell Structure
Your body is made of trillions of tiny structures called cells. **Interpreting Photographs** *What structure forms the outside boundary of the cell?*

Chapter 14 ◆ 469

Lab zone Try This Activity

How Is a Book Organized?
In this activity, you will analyze the levels of organization in a book.

1. Examine this textbook to see how it is subdivided—into chapters, sections, and so on.
2. Make a concept map that shows this pattern of organization. Place the largest subdivision at the top of the map and the smallest at the bottom.
3. Compare the levels of organization in this textbook to those in the human body.

Making Models Which level of organization in the textbook represents cells? Which represents tissues? Organs? Organ systems?

Lab zone Try This Activity

Skills Focus Making models
Materials student textbook
Time 15 minutes
Tips To help students make their concept maps, suggest they study the table of contents. Also refer students to the section on concept mapping in the Skills Handbook.

Expected Outcome Sample answer: sentences—cells; subsections—tissues; sections—organs; chapters—organ systems

Extend Ask students to think of another object or situation that can be organized into different levels. *(Sample answers: Individuals, families, towns, county; bricks, walls, rooms, building)* **learning modality: logical/mathematical**

469

Tissues

Teach Key Concepts L2

Types of Tissues

Focus Refer students to Figure 2.

Teach Explain that cells are specialized to perform different functions and that groups of similar cells join to form tissues. Ask a student volunteer to read the captions describing the different types of tissue. Ask: **What is the main function of muscle tissue?** *(Allow movement)* **Nerve tissue?** *(Carry messages through the body)* **Connective tissue?** *(Support and connect parts)* **Epithelial tissue?** *(Protect delicate structures)* Point out that the types of cells shown are representative of each type of tissue. Within each type, tissues vary. For example, red blood cells and bones are both connective tissue, but the cells that make up each of them look and function differently.

Apply Ask students to identify the type of tissue in the following body parts: **Tendons that attach muscle to bone** *(Connective)*, **spinal cord** *(Nerve)*, **lining of the mouth** *(Epithelial)*, **stomach wall that moves to mix food** *(Muscle)*. **learning modality: visual**

Observing Cells and Tissues

Materials prepared slides of different types of tissue, such as red blood cells, liver, nerve, and muscle; microscope

Time 20 minutes

Focus Tell students that the structure of cells is related to their function.

Teach Set up several slides and microscopes at stations around the room. Have students observe the slides under high and low powers, and make labeled sketches of their observations.

Apply Ask students to explain how the structure of different tissues relates to their function. *(Sample answers: The cells in epithelial tissue are packed closely together to form a protective barrier. Nerve cells have long extensions to carry messages.)* **learning modality: visual**

FIGURE 2
Types of Tissues

Your body contains four kinds of tissues: muscle, nervous, connective, and epithelial.

Comparing and Contrasting *How is the function of nervous tissue different from that of epithelial tissue?*

Muscle Tissue
Every movement you make depends on muscle tissue. The muscle tissue shown here allows your body to move.

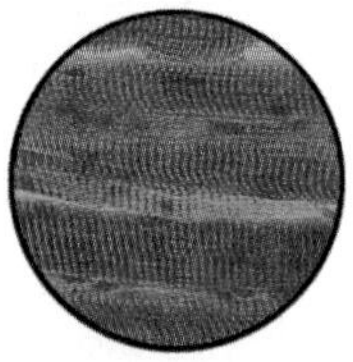

Nervous Tissue
Nervous tissue, such as the brain cells shown here, enables you to see, hear, and think.

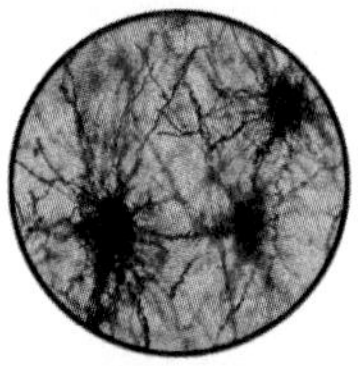

Connective Tissue
Connective tissue, such as the bone shown here, connects and supports parts of your body.

Epithelial Tissue
Epithelial tissue, such as the skin cells shown here, covers the surfaces of your body and lines your internal organs.

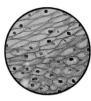

Tissues

The next largest unit of organization in your body is a tissue. A **tissue** is a group of similar cells that perform the same function. The human body contains four basic types of tissue: muscle tissue, nervous tissue, connective tissue, and epithelial tissue. To see examples of each of these tissues, look at Figure 2.

Like the muscle cells that form it, **muscle tissue** can contract, or shorten. By doing this, muscle tissue makes parts of your body move. While muscle tissue carries out movement, **nervous tissue** directs and controls the process. Nervous tissue carries electrical messages back and forth between the brain and other parts of the body. Another type of tissue, **connective tissue,** provides support for your body and connects all its parts. Bone tissue and fat are connective tissues.

The surfaces of your body, inside and out, are covered by **epithelial tissue** (ep uh THEE lee ul). Some epithelial tissue, such as your skin, protects the delicate structures that lie beneath it. The lining of your digestive system consists of epithelial tissue that allows you to digest and absorb the nutrients in your food.

 Reading Checkpoint **What is the job of muscle tissue?**

Organs and Organ Systems

Your stomach, heart, brain, and lungs are all organs. An **organ** is a structure that is composed of different kinds of tissue. Like a tissue, an organ performs a specific job. The job of an organ, however, is generally more complex than that of a tissue. The heart, for example, pumps blood throughout your body, over and over again. The heart contains all four kinds of tissue—muscle, nervous, connective, and epithelial. Each type of tissue contributes to the organ's overall job of pumping blood.

Each organ in your body is part of an **organ system,** which is a group of organs that work together to perform a major function. Your heart is part of your circulatory system, which carries oxygen and other materials throughout the body. Besides the heart, blood vessels are major structures in the circulatory system. Figure 3 shows some of the major organ systems in the human body.

FIGURE 3
Organ Systems
The human body is made up of eleven organ systems. Eight of the systems are shown here.
Interpreting Diagrams *Which two systems work together to get oxygen to your cells?*

Circulatory System
Transports materials to and from cells.

Skeletal System
Supports and protects the body.

Digestive System
Breaks down food and absorbs nutrients.

Nervous System
Detects information from the environment and controls body functions.

Endocrine System
Controls many body processes by means of chemicals.

Respiratory System
Takes in oxygen and eliminates carbon dioxide.

Muscular System
Enables movement of the body and internal organs.

Excretory System
Removes wastes.

Organs and Organ Systems

Teach Key Concepts L2

Organs Work Together

Focus Ask: **Where in the organizational level of the body are organs?** *(Third—after tissues)*

Teach Explain that an organ performs a specific function, as a tissue does. However, an organ can be made of different types of tissue. Ask: **What is the level of organization after organs?** *(Organ systems)* Refer students to Figure 3, and review the organ systems by asking questions such as: **What is the function of the skeletal system?** *(To support and protect the body)* **What are the structures of the nervous system?** *(The brain, spinal cord, and nerves)* **Which system chemically controls many body processes?** *(The endocrine system)* Then ask: **What is the relationship between organs and organ systems?** *(Each organ performs one function that is related to the function of the other organs in the system. The organs work together to carry out one major function in the organ system.)*

Apply Point out that the highest level of organization is the entire body. Have students use Figure 3 to write a paragraph relating the functions of different organ systems to their own lives. *(Sample answers: My nervous system helps me to be aware of my environment and to learn new information. My digestive system breaks down the food I ate for breakfast.)* **learning modality: verbal**

Monitor Progress L2

Writing Have students list the tissue types found in the hand. *(Sample answer: The hand has nervous tissue, connective tissue such as bone and blood, muscle tissue, and epithelial tissue such as skin.)*

Answers
Figure 2 Nervous tissue carries messages back and forth; epithelial tissue protects and lines structures.
Figure 3 Circulatory and respiratory systems.

 Reading Checkpoint To make parts of your body move

Differentiated Instruction

English Learners/Beginning L1
Comprehension: Link to Visual Review the terms *cells*, *tissues*, *organs*, and *organ systems*. Using Figure 3 as a guide, construct a concept circle with the name of one body system in the center and the structures and functions of that body system connected to the center by lines. Then choose another body system and have students help you repeat the activity. **learning modality: visual**

English Learners/Intermediate L2
Comprehension: Link to Visual Extend the Beginning activity by having pairs of students work together to construct concept circles for body systems not yet covered. Circulate among students, helping them as necessary. **learning modality: visual**

Homeostasis

Teach Key Concepts
Keeping the Body Balanced

Focus Ask: **What happens to your breathing when you run?** (*You breathe faster and deeper.*)

Teach Explain that when you run, your breathing changes to get more air into your lungs and more oxygen to your muscles. Ask: **What happens in homeostasis?** (*Organ systems constantly work together to keep conditions inside the body balanced.*) **How does your body help maintain homeostasis when you are cold?** (*You shiver.*) **When you are hot?** (*You sweat.*) **How does the release of adrenaline during times of stress help maintain homeostasis?** (*Adrenaline gives you energy and helps you to take action to get through the stressful event.*)

Apply Ask students to think of other ways the body maintains homeostasis. (*Sample answers: When your body needs water, you get thirsty. When you body needs energy, you get hungry.*) **learning modality: verbal**

Build Inquiry L1

Communicating Ways to Manage Stress

Materials posters, markers, discarded magazines, reliable health references (books or Internet printouts)

Time 30 minutes

Focus Explain that negative stress that lasts for a long time can be unhealthy.

Teach Have students use the resources provided and work in small groups to identify warning signs of negative stress and healthful ways to manage it. Ask them to prepare and present a poster and a skit or role-play of a stressful situation, such as declining grades, and healthful ways to manage the stress.

Apply Ask students to volunteer methods of dealing with stress that work for them. Brainstorm a list of ways that are not healthful or do not deal with the problem, such as using alcohol or tobacco, watching a lot of television, or sleeping too much. **learning modality: visual**

Go Online
SciLINKS NSTA
For: Links on body systems
Visit: www.SciLinks.org
Web Code: scn-0411

Homeostasis

The different organ systems work together and depend on one another. When you ride a bike, you use your muscular and skeletal systems to steer and push the pedals. But you also need your nervous system to direct your arms and legs to move. Your respiratory, digestive, and circulatory systems work together to fuel your muscles with the energy they need. And your excretory system removes the wastes produced while your muscles are hard at work.

All the systems of the body work together to maintain **homeostasis** (hoh mee oh STAY sis), the body's tendency to keep an internal balance. **Homeostasis is the process by which an organism's internal environment is kept stable in spite of changes in the external environment.**

Homeostasis in Action To see homeostasis in action, all you have to do is take your temperature when the air is cold. Then, take it again in an overheated room. No matter what the temperature of the air around you, your internal body temperature will be close to 37°C. Of course, if you become sick, your body temperature may rise. But when you are well again, it returns to 37°C.

Maintaining Homeostasis Your body has various ways of maintaining homeostasis. For example, when you are too warm, you sweat. Sweating helps to cool your body. On the other hand, when you are cold, you shiver. Shivering occurs when your muscles rapidly contract and relax. This action produces heat that helps keep you warm. Both of these processes help your body maintain homeostasis by regulating your temperature.

FIGURE 4
Maintaining Homeostasis
Regardless of the surrounding temperature, your body temperature remains fairly constant at about 37°C. Sweating (left) and shivering (right) help regulate your body temperature.
Applying Concepts What is the term for the body's tendency to maintain a stable internal environment?

472 ◆

Differentiated Instruction

Less Proficient Readers L1
Organizing Information Have students organize the information on homeostasis into a cause-and-effect table. Model an example: Cause—room gets cold; Effect—you shiver. Have them read the text and find other examples. Encourage them to think of examples on their own. **learning modality: verbal**

Gifted and Talented L3
Researching Variations in Body Temperature Ask students to measure and record their temperature several times in one day. Have them record what they were doing just before they measured it. Students will discover that body temperature varies slightly during a day. Ask them to graph and explain their results using references. **learning modality: logical/mathematical**

Stress and Homeostasis Sometimes, things can happen to disrupt homeostasis. As a result, your heart may beat more rapidly or your breathing may increase. These reactions of your circulatory and respiratory systems are signs of stress. **Stress** is the reaction of your body to potentially threatening, challenging, or disturbing events.

Think about what happens when you leave the starting line in a bike race. As you pedal, your heart beats faster and your breathing increases. What is happening in your body? First, your endocrine system releases a chemical called adrenaline into your bloodstream. Adrenaline gives you a burst of energy and prepares your body to take action. As you pedal, your muscles work harder and require more oxygen. Oxygen is carried by the circulatory system, so your heart beats even faster to move more blood to your muscles. Your breath comes faster and faster, too, so that more oxygen can get into your body. Your body is experiencing stress.

If stress is over quickly, your body soon returns to its normal state. Think about the bike race again. After you cross the finish line, you continue to breathe hard for the next few minutes. Soon, however, your breathing and heart rate return to normal. The level of adrenaline in your blood returns to normal. Thus, homeostasis is restored after just a few minutes of rest.

 **What is stress?**

FIGURE 5
Stress
Your body reacts to stress, such as the start of a bike race, by releasing adrenaline and carrying more oxygen to body cells.

Section 1 Assessment

Target Reading Skill Outlining Use the information in your outline to help you answer the questions below.

Reviewing Key Concepts

1. a. Identifying List the four levels of organization in the human body from smallest to largest. Give an example of each level.
 b. Comparing and Contrasting What is the difference between tissues and organs?
 c. Applying Concepts What systems of the body are involved when you prepare a sandwich and then eat it?

2. a. Defining What is homeostasis?
 b. Explaining How does stress affect homeostasis?
 c. Relating Cause and Effect Describe what happens inside your body as you give an oral report in front of your class.

Writing in Science

Summary Write a paragraph that explains what body systems are involved when you sit down to do your homework. Be sure to begin your paragraph with a topic sentence and include supporting details.

Chapter 14 ◆ 473

Lab zone Chapter Project

Keep Students on Track Check that students have begun experimenting with various objects and making sketches of their model. Remind them that the models need to pivot and have a hinge action. Have them evaluate their design for practicality; the design should not be too complicated to build. Meet with students who are having difficulty choosing materials.

Writing in Science

Writing Mode Description
Scoring Rubric
4 Includes correct, complete descriptions of all functions; description is interesting and detailed
3 Includes all criteria, but description is uninteresting
2 Includes only brief descriptions
1 Includes inaccurate descriptions

Monitor Progress ___ L2
Answers
Figure 4 Homeostasis

Reading Checkpoint The reaction of your body to threatening, challenging, or disturbing events

Assess

Reviewing Key Concepts

1. a. Sample answer: Cell—bone cell; tissue—muscle tissue; organ—heart; organ system—nervous system **b.** A tissue is a group of similar cells that perform the same function. An organ performs one function also, but is composed of different types of tissue. Its job is more complex than that of a tissue. **c.** Skeletal, nervous, muscular, circulatory, and digestive systems
2. a. The process by which an organism's internal environment is kept stable in spite of changes in the external environment **b.** Stress can throw your body out of balance. **c.** Your endocrine system releases adrenaline into your bloodstream. Your heart beats faster so that more blood is moving to the muscles. Your breathing quickens so that more oxygen gets into your body.

Reteach L1
Use Figure 3 to identify several different body systems.

Performance Assessment L2
Skills Check Have students make a flowchart that sequences the events that occur when a person is stressed.

All in One Teaching Resources, Unit 3

• Section Summary: *Body Organization and Homeostasis*
• Review and Reinforce: *Body Organization and Homeostasis*
• Enrich: *Body Organization and Homeostasis*

473

The Skeletal System

Objectives

After this lesson, students will be able to
14.2.1 Identify the functions of the skeleton.
14.2.2 Explain the role that joints play in the body.
14.2.3 Describe the characteristics of bone and how to keep bones strong and healthy.

Target Reading Skill

Asking Questions Explain that changing a head into a question helps students anticipate the ideas, facts, and events they are going to read about.

Answers

Sample answers:
What does the skeleton do? (*The skeleton provides shape and support, helps you to move, protects organs, produces blood cells, and stores minerals and other materials.*) **How do joints move?** (*Joints can move forward or backward, in a circle, in a rotating motion, and in a gliding motion.*) **How strong are bones?** (*Bones can absorb more force without breaking than granite or concrete.*) **What can I do to care for my bones?** (*Eat a well-balanced diet and get plenty of exercise.*)

All in One Teaching Resources, Unit 3

• Transparency LS138

Preteach

Build Background Knowledge   L1

What Bones Look Like
Ask students to feel the bones beneath the skin in one of their hands and then have them draw a picture of what they think the bones look like. Have students brainstorm what they know or think they know about bones. List these on a piece of poster paper, and address misconceptions as you teach the section.

The Skeletal System

Reading Preview

Key Concepts
• What are the functions of the skeleton?
• What role do joints play in the body?
• What are the characteristics of bone, and how can you keep your bones strong and healthy?

Key Terms
• skeleton • vertebrae • joint
• ligament • cartilage
• compact bone • spongy bone
• marrow • osteoporosis

Target Reading Skill
Asking Questions Before you read, preview the red headings. In a graphic organizer like the one below, ask a *what* or *how* question for each heading. As you read, answer your questions.

The Skeletal System

Question	Answer
What does the skeleton do?	The skeletal system provides shape . . .

Lab zone Discover Activity

Hard as a Rock?

1. Your teacher will give you a rock and a leg bone from a cooked turkey or chicken.
2. Use a hand lens to examine both the rock and the bone.
3. Gently tap both the rock and the bone on a hard surface.
4. Pick up each object to feel how heavy it is.
5. Wash your hands. Then make notes of your observations.

Think It Over
Observing Based on your observations, why do you think bones are sometimes compared to rocks? List some ways in which bones and rocks are similar and different.

A high rise construction site is a busy place. After workers have prepared the building's foundation, they begin to assemble thousands of steel pieces into a frame for the building. People watch as the steel pieces are joined to create a rigid frame that climbs toward the sky. By the time the building is finished, however, the building's framework will no longer be visible.

Like a building, you also have an inner framework, but it isn't made up of steel. Your framework, or **skeleton,** is made up of all the bones in your body. The number of bones in your skeleton, or skeletal system, depends on your age. A newborn has about 275 bones. An adult, however, has about 206 bones. As a baby grows, some of the bones in the body fuse together. For example, as you grew, some of the bones in your skull fused together.

What the Skeletal System Does

Just as a building could not stand without its frame, you would collapse without your skeleton. **Your skeleton has five major functions. It provides shape and support, enables you to move, protects your organs, produces blood cells, and stores minerals and other materials until your body needs them.**

Lab zone Discover Activity

Skills Focus Observing   L1

Materials leg bone from a cooked chicken or turkey, rock of similar size, hand lens

Time 10 minutes

Tips Remind students to observe as many characteristics as possible, such as size, shape, color, texture, composition, and strength. Make sure the chicken or turkey bone has been thoroughly cooked and washed.

Think It Over Possible answer: They are both hard; bone is not as dense as rock and has a definite structure. Bone is living, while rock is not.

Shape and Support Your skeleton determines the shape of your body, much as a steel frame determines the shape of a building. The backbone, or vertebral column, is the center of the skeleton. Locate the backbone in Figure 6. Notice that the bones in the skeleton are in some way connected to this column. If you move your fingers down the center of your back, you can feel the 26 small bones, or **vertebrae** (VUR tuh bray) (singular: *vertebra*), that make up your backbone. Bend forward at the waist and feel the bones adjust as you move. You can think of each individual vertebra as a bead on a string. Just as a beaded necklace is flexible and able to bend, so too is your vertebral column. If your backbone were just one bone, you would not be able to bend or twist.

✔ **Reading Checkpoint** Why is the vertebral column considered the center of the skeleton?

FIGURE 6
The Skeleton
The skeleton provides a framework that supports and protects many other body parts. **Comparing and Contrasting** *In what ways is the skeleton like the steel framework of a building? In what ways is it different?*

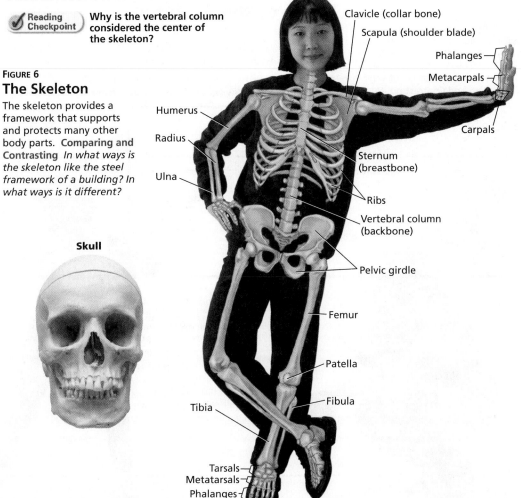

Skull

Clavicle (collar bone)
Scapula (shoulder blade)
Phalanges
Metacarpals
Humerus
Radius
Carpals
Ulna
Sternum (breastbone)
Ribs
Vertebral column (backbone)
Pelvic girdle
Femur
Patella
Fibula
Tibia
Tarsals
Metatarsals
Phalanges

Instruct

What the Skeletal System Does

Teach Key Concepts L2
Functions of the Skeleton

Focus Ask: **What would your body be like if you did not have a skeleton?** *(Sample answers: You would not have a shape; you would not be able to stand or perform any other movements.)*

Teach Ask students to identify as many functions of the skeletal system as they can by examining Figure 6. *(Helps you to move, provides shape, provides support, protects organs)* Ask: **Why are vertebrae important?** *(They are the bones that make up your backbone, and all other bones are connected to the backbone.)* **What other functions does the skeletal system perform?** *(It produces certain blood cells and stores minerals.)*

Apply Explain that a bone's structure relates to its function. Ask students to locate these bones in Figure 6 and identify their primary function: **Sternum** *(Protection)*, **Carpals** *(Movement)*, **Femur** *(Support and movement)*, **Ribs** *(Protection)*, **Vertebral column** *(Protection, support, and movement)* **learning modality: visual**

All in One Teaching Resources, Unit 3
• Transparency LS139

Independent Practice L2

All in One Teaching Resources, Unit 3
• Guided Reading and Study Worksheet: *The Skeletal System*

💿 **Student Edition on Audio CD**

Monitor Progress _____ L2

Writing Ask students to list the five main functions of the skeletal system.

Answers
Figure 6 Like the steel framework, the skeleton shapes and supports the body. Unlike the framework, the skeleton is living, produces necessary materials, and is flexible.

✔ **Reading Checkpoint** The bones in the skeleton are in some way connected to the backbone.

Joints of the Skeleton

Teach Key Concepts L2
The Role of Joints

Focus Ask students to bend their right elbows. Ask: **What is the point where your elbow bends?** (*Most students will know that it is a joint.*)

Teach Explain that joints hold bones together. Not all joints are movable; two bones can come together and not move—for example, in the skull. Have volunteers read aloud the captions in Figure 7. Ask a question about each type of movable joint, such as: **What types of movements does the ball-and-socket joint in the shoulder allow the arm to make?** (*Up and down, backward and forward, shrugging, in a circle*) Then ask: **What do ligaments do?** (*They hold together the bones in movable joints.*) **What substance keeps bones from rubbing against each other?** (*Cartilage*)

Apply Instruct students to move one ear back and forth, then the tip of their nose. Explain that the flexible part is cartilage, the same material that covers the ends of bones.

Extend The Active Art will show students how joints move. **learning modality: visual**

All in One **Teaching Resources, Unit 3**
• Transparency LS140

Help Students Read

Comparing and Contrasting As students read the section, have them create a table that compares and contrasts the types of joint.

Go Online
active art

For: Movable Joints activity
Visit: PHSchool.com
Web Code: cep-4012

FIGURE 7
Movable Joints

Without movable joints, your body would be as stiff as a board. The different kinds of joints allow your body to move in a variety of ways. **Comparing and Contrasting** *How is the movement of a hinge joint different from that of a ball-and-socket joint?*

Movement and Protection Your skeleton allows you to move. Most of the body's bones are associated with muscles. The muscles pull on the bones to make the body move. Bones also protect many of the organs in your body. For example, your skull protects your brain, and your breastbone and ribs form a protective cage around your heart and lungs.

Production and Storage of Substances Some of your bones produce substances that your body needs. You can think of the long bones of your arms and legs as factories that make certain blood cells. Bones also store minerals such as calcium and phosphorus. When the body needs these minerals, the bones release small amounts of them into the blood.

Joints of the Skeleton

Suppose that a single long bone ran the length of your leg. How would you get out of bed or run for the school bus? Luckily, your body contains many small bones rather than fewer large ones. A **joint** is a place in the body where two bones come together. **Joints allow bones to move in different ways.** There are two kinds of joints—immovable joints and movable joints.

Hinge Joint
A hinge joint allows forward or backward motion. Your knee is a hinge joint that allows you to bend and straighten your leg. Your elbow is also a hinge joint.

Ball-and-Socket Joint
Ball-and-socket joints allow the greatest range of motion. The ball-and-socket joint in your shoulder allows you to swing your arm freely in a circle. Your hips also have ball-and-socket joints.

476 ◆

Immovable Joints Some joints in the body connect bones in a way that allows little or no movement. These joints are called immovable joints. The bones of the skull are held together by immovable joints.

Movable Joints Most of the joints in the body are movable joints. Movable joints allow the body to make a wide range of movements. Look at Figure 7 to see the variety of movements that these joints make possible.

The bones in movable joints are held together by strong connective tissues called **ligaments.** Most joints have a second type of connective tissue, called **cartilage** (KAHR tuh lij), which is more flexible than bone. Cartilage covers the ends of the bones and keeps them from rubbing against each other. For example, in the knee, cartilage acts as a cushion that keeps your femur (thighbone) from rubbing against the bones of your lower leg. In addition, a fluid lubricates the ends of the bones, allowing them to move smoothly over each other.

 Reading Checkpoint How are movable joints held together?

 **Go Online**
active.art

For: Movable Joints activity
Visit: PHSchool.com
Web Code: cep-4012

Students explore the skeletal and muscular systems.

Lab zone **Build Inquiry** L1

Observing Joints

Materials model of a human skeleton

Time 5 minutes whole class; 5 minutes per pair or small group of students

Focus Show students the model and ask: **How does the human skeleton enable you to move?** *(Bones are connected at joints and can rotate, pivot, and bend back and forth.)*

Teach Move one joint of each type on the model, and state the type of joint as you move it. Instruct students to take turns examining the model in pairs, spending no more than 5 minutes manipulating the bones to see how the joints of the skeleton move. Tell them to write down their observations. You might schedule this activity while students are working on their Chapter Projects or doing independent seat work.

Apply Make copies of a human skeleton, and have students indicate each joint they felt on the model and the name of the type of joint. **learning modality: kinesthetic**

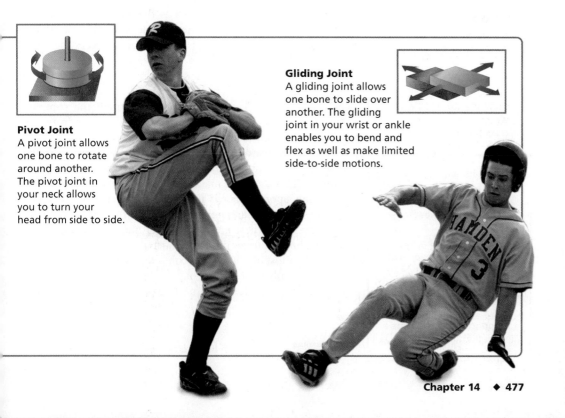

Pivot Joint
A pivot joint allows one bone to rotate around another. The pivot joint in your neck allows you to turn your head from side to side.

Gliding Joint
A gliding joint allows one bone to slide over another. The gliding joint in your wrist or ankle enables you to bend and flex as well as make limited side-to-side motions.

Chapter 14 ◆ 477

Monitor Progress L2

Skills Check Ask students to identify different types of movable joints in addition to the ball-and-socket joints in the picture of the batter. *(Sample answer: Neck—pivot joint; hands—gliding; knees—hinge)* Ask students to give an example of a joint that is immovable. *(Sample answer: The bones of the skull)*

Answers
Figure 7 A hinge joint allows only one type of movement—forward or backward motion. A ball-and-socket joint permits movement in many directions.

 Reading Checkpoint By strong connective tissues called ligaments

Bones—Strong and Living

Characteristics of Bone

Focus Ask: **Which function of the skeletal system gives you a clue that bones are not dead or solid?** *(Bones make blood cells and release small amounts of minerals into the blood when needed.)*

Teach Refer students to Figure 8. Have them locate and examine each part of the femur. Ask: **What covers the bone except for the ends?** *(A thin, tough membrane)* **What is just beneath this membrane?** *(Compact bone)* **How do blood and other materials get to the living cells inside the bone?** *(Blood vessels run through canals in the compact bone.)* **How does the structure of spongy bone relate to its function?** *(Spongy bone has many small spaces that make it lightweight but strong.)* **Where is marrow produced?** *(In the spaces in bone)* **What is marrow?** *(Two types of soft, connective tissue; one type produces most types of blood cells, the other type stores fat.)* **Does new bone tissue stop forming after you stop growing?** *(No; bones make new tissue when they absorb the force of your weight and when a bone has broken.)*

Apply Have students write a paragraph describing how the structure of bones allows the bones to grow and makes them strong. *(Sample answer: The membrane allows blood vessels to run through canals in the compact bone to deliver materials the bone needs to function. Spongy bone has spaces within it that allow it to absorb large amounts of force.)*
learning modality: visual

All in One Teaching Resources, Unit 3

- Transparency LS141

FIGURE 8
Bone Structure

The most obvious feature of a long bone, such as the femur, is its long shaft. Running through the compact bone tissue within the shaft is a system of canals. The canals bring materials to the living bone cells.
Interpreting Diagrams *What different tissues make up the femur?*

Femur

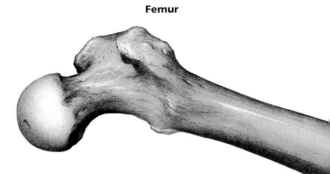

Bones—Strong and Living

When you think of a skeleton, you may think of the paper cutouts that are used as decorations at Halloween. Many people connect skeletons with death. The ancient Greeks did, too. The word *skeleton* actually comes from a Greek word meaning "a dried body." The bones of your skeleton, however, are not dead at all. **Bones are complex living structures that undergo growth and development.**

Bone Structure Figure 8 shows the structure of the femur, or thighbone. The femur, which is the body's longest bone, connects the pelvic bones to the lower leg bones. Notice that a thin, tough membrane covers all of the bone except the ends. Blood vessels and nerves enter and leave the bone through the membrane. Beneath the bone's outer membrane is a layer of **compact bone,** which is hard and dense, but not solid. As you can see in Figure 8, small canals run through the compact bone. These canals carry blood vessels and nerves from the bone's surface to the living cells within the bone.

Just inside the femur's compact bone is a layer of spongy bone. Like a sponge, **spongy bone** has many small spaces within it. This structure makes spongy bone tissue lightweight but strong. Spongy bone is also found at the ends of the bone.

The spaces in many bones contain a soft, connective tissue called **marrow.** There are two types of marrow—red and yellow. Red bone marrow produces most of the body's blood cells. As a child, most of your bones contained red bone marrow. As a teenager, only the ends of your femurs, skull, hip bones, and sternum (breastbone) contain red marrow. Your other bones contain yellow marrow. This marrow stores fat that can serve as an energy reserve.

 Reading Checkpoint What are the two types of bone marrow?

Lab zone Try This **Activity**

Soft Bones?

In this activity, you will explore the role that calcium plays in bones.

1. Put on protective gloves. Soak one clean chicken bone in a jar filled with water. Soak a second clean chicken bone in a jar filled with vinegar. (Vinegar causes calcium to dissolve out of bone.)
2. After one week, put on protective gloves and remove the bones from the jars.
3. Compare how the two bones look and feel. Note any differences between the two bones.

Drawing Conclusions Based on your results, explain why it is important to consume a diet that is high in calcium.

Lab zone Try This **Activity**

Skills Focus Drawing conclusions

Materials 2 plastic jars with lids, vinegar, water, 2 clean chicken bones, gloves

Time 15 minutes for setup; 15 minutes for observation

Tips
CAUTION: *After students examine the chicken bones, make sure they wash their hands after removing the gloves.*

Expected Outcome Bones soaked in vinegar lose their calcium and become rubbery; a diet high in calcium helps keep bones hard.

Extend Ask students to examine food labels at home to find food sources rich in calcium, and then report their findings to the class. **learning modality: kinesthetic**

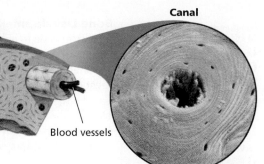

Compact Bone

Canal

Blood vessels

Compact bone

Spongy bone

Bone marrow

Outer membrane

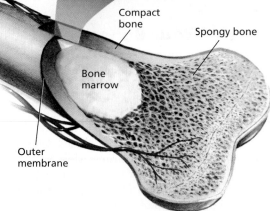

Bone Strength

The structure of bone makes it both strong and lightweight. In fact, bones are so strong that they can absorb more force without breaking than can concrete or granite rock. Yet, bones are much lighter than these materials. In fact, only about 20 percent of an average adult's body weight is bone.

Have you ever heard the phrase "as hard as a rock"? Most rock is hard because it is made up of minerals that are packed tightly together. In a similar way, bones are hard because they contain minerals—primarily phosphorus and calcium.

Bone Growth

Bones are alive—they contain cells and tissues, such as blood and nerves. Because they are alive, bones also form new bone tissue as you grow. Even after you are grown, however, bone tissue continues to form within your bones. For example, every time you play soccer or basketball, some of your bones absorb the force of your weight. They respond by making new bone tissue.

Sometimes, new bone tissue forms after an accident. If you break a bone, for example, new bone tissue forms to fill the gap between the broken ends of the bone. In fact, the healed region of new bone may be stronger than the original bone!

FIGURE 9
Bone Strength
You can jump up and down or turn cartwheels without breaking bones.

Chapter 14 ◆ 479

Lab zone **Build Inquiry** L2

Observing Bone Structure

Materials leg bones from thoroughly cooked chickens or turkeys, dissecting trays, gloves, hand lens; before class, use a small kitchen saw to slice one leg bone crosswise and one lengthwise for each group. Place the bones in the trays.

Time 15 minutes setup; 15 minutes class

Focus Remind students that bones are organs that are composed of different types of tissue.

Teach
Have groups of students use Figure 8 to identify the various parts of the bones. Ask them to write down and sketch their observations. **CAUTION:** *After students examine the chicken bones, make sure they wash their hands after removing the gloves.*

Apply Ask: **Where did you find the largest concentration of compact bone and spongy bone?** *(Compact in the shaft, spongy at the ends)* Explain that short bones, such as those in the fingers, are mostly spongy bone. Ask students to infer why long bones have more compact bone. *(Long bones, such as those in the legs, must have harder, denser compact bone to support the body.)* **learning modality: visual**

Monitor Progress L2

Skills Check Have students draw concept maps showing the structure of bone. Suggest that students draw concentric circles indicating the layers of tissue and draw arrows where blood vessels and nerves flow through. Students can save their concept maps in their portfolios.

Portfolio

Answers
Figure 8 Connective tissue and nervous tissue

 Reading Checkpoint Red marrow and yellow marrow

Differentiated Instruction

Gifted and Talented L3
Investigating the Effects of Microgravity Tell students that weight-bearing exercise promotes bone growth and prevents bone loss. Exercises performed against the force of gravity stimulate osteoblasts, the cells that make bone. Ask students to find out the effects of microgravity on the bones of astronauts and how scientists are using this

information to help people with spinal cord injuries and people with osteoporosis. *(Students may discover some interesting facts, for example, that some astronauts on the space station Mir lost more than 10% of their bone mass, mostly from the legs.)* Ask students to present a report to the class. **learning modality: verbal**

Address Misconceptions ▪ L1

Bones Are Living

Focus Some students might think that bone is dead.

Teach Explain that some people think of bones as lifeless because they see skeletons in movies or skeletons of dead animals. Bone does contain nonliving material, such as calcium. However, it is composed of living tissue. Ask: **What are the levels of organization before bones?** *(Cells, then tissues)* **What kinds of functions do these perform?** *(Cells grow, reproduce, and take in energy. Tissues perform a specific function.)* Point out that bones are living because they are made of cells which compose all living things.

Apply Ask: **Would a bone bleed if it were cut?** *(Yes, because bones have blood vessels)* **Would it hurt?** *(Yes, because bones have nerves)* **learning modality: verbal**

Taking Care of Your Bones

Teach Key Concepts ▪ L2

Habits for Strong, Healthy Bones

Focus Remind students that calcium is a mineral that helps bones to be hard.

Teach Ask: **How can you get enough calcium?** *(Eat a well-balanced diet that includes good sources of calcium.)* **What kind of exercise helps your bones grow stronger and denser?** *(Activities in which your bones support the weight of your body)* **How can you reduce your risk of osteoporosis?** *(Eat calcium-rich foods and get plenty of exercise)* Tell students that osteoporosis can be largely prevented by building bone mass during adolescence and young adulthood.

Apply Encourage students to create a list of activities that are weight-bearing and a list of those that are not. *(Weight-bearing activities include jogging, aerobics, walking, jumping rope, weight lifting, skating, dancing, soccer, and basketball. Non-weight-bearing activities include cycling and swimming.)* **learning modality: verbal**

Bones, Muscle, and Skin

Video Preview
▶ Video Field Trip
Video Assessment

Bone Development Try this activity: Move the tip of your nose from side to side with your fingers. Notice that the tip of your nose is not stiff. That is because it contains cartilage. As an infant, much of your skeleton was cartilage. Over time, most of the cartilage was replaced with hard bone tissue.

The replacement of cartilage by bone tissue usually is complete by the time you stop growing. You've seen, however, that not all of your body's cartilage is replaced by bone. Even in adults, many joints contain cartilage that protects the ends of the bones.

Taking Care of Your Bones

Because your skeleton performs so many necessary functions, it is important to keep it healthy. **A combination of a balanced diet and regular exercise are important for a lifetime of healthy bones.**

Diet One way to help ensure healthy bones is to eat a well-balanced diet. A well-balanced diet includes enough calcium and phosphorus to keep your bones strong while they are growing. Meats, whole grains, and leafy green vegetables are all good sources of both calcium and phosphorus. Dairy products, including yogurt, are good sources of calcium.

Exercise Another way to build and maintain strong bones is to get plenty of exercise. During activities such as running, skating, or dancing, your bones support the weight of your entire body. These weight-bearing activities help your bones grow stronger and denser. To prevent injuries while exercising, be sure to wear appropriate safety equipment, such as a helmet and pads.

 Reading Checkpoint What are two ways to keep your bones healthy?

FIGURE 10
Caring for Your Bones
Exercising regularly and eating a balanced diet help to keep your bones strong and healthy.

480 ◆

Bones, Muscles, and Skin

Show the Video Field Trip to let students experience a trip through a bone and understand the structure and function of bones. Discussion question: **What happens to the cartilage that makes up much of an infant's skeleton?** *(It is replaced by bone tissue as the child grows.)*

Healthy Spine

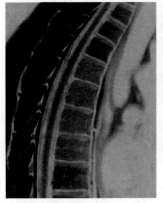

Spine with Osteoporosis

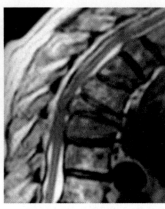

FIGURE 11
Osteoporosis
Without enough calcium in the diet, a person's bones weaken. These photos show how the shape and structure of vertebrae in a healthy spine compare with those in a person with osteoporosis.
Relating Cause and Effect *What can you do to prevent osteoporosis?*

Osteoporosis As people become older, their bones begin to lose some of the minerals they contain. Mineral loss can lead to **osteoporosis** (ahs tee oh puh ROH sis), a condition in which the body's bones become weak and break easily. You can see the effect of osteoporosis in Figure 11. Osteoporosis is more common in women than in men. Evidence indicates that regular exercise throughout life can help prevent osteoporosis. A diet with enough calcium can also help prevent osteoporosis. If you eat enough calcium-rich foods now, during your teenage years, you may help prevent osteoporosis later in life.

Section 2 Assessment

Target Reading Skill **Asking Questions** Work with a partner to check the answers in your graphic organizer.

Reviewing Key Concepts

1. **a. Listing** What are five functions of the skeleton?
   b. Explaining How does the skeleton protect the body?
   c. Predicting How would your life be different if your backbone consisted of just one long bone?
2. **a. Naming** What are four types of movable joints?
   b. Comparing and Contrasting Compare immovable joints with movable joints.
   c. Classifying Which of your movable joints are ball-and-socket joints?
3. **a. Identifying** What are three layers within the femur?
   b. Relating Cause and Effect How does the structure of bones make them both strong and lightweight?
   c. Applying Concepts How do a well-balanced diet and weight-bearing exercise help keep bones strong?

Lab zone **At-Home Activity**

Model Joints Choose two examples of movable joints from Figure 7. Ask a family member to perform separate movements that involve one joint and then the other. Make drawings to represent the joints and bones involved in each movement. Use the drawings to explain to your family how the motions of the two joints differ.

Chapter 14 ◆ **481**

Lab zone **Chapter Project**

Keep Students on Track Check that students have completed their designs and sketches of the model hands, and that they have begun building their models. Approve all designs, and help students locate materials. Remind students that they can use parts from other devices, such as discarded or broken toys.

Lab zone **At-Home Activity**

Model Joints **L2** As a class, review the different types of joints and their movements. Suggest that students closely note the direction of the movement when a family member performs it. Advise them to keep their drawings simple to emphasize the movement.

Assess

Reviewing Key Concepts

1. **a.** Provide shape and support, enable you to move, protect your organs, produce blood cells, and store minerals and other materials **b.** The skull protects the brain, and the breastbone and ribs protect the heart and lungs. **c.** Sample answer: You could not bend at the waist or twist. You would not be able to do some activities you do now, such as certain sports, twisting to get something behind you, or getting out of bed the same way.
2. **a.** Hinge, ball-and-socket, pivot, and gliding **b.** Both immovable and movable joints join two bones. Immovable joints allow little or no movement. Movable joints allow the body to make a wide range of movements. **c.** Shoulders and hips
3. **a.** Compact bone, spongy bone, and marrow. Students may also list the thin tough outer membrane. **b.** Compact bone is hard and dense. Spongy bone has many small spaces within it that make it strong but lightweight.
   c. A well-balanced diet contains calcium and phosphorus, which bones need to keep them strong. Weight-bearing exercises help bones grow stronger and denser.

Reteach L1

Call on students to define the Key Terms in this section and relate each to the Key Concepts.

Performance Assessment L2

Writing Ask students to describe one of the major functions of the human skeleton and explain how the skeleton carries out that function.

All in One **Teaching Resources, Unit 3**
- Section Summary: *The Skeletal System*
- Review and Reinforce: *The Skeletal System*
- Enrich: *The Skeletal System*

Section
3
The Muscular System

Objectives

After this lesson, students will be able to

14.3.1 Identify the types of muscles found in the body.

14.3.2 Explain why skeletal muscles work in pairs.

Target Reading Skill

Previewing Visuals Explain that looking at the visuals before they read helps students activate prior knowledge and predict what they are about to read.

Answers

Sample answers:

How does skeletal muscle help my body move? *(Skeletal muscles are attached to the ends of bones and provide the force to move them.)* **Where is smooth muscle found?** *(The inside of many internal organs)* **Why is cardiac muscle considered a special type?** *(It is found only in the heart; it is like smooth muscle because it is involuntary and like skeletal muscle because it is striated.)*

All in One **Teaching Resources, Unit 3**

• Transparency LS142

Preteach

Build Background Knowledge L2

How Muscles Move

Ask each student to hold a science book in one hand. Have students stand and hold the books down at their sides. Ask them to lift the books while feeling their arm muscles with the opposite hand. Ask: **What muscles did you feel contract? What else did you notice?** *(Sample answer: Muscles in the upper arm; fibers [tendons] stood out through the skin.)* Record their observations on the board.

Reading Preview

Key Concepts

• What types of muscles are found in the body?

• Why do skeletal muscles work in pairs?

Key Terms

• involuntary muscle
• voluntary muscle
• skeletal muscle
• tendon
• striated muscle
• smooth muscle
• cardiac muscle

Target Reading Skill

Previewing Visuals When you preview, you look ahead at the material to be read. Preview Figure 12. Then, in a graphic organizer like the one below, write two questions that you have about the diagram. As you read, answer your questions.

Types of Muscle

Q.	How does skeletal muscle help my body move?
A.	
Q.	

Lab zone Discover Activity

How Do Muscles Work?

1. Grip a spring-type clothespin with the thumb and index finger of your writing hand. Squeeze the clothespin open and shut as quickly as possible for two minutes. Count how many times you can squeeze the clothespin before your muscles tire.

2. Rest for one minute. Then, repeat Step 1.

Think It Over

Predicting What do you think would happen if you repeated Steps 1 and 2 with your other hand? Give a reason for your prediction. Then, test your prediction.

A rabbit becomes still when it senses danger. The rabbit sits so still that it doesn't seem to move a muscle. Could you sit without moving any muscles? Saliva builds up in your mouth. You swallow. You need to breathe. Your chest expands to let air in. All of these actions involve muscles. It is impossible to sit absolutely still without muscle movement.

There are about 600 muscles in your body. Muscles have many functions. For example, they keep your heart beating, pull your mouth into a smile, and move the bones of your skeleton. The girl doing karate on the next page uses many of her muscles to move her arms, legs, hands, feet, and head. Other muscles expand and contract her chest and allow her to breathe.

Types of Muscle

Some of your body's movements, such as smiling, are easy to control. Other movements, such as the beating of your heart, are impossible to control completely. That is because some of your muscles are not under your conscious control. Those muscles are called **involuntary muscles.** Involuntary muscles are responsible for such essential activities as breathing and digesting food.

482 ◆

Lab zone Discover Activity

Skills Focus Predicting L1

Materials spring-type clothespin

Time 15 minutes

Tips Caution students not to move so fast that they lose their grip; otherwise they might pinch their fingers in the spring.

Expected Outcome The muscles can respond repetitively but tire easily. Most

students will find that the number of times they are able to squeeze the clothespin decreases in Step 2.

Think It Over Students might predict that repeating the steps with the other hand would produce the same pattern, but that they will not be able to squeeze the clothespin as many times as in the first trial because the writing hand is stronger.

The muscles that are under your conscious control are called **voluntary muscles.** Smiling, turning a page in a book, and getting out of your chair when the bell rings are all actions controlled by voluntary muscles.

Your body has three types of muscle tissue—skeletal muscle, smooth muscle, and cardiac muscle. Some of these muscle tissues are involuntary, and some are voluntary. In Figure 12, you see a magnified view of each type of muscle in the body. Both skeletal and smooth muscles are found in many places in the body. Cardiac muscle is found only in the heart. Each muscle type performs specific functions in the body.

FIGURE 12
Types of Muscle
Your body has three types of muscle tissue: skeletal muscle, smooth muscle, and cardiac muscle. **Classifying** *Which type of muscle is found only in the heart?*

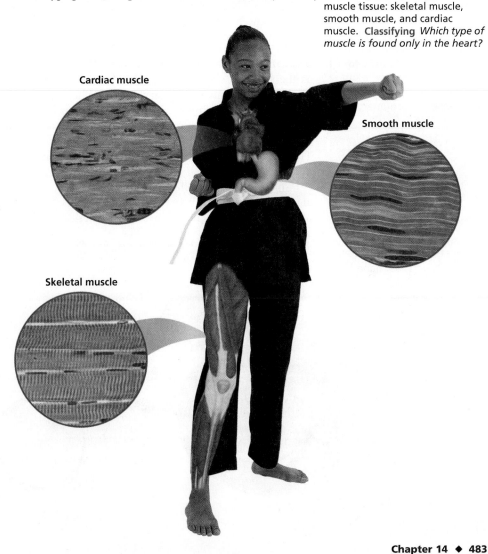

Cardiac muscle

Smooth muscle

Skeletal muscle

Chapter 14 ◆ 483

Lab zone Build **Inquiry** L3

Observing Muscle Tissue

Materials prepared slides of skeletal, smooth, and cardiac muscle; microscope

Time 20 minutes

Focus Review the three types of muscle.

Teach

CAUTION: *Tell students to be careful handling the slides.* Ask them to observe the slides with a low-power lens, then at high power. Have them sketch each type of muscle, noting whether cells contain striations, and labeling the nucleus and cytoplasm for each cell type. The cell membrane may or may not be distinguishable because cells may be tightly packed.

Apply Ask students how the nuclei of striated muscle tissue differ from the nuclei of cardiac and smooth. *(Striated have more nuclei.)* Tell students that skeletal muscle tissue is actually many individual cells, each with a nucleus, that have joined to make one muscle fiber. A muscle fiber can be several centimeters long. Smooth and cardiac muscle tissues are composed of individual cells, each with its own nucleus. **learning modality: visual**

Help Students Read L1

Anticipation Guide Before students read the next two sections, write these statements on the board:

- **Muscle cells shorten and lengthen to move a muscle.**
- **Exercise causes more muscle cells to be produced.**

Ask students whether they agree with the statements. Discuss their responses, and then have them read the sections and evaluate their initial answers. *(Both statements are false. Muscle cells shorten only, and exercise makes individual muscle cells grow in size.)*

Lab zone Try This **Activity**

Get a Grip

Are skeletal muscles at work when you're not moving?

1. Hold a stirrer in front of you, parallel to a table top. Do not touch the table.
2. Have a partner place a hairpin on the stirrer.
3. Raise the stirrer until the "legs" of the hairpin just touch the table. The "head" of the hairpin should rest on the stirrer.
4. Hold the stirrer steady for 20 seconds. Observe what happens to the hairpin.
5. Grip the stirrer tighter and repeat Step 4. Observe.

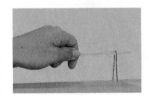

Inferring Are the skeletal muscles in your hand at work when you hold your hand still? Explain.

Skeletal Muscle Every time you walk across a room, you are using skeletal muscles. **Skeletal muscles** are attached to the bones of your skeleton and provide the force that moves your bones. At each end of a skeletal muscle is a tendon. A **tendon** is a strong connective tissue that attaches muscle to bone. Skeletal muscle cells appear banded, or striated. For this reason, skeletal muscle is sometimes called **striated** (STRY ay tid) **muscle.**

Because you have conscious control of skeletal muscles, they are classified as voluntary muscles. One characteristic of skeletal muscles is that they react very quickly. Think about what happens during a swim meet. Immediately after the starting gun sounds, a swimmer's leg muscles push the swimmer off the block into the pool. However, another characteristic of skeletal muscles is that they tire quickly. By the end of the race, the swimmer's muscles are tired and need a rest.

Smooth Muscle The inside of many internal organs, such as the stomach and blood vessels, contain **smooth muscles.** Smooth muscles are involuntary muscles. They work automatically to control certain movements inside your body, such as those involved in digestion. For example, as the smooth muscles of your stomach contract, they produce a churning action. The churning mixes the food with chemicals, and helps to digest the food.

Unlike skeletal muscles, smooth muscle cells are not striated. Smooth muscles behave differently than skeletal muscles, too. Smooth muscles react more slowly and tire more slowly.

Reading Checkpoint Where is smooth muscle found?

484 ◆

Lab zone Try This **Activity**

Skills Focus Inferring L2

Materials wooden stirrer, hairpin

Time 10 minutes

Tips Ask students to predict what may happen to the hairpin as they hold the stirrer out in front of them.

Expected Outcome Even when students hold their hands still, some of the muscles are at work as evidenced by the movement, or "walking," of the hairpin.

Extend Have students rest a hand on their desks, make a fist, and then extend the index finger. Tell them to hold the index finger still. If students watch carefully, they can probably see the finger trembling slightly. **learning modality: kinesthetic**

Cardiac Muscle The tissue called **cardiac muscle** is found only in your heart. Cardiac muscle has some characteristics in common with both smooth muscle and skeletal muscle. Like smooth muscle, cardiac muscle is involuntary. Like skeletal muscle, cardiac muscle cells are striated. However, unlike skeletal muscle, cardiac muscle does not get tired. It can contract repeatedly. You call those repeated contractions heartbeats.

Muscles at Work

Has anyone ever asked you to "make a muscle"? If so, you probably tightened your fist, bent your arm at the elbow, and made the muscles in your upper arm bulge. Like other skeletal muscles, the muscles in your arm do their work by contracting, becoming shorter and thicker. Muscle cells contract when they receive messages from the nervous system. **Because muscle cells can only contract, not extend, skeletal muscles must work in pairs. While one muscle contracts, the other muscle in the pair relaxes to its original length.**

Muscles Work in Pairs Figure 13 shows the muscle action involved in bending the arm at the elbow. First, the biceps muscle on the front of the upper arm contracts to bend the elbow, lifting the forearm and hand. As the biceps contracts, the triceps on the back of the upper arm relaxes and returns to its original length. Then, to straighten the elbow, the triceps muscle contracts. As the triceps contracts to extend the arm, the biceps relaxes and returns to its original length. Another example of muscles that work in pairs are those in your thigh that bend and straighten the knee joint.

Go Online
PHSchool.com

For: More on muscle types
Visit: PHSchool.com
Web Code: ced-4014

FIGURE 13
Muscle Pairs

Because muscles can only contract, or shorten, they must work in pairs. To bend the arm at the elbow, the biceps contracts while the triceps returns to its original length. *Interpreting Diagrams What happens to each muscle to straighten the arm?*

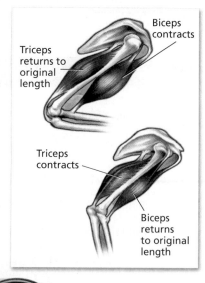

Triceps returns to original length

Biceps contracts

Triceps contracts

Biceps returns to original length

Chapter 14 ◆ 485

Muscles at Work

Teach Key Concepts L2
Muscles Work in Pairs

Focus Refer students to Figure 13.

Teach Ask students to bend their elbows so they can feel their muscles contract and relax as shown in the figure. Explain that muscles can only contract, or become shorter. They cannot extend, or become longer. Ask: **How does your biceps change as you bend your arm?** *(It gets shorter and thicker and feels firmer.)* **What happens to your arm when your triceps contracts?** *(The arm straightens and the biceps returns to its original length.)*

Apply Explain that the nervous system determines the strength of muscle contractions. If a person lifts something light, only a few muscle cells will contract; if the object is heavy, many muscle cells will contract. **learning modality: kinesthetic**

All in One Teaching Resources, Unit 3
• Transparency LS143

Lab zone Build Inquiry L2

Modeling How Skeletal Muscles Work

Materials strips of cardboard; thick, long elastic bands; brass fasteners

Time 25 minutes

Focus Review how muscles work in pairs.

Teach Have students work in small groups to build models to show how muscle pairs work together and then have them demonstrate and explain the model.

Apply Ask students to examine a diagram of a human skeleton and list the bones that are moved by muscle pairs. **learning modality: kinesthetic**

Monitor Progress _____ L2

Drawing Have students observe which muscles contract when they stand and bend a knee. Then have them sketch the bones and muscles in the thigh in each position and indicate which muscle is contracted. Have students place their drawings in their portfolios.

Answers
Figure 13 The triceps contracts and the biceps returns to its original length.

Reading Checkpoint On the inside of many internal organs

Differentiated Instruction

Less Proficient Readers L1
Comparing and Contrasting Ask students to organize the information on types of muscle tissue in a compare/contrast table. Columns are *Type of Tissue, How It Is Controlled,* and *Where It Is Found.* **learning modality: visual**

Gifted and Talented L3
Improving Flexibility Flexibility is the ability to use a muscle throughout its entire range of motion. Flexibility is just as important as having strong muscles. Have students ask a physical education teacher to show them how to correctly perform stretches for flexibility. Students can lead the class in performing the stretches. **learning modality: kinesthetic**

Reading Checkpoint) Stretch and warm up thoroughly.

Assess

Skeletal, smooth, and cardiac   A person can control voluntary muscles, such as skeletal muscles. A person cannot control involuntary muscles, such as smooth or cardiac muscles. Also, voluntary muscles tire more easily than involuntary muscles.

The person would not be able to move the finger because the muscle would not be connected to the bone.

Attached to the bones of the skeleton; for example, in the upper arms and thighs

To bend the arm, the biceps shortens, pulling the forearm up toward the shoulder. To straighten the arm, the triceps contracts while the biceps returns to its original length.   Sample answer: Because paired muscles must work together, and exercise makes individual muscle cells grow in size, exercising both muscles in a pair will make them grow equally strong.

L1

Name several different body parts, including internal organs, and ask students to identify the type of muscle found there and its function.

f

Have students write a paragraph explaining why having involuntary muscles is important.

All in One

- Section Summary: *The Muscular System*
- Review and Reinforce: *The Muscular System*
- Enrich: *The Muscular System*

FIGURE 14
Preventing Muscle Injuries
When you warm up before exercising, you increase the flexibility of your muscles.

Muscular Strength and Flexibility Regular exercise is important for maintaining both muscular strength and flexibility. Exercise makes individual muscle cells grow in size. As a result, the whole muscle becomes thicker. The thicker a muscle is, the stronger the muscle is. When you warm up thoroughly before exercising, the blood flow to your muscles increases and they become more flexible. Stretching after you warm up helps prepare your muscles for the more vigorous exercise or play ahead.

Sometimes, despite taking proper precautions, muscles can become injured. A muscle strain, or pulled muscle, can occur when muscles are overworked or overstretched. Tendons can also be overstretched or partially torn. After a long period of exercise, a skeletal muscle can cramp. When a muscle cramps, the entire muscle contracts strongly and stays contracted. If you injure a muscle or tendon, it is important to follow medical instructions and to rest the injured area so it can heal.

 Reading Checkpoint) **What are two ways to prepare the muscles for exercise?**

Section 3 Assessment

Target Reading Skill Previewing Visuals Refer to your questions and answers about Figure 12 to help you answer Question 1 below.

Reviewing Key Concepts

1. a. **Identifying** What are the three types of muscle tissue?
   b. **Comparing and Contrasting** How do voluntary and involuntary muscles differ? Give an example of each type of muscle.
   c. **Predicting** The muscles that move your fingers are attached to the bones in your fingers by tendons. Suppose one of the tendons in a person's index finger were cut. How would it affect movement in the finger?
2. a. **Identifying** Where might you find muscle pairs?
   b. **Describing** Describe how the muscles in your upper arm work together to bend and straighten your arm.
   c. **Applying Concepts** When exercising to build muscular strength, why is it important to exercise both muscles in a muscle pair equally?

Writing in Science

Comparison Paragraph Write a paragraph comparing smooth muscle tissue and skeletal muscle tissue. Include whether these muscle tissues are voluntary or involuntary, where they are found and what their functions are. In addition, describe what you might expect to see if you looked at these muscle tissues under a microscope.

486 ◆

Lab zone Chapter **Project**

Models

should be complete or nearly so. Provide time for testing and revising of designs. Suggest that students try different materials if some materials aren't working. Before conducting the tests, have students review the criteria they will use to evaluate their model's performance.

Writing in Science

Description

Includes the function, structure, and location of smooth and skeletal muscle; description uses examples and many supporting details

Includes all criteria, but does not include examples or many details

Includes incomplete description

Includes inaccurate description

A Look Beneath the Skin

Problem

What are some characteristics of skeletal muscles? How do skeletal muscles work?

Skills Focus

observing, inferring, classifying

Materials

- water
- paper towels
- scissors
- dissecting tray
- uncooked chicken wing, treated with bleach

Procedure

1. Put on goggles, an apron, and protective gloves. **CAUTION:** *Wear gloves whenever you handle the chicken.*

2. Your teacher will give you a chicken wing. Rinse it well with water, dry it with paper towels, and place it in a dissecting tray.

3. Carefully extend the wing to find out how many major parts it has. Draw a diagram of the external structure. Label the upper arm, elbow, lower arm, and hand (wing tip).

4. Use scissors to remove the skin. Cut only through the skin. **CAUTION:** *Cut away from your body and your classmates.*

5. Examine the muscles, which are the bundles of pink tissue around the bones. Find the two groups of muscles in the upper arm. Hold the arm down at the shoulder, and alternately pull on each muscle group. Observe what happens.

6. Find the two groups of muscles in the lower arm. Hold down the arm at the elbow, and alternately pull on each muscle group. Then, make a diagram of the wing's muscles.

7. Find the tendons—shiny white tissue at the ends of the muscles. Notice what parts the tendons connect. Add the tendons to your diagram.

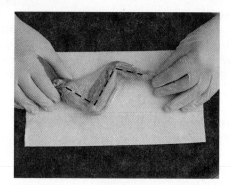

8. Remove the muscles and tendons. Find the ligaments, which are the whitish ribbon-shaped structures between bones. Add them to your diagram.

9. Dispose of the chicken parts according to your teacher's instructions. Wash your hands.

Analyze and Conclude

1. **Observing** How does a chicken wing move at the elbow? How does the motion compare to how your elbow moves? What type of joint is involved?

2. **Inferring** What happened when you pulled on one of the arm muscles? What muscle action does the pulling represent?

3. **Classifying** Categorize the muscles you observed as smooth, cardiac, or skeletal.

4. **Communicating** Why is it valuable to record your observations with accurate diagrams? Write a paragraph in which you describe what your diagrams show.

More to Explore

Use the procedures from this lab to examine an uncooked chicken thigh and leg. Compare how the chicken leg and a human leg move. *Obtain your teacher's permission before carrying out your investigation.*

Expected Outcome

Students will be able to observe skeletal muscles working in pairs.

Analyze and Conclude

1. Up and down; similar; hinge
2. If students pulled on the biceps, they bent the arm at the elbow. If they pulled on the triceps, the arm straightened. The pulling represents muscle contraction.
3. Skeletal

4. Paragraphs should describe the structures and locations of the muscles as shown in students' diagrams. Students might note that diagrams serve as a record of what they observed and allow comparison of structures that cannot be seen simultaneously.

Extend Inquiry

More to Explore Advise students to use chicken leg quarters with the thighs and legs attached, and to repeat all safety procedures.

A Look Beneath the Skin

L2

Prepare for Inquiry

Skills Objectives

After this lab, students will be able to

- observe the structure and function of the muscles in a chicken wing
- infer how the muscles work together to move the wing
- classify muscles as smooth, cardiac, or skeletal

Prep Time 60 minutes

Class Time 30 minutes

Advance Planning

- Use only fresh chicken wings. Refrigerate and use them within 24 hours of purchase.
- Soak wings in a solution of 2 parts household bleach and 8 parts water for 2 hours before the lab. Rinse with water to remove the bleach.
- Use disposable latex or vinyl gloves.

Safety

 After students dispose of the wings, have them remove their gloves and wash their hands thoroughly with soap and water. Remind students to cut away from themselves and others at all times. Review the safety guidelines in Appendix A.

All in One Teaching Resources, Unit 3

- Lab Worksheet: *A Look Beneath the Skin*

Guide Inquiry

Introduce the Procedure

Direct students' attention to the photo showing where to make the cut lines. Tell them that the skin is relatively thin, and the muscles lie directly beneath the skin.

Troubleshooting the Experiment

Remind students to work slowly so they do not damage the wing.

Objectives

After this lesson, students will be able to

14.4.1 Describe the functions and the structures of skin.

14.4.2 Identify habits that can help keep skin healthy.

Target Reading Skill ↻

Identifying Main Ideas Explain that identifying main ideas and details helps students organize facts into groups. Each group can have a main topic, subtopics, and details.

Answers

Sample details:

The skin forms a barrier against disease-causing microorganisms and harmful substances, and prevents the loss of important fluids; the skin helps the body maintain a steady temperature; the skin helps to eliminate wastes through perspiration; the skin contains nerves that gather information about the environment; skin cells produce vitamin D that helps your body absorb calcium.

All in One Teaching Resources, Unit 3

• Transparency LS144

Preteach

Build Background Knowledge   L1

What Skin Does

Have students look at the skin on their arms and hands. Ask them to speculate about what they think their skin does. *(Sample answers: It protects body tissues underneath, keeps bacteria out of the body, produces sweat, and provides feeling through the sense of touch.)*

Reading Preview

Key Concepts

• What are the functions and the structures of skin?

• What habits can help keep your skin healthy?

Key Terms

• epidermis • melanin
• dermis • pore • follicle
• cancer

↻ Target Reading Skill

Identifying Main Ideas As you read the section titled The Body's Tough Covering, write the main idea—the biggest or most important idea—in a graphic organizer like the one below. Then, write five supporting details. The supporting details give examples of the main idea.

Main Idea

The skin has several important functions.

Detail	Detail	Detail

Lab zone Discover Activity

What Can You Observe About Skin?

1. Using a hand lens, examine the skin on your hand. Look for pores and hairs on both the palm and back of your hand.

2. Place a plastic glove on your hand. After five minutes, remove the glove. Then, examine the skin on your hand with the hand lens.

Think It Over

Inferring Compare your hand before and after wearing the glove. What happened to the skin when you wore the glove? Why did this happen?

Here's a question for you: What's the largest organ in the human body? If your answer is the skin, you are right! If an adult's skin were stretched out flat, it would cover an area larger than 1.5 square meters—about the size of a mattress on a twin bed. You may think of the skin as nothing more than a covering that separates the inside of the body from the outside environment. If so, you'll be surprised to learn about the many important roles that the skin plays.

The Body's Tough Covering

The skin performs several major functions in the body. **The skin covers and protects the body from injury, infection, and water loss. The skin also helps regulate body temperature, eliminate wastes, gather information about the environment, and produce vitamin D.**

Protecting the Body The skin protects the body by forming a barrier that keeps disease-causing microorganisms and harmful substances outside the body. In addition, the skin helps keep important substances inside the body. Like plastic wrap that keeps food from drying out, the skin prevents the loss of important fluids such as water.

Lab zone Discover Activity

Skills Focus Inferring

Materials hand lens, plastic gloves

Time 15 minutes

Tips Ask students to predict what structures they expect to see on the surface of their skin.

L1

Expected Outcome Students will observe perspiration, hairs on the back of the hands, and ridges.

Think It Over After students have worn the plastic glove, moisture covering the skin's surface will be noticeable. Perspiration is one of the functions of the skin.

Maintaining Temperature Another function of the skin is to help the body maintain a steady temperature. Many blood vessels run throughout the skin. When you become too warm, these blood vessels enlarge and the amount of blood that flows through them increases. These changes allow heat to move from your body into the outside environment. In addition, sweat glands in the skin respond to excess heat by producing perspiration. As perspiration evaporates from your skin, your skin is cooled.

Eliminating Wastes Perspiration contains dissolved waste materials that come from the breakdown of chemicals during cellular processes. Thus, your skin is also helping to eliminate wastes whenever you perspire. For example, some of the wastes that come from the breakdown of proteins are eliminated in perspiration.

Gathering Information The skin also gathers information about the environment. To understand how the skin does this, place your fingertips on the skin of your arm and press down firmly. Then lightly pinch yourself. You have just tested some of the nerves in your skin. The nerves in skin provide information about such things as pressure, pain, and temperature. Pain messages are important because they warn you that something in your surroundings may have injured you.

Producing Vitamin D Lastly, some of the skin cells produce vitamin D in the presence of sunlight. Vitamin D is important for healthy bones because it helps the cells in your digestive system to absorb the calcium in your food. Your skin cells need only a few minutes of sunlight to produce all the vitamin D you need in a day.

 Reading Checkpoint How does your skin gather information about the environment?

FIGURE 15
Eliminating Wastes
Sweat glands in the skin produce perspiration, which leaves the body through pores. The inset photo shows beads of sweat on skin.
Relating Cause and Effect In addition to eliminating wastes, what is another important function of perspiration?

Differentiated Instruction

Special Needs L1
Demonstrating Skin Functions Gently squeeze students' hands, and explain that the nerves in skin help them to feel the pressure. Have students touch a chilled object to demonstrate that the skin senses temperature. Have students dip a finger into a cup of water, then hold the finger in the air. Ask: **How does your finger feel?** (*Cool*) Explain that this is similar to what happens when people sweat. The sweat, like the water, removes heat from the body and makes a person feel cooler. **learning modality: kinesthetic**

Teach Key Concepts L1
The Functions of Skin

Focus Have students look at the other people in the class. Ask: **What is the most obvious function of skin?** (*To cover and protect the body*)

Teach Explain that the skin keeps out harmful microorganisms and substances and keeps in fluids, but skin has other functions, too. Ask: **How does skin regulate temperature?** (*When you are too warm, blood vessels in the skin enlarge to allow heat to move out of your body. The evaporation of perspiration cools the skin.*) **How is waste eliminated by the skin?** (*Through perspiration*) **What information can you gather from the environment through your skin?** (*Pressure, pain, and temperature*) **How does your skin help you to have healthy bones?** (*Some skin cells produce vitamin D that helps your digestive system to absorb calcium, which is needed for strong bones.*)

Apply Ask students to identify how each function of skin helps the body maintain homeostasis—for example, helping to maintain water balance. **learning modality: verbal**

Independent Practice L2
All in One Teaching Resources, Unit 3

• Guided Reading and Study Worksheet: *The Skin*

Student Edition on Audio CD

Monitor Progress L2

Skills Check Maintaining a body temperature. Have students create concept maps of the skin's functions.

Answers
Figure 15 Maintaining body temperature; as perspiration evaporates from the skin, heat moves from the body into the environment

 Reading Checkpoint Nerves in skin provide information about pressure, pain, and temperature.

Help Students Read

SQ3R Have students **survey** the diagrams, photos, and graph in this section, and write a short explanation of each. Then have them write **questions, read** the section, **recite** their questions, and give the answers in their own words. Tell students to **review** the section by writing their answers, and then answer the Key Concepts questions on the first page of the section. For more information on SQ3R, refer to the **Content Refresher.**

The Epidermis

Teach Key Concepts

The First Layer of Skin

Focus Tell students that the epidermis is the layer of skin you can see.

Teach Refer students to Figure 16. Ask: **What is the epidermis made of?** (*A layer of dead cells*) **How do these dead cells protect you?** (*The dead cells on your fingertips cushion the fingertips, shedding of dead cells carries away bacteria, and some cells produce hard fingernails.*)

Apply Ask: **What is the advantage of having dead cells make up the outer layer of skin instead of living tissue?** (*Living tissue has nerves and blood vessels. You would feel pain more easily from cuts and pressure. You would bleed more easily.*) **learning modality: verbal**

All in One Teaching Resources, Unit 3
- Transparency LS145

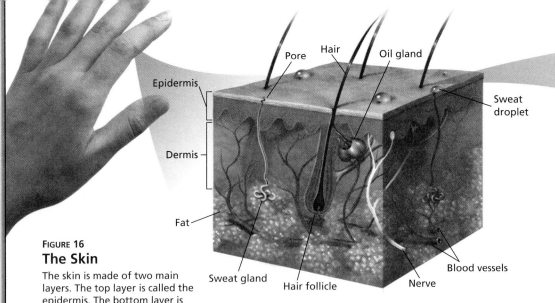

FIGURE 16
The Skin
The skin is made of two main layers. The top layer is called the epidermis. The bottom layer is called the dermis.
Interpreting Diagrams *In which layer of the skin do you find blood vessels?*

The Epidermis

The skin is organized into two main layers, the epidermis and the dermis. The **epidermis** is the outer layer of the skin. In most places, the epidermis is thinner than the dermis. The epidermis does not have nerves or blood vessels. This is why you usually don't feel pain from very shallow scratches, and why shallow scratches do not bleed.

Epidermis Structure Like all cells, the cells in the epidermis have a life cycle. Each epidermal cell begins life deep in the epidermis, where cells divide to form new cells. The new cells mature and move upward in the epidermis as new cells form beneath them. After about two weeks, the cells die and become part of the epidermal surface layer. Under a microscope, this surface layer of dead cells resembles flat bags laid on top of one another. Cells remain in this layer for about two weeks. Then, they are shed and replaced by the dead cells below.

Epidermis Function In some ways, the cells of the epidermis are more valuable dead than alive. Most of the protection provided by the skin is due to the layer of dead cells on the surface. The thick layer of dead cells on your fingertips, for example, protects and cushions your fingertips. Also, the shedding of dead cells carries away bacteria and other substances that settle on the skin. Every time you rub your hands together, you lose thousands of dead skin cells and any bacteria on them.

490 ◆

Differentiated Instruction

English Learners/Beginning L1
Vocabulary: Science Glossary
Pronounce the key terms *epidermis, dermis, pores,* and *follicles* as you point to them in Figure 16. Have students use their first language to write descriptions of these structures. Students can then draw the structures and label them with English terms. **learning modality: verbal**

English Learners/Intermediate L2
Vocabulary: Word Knowledge Contrast the meanings of *dermis* and *epidermis.* Point out that *dermis* means "skin" and the prefix *epi* means "outside." Ask students to relate these terms. (*The epidermis is on the outside of the dermis.*) **learning modality: verbal**

Hair follicle

Some cells in the inner layer of the epidermis help to protect the body, too. On your fingers, for example, some cells produce hard fingernails, which protect the fingertips from injury and help you scratch and pick up objects.

Other cells deep in the epidermis produce **melanin,** a pigment, or colored substance, that gives skin its color. The more melanin in your skin, the darker it is. Exposure to sunlight stimulates the skin to make more melanin. Melanin production helps to protect the skin from burning.

The Dermis

The **dermis** is the inner layer of the skin. Find the dermis in Figure 16. Notice that it is located below the epidermis and above a layer of fat. This fat layer pads the internal organs and helps keep heat in the body.

The dermis contains nerves and blood vessels. The dermis also contains sweat glands, hairs, and oil glands. Sweat glands produce perspiration, which reaches the surface through openings called **pores.** Strands of hair grow within the dermis in structures called **follicles** (FAHL ih kulz). The hair that you see above the skin's surface is made up of dead cells. Oil produced in glands around the hair follicles help to waterproof the hair. In addition, oil that reaches the surface of the skin helps to keep the skin moist.

 Reading Checkpoint What is the function of pores in the skin?

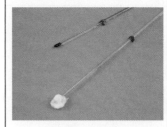

Lab zone Try This **Activity**

Sweaty Skin
This activity illustrates one of the skin's functions.

1. Wrap a wet cotton ball around the bulb of one thermometer. Place a second thermometer next to the first one.

2. After two minutes, record the temperature reading on each thermometer.

3. Using a piece of cardboard, fan both of the thermometers for several minutes. The cardboard should be at least 10 cm from the thermometers. Record the temperatures.

Measuring Which of the thermometers had a lower temperature after Step 3? How does this activity relate to the role of skin in regulating body temperature?

Chapter 14 ◆ 491

Lab zone Try This **Activity**

Skills Focus Measuring **L2**

Materials 2 thermometers, wet cotton ball, piece of cardboard

Time 15 minutes

Tips CAUTION: *Advise students to use care when handling the thermometers.* Have students note the temperatures on both thermometers before beginning.

Expected Outcome The thermometer wrapped in wet cotton has a lower temperature after it is fanned. When skin is moist, sweat evaporates, removing body heat and lowering the body temperature.

Extend Ask students why they might put on a heavy sweatshirt after vigorous physical activity. (*To keep from getting chilled when sweat evaporates*) **learning modality: logical/mathematical**

The Dermis

Teach Key Concepts
The Second Layer of Skin

Focus Refer students to Figure 16.

Teach Ask students to note differences between the epidermis and the dermis. (*The dermis is thicker. It has blood vessels, nerves, hair follicles, sweat glands, and fat.*) **What are the functions of the dermis?** (*The fat pads internal organs and helps keep heat in the body. Sweat glands produce perspiration. Oil helps moisten the skin.*)

Apply Ask: **How does the dermis help regulate temperature when you are hot?** (*It contains blood vessels that widen to help move heat from the body.*) Ask students to infer what happens to blood vessels in the dermis when a person is cold. (*They narrow to conserve heat.*) **learning modality: verbal**

Use Visuals: Figure 16 **L1**
Epidermis and Dermis

Focus Ask students to identify the openings in the epidermis. (*Pores and openings of hair follicles*)

Teach Ask: **What are the pores connected to?** (*Sweat glands*) **Where is oil produced?** (*In glands around the hair*) Call students' attention to the inset of the hair. Ask: **What are the scalelike structures?** (*Dead epidermal cells*)

Apply Ask students to infer the relationship between the hairs and the nerves in the dermis. (*When something touches or blows against the hairs, the nerves pick up the sensation.*) **learning modality: visual**

Monitor Progress _____ **L2**

Writing Have students write paragraphs that compare and contrast the structure and function of the dermis and epidermis.

Answers
Figure 16 The dermis

Reading Checkpoint They are the openings through which perspiration from sweat glands in the dermis reaches the skin's surface.

Caring for Your Skin

Teach Key Concepts [L2]

Habits to Keep Skin Healthy

Focus Tell students that acne is the most common skin problem for teens.

Teach Ask: **What is a healthful habit to help control acne?** *(Keep your face clean.)* **What are other habits to care for your skin?** *(Eat a well-balanced diet, drink plenty of water, and protect your skin from sun damage.)*

Apply Tell students that people with acne should wash their face twice a day with a mild cleanser. More frequent washing or scrubbing with strong soap or scrub pads can make acne worse. **learning modality: verbal**

Math ▶ Analyzing Data

Math Skills Making and interpreting graphs

Focus Remind students that wearing sunscreen is one way to reduce the risk of skin cancer.

Teach Tell students that the skin's relative resistance to sunburn, as well as the strength of sunscreen used, affects how long you can safely stay in the sun. However, limiting sun exposure is recommended for everyone as the best method of preventing overexposure.

Answers

1. The height of each bar represents the amount of time that person can spend in the sun before burning.

2. about 20 minutes; about 80 minutes; 5 hours

3. Person C would need to use SPF 15 sunscreen because SPF 4 would protect the individual for only four hours.

4. SPF 15 is 3.75 times more effective at preventing sunburn. Sample calculations: 2.5 hours compared to 40 minutes, or 150 minutes/40 minutes = 3.75; 5 hours

---

Math ▶ Analyzing Data

Sunscreen Ratings

The graph shows how sunscreens with different sun protection factor (SPF) ratings extend the time three people can stay in the sun without beginning to get a sunburn.

1. **Reading Graphs** What does the height of each bar in the graph represent?

2. **Interpreting Data** How long can Person B stay in the sun without sunscreen before starting to burn? With a sunscreen of SPF 4? SPF 15?

3. **Inferring** Suppose that Person C was planning to attend an all-day picnic. Which sunscreen should Person C apply? Use data to support your answer.

4. **Calculating** Which is more effective at preventing sunburn—a sunscreen with SPF 4 or one with SPF 15? How much more effective is it? Show your work.

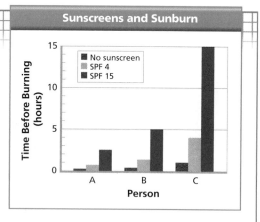

Sunscreens and Sunburn

5. **Drawing Conclusions** What does the number in the SPF rating stand for? *(Hint: Note the length of time each person can stay in the sun without sunscreen and compare this value to the length of time each can stay in the sun using SPF 4. Then, do the same for SPF 15.)*

Caring for Your Skin

Because your skin has so many vital functions, taking care of it is important. **Three simple habits can help you keep your skin healthy. Eat a healthful diet. Keep your skin clean and dry. Limit your exposure to the sun.**

Healthful Diet Your skin is always active. Eating a well-balanced diet provides the energy and raw materials needed for the growth and replacement of hair, nails, and skin cells. In addition to what you eat, a healthful diet also includes drinking plenty of water. That way, you can replace the water lost in perspiration.

Keeping Skin Clean When you wash your skin with mild soap, you get rid of dirt and harmful bacteria. Washing your skin also helps to control oiliness.

Good washing habits are particularly important during the teenage years when oil glands are more active. When glands become clogged with oil, the blackheads and whiteheads of acne can form. If acne becomes infected by skin bacteria, your doctor may prescribe an antibiotic to help control the infection.

---

compared to 80 minutes, or 300 minutes/ 80 minutes = 3.75

5. It stands for the level of protection against sunburn—the higher the level is, the greater the protection. SPF 4 means a person can safely stay four times longer in the sun than without the sunscreen; SPF 15—15 times longer.

Limiting Sun Exposure It is important to protect your skin from the harmful effects of the sun. Repeated exposure to sunlight can damage skin cells, and possibly lead to skin cancer. **Cancer** is a disease in which some cells in the body divide uncontrollably. In addition, repeated exposure to the sun can cause the skin to become leathery and wrinkled.

There are many things you can do to protect your skin from damage by the sun. When you are outdoors, always wear a hat, sunglasses, and use a sunscreen on exposed skin. Choose clothing made of tightly woven fabrics for the greatest protection. In addition, avoid exposure to the sun between the hours of 10 A.M. and 4 P.M. That is the time when sunlight is the strongest.

 Reading Checkpoint What health problems can result from repeated sun exposure?

FIGURE 17
Skin Protection
This person is wearing a hat to protect his skin from the sun.
Applying Concepts *What other behaviors can provide protection from the sun?*

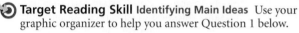

Section 4 Assessment

Target Reading Skill Identifying Main Ideas Use your graphic organizer to help you answer Question 1 below.

Reviewing Key Concepts

1. a. **Listing** What are five important functions of the skin?
   b. **Identifying** How does the epidermis protect the body? What structure in the dermis helps to maintain body temperature?
   c. **Inferring** What could happen if the pores in your dermis become blocked?
2. a. **Identifying** What are three things you can do to keep your skin healthy?
   b. **Explaining** Why is it important to use sunscreen to protect your skin when outside?
   c. **Making Judgments** Do you think it is possible to wash your skin too much and damage it as a result? Why or why not?

Lab zone **At-Home Activity**

Protection From the Sun With a family member, look for products in your home that provide protection from the sun. You may also want to visit a store that sells these products. Make a list of the products and place them in categories, such as sunblocks, clothing, eye protectors, and other forms of protection. Explain to your family member why it is important to use such products.

Chapter 14 ◆ 493

Answers
Figure 17 Wearing sunscreen and avoiding exposure to the sun between 10 A.M. and 2 P.M.

 Reading Checkpoint Damage to skin cells, cancer, and wrinkled, leathery skin.

Assess

Reviewing Key Concepts

1. a. The skin protects the body from injury, infection, and water loss; helps regulate body temperature; eliminates waste; gathers information about the environment; and produces vitamin D. **b.** The epidermis consists of a layer of dead cells that protect the inner parts of the skin. The dermis contains a fat layer that helps keep in heat and sweat glands that help cool the body. **c.** If pores in the dermis become blocked, the blackheads and whiteheads of acne can form.
2. a. Accept any three: Eat properly, drink enough water, limit exposure to the sun, and keep skin clean and dry. **b.** It is important to use sunscreen when outdoors because unprotected skin can burn. Also, repeated exposure to sunlight can damage skin cells, causing them to become cancerous. **c.** Sample answer: Washing the skin too much may cause dryness and remove dead skin cells that are necessary to protect the skin.

Reteach L1

Use Figure 16 to review how each structure relates to the function of the skin.

Performance Assessment
Writing Have students develop a pamphlet explaining to other teens how to take care of their skin.

All in One Teaching Resources, Unit 3

- Section Summary: *The Skin*
- Review and Reinforce: *The Skin*
- Enrich: *The Skin*

Lab zone **At-Home Activity**

Protection From the Sun L2
Before students perform this activity, have them identify ways that people protect themselves from the sun. Encourage students to include items such as hats, sunglasses, and beach umbrellas.

Sun Safety L2

Prepare for Inquiry

Key Concept
The higher a product's SPF rating, the better it protects individuals from the sun.

Skills Objectives
After this lab, students will be able to
- observe the effectiveness of different levels of sun protection
- predict which sunscreen provides more protection
- interpret data on which fabrics protect against sun exposure
- draw conclusions about which fabric provided the most protection

🕐 **Prep Time** 20 minutes
Class Time 45 minutes, follow-up 20 minutes

Advance Planning
- Obtain photosensitive paper from science supply houses, or a toy or craft store.
- Collect fabric or have students bring in scraps of fabric. Choose fabrics commonly worn by students, such as T-shirt material and denim.
- Before the activity, test a strip of photosensitive paper in the window of your classroom, if present, to determine whether UV rays pass through that particular glass.

Safety
Remind students to be careful when using scissors. Caution them not to get any sunscreen into their eyes or mouths. Advise them to wash their hands after the lab. If sunlamps are used, be sure students do not look at the light source and if possible, provide UV-protective goggles. Review the safety guidelines in Appendix A.

All in One **Teaching Resources, Unit 3**
- Lab Worksheet: *Sun Safety*

Sun Safety

Problem
How well do different materials protect the skin from the sun?

Skills Focus
observing, predicting, interpreting data, drawing conclusions

Materials
- scissors
- photosensitive paper
- metric ruler
- white construction paper
- stapler
- pencil
- resealable plastic bag
- plastic knife
- 2 sunscreens with SPF ratings of 4 and 30
- staple remover
- 3 different fabrics

Procedure ✂

PART 1 Sunscreen Protection

1. Read over the procedure for Part 1. Then, write a prediction about how well each of the sunscreens will protect against the sun.
2. Use scissors to cut two strips of photosensitive paper that measure 5 cm by 15 cm.
3. Divide each strip into thirds by drawing lines across the strips.
4. Cover one third of each strip with a square of white construction paper. Staple each square down.
5. Use a pencil to write the lower SPF rating on the back of the first strip. Write the other SPF rating on the back of the second strip.

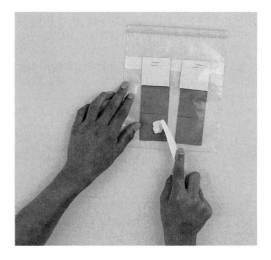

6. Place the two strips side by side in a plastic bag. Seal the bag, then staple through the white squares to hold the strips in place.
7. With a plastic knife, spread a thin layer of each sunscreen on the bag over the bottom square of its labeled strip. This is shown in the photo above. Make certain each strip has the same thickness of sunscreen. Be sure not to spread sunscreen over the middle squares.
8. Place the strips in sunlight until the color of the middle squares stops changing. Make sure the bag is sunscreen-side up when you place it in the sunlight.
9. Remove the staples from the bag, and then take out the strips. Take off the construction paper. Rinse the strips for one minute in cold water, then dry them flat.
10. Observe all the squares. Then, record your observations.

Guide Inquiry

Introduce the Procedure
- Demonstrate how to cut the photosensitive and construction paper strips and staple them in place in the plastic bag. Demonstrate the technique for coating the bag with sunscreen.

- Check that students understand that the white construction paper allows them to control the experiment and compare their results. Ask: **What are some other controls?** (*Using the same amount of sunscreen and making sure the strips are exposed to direct sunlight*)

PART 2 Fabric Protection

11. Your teacher will provide three fabric pieces of different thicknesses.

12. Based on the procedure in Part 1, design an experiment to test how effective the three fabrics are in protecting against the sun. Write a prediction about which fabric you think will be most effective, next most effective, and least effective.

13. Obtain your teacher's approval before carrying out your experiment. Record all of your observations.

Analyze and Conclude

1. **Observing** Did the sunscreens protect against sun exposure? How do you know?

2. **Predicting** Which sunscreen provided more protection? Was your prediction correct? How would you predict a sunscreen with an SPF of 15 would compare to the sunscreens you tested?

3. **Interpreting Data** Did the fabrics protect against sun exposure? How do you know?

4. **Drawing Conclusions** Which of the fabrics provided the most protection? The least protection? How did your results compare with your predictions?

5. **Communicating** What advice would you give people about protecting their skin from the sun? Create a pamphlet in which you address this question by comparing the different sunscreens and fabrics you tested.

More to Explore

Design another experiment, this time to find out whether ordinary window glass protects skin against sun exposure. *Obtain your teacher's permission before carrying out your investigation.*

- Place the strips where they will receive direct sunlight. You could use an artificial source of ultraviolet light such as a sunlamp.

Expected Outcome
The sunscreens with the highest SPF and the materials with the tightest weave provide the most protection.

Analyze and Conclude
1. Yes; sections not covered by sunscreen changed color drastically. The covered sections changed color slightly or not at all.

2. The sunscreen with SPF 30 provided more protection. Yes, if students predicted this result. A sunscreen with an SPF of 15 would provide more protection than SPF 4 but less protection than SPF 30.

3. Yes; the sections covered by fabric did not change color as much as the uncovered areas.

4. The heaviest or most tightly woven fabric, such as denim, provided the most protection. Thin fabrics, such as T-shirt material or light gauze, provided the least protection. Sample answer: My predictions matched the results.

5. Sample answer: Wear sunscreen, limit exposure to the sun, and wear clothing that blocks the sun. The pamphlet should include choosing a sunscreen with a high SPF rating and wearing clothing that blocks the sun. (You may want to share with students that lightweight clothing specially made to block UV rays is available.)

Extend Inquiry

More to Explore Students' designs should include placing one strip of photosensitive paper in direct sunlight and one on an inside window sill or under a piece of window glass. Check that students control variables such as the angle and amount of sunlight received.

Chapter 14 ◆ 495

Interactive Textbook

- Complete student edition
- Section and chapter self-assessments
- Assessment reports for teachers

Help Students Read **L1**

Building Vocabulary

Word Origins Have students look in a dictionary to find the origins of some names of bones. For example, the word *femur* comes from the Latin word for "thigh." *Tibia* comes from the Latin word meaning "shin." Challenge students to find the derivation of as many words as possible.

Latin Plural Form Explain that the word *nucleus* comes from the Latin word meaning "kernel," which is a grain or seed. The word *vertebra* comes from the Latin word meaning "turning joint." Ask students to discuss how the definition of each term relates to its Latin origin. *(Like the kernel of a nut, the nucleus is a small mass at the center of the cell. The vertebrae allow a person to twist and turn.)* Remind students that the plural of the nucleus is *nuclei* and the plural of the word vertebra is *vertebrae.*

Connecting Concepts

Concept Maps Help students develop one way to show how the information in this chapter is related. The human body consists of body systems that include the skeletal system and the muscular system, which work together to allow movement and are protected by the skin. Have students brainstorm to identify Key Concepts, Key Terms, details, and examples, then write each one on a sticky note and attach it at random on chart paper or on the board.

Tell students that this concept map will be organized in hierarchical order to begin at the top with the Key Concepts. Ask students these questions to guide them to categorize the information on the sticky notes: **How is the body organized? What are the functions of the skeletal system and the muscular system? How do the two systems work together? What are the functions of the skin?**

① Body Organization and Homeostasis

Key Concepts

- The levels of organization in the body consist of cells, tissues, organs, and organ systems.
- Homeostasis is the process by which an organism's internal environment is kept stable in spite of changes in the external environment.

Key Terms

cell	connective tissue
cell membrane	epithelial tissue
nucleus	organ
cytoplasm	organ system
tissue	homeostasis
muscle tissue	stress
nervous tissue	

② The Skeletal System

Key Concepts

- Your skeleton provides shape and support, enables you to move, protects your organs, produces blood cells, and stores minerals and other materials until your body needs them.
- Joints allow bones to move in different ways.
- Bones are complex living structures that undergo growth and development.
- A balanced diet and regular exercise are important for a lifetime of healthy bones.

Key Terms

skeleton
vertebrae
joint
ligament
cartilage
compact bone
spongy bone
marrow
osteoporosis

③ The Muscular System

Key Concepts

- Your body has three types of muscle tissue—skeletal, smooth, and cardiac.
- Skeletal muscles work in pairs. While one muscle contracts, the other muscle in the pair relaxes to its original length.

Key Terms

involuntary muscle	striated muscle
voluntary muscle	smooth muscle
skeletal muscle	cardiac muscle
tendon	

④ The Skin

Key Concepts

- The skin has several functions: protection, maintaining temperature, eliminating wastes, gathering information, and making vitamin D.
- The two skin layers are epidermis and dermis.
- Three simple habits can help you keep your skin healthy. Eat a healthful diet. Keep your skin clean and dry. Limit your sun exposure.

Key Terms

epidermis	pore
melanin	follicle
dermis	cancer

Prompt students by using connecting words or phrases, such as "classified as" and "consists of," to indicate the basis for the organization of the map. The phrases should form a sentence between or among a set of concepts.

Answer
Accept logical presentations by students.

All in One Teaching Resources, Unit 3

- Key Terms Review: *Bones, Muscles, and Skin*
- Connecting Concepts: *Bones, Muscles, and Skin*

Review and Assessment

Go Online
PHSchool.com
For: Self-Assessment
Visit: PHSchool.com
Web Code: cha-3140

Organizing Information

Concept Mapping Copy the concept map about the types of muscles onto a separate sheet of paper. Then complete it and add a title. (For more on Concept Mapping, see the Skills Handbook.)

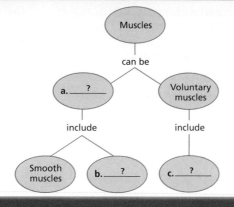

Reviewing Key Terms

Choose the letter of the best answer.

1. A group of similar cells that perform a similar function is called a(n)
   a. cell.   **b.** organ.
   c. tissue.   **d.** organ system.

2. Which type of body tissue covers the surfaces of the body?
   a. muscle tissue
   b. nervous tissue
   c. connective tissue
   d. epithelial tissue

3. A soft, connective tissue found inside some bones is
   a. cytoplasm.
   b. marrow.
   c. cartilage.
   d. osteoporosis.

4. Muscles that help the skeleton move are
   a. cardiac muscles.
   b. smooth muscles.
   c. skeletal muscles.
   d. involuntary muscles.

5. A colored substance that helps to keep the skin from burning is
   a. the dermis.   **b.** the epidermis.
   c. melanin.   **d.** a follicle.

If the statement is true, write *true*. If the statement is false, change the underlined word or words to make the statement true.

6. The <u>cytoplasm</u> directs the cell's activities.

7. Spongy bone is filled with <u>cartilage.</u>

8. <u>Skeletal</u> muscle is called striated muscle.

9. The <u>epidermis</u> contains nerve endings and blood vessels.

10. Strands of hair grow within the dermis in structures called <u>pores.</u>

Writing in Science

Descriptive Paragraph Pretend you are a writer for a science magazine for children. Write a few paragraphs that compare the characteristics of cartilage with the characteristics of bones. Be sure to explain the advantages of both types of materials.

Bones, Muscles, and Skin
Video Preview
Video Field Trip
▶ Video Assessment

Go Online
PHSchool.com
For: Self-Assessment
Visit: PHSchool.com
Web Code: cha-3140

Students can take a practice test online that is automatically scored.

All in One Teaching Resources, Unit 3
• Transparency LS146
• Chapter Test
• Performance Assessment Teacher Notes
• Performance Assessment Student Worksheet
• Performance Assessment Scoring Rubric

ExamView® **Computer Test Bank CD-ROM**

Review and Assessment

Organizing Information
a. Involuntary muscles
b. Cardiac muscles
c. Skeletal muscles

Reviewing Key Terms
1. c **2.** d **3.** b **4.** c **5.** c
6. false; nucleus
7. false; marrow
8. true
9. false; dermis
10. false; follicles

Writing in Science

Writing Mode Description
Scoring Rubric
4 Includes detailed, accurate description and explanation; writing is engaging
3 Includes all criteria, writing is unengaging
2 Includes accurate description but few details
1 Includes inaccurate information

Video Assessment

Bones, Muscles, and Skin

Show the Video Assessment to review chapter content and as a prompt for the writing assignment. Discussion questions: **What property of cartilage makes it a good material to protect an infant's body?** (*Flexibility*) **How does spongy bone distribute the forces created when we jump up and down?** (*The network of arches in spongy bone function like the arches that make up the frame of a building, spreading the weight evenly.*)

Checking Concepts

11. A cell is the basic unit of structure and function in a living thing. A tissue is a group of similar cells that perform the same function. An organ is composed of different kinds of tissue. An organ system consists of several organs that work together to perform a major function.

12. The four kinds of movable joints are ball-and-socket—allows range of motion through a complete circle; pivot—allows one bone to rotate around another; gliding—allows one bone to slide over another; and hinge—allows forward and backward motion.

13. Bone is covered by a thin, tough membrane except at its ends. Blood vessels and nerves enter and leave the bone through the membrane. Compact bone, which contains canals that have blood vessels and nerves, is directly under the membrane. Spongy bone is found under compact bone and also at the ends of the bone. Marrow fills the spaces in bone.

14. Eating a well-balanced diet, which includes enough calcium and phosphorus, keeps bones strong while they are growing. Weight-bearing exercises help bones grow stronger and denser.

15. Skeletal muscle cells appear banded, or striated. Smooth muscle is not striated.

16. Because each skeletal muscle can only contract and thereby pull a bone in one direction, there is another muscle attached to the bone that can pull the bone in the opposite direction.

17. The skin protects the body by forming a barrier that keeps disease-causing microorganisms and harmful substances outside the body. Skin also helps to prevent the loss of fluids from the body.

Review and Assessment

Checking Concepts

11. Explain the relationship among cells, tissues, organs, and organ systems.

12. List the four kinds of movable joints. Describe the type of movement each joint allows.

13. Describe the structure of a bone.

14. How does eating a well-balanced diet and exercising regularly contribute to healthy bones?

15. How does the appearance of smooth muscle differ from that of skeletal muscle?

16. Explain how skeletal muscles work in pairs.

17. How does the skin protect your body?

Thinking Critically

18. Classifying Identify each of the labeled parts of the cell.

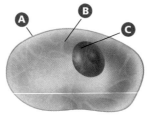

19. Inferring In addition to bone, cartilage, and fat, scientists classify blood as a connective tissue. Explain why.

20. Making Generalizations How is homeostasis important to survival?

21. Predicting If smooth muscle had to be controlled consciously, what problems could you foresee in day-to-day living?

22. Making Judgments Suppose a member of your running team suggests eliminating "warm-up time" because it takes too much time away from practice. Do you think this suggestion is a good idea? Why or why not?

23. Relating Cause and Effect A person who is exposed to excessive heat may suffer from heatstroke. The first sign of heatstroke is that the person stops sweating. Why is heatstroke a life-threatening emergency?

Applying Skills

Use the graph to answer Questions 24–26.

The graph below shows the effects of the temperature of the environment on a boy's skin temperature and on the temperature inside his body.

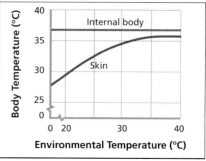

24. Interpreting Data As the temperature of the environment rises, what happens to the boy's internal body temperature? How does this demonstrate homeostasis?

25. Inferring What happens to the temperature of the boy's skin? Why is this pattern different from the pattern shown by the boy's internal body temperature?

26. Predicting Suppose the boy went outdoors on a chilly fall morning. Predict what would happen to his internal body temperature and his skin temperature. Explain.

Lab zone Chapter **Project**

Performance Assessment Before testing your prosthetic hand, explain to your classmates how and why you designed the hand the way you did. When you test the hand, observe how it picks up objects. How does it compare with a real human hand? How could you improve the function of your prosthetic hand?

Lab zone Chapter **Project**

Performance Assessment Give students the opportunity to explain their design goals and criteria. Criteria should focus on ease of use and the range of activities that can be performed. Ask students to describe any challenges they faced and how they resolved them. For example, students might have increased the rigidity after testing the model.

Reflect and Record Students will reflect that it is hard to design and build a model that can perform the same functions as the human hand. Encourage students to evaluate how well they met their goals and what they could have done differently.

Standardized Test Prep

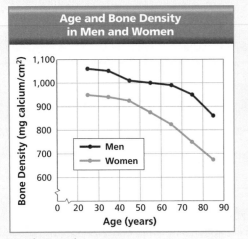

Sample Question
Which of the following relationships is plotted on the graph?
   A how exercise affects bone density
   B how bone density changes with age
   C how calcium intake affects bone density
   D how calcium intake changes with age

Answer
The correct answer is **B**. Both the graph title and the labels on the axes tell you that the graph shows the relationship between age and bone density. Choices **A**, **C**, and **D** are incorrect because the graph does not include any information on exercise or calcium intake.

Choose the letter of the best answer.

1. Which of the following statements is true according to the graph shown at left?
   A The bones of women are more dense than the bones of men.
   B The bones of men contain less calcium than do the bones of women.
   C The bone density of both men and women decreases as they age.
   D An average 55-year-old woman has stronger bones than an average 55-year-old man.

2. Which of the following is a function of the skin?
   F eliminates wastes
   G produces vitamin D
   H protects the body against microorganisms
   J all of the above

3. The muscles that you use to lift a book are
   A cardiac muscles.
   B smooth muscles.
   C involuntary muscles.
   D skeletal muscles.

4. Which of the following is *not* an important function of the skeletal system?
   F It protects internal organs.
   G It stores minerals until they are needed by the body.
   H It allows the body to move.
   J It regulates body temperature.

5. Which of the following represents the smallest level of organization in the body?
   A cardiac muscle tissue
   B the heart
   C a muscle cell
   D the circulatory system

Constructed Response

6. Compare the dermis and the epidermis layers of the skin. Discuss the following: their thickness, location, nerves, blood vessels, sweat glands, and cell life cycle.

Thinking Critically

18. A: cell membrane; B: cytoplasm; C: nucleus

19. Connective tissue provides support for your body and connects all its parts. Blood carries nutrients and oxygen to all the cells in the body.

20. If living things could not maintain a stable internal environment, body functions could not take place. For example, if a person did not get hungry and the body did not have a steady supply of food, the cells would not obtain the materials they need.

21. Sample answer: People would have to spend a lot of time consciously controlling processes that normally happen automatically, such as digestion. People would not be able to sleep, because life processes would not happen automatically.

22. Sample answer: This is probably not a good idea because warming up helps prepare muscles for exercise by making them more flexible. Exercising without warming up first might lead to injury.

23. Without being able to sweat, a person cannot get rid of excess body heat to maintain homeostasis.

Applying Skills

24. The boy's internal temperature stays constant as the environmental temperature rises. This demonstrates the stability of his internal temperature despite changes in the external temperature.

25. His skin temperature rises as the external temperature increases. His skin is in direct contact with the external environment (the air) and thus warms as the external temperature increases. Several processes combine to keep the internal body temperature constant.

26. Most students will predict that his internal temperature would remain constant due to homeostasis, while his skin temperature would decline.

Standardized Test Prep

1. C **2.** J **3.** D **4.** J **5.** C
6. Sample answer: The epidermis is the outermost layer of the skin. It is usually thinner than the dermis, the innermost layer. The dermis contains nerves, blood vessels, hair, and sweat and oil glands; the epidermis has none of these structures. Cells in the epidermis begin life deep in the epidermal layer. They gradually move upward and die after about two weeks. Once dead, the cells protect living cells located below them.

Chapter at a Glance

PRENTICE HALL
TeacherEXPRESS™
Plan • Teach • Assess

 Chapter **Project** *What's for Lunch?*

Technology

Local Standards

All in One Teaching Resources, Unit 3
• Chapter Project Teacher Notes, pp. 88–89
• Chapter Project Student Overview, pp. 90–91
• Chapter Project Student Worksheets, pp. 92–93
• Chapter Project Scoring Rubric, p. 94

DISCOVERY CHANNEL SCHOOL
Video Preview

Section 1

3 periods
1 1/2 blocks

Food and Energy
15.1.1 Explain why the body needs food.
15.1.2 Describe how the six nutrients needed by the body help carry out essential processes.
15.1.3 Explain how the MyPyramid Plan and food labels can help in planning a healthy diet.

Go Online
SciLINKS NSTA

DISCOVERY CHANNEL SCHOOL
Video Field Trip

Go Online
active art

Section 2

2 periods
1 block

The Digestive Process Begins
15.2.1 Describe the functions carried out in the digestive system.
15.2.2 Explain the roles of the mouth, esophagus, and stomach in digestion.

Go Online
SciLINKS NSTA

Section 3

1 period
1/2 block

Final Digestion and Absorption
15.3.1 Describe the digestive processes that occur in the small intestine and how other digestive organs are involved.
15.3.2 Explain the role of the large intestine in digestion.

Go Online
PHSchool.com

Review and Assessment

Test Preparation

All in One Teaching Resources, Unit 3
• Key Terms Review, p. 123
• Transparency LS154
• Performance Assessment Teacher Notes, p. 132
• Performance Assessment Scoring Rubric, p. 133
• Performance Assessment Student Worksheet, p. 134
• Chapter Test, pp. 135–138

Go Online
PHSchool.com

DISCOVERY CHANNEL SCHOOL
Video Assessment

Test Preparation Blackline Masters

Lab zone **Chapter Activities Planner**

For more activities
LAB ZONE
Easy Planner
CD-ROM

Student Edition	Inquiry	Time	Materials	Skills	Resources
Chapter Project, p. 501	Open-Ended	Ongoing (2 weeks)	**All in One Teaching Resources, Unit 3**, p. 88	Observing, measuring, graphing, comparing and contrasting, interpreting diagrams	**Lab zone Easy Planner** **All in One Teaching Resources, Unit 3**, Support pp. 88–89
Section 1					
Discover Activity, p. 502	Guided	15 minutes	None	Posing questions	**Lab zone Easy Planner**
Skills Activity, p. 505	Directed	20 minutes	Fruits and vegetables (potatoes, rice, bread, and breakfast cereals), soft drinks (diet and regular), iodine solution, plastic dropper, test tubes, notebook	Predicting	**Lab zone Easy Planner**
Consumer Lab, p. 515	Directed	Prep: 20 minutes Class: 40 minutes	Raisin and bran cereal (several brands), balance, beaker (250-mL beaker)	Measuring, calculating, controlling variables	**Lab zone Easy Planner** **Lab Activity Video** 📼 **All in One Teaching Resources, Unit 3**, Consumer Lab: *Raisin' the Raisin Question*, pp. 105–106
Section 2					
Discover Activity, p. 516	Directed	15 minutes	2 plastic jars with lids, water, sugar cubes	Predicting	**Lab zone Easy Planner**
Try This Activity, p. 519	Guided	15 minutes	20-cm clear, flexible, plastic straw (about 6 mm in diameter); round bead (5–6 mm in diameter)	Making models	**Lab zone Easy Planner**
Skills Lab, pp. 522–523	Directed	Prep: 40 minutes Class: 40 minutes	Test tube rack, pepsin, water, litmus paper, cubes of boiled egg white, 10-mL plastic graduated cylinder, 4 test tubes with stoppers, marking pencil, diluted hydrochloric acid, plastic stirrers	Interpreting data, controlling variables, drawing conclusions	**Lab zone Easy Planner** **Lab Activity Video** 📼 **All in One Teaching Resources, Unit 3**, Skills Lab: *As the Stomach Churns*, pp. 114–116
Section 3					
Discover Activity, p. 524	Guided	10 minutes	1 m string, metric ruler	Predicting	**Lab zone Easy Planner**
Try This Activity, p. 525	Directed	15 minutes	2 jars, baking soda, oil, stirring rod or spoon	Observing	**Lab zone Easy Planner**

Section 1 Food and Energy

 3 periods, 1 1/2 blocks

ABILITY LEVELS
L1 Basic to Average
L2 For All Students
L3 Average to Advanced

Objectives

15.1.1 Explain why the body needs food.

15.1.2 Describe how the six nutrients needed by the body help carry out essential processes.

15.1.3 Explain how the MyPyramid Plan and food labels can help in planning a healthy diet.

Local Standards

Key Terms

• nutrient • calorie • carbohydrate • glucose • fat • protein • amino acid
• vitamin • mineral • Percent Daily Value • Dietary Reference Intakes (DRIs)

Preteach

Build Background Knowledge

Have students name foods that they think supply them with energy and discuss what a Calorie is.

Lab zone Discover Activity *Food Claims—Fact or Fiction?* **L1**

Targeted Print and Technology Resources

All in One Teaching Resources, Unit 3

L2 Reading Strategy Transparency
LS147: Outlining

○ PresentationEXPRESS™ CD-ROM

Instruct

Why You Need Food Compare the Calories in common foods, and discuss why the body needs food.

Carbohydrates Compare and contrast simple and complex carbohydrates, and explain that carbohydrates are the major energy source for cells.

Fats Use a graph to discuss fats, and describe how fats are beneficial to the body.

Proteins Use a photo to identify types of proteins, and consider why teens need adequate protein.

Vitamins and Minerals Ask leading questions for a discussion on the role of vitamins and minerals.

Water Describe why water is needed by the body.

Guidelines for a Healthy Diet Apply the concepts of the USDA guidelines to planning a healthy diet.

Food Labels Use a sample food label to interpret the information, and then apply the information to an analysis of snack foods.

Lab zone Consumer Lab *Raisin' the Raisin Question* **L2**

Targeted Print and Technology Resources

All in One Teaching Resources, Unit 3

L2 Guided Reading, pp. 97–102
L2 Transparencies LS148, LS149
L2 Consumer Lab: *Raisin' the Raisin Question*, pp. 105–106

▭ Lab Activity Video/DVD
Consumer Lab: *Raisin' the Raisin Question*

www.SciLinks.org Web Code: scn-0421

DISCOVERY
CHANNEL
SCHOOL
Video Field Trip

PHSchool.com Web Code: cep-4022

○ Student Edition on Audio CD

Assess

Section Assessment Questions

⟳ Have students use their completed outlines to answer the questions.

Reteach

Have students compare and contrast the subcategories of carbohydrates, fats, fond proteins.

Targeted Print and Technology Resources

All in One Teaching Resources, Unit 3

• Section Summary, p. 96
L1 Review and Reinforce, p. 103
L3 Enrich, p. 104

Section 2 The Digestive Process Begins

🕐 *2 periods, 1 block*

Objectives

15.2.1 Describe the functions carried out in the digestive system.

15.2.2 Explain the roles of the mouth, esophagus, and stomach in digestion.

Key Terms

• digestion • absorption • saliva • enzyme • epiglottis • esophagus • mucus
• peristalsis • stomach

Local Standards

Preteach

Build Background Knowledge

Name a food, and invite students to describe what they think happens after they eat it.

Lab zone Discover Activity *How Can You Speed Up Digestion?* L1

Targeted Print and Technology Resources

All in One Teaching Resources, Unit 3

L2 Reading Strategy Transparency
LS150: Using Prior Knowledge

🔘 **PresentationEXPRESS™ CD-ROM**

Instruct

Functions of the Digestive System Use the example of eating a pizza to describe and distinguish among mechanical digestion, chemical digestion, and absorption.

The Mouth Use a cross-section diagram of the mouth to discuss the function of each part in digestion.

The Esophagus Discuss the functions of the epiglottis and the esophagus.

The Stomach Use a diagram to examine the structure of and analyze the functions of the stomach.

Lab zone Skills Lab *As the Stomach Churns* L2

Targeted Print and Technology Resources

All in One Teaching Resources, Unit 3

L2 Guided Reading, pp. 109–111
L2 Transparency LS151
L2 Skills Lab: *As the Stomach Churns,* pp. 114–116

📼 **Lab Activity Video/DVD**
Skills Lab: *As the Stomach Churns*

www.SciLinks.org Web Code: scn-0423

🔘 **Student Edition on Audio CD**

Assess

Section Assessment Questions

🎯 Have students revise their graphic organizers based on what they have learned.

Reteach

Use diagrams to review the structures and functions of the digestive system.

Targeted Print and Technology Resources

All in One Teaching Resources, Unit 3

• Section Summary, p. 108
L1 Review and Reinforce, p. 112
L3 Enrich, p. 113

Section 3 **Final Digestion and Absorption**

 1 period, 1/2 block

ABILITY LEVELS
L1 Basic to Average
L2 For All Students
L3 Average to Advanced

Objectives

15.3.1 Describe the digestive processes that occur in the small intestine and how other digestive organs are involved.

15.3.2 Explain the role of the large intestine in digestion.

Key Terms

• small intestine • liver • bile • gallbladder • pancreas • villus • large intestine
• rectum • anus

Local Standards

Preteach

Build Background Knowledge

Ask students to recall the purpose of digestion and the ways that food particles are broken down.

Lab zone **Discover Activity** *Which Surface Is Larger?* **L1**

Targeted Print and Technology Resources

All in One Teaching Resources, Unit 3

L2 Reading Strategy Transparency
LS152: Identifying Main Ideas

◉ PresentationEXPRESS™ CD-ROM

Instruct

The Small Intestine Ask leading questions to help students identify the functions of the small intestine and of digestive organs through which food does not pass.

The Large Intestine Discuss the functions of the large intestine, and apply that information to the importance of fiber.

Targeted Print and Technology Resources

All in One Teaching Resources, Unit 3

L2 Guided Reading, pp. 119–120
L2 Transparency LS153

PHSchool.com Web Code: ced-4024

◉ Student Edition on Audio CD

Assess

Section Assessment Questions

Have students use their main ideas graphic organizer to answer the questions.

Reteach

Help students understand the functions of the organs involved in final digestion and absorption.

Targeted Print and Technology Resources

All in One Teaching Resources, Unit 3

• Section Summary, p. 118
L1 Review and Reinforce, p. 121
L3 Enrich, p. 122

Chapter 15 **Content Refresher**

Go Online

NSTA-PD*LINKS*

For: For professional development support
Visit: www.SciLinks.org/PDLinks
Web Code: scf-0420

Professional Development

Section 1 **Food and Energy**

Omega 3 Fatty Acids One type of unsaturated fat called omega-3 fatty acids may affect health in positive ways. Omega-3 fatty acids are found in all seafood, especially cold-water fishes such as salmon. Lesser amounts are found in flaxseeds, soybeans, and canola oil. Research has shown that omega-3 fatty acids reduce the risk of coronary heart disease by decreasing the incidence of blood clots and irregular heartbeat, and lowering blood pressure and triglyceride levels.

Address Misconceptions

Some students may think that if low fat is good for you, then no fat is better. A certain amount of fat is needed by the body. For a strategy for overcoming this misconception, see **Address Misconceptions** in the section *Food and Energy*.

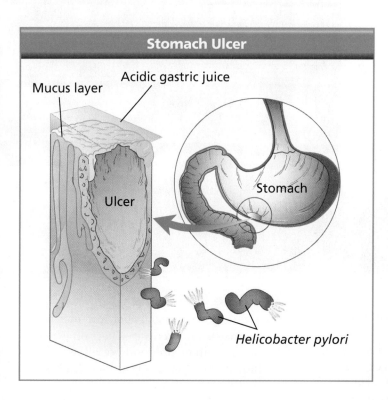

Stomach Ulcer

Mucus layer

Acidic gastric juice

Ulcer

Stomach

Helicobacter pylori

Section 2 **The Digestive Process Begins**

Ulcers The lining of the stomach is covered with mucus. Beneath the mucus is a layer of mucus-producing epithelial cells, the mucosa. Beneath the mucosa is the submucosal layer, which contains blood vessels and nerves. Muscles are located beneath the submucosa. As the illustration shows, a stomach ulcer is a break in the tissue lining the stomach.

Most ulcers are caused by a bacterium, *Helicobacter pylori*. However, infection is usually not the only cause. Instead, a person's stomach is probably first changed by *H. pylori*. The person then develops a severe stomach infection or uses a medication that changes the stomach's chemical balance. The infection or medication, along with *H. pylori*, produces the ulcer.

Section 3 **Final Digestion and Absorption**

Parts of the Small Intestine The small intestine is divided into three parts. The first segment is the duodenum. The duodenum receives digestive enzymes from the pancreas, and bile is released from the gallbladder. Most absorption occurs in the second and third parts of the small intestine, the jejunum and the ileum. Absorption is facilitated by peristalsis and the surface area of the villi. Enzymes to complete the breakdown of nutrients continue to be released in small amounts, and water from the intestinal wall helps to dissolve remaining food.

Help Students Read

Predicting
Previewing to Predict Content

Strategy
1. Introduce students to the topic by having them read the headings and subheadings. Ask students what they think they will learn about the topic.
2. Have a student read aloud the first Key Concept in the Reading Preview.
3. Based on what they have read so far, ask students to predict the content of the section. Write their predictions on the board.
4. Have students read through the section independently. Afterward, ask which of their predictions were confirmed. Point out that there is nothing wrong with making an incorrect prediction.

Interactive Textbook
- Complete student edition
- Video and audio
- Simulations and activities
- Section and chapter activities

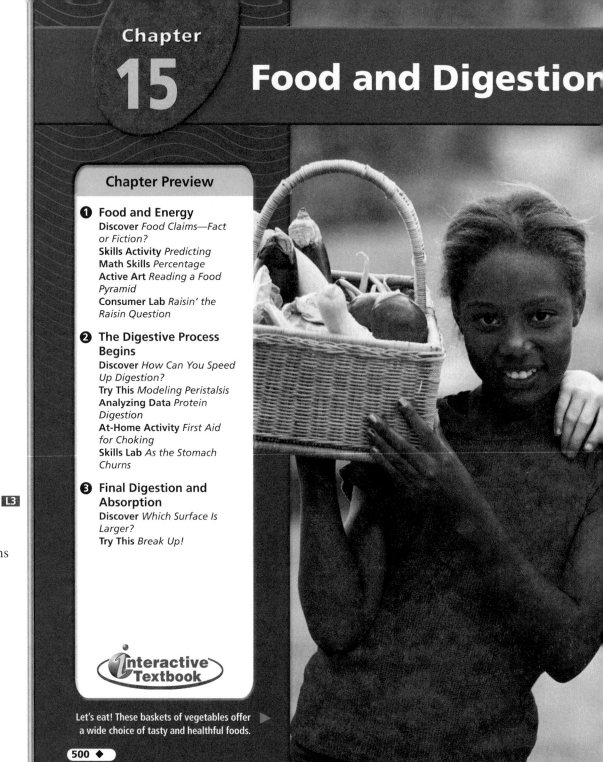

Chapter

15 Food and Digestion

Interactive Textbook

Let's eat! These baskets of vegetables offer a wide choice of tasty and healthful foods. ▶

500 ◆

Lab zone — Chapter **Project**   L3

Objectives
Students will compare their eating patterns to the recommendations in the USDA's MyPyramid plans. After this Chapter Project, students will be able to
- observe and maintain records of their eating habits
- measure or estimate the size of food servings
- graph data from their data tables
- compare and contrast their data with the recommendations
- interpret their diagrams and make judgments about how to improve their own diets

Skills Focus
Observing, measuring, graphing, comparing and contrasting, interpreting diagrams

Project Time Line   2 weeks

All in One Teaching Resources, Unit 3
- Chapter Project Teacher Notes
- Chapter Project Overview
- Chapter Project Worksheet 1
- Chapter Project Worksheet 2
- Chapter Project Scoring Rubric

Developing a Plan
Explain to students that they will have three days to record their food intake, three or four days to analyze their data, and three more days to implement a diet based on their recommended MyPyramid Plan. Have students brainstorm ways they can record the foods they eat and the amounts, so they can easily convert food listings into servings. Write a sample of a food record on the board.

Possible Materials
- Provide graph paper, paper, and pencils.
- You may want to create a chart on which students can record foods, or allow students to develop one as they discuss recordkeeping as a class.

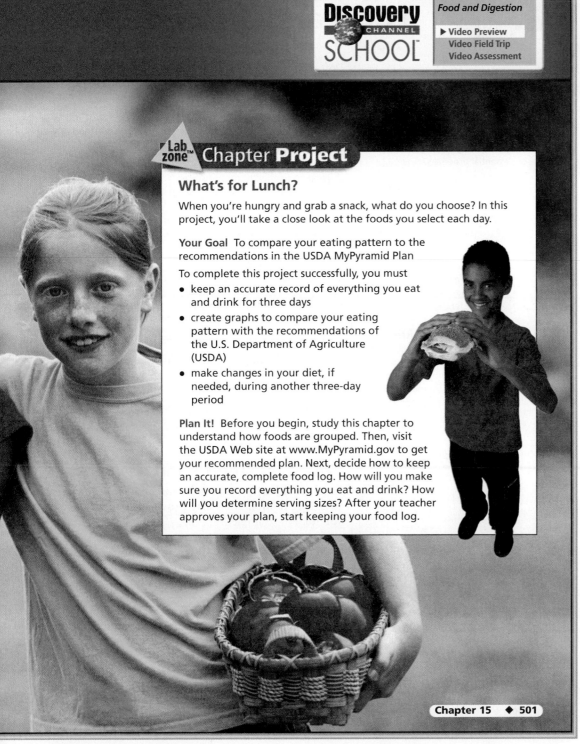

Lab zone™ Chapter **Project**

What's for Lunch?

When you're hungry and grab a snack, what do you choose? In this project, you'll take a close look at the foods you select each day.

Your Goal To compare your eating pattern to the recommendations in the USDA MyPyramid Plan

To complete this project successfully, you must

- keep an accurate record of everything you eat and drink for three days
- create graphs to compare your eating pattern with the recommendations of the U.S. Department of Agriculture (USDA)
- make changes in your diet, if needed, during another three-day period

Plan It! Before you begin, study this chapter to understand how foods are grouped. Then, visit the USDA Web site at www.MyPyramid.gov to get your recommended plan. Next, decide how to keep an accurate, complete food log. How will you make sure you record everything you eat and drink? How will you determine serving sizes? After your teacher approves your plan, start keeping your food log.

Chapter 15 ◆ 501

Food and Digestion

Show the Video Preview to introduce the Chapter Project and overview the chapter content. Discussion Questions: **What changes have the Pittsburgh Steelers made in their eating habits since they started working with a nutritionist?** (*They are eating more healthful food.*)

Performance Assessment

The Chapter Project Scoring Rubric will help you evaluate how well students complete the Chapter Project. You might want to share the rubric with your students so that they know what is expected. Students will be assessed on

- how thoroughly they keep records of the types and amounts of food they eat
- the completeness of their graphs, including the conversion of servings into totals
- how well they analyze their diets based on the USDA's recommendations
- the thoroughness and organization of their written presentations and how well they show an understanding of food choices and healthy and unhealthy diets

Portfolio

Launching the Project

Ask students to write down what they have eaten so far today. Explain to students that their notes and lab reports will be kept confidential, so no one else will know what they have eaten. Using the illustration of the MyPyramid Plan as a guide, ask the students to try to sort their food items into the appropriate groups.

Allow time for students to read the description of the project in their text. Then discuss the MyPyramid Plan and talk about the kind of diet it describes as optimal. Discuss how a person's recommended plan depends on his or her age and activity level.

501

Objectives

After completing this lesson, students will be able to

15.1.1 Explain why the body needs food.

15.1.2 Describe how the six nutrients needed by the body help carry out essential processes.

15.1.3 Explain how the MyPyramid Plan and food labels can help in planning a healthy diet.

Target Reading Skill 🎯

Outlining Explain that using an outline format helps students organize information by main topic, subtopic, and details.

Sample Answer

Food and Energy
I. Why You Need Food
    A. Nutrients
    B. Energy
II. Carbohydrates
    A. Simple Carbohydrates
    B. Complex Carbohydrates
III. Fats
    A. Kinds of Fats
    B. Cholesterol
    C. Nutritionists' Recommendations
IV. Proteins
    A. Amino Acids
    B. Complete and Incomplete Proteins
V. Vitamins and Minerals
    A. Fat-Soluble and Water-Soluble Vitamins
    B. Importance of Vitamins
    C. Importance of Minerals
VI. Water

All in One Teaching Resources, Unit 3

• Transparency LS147

Preteach

Build Background Knowledge   L2

Energy and Calories

Ask students to name foods that they think supply them with energy. Write their responses on the board. Then ask them what they think a Calorie is and write those responses on the board. Revisit the responses once students have read the section.

Food and Energy

Reading Preview

Key Concepts
• Why does your body need food?
• How do the six nutrients needed by the body help carry out essential processes?
• How can food pyramids and food labels help you have a healthy diet?

Key Terms
• nutrient • calorie
• carbohydrate • glucose • fat
• protein • amino acid
• vitamin • mineral
• Percent Daily Value
• Dietary Reference Intakes (DRIs)

🎯 Target Reading Skill

Outlining As you read, make an outline about the six groups of nutrients needed by the body. Use the red headings for the main ideas and the blue headings for the supporting ideas.

Food and Energy
I. Why You Need Food
A. Nutrients
B.
II. Carbohydrates
A.

Lab zone Discover Activity

Food Claims—Fact or Fiction?

1. Examine the list of statements at the right. Copy the list onto a separate sheet of paper.

2. Next to each statement, write *agree* or *disagree*. Give a reason for your response.

3. Discuss your responses with a small group of classmates. Compare the reasons you gave for agreeing or disagreeing with each statement.

Think It Over

Posing Questions List some other statements about nutrition that you have heard. How could you find out whether the statements are true?

Fact or Fiction?
a. Athletes need more protein in their diets than other people do.
b. The only salt that a food contains is the salt that you have added to it.
c. As part of a healthy diet, everyone should take vitamin supplements.

Imagine a Thanksgiving dinner. You see roast turkey on a platter, delicious stuffing, lots of vegetables, and pumpkin pie. The dinner includes an abundance of colors and delicious aromas. Food is a central part of many celebrations, of times shared with friends and family. Food is also essential. Every living thing needs food to stay alive.

Why You Need Food

Food provides your body with materials for growing and for repairing tissues. Food also provides energy for everything you do. For example, running, playing a musical instrument, reading, and even sleeping require energy. Food also helps your body maintain homeostasis, or a stable internal environment. By filling your energy needs, food enables your body to keep this balance during all your activities.

Nutrients Your body breaks down the foods you eat into nutrients. **Nutrients** (NOO tree unts) are the substances in food that provide the raw materials and energy the body needs to carry out all its essential processes. There are six groups of nutrients necessary for human health—carbohydrates, fats, proteins, vitamins, minerals, and water.

Lab zone Discover Activity

Skills Focus Posing questions

Materials none

Time 15 minutes

Tips Write the statements on the board or use an overhead projector to project the statements on a screen.

Expected Outcome All the statements are false. At this stage, you may wish to

L1 collect students' opinions and look for misconceptions, then address specific issues later as you teach the chapter.

Think It Over Encourage students to volunteer additional statements about nutrition and to discuss whether the statements are true.

Energy When nutrients are used by the body for energy, the amount of energy they release can be measured in units called calories. One **calorie** is the amount of energy needed to raise the temperature of one gram of water by one degree Celsius. Most foods contain many thousands of calories of energy. Biologists use the term *Calorie*, with a capital *C*, to measure the energy in foods. One Calorie is the same as 1 kilocalorie (kcal) or 1,000 calories. For example, one serving of popcorn may contain 60 Calories (60 kcal), or 60,000 calories, of energy. The more Calories a food has, the more energy it contains.

You need to eat a certain number of Calories each day to meet your body's energy needs. Your daily energy requirement depends on your level of physical activity. Your needs also change as you grow and age. As an infant and child, you grew very rapidly, so you likely had very high energy needs. Your current growth and level of physical activity affect the number of Calories you need now. The more active you are, the greater your energy needs are.

✓ Reading Checkpoint How is energy in foods measured?

Playing basketball

Walking

Reading

FIGURE 1
Burning Calories
The number of Calories you burn depends on your weight as well as your level of activity. The more active you are, the more Calories you burn.
Applying Concepts *Which activity do you think burns the most Calories per hour—playing basketball, walking, or reading?*

Chapter 15 ◆ 503

Instruct

Why You Need Food

Teach Key Concepts   L2
Calories and Energy

Focus Ask: **What are some reasons that your body needs food?** *(Sample answers: To feel your best, to perform well in school and sports, to reduce your risk of illness)*

Teach Ask: **How do a slice of pizza and a slice of bread compare in Calories and the energy each provides?** *(The pizza has more Calories, so it provides more energy.)* **Why do you need to eat a certain number of Calories each day?** *(To provide your body's energy needs and to grow properly)*

Apply Ask students to hypothesize what might happen if a person their age does not take in enough Calories. *(The person might lose weight and would not have the energy needed to grow and to repair tissues.)*
learning modality: logical/mathematical

Independent Practice   L2

All in One **Teaching Resources, Unit 3**
• Guided Reading and Study Worksheet: *Food and Energy*

⊙ **Student Edition on Audio CD**

Monitor Progress   L2

Writing Have students explain why they need food and list the six main types of nutrients. Students can save their responses in their portfolios.

Portfolio

Answers
Figure 1 Playing basketball

✓ Reading Checkpoint In Calories; 1 Calorie is the same as 1 kilocalorie, or 1,000 calories

Differentiated Instruction

Less Proficient Readers   L1
Recording Information Help students create a framework for a three-column table on the board. Label the columns *Nutrient, Function,* and *Source.* Then have a volunteer read aloud the boldfaced sentence under *Why You Need Food* that names the six nutrients. List them in the first column of the table. Review key words or phrases within the text that provide clues for understanding the functions of each nutrient, such as *perform, provide,* and *helps.* Students can copy the table and fill in the remaining columns as they read.
learning modality: verbal

503

Carbohydrates

Teach Key Concepts `L2`
The Two Groups of Carbohydrates

Focus Ask: **What are some examples of carbohydrates?** (*Sample answers: Bread, potatoes, corn*)

Teach Explain that carbohydrates are categorized into two groups. Ask: **How are the two groups alike?** (*Both are made of sugar molecules.*) Ask: **How are they different?** (*Simple carbohydrates are known as sugars and provide quick energy for the body. Complex carbohydrates are made of many sugar molecules that must be broken down by the body before they can be used.*) Ask: **Why do you need a large proportion of Calories to come from carbohydrates?** (*The glucose in carbohydrates is the major source of energy for your body's cells.*)

Apply Ask: **Why are foods that are made with a lot of sugar not a good source of fiber?** (*Fiber is a complex carbohydrate; foods with a lot of sugar are generally simple carbohydrates.*) **learning modality: logical/mathematical**

Integrating Chemistry `L3`
Write the chemical formula for glucose on the board: $C_6H_{12}O_6$. Explain that fructose has the same formula, but its atoms are arranged differently than those of glucose. Sucrose, or "table sugar," is a simple carbohydrate made up of two molecules, glucose and fructose, that are combined chemically. A carbohydrate that is made up of only one or two sugar molecules is considered a simple carbohydrate. Tell students the sugar found in milk, lactose, is a compound made of two single sugars, glucose and galactose, that are combined chemically. Although its molecules each consists of two sugar subunits, lactose is still considered a simple carbohydrate.

To illustrate the chemical difference between the simple and complex carbohydrates, show students a chain of beads and tell them it represents a carbohydrate. Ask: **What does each bead represent?** (*One sugar molecule*) **What does the chain represent?** (*A complex carbohydrate*) **learning modality: visual**

FIGURE 2
Carbohydrates

Simple carbohydrates, or sugars, are found in fruits, milk, and some vegetables. Sugars are also added to cookies, candies, and soft drinks. Complex carbohydrates are found in rice, corn, pasta, and bread. Fruits, vegetables, nuts, and whole-grain foods also contain fiber.
Applying Concepts *Why is fiber important in the diet?*

Simple Carbohydrates

Brownie (1 square)	
Total Carbohydrates 18 g	
Sugars	10 g
Starches	7 g
Fiber	1 g

Watermelon (1 slice)	
Total Carbohydrates 22 g	
Sugars	18 g
Starches	3 g
Fiber	1 g

Milk (1 cup)	
Total Carbohydrates 12 g	
Sugars	12 g
Starches	0 g
Fiber	0 g

Carbohydrates

The nutrients called **carbohydrates** (kahr boh HY drayts), which are composed of carbon, oxygen, and hydrogen, are a major source of energy. One gram of carbohydrate provides your body with four Calories of energy. **In addition to providing energy, carbohydrates provide the raw materials to make cell parts.** Based on their chemical structure, carbohydrates are divided into simple carbohydrates and complex carbohydrates.

Simple Carbohydrates Simple carbohydrates are also known as sugars. One sugar, **glucose** (GLOO kohs), is the major source of energy for your body's cells. However, most foods do not contain large amounts of glucose. The body converts other types of sugars, such as the sugar found in fruits, into glucose. Glucose is the form of sugar the body can most easily use.

Complex Carbohydrates Complex carbohydrates are made up of many sugar molecules linked together in a chain. Starch is a complex carbohydrate found in foods from plants, such as potatoes, rice, wheat, and corn. To use starch as an energy source, your body first breaks it down into smaller, individual sugar molecules. Only then can your body release the molecules' energy.

Like starch, fiber is a complex carbohydrate found in plants. But unlike starch, fiber cannot be broken down into sugar molecules by your body. Instead, fiber passes through the body and is eliminated.

504 ◆

Complex Carbohydrates

Yellow Corn (1 ear)
Total Carbohydrates 19 g
Sugars   2 g
Starches   15 g
Fiber   2 g

Pasta (1 cup)
Total Carbohydrates 40 g
Sugars   1 g
Starches   37 g
Fiber   2 g

Wheat Bread (1 slice)
Total Carbohydrates 17 g
Sugars   3.5 g
Starches   12.0 g
Fiber   1.5 g

Because your body cannot digest it, fiber is not considered a nutrient. Fiber is an important part of the diet, however, because it helps keep the digestive system functioning properly.

Nutritionists' Recommendations Nutritionists recommend that 45 to 65 percent of the Calories in a diet come from carbohydrates. It is better to eat more complex carbohydrates, such as whole grains, than simple carbohydrates. Foods made with whole grains usually contain a variety of other nutrients. Foods made with a lot of sugar, such as candy and soft drinks, have few valuable nutrients. Also, while sugars can give you a quick burst of energy, starches provide a more even, long-term energy source.

 Reading Checkpoint What are two types of carbohydrates? Give an example of each.

Fats

Like carbohydrates, **fats** are energy-containing nutrients that are composed of carbon, oxygen, and hydrogen. However, fats contain more than twice the energy of an equal amount of carbohydrates. One gram of fat provides your body with nine Calories of energy. **In addition to providing energy, fats have other important functions. Fats form part of the cell membrane, the structure that forms the boundary of a cell. Fatty tissue protects and supports your internal organs and insulates your body.**

Lab zone Skills Activity

Predicting
You can do a test to see which foods contain starch.

1. Put on your apron.
2. Obtain food samples from your teacher. Predict which ones contain starch. Write down your predictions.
3. Use a plastic dropper to add three drops of iodine to each food sample. **CAUTION:** *Iodine can stain skin and clothing.* Handle it carefully. If the iodine turns blue-black, starch is present.

Which foods contain starch? Were your predictions correct?

Lab zone Skills Activity

Skills Focus Predicting **L1**

Materials fruits and vegetables (potatoes, rice, bread, and breakfast cereals), soft drinks (diet and regular), iodine solution, plastic dropper, test tubes, notebook

Time 20 minutes

Tips Place each food sample in a labeled test tube. Set up stations and have students rotate in groups of three or four from station to station.

Expected Outcome Foods such as potatoes, pasta, rice, and cereal contain starch. Other fruits and vegetables also may contain small amounts of starch.

Extend Have students group the foods tested into simple and complex carbohydrates. **learning modality: visual**

Lab zone Build Inquiry **L2**

Calculating Calorie Content

Materials Calorie requirement charts for different age groups, references providing the nutrient content and calories of foods

Time 20 minutes

Focus Ask students to list foods that they commonly eat.

Teach Have students work in groups to determine their recommended daily Calorie intake. Then have them use nutrition textbooks or calorie-counting references to find and list the nutrient content and Calories of the foods they commonly eat.

Apply Have students use the information on their lists to calculate the nutrient and Calorie content of one day's meals and snacks. Ask them to calculate the proportion of Calories that came from carbohydrates. If the proportion is above or below the recommended percentage, have them describe how they can modify their intake to meet recommended percentages. **learning modality: logical/mathematical**

Monitor Progress _____ **L2**

Skills Check Have students make compare/ contrast tables for simple and complex carbohydrates and saturated and unsaturated fats, giving an example of each. Students can place their tables in their portfolios.

Answers
Figure 2 It helps keep the digestive system functioning properly.

Reading Checkpoint Simple and complex; an example of a simple carbohydrate is glucose. An example of a complex carbohydrate is starch.

Fats

Teach Key Concepts L2
Types of Fats

Focus Refer students to Figure 3.

Teach Ask students to identify the main type of fat in the foods shown. Point out that foods can contain different types of fats. Ask: **What is the basis for classifying fats?** *(Chemical structure)* **How are fats beneficial?** *(They provide energy, form part of cell membranes, protect and support internal organs, and insulate your body.)*

Apply Ask: **Which food item shown has the healthiest type of fat?** *(Olive oil)* **learning modality: visual**

Teacher **Demo** L1

Identifying Fats in Foods

Materials foods or pictures of foods that are mostly fats or contain fats, such as a can of vegetable shortening, a bottle of olive oil, a bag of chips, and a box of cereal or crackers

Time 5 minutes

Focus Ask students to recall the three types of fats.

Teach Show each food item and have students classify it by the main type of fat it contains. Students may have difficulty with the food items in boxes. Explain that reading food labels can help determine the presence of saturated fats and trans fats. The words "hydrogenated" or "partially hydrogenated" on the ingredient list indicate trans fats. Pass around a container on which this information appears for students to examine.

Apply Ask: **How can you reduce the amount of saturated fats and trans fats in your diet?** *(Possible answers: Eat low-fat dairy products, read food labels to try to limit the amount of foods you eat that have trans fat, and cook with unsaturated rather than saturated fats.)* **learning modality: visual**

FIGURE 3
Many foods contain saturated, unsaturated, and trans fats. Unsaturated fats are considered to be more healthful than saturated fats and trans fats.
Interpreting Graphs *Which item has the most unsaturated fat— butter, tub margarine, or olive oil?*

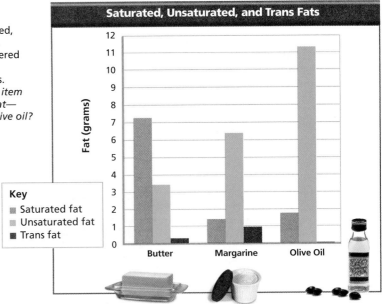

Kinds of Fats Fats may be classified as unsaturated or saturated based on their chemical structure. Unsaturated fats are usually liquid at room temperature. Most cooking oils are unsaturated fats. Saturated fats are usually solid at room temperature. Meat and dairy products contain relatively large amounts of saturated fat.

You may have heard about trans fat. Trans fats are made when manufacturers add hydrogen to vegetable oils. Foods containing trans fats stay fresh longer than foods containing unsaturated fats. Trans fats are found in margarine, chips, and commercially baked goods. Both trans fats and saturated fats are considered to be less healthful than unsaturated fats.

Cholesterol Cholesterol (kuh LES tur awl) is a waxy, fatlike substance found only in animal products. Like fats, cholesterol is an important part of your body's cells. Your liver can make all of the cholesterol your body needs. Therefore, cholesterol is not a necessary part of the diet.

Nutritionists' Recommendations Nutritionists recommend that no more than 30 percent of the Calories eaten each day come from fats. Extra fats and cholesterol in the diet can lead to a buildup of fatty material in the blood vessels. This fatty buildup can cause heart disease.

 Reading Checkpoint What is cholesterol?

FIGURE 4
Complete and Incomplete Proteins
Animal products such as meats and eggs contain complete proteins. Incomplete proteins are found in beans, nuts, and grains.

Proteins

Proteins are nutrients that contain nitrogen as well as carbon, hydrogen, and oxygen. **Proteins are needed for tissue growth and repair. They also play an important part in chemical reactions within cells.** Proteins can serve as a source of energy, but they are a less important source of energy than carbohydrates or fats. About 10 to 35 percent of your daily Calorie intake should come from proteins.

Amino Acids Proteins are made up of small units called **amino acids** (uh MEE noh), which are linked together chemically to form large protein molecules. Thousands of different proteins are built from only about 20 different amino acids. Your body can make about half of the amino acids it needs. The others, called essential amino acids, must come from the foods you eat.

Complete and Incomplete Proteins Foods from animal sources, such as meat and eggs, are sources of complete proteins because these foods contain all the essential amino acids. Proteins from plant sources, such as beans, grains, and nuts, are called incomplete proteins because they are missing one or more essential amino acid. Different plant sources lack different amino acids. Therefore, to obtain all the essential amino acids from plant sources alone, people need to eat a wide variety of plant foods.

 Reading Checkpoint What are the units that make up proteins?

Math Skills

Percentage

A percentage (%) is a ratio that compares a number to 100. For example, 30% means 30 out of 100.

Suppose that a person eats a total of 2,000 Calories in one day. Of those Calories, 300 come from protein. Follow these steps to calculate the percentage of Calories that come from protein.

1. Write the comparison as a fraction:
$$\frac{300}{2,000}$$

2. Multiply the fraction by 100% to express it as a percentage:
$$\frac{300}{2,000} \times 100\% = 15\%$$

Practice Problem Suppose that 540 Calories of the person's 2,000 Calorie total come from fats. What percentage of the Calories comes from fats?

Chapter 15 ◆ 507

Differentiated Instruction

Gifted and Talented L3
Preparing a Display Have students use reliable sources, such as the American Dietetic Association or the American Heart Association, to prepare a display with information on healthful vegetarian diets. Some of the information they may wish to present includes the following

recommendation: Foods with incomplete proteins do not have to be combined to provide complete proteins within a given meal, but should be eaten over the course of a day to provide essential amino acids.
learning modality: logical/mathematical

Address Misconceptions L2
The Role of Fat in a Healthful Diet

Focus Students may think that if low fat is good for you, then no fat is better.

Teach Tell students that some fats contain essential fatty acids, which help regulate blood pressure, blood clotting, and the immune response. Healthy skin and hair also are maintained by fat.

Apply Ask: **How might a person's health be affected by eating too little fat?** (*The person might develop irritated skin and infections.*)
learning modality: logical/mathematical

Proteins

Teach Key Concepts L2

Focus Refer students to Figure 4.

Teach Ask: **What kinds of foods have complete proteins, and what kinds have incomplete proteins?** (*Meats contain all the essential amino acids. Plant foods lack one or more essential amino acids.*)

Apply Ask: **Why is it important for teens to get enough protein?** (*Proteins are needed for tissue growth, and teens are growing rapidly.*)
learning modality: logical/mathematical

Math Skill Calculating percent

Focus Tell students that calculating the percent of Calories from different nutrients helps them to get the recommended amounts.

Teach Remind students which numbers to use in the fraction.

Answer
27%

Monitor Progress _____ L2

Writing Have students explain why protein is important to health.

Answers
Figure 3 Olive oil has the most unsaturated fat.

 Reading Checkpoint Cholesterol is a waxy, fatlike substance found only in animal products.

 Reading Checkpoint Amino acids make up proteins.

Vitamins and Minerals

Teach Key Concepts
The Role of Vitamins

Focus Students may think that all nutrients provide energy. Remind them that a nutrient is a substance in food that provides the raw materials and energy the body needs to carry out all its essential processes.

Teach Ask: **Are vitamins and minerals sources of energy?** *(No)* **Why are vitamins and minerals nutrients?** *(They help to carry out chemical processes.)* Explain that chemical reactions must take place for processes to occur in the body, such as blood clotting, helping the body get energy from foods, and sending messages through the nervous system. Ask: **Why is it important to get vitamins and minerals from food?** *(The body cannot make minerals and some vitamins.)* **Which group of vitamins are important to include every day in the diet and why?** *(Water-soluble vitamins because they cannot be stored in the body)*

Apply Tell students that a nutrient-dense food provides many nutrients relative to the number of Calories. Many nutrient-dense foods contain important vitamins and minerals. Refer students to Figure 6. Ask them to use the information in the chart with what they have learned in this section to give some examples of nutrient-dense foods. *(Sample answers: Dairy products have protein, some carbohydrates, calcium, and some B vitamins. Fruits have carbohydrates, vitamins, and minerals.)* **learning modality: logical/mathematical**

Go Online
SciLINKS

For: Links on foods and energy
Visit: www.SciLinks.org
Web Code: scn-0421

Download a worksheet that will guide students' review of Internet resources on essential nutrients.

Go Online
SciLINKS

For: Links on foods and energy
Visit: www.SciLinks.org
Web code: scn-0421

FIGURE 5
Eat Your Vegetables!
Fresh vegetables are full of vitamins and are fun to pick as well.

Vitamins and Minerals

Two kinds of nutrients—vitamins and minerals—are needed by the body in very small amounts. Unlike the other nutrients, vitamins and minerals do not provide the body with energy or raw materials. Instead, they help the body carry out various processes.

Vitamins act as helper molecules in a variety of chemical reactions in the body. Vitamin K, for example, helps your blood to clot when you get a cut or a scrape. Figure 6 lists the vitamins necessary for health. The body can make a few of these vitamins. For example, your skin can make vitamin D when exposed to sunlight. Most vitamins, however, must be obtained from foods.

Fat-Soluble and Water-Soluble Vitamins Vitamins are classified as either fat-soluble or water-soluble. Fat-soluble vitamins dissolve in fat, and they are stored in fatty tissues in the body. Vitamins A, D, E, and K are all fat-soluble vitamins. Water-soluble vitamins dissolve in water and are not stored in the body. This fact makes it especially important to include sources of water-soluble vitamins—vitamin C and all of the B vitamins—in your diet every day.

Importance of Vitamins Although vitamins are only needed in small amounts, a lack of certain vitamins in the diet can lead to health problems. In the 1700s, sailors on long voyages survived on hard, dry biscuits, salted meat, and not much else. Because of this limited diet, many sailors developed a serious disease called scurvy. People with scurvy suffer from bleeding gums, stiff joints, and sores that do not heal. Some may even die.

A Scottish doctor, James Lind, hypothesized that scurvy was the result of the sailors' poor diet. Lind divided sailors with scurvy into groups and fed different foods to each group. The sailors who were fed citrus fruits—oranges and lemons—recovered from the disease. Lind recommended that all sailors eat citrus fruits. When Lind's recommendations were carried out, scurvy disappeared. Today scientists know that scurvy is caused by the lack of vitamin C, which is found in citrus fruits.

Reading Checkpoint List the fat-soluble vitamins.

FIGURE 6
Essential Vitamins

Both fat-soluble vitamins and water-soluble vitamins are necessary to maintain health. **Interpreting Tables** *What foods provide a supply of both vitamins E and K?*

Fat-Soluble Vitamins		
Vitamin	**Sources**	**Function**
A	Dairy products; eggs; liver; yellow, orange, and dark green vegetables; fruits	Maintains healthy skin, bones, teeth, and hair; aids vision in dim light
D	Fortified dairy products; fish; eggs; liver; made by skin cells in presence of sunlight	Maintains bones and teeth; helps in the use of calcium and phosphorus
E	Vegetable oils; margarine; green, leafy vegetables; whole-grain foods; seeds; nuts	Aids in maintenance of red blood cells
K	Green, leafy vegetables; milk; liver; made by bacteria in the intestines	Aids in blood clotting

Water-Soluble Vitamins		
Vitamin	**Sources**	**Function**
B1 (thiamin)	Pork; liver; whole-grain foods; legumes; nuts	Needed for breakdown of carbohydrates
B2 (riboflavin)	Dairy products; eggs; whole-grain breads and cereals; green, leafy vegetables	Needed for normal growth
B3 (niacin)	Many protein-rich foods; milk; eggs; meat; fish; whole-grain foods; nuts; peanut butter	Needed for release of energy
B6 (pyridoxine)	Green, leafy vegetables; meats; fish; legumes; fruits; whole-grain foods	Helps in the breakdown of proteins, fats, and carbohydrates
B12	Meats; fish; poultry; dairy products; eggs	Maintains healthy nervous system; needed for red blood cell formation
Biotin	Liver; meat; fish; eggs; legumes; bananas; melons	Aids in the release of energy
Folic acid	Green, leafy vegetables; legumes; seeds; liver	Needed for red blood cell formation
Pantothenic acid	Liver; meats; fish; eggs; whole-grain foods	Needed for the release of energy
C	Citrus fruits; tomatoes; potatoes; dark green vegetables; mangoes	Needed to form connective tissue and fight infection

Chapter 15 ◆ 509

Use Visuals: Figure 6 [L2]
Essential Vitamins

Focus Refer students to Figure 6.

Teach Have students identify the water-soluble vitamins. (*B vitamins, biotin, folic acid, pantothenic acid, vitamin C*) Ask: **What is a primary function of these vitamins?** (*Most are involved in breaking down other nutrients and releasing energy.*) **Which foods are good sources of this type of vitamin?** (*Answers should reflect information in the table.*)

Apply Ask: **What might be some effects of a deficiency of water-soluble vitamins?** (*Not growing properly, tiredness, anemia, infections*) **learning modality: visual**

 **Build Inquiry** [L2]

Interpreting Data About Vitamins

Materials printouts of information from reliable Internet sources, reference books on nutrition

Time 20 minutes

Focus Remind students that they need to eat a variety of foods to get the kinds and amounts of vitamins they need.

Teach Divide the class into small groups, and assign each group three or four of the vitamins listed in Figure 6. Have students use the reference materials to find the daily amount of each vitamin recommended for people their age, additional foods that provide each vitamin, and additional functions of each vitamin. Have the groups present their findings to the class.

Apply Ask students to prepare a sample menu for one day of three meals and two snacks that includes all of the vitamins they should take in during a day. **learning modality: logical/mathematical**

Differentiated Instruction

English Learners/Intermediate [L2]
Vocabulary: Link to Visual Pair students with native English speakers. Have them create a vitamin chart similar to the one in Figure 6, listing food sources for each of the vitamins in both English and their native languages. Provide nutrition books and cookbooks to help English learners connect the words to the visuals. **learning modality: visual**

English Learners/Advanced [L3]
Comprehension: Key Concepts Have students look in magazines for foods in Figure 6, for example, *dark green vegetables* and *broccoli*. Then have them list the foods in English along with the nutrients each food contains. Example: broccoli—carbohydrates and vitamins. **learning modality: verbal**

Monitor Progress [L2]

Skills Check Have students list their favorite foods and then classify them according to the vitamins the foods provide.

Answers
Figure 6 Green, leafy vegetables

 A, D, E, K

509

Use Visuals: Figure 7 L2

Essential Minerals

Focus Have students review the minerals in the chart.

Teach Ask: **To obtain enough calcium, what foods should people eat if they do not drink milk?** (*Cheese, dark green, leafy vegetables, tofu, legumes*) **What does the body use calcium for?** (*Building bones and teeth, clotting blood, and nerve and muscle function*)

Apply Tell students that most teens do not get the recommended amount of calcium, which is 1,300 mg per day. Ask them to use the chart to name specific foods people could eat if they do not like milk or cannot drink milk. (*Spinach, broccoli, peas, beans, tofu, cheese*) **learning modality: visual**

FIGURE 7
Eating a variety of foods each day provides your body with the minerals it needs. **Interpreting Tables** *Which minerals play a role in regulating water levels in the body?*

Essential Minerals		
Mineral	**Sources**	**Function**
Calcium	Milk; cheese; dark green, leafy vegetables; tofu; legumes	Helps build bones and teeth; aids in blood clotting; muscle and nerve function
Chlorine	Table salt; soy sauce	Helps maintain water balance
Fluorine	Fluoridated drinking water; fish	Helps form bones and teeth
Iodine	Seafood, iodized salt	Helps in the release of energy
Iron	Red meats; seafood; green, leafy vegetables; legumes; dried fruits	Needed for red blood cell function
Magnesium	Green, leafy vegetables; legumes; nuts; whole-grain foods	Aids in muscle and nerve function; helps in the release of energy
Phosphorus	Meat; poultry; eggs; fish; dairy products	Helps produce healthy bones and teeth; helps in the release of energy
Potassium	Grains; fruits; vegetables; meat; fish	Helps maintain water balance; muscle and nerve function
Sodium	Table salt; soy sauce	Helps maintain water balance; nerve function

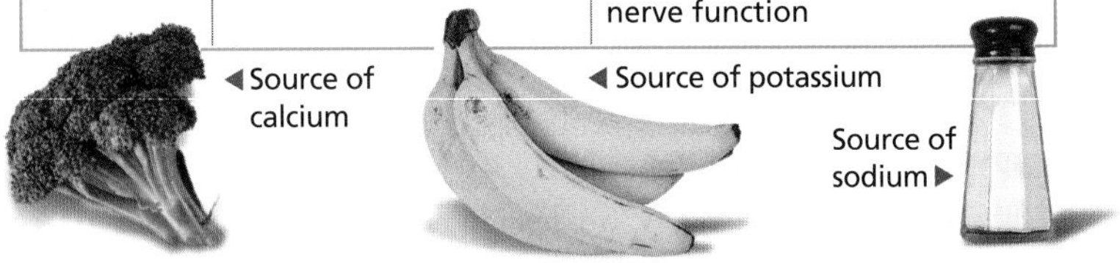

◄ Source of calcium   ◄ Source of potassium   Source of sodium ►

Importance of Minerals Nutrients that are not made by living things are called **minerals.** Minerals are present in soil and are absorbed by plants through their roots. You obtain minerals by eating plant foods or animals that have eaten plants. Figure 7 lists some minerals you need. You probably know that calcium is needed for strong bones and teeth. Iron is needed for the proper functioning of red blood cells.

Both vitamins and minerals are needed by your body in small amounts to carry out chemical processes. If you eat a wide variety of foods, you probably will get enough vitamins and minerals. Most people who eat a balanced diet do not need to take vitamin or mineral supplements.

Reading Checkpoint What are minerals?

FIGURE 8
Water—An Essential Nutrient
All living things need water. Without regular water intake, an organism would not be able to carry out the processes that keep it alive.

Water

Imagine that a boat is sinking. The people on board are getting into a lifeboat. They have room for only one of these items: a bag of fruit, a can of meat, a loaf of bread, or a jug of water. Which item should they choose?

You might be surprised to learn that the lifeboat passengers should choose the water. Although people can probably survive for weeks without food, they will die within days without fresh water. Water is the most abundant substance in the body. It accounts for about 65 percent of the average person's body weight.

Water is the most important nutrient because the body's vital processes—including chemical reactions such as the breakdown of nutrients—take place in water. All the cells in your body are composed mostly of water. Water makes up most of the body's fluids, including blood. Nutrients and other important substances are carried throughout the body dissolved in the watery part of the blood. The water in blood also carries waste materials that must be removed from your body.

On a hot day or after exercising, your body produces perspiration, or sweat. Perspiration consists of chemicals dissolved in water. The water in perspiration comes from body tissues. Sweat glands in your skin release the water on the surface of your body. Perspiration helps regulate body temperature by cooling the body. Some waste chemicals are dissolved in perspiration. Therefore, when you perspire, you are also removing wastes.

Under normal conditions, you need to take in about 2 liters of water every day. When you perspire a lot, you need more water. You can obtain water by drinking water and other beverages. In addition, you take in water when you eat foods that contain a lot of water. Fruits and vegetables such as melons and tomatoes have a large amount of water.

 Reading Checkpoint What is the most abundant substance in the body?

Food and Digestion

Video Preview
▶ Video Field Trip
Video Assessment

Teach Key Concepts L2
Getting Enough Water

Focus Ask: **How much water do you think you take in every day?** (*Encourage students to include beverages other than water, such as fruit juices, and fruits and vegetables.*)

Teach Ask: **How does water work with vitamins and minerals to carry out body processes?** (*Vitamins and minerals help carry out chemical reactions, which take place in water.*) Tell students that water contains substances called electrolytes that regulate many processes in cells. Heavy perspiring can result in a reduction in the body's water content and electrolytes. Signs of losing too much water include weakness, rapid breathing, and weak heartbeat.

Apply Ask: **How can you help prevent dehydration when you are very physically active?** (*Drink water before, during, and after participating in physical activities; be alert to signs of dehydration*) **learning modality: logical/mathematical**

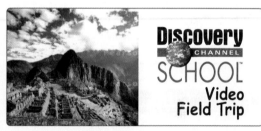

Food and Digestion

Show students the Video Field Trip to help them understand the importance of the digestive system. Discussion Question: **According to the Food Guide Pyramid, what category of food should we consume the most servings of?** (*Foods rich in complex carbohydrates*)

Monitor Progress ————— L2
Answers
Figure 7 Chlorine, potassium, and sodium

 Reading Checkpoint Nutrients that are not made by living things

 Reading Checkpoint Water

511

Guidelines for a Healthy Diet

Teach Key Concepts L2

Shape of a Food Pyramid

Focus Refer students to Figure 9.

Teach Ask: **What does the width of each band represent?** *(The proportions of each food group you need daily)*

Apply Ask: **How do the types and amounts of food in each group reflect the recommendations for the percentage of Calories that should come from the different nutrients?** *(The highest percentage of Calories should come from grains and vegetables. As shown in the pyramid, the intake of oils should be limited.)* **learning modality: visual**

All in One Teaching Resources, Unit 3

• Transparency LS148

Go Online
active art

For: Reading a Food Pyramid activity
Visit: PHSchool.com
Web Code: cep-4022

Students learn about the food groups and how they can be combined to form a healthy diet.

Lab zone Build Inquiry L2

Classifying Foods

Materials note cards

Time 15 minutes

Focus Ask each student to list a favorite food on each of ten note cards.

Teach Have students work in small groups to classify the foods, using a USDA MyPyramid Plan. Explain that some foods, such as pizza, fall into more than one category. Then have students use their cards to plan nutritious meals.

Apply Ask students to write a paragraph describing whether they need to include more or less of any food groups in their daily diets. **learning modality: logical/ mathematical**

512

Guidelines for a Healthy Diet

In 2005, the United States Department of Agriculture (USDA) introduced a new set of guidelines to promote healthy eating and physical activity. **The USDA guidelines provide a personalized way to help people make healthy food choices based on their age, sex, and amount of physical activity.** You can get more information about the USDA dietary guidelines by visiting its Web site on the Internet.

Go Online
active art

For: Reading a Food Pyramid activity
Visit: PHSchool.com
Web Code: cep-4022

FIGURE 9
Reading a Food Pyramid

This food pyramid recommends the proportion of foods from each group that make up a healthy diet.

Stay Active
Daily physical activity is an important part to staying healthy.

Know Your Food Groups
The pyramid is divided into six colored bands, representing the five food groups, plus oils.

Know Your Calorie Needs
Depending on physical activity, a 13-year-old girl needs 1600–2200 Calories per day. A 13-year-old boy needs 1800–2400 Calories per day.

Balance Your Diet
The proportions of each food group you need daily are shown by the width of each band.

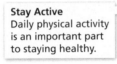

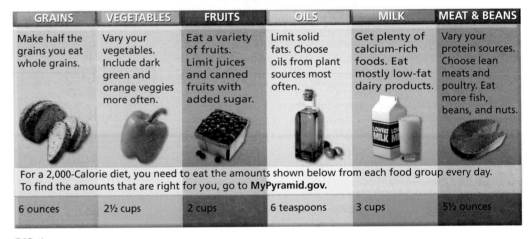

GRAINS	VEGETABLES	FRUITS	OILS	MILK	MEAT & BEANS
Make half the grains you eat whole grains.	Vary your vegetables. Include dark green and orange veggies more often.	Eat a variety of fruits. Limit juices and canned fruits with added sugar.	Limit solid fats. Choose oils from plant sources most often.	Get plenty of calcium-rich foods. Eat mostly low-fat dairy products.	Vary your protein sources. Choose lean meats and poultry. Eat more fish, beans, and nuts.

For a 2,000-Calorie diet, you need to eat the amounts shown below from each food group every day. To find the amounts that are right for you, go to **MyPyramid.gov.**

6 ounces	2½ cups	2 cups	6 teaspoons	3 cups	5½ ounces

512 ◆

Food Labels

After a long day, you and your friends stop into a store on your way home from school. What snack should you buy? How can you make a wise choice? One thing you can do is to read the information provided on food labels. **Food labels allow you to evaluate a single food as well as to compare the nutritional value of two different foods.**

How to Read a Food Label Figure 10 shows a food label that might appear on a box of cereal. Refer to that label as you read about some of the important nutritional information it contains.

❶ Serving Size This information tells you the size of a single serving and the number of servings in the container. The information on the rest of the label is based on serving size. If you eat twice the serving size, then you'll consume twice the number of Calories.

❷ Calories This information tells you how much energy you get from one serving of this food, including how many Calories come from fat.

❸ Percent Daily Value The **Percent Daily Value** shows you how the nutritional content of one serving fits into the recommended diet for a person who consumes 2,000 Calories per day. For example, one serving of this cereal contains 12% of the total amount of sodium a person should consume in one day. You might eat more or less than 2,000 Calories per day. But, you can still use this percentage as a general guide.

❹ Ingredients The ingredients are listed in order by weight, starting with the main ingredient. The list can alert you to substances that have been added to a food to improve its flavor or color, or to keep it from spoiling. In addition, reading ingredients lists can help you avoid substances that make you ill.

Using Food Labels Food labels can help you make healthful food choices. Suppose you are shopping for breakfast cereals. By reading the labels, you might find that one cereal contains little fat and a high percentage of the Daily Values for complex carbohydrates and several vitamins. Another cereal might have fewer complex carbohydrates and vitamins, and contain significant amounts of fat. You can see that the first cereal would be a better choice as a regular breakfast food.

FIGURE 10
Food Label
By law, specific nutritional information must be listed on food labels.
Calculating *How many servings of this product would you have to eat to get 90% of the Daily Value for iron?*

Nutrition Facts

Serving Size		1 cup (30g)
Servings Per Container		About 10

Amount Per Serving

Calories 110	Calories from Fat 15

	% Daily Value*
Total Fat 2g	3%
Saturated Fat 0g	0%
Trans Fat 0g	0%
Cholesterol 0mg	0%
Sodium 280mg	12%
Total Carbohydrate 22g	7%
Dietary Fiber 3g	12%
Sugars 1g	
Protein 3g	

Vitamin A	10%	• Vitamin C	20%
Calcium	4%	• Iron	45%

* Percent Daily Values are based on a 2,000 Calorie diet. Your daily values may be higher or lower depending on your caloric needs:

		Calories	2,000	2,500
Total Fat	Less than		65g	80g
Sat. Fat	Less than		20g	25g
Cholesterol	Less than		300mg	300mg
Sodium	Less than		2,400mg	2,400mg
Total Carbohydrate			300g	375g
Fiber			25g	30g

Calories per gram:
Fat 9 • Carbohydrate 4 • Protein 4

Ingredients: Whole grain oats, sugar, salt, milled corn, oat fiber, dried whey, honey, alm...

Food Labels

Teach Key Concepts ▢L2
Interpreting Food Labels

Focus Tell students that the Food Guide Pyramid helps you plan your food choices, but it does not tell you the amounts of specific nutrients you need.

Teach Refer students to Figure 10. Ask students to locate the different types of information on the food label as a student volunteer reads aloud the explanation for each item. Reinforce that food labels are only a guide; teens may need more nutrients than the Percent Daily Values indicate.

Apply Have students bring in food labels from their favorite snacks, work in small groups to read and interpret the labels, and then prepare a chart comparing the nutritional value of two or more snacks.
learning modality: visual

All in One Teaching Resources, Unit 3
• Transparency LS149

Lab zone Build Inquiry ▢L2

Calculating Percent of Calories From Fat

Focus Explain that the Calories from fat in every single food you eat do not have to be less than 35%. Some foods can be higher in fat as long as others are lower.

Teach Model how to use labels from snacks to find the percent of Calories that come from fat.

Example: 30 potato chips	
Calories	340
Calories from Fat	200

$200 \div 340 \times 100 = 58.8\%$

Apply Have students use food labels from their favorite snack foods to calculate the percentage of fat in each serving. **learning modality: logical/mathematical**

Monitor Progress ▢L2
Answers
Figure 10 Two; one serving provides 45%.

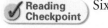 Six

Answer

✓ Reading Checkpoint   Guidelines for the amounts of nutrients needed daily

Assess

Reviewing Key Concepts

1. a. Any two: growing, repairing tissues, providing energy, maintaining homeostasis
b. The amount of energy needed to raise the temperature of one gram of water by one degree Celsius; the more Calories a food has, the more energy it contains. **c.** Individuals who are growing and who are very active have high energy needs.
2. a. Carbohydrates, fats, proteins, vitamins, minerals, and water
b. Carbohydrates and fats provide energy and raw materials the body needs; and fatty tissue supports, protects, and insulates the body. Proteins are needed for growth and repair, and for chemical reactions. Vitamins and minerals act as helper molecules in chemical reactions. Water is needed because all the body's chemical reactions take place in water. **c.** Proteins in plant foods are incomplete proteins. However, if vegetarians eat different plant foods in combination, they will get all the essential amino acids.
3. a. Food pyramids classify food into six groups, and a food label contains nutritional information about the food. **b.** A food pyramid indicates how much from each food group you should eat every day to maintain a healthy diet. You can use food labels to evaluate a single food and to compare the nutritional value of different foods in planning a healthy meal.

Reteach   L1
Help students compare subcategories of carbohydrates, fats, and proteins—for example, simple and complex carbohydrates.

Performance Assessment   L2
Drawing Have small groups of students prepare posters showing one nutrient, its functions, and sources of the nutrient.

All in One Teaching Resources, Unit 3
• Section Summary: *Food and Energy*
• Review and Reinforce: *Food and Energy*
• Enrich: *Food and Energy*

FIGURE 11
Reading Food Labels
Food labels allow you to compare the nutritional content of similar kinds of foods.

Dietary Reference Intakes Food labels can also help you monitor the nutrients in your diet. Guidelines that show the amounts of nutrients that are needed every day are known as **Dietary Reference Intakes (DRIs).** For example, the DRIs for vitamins recommend that people your age get 45 milligrams of vitamin C every day.

DRIs also show how the Calories that people eat each day should be split among carbohydrates, fats, and proteins. The Percent Daily Values listed on food labels can help you make sure that you are meeting the DRIs for different nutrients.

✓ Reading Checkpoint   **What are Dietary Reference Intakes?**

Section 1 Assessment

↻ **Target Reading Skill** **Outlining** Use the information in your outline about nutrients to help you answer the questions below.

Reviewing Key Concepts
1. a. Identifying Name two ways in which foods are used by the body.
  b. Defining What is a calorie? How does it relate to the amount of energy in foods?
  c. Inferring Why do young children and active teenagers have high energy needs?
2. a. Listing List the six nutrients that are needed by the body.
  b. Summarizing For each nutrient you listed, briefly describe the role it plays in the body.
  c. Applying Concepts Why is it especially important that vegetarians eat a varied diet?

3. a. Reviewing What kinds of information are found in food pyramids and on food labels?
  b. Applying Concepts How can you use this information to plan a healthy meal?

Math   Practice

4. Percentage Suppose that a person eats 2,500 Calories in one day. Of those Calories, 1,200 are from carbohydrates, 875 are from fat, and the rest are from protein. What percentages of the person's Calories are from carbohydrates, from fats, and from proteins?

Lab zone Chapter Project

Keep Students on Track Remind students to record foods soon after they eat, as remembering later can be difficult. Encourage students not to modify their diets during the project. Recording what they eat will help them better understand how their habits affect their health.

Math   Practice

Math Skill Calculating percent
Answers
4. Carbohydrates: 1200 ÷ 2500 = 0.48; 0.48 × 100 = 48% Fats: 875 ÷ 2500 = 0.35; 0.35 × 100 = 35%
Proteins: 48% + 35% = 83%; 100% − 83% = 17%

Raisin' the Raisin Question

Problem

Raisins are a good source of the mineral iron. Which raisin bran cereal contains the most raisins?

Skills Focus

measuring, calculating, controlling variables

Materials

- balance
- beaker (250 mL)
- raisin bran cereals (several brands)

Procedure

1. Use a balance to find the mass of a clean 250-mL beaker. Record the mass in a data table like the one below.

2. Fill the beaker to the top with one of the brands of raisin bran cereal, but do not pack down the cereal. **CAUTION:** *Do not put any cereal in your mouth.* Write the brand name in the data table. Measure and record the mass of the beaker plus cereal. Subtract the mass of the empty beaker to get the mass of the cereal alone. Record the result.

3. Pour the cereal onto a paper towel. Separate the raisins from the bran and place the raisins back in the beaker. Measure and record the mass of the beaker plus raisins. Subtract the mass of the empty beaker to get the mass of the raisins alone. Record the result.

4. Repeat Steps 1–3 with each of the other brands of cereal.

Analyze and Conclude

1. **Measuring** Why did you first measure the mass of an empty beaker and then the mass of the beaker plus cereal?

2. **Calculating** Calculate the percentage mass of raisins in each cereal as follows:

$$\% \text{ Mass of raisins} = \frac{\text{Mass of raisins}}{\text{Mass of cereal}} \times 100\%$$

Record the results in your data table.

3. **Interpreting Data** Based on your observations, which brand of cereal had the greatest percentage of raisins by mass?

4. **Controlling Variables** Was it important that all of the cereal samples were collected in the same-size beaker? Why or why not?

5. **Communicating** Based on your results, write a paragraph that could be printed on a box of raisin bran cereal that would help consumers understand that this brand is the best source of iron.

Design an Experiment

In this investigation, you examined a *sample* of cereal rather than the contents of the entire box. Scientists often use samples because it is a more practical way to make observations. Redesign this experiment to improve upon the sampling technique and increase the accuracy of your results. *Obtain your teacher's permission before carrying out your investigation.*

Data Table						
Cereal Brand	Mass (g)					Percentage Mass of Raisins (%)
	Empty Beaker	Beaker plus Cereal	Cereal	Beaker plus Raisins	Raisins	

Analyze and Conclude

1. So that the mass of the beaker is not included in the calculations.
2. Answers will depend on brands used.
3. Answers will depend on brands used.
4. The way the flakes fit into different sized containers may influence the packing, and the size of the sample influences the percentage error, so the containers should be the same for each sample.
5. Accept answers that correctly identify the raisin bran with most raisins based on the data table, that explain how sampling was done, and how the data were analyzed.

Extend Inquiry

Design an Experiment

Samples contain random errors. The best way to reduce error is to measure several samples and average the results.

Raisin' the Raisin Question

Preparing for Inquiry

Skills Objectives

Students will be able to:

- measure the masses of the components of a consumer product
- calculate the percentage by mass of the components of a consumer product
- understand why a variable in an experiment was controlled

 Prep Time 20 minutes
Class Time 40 minutes

Safety

 Warn students not to eat the cereal or raisins.

Guide Inquiry

Introducing the Procedure

Ask: **How do you calculate the percentage of part of a mixture if you know the amount of the mixture and the amount of the part?** *(Divide the amount of the part by the amount of the mixture, and multiply by 100.)*

Troubleshooting the Experiment

- Students should place raisins back into the empty beaker as they find them. After students separate all the raisins from the flakes, they should go through the flakes one more time to make sure no raisins are left behind.
- Students should re-zero the balance between cereals, and remeasure the mass of the empty beaker as well.
- No form of packing should be done, including banging the container on the tabletop.
- Depending on the level of the student, you may wish to introduce the concept of significant figures. For lower level students, suggest that they round off calculations to 1 or 2 decimal places.

Expected Outcome

Commercial raisin brans are about 30 to 35 percent raisins by mass.

Objectives

After completing this lesson, students will be able to

15.2.1 Describe the functions carried out in the digestive system

15.2.2 Explain the roles of the mouth, esophagus, and stomach in digestion

Target Reading Skill

Using Prior Knowledge Explain that using prior knowledge helps students connect what they already know to what they are about to read.

Answer

Graphic organizers should have two columns: "What You Know" and "What You Learned." Have students write what they know in the first column. Then as they read, they can add new facts to the second column.

All in One Teaching Resources, Unit 3

• Transparency LS150

Preteach

Build Background Knowledge   L2

What Happens During Digestion

Ask students to describe what they think happens after they eat a food item. Give students an example, such as a baked potato, and have them discuss what they know about the processes that change it from a potato to nutrients and energy.

The Digestive Process Begins

Reading Preview

Key Concepts
• What functions are carried out in the digestive system?
• What roles do the mouth, esophagus, and stomach play in digestion?

Key Terms
• digestion • absorption
• saliva • enzyme • epiglottis
• esophagus • mucus
• peristalsis • stomach

Target Reading Skill

Using Prior Knowledge Before you read, look at the section headings and visuals to see what this section is about. Then write what you know about the digestive system in a graphic organizer like the one below. As you read, continue to write in what you learn.

What You Know
1. Food is digested in the stomach.
2.

What You Learned
1.
2.

Lab zone Discover Activity

How Can You Speed Up Digestion?

1. Obtain two plastic jars with lids. Fill the jars with equal amounts of water at the same temperature.
2. Place a whole sugar cube into one jar. Place a crushed sugar cube into the other jar.
3. Fasten the lids on the jars. Holding one jar in each hand, shake the two jars gently and for equal amounts of time.
4. Place the jars on a flat surface. Observe whether the whole cube or the crushed cube dissolves faster.

Think It Over
Predicting Use the results of this activity to predict which would take longer to digest: a large piece of food or one that has been cut up into many small pieces. Explain your answer.

In 1822, a man named Alexis St. Martin was wounded in the stomach. Dr. William Beaumont saved St. Martin's life. The wound, however, left an opening in St. Martin's stomach that never healed completely. Beaumont realized that by looking through the opening in St. Martin's abdomen, he could observe what was happening inside the stomach.

Beaumont observed that food changed chemically inside the stomach. He hypothesized that chemical reactions in the stomach broke down foods into smaller particles. Beaumont removed liquid from St. Martin's stomach and analyzed it. The stomach liquid contained an acid that played a role in the breakdown of foods into simpler substances.

Functions of the Digestive System

Beaumont's observations helped scientists understand the role of the stomach in the digestive system. **The digestive system has three main functions. First, it breaks down food into molecules the body can use. Then, the molecules are absorbed into the blood and carried throughout the body. Finally, wastes are eliminated from the body.** Figure 12 shows the organs of the digestive system, which is about 9 meters long from beginning to end.

Lab zone Discover Activity

Skills Focus Predicting   L1

Materials 2 plastic jars with lids, water, sugar cubes

Time 15 minutes

Tips Pair students; each student can shake one jar. The jars must receive equal shaking. Have students synchronize their shaking techniques and predict what will happen to the sugar in each jar.

Expected Outcome The crushed sugar cube will dissolve more quickly than the whole cube.

Think It Over A large piece of food would take longer to digest than one that has been cut up in many small pieces because the large piece has to be broken down first.

Digestion The process by which your body breaks down food into small nutrient molecules is called **digestion**. There are two kinds of digestion—mechanical and chemical. In mechanical digestion, foods are physically broken down into smaller pieces. Mechanical digestion occurs when you bite into a sandwich and chew it into small pieces.

In chemical digestion, chemicals produced by the body break foods into their smaller chemical building blocks. For example, the starch in bread is broken down into individual sugar molecules.

Absorption and Elimination After your food is digested, the molecules are ready to be transported throughout your body. **Absorption** (ab SAWRP shun) is the process by which nutrient molecules pass through the wall of your digestive system into your blood. Materials that are not absorbed, such as fiber, are eliminated from the body as wastes.

Go Online
SciLINKS NSTA

For: Links on digestion
Visit: www.SciLinks.org
Web Code: scn-0423

> **Reading Checkpoint** What is chemical digestion?

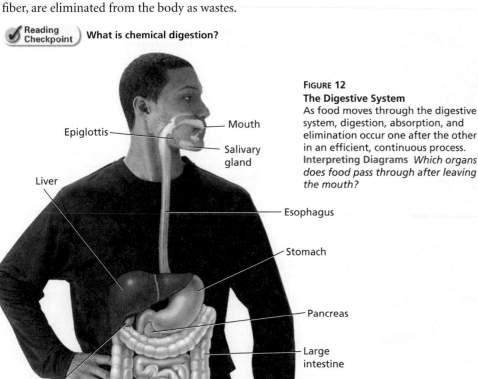

FIGURE 12
The Digestive System
As food moves through the digestive system, digestion, absorption, and elimination occur one after the other in an efficient, continuous process. *Interpreting Diagrams Which organs does food pass through after leaving the mouth?*

Epiglottis

Mouth

Salivary gland

Liver

Esophagus

Stomach

Pancreas

Large intestine

Small intestine

Gallbladder

Rectum

Chapter 15 ◆ 517

Differentiated Instruction

English Learners/Beginning [L1]
Vocabulary: Prior Knowledge Point to each part of the digestive system labeled in Figure 12. Pronounce the terms and have students repeat them. Then have students write the terms in English and in their native languages. **learning modality: visual**

English Learners/Intermediate [L2]
Vocabulary: Science Glossary Conduct the same activity as described for Beginning students. As students read this section and the next one, have them write a sentence in their own words that describes the function of each of the terms. **learning modality: verbal**

Instruct

Functions of the Digestive System

Teach Key Concepts [L2]
Types of Digestion

Focus Review the difference between mechanical and chemical changes.

Teach Ask: **What happens to the pizza during chemical digestion?** *(It is broken down into molecules that the body can use.)* **What nutrients in the cheese and crust would be absorbed?** *(Protein, fat, and calcium from cheese; carbohydrates and B vitamins from the crust)*

Apply Refer students to Figure 12. Explain that both types of digestion can occur at the same time in the same organ. Have students trace the path of food through the digestive system. **learning modality: visual**

 **Teaching Resources, Unit 3**

• Transparency LS151

Independent Practice [L2]

Teaching Resources, Unit 3

• Guided Reading and Study Worksheet: *The Digestive Process Begins*

⊙ Student Edition on Audio CD

Go Online
SciLINKS NSTA

For: Links on digestion
Visit: www.SciLinks.org
Web Code: scn-0423

Download a worksheet that will guide students' review of Internet resources on digestion.

Monitor Progress [L2]

Writing Have students explain what happens to food when it is digested.

Answers
Figure 12 The esophagus, stomach, small intestine, and large intestine

> **Reading Checkpoint** The process in which chemicals produced by the body break foods into their smaller chemical building blocks

The Mouth

Teach Key Concepts L2
Digestion Begins

Focus Review chemical and mechanical digestion.

Teach Refer students to Figure 13. Ask them to discuss the function of each part of the mouth: **Salivary glands** (*Produce saliva, which moistens food and contains an enzyme that breaks down starch*); **Salivary duct** (*Narrow tube that conveys saliva from the salivary gland to the mouth*); **Tongue** (*Helps mix food with saliva and assists in swallowing*); **Teeth** (*Cut, tear, and grind food*).

Apply Ask: **Why is it important to keep your teeth healthy?** (*Healthy teeth allow you to eat different foods to obtain the variety of nutrients you need.*) **learning modality: visual**

Teacher Demo L3

Action of Enzymes

Materials meat tenderizer, milk, orange juice, 2 flasks or clear glasses, 2 stirrers

Time 10 minutes

Focus Show students the container of meat tenderizer. Ask: **What is meat tenderizer used for?** (*It is sprinkled on meats before cooking to make them more tender.*) Explain that meat tenderizer contains papain, an enzyme that breaks down protein.

Teach At the beginning of class, place 2 tablespoons of milk into one flask and the same amount of orange juice in another. Add 1 tablespoon of the meat tenderizer to each flask, and stir well with separate stirrers. Ask: **What will happen to the milk and orange juice?** (*The papain will act on the milk solution but not the orange juice because milk contains protein, while orange juice does not.*) Set aside the flasks until the end of class, then display both flasks. The milk solution will be thick; the orange juice will be unchanged.

Apply Ask: **What can you say about the action of digestive enzymes based on this demonstration?** (*An enzyme acts on only one type of nutrient.*) **learning modality: visual**

The Mouth

Have you ever walked past a bakery or restaurant and noticed your mouth watering? Smelling or even just thinking about food when you're hungry is enough to start your mouth watering. This response isn't accidental. When your mouth waters, your body is preparing for the delicious meal it expects. **Both mechanical and chemical digestion begin in the mouth.** The fluid released when your mouth waters is **saliva** (suh LY vuh). Saliva plays an important role in both kinds of digestion.

Mechanical Digestion in the Mouth Your teeth carry out the first stage of mechanical digestion. Your center teeth, or incisors (in SY zurz), cut the food into bite-sized pieces. On either side of the incisors there are sharp, pointy teeth called canines (KAY nynz). These teeth tear and slash the food into smaller pieces. Behind the canines are the premolars and molars, which crush and grind the food. As the teeth do their work, saliva moistens the pieces of food into one slippery mass.

Chemical Digestion in the Mouth As mechanical digestion begins, so does chemical digestion. If you take a bite of a cracker and suck on it, the cracker begins to taste sweet. It tastes sweet because a chemical in the saliva has broken down the starch molecules in the cracker into sugar molecules.

FIGURE 13
Digestion in the Mouth
Mechanical digestion begins in the mouth, where the teeth cut and tear food into smaller pieces. Salivary glands release enzymes that begin chemical digestion. **Observing** *Which teeth are best suited for biting into a juicy apple?*

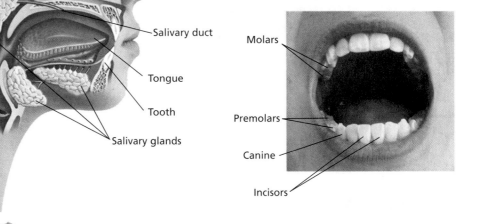

Salivary duct

Tongue

Tooth

Salivary glands

Molars

Premolars

Canine

Incisors

FIGURE 14
How Enzymes Work
The shape of an enzyme molecule is specific to the shape of the food molecule it breaks down. Here, an enzyme breaks down a starch into sugars.

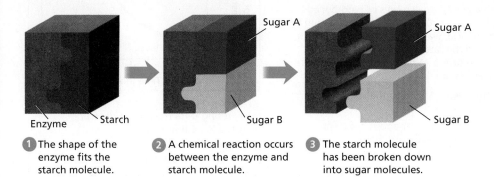

1. The shape of the enzyme fits the starch molecule.

2. A chemical reaction occurs between the enzyme and starch molecule.

3. The starch molecule has been broken down into sugar molecules.

The chemical in saliva that digests starch is an enzyme. **Enzymes** are proteins that speed up chemical reactions in the body. Your body produces many different enzymes. Each enzyme has a specific chemical shape. Its shape enables it to take part in only one kind of chemical reaction. An example of enzyme action is shown in Figure 14.

The Esophagus

If you've ever choked on food, your food may have "gone down the wrong way." That's because there are two openings at the back of your mouth. One opening leads to your windpipe, which carries air into your lungs. As you swallow, a flap of tissue called the **epiglottis** (ep uh GLAHT is) seals off your windpipe, preventing the food from entering. The food goes into the **esophagus** (ih SAHF uh gus), a muscular tube that connects the mouth to the stomach. The esophagus is lined with **mucus,** a thick, slippery substance produced by the body. Mucus makes food easier to swallow and move along.

Food remains in the esophagus for only about 10 seconds. **After food enters the esophagus, contractions of smooth muscles push the food toward the stomach.** These involuntary waves of muscle contraction are called **peristalsis** (pehr ih STAWL sis). Peristalsis also occurs in the stomach and farther down the digestive system. These muscular waves keep food moving in one direction.

Reading Checkpoint How is food prevented from entering the windpipe?

Lab zone Try This **Activity**

Modeling Peristalsis

1. Obtain a clear, flexible plastic straw.

2. Hold the straw vertically and insert a small bead into the top of the straw. The bead should fit snugly into the straw. **CAUTION:** *Do not put the straw in your mouth or blow into the straw.*

3. Pinch the straw above the bead so the bead begins to move down the length of the tubing.

4. Repeat Step 3 until the bead exits the straw.

Making Models How does this action compare with peristalsis? What do the bead and the straw represent?

Chapter 15 ◆ 519

Lab zone Try This **Activity**

Skills Focus Making models ⬛L2

Materials 20-cm clear, flexible, plastic straw (about 6 mm in diameter); round bead (5–6 mm in diameter)

Time 15 minutes

Tips You may substitute a seed, pebble, or other object for the bead.

Expected Outcome The bead will move ahead of where the straw is being pinched. The pinching motion models the contractions of the muscles around the esophagus. The straw models the esophagus, and the bead represents food. **learning modality: kinesthetic**

The Esophagus

Teach Key Concepts ⬛L2
The Function of the Esophagus

Focus Ask students to swallow and try to breathe at the same time. They will note that for a very brief time, they are not able to breathe.

Teach Ask: **Why weren't you able to breathe when you swallowed?** *(The epiglottis sealed off the windpipe.)* Tell students that the large, hollow organs of the digestive system contain muscles that help their walls to move. Ask: **How do the muscles of the esophagus help food to move through the digestive system?** *(Muscles in the esophagus push food toward the stomach.)*

Apply Ask: **How does peristalsis explain how astronauts are able to eat in space?** *(Gravity doesn't affect how food travels from the mouth to the stomach. The muscles in the esophagus contract and push the food down into the stomach.)* **learning modality: logical/mathematical**

Monitor Progress ⬛L2

Skills Check

Have students compare and contrast mechanical and chemical digestion.

Answers
Figure 13 Incisors

Reading Checkpoint As you swallow, a flap of tissue called the epiglottis seals off the windpipe, preventing the food from entering.

Math Skill Making and interpreting Graphs

Focus Remind students that a line graph is often used to show changes over time.

Teach Ask: **What is being represented by the graph?** (*The time it takes for egg white to be digested*)

Answers
1. Percentage of egg white digested
2. About 14 hours
3. About 70%
4. From 12 to 16 hours

The Stomach

Teach Key Concepts   L2

Function of the Stomach

Focus Ask: **What is one way your stomach lets you know it is empty?** (*Sample answers: You feel hunger pangs; your stomach "growls" or rumbles.*) Explain that these sounds are caused by hunger contractions, or peristaltic contractions in the stomach when it has been empty for a long time. People sometimes experience a sensation of pain, called hunger pangs.

Teach Refer students to Figure 15. Ask: **How do the muscles in the stomach help it to perform its function?** (*They contract to squeeze food and mix it with fluids.*) **What happens to food in the stomach?** (*Food enters the stomach from the esophagus, where it is mixed with fluids. The proteins are chemically digested. Then the food is released into the small intestine.*)

Apply Have students use what they have learned in this section to summarize where mechanical and chemical digestion have taken place to this point. (*Mouth: chemical and mechanical digestion; esophagus: none; stomach: chemical and mechanical digestion*) Ask: **Where is mechanical digestion complete?** (*The stomach*) **Is chemical digestion complete here?** (*No; it is complete in the small intestine.*) **learning modality: visual**

Protein Digestion

A scientist performed an experiment to determine the amount of time needed to digest protein. He placed small pieces of hard-boiled egg white (a protein) in a test tube containing hydrochloric acid, water, and the enzyme pepsin. He measured the rate at which the egg white was digested over a 24-hour period. His data are recorded in the graph.

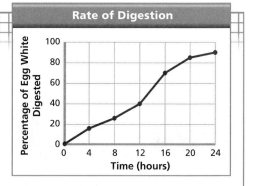

Rate of Digestion

1. **Reading Graphs** What do the values on the *y*-axis represent?

2. **Interpreting Data** After about how many hours would you estimate that half of the protein was digested?

3. **Interpreting Data** How much digestion occurred in 16 hours?

4. **Drawing Conclusions** During which 4-hour period did the most digestion take place?

The Stomach

When food leaves the esophagus, it enters the **stomach,** a J-shaped, muscular pouch located in the abdomen. As you eat, your stomach expands to hold all of the food that you swallow. **Most mechanical digestion and some chemical digestion occur in the stomach.**

Mechanical Digestion in the Stomach The process of mechanical digestion occurs as three strong layers of smooth muscle contract to produce a churning motion. This action mixes the food with fluids in somewhat the same way that clothes and soapy water are mixed in a washing machine.

Chemical Digestion in the Stomach Chemical digestion occurs as the churning food makes contact with digestive juice, a fluid produced by cells in the lining of the stomach. Digestive juice contains the enzyme pepsin. Pepsin chemically digests the proteins in your food, breaking them down into short chains of amino acids.

Digestive juice also contains hydrochloric acid, a very strong acid. Without this strong acid, your stomach could not function properly. First, pepsin works best in an acid environment. Second, the acid kills many bacteria that you swallow with your food.

Why doesn't stomach acid burn a hole in your stomach? The reason is that cells in the stomach lining produce a thick coating of mucus, which protects the stomach lining. Also, the cells that line the stomach are quickly replaced as they are damaged or worn out.

520 ◆

Differentiated Instruction

Less Proficient Readers   L1
Making a Table Have students draw a table with three columns: *Organ, Type of Digestion*, and *What Happens*. As they read this section and the next, have them complete the table. Model the first row for them: Organ—Mouth; Type of Digestion—Chemical and Mechanical; What Happens—Teeth cut, tear and grind food; tongue mixes food and helps in swallowing; enzymes in saliva break down carbohydrates. **learning modality: visual**

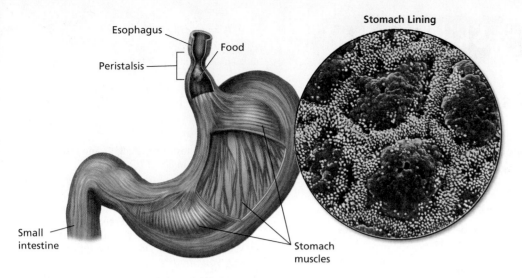

Esophagus

Food

Peristalsis

Stomach Lining

Small intestine

Stomach muscles

Food remains in the stomach until all of the solid material has been broken down into liquid form. A few hours after you finish eating, the stomach completes mechanical digestion of the food. By that time, most of the proteins have been chemically digested into shorter chains of amino acids. The food, now a thick liquid, is released into the next part of the digestive system. That is where final chemical digestion and absorption will take place.

 Reading Checkpoint What is pepsin?

FIGURE 15
The Stomach
The stomach has three layers of muscle that help to break down foods mechanically. The inset photo shows a microscopic view of the stomach lining. The yellow dots are mucus.
Relating Cause and Effect *What role does mucus play inside the stomach?*

Section 2 Assessment

Target Reading Skill Using Prior Knowledge Review your graphic organizer and revise it based on what you just learned in the section.

Reviewing Key Concepts
1. **a. Listing** What are the functions of the digestive system?
   b. Comparing and Contrasting Distinguish between mechanical and chemical digestion.
   c. Inferring Why must mechanical digestion start before chemical digestion?
2. **a. Reviewing** What key chemicals do the mouth and stomach contain?
   b. Describing How do pepsin and hydrochloric acid work together to digest food in the stomach?
   c. Predicting What could happen if your stomach didn't produce enough mucus? Explain.

Lab zone **At-Home Activity**

First Aid for Choking Explain to your family what happens when people choke on food. With your family, find out how to recognize when a person is choking and what to do to help the person. Learn about the Heimlich maneuver and how it is used to help someone who is choking.

Chapter 15 ◆ 521

Monitor Progress _____ L2

Answers
Figure 15 Mucus coats and protects the stomach lining.

Reading Checkpoint Pepsin is an enzyme that is part of the digestive juice. It breaks down protein into short chains of amino acids.

Assess

Reviewing Key Concepts
1. **a.** To break down food into molecules that can be used by the body, to absorb the food molecules into the blood, and to eliminate wastes from the body **b.** In mechanical digestion, foods are physically broken down into smaller pieces. In chemical digestion, chemicals produced by the body break foods into their smaller chemical building blocks. **c.** Mechanical digestion helps prepare food for chemical digestion by making smaller pieces that enzymes can act upon.
2. **a.** Mouth: an enzyme that breaks down starch; stomach: pepsin and hydrochloric acid **b.** HCl provides an acid environment, in which pepsin works best. **c.** The stomach lining would become irritated and might develop sores from the acid produced by the stomach.

Reteach L1
Use the illustrations in this section to review the parts and functions of the digestive system.

Performance Assessment L2
Skills Check Have students prepare flowcharts that show the process of digestion from the mouth through the stomach.

All in One Teaching Resources, Unit 3
- Section Summary: *The Digestive Process Begins*
- Review and Reinforce: *The Digestive Process Begins*
- Enrich: *The Digestive Process Begins*

Lab zone **Chapter Project**

Keep Students on Track Students will have completed three days of record keeping. Provide resources to help them create bar graphs to compare their food intake to the numbers of servings recommended in the Food Guide Pyramid. Ask them to analyze their graphs to identify changes they could make in their diets.

Lab zone **At-Home Activity**

First Aid for Choking L2 Suggest that students and their parents consult first-aid manuals or a health-care professional to learn the symptoms of choking and how to use the Heimlich maneuver. Encourage them to learn how to distinguish between situations in which the person can breathe and situations in which the Heimlich maneuver is required.

521

As the Stomach Churns

Prepare for Inquiry

Key Concept
In the stomach, proteins are digested by the chemicals in the digestive juices and by the mechanical processes as the stomach churns.

Skills Objectives
After this lab students will be able to
- interpret data and draw conclusions about the conditions needed for the digestion of proteins in the stomach
- control variables to test their predictions
- draw conclusions about the role of pepsin in protein digestion

 Prep Time 40 minutes
Class Time 40 minutes

Advance Planning
Obtain blue litmus paper and a 0.2% solution of hydrochloric acid. Boil eggs and cut whites into 1-cm cubes. Prepare enough eggs for students to have 3 cubes per test tube.

Safety

Make sure all students, teachers, and visitors wear goggles and aprons throughout the lab. Hydrochloric acid can cause burns. Review the safety guidelines in Appendix A.

All in One Teaching Resources, Unit 3
- Lab Worksheet: *As the Stomach Churns*

Guide Inquiry

Invitation
Ask students to name some foods that contain protein. (*Sample answers: meat, poultry, fish, dairy products, nuts, beans, and lentils*) Ask: **What role does protein play in nutrition?** (*It aids in tissue growth and repair.*) Ask: **Why is it important for the stomach to be acidic?** (*To create an environment in which pepsin can act*)

Lab zone Skills Lab

As the Stomach Churns

Problem
What conditions are needed for the digestion of proteins in the stomach?

Skills Focus
interpreting data, controlling variables, drawing conclusions

Materials
- test-tube rack
- pepsin
- water
- 4 strips blue litmus paper
- cubes of boiled egg white
- 10-mL plastic graduated cylinder
- 4 test tubes with stoppers
- marking pencil
- diluted hydrochloric acid
- plastic stirrers

Procedure

1. In this lab, you will investigate how acidic conditions affect protein digestion. Read over the entire lab to see what materials you will be testing. Write a prediction stating which conditions you think will speed up protein digestion. Then, copy the data table into your notebook.

2. Label four test tubes A, B, C, and D, and place them in a test-tube rack.

3. In this lab, the protein you will test is boiled egg white, which has been cut into cubes about 1 cm on each side. Add 3 cubes to each test tube. Note and record the size and overall appearance of the cubes in each test tube. **CAUTION:** *Do not put any egg white into your mouth.*

4. Use a graduated cylinder to add 10 mL of the enzyme pepsin to test tube A. Observe the egg white cubes to determine whether an immediate reaction takes place. Record your observations under Day 1 in your data table. If no changes occur, write "no immediate reaction."

5. Use a clean graduated cylinder to add 5 mL of pepsin to test tube B. Then rinse out the graduated cylinder and add 5 mL of water to test tube B. Observe whether or not an immediate reaction takes place.

6. Use a clean graduated cylinder to add 10 mL of hydrochloric acid to test tube C. Observe whether or not an immediate reaction takes place. **CAUTION:** *Hydrochloric acid can burn skin and clothing. Avoid direct contact with it. Wash any splashes or spills with plenty of water, and notify your teacher.*

Test Tube	Egg White Appearance		Litmus Color	
	Day 1	Day 2	Day 1	Day 2
A				
B				
C				
D				

Data Table

Introducing the Procedure
Review the litmus test procedure. Discuss ways to prevent cross-contamination of the test tubes by using a clean stirrer for each litmus test and by using clean graduated cylinders when adding fluids to a new test tube.

Troubleshooting the Experiment
Students' results may be unconvincing if the egg white cubes are too large or if the hydrochloric acid solution is too weak.

7. Use a clean graduated cylinder to add 5 mL of pepsin to test tube D. Then, rinse the graduated cylinder and add 5 mL of hydrochloric acid to test tube D. Observe whether or not an immediate reaction takes place. Record your observations.

8. Obtain four strips of blue litmus paper. (Blue litmus paper turns pink in the presence of an acid.) Dip a clean plastic stirrer into the solution in each test tube, and then touch the stirrer to a piece of litmus paper. Observe what happens to the litmus paper. Record your observations.

9. Insert stoppers in the four test tubes and store the test tube rack as directed by your teacher.

10. The next day, examine the contents of each test tube. Note any changes in the size and overall appearance of the egg white cubes. Then, test each solution with litmus paper. Record your observations in your data table.

Analyze and Conclude

1. **Interpreting Data** Which materials were the best at digesting the egg white? What observations enabled you to determine this?

2. **Inferring** Is the chemical digestion of protein in food a fast or a slow reaction? Explain.

3. **Controlling Variables** Why was it important that the cubes of egg white all be about the same size?

4. **Drawing Conclusions** What did this lab show about the ability of pepsin to digest protein?

5. **Communicating** Write a paragraph in which you describe the purpose of test tube A and test tube C as they relate to the steps you followed in the procedure.

Design an Experiment

Design a way to test whether protein digestion is affected by the size of the food pieces. Write down your hypothesis and the procedure you will follow. *Obtain your teacher's permission before carrying out your investigation.*

◆ 523

Extend Inquiry

Final Digestion and Absorption

Objectives

After completing this lesson, students will be able to

15.3.1 Describe the digestive processes that occur in the small intestine and how other digestive organs are involved

15.3.2 Explain the role of the large intestine in digestion

Target Reading Skill

Identifying Main Ideas Explain that identifying main ideas and details helps students sort the facts from the information into groups. Each group can have a main topic, subtopics, and details.

Answer

Main Idea: Chemical digestion takes place in the small intestine. **Details:** Food mixes with enzymes and secretions; starches, proteins, and fats are digested chemically. Enzymes and secretions are produced by the small intestine, liver, and pancreas.

All in One Teaching Resources, Unit 3

• Transparency LS152

Preteach

Build Background Knowledge [L2]

Breakdown of Foods

Ask students to recall the purpose of digestion. (*To change food into smaller nutrient molecules so that they can be absorbed into the blood and carried to cells throughout the body*) Ask: **What are some ways that food particles are broken down?** (*Chewed, mixed, dissolved in liquid, broken down chemically*)

Final Digestion and Absorption

Reading Preview

Key Concepts

• What digestive processes occur in the small intestine, and how are other digestive organs involved?

• What role does the large intestine play in digestion?

Key Terms

• small intestine • liver • bile
• gallbladder • pancreas
• villus • large intestine
• rectum • anus

Target Reading Skill

Identifying Main Ideas As you read the section titled The Small Intestine, write the main idea in a graphic organizer like the one below. Then, write three supporting details that further explain the main idea.

Main Idea

Chemical digestion takes place in the . . .

Detail	Detail	Detail

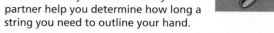

Discover Activity

Which Surface Is Larger?

1. Work with a partner to carry out this investigation.

2. Begin by placing your hand palm-side down on a table. Keep your thumb and fingers tightly together. Lay string along the outline of your hand. Have your partner help you determine how long a string you need to outline your hand.

3. Use a metric ruler to measure the length of that string.

Think It Over

Predicting How long would you expect your hand outline to be if you spread out your thumb and fingers? Use string to test your prediction. Compare the two string lengths.

Have you ever been part of a huge crowd attending a concert or sports event? Barriers and passageways often guide people in the right direction. Ticket takers make sure that people enter in an orderly fashion.

In some ways, the stomach can be thought of as the "ticket taker" of the digestive system. Once the food has been changed into a thick liquid, the stomach releases a little of the liquid at a time into the next part of the digestive system. This slow, smooth passage of food through the digestive system ensures that digestion and absorption can take place efficiently.

The Small Intestine

After the thick liquid leaves the stomach, it enters the small intestine. The **small intestine** is the part of the digestive system where most chemical digestion takes place. You may wonder how the small intestine got its name. After all, at about 6 meters—longer than some full-sized cars—it makes up two thirds of the length of the digestive system. The small intestine was named for its small diameter. It is from 2 to 3 centimeters wide, about half the diameter of the large intestine.

Discover Activity

Skills Focus Predicting

Materials 1 m string, metric ruler

Time 10 minutes

Tips Have students clearly mark the end of the string by holding it with their fingers and tying a knot or by marking it with a marker.

[L1]

Think It Over Students' predictions will vary. The length of string needed to outline the hand with outspread fingers should be about twice as long as the length needed to outline the hand when the fingers are held tightly together.

When food reaches the small intestine, it has already been mechanically digested into a thick liquid. But chemical digestion has just begun. Starches and proteins have been partially broken down, but fats haven't been digested at all. **Almost all chemical digestion and absorption of nutrients takes place in the small intestine.** As the liquid moves into the small intestine, it mixes with enzymes and secretions that are produced by the small intestine, the liver, and the pancreas. The liver and the pancreas deliver their substances to the small intestine through small tubes.

The Liver As you can see in Figure 16, the **liver** is located in the upper right portion of the abdomen. It is the largest organ inside the body. The liver is like an extremely busy chemical factory and plays a role in many body processes. For example, it breaks down medicines, and it helps eliminate nitrogen from the body. **The role of the liver in the digestive system is to produce bile.**

Bile is a substance that breaks up fat particles. Bile flows from the liver into the **gallbladder,** the organ that stores bile. After you eat, bile passes through a tube from the gallbladder into the small intestine.

Bile is not an enzyme. It does not chemically digest foods. It does, however, physically break up large fat particles into smaller fat droplets. You can compare the action of bile on fats with the action of soap on a greasy frying pan. Soap physically breaks up the grease into small droplets that can mix with the soapy water and be washed away. Bile mixes with the fats in food to form small fat droplets. The droplets can then be chemically broken down by enzymes produced in the pancreas.

FIGURE 16
The Liver and Pancreas
Substances produced by the liver and pancreas aid in digestion.
Predicting How would digestion be affected if the tube leading from the gallbladder to the small intestine became blocked?

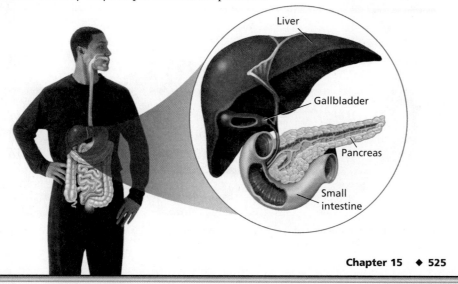

Liver

Gallbladder

Pancreas

Small intestine

Chapter 15 ◆ 525

525

Use Visuals: Figure 17 ▪L2▪

How Nutrients Are Absorbed

Focus Make sure students understand that each diagram in the series is a closer view of the part of the small intestine shown in the previous diagram.

Teach Ask: **What structures are inside the single villus in the diagram?** (*Blood vessels run through it.*) Ask: **How do nutrients from the small intestine get to the rest of the body?** (*They pass from the cells on the villi into blood vessels.*)

Apply Ask: **What types of molecules are being absorbed that were broken down from carbohydrates?** (*Glucose*) **From proteins?** (*Amino acids*) **learning modality: visual**

 **Teaching Resources, Unit 3**

• Transparency LS153

 **Build Inquiry** ▪L2▪

Interpreting Diagrams of the Digestive System

Focus After completing this section, call on students to name the digestive organs.

Teach Have pairs of students draw diagrams of the digestive system as shown in Figure 12 and include each organ's role, enzymes and secretions, and the nutrients each organ digests.

Apply Have pairs of students write five questions about the digestive system, and then quiz their partners, using their diagrams to answer the questions. **learning modality: visual**

Go Online
PHSchool.com

For: More on the digestive system
Visit: PHSchool.com
Web Code: ced-4024

Students can review the digestive system in an online activity.

526

Go Online
PHSchool.com

For: More on the digestive system
Visit: PHSchool.com
Web Code: ced-4024

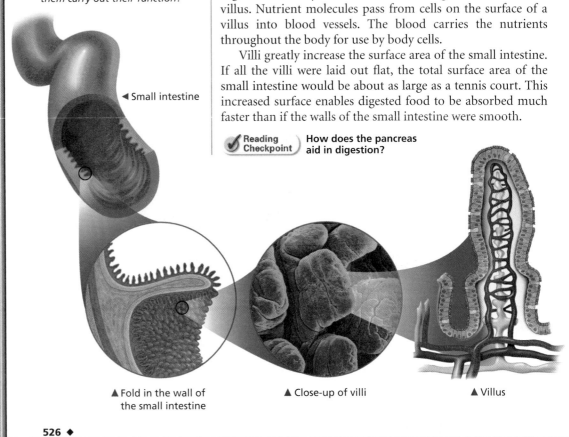

FIGURE 17
The Small Intestine
Tiny finger-shaped projections called villi line the inside of the small intestine. Blood vessels in the villi are covered by a single layer of cells.
Relating Cause and Effect *How does the structure of the villi help them carry out their function?*

◄ Small intestine

▲ Fold in the wall of the small intestine

▲ Close-up of villi

▲ Villus

526 ◆

The Pancreas The **pancreas** is a triangular organ that lies between the stomach and the first part of the small intestine. Like the liver, the pancreas plays a role in many body processes. **As part of the digestive system, the pancreas produces enzymes that flow into the small intestine and help break down starches, proteins, and fats.**

Digestive enzymes do not break down all food substances. Recall that the fiber in food isn't broken down. Instead, fiber thickens the liquid material in the intestine. This thickening makes it easier for peristalsis to push the material forward.

Absorption in the Small Intestine After chemical digestion takes place, the small nutrient molecules are ready to be absorbed by the body. The structure of the small intestine makes it well suited for absorption. The inner surface, or lining, of the small intestine looks bumpy. Millions of tiny finger-shaped structures called **villi** (VIL eye) (singular *villus*) cover the surface. The villi absorb nutrient molecules. Notice in Figure 17 that tiny blood vessels run through the center of each villus. Nutrient molecules pass from cells on the surface of a villus into blood vessels. The blood carries the nutrients throughout the body for use by body cells.

Villi greatly increase the surface area of the small intestine. If all the villi were laid out flat, the total surface area of the small intestine would be about as large as a tennis court. This increased surface enables digested food to be absorbed much faster than if the walls of the small intestine were smooth.

✓ **Reading Checkpoint** **How does the pancreas aid in digestion?**

Differentiated Instruction

Special Needs ▪L1▪
Visualizing Surface Area Give each student two pieces of blank paper of the same size. Ask them to make accordion folds in one of the pieces and place both pieces on a desk or table top. Explain that both pieces still have the same surface area. However, the folded piece takes up less surface area on the desk or table top. Have students describe how the folded paper models the villi in the small intestine. (*The villi allow for greater surface area, yet take up relatively little space in the body.*) If students have difficulty with this concept, ask them to smooth out the folded paper and place it against the flat paper. **learning modality: kinesthetic**

The Large Intestine

By the time material reaches the end of the small intestine, most nutrients have been absorbed. The remaining material moves from the small intestine into the large intestine. The **large intestine** is the last section of the digestive system. It is about 1.5 meters long—about as long as the average bathtub. It runs up the right-hand side of the abdomen, across the upper abdomen, and then down the left-hand side. The large intestine contains bacteria that feed on the material passing through. These bacteria normally do not cause disease. In fact, they are helpful because they make certain vitamins, including vitamin K.

The material entering the large intestine contains water and undigested food. **As the material moves through the large intestine, water is absorbed into the bloodstream. The remaining material is readied for elimination from the body.**

The large intestine ends in a short tube called the **rectum.** Here, waste material is compressed into a solid form. This waste material is eliminated from the body through the **anus,** a muscular opening at the end of the rectum.

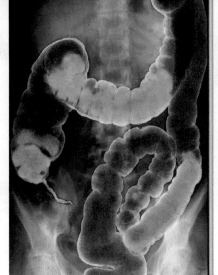

FIGURE 18
The Large Intestine
As material passes through the large intestine, most of the water is absorbed by the body. The remaining material will be eliminated from the body.

 Reading Checkpoint What role do bacteria play in the large intestine?

Section 3 Assessment

Target Reading Skill
Identifying Main Ideas Use your graphic organizer to help you answer Question 1 below.

Reviewing Key Concepts

1. **a. Reviewing** What two digestive processes occur in the small intestine?
   b. Explaining Explain how bile produced by the liver and enzymes produced in the pancreas function in the small intestine.
   c. Relating Cause and Effect Some people are allergic to a protein in wheat. When these people eat foods made with wheat, a reaction destroys the villi in the small intestine. What problems would you expect these people to experience?
2. **a. Identifying** Which key nutrient is absorbed in the large intestine?

   b. Describing What happens as food moves through the large intestine?
   c. Applying Concepts Diarrhea is a condition in which waste material that is eliminated contains too much water. How might diarrhea upset homeostasis in the body? How could a person reduce the effects of diarrhea on the body?

Writing in Science

Sequence of Events Describe the journey of a bacon, lettuce, and tomato sandwich through a person's digestive system, starting in the mouth and ending with absorption. Include where digestion of fats, carbohydrates, and proteins take place. Use words like *first, next,* and *finally* in your writing.

The Large Intestine

Teach Key Concepts L2
Role of the Large Intestine

Focus Ask: **Where does digestion take place?** (*Mouth, stomach, small intestine*)

Teach Ask: **What is the role of the large intestine?** (*To absorb water into the bloodstream and get remaining material ready for elimination*) **Do you think the large intestine contains muscles?** (*Yes; it moves material from the small intestine to the anus.*)

Apply Ask: **Why is fiber important?** (*It helps the large intestine move waste materials out of the body.*) **learning modality: logical/mathematical**

Monitor Progress ———— L2

Answers
Figure 17 Single layers of cells on the villi absorb nutrients that pass into blood vessels. The finger-like shape of the villi increases the surface area of the small intestine.

Reading Checkpoint The pancreas produces enzymes that help break down starches, proteins, and fats.

Reading Checkpoint Bacteria in the large intestine make certain vitamins, including vitamin K.

Assess

Reviewing Key Concepts

1. **a.** Chemical digestion and absorption
b. Bile breaks up fat particles. Enzymes from the pancreas help break down starches, proteins, and fats. **c.** Without villi to absorb nutrients, the person would not obtain sufficient nutrients.
2. **a.** Water **b.** Water is absorbed into the bloodstream, and the remaining material is readied for elimination from the body.
c. The person might lose too much water; by drinking more water.

Reteach L1
Have students tell the functions of the organs presented in this section.

All in One Teaching Resources, Unit 3
- Section Summary: *Final Digestion and Absorption*
- Review and Reinforce: *Final Digestion and Absorption*
- Enrich: *Final Digestion and Absorption*

Lab zone Chapter Project

Keep Students on Track Have students graph their food intake during the three days of eating a more healthful diet. Encourage them to develop plans for improving their diets that they can maintain on a long-term basis. Remind them not to make drastic changes.

Writing in Science

Writing Mode Description
Scoring Rubric
4 Includes full description of how food moves through the digestive system; account is logical and engaging
3 Includes all criteria but is not entertaining
2 Includes only some criteria
1 Includes partial or inaccurate summary

Study Guide

nteractive
Textbook

- Complete student edition
- Section and chapter self-assessments
- Assessment reports for teachers

Help Students Read L1

Building Vocabulary

Word/Part Analysis Ask students to look up the key terms *epiglottis, esophagus,* and *pancreas* in a dictionary and list the meanings of each word part. (*Epiglottis*: *epi* means "upon," and *glotta* means "tongue;" *Esophagus*: *eso* is derived from *oisein,* meaning "to carry," and *phagein* meaning "to eat;" *Pancreas*: *pan* means "all," and *kreas* means "flesh.")

Vocabulary Rating Chart Have students construct a chart with four columns labeled *Term, Can Define or Use It, Heard or Seen It,* and *Don't Know* to rate their knowledge of each term. If students did not check the *Can Define* or *Use It* column, have them re-read passages with those terms, then work with a partner to review the term.

Connecting Concepts

Concept Maps Help students develop one way to show how the information in this chapter is related. Foods can be classified by type of nutrient to help in planning a healthy diet. Foods must be broken down by the digestive system to be used by cells. Have students brainstorm to identify the Key Concepts, Key Terms, details, and examples and then write each one on a sticky note and attach it at random on chart paper or on the board.

Tell students that this concept map will be organized in hierarchical order and to begin at the top with the key concepts. Ask students these questions to guide them to categorize the information on the stickies: **What do the different types of nutrients do, and how are they classified in USDA MyPyramid food plans? How does food move through the digestive system, and what happens in each organ?**

Prompt students by using connecting words or phrases, such as "is used for," "is

broken down," and "contains," to indicate the basis for the organization of the map. The phrases should form a sentence between or among a set of concepts.

Answer Accept logical presentations by students.

All in One **Teaching Resources, Unit 3**

- Key Terms Review: *Food and Digestion*
- Connecting Concepts: *Food and Digestion*

① Food and Energy

Key Concepts

- Food provides the body with raw materials and energy.
- Carbohydrates provide energy as well as the raw materials to make cell parts.
- Fats provide energy and form part of the cell membrane. Fatty tissue protects and insulates the body.
- Proteins are needed for tissue growth and repair. They also play an important part in chemical reactions within cells.
- Vitamins and minerals are needed in small amounts to carry out chemical processes.
- Water is the most important nutrient because the body's vital processes take place in water.
- The USDA guidelines provide a personalized way to help people make healthy food choices based on their age, sex, and amount of physical activity.

Key Terms

nutrient
calorie
carbohydrate
glucose
fat
protein
amino acid
vitamin
mineral
Percent Daily Value
Dietary Reference Intakes (DRIs)

② The Digestive Process Begins

Key Concepts

- The digestive system breaks down food into molecules the body can use. Then, the molecules are absorbed into the blood and carried throughout the body. Finally, wastes are eliminated.
- Both mechanical and chemical digestion begin in the mouth.
- In the esophagus, contractions of smooth muscles push the food toward the stomach.
- Most mechanical digestion and some chemical digestion occur in the stomach.

Key Terms

digestion	esophagus
absorption	mucus
saliva	peristalsis
enzyme	stomach
epiglottis	

③ Final Digestion and Absorption

Key Concepts

- Almost all chemical digestion and absorption of nutrients takes place in the small intestine.
- The liver produces bile, which breaks up fats.
- The pancreas produces enzymes that help break down starches, proteins, and fats.
- In the large intestine, water is absorbed into the bloodstream. The remaining material is readied for elimination.

Key Terms

small intestine	villus
liver	large intestine
bile	rectum
gallbladder	anus
pancreas	

Review and Assessment

Go Online
PHSchool.com
For: Self-Assessment
Visit: PHSchool.com
Web Code: cha-3150

Organizing Information

Sequencing Copy the flowchart about digestion onto a separate sheet of paper. Then, complete it and add a title. (For more on Sequencing, see the Skills Handbook.)

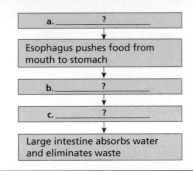

a. _____?_____

↓

Esophagus pushes food from mouth to stomach

↓

b. _____?_____

↓

c. _____?_____

↓

Large intestine absorbs water and eliminates waste

Reviewing Key Terms

Choose the letter of the best answer.

1. The building blocks of proteins are
   a. vitamins.
   b. minerals.
   c. amino acids.
   d. fats.

2. Which of the following groups of nutrients is a major source of energy for the body?
   a. proteins
   b. vitamins
   c. minerals
   d. carbohydrates

3. The enzyme in saliva chemically breaks down
   a. fats.
   b. proteins.
   c. glucose.
   d. starches.

4. Most mechanical digestion takes place in the
   a. liver.
   b. esophagus.
   c. stomach.
   d. small intestine.

5. Bile is produced by the
   a. liver.
   b. pancreas.
   c. small intestine.
   d. large intestine.

If the statement is true, write _true_. If it is false, change the underlined word or words to make the statement true.

6. Proteins that come from animal sources are <u>incomplete</u> proteins.

7. <u>Vitamins</u> are nutrients that are not made by living things.

8. To determine which of two cereals supplies more iron, check the <u>Percent Daily Value</u> on the food label.

9. <u>Absorption</u> moves food through the digestive system.

10. Most materials are absorbed into the bloodstream in the <u>large</u> intestine.

Writing in Science

Information Sheet You are a nutritionist assigned to work with a family trying to eat a more healthful diet. Write an instruction sheet outlining what kinds of foods they should eat. Provide some examples of each kind of food.

DISCOVERY CHANNEL SCHOOL

Food and Digestion
Video Preview
Video Field Trip
▶ Video Assessment

Chapter 15 ◆ 529

Review and Assessment

Organizing Information
a. In the mouth, the teeth break food into smaller pieces and saliva begins to break down starches.
b. In the stomach, food is churned and mixed with digestive juices that break down protein.
c. In the small intestine, almost all chemical digestion and absorption occurs.

Reviewing Key Terms
1. c **2.** d **3.** d **4.** c **5.** a
6. complete
7. Minerals
8. true
9. Peristalsis
10. small

Writing in Science

Writing Mode Exposition
Scoring Rubric
4 Advice is clearly stated and gives several facts from the chapter to support it.
3 Includes several facts but is not clearly stated
2 Includes few facts and is not clearly stated
1 Does not include facts to support the advice

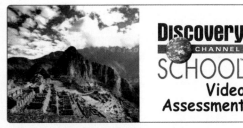

DISCOVERY CHANNEL SCHOOL Video Assessment

Food and Digestion

Show the Video Assessment to review chapter content and as a prompt for the writing assignment.

Go Online
PHSchool.com
For: Self-Assessment
Visit: PHSchool.com
Web Code: cha-3150

Students can take a practice test online that is automatically scored.

All in One Teaching Resources, Unit 3
- Transparency LS154
- Chapter Test
- Performance Assessment Teacher Notes
- Performance Assessment Student Worksheet
- Performance Assessment Scoring Rubric

💿 *ExamView® Computer Test Bank CD-ROM*

Checking Concepts

11. The more physical activity a person does, the higher his or her daily energy needs are.

12. Fiber helps keep the digestive system functioning properly.

13. The ingredients are listed in order by weight, starting with the main ingredient.

14. The epiglottis is located in the back of your mouth and seals off your windpipe when you swallow to prevent food from entering.

15. It pushes food and undigested material through the digestive system.

16. The pancreas produces enzymes that flow into the small intestine and help break down starches, proteins, and fats.

17. Villi absorb nutrient molecules. They cover the surface of the small intestine.

Review and Assessment

Checking Concepts

11. How does a person's level of physical activity affect his or her daily energy needs?

12. Why is fiber necessary in a person's diet?

13. In what order are the ingredients listed on a food label?

14. Describe the function of the epiglottis.

15. Explain the role of peristalsis.

16. What is the function of the pancreas in the digestive process?

17. What is the function of villi?

Thinking Critically

18. Applying Concepts Before winter, animals that hibernate often prepare by eating foods high in fat. How is this behavior helpful?

19. Predicting Suppose a medicine killed all the bacteria in your body. How might this affect vitamin production in your body?

20. Inferring Why is it important for people to chew their food thoroughly before swallowing?

21. Relating Cause and Effect How does the condition illustrated in the diagram below affect the esophagus?

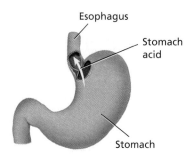

Esophagus

Stomach acid

Stomach

22. Comparing and Contrasting The digestive system is sometimes said to be "an assembly line in reverse." Identify some similarities and some differences between your digestive system and an assembly line.

Math Practice

23. Percentage Your aunt eats 250 Calories of protein and 1,800 Calories total for the day. Did she get enough protein on that particular day? Show your calculations.

Applying Skills

Use the table to answer Questions 24–27.

Comparing Nutrient Data

Food (1 cup)	Calcium (% Daily Value)	Calories	Calories From Fat
Chocolate milk	30	230	80
Low-fat milk	35	110	20
Plain yogurt	35	110	35

24. Classifying To which group in a food pyramid do the foods in the chart belong? How does the body benefit from calcium in the diet?

25. Interpreting Data How many cups of low-fat milk provide 100% of the day's Daily Value for calcium?

26. Calculating Which of the foods meet the recommendation that no more than 30 percent of a food's Calories come from fat? Explain.

27. Making Judgments Which of the foods would be the most healthful choice for an afterschool snack? Explain your reasoning.

Lab zone Chapter **Project**

Performance Assessment Write a summary of what you've learned from keeping a food log. How close were your eating patterns to those recommended in your USDA MyPyramid Plan? How successful were you in making changes in your diet to match the MyPyramid Plan?

Lab zone Chapter **Project** L3

Performance Assessment Summaries should document how students' analyses of their eating habits led to changes and describe the changes that students implemented. This project may involve sensitive issues for some students. Assure them that their summaries will be held in confidence.

Reflect and Record Have students write achievable plans for maintaining healthy eating habits, including strategies for dealing with unhealthful habits. Remind students to focus on the overall diet rather than on individual foods. Every meal or snack does not have to meet the guidelines if the overall diet is healthful.

Standardized Test Prep

Choose the letter of the best answer.

1. Which of the following parts of the digestive system is *best* paired with its function?
  A esophagus—digests carbohydrates
  B stomach—digests fats
  C small intestine—absorbs water
  D liver—produces bile

2. A food label on a cereal box gives you the following information: a serving size equals one cup and there are 110 Calories per serving. You measure the amount of cereal you plan to eat and find that it measures 1 1/2 cups. How many Calories will you consume?
  F 110 Calories
  G 165 Calories
  H 220 Calories
  J 1,100 Calories

Use the table below and your knowledge of science to answer Questions 3 and 4.

Length of Time Food Stays in Organ	
Organ	**Time**
Mouth	Less than 1 minute
Esophagus	Less than 1 minute
Stomach	1–3 hours
Small Intestine	1–6 hours
Large Intestine	12–36 hours

3. If a meal is eaten at noon, what is happening to the food at 1 P.M.?
  A Saliva is breaking down starch into sugar.
  B Proteins are being digested into short chains of amino acids.
  C Fats are being digested.
  D Digested food is being absorbed into the blood.

4. For food eaten at noon, absorption cannot have begun by
  F 1 P.M.
  G 7 P.M.
  H 9 P.M.
  J noon the next day.

5. Which of the following organs is *not* just a digestive organ?
  A stomach
  B liver
  C small intestine
  D large intestine

Constructed Response

6. Compare the processes of mechanical and chemical digestion. How are they similar? How are they different? In what parts of the digestive system do the two processes take place? How do the processes occur?

Thinking Critically

18. Fats provide more than twice the energy of carbohydrates or proteins. The fat will be stored as an energy source to be used when the animal is hibernating and not taking in food as energy.

19. Bacteria in the large intestine produce vitamin K. If they were killed by the medicine, vitamin K would no longer be produced.

20. Chewing thoroughly breaks food into smaller particles, making it easier for chemical digestion to occur. It also reduces the risk of choking.

21. Because acid can burn human tissue, stomach acid can burn the esophagus. The diagram shows stomach acid passing into the esophagus. The condition, called heartburn, produces a burning pain in the esophagus behind the lower breastbone, which is close to the heart; this is how it got the name.

22. Similarity: Both an assembly line and the digestive system perform specific jobs in a sequence of steps. Difference: In an assembly line, something is constructed from many small parts in many steps; in digestion, the process is reversed— something is broken down into smaller parts step by step.

Math Practice

23. 250 Calories/1,800 Calories=13.8%; since about 10 to 35 percent of a person's daily intake should come from proteins, your aunt did get enough protein for that day.

Applying Skills

24. Milk group; calcium helps build bones and teeth, aids in blood clotting, and is involved in nerve and muscle function

25. About three cups

26. Low-fat milk: $20 \div 110 \times 100\% \div 1 = 18\%$. The other foods get 32% (yogurt) and 35% (chocolate milk) of their Calories from fat.

27. Sample: The low-fat milk because it gives 35% of the daily value of calcium while providing the lowest percentage of Calories from fat.

Standardized Test Prep

1. D **2.** G **3.** B **4.** F **5.** B
6. Mechanical digestion causes a physical change as the pieces of food are broken down into smaller pieces. In chemical digestion, foods are broken down chemically into their smaller building blocks with the help of enzymes. The processes are similar in that they break down food into smaller pieces or components. The processes are different in that mechanical digestion does not involve chemical reactions that use enzymes. Mechanical digestion occurs in the mouth and stomach. Chemical digestion occurs in the mouth, stomach, and small intestine.

Chapter at a Glance

 Chapter Project *Travels of a Red Blood Cell*

All in One Teaching Resources, Unit 3
- Chapter Project Teacher Notes, pp. 148–149
- Chapter Project Student Overview, pp. 150–151
- Chapter Project Student Worksheets, pp. 152–153
- Chapter Project Scoring Rubric, p. 154

Technology

Video Preview

Local Standards

 The Body's Transport System

3 periods
1 1/2 blocks

16.1.1 Explain the functions of the cardiovascular system.
16.1.2 Describe the function and structure of the heart.
16.1.3 Sequence the path taken by blood through the cardiovascular system.
16.1.4 Describe the functions and structures of arteries, capillaries, and veins.

 Go Online active art
 Video Field Trip
 Go Online PHSchool.com

 Blood and Lymph

1 period
1/2 block

16.2.1 Describe the components of blood.
16.2.2 Explain what determines the type of blood that a person can receive in a transfusion.
16.2.3 Name the structures and functions of the lymphatic system.

 Go Online SciLINKS NSTA

 Cardiovascular Health

2 periods
1 block

16.3.1 Identify some diseases of the cardiovascular system.
16.3.2 Describe behaviors that can help maintain cardiovascular health.

 Go Online SciLINKS NSTA

Review and Assessment

All in One Teaching Resources, Unit 3
- Key Terms Review, p. 182
- Transparency LS163
- Performance Assessment Teacher Notes, p. 189
- Performance Assessment Scoring Rubric, p. 190
- Performance Assessment Student Worksheet, p. 191
- Chapter Test, pp. 192–195

 Go Online PHSchool.com
 Video Assessment

Test Preparation

Test Preparation Blackline Masters

Lab zone Chapter Activities Planner

For more activities
LAB ZONE Easy Planner CD-ROM

Student Edition	Inquiry	Time	Materials	Skills	Resources
Chapter Project, p. 533	Open-ended	2 to 3 weeks	**All in One Teaching Resources, Unit 3**, p. 148	Describing, making models, communicating	**Lab zone Easy Planner** **All in One Teaching Resources, Unit 3**, Support pp. 148–149
Section 1					
Discover Activity, p. 534	Guided	20 minutes	Newspapers, paper towels, two large plastic containers, cup with capacity of about 60 mL, watch or clock with a second hand, water	Inferring	**Lab zone Easy Planner**
Skills Activity, p. 538	Guided	15 minutes	Paper and pencil	Creating data tables	**Lab zone Easy Planner**
Skills Lab, p. 544	Directed	40 minutes	Watch with second hand or heart rate monitor, graph paper	Graphing, interpreting data, drawing conclusions	**Lab zone Easy Planner** **Lab Activity Video** **All in One Teaching Resources, Unit 3**, Skills Lab: *Heart Beat, Health Beat*, pp. 164–165
Section 2					
Discover Activity, p. 545	Open-ended	15 minutes	Microscope, prepared slides of human blood	Observing	**Lab zone Easy Planner**
Try This Activity, p. 548	Directed	15 minutes	2 plastic cups, 20-cm-square piece of cheesecloth, rubber band, water, paper clips, coins, newspapers, paper towels	Making models	**Lab zone Easy Planner**
Section 3					
Discover Activity, p. 552	Open-ended	20 minutes	Assortment of foods	Forming operational definitions	**Lab zone Easy Planner**
Try This Activity, p. 553	Directed	20 minutes	Plastic funnel, plastic jar, graduated cylinder, stopwatch or clock, paste, plastic knife, toothpick, newspaper, paper towels	Predicting	**Lab zone Easy Planner**
Skills Lab, p. 557	Directed	Prep: 15 minutes Class: 40 minutes	4 paper cups, 4 plastic droppers, 8 plastic petri dishes, white paper, marking pen, toothpicks, four model "blood" types	Interpreting data, drawing conclusions	**Lab zone Easy Planner** **Lab Activity Video** **All in One Teaching Resources, Unit 3**, Skills Lab: *Do You Know Your A-B-O's?*, pp. 180–181

Section 1 The Body's Transport System

3 periods, 1 1/2 blocks

Objectives

16.1.1 Explain the functions of the cardiovascular system.

16.1.2 Describe the function and structure of the heart.

16.1.3 Sequence the path taken by blood through the cardiovascular system.

16.1.4 Describe the functions and structures of arteries, capillaries, and veins.

Local Standards

Key Terms

• cardiovascular system • heart • atrium • pacemaker • ventricle • valve
• artery • capillary • vein • aorta

Preteach

Build Background Knowledge

Students compare a vehicle transportation system to the body's cardiovascular system.

 **Discover Activity** *How Hard Does Your Heart Work?* L1

Targeted Print and Technology Resources

 **Teaching Resources, Unit 3**

L2 Reading Strategy Transparency LS155: Sequencing

○ **PresentationEXPRESS™ CD-ROM**

Instruct

The Cardiovascular System Lead students in a discussion of the functions of the cardiovascular system.

The Heart Use a diagram to examine the anatomy of the heart and relate its structure to its functions.

Two Loops Analyze how the two-looped path of blood in the circulatory system relates to blood oxygen content in different parts of the body.

Arteries Sketch and describe a cross-section drawing of an artery.

Capillaries Relate the structure of capillary walls to their function.

Veins Discuss the factors that help blood move through the veins and how exercise affects blood flow.

Blood Pressure Identify what causes blood pressure and relate this to how blood pressure is measured.

 Skills Lab *Heart Beat, Health Beat* L2

Targeted Print and Technology Resources

 Teaching Resources, Unit 3

L2 Guided Reading, pp. 157–161

L2 Transparencies LS156, LS157, LS158, LS159

L3 Skills Lab: *Heart Beat, Health Beat,* pp. 164–165

■ **Lab Activity Video/DVD**
Skills Lab: *Heart Beat, Health Beat*

PHSchool.com Web Code: cep-4031
PHSchool.com Web Code: ced-4032

SCHOOL
Video Field Trip

○ **Student Edition on Audio CD**

Assess

Section Assessment Questions

Have students use their completed cycle diagrams to help them answer the questions.

Reteach

Students summarize the structures and functions of the three types of blood vessels.

Targeted Print and Technology Resources

Teaching Resources, Unit 3

• Section Summary, p. 156

L1 Review and Reinforce, p. 162

L3 Enrich, p. 163

Section 2 Blood and Lymph

1 period, 1/2 block

ABILITY LEVELS
L1 Basic to Average
L2 For All Students
L3 Average to Advanced

Objectives

16.2.1 Describe the components of blood.

16.2.2 Explain what determines the type of blood that a person can receive in a transfusion.

16.2.3 Name the structures and functions of the lymphatic system.

Key Terms

• plasma • red blood cell • hemoglobin • white blood cell • platelet
• lymphatic system • lymph • lymph node

Local Standards

Preteach

Build Background Knowledge

Students name the components of blood with which they are familiar.

 **Discover Activity** *What Kinds of Cells Are in Blood?* **L1**

Targeted Print and Technology Resources

 Teaching Resources, Unit 3

L2 Reading Strategy Transparency LS160: Identifying Main Ideas

⊙ **PresentationEXPRESS™ CD-ROM**

Instruct

Blood Discuss the functions of the different types of blood cells.

Blood Types Evaluate the appropriate blood type combinations for transfusions.

The Lymphatic System Introduce the structures and functions of the lymphatic system and relate them to the circulatory system.

Targeted Print and Technology Resources

 Teaching Resources, Unit 3

L2 Guided Reading, pp. 168–170
L2 Transparency LS161
www.SciLinks.org Web Code: scn-0433

⊙ **Student Edition on Audio CD**

Assess

Section Assessment Questions

⤺ Have students use their Identifying Main Ideas graphic organizers to answer the questions.

Reteach

Students work in pairs to describe characteristics of blood components.

Targeted Print and Technology Resources

Teaching Resources, Unit 3

• Section Summary, p. 167
L1 Review and Reinforce, p. 171
L3 Enrich, p. 172

Section 3 Cardiovascular Health

⏱️ *2 periods, 1 block*

ABILITY LEVELS
- **L1** Basic to Average
- **L2** For All Students
- **L3** Average to Advanced

Objectives

16.3.1 Identify some diseases of the cardiovascular system.

16.3.2 Describe behaviors that can help maintain cardiovascular health.

Local Standards

Key Terms

- atherosclerosis • heart attack • hypertension

Preteach

Build Background Knowledge

Students discuss factors that make a person at higher risk for a heart attack.

 **Discover Activity** *Which Foods Are "Heart Healthy"?* **L2**

Targeted Print and Technology Resources

 Teaching Resources, Unit 3

L2 Reading Strategy Transparency
LS162: Asking Questions

🔘 **PresentationEXPRESS™ CD-ROM**

Instruct

Cardiovascular Diseases Compare healthy arteries with diseased arteries and discuss how atherosclerosis affects the heart.

Keeping Healthy Identify health behaviors that help prevent cardiovascular disease.

 Skills Lab *Do You Know Your A-B-O's?* **L2**

Targeted Print and Technology Resources

 Teaching Resources, Unit 3

L2 Guided Reading, pp. 175–177
L2 Skills Lab: *Do You Know Your A-B-O's?*, pp. 180–181

📼 **Lab Activity Video/DVD**
Skills Lab: *Do You Know Your A-B-O's?*

www.SciLinks.org Web Code: scn-0434

🔘 **Student Edition on Audio CD**

Assess

Section Assessment Questions

🎯 Have students use their completed graphic organizers to answer the questions.

Reteach

Students make a table on the causes and prevention of cardiovascular disease.

Targeted Print and Technology Resources

 Teaching Resources, Unit 3

- Section Summary, p. 174
- **L1** Review and Reinforce, p. 178
- **L3** Enrich, p. 179

Go Online

NSTA–PD*i*LINKS

For: Professional development support
Visit: www.SciLinks.org/PDLinks
Web Code: scf-0430

Professional Development ★

Section 1 **The Body's Transport System**

Transport of Carbon Dioxide   Some of the carbon dioxide produced by cells dissolves directly into the bloodstream and some is bound to hemoglobin. However, most of the carbon dioxide carried by the blood is first converted to carbonic acid by carbonic anhydrase, an enzyme found in red blood cells. The carbonic acid readily dissolves in blood, which contains substances that act as buffers and prevent the blood from becoming dangerously acidic. In the lungs, the carbonic acid is converted back into carbon dioxide, which diffuses across the capillary walls into air in the lungs.

Address Misconceptions

Some students may think that some blood is actually blue. Although illustrations of the circulatory system often show oxygen-poor blood as blue, it is in fact dark red. For a strategy for helping students understand the actual colors of blood, see **Address Misconceptions** *in the section* The Body's Transport System.

Section 2 **Blood and Lymph**

The Lymphatic System   The lymphatic system has three major functions: to maintain the blood's fluid balance, to help fight disease, and to absorb fats from digested food in the small intestine and transport them to the bloodstream.

Blood loses about 1% of its liquid volume to cells and interstitial fluid when traveling through the capillaries. The lost fluid eventually ends up in the lymphatic system. The fluid, now called lymph, is filtered through lymph nodes, which contain a multitude of white blood cells called lymphocytes. These white blood cells fight bacteria and viruses filtered by the lymph nodes during an infection.

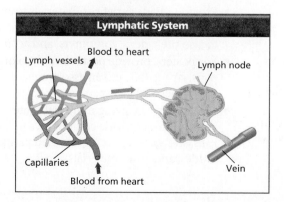

Lymphatic System

Lymph vessels
Blood to heart
Lymph node
Capillaries
Vein
Blood from heart

Section 3 **Cardiovascular Health**

Arteriosclerosis and Atherosclerosis

Arteriosclerosis is the medical term for hardening of the arteries. As people age, many experience calcium deposits in the walls of their arteries. The calcium causes the arteries to become narrow and stiff, restricting the flow of blood and causing pain in their limbs and organs.

Arteries can develop plaques, or buildups of lipids, such as cholesterol, on their walls. The plaques (also called atheromas) can become hard due to calcium deposits, causing a condition called atherosclerosis. Atherosclerosis is dangerous because it can cause complete blockage of arteries that service major organs, such as the heart. When the heart muscle does not receive enough oxygen, the muscle cells die, causing a condition known as a myocardial infarction, or heart attack.

Factors that contribute to the buildup of plaques on artery walls are a high-cholesterol diet, lack of exercise, obesity, high blood pressure, smoking, stress, diabetes, gender, genetics, and age. Treatment can involve lifestyle changes to reduce risk factors; medicines that reduce cholesterol, thin the blood, and/or dilate the veins; and surgery that removes deposits or opens up arteries.

Help Students Read

Summarize

Briefly Stating the Main Ideas

Strategy   Help students understand a topic by restating the main ideas. Students read a section of the text and then identify main ideas and supporting details. They summarize what they have read by briefly restating the main concepts in a sentence or two.

Example

1. Ask students to carefully read the selected passage. Then have them review the passage and identify the main ideas. Demonstrate this process by using the bold headings, key concept statements, and Key Terms as aids in determining what the passage is mostly about. List the main ideas on the board.
2. Direct students to write brief summaries of the passage by restating each of the main ideas in one or two sentences, using their own words. Remind students to focus on the most important concepts, omitting details and examples.
3. Assign the next passage for students to read and summarize. You may want to have students work in small groups to compare summaries.

Interactive Textbook
- Complete student edition
- Video and audio
- Simulations and activities
- Section and chapter activities

Chapter 16

Circulation

Interactive Textbook

Blood cells travel in blood vessels to all parts of the body. ▶

532 ◆

Chapter Project L3

Objectives
Students will design a display that shows what happens as blood moves through the body. After this Chapter Project, students will be able to
- describe the two main circuits in the circulatory system of the human body
- make a model in the form of visual displays showing the two circuits traveled by red blood cells
- communicate information concerning the function of the two circuits

Skills Focus
Describing, making models, communicating

Project Time Line 2 to 3 weeks

All in One Teaching Resources, Unit 3
- Chapter Project Teacher Notes
- Chapter Project Overview
- Chapter Project Worksheet 1
- Chapter Project Worksheet 2
- Chapter Project Scoring Rubric

Developing a Plan
On the first day, class time should be allowed for students to exchange ideas on ways to create visual displays. On the second day, have students work on ideas for their own displays and talk with you about their plans. Have students present detailed sketches of their plans to you during the next few days. When you have approved their plans, students will spend eight to ten days building their displays. Allow one or two class periods at the end of the project for students to present their displays.

Possible Materials
- Provide a wide variety of materials from which students can choose. Encourage them to also use videos, computers, and art media.
- For posters, provide poster board, colored pens, string, foil, and an assortment of magazines and newspapers.
- For displays involving more elaborate construction, provide cardboard, cardboard rolls, straws, scrap wood, assorted plastic bottles, and other materials.

Discovery CHANNEL **SCHOOL**™

Circulation
▶ Video Preview
Video Field Trip
Video Assessment

Lab zone™ Chapter **Project**

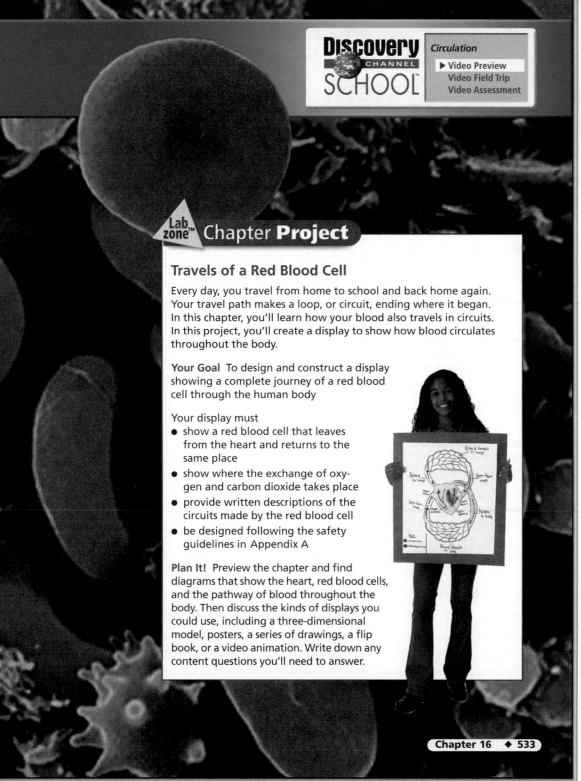

Travels of a Red Blood Cell

Every day, you travel from home to school and back home again. Your travel path makes a loop, or circuit, ending where it began. In this chapter, you'll learn how your blood also travels in circuits. In this project, you'll create a display to show how blood circulates throughout the body.

Your Goal To design and construct a display showing a complete journey of a red blood cell through the human body

Your display must
- show a red blood cell that leaves from the heart and returns to the same place
- show where the exchange of oxygen and carbon dioxide takes place
- provide written descriptions of the circuits made by the red blood cell
- be designed following the safety guidelines in Appendix A

Plan It! Preview the chapter and find diagrams that show the heart, red blood cells, and the pathway of blood throughout the body. Then discuss the kinds of displays you could use, including a three-dimensional model, posters, a series of drawings, a flip book, or a video animation. Write down any content questions you'll need to answer.

Chapter 16 ◆ 533

Launching the Project

Compare blood circulation to a rural mail route. Each morning a mail carrier goes to the post office and picks up the mail, much as blood picks up oxygen in the lungs. The carrier then drives to where the customers live and delivers the mail, as oxygen is delivered to cells. The carrier picks up mail from the customer and returns to the post office, as carbon dioxide is picked up by the blood to be returned to the lungs.

Ask: **What words describe the path that blood travels?** (Sample answers: Circuit and loop) Help students modify overly ambitious or expensive plans; approve creative ideas that can be completed within the time period and with the resources available.

Discovery CHANNEL **SCHOOL**™

Video Preview

Circulation

Show the Video Preview to introduce the Chapter Project and present an overview of the chapter content. Discussion question: **What is one negative effect of eating a diet high in fat?** (The fat and cholesterol can cling to the walls of blood vessels and form plaque, which over time can block the flow of blood.)

Performance Assessment

The Chapter Project Scoring Rubric will help you evaluate how well students complete the Chapter Project. You may want to share the scoring rubric with your students so they are clear about what will be expected of them. Students will be assessed on

- the thoroughness of their research on the circulatory system and their plans for creating the display
- the accuracy and creativity of their display and whether it was completed on time
- the thoroughness and organization of their presentation to the rest of the class
- how well students work with others and participate in class discussions

Portfolio

Objectives

After this lesson, students will be able to

16.1.1 Explain the functions of the cardiovascular system.

16.1.2 Describe the function and structure of the heart.

16.1.3 Sequence the path taken by blood through the cardiovascular system.

16.1.4 Describe the functions and structures of arteries, capillaries, and veins.

Target Reading Skill

Sequencing Explain that organizing information from beginning to end helps students understand a step-by-step process.

Answers

Bottom oval: Left side of heart; left oval: Body

All in One Teaching Resources, Unit 3

• Transparency LS155

Preteach

Build Background Knowledge L1

Transportation Systems

Display a map of a subway, bus, train, or local highway system. Ask: **What is the function of this transportation system?** (*To pick up and deliver passengers at various points along a route*) Tell students that the cardiovascular system transports blood and other materials through the body in the same way. They will learn how in this chapter.

Section

1 The Body's Transport System

Reading Preview

Key Concepts

• What are the functions of the cardiovascular system?

• What is the function and structure of the heart?

• What path does blood take through the cardiovascular system?

• What are the functions and structures of arteries, capillaries, and veins?

Key Terms

• cardiovascular system • heart
• atrium • pacemaker
• ventricle • valve • artery
• capillary • vein • aorta
• coronary artery • pulse
• diffusion • blood pressure

Target Reading Skill

Sequencing As you read, make a cycle diagram like the one below that shows the path that blood follows as it circulates throughout the body. Write each step of the pathway in a separate circle.

Pathway of Blood

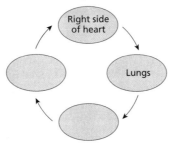

Right side of heart → Lungs

Lab zone Discover **Activity**

How Hard Does Your Heart Work?

1. Every minute, your heart beats about 75 to 85 times. With each beat, it pumps about 60 milliliters of blood. Can you work as hard and fast as your heart does?

2. Cover a table or desk with newspapers. Place two large plastic containers side by side on the newspapers. Fill one with 2.5 liters of water, which is about the volume of blood that your heart pumps in 30 seconds. Leave the other container empty.

3. With a plastic cup that holds about 60 milliliters, transfer water as quickly as possible into the empty container, trying not to spill any. **CAUTION:** *Wipe up spills on the floor immediately.* Have a partner time you for 30 seconds. As you work, count how many transfers you make in 30 seconds.

4. Multiply your results by 2 to find the number of transfers in 1 minute.

Think It Over

Inferring Compare your performance with the number of times your heart beats every minute. What do your results tell you about the strength and speed of a heartbeat?

Late at night, a truck rolls through the darkness. Loaded with fresh fruits and vegetables, the truck is headed for a city supermarket. The driver steers off the interstate and onto a smaller highway. Finally, after driving through narrow city streets, the truck reaches its destination. As dawn breaks, store workers unload the cargo. At the same time, a garbage truck removes yesterday's trash and drives off down the road.

The Cardiovascular System

Like the roads that link all parts of the country, your body has a "highway" network, called the cardiovascular system, that links all parts of your body. The **cardiovascular system,** also called the circulatory system, consists of the heart, blood vessels, and blood. **The cardiovascular system carries needed substances to cells and carries waste products away from cells. In addition, blood contains cells that fight disease.**

Lab zone Discover **Activity**

Skills Focus Inferring L1

Materials newspapers, paper towels, two large plastic containers, cup with capacity of about 60 mL, watch or clock with a second hand, water

Time 20 minutes

Tips Set up with newspapers, towels, or other materials for quick cleanup. Put large plastic containers in a larger container to catch spills. Advise students to wear aprons. Consider doing this activity outdoors.

Expected Outcome Results will vary. Students probably cannot make 75 transfers of water.

Think It Over The heart is very strong to be able to pump continuously and at the speed it does.

Delivering Needed Materials Most substances that need to get from one part of the body to another are carried by blood. For example, blood carries oxygen from your lungs to your other body cells. Blood also transports the glucose your cells use to produce energy.

Removing Waste Products The cardiovascular system picks up wastes from cells. For example, when cells break down glucose, they produce carbon dioxide as a waste product. The carbon dioxide passes from the cells into the blood. The cardiovascular system then carries carbon dioxide to the lungs, where it is exhaled.

Fighting Disease The cardiovascular system also transports cells that attack disease-causing microorganisms. This process can help keep you from becoming sick. If you do get sick, these disease-fighting blood cells will kill the microorganisms and help you get well.

✓ **Reading Checkpoint** How does the cardiovascular system help fight disease?

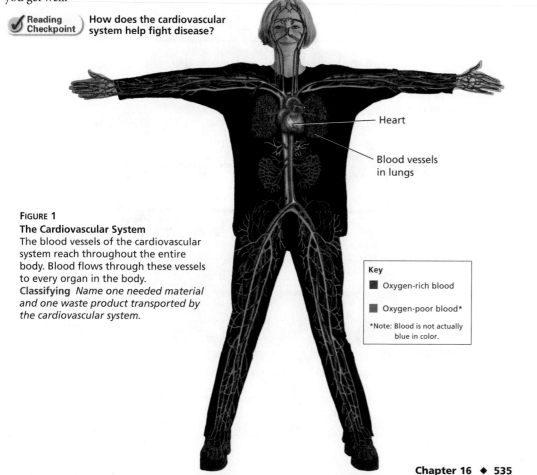

Heart

Blood vessels in lungs

FIGURE 1
The Cardiovascular System
The blood vessels of the cardiovascular system reach throughout the entire body. Blood flows through these vessels to every organ in the body.
Classifying *Name one needed material and one waste product transported by the cardiovascular system.*

Key
■ Oxygen-rich blood
■ Oxygen-poor blood*
*Note: Blood is not actually blue in color.

The Cardiovascular System

Help Students Read 　 L1
Previewing Visuals Before students read, have them look at the images in this section and predict what they are about to read. The arrows in the visuals might suggest that they will be learning about pathways and the direction of blood flow in the body.

Teach Key Concepts 　 L2
System Functions

Focus Remind students that the cardiovascular system removes as well as delivers materials.

Teach Ask: **What are some materials that the cardiovascular system delivers throughout the body?** *(Oxygen and glucose)* **How does the cardiovascular system get rid of carbon dioxide?** *(Carbon dioxide is passed from cells into the blood, and then carried to the lungs, where it is exhaled.)* Refer students to Figure 1. Ask: **Why do you think the lungs have a dense network of blood vessels?** *(The lungs are the only place where the exchange of gases between the body and the environment occurs, so many blood vessels must be in the lungs to do this work quickly and efficiently.)*

Apply Display two 2-liter bottles and one 1-liter bottle, or an equivalent capacity in other containers. Tell students that an adult of average size has 5 liters of blood circulating at any one time—an amount that would fill the containers. **learning modality: visual**

 **Teaching Resources, Unit 3**
• Transparency LS156

Independent Practice 　 L2
 **Teaching Resources, Unit 3**
• Guided Reading and Study Worksheet: *The Body's Transport System*

◉ **Student Edition on Audio CD**

Monitor Progress _____ L2
Answers
Figure 1 Needed materials: oxygen and glucose; waste product: carbon dioxide

 Reading Checkpoint It transports cells that attack disease-causing microorganisms.

The Heart

Go Online
active art

For: The Heart Activity
Visit: PHSchool.com
Web Code: cep-4031

Students learn the parts of the heart and see the flow of blood through the heart.

Teach Key Concepts **L2**

The Heart

Focus Refer students to Figures 2 and 3.

Teach Ask volunteers to read the descriptions of the parts of the heart in Figure 2. Explain that the human heart has four chambers. Ask: **What are the four chambers of the heart?** (*Right atrium, right ventricle, left atrium, left ventricle*) Ask: **Which chambers contain oxygen-rich blood?** (*The left atrium and left ventricle*) Explain that the valves separate the chambers from each other and from other parts of the body. Valves are located between the left atrium and the left ventricle, the right atrium and the right ventricle, and the right ventricle and the artery to the lungs. Have students look at Figure 3. Then ask: **Where in Figure 2 is this valve shown?** (*Between the right ventricle and the artery to the lungs*) Show the transparency of Figure 2 and have individual students state each step in the flow of blood through the heart while you trace it with a pencil eraser or other object.

Apply Point out that the walls of the ventricles are much thicker than the walls of the atria. Ask: **How could having thick walls benefit the ventricles?** (*Thick walls give ventricles the muscular strength to pump blood out of the heart.*)

Extend The Active Art will show students how the heart pumps. **learning modality: visual**

All in One Teaching Resources, Unit 3

• Transparency LS157

The Heart

Without the heart, blood wouldn't go anywhere. The **heart** is a hollow, muscular organ that pumps blood throughout the body. **Each time the heart beats, it pushes blood through the blood vessels of the cardiovascular system.**

Your heart, shown in Figure 2, is about the size of your fist. It is located in the center of your chest. The heart lies behind the sternum (breastbone) and inside the rib cage. It is made of cardiac muscle, which can contract over and over without getting tired.

Go Online
active art

For: The Heart activity
Visit: PHSchool.com
Web Code: cep-4031

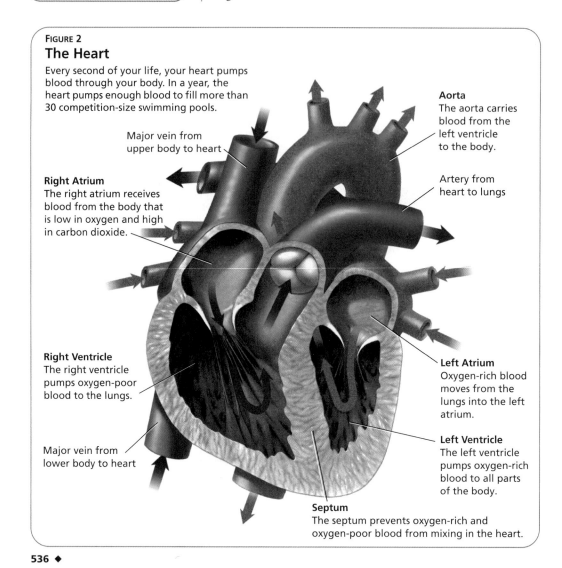

FIGURE 2
The Heart
Every second of your life, your heart pumps blood through your body. In a year, the heart pumps enough blood to fill more than 30 competition-size swimming pools.

Major vein from upper body to heart

Aorta
The aorta carries blood from the left ventricle to the body.

Right Atrium
The right atrium receives blood from the body that is low in oxygen and high in carbon dioxide.

Artery from heart to lungs

Right Ventricle
The right ventricle pumps oxygen-poor blood to the lungs.

Left Atrium
Oxygen-rich blood moves from the lungs into the left atrium.

Left Ventricle
The left ventricle pumps oxygen-rich blood to all parts of the body.

Major vein from lower body to heart

Septum
The septum prevents oxygen-rich and oxygen-poor blood from mixing in the heart.

536 ◆

Differentiated Instruction

English Learners/Beginning **L1**
Vocabulary: Link to Visual Refer students to Figure 2, and point out the parts of the heart as you read the captions. Make sure students understand that *right* and *left* are correct, and that the diagram is positioned as if looking at another person. Distribute an unlabeled diagram and have students label and color in the right and left atria and ventricles. **learning modality: visual**

English Learners/Intermediate **L2**
Vocabulary: Link to Visual Have students do the beginning-level activity. Then pair students with English-proficient students to write four sentences describing the functions of the right and left atria and ventricles in their own words. **learning modality: verbal**

The Heart's Structure The heart has a right side and a left side. **The right side of the heart is completely separated from the left side by a wall of tissue called the septum. Each side has two compartments, or chambers—an upper chamber and a lower chamber.** Each of the two upper chambers, called an **atrium** (AY tree um) (plural *atria*), receives blood that comes into the heart. Located in the right atrium is a group of heart cells called the **pacemaker,** which sends out signals that make the heart muscle contract.

Each lower chamber, called a **ventricle,** pumps blood out of the heart. The atria are separated from the ventricles by valves. A **valve** is a flap of tissue that prevents blood from flowing backward. Valves are also located between the ventricles and the large blood vessels that carry blood away from the heart.

How the Heart Works The action of the heart has two main phases. In one phase, the heart muscle relaxes and the heart fills with blood. In the other phase, the heart muscle contracts and pumps blood forward. A heartbeat, which sounds something like *lub-dup*, can be heard during the pumping phase.

When the heart muscle relaxes, blood flows into the chambers. Then, the atria contract, squeezing blood out of the atria, through the valves, and into the ventricles. Next, the ventricles contract. This contraction closes the valves between the atria and ventricles, making the *lub* sound and squeezing blood into large blood vessels. As the valves between the ventricles and the blood vessels snap shut, they make the *dup* sound.

When muscle cells in the ventricles contract, they exert a force on the blood. A force is a push or a pull. The force exerted by the ventricles pushes blood out of your heart and into arteries. The contraction of the left ventricle exerts much more force than the contraction of the right ventricle.

 Reading Checkpoint What is the role of the pacemaker?

DISCOVERY CHANNEL SCHOOL

Circulation

Video Preview
▶ Video Field Trip
Video Assessment

FIGURE 3
Open and Closed Heart Valves
As blood flows out of the heart and toward the lungs, it passes through a valve like the one in the photograph. **Applying Concepts** *What is the function of a closed heart valve?*

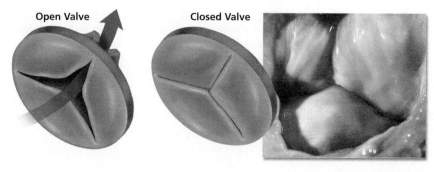

Open Valve   Closed Valve

Chapter 16   ◆   537

Lab zone **Build Inquiry**   L2

Observing Your Heartbeat

Materials stethoscope
Time 15 minutes

Focus Explain that you can use a stethoscope to hear the sound of heart valves closing.

Teach Have students use the stethoscope to listen to their own heartbeats. (After each use, use rubbing alcohol to clean the parts of the stethoscope that are inserted into the ears.) Ask: **What sounds do you hear as your heart beats?** (*There is a deeper sound, "lub," and a higher sound, "dup."*)

Apply Ask: **How do the sounds of the heartbeat relate to the muscle contractions in the heart?** (*The "lub" sound comes from the closing of the valves between the atria and ventricles, while the "dup" sound comes from the closing of the valves between the ventricles and the blood vessels.*) **learning modality: kinesthetic**

DISCOVERY CHANNEL SCHOOL
Video Field Trip

Circulation
Show the Video Field Trip to let students experience the intense exercise regimens of top athletes and understand how the training helps to improve the efficiency of the cardiovascular system. Discussion question: **How does the circulatory system get rid of carbon dioxide waste in the blood?** (*The blood carries the carbon dioxide from the cells to the lungs, where it is exhaled into the air.*)

Differentiated Instruction

Special Needs   L1
Model Heart Have students examine a model heart with removable parts. Invite students to hold each part of the heart as you describe its function. Point out the difference in the size of the chambers and the thickness of the walls. Have students describe the different sizes of the blood vessels that lead in and out of the chambers. Give each student a beanbag or small, soft ball. Demonstrate how to squeeze the item at a steady rate to approximate 80 beats per minute, then have them do it. Emphasize that the heart works continuously like this for a person's lifetime. **learning modality: kinesthetic**

Monitor Progress   L2

Drawing Have students draw a heart, label its chambers, and write brief captions describing the function of each chamber. Have students place their drawings in their portfolios.

Portfolio

Answer
Figure 3 Valves prevent blood from flowing backward.

Build Inquiry

Interpreting Pulse Data

Materials watch with a second hand

Time 10 minutes each day over one week

Focus Remind students that heart rate changes with changing oxygen needs.

Teach Show students how to locate their pulse by placing the index finger of one hand on the other wrist at the base of the thumb and moving the fingers slightly until the pulse is felt. Explain that the pulse is caused by a spurt of blood passing through an artery. By measuring their pulse, students can measure their heart rate. Have them count the number of beats in the pulse for exactly one minute, and allow time for practice. Then direct students to take their pulse three times a day for one school week—when they wake up in the morning, after exercising, before going to bed—and record their pulse rates in data tables. **CAUTION:** *Advise students not to exercise if they have a medical condition that rules out vigorous exercise.* At the end of the week, ask students to look for patterns in their data.

Apply Ask: **How does your heart rate at certain times of the day or during certain activities relate to your body's need for oxygen at that time?** (*The heart rate increases when there is a high demand for oxygen.*)
learning modality: logical/mathematical

Two Loops

Teach Key Concepts

Following the Two-Looped Path

Focus Refer students to Figure 5.

Teach Have students place a finger on the right atrium and follow the arrows to trace the path of blood as you read the passage. Then ask: **What is the difference between arteries and veins?** (*Arteries carry blood away from the heart; veins carry blood to the heart.*) **What are the two loops of blood flow?** (*Heart to the lungs and back to the heart; heart to the body and back to the heart*)

Apply Ask: **When blood is pumped to the body cells, is it oxygen-rich?** (*Yes; it has just come from the lungs where it released carbon dioxide and picked up oxygen.*) **learning modality: visual**

FIGURE 4
Getting Blood to Body Cells
During strenuous exercise, such as swimming, the pattern of blood flow through the body ensures that body cells get the oxygen they need quickly and efficiently.

Skills Activity

Creating Data Tables
Scientists measured the volume of blood that different organs receive, at rest and during vigorous exercise.

- At rest, the organs of the abdomen received about 1,400 mL of blood per minute (mL/min). During vigorous exercise, they received 600 mL/min.
- At rest, skeletal muscles received 1,200 mL/min. During vigorous exercise, they received about 12,500 mL/min.
- At rest, the kidneys received 1,100 mL/min. During vigorous exercise, they received about 600 mL/min.

Create a table to record these data. Then, use the data to explain why some organs receive more blood during exercise than others.

538 ◆

Two Loops

After leaving the heart, blood travels in blood vessels through the body. Your body has three kinds of blood vessels—arteries, capillaries, and veins. **Arteries** are blood vessels that carry blood away from the heart. From the arteries, blood flows into tiny, narrow vessels called **capillaries.** In the capillaries, substances are exchanged between the blood and body cells. From capillaries, blood flows into **veins,** blood vessels that carry blood back to the heart.

Pattern of Blood Flow The overall pattern of blood flow through the body is something like a figure eight. The heart is at the center where the two loops cross. **In the first loop, blood travels from the heart to the lungs and then back to the heart. In the second loop, blood is pumped from the heart throughout the body and then returns again to the heart.** The heart is really two pumps, one on the right and one on the left. The right side pumps blood to the lungs, and the left side pumps blood to the rest of the body.

Blood travels in only one direction. If you were a drop of blood, you could start at any point and eventually return to the same point. The entire trip would take less than a minute. As you read about the path that blood takes through the cardiovascular system, trace the path in Figure 5.

Loop One: To the Lungs and Back When blood from the body flows into the right atrium, it contains little oxygen but a lot of carbon dioxide. This oxygen-poor blood is dark red. The blood then flows from the right atrium into the right ventricle. Then, the ventricle pumps the oxygen-poor blood into the arteries that lead to the lungs.

Skills Activity

Skills Focus Creating data tables

Materials paper and pencil

Time 15 minutes

Tips Suggest that students' tables contain a column for volume of blood per minute at rest and volume of blood per minute during vigorous exercise.

Expected Outcome The skeletal muscles need extra oxygen and glucose during exercise, so the amount of blood flowing to other organs is adjusted.

Extend Have students graph the data.
learning modality: logical/mathematical

As blood flows through the lungs, large blood vessels branch into smaller ones. Eventually, blood flows through tiny capillaries that are in close contact with the air that comes into the lungs. The air in the lungs has more oxygen than the blood in the capillaries, so oxygen moves from the lungs into the blood. For the same reason, carbon dioxide moves in the opposite direction—from the blood into the lungs. As the blood leaves the lungs, it is now rich in oxygen and poor in carbon dioxide. This blood, which is bright red, flows to the left side of the heart and will be pumped through the second loop.

Loop Two: To the Body and Back The second loop begins as the left atrium fills with oxygen-rich blood coming from the lungs. The blood then moves into the left ventricle. From the left ventricle, the blood is pumped into the **aorta** (ay AWR tuh), the largest artery in the body.

Eventually, after passing through branching arteries, blood flows through tiny capillaries in different parts of your body, such as your brain, liver, and legs. These vessels are in close contact with body cells. Oxygen moves out of the blood and into the body cells. At the same time, carbon dioxide passes from the body cells and into the blood. This blood, which is low in oxygen, then flows back to the right atrium of the heart through veins, completing the second loop.

FIGURE 5
Direction of Blood Flow
Blood circulates through the body in two loops, with the heart at the center. Loop one goes from the heart to the lungs and back. Loop two circulates blood throughout the rest of the body.
Interpreting Diagrams Where does the blood that enters the left atrium come from?

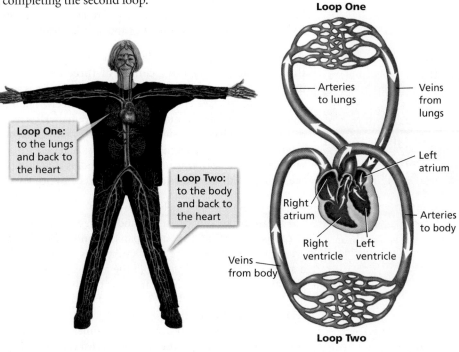

Loop One

Arteries to lungs

Veins from lungs

Left atrium

Right atrium

Arteries to body

Right ventricle

Left ventricle

Veins from body

Loop Two

Loop One: to the lungs and back to the heart

Loop Two: to the body and back to the heart

All in One Teaching Resources, Unit 3
• Transparency LS158

Address Misconceptions L1

The Color of Blood

Focus Some students may think that some blood is actually blue.

Teach Tell students that oxygen-poor blood is dark red, not blue. Illustrations of the cardiovascular system often show vessels in blue and red to distinguish vessels that carry oxygen-rich blood from those that carry oxygen-poor blood. Ask: **Why is some blood dark red?** *(It contains little oxygen.)* **Where does it change to bright red?** *(In the lungs; wastes move from blood to the air, while oxygen in air moves into blood. Blood that is rich in oxygen is bright red.)*

Apply Ask: **Why is blood in the veins traveling from the body to the right atrium dark red?** *(Body cells use up the oxygen in the blood and add wastes, so the blood in these veins would be low in oxygen and high in wastes—dark red.)* **learning modality: verbal**

Monitor Progress L2

Skills Check Have students make flowcharts of the path of blood from one point until it reaches the same point again.

Answer
Figure 5 The lungs

Differentiated Instruction

Gifted and Talented L3
Researching Pacemakers Explain to students that in the case of disease or accident where a person's pacemaker becomes damaged, an artificial pacemaker can be implanted beneath the skin and connected to the heart by wires. Tiny electrical impulses travel from the battery through the wires, and make the heart contract. Have students research artificial pacemakers that are sensitive to changes in body temperature and oxygen needs. Ask: **Why would these be more efficient than pacemakers that do not have these functions?** *(They could match the person's heart rate with his or her activity level.)* Have students present their findings in a poster or visual presentation to the class. **learning modality: visual**

Arteries

Teach Key Concepts **L2**
Functions of Arteries

Focus Remind students that arteries carry blood away from the heart.

Teach Explain that the heart itself must receive oxygen-rich blood to function. Ask: **How does it get this blood?** (*Coronary arteries supply blood to the heart.*) Sketch a cross-section of an artery. Ask: **How does the structure of an artery relate to its function?** (*The smooth inner layer helps blood to flow freely. The muscular middle layer expands and relaxes in response to the heart pumping. The outer connective tissue makes the artery strong yet flexible.*) **What are you feeling when you take a pulse?** (*A spurt of blood pushing the artery walls and making them expand*)

Apply Refer students to Figure 6. Ask: **What is the main difference between the structure of arteries and veins, and why is this?** (*Arteries are thicker because the force of blood pumped through these vessels is stronger than the force flowing through the veins.*)
learning modality: visual

Math Skill Calculating a rate

Focus Tell students that the units of pulse rate are heartbeats per minute.

Teach Explain that people often calculate heart rate by counting the pulse for 10, 15, or 30 seconds and then multiplying.

Answer
68 beats per minute

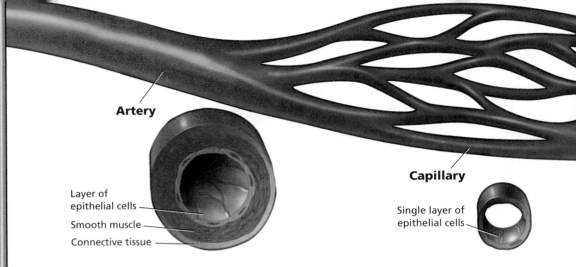

Artery

Layer of epithelial cells

Smooth muscle

Connective tissue

Capillary

Single layer of epithelial cells

FIGURE 6
Artery, Capillary, and Vein
The walls of arteries and veins have three layers. The walls of capillaries are only one cell thick. **Relating Cause and Effect** *How does material get from inside capillaries to body cells?*

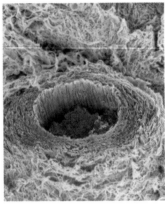

▲ The artery wall appears as a thick pink band surrounding a clump of red blood cells.

Arteries

When blood leaves the heart, it travels through arteries. The right ventricle pumps blood into the arteries that go to the lungs. The left ventricle pumps blood into the aorta. Smaller arteries branch off the aorta. The first branches, called the **coronary arteries,** carry blood to the heart itself. Other branches carry blood to the brain, intestines, and other organs. Each artery branches into smaller and smaller arteries.

Artery Structure **The walls of arteries are generally very thick. In fact, artery walls consist of three cell layers.** The innermost layer, which is made up of epithelial cells, is smooth. This smooth surface enables blood to flow freely. The middle layer consists mostly of muscle tissue. The outer wall is made up of flexible connective tissue. Because of this layered structure, arteries have both strength and flexibility. Arteries are able to withstand the enormous pressure of blood as it is pumped by the heart and to expand and relax between heart beats.

Pulse If you lightly touch the inside of your wrist, you can feel the artery in your wrist rise and fall repeatedly. This **pulse** is caused by the alternating expansion and relaxation of the artery wall. Every time the heart's ventricles contract, they send a spurt of blood out through all the arteries in your body. As this spurt travels through the arteries, it pushes the artery walls and makes them expand. After the spurt passes, the artery walls relax and become narrower again.

When you count the number of times an artery pulses beneath your fingers, you are counting heartbeats. By taking your pulse rate, you can determine how fast your heart is beating.

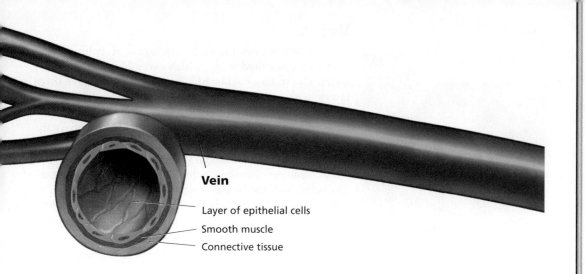

Vein

Layer of epithelial cells
Smooth muscle
Connective tissue

Regulating Blood Flow The layer of muscle in an artery acts as a control gate, adjusting the amount of blood sent to different organs. When the muscle contracts, the opening in the artery becomes smaller. When the muscle relaxes, the opening becomes larger. For example, after you eat, your stomach and intestines need a greater blood supply for digestion. The arteries leading to those organs open wider, and more blood flows through them. In contrast, when you are running, your stomach and intestines need less blood than the muscles in your legs. The arteries leading to the digestive organs become narrower, decreasing the blood flow to these organs.

 Reading Checkpoint What causes your pulse?

Capillaries

Eventually, blood flows from small arteries into the tiny capillaries. **In the capillaries, materials are exchanged between the blood and the body's cells. Capillary walls are only one cell thick.** Thus, materials can pass easily through them. Materials such as oxygen and glucose pass from the blood, through the capillary walls, to the cells. Cellular waste products travel in the opposite direction—from cells, through the capillary walls, and into the blood.

One way that materials are exchanged between the blood and body cells is by diffusion. **Diffusion** is the process by which molecules move from an area of higher concentration to an area of lower concentration. For example, glucose is more highly concentrated in the blood than it is in the body cells. Therefore, glucose diffuses from the blood into the body cells.

Math Skills

Calculating a Rate
A rate is the speed at which something happens. When you calculate a rate, you compare the number of events with the time period in which they occur. Here's how to calculate the pulse rate of a person whose heart beats 142 times in 2 minutes.

1. Write the comparison as a fraction.

$$\frac{142 \text{ heartbeats}}{2 \text{ minutes}}$$

2. Divide the numerator and the denominator by 2.

$$\frac{142 \div 2}{2 \div 2} = \frac{71}{1}$$

The person's pulse rate is 71 heartbeats per minute.

Practice Problem Calculate your pulse rate if your heart beats 170 times in 2.5 minutes.

Capillaries

Teach Key Concepts L1
Function of Capillaries
Focus Refer students to Figure 6.

Teach Ask: **Why are capillary walls so thin?** *(Materials must be able to pass easily between them and body cells.)*

Apply Tell students that blood cells must pass through capillaries in single file.
learning modality: visual

 **Teaching Resources, Unit 3**
• Transparency LS159

Lab zone **Teacher Demo** L1

Observing Diffusion

Materials 2 beakers, food coloring, salt, teaspoon

Time 10 minutes over two days

Focus Review the process of diffusion.

Teach Pour water into a beaker until it is one-third full. Add one-half teaspoon of salt and a few drops of food coloring. Stir until you have a uniform solution. Pour water into a second beaker until it is one-half full. Next, carefully pour the contents of the first beaker into the second. The salt water will sink to the bottom. Let the beaker stand overnight. The liquid will be uniformly colored.

Apply Ask: **How is this process like diffusion in capillaries?** *(The concentration of salt in the salt water was higher than that in the fresh water; thus, the salt water diffused into the fresh. Glucose is higher in concentration in blood than in body cells, so it moves from the blood to body cells.)* **learning modality: visual**

Differentiated Instruction

Less Proficient Readers L1
Illustrating Blood Vessels Have students draw each type of blood vessel. The drawing should include leader lines labeling any parts discussed in the text and captions describing the functions of each type of vessel. Pair students with more proficient readers to read the corresponding text and to identify information to include in the drawings. Students can copy and expand upon the illustrations in the text or their own charts. Encourage students to use different-colored markers to distinguish structures. **learning modality: visual**

Monitor Progress L2

Writing Ask students to explain the differences between arteries and capillaries.

Answers
Figure 6 By diffusion

 Reading Checkpoint Alternating expansion and relaxation of the artery wall

Veins

Teach Key Concepts

Returning Blood to the Heart

Focus Review the function of veins.

Teach Ask: **How does the pushing force of the heart in veins compare to the pushing force in arteries?** (*The pushing force of the heart has less effect by the time blood reaches the veins.*) **What factors help move blood through veins?** (*Contraction of skeletal muscles, valves, and breathing movements*)

Apply Ask: **Would your blood move best through the veins while you were sitting for 45 minutes or while you were playing soccer for 45 minutes? Why?** (*Playing soccer; skeletal muscles help push blood along when they contract.*) **learning modality: logical/ mathematical**

Blood Pressure

Teach Key Concepts

What Causes Blood Pressure

Focus Ask: **What happens to the force of blood as moves away from the heart?** (*It decreases.*)

Teach Explain that blood pressure is caused when the heart contracts and produces a wave of fluid pressure through the arteries. Blood pressure decreases when the heart relaxes, but the system still remains under pressure. Ask: **How do these differences explain the different numbers in a blood pressure reading?** (*The first number measures the blood pressure when the heart contracts, so it is higher. The second number is lower because it shows the pressure when the heart relaxes.*)

Apply Ask: **Why is a cut in an artery generally a more serious injury than a cut in a vein of the same size?** (*Blood pressure is higher in arteries, so blood loss from a cut artery can occur more rapidly.*) **learning modality: verbal**

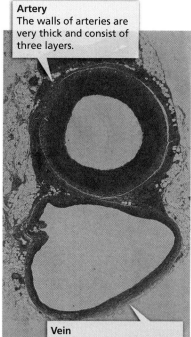

Artery
The walls of arteries are very thick and consist of three layers.

Vein
Although the walls of veins also consist of three layers, they are much thinner than the walls of arteries.

FIGURE 7
Artery and Vein
In this photo, you can compare the wall of an artery (top) with the wall of a vein (bottom).
Comparing and Contrasting
Where is the pushing force of the heart greater—in arteries or in veins?

Veins

After blood moves through capillaries, it enters larger blood vessels called **veins**, which carry blood back to the heart. **The walls of veins, like those of arteries, have three layers, with muscle in the middle layer.** However, the walls of veins are generally much thinner than those of arteries.

By the time blood flows into veins, the pushing force of the heart has much less effect than it did in the arteries. Several factors help move blood through veins. First, because many veins are located near skeletal muscles, the contraction of the muscles helps push the blood along. For example, as you run or walk, the skeletal muscles in your legs contract and squeeze the veins in your legs. Second, larger veins in your body have valves in them that prevent blood from flowing backward. Third, breathing movements, which exert a squeezing pressure against veins in the chest, also force blood toward the heart.

 Reading Checkpoint How do skeletal muscles help move blood in veins?

Blood Pressure

Suppose that you are washing a car. You attach the hose to the faucet and turn on the faucet. The water flows out in a slow, steady stream. Then, while your back is turned, your little brother turns the faucet on all the way. Suddenly, the water spurts out rapidly, and the hose almost jumps out of your hand.

As water flows through a hose, it pushes against the walls of the hose, creating pressure on the walls. **Pressure** is the force that something exerts over a given area. When your brother turned on the faucet all the way, the additional water flow increased the pressure exerted on the inside of the hose. The extra pressure made the water spurt out of the nozzle faster.

What Causes Blood Pressure? Blood traveling through blood vessels behaves in a manner similar to that of water moving through a hose. Blood exerts a force, called **blood pressure,** against the walls of blood vessels. Blood pressure is caused by the force with which the ventricles contract. In general, as blood moves away from the heart, blood pressure decreases. This change happens because the farther away from the ventricle the blood moves, the lower its force is. Blood flowing through the arteries exerts the highest pressure. Blood pressure in arteries farther from the heart is much lower.

Measuring Blood Pressure Blood pressure can be measured with an instrument called a sphygmomanometer (sfig moh muh NAHM uh tur). A cuff is wrapped around the upper arm. Air is pumped into the cuff until the blood flow through the artery is stopped. As the pressure is released, the examiner listens to the pulse and records two numbers. Blood pressure is expressed in millimeters of mercury. The first number is a measure of the blood pressure while the heart's ventricles contract and pump blood into the arteries. The second number, which is lower, measures the blood pressure while the ventricles relax. The two numbers are expressed as a fraction: the contraction pressure over the relaxation pressure.

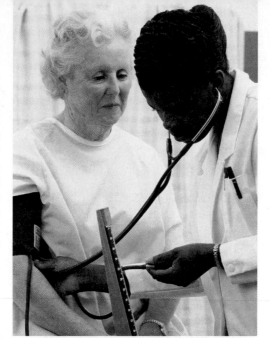

FIGURE 8
Measuring Blood Pressure
Blood pressure can be measured with a sphygmomanometer. A typical blood pressure reading for a healthy person is 120/80 or lower.

Section 1 Assessment

Target Reading Skill **Sequencing** Refer to your cycle diagram about the pathway of blood flow as you answer Question 3.

Reviewing Key Concepts

1. a. **Reviewing** What does the cardiovascular system consist of?
   b. **Classifying** What three functions does the cardiovascular system perform?
2. a. **Identifying** What function does the heart perform?
   b. **Summarizing** What are the four chambers of the heart? What structures separate one chamber from another?
   c. **Predicting** What would happen if the valve between the right atrium and the right ventricle did not work properly?
3. a. **Identifying** Where does blood returning from the body enter the heart?
   b. **Sequencing** Where does the blood move next?

4. a. **Describing** What roles do arteries, capillaries, and veins play in the cardiovascular system?
   b. **Comparing and Contrasting** How are the structures of arteries, capillaries, and veins similar? How are they different?

Math Practice

Before a run, you take your pulse rate for 30 seconds and count 29 beats. Immediately after the run, you count 63 beats in 30 seconds.

5. **Calculating a Rate** What was your pulse rate per minute before the run?
6. **Calculating a Rate** What was your pulse rate immediately after the run?

Lab zone Chapter **Project**

Keep Students on Track See that students have sketched out the two loops correctly. Advise them to begin planning how they will construct their displays and to start a list of materials or equipment they will need. Ask them to think about how they will show movement of blood cells. Check to make sure that their plans are realistic.

Math Practice

Math Skills Calculating a rate
Answers
5. 58 (29 × 2 = 58)
6. 126 (63 × 2 = 126)

543

Heart Beat, Health Beat

Prepare for Inquiry

Skills Objectives
After this lab, students will be able to
- graph their pulse rate under different conditions
- interpret data on pulse rate
- draw conclusions about the relationship between physical activity and pulse rate

Prep Time none

Class Time 40 minutes

Advance Planning
Students with relevant health problems can keep time and record data.

Safety
Students with medical reasons to avoid exercise should do only steps 1–3. Review the safety guidelines in Appendix A.

All in One Teaching Resources, Unit 3
- Lab Worksheet: *Heart Beat, Health Beat*

Guide Inquiry

Introduce the Procedure
Have students practice taking their pulse.

Troubleshooting the Experiment
Ask the class to be quiet during the lab.

Expected Outcome
Pulse will increase more when running than walking, then return to a resting rate (70–80 beats per minute).

Analyze and Conclude
1. Graphs will reflect data similar to those in the table. Graphs should be clearly labeled.

2. The pulse returns to the resting rate.

3. The heart is beating faster.

4. Pulse rate increases during exercise.

5. Answers should include the idea that taking many measurements and finding an average improves accuracy.

For: Data sharing
Visit: PHSchool.com
Web Code: ced-4032

Students can share data online.

Heart Beat, Health Beat

Problem
How does physical activity affect your pulse rate?

Skills Focus
graphing, interpreting data, drawing conclusions

Materials
- graph paper
- watch with second hand or heart rate monitor

Procedure
1. Predict how your pulse rate will change as you go from resting to being active, then back to resting again. Then, copy the data table into your notebook.

2. Locate your pulse by placing the index and middle finger of one hand on your other wrist at the base of your thumb. Move the two fingers slightly until you feel your pulse. If you are using a heart rate monitor, see your teacher for instructions.

3. Work with a partner for the rest of this lab. Begin by determining your resting pulse rate. Count the number of beats in your pulse for exactly 1 minute while your partner times you. Record your resting pulse rate in your data table. **CAUTION:** *Do not complete the rest of this lab if there is any medical reason why you should avoid physical activities.*

Data Table	
Activity	**Pulse Rate**
Resting	
Walking	
Running	
Resting after exercise (1 min)	
Resting after exercise (3+ min)	

4. Walk in place for 1 minute while your partner times you. Stop and immediately take your pulse for 1 minute. Record the number in your data table.

5. Run in place for 1 minute. Take your pulse again, and record the result.

6. Sit down right away, and have your partner time you as you rest for 1 minute. Then, take your pulse rate again.

7. Have your partner time you as you rest for 3 more minutes. Then take your pulse rate again and record it.

Analyze and Conclude
1. **Graphing** Use the data you obtained to create a bar graph of your pulse rate under the different conditions you tested.

2. **Interpreting Data** What happens to the pulse rate when the physical activity has stopped?

3. **Inferring** What can you infer about the heartbeat when the pulse rate increases?

4. **Drawing Conclusions** What conclusion can you draw about the relationship between physical activity and a person's pulse rate?

5. **Communicating** How could you improve the accuracy of your pulse measurements? Write a paragraph in which you discuss this question in relation to the steps you followed in your procedure.

Design an Experiment
Design an experiment to determine whether the resting pulse rates of adults, teens, and young children differ. *Obtain your teacher's permission before carrying out your investigation.*

For: Data sharing
Visit: PHSchool.com
Web Code: ced-4032

Extend Inquiry

Design an Experiment Students' plans will include measuring the resting pulse rate of people of different ages.

Reading Preview

Key Concepts
- What are the components of blood?
- What determines the type of blood that a person can receive in a transfusion?
- What are the structures and functions of the lymphatic system?

Key Terms
- plasma • red blood cell
- hemoglobin
- white blood cell • platelet
- lymphatic system • lymph
- lymph node

 Target Reading Skill

Identifying Main Ideas As you read the section titled Blood, write the main idea in a graphic organizer like the one below. Then, write four supporting details that give examples of the main idea.

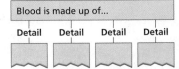

Main Idea

Blood is made up of...

Detail	Detail	Detail	Detail

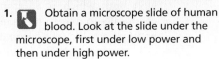 **Lab zone Discover Activity**

What Kinds of Cells Are in Blood?

1. Obtain a microscope slide of human blood. Look at the slide under the microscope, first under low power and then under high power.
2. Look carefully at the different kinds of cells that you see.
3. Make several drawings of each kind of cell. Use red pencil for the red blood cells.

Think It Over
Observing How many kinds of cells did you see? How do they differ from one another?

While riding your bike through the neighborhood, you take a tumble and scrape your knee. Your knee begins to sting, and you notice blood oozing from the wound. You go inside to clean the wound. As you do, you wonder, "Just what is blood?"

Blood

Blood may seem like just a plain red liquid, but it is actually a complex tissue that has several parts. **Blood is made up of four components: plasma, red blood cells, white blood cells, and platelets.** About 45 percent of the volume of blood is cells. The rest is plasma.

Plasma Most of the materials transported in the blood travel in the plasma. **Plasma** is the liquid part of the blood. Water makes up 90 percent of plasma. The other 10 percent is dissolved materials. Plasma carries nutrients, such as glucose, fats, vitamins, and minerals. Plasma also carries chemical messengers that direct body activities such as the uptake of glucose by your cells. In addition, many wastes produced by cell processes are carried away by plasma.

Protein molecules give plasma its yellow color. There are three groups of plasma proteins. One group helps to regulate the amount of water in blood. The second group, which is produced by white blood cells, helps fight disease. The third group of proteins interacts with platelets to form blood clots.

Chapter 16 ◆ 545

Section
2
Blood and Lymph

Objectives
After completing the lesson, students will be able to
16.2.1 Describe the components of blood.
16.2.2 Explain what determines the type of blood that a person can receive in a transfusion.
16.2.3 Name the structures and functions of the lymphatic system.

Target Reading Skill

Identifying Main Ideas Explain that identifying main ideas and details helps students sort the facts from the information into groups. Each group can have a main topic, subtopics, and details.

Answers
Sample details: Plasma is the liquid part of blood: red blood cells take up oxygen and deliver it to cells in the body; white blood cells fight disease; platelets help form blood clots.

All in One Teaching Resources, Unit 3
- Transparency LS160

Preteach

Build Background Knowledge **L1**

Components of Blood
Ask students to name what blood is made of. *(Students may mention red blood cells, cells that attack disease-causing organisms, glucose, and waste products.)* Do not comment on their answers at this time. Tell them that blood is actually a tissue that contains dissolved substances and specialized cells.

Lab zone Discover Activity

Skills Focus Observing **L2**

Materials microscope, prepared slides of human blood

Time 15 minutes

Tips Remind students to note the shapes and sizes of cells. **CAUTION:** *Advise students to handle the slides carefully to avoid breakage or cuts.*

Expected Outcome Students will observe three kinds of blood cells. They will see many more red blood cells than white blood cells or platelets.

Think It Over Students will describe three types of cells: round with a depressed center (red blood cells); irregularly shaped cells (white blood cells); and flat, fragmented bodies (platelets).

Blood

Teach Key Concepts L2
Structure and Function of Blood

Focus Remind students that the cardiovascular system carries oxygen and glucose to all parts of the body, and picks up waste materials.

Teach Ask: **What makes up the greatest part of blood?** (*Plasma makes up about 55%.*) **What does plasma do?** (*Carries nutrients, chemical messengers, and wastes*) **How do red blood cells perform their function?** (*The hemoglobin in red blood cells binds to oxygen so the cells can deliver oxygen throughout the body.*) **What do white blood cells do?** (*Recognize disease-causing organisms and kill them*) **How do platelets protect you?** (*They prevent loss of blood by forming blood clots when a vessel is cut.*)

Apply Ask: **What do you think happens to the total number of white blood cells when the body is fighting an infection?** (*The number increases.*) **learning modality: verbal**

Independent Practice L2

All in One Teaching Resources, Unit 3

- Guided Reading and Study Worksheet: *Blood and Lymph*

🔘 **Student Edition on Audio CD**

Help Students Read L1
Building Vocabulary Before students read this section, have them work in small groups and use the glossary to create vocabulary worksheets that include definitions for the boldface terms. Offer suggestions such as matching activities or fill-in-the-blank activities. Direct groups to exchange worksheets and complete them as they read the section.

Red Blood Cells Without red blood cells, your body could not use the oxygen that you breathe in. **Red blood cells** take up oxygen in the lungs and deliver it to cells elsewhere in the body. Red blood cells, like most blood cells, are produced in bone marrow. Under a microscope, these cells look like disks with pinched-in centers. Because of their pinched shape, red blood cells are thin in the middle and can bend and twist easily. This flexibility enables them to squeeze through narrow capillaries.

A red blood cell is made mostly of **hemoglobin** (HEE muh gloh bin), which is an iron-containing protein that binds chemically to oxygen molecules. When hemoglobin combines with oxygen, the cells become bright red. Without oxygen, the cells are dark red. Thus, blood leaving the heart through the aorta is bright red, whereas blood returning from the body to the heart through veins is dark red. Hemoglobin picks up oxygen in the lungs and releases it as blood travels through capillaries in the rest of the body. Hemoglobin also picks up some of the carbon dioxide produced by cells. However, most of the carbon dioxide is carried by plasma. The blood carries the carbon dioxide to the lungs, where it is released from the body.

Mature red blood cells have no nuclei. Without a nucleus, a red blood cell cannot reproduce or repair itself. Mature red blood cells live only about 120 days. Every second, about 2 million red blood cells in your body die. Fortunately, your bone marrow produces new red blood cells at the same rate.

✓ **Reading Checkpoint** What is hemoglobin?

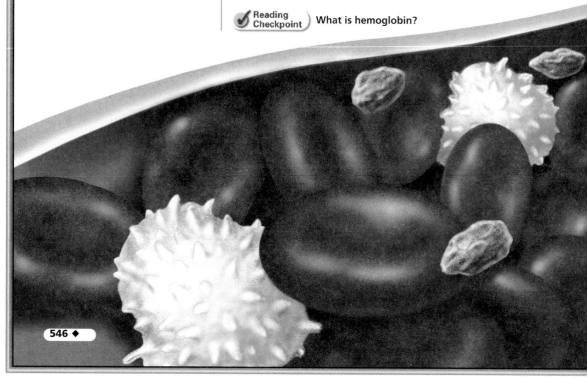

546 ◆

White Blood Cells Like red blood cells, white blood cells are produced in bone marrow. **White blood cells** are the body's disease fighters. Some white blood cells recognize disease-causing organisms, such as bacteria, and alert the body that it has been invaded. Other white blood cells produce chemicals to fight the invaders. Still others surround and kill the organisms.

White blood cells are different from red blood cells in several important ways. There are fewer of them—only about one white blood cell for every 500 to 1,000 red blood cells. White blood cells are also larger than red blood cells. In addition, white blood cells contain nuclei. Most white blood cells can live for months or even years.

FIGURE 9
Parts of Blood
Blood consists of liquid plasma and three kinds of cells—red blood cells, white blood cells, and platelets.
Observing *Describe the shape of a red blood cell.*

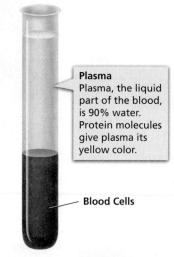

Plasma
Plasma, the liquid part of the blood, is 90% water. Protein molecules give plasma its yellow color.

Blood Cells

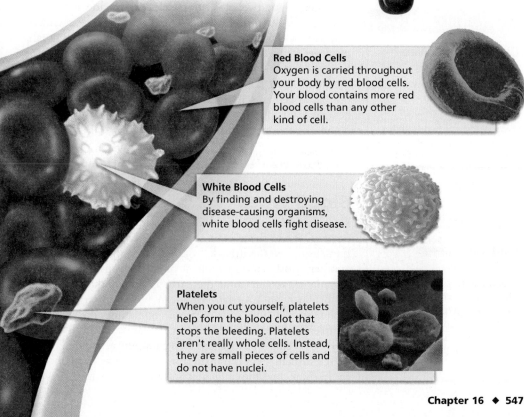

Red Blood Cells
Oxygen is carried throughout your body by red blood cells. Your blood contains more red blood cells than any other kind of cell.

White Blood Cells
By finding and destroying disease-causing organisms, white blood cells fight disease.

Platelets
When you cut yourself, platelets help form the blood clot that stops the bleeding. Platelets aren't really whole cells. Instead, they are small pieces of cells and do not have nuclei.

Chapter 16 ◆ 547

Blood Types

L2

Teach Key Concepts

Determinants of Blood Type

Focus Refer students to Figure 11.

Teach Ask: **What type of marker molecule is on type B blood?** *(B marker)* **Why are clumping proteins in type B blood anti-A?** *(Clumping proteins recognize markers that are foreign or different. Because type B blood contains B markers, it recognizes A markers as foreign and is therefore anti-A.)* **What would happen if a person with type B blood received type A blood?** *(The type A cells would clump together; the person would get sick and could die.)* **Why can a person with type B blood receive type O in a transfusion?** *(Type O has no markers.)*

Apply Tell students that blood type O is often referred to as the "universal donor" because it has no markers. Ask students to explain why type AB is called the "universal recipient." *(People with this blood type can receive type O, and they have markers for A and B, so they also can receive A, B, and AB.)*
learning modality: visual

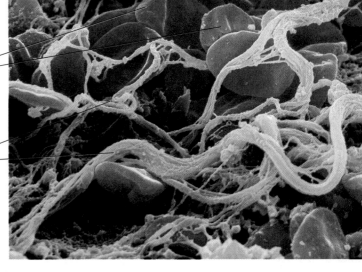

Red blood cells

Fibrin

FIGURE 10
Formation of a Blood Clot
When you cut your skin, a blood clot forms. The blood clot consists of blood cells trapped in a fiber net.
Relating Cause and Effect *How is this net of fibers produced?*

Try This **Activity**

Caught in the Web

In this activity, you will model part of the process by which a blood clot forms.

1. Cover the opening of a sturdy plastic cup with a piece of cheesecloth. Use a rubber band to hold the cheesecloth in place.
2. Put some water, paper clips, and coins in another cup.
3. Carefully pour the water, coins, and paper clips into the middle of the cheesecloth.

Making Models The paper clips and coins represent blood cells. What does the cheesecloth represent? What starts the production of the substance that the cheesecloth represents?

Platelets When you scraped your knee, blood oozed out of the wound. After a short time, however, a blood clot formed, stopping the blood flow. **Platelets** (PLAYT lits) are cell fragments that play an important part in forming blood clots.

When a blood vessel is cut, platelets collect and stick to the vessel at the site of the wound. The platelets release chemicals that start a chain reaction. This series of reactions eventually produces a protein called fibrin (FY brin). Fibrin gets its name from the fact that it weaves a net of tiny fibers across the cut in the blood vessel. Look at Figure 10 to see how the fiber net traps the blood cells. As more and more platelets and blood cells become trapped in the net, a blood clot forms. A scab is a dried blood clot on the skin surface.

Reading Checkpoint What is the role of platelets?

Blood Types

If a person loses a lot of blood—either from a wound or during surgery—he or she may be given a blood transfusion. A blood transfusion is the transfer of blood from one person to another. Most early attempts at blood transfusion failed, but no one knew why until the early 1900s. At that time, Karl Landsteiner, an Austrian American physician, tried mixing blood samples from pairs of people. Sometimes the two blood samples blended smoothly. In other cases, however, the red blood cells clumped together. This clumping accounted for the failure of many blood transfusions. If clumping occurs within the body, it clogs the capillaries and may lead to death.

548 ◆

Try This **Activity**

Skills Focus Making models   L2

Materials two plastic cups, 20-cm-square piece of cheesecloth, rubber band, water, paper clips, coins, newspapers, paper towels

Time 15 minutes

Tips Have students spread newspapers on their work areas and place their cups on the newspapers.

Expected Outcome The cheesecloth represents the fibrin net. Platelets release chemicals that eventually result in the production of fibrin.

Extend Ask: **What would happen if people did not have platelets?** *(Their blood could not clot and they might bleed to death if the bleeding were not stopped some other way.)* **learning modality: kinesthetic**

Marker Molecules Landsteiner went on to discover that there are four major types of blood—A, B, AB, and O. Blood types are determined by proteins known as marker molecules that are on the red blood cells. If your blood type is A, you have the A marker. If your blood type is B, you have the B marker. People with type AB blood have both A and B markers. People with type O blood have neither A nor B markers.

Your plasma contains clumping proteins that recognize red blood cells with "foreign" markers (not yours) and make those cells clump together. For example, if you have blood type A, your blood contains clumping proteins that act against cells with B markers. So, if you receive a transfusion of type B blood, your clumping proteins will make the "foreign" type B cells clump together.

Safe Transfusions Landsteiner's work led to a better understanding of transfusions. **The marker molecules on your red blood cells determine your blood type and the type of blood that you can safely receive in transfusions.** A person with type A blood can receive transfusions of either type A or type O blood. Neither of these two blood types has B markers. Thus they would not be recognized as foreign by the clumping proteins in type A blood. A person with type AB blood can receive all blood types in transfusion because type AB blood has no clumping proteins. Figure 11 shows which transfusions are safe for each blood type.

If you ever receive a transfusion, your blood type will be checked first. Then, donated blood that you can safely receive will be found. This process is called cross matching. You may have heard a doctor on a television show give the order to "type and cross." The doctor wants to find out what blood type the patient has and then cross match it with donated blood.

Go Online
SciLINKS NSTA

For: Links on blood
Visit: www.SciLinks.org
Web Code: scn-0433

FIGURE 11
Blood Types and Their Markers
The chemical markers on a person's red blood cells determine the types of blood he or she can safely receive in a transfusion.
Interpreting Tables *What types of blood can be given safely to a person with blood type AB?*

Blood Types and Their Markers				
Blood Type Characteristic	**Blood Type A**	**Blood Type B**	**Blood Type AB**	**Blood Type O**
Marker Molecules on Red Blood Cells	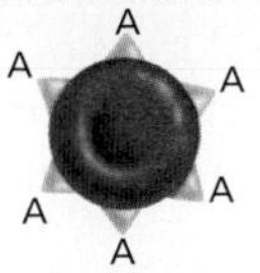	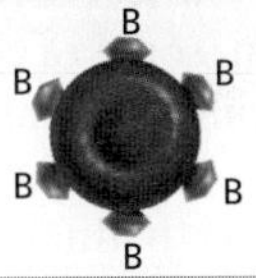	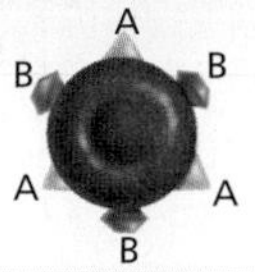	
Clumping Proteins	anti-B	anti-A	no clumping proteins	anti-A and anti-B
Blood Types That Can Be Safely Received in a Transfusion	A and O	B and O	A, B, AB, and O	O

Go Online
SciLINKS NSTA

For: Links on blood
Visit: www.SciLinks.org
Web Code: scn-0433

Download a worksheet to guide students' review of Internet resources on capillaries.

Differentiated Instruction

Less Proficient Readers ▪L1
Using Visuals Have students take turns with a partner describing the main idea behind each figure in the section while their partner takes notes. Then have them identify which figures go with each major heading in the section. Finally, have them combine their notes and the headings into an outline that they can use when answering assessment questions. **learning modality: visual**

Monitor Progress _____ L2

Writing Have students choose one blood type, identify which other blood types a person with that blood type may safely receive in a transfusion, and explain why this is the case.

Answers
Figure 10 Platelets collect at the site of a wound and release chemicals that lead to the production of fibrin, which forms a net that traps blood cells and forms a clot.
Figure 11 A, B, AB, or O

 Platelets play a role in forming blood clots.

549

Math Skill Making and interpreting graphs
Focus Remind students that there are eight, not four, blood types, taking the Rh factor into account.

Teach Ask: **Why is a circle graph the best way to show this data?** *(A circle graph shows parts of a whole, in this case, the population of the U.S.)*

Answers
1. The percentage of each blood type found in the United States population
2. AB (4%), B (11%), A (40%), O (45%)
3. 84%; 16%
4. O negative or B negative blood; 9%
5. The data should be arranged in three columns and eight rows.

The Lymphatic System

Teach Key Concepts   L2
Functions of the Lymphatic System

Focus Ask students to recall whether a physician or nurse has ever felt below their ears for swollen lymph nodes.

Teach Ask: **What would swollen lymph nodes under the ears indicate?** *(That the body is fighting infection)* **What role do lymph nodes have in the lymphatic system?** *(The lymphatic system is a network of vessels that filter lymph through lymph nodes and trap disease-causing organisms.)*

Apply Ask: **How are the circulatory and lymphatic systems related?** *(Lymph vessels empty into the large veins of the chest, from which lymph reenters the bloodstream to become part of blood plasma.)* **learning modality: verbal**

All in One Teaching Resources, Unit 3
• Transparency LS161

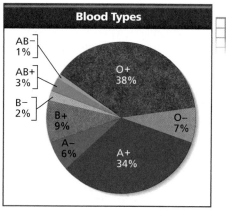

Blood Types

AB– 1%
AB+ 3%
B– 2%
B+ 9%
A– 6%
A+ 34%
A+ 34%
O+ 38%
O– 7%

Blood Type Distribution

The circle graph shows the percentage of each blood type found in the U.S. population.

1. **Reading Graphs** What does each wedge of the graph represent?

2. **Interpreting Data** Rank the four major blood types—A, B, AB, and O—from least common to most common. What is the percentage of each type?

3. **Calculating** According to the graph, what percentage of the population is Rh positive? What percentage is Rh negative?

4. **Predicting** What type of blood can someone who is B negative (blood type B and Rh negative) receive? What percentage of the population does that represent?

5. **Creating Data Tables** Use the data to make a table of the eight possible blood types. Include columns for the A, B, AB, and O blood types and Rh factor (positive or negative), and a row for percentage of the population.

Rh Factor Landsteiner also discovered the presence of another protein on red blood cells, which he called Rh factor. About 85 percent of the people he tested had this protein, and about 15 percent lacked it. Like the A, B, AB, and O blood types, the presence of Rh factor is determined by a marker on the red blood cell. If your blood type is Rh positive, you have the Rh marker. If your blood type is Rh negative, you lack the marker on your cells. If you are Rh negative and ever received Rh positive blood, you would develop Rh clumping proteins in your plasma. This situation is potentially dangerous.

 Reading Checkpoint   **Where is the Rh marker found?**

The Lymphatic System

As blood travels through the capillaries in the cardiovascular system, some of the fluid leaks out. It moves through the walls of capillaries and into surrounding tissues. This fluid carries materials that the cells in the tissues need.

After bathing the cells, this fluid moves into your body's drainage system, called the **lymphatic system** (lim FAT ik). **The lymphatic system is a network of veinlike vessels that returns the fluid to the bloodstream.** The lymphatic system acts something like rain gutters after a rainstorm, carrying the excess fluid away.

Lymph Once the fluid is inside the lymphatic system, it is called **lymph**. Lymph consists of water and dissolved materials such as glucose. It also contains some white blood cells that have left the capillaries.

The lymphatic system has no pump, so lymph moves slowly. Lymphatic vessels, which are part of the cardiovascular system, connect to large veins in the chest. Lymph empties into these veins, and the fluid once again becomes part of blood plasma.

Lymph Nodes As lymph flows through the lymphatic system, it passes through small knobs of tissue called lymph nodes. The **lymph nodes** filter lymph, trapping bacteria and other disease-causing microorganisms in the fluid. When the body is fighting an infection, the lymph nodes enlarge. If you've ever had "swollen glands" when you've been sick, you've actually had swollen lymph nodes.

 Reading Checkpoint What is lymph?

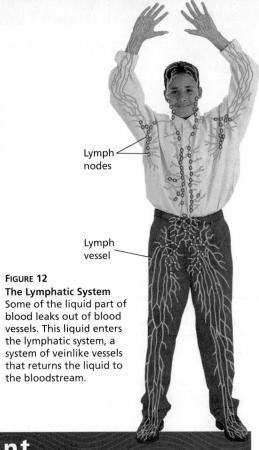

Lymph nodes

Lymph vessel

FIGURE 12
The Lymphatic System
Some of the liquid part of blood leaks out of blood vessels. This liquid enters the lymphatic system, a system of veinlike vessels that returns the liquid to the bloodstream.

Section 2 Assessment

Target Reading Skill Identifying Main Ideas Use your graphic organizer to help you answer Question 1 below.

Reviewing Key Concepts

1. **a. Listing** Name the four components of blood. Identify whether each is a cell, a part of a cell, or a liquid.
   b. Summarizing Briefly describe what happens to stop the bleeding when you cut yourself.
   c. Relating Cause and Effect People with the disorder hemophilia do not produce the protein fibrin. Explain why hemophilia is a serious disorder.
2. **a. Reviewing** What is a marker molecule?
   b. Explaining Explain why a person with type O blood cannot receive a transfusion of type A blood.

   c. Predicting Can a person with type AB, Rh negative blood safely receive a transfusion of type O, Rh negative blood? Explain.
3. **a. Identifying** Where does lymph come from?
   b. Sequencing What happens to lymph after it travels through the lymphatic system?

Lab zone At-Home **Activity**

What's Your Blood Type? If possible, find out your blood type. Explain to family members the types of blood you can receive and to whom you can donate blood. Create a chart to help with your explanation.

Chapter 16 ◆ 551

Lab zone Chapter **Project**

Keep Students on Track Advise students to begin constructing their displays if they haven't begun. Help students determine the best way to organize the information for their own understanding. Suggest that students begin to prepare a rough draft of their written descriptions. Suggest students make flowcharts to help them prepare rough drafts.

Lab zone At-Home **Activity**

What's Your Blood Type? ▪L2▪
Direct students to the table in Figure 11. Have them use this table to help in creating their personal charts.

551

Objectives

After completing this lesson, students will be able to

16.3.1 Identify some diseases of the cardiovascular system.
16.3.2 Describe behaviors that can help maintain cardiovascular health.

Target Reading Skill 🔄

Asking Questions Explain that changing a head into a question helps students anticipate the ideas, facts, and events they are going to read about.

Answers

Possible question and answer include: **What are some cardiovascular diseases?** *Cardiovascular diseases include atherosclerosis and hypertension.* **How can a person keep a healthy cardiovascular system?** *Exercise regularly, eat a healthy diet, and avoid smoking*

All in One Teaching Resources, Unit 3

• Transparency LS162

Preteach

Build Background Knowledge
L1

Risk Factors for Heart Attacks
Ask: **What factors do you think make a person more likely to have a heart attack?** *(Sample answers: High-fat diet, high salt intake, and little or no exercise)* Tell students that in this section they will learn about heart disease and the steps they can take to prevent it.

Reading Preview

Key Concepts
• What are some diseases of the cardiovascular system?
• What behaviors can help maintain cardiovascular health?

Key Terms
• atherosclerosis • heart attack
• hypertension

🔄 Target Reading Skill
Asking Questions Before you read, preview the red headings. In a graphic organizer like the one below, ask a *what* or *how* question for each heading. As you read, write the answers to your questions.

Cardiovascular Health

Question	Answer
What are some cardiovascular diseases?	Cardiovascular diseases include...

FIGURE 13
Exercising for Health
Strenuous exercise, such as rowing, requires a healthy cardiovascular system. In turn, exercise keeps the cardiovascular system healthy.

552 ◆

Lab zone Discover Activity

Which Foods Are "Heart Healthy"?

1. Your teacher will give you an assortment of foods. If they have nutrition labels, read the information.
2. Sort the foods into three groups. In one group, put those foods that you think are good for your cardiovascular system. In the second group, put foods that you think might damage your cardiovascular system if eaten often. Place foods you aren't sure about in the third group.

Think It Over
Forming Operational Definitions How did you define a "heart-healthy" food?

Shortly after sunrise, when most people are just waking up, a team of rowers is already out on the river. Rhythmically, with perfectly coordinated movement, the rowers pull on the oars, making the boat glide swiftly through the water. Despite the chilly morning air, sweat glistens on the rowers' faces and arms. Inside their chests, their hearts are pounding, delivering blood to the arm and chest muscles that power the oars.

Lab zone Discover Activity

Skills Focus Forming operational definitions

Materials assortment of foods

Time 20 minutes

Tips Provide heart-healthy foods such as fresh fruit and vegetables, unbuttered popcorn, low-fat yogurt, and skim milk. Also provide items such as potato chips,

L2

crackers, and processed foods high in sodium or fat (especially saturated fat). Information about sodium and fat content is found on food labels.

Think It Over Students' answers will depend on their knowledge of nutrition and the cardiovascular system. Heart-healthy foods include those low in fat and sodium.

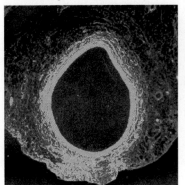
Healthy, unblocked artery

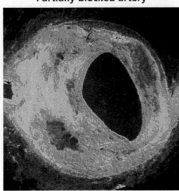
Partially blocked artery

FIGURE 14
Effect of Atherosclerosis
The artery on the right shows atherosclerosis, which is caused by deposits of fat on the artery walls.
Relating Cause and Effect *What kind of diet can lead to atherosclerosis?*

Cardiovascular Diseases

Rowers cannot perform at their peaks unless their cardiovascular systems are in excellent condition. But cardiovascular health is important for all people, not just for athletes. Cardiovascular disease is the leading cause of death in the United States today. **Diseases of the cardiovascular system include atherosclerosis and hypertension.**

Atherosclerosis Compare the photos of the two arteries in Figure 14. The one on the left is a healthy artery. It has a large space in the center through which blood can flow easily. The artery on the right, in contrast, has a smaller space in the middle. This artery exhibits **atherosclerosis** (ath uh roh skluh ROH sis), a condition in which an artery wall thickens as a result of the buildup of fatty materials. One of these fatty materials is cholesterol, a waxy substance. Atherosclerosis results in a reduced flow of blood in the affected artery.

Atherosclerosis can develop in the coronary arteries, which supply the heart muscle. When that happens, the heart muscle receives less blood and therefore less oxygen. This condition may lead to a heart attack. A **heart attack** occurs when blood flow to part of the heart muscle is blocked. Cells die in the part of the heart that does not receive blood and oxygen. This permanently damages the heart.

Treatment for mild atherosclerosis usually includes a low-fat diet and a moderate exercise program. In addition, medications that lower the levels of cholesterol and fats in the blood may be prescribed. People with severe atherosclerosis may need to undergo surgery or other procedures to unclog the blocked arteries.

Lab zone Try This **Activity**

Blocking the Flow
Use this activity to model how fatty deposits affect the flow of blood through an artery.

1. Put a funnel in the mouth of a plastic jar. The funnel will represent an artery.
2. Slowly pour 100 mL of water into the funnel. Have your partner time how many seconds it takes for all the water to flow through the funnel. Then, discard the water.
3. Use a plastic knife to spread a small amount of paste along the bottom of the funnel's neck. Then, with a toothpick, carve out a hole in the paste so that the funnel is partly, but not completely, clogged.
4. Repeat Steps 1 and 2.

Predicting If the funnels were arteries, which one—blocked or unblocked—would do a better job of supplying blood to tissues? Explain.

Lab zone Try This **Activity**

Skills Focus Predicting L1

Materials plastic funnel, plastic jar, graduated cylinder, stopwatch or clock, paste, plastic knife, toothpick, newspaper, paper towels

Time 20 minutes

Tips If paste is not available, use modeling clay to block the funnel.

Expected Outcome The unblocked funnel would do a better job of supplying blood, because more liquid can flow through it.

Extend Ask: **Which photo in Figure 14 represents the paste clogged funnel?** (*The one on the right*) **learning modality: kinesthetic**

Instruct

Cardiovascular Diseases

Teach Key Concepts L2
Exploring Atherosclerosis

Focus Remind students that the cross-section of a cylinder is a circle. The diameter is a line that goes across its center.

Teach Have students compare the two cross-section views of arteries in Figure 14. Ask: **How do the outer diameters of the arteries compare?** (*The outer diameters are similar.*) **The inner diameters?** (*The inner diameter of the artery on the right is smaller than the inner diameter of the artery on the left.*) **Which one is diseased, and how can it lead to a heart attack in the case of a coronary artery?** (*The one on the right because blood flow is restricted; the heart does not receive as much oxygen. If the heart receives too little oxygen, a heart attack can result.*) **How are hypertension and atherosclerosis linked?** (*As arteries narrow, blood pressure increases.*)

Apply Point out that young people can develop high blood pressure, especially if they are overweight and do not exercise.
learning modality: visual

Help Students Read L1
Relating Cause and Effect As students read, encourage them to list the cardiovascular diseases described in the text and the causes of those diseases. Then have them list healthy habits that can lead to cardiovascular health.

Independent Practice

All in One Teaching Resources, Unit 3
• Guided Reading and Study Worksheet: *Cardiovascular Health*

 **Student Edition on Audio CD**

Monitor Progress _____ L2

Writing Have students describe how atherosclerosis causes heart attacks.

Answer
Figure 14 One that is high in fat and cholesterol

 **Build Inquiry** L2

Predicting High Sodium in Foods

Materials empty food containers with nutrition labels

Time 15 minutes

Focus Remind students that sodium can exacerbate high blood pressure.

Teach Ask students to name foods that they think are high in sodium and foods that they think are low in sodium. Have them bring in food containers from home of these types of foods. Have group members work together to examine the labels on all the containers and compare the label information with their predictions. Students may be surprised at the amounts of sodium in foods they might otherwise think of as healthy.

Apply Have students list which foods they normally eat and determine whether their diet is high in sodium compared to recommended daily amounts. **learning modality: logical/mathematical**

Hypertension High blood pressure, or **hypertension** (hy pur TEN shun), is a disorder in which a person's blood pressure is consistently higher than normal—usually defined as greater than 140/90.

Hypertension makes the heart work harder to pump blood throughout the body. It also may damage the walls of the blood vessels. Over time, both the heart and arteries can be severely harmed by hypertension. Because people with hypertension often have no obvious symptoms to warn them of the danger until damage is severe, hypertension is sometimes called the "silent killer."

• Tech & Design in History •

Advances in Cardiovascular Medicine

Scientists today have an in-depth understanding of how the cardiovascular system works and how to treat cardiovascular problems. This timeline describes some of the advances in cardiovascular medicine.

1958
Artificial Pacemaker
Electrical engineer Earl Baaken developed an external pacemaker to correct irregular heartbeats. A small electric generator connected to the pacemaker generated electric pulses that regulated heart rate. The first pacemakers had a fixed rate of 70 to 75 pulses per minute.

1961
Heart Valve Replacement
The first successful artificial heart valve was inserted into a patient's heart by surgeons Albert Starr and M. L. Edwards in Oregon. The valve was a rubberlike ball inside a stainless steel cage.

1930s–1940s
Blood Banks
Charles Drew demonstrated that emergency blood transfusions could be done with plasma if whole blood was not available. During World War II, Drew established blood banks for storing donated blood. His work helped save millions of lives on and off the battlefield.

| 1930 | 1940 | 1950 | 1960 |

Differentiated Instruction

English Learners/Beginning L1
Vocabulary: Science Glossary Provide pictures from reference books and encourage students to make drawings to illustrate the Key Terms in the section, not necessarily technical diagrams. For example, students might draw a blood vessel with a closed faucet head and a pressure gauge that indicates high pressure. **learning modality: visual**

English Learners/Intermediate L2
Vocabulary: Science Glossary Have students complete the activity described for beginning students, then write sentences in their own words for each Key Term. **learning modality: verbal**

Hypertension and atherosclerosis are closely related. As the arteries narrow, blood pressure increases. For mild hypertension, regular exercise and careful food choices may be enough to lower blood pressure. People with hypertension may need to limit their intake of sodium, which can increase blood pressure. Sodium is found in table salt and in processed foods such as soups and packaged snack foods. For many people who have hypertension, however, medications are needed to reduce their blood pressure.

 Reading Checkpoint Why is hypertension called the "silent killer"?

Writing in Science

Research and Write Choose one of the scientists whose work is described in the timeline. Imagine that you are on a committee that has chosen this scientist to receive an award. Write the speech you would give at the award ceremony, explaining the scientist's contributions.

1967
First Heart Transplant
Christiaan Barnard, a South African surgeon, performed the first transplant of a human heart. Louis Washkansky, the man who received the heart, lived for only 18 days after the transplant. But Barnard's work paved the way for future successes in transplanting hearts and other organs.

1977
Angioplasty
The first coronary balloon angioplasty was performed by Andreas Gruentzig and a team of surgeons in San Francisco. A balloon is inserted into the coronary artery and inflated, thus opening the artery. In 2001, more than two million angioplasties were performed worldwide.

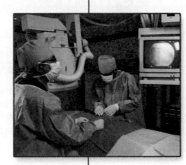

2001
Replacement Heart
The first replacement heart was implanted by a team of surgeons in Louisville, Kentucky. Unlike the first artificial heart, the Jarvik-7, the replacement heart has its own internal batteries. The patient does not have to be "plugged in" to an external power source. The first patient to receive the replacement heart lived for more than 500 days.

| 1970 | 1980 | 1990 | 2000 |

Background

Facts and Figures After World War II, America experienced an epidemic of heart disease. In 1948, the U.S. Public Health Service conducted the Framingham (Massachusetts) Heart Study with 5,209 healthy volunteers. Since that time, participants have had health checkups every two years.

Among the findings:
- High blood pressure appears to trigger heart attacks.
- Cigarette smoking is bad for the heart.
- Too much cholesterol in the blood raises the risk of heart attacks.
- Physical exercise lowers the risk of heart disease; being overweight increases it.
- Diabetes contributes to heart disease.

• Tech & Design in History •

Focus Help students understand the context of the timeline by mentioning significant events or inventions that have taken place over these years. For example, mention that people were just beginning to drive cars in the early 1900s and that the laser wasn't invented until the late 1950s.

Teach Ask student volunteers to read each caption. Ask: **How did the treatment of cardiovascular diseases change in the twentieth century?** (*Sample answer: The development of technologies, such as artificial heart valves, enabled scientists and physicians to treat diseases that before were untreatable.*) Ask: **Why would some kinds of surgery have been impossible before the discovery of blood types?** (*Some kinds of surgery require blood transfusions.*)

Writing in Science

Writing Mode Description
Scoring Rubric
4 Includes a complete and accurate description of the scientist's work and contributions; written from first-person point of view and reflects emotional responses
3 Includes a complete and accurate description, but lacks the personal aspect
2 Includes accurate but brief description
1 Includes inaccurate description

Portfolio

Monitor Progress _____ L2

Writing Ask students to list and describe at least three cardiovascular advances made since 1900. Students can place their descriptions in their portfolios.

Portfolio

Answer
✓ **Reading Checkpoint** People with hypertension often have no symptoms to warn them of the disease, even though their hearts and arteries are becoming badly damaged.

Keeping Healthy

Teach Key Concepts
Maintaining Cardiovascular Health

Focus Remind students that cardiovascular disease takes years to develop, and that they can practice behaviors now to prevent it.

Teach Ask: **How does exercise help prevent cardiovascular disease?** *(It strengthens the heart muscle and prevents atherosclerosis.)* **Why should you limit foods high in fat and cholesterol?** *(These foods can lead to the buildup of fatty deposits on artery walls.)*

Apply Have students brainstorm ways they can fit more exercise into their schedules.
learning modality: verbal

Monitor Progress

Answers
Figure 15 Fruits, vegetables, low-fat dairy products, low-fat whole-grain products

 Red meats, eggs, and cheese

Assess

Reviewing Key Concepts

1. a. Atherosclerosis is a condition in which artery walls thicken; hypertension is a disorder in which a person's blood pressure is consistently higher than normal **b.** They make the heart work harder. If atherosclerosis develops in the coronary arteries, it can cause a heart attack.
2. a. Exercise regularly, eat a healthy diet, and avoid smoking **b.** Exercise strengthens heart muscle and helps prevent atherosclerosis. **c.** Sample answer: Americans generally have diets high in fat, cholesterol, and sodium, and do not exercise enough.

Reteach
Have students make and complete a three-column table on the causes and prevention of cardiovascular diseases.

All in One Teaching Resources, Unit 3
- Section Summary: *Cardiovascular Health*
- Review and Reinforce: *Cardiovascular Health*
- Enrich: *Cardiovascular Health*

FIGURE 15
Eating for Health
Eating foods that are low in fat can help keep your cardiovascular system healthy.
Applying Concepts *What are some heart-healthy low-fat foods?*

Keeping Healthy

Few young people have heart attacks, but signs of atherosclerosis can be found in some people as young as 18 to 20 years old. You can establish habits now that will lessen your risk of developing atherosclerosis and hypertension. **To help maintain cardiovascular health, people should exercise regularly; eat a balanced diet that is low in saturated fats and trans fats, cholesterol, and sodium; and avoid smoking.**

Exercise and Diet Do you participate in sports, ride a bike, swim, dance, or climb stairs instead of taking the elevator? Every time you do one of those activities, you are helping to strengthen your heart muscle and prevent atherosclerosis.

Foods that are high in cholesterol, saturated fats, and trans fats can lead to atherosclerosis. Foods such as red meats, eggs, and cheese are high in cholesterol. But because they also contain substances that your body needs, a smart approach might be to eat them only in small quantities. Foods that are high in saturated fat include butter, whole milk, and ice cream. Foods high in trans fat include margarine, potato chips, and doughnuts.

Avoid Smoking Smokers are more than twice as likely to have a heart attack as are nonsmokers. Every year, about 180,000 people in the United States who were smokers die from cardiovascular disease. If smokers quit, however, their risk of death from cardiovascular disease decreases.

 What are some foods that are high in cholesterol?

Section 3 Assessment

Target Reading Skill **Asking Questions** Use the answers to the questions you wrote about the headings to help you answer the questions below.

Reviewing Key Concepts
1. a. Defining What is atherosclerosis? What is hypertension?
   b. Relating Cause and Effect How do these two diseases affect the heart?
2. a. Listing List three things you can do to help your cardiovascular system stay healthy.
   b. Explaining Why it is important to exercise?
   c. Inferring Coronary heart disease is less common in some countries than in the United States. What factors might account for this difference?

Lab zone At-Home Activity

Heart-Healthy Activities With your family, discuss things you all can do to maintain heart health. Make a list of activities that you can enjoy together. You might also work with your family to cook and serve a "heart-healthy" meal. List the foods you would serve at the meal.

Lab zone Chapter Project

Keep Students on Track Make sure students are completing their displays. Have students test their displays or practice their presentations as they add the finishing touches. Remind them to check their final written descriptions against their displays to make sure that they match and are both correct.

Lab zone At-Home Activity

Heart-Healthy Activities L2
Provide students with information about community activities such as walks, bike rides, or "fun runs." Bring cookbooks or magazines with simple low-fat recipes to class. Provide time for students to look at the recipes and choose several they think they would like. Students may choose to make their own cookbooks with low-fat recipes.

Skills Lab

Do You Know Your A-B-O's?

Problem

Which blood types can safely receive transfusions of type A blood? Which can receive type O blood?

Skills Focus

interpreting data, drawing conclusions

Materials

- 4 paper cups
- 8 plastic petri dishes
- marking pen
- 4 plastic droppers
- white paper
- toothpicks
- four model "blood" types

Procedure

1. Write down your ideas about why type O blood might be in higher demand than other blood types. Then, make two copies of the data table in your notebook.

2. Label four paper cups A, B, AB, and O. Fill each cup about one-third full with the model "blood" supplied by your teacher. Place one clean plastic dropper into each cup. Use each dropper to transfer only that one type of blood.

3. Label the side of each of four petri dishes with a blood type: A, B, AB, or O. Place the petri dishes on a sheet of white paper.

Data Table			
Donor: Type _____			
Potential Receiver	Original Color	Final Color of Mixture	Safe or Unsafe?
A			
B			
AB			
O			

4. Use the plastic droppers to place 10 drops of each type of blood in its labeled petri dish. Each sample represents the blood of a potential receiver of a blood transfusion. Record the original color of each sample in your data table as yellow, blue, green, or colorless.

5. Label your first data table Donor: Type A. To test whether each potential receiver can safely receive type A blood, add 10 drops of type A blood to each sample. Stir each mixture with a separate, clean toothpick.

6. Record the final color of each mixture in the data table. If the color stayed the same, write "safe" in the last column. If the color of the mixture changed, write "unsafe."

7. Label your second data table Donor: Type O. Obtain four clean petri dishes, and repeat Steps 3 through 6 to determine who could safely receive type O blood.

Analyze and Conclude

1. **Interpreting Data** Which blood types can safely receive a transfusion of type A blood? Type O blood?

2. **Inferring** Use what you know about marker molecules to explain why some transfusions of type A blood are safe while others are unsafe.

3. **Drawing Conclusions** If some blood types are not available, how might type O blood be useful?

4. **Communicating** Write a paragraph in which you discuss why it is important for hospitals to have an adequate supply of different types of blood.

More to Explore

Repeat this activity to find out which blood types can safely receive donations of type B and type AB blood.

Skills Lab

Do You Know Your A-B-O's?

Prepare for Inquiry

Skills Objectives

Students will be able to
- interpret data on blood types
- draw conclusions about the supply of blood and how type O might be useful

Prep Time 15 minutes
Class Time 40 minutes

Advance Planning

To make up the "blood types" use uncolored water for type O. For A, use 20 drops of yellow dye, such as food coloring, per liter of water. For B, use 20 drops of blue dye per liter of water. For AB, use 50 drops of yellow plus 50 drops of blue per liter of water. To test the colors, place 10 drops of AB solution in each of four petri dishes. Then add 10 drops of a different "blood type" to each. Mix with separate toothpicks; the four mixtures should be about the same green. If some mixtures are too yellowish or bluish, add more dye to darken the AB solution.

Safety

Ensure that students wear lab aprons to protect their clothing from food coloring. Caution students not to taste any mixtures and to wash their hands thoroughly after the activity. Review the safety guidelines in Appendix A.

All in One Teaching Resources, Unit 3
- Lab Worksheet: *Do You Know Your A-B-O's?*

Guide Inquiry

Troubleshooting the Experiment

Make sure students do not interpret a change in intensity as a change in color.

Expected Outcome

Colors will change only when A is added to B and O.

Extend Inquiry

More to Explore Colors should change when B is added to A or O, and when AB is added to A, B, or O.

Analyze and Conclude

1. Types A and AB can receive type A. Types A, B, AB, and O can receive type O.

2. People with type A or AB blood can safely receive a transfusion of type A blood because their blood has type A marker molecules and will not produce anti-A clumping proteins. People with type B or O blood have no A markers, so they will produce anti-A clumping proteins and the transfusion would not be safe. (Some students may answer in terms of Rh: People who are A positive can safely receive a transfusion of A positive or A negative blood, but a person who is Rh negative lacks the Rh marker and will produce clumping proteins if given A positive blood.)

3. Type O can safely be given to anyone.

4. To provide blood for people who have lost blood through injury, who are having surgery, or who need regular transfusions

Study Guide

interactive Textbook

- Complete student edition
- Section and chapter self-assessments
- Assessment reports for teachers

Help Students Read

Building Vocabulary

Vocabulary Rating Chart Have students construct a chart with five columns: *Term, Can Define or Use It, Heard or Seen It, Can Connect to Other Key Terms, Don't Know.* Students can copy the vocabulary terms for each section under the first column. They can then place a checkmark under one of the columns for each term to assess their familiarity with the terms and guide their studying.

Words in Context Select Key Terms from the chapter. Have students write a sentence for each term that places the term in a correct context. Provide them with one example before they begin. *Coronary artery: The heart muscle receives blood from the coronary arteries.*

Connecting Concepts

Concept Maps Help students develop one way to show how the information in this chapter is related. The cardiovascular system is made up of the heart, the blood, and a network of blood vessels that transport needed substances to all of the body's cells and carry away waste products. Have students brainstorm to identify the Key Concepts, Key Terms, details, and examples, then write each one on a sticky note and attach it at random on chart paper or on the board.

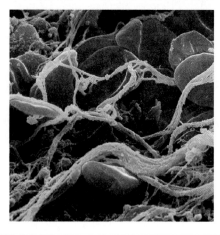

① The Body's Transport System

Key Concepts

- The cardiovascular system carries needed substances to cells and carries waste products away from cells. In addition, blood contains cells that fight disease.

- The heart pushes blood through the cardiovascular system. The right side of the heart is separated from the left side by the septum. Each side has an upper chamber and a lower chamber.

- Blood circulates in two loops. First, it travels from the heart to the lungs and then back to the heart. Second, it is pumped from the heart to the body and then it returns to the heart.

- Blood leaves the heart through arteries. When it reaches the capillaries, materials are exchanged between the blood and the body's cells. Veins carry blood back to the heart. The walls of arteries and veins consist of three layers. Capillary walls are only one cell thick.

Key Terms

cardiovascular system	capillary
heart	vein
atrium	aorta
pacemaker	coronary artery
ventricle	pulse
valve	diffusion
artery	blood pressure

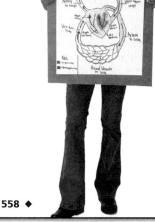

② Blood and Lymph

Key Concepts

- Blood is made up of four components: plasma, red blood cells, white blood cells, and platelets.

- The marker molecules on your red blood cells determine your blood type and the type of blood that you can safely receive in transfusions.

- The lymphatic system is a network of vein-like vessels that returns the fluid to the bloodstream.

Key Terms

plasma	platelet
red blood cell	lymphatic system
hemoglobin	lymph
white blood cell	lymph node

③ Cardiovascular Health

Key Concepts

- Diseases of the cardiovascular system include atherosclerosis and hypertension.

- To help maintain cardiovascular health, people should exercise regularly; eat a balanced diet that is low in saturated fats and trans fats, cholesterol, and sodium; and avoid smoking.

Key Terms

atherosclerosis	hypertension
heart attack	

Tell students that this concept map will be organized in hierarchical order and to begin at the top with the Key Concepts. Ask students these questions to guide them to categorize the information on the stickies: **What is the structure and function of the cardiovascular system? How do blood vessels differ in structure and function? What are the different components of blood? How can you maintain cardiovascular health?**

Prompt students by using connecting words or phrases, such as "consists of," "can be prevented by," and "is caused by," to indicate the basis for the organization of the map. The phrases should form a sentence between or among a set of concepts.

Answer

Accept logical presentations by students.

All in One Teaching Resources, Unit 3

- Key Terms Review: *Circulation*
- Connecting Concepts: *Circulation*

Review and Assessment

Go Online
PHSchool.com
For: Self-Assessment
Visit: PHSchool.com
Web Code: cha-3160

Organizing Information

Comparing and Contrasting Copy the compare/contrast table about the two loops of the circulatory system onto a sheet of paper. Then complete it and add a title. (For more on Comparing and Contrasting, see the Skills Handbook.)

Loop	Side of heart where loop starts	Where blood flows to	Where blood returns to
Loop One	a. ___?___	Lungs	b. ___?___
Loop Two	Left side	c. ___?___	d. ___?___

Reviewing Key Terms

Choose the letter of the best answer.

1. The heart's upper chambers are called
   a. ventricles.
   b. atria.
   c. valves.
   d. arteries.

2. Nutrients are exchanged between the blood and body cells in the
   a. capillaries.
   b. veins.
   c. aorta.
   d. arteries.

3. The alternating expansion and relaxation of the artery that you feel in your wrist is your
   a. pulse.
   b. coronary artery.
   c. blood pressure.
   d. plasma.

4. Blood components that help the body to control bleeding are
   a. platelets.
   b. red blood cells.
   c. white blood cells.
   d. hemoglobin.

5. Cholesterol is a waxy substance associated with
   a. lymph nodes.
   b. white blood cells.
   c. atherosclerosis.
   d. plasma.

If the statement is true, write *true*. If it is false, change the underlined word or words to make the statement true.

6. The two lower chambers of the heart are called <u>atria</u>.

7. The <u>veins</u> are the narrowest blood vessels in the body.

8. <u>White blood cells</u> contain hemoglobin.

9. The <u>lymphatic system</u> is involved in returning fluid to the bloodstream.

10. Elevated blood pressure is called <u>atherosclerosis</u>.

Writing in Science

Letter Write a letter to a friend describing what you do to stay active. For example, do you participate in team sports, jog, or take long walks with your dog? Include in your letter additional ways you can be even more active.

Discovery CHANNEL SCHOOL

Circulation
Video Preview
Video Field Trip
▶ Video Assessment

Go Online
PHSchool.com
For: Self-Assessment
Visit: PHSchool.com
Web Code: cha-3160

Students can take a practice test online that is automatically scored.

All in One Teaching Resources, Unit 3
• Transparency LS163
• Chapter Test
• Performance Assessment Teacher Notes
• Performance Assessment Student Worksheet
• Performance Assessment Scoring Rubric

◉ *ExamView*® **Computer Test Bank CD-ROM**

Review and Assessment

Organizing Information
a. Right side
b. Left atrium
c. Body
d. Right atrium

Reviewing Key Terms
1. b 2. a 3. a 4. a 5. c
6. ventricles
7. capillaries
8. red blood cells
9. true
10. hypertension

Writing in Science

Writing Mode Description
Scoring Rubric
4 Includes a description of activities, using specific examples as applicable; describes several sensible ideas for increasing activity in safe and enjoyable settings; takes the form of a friendly letter
3 Includes ideas for several reasonable activities, but does not take letter form
2 Includes only one or two ideas for activities, and does not take letter form
1 Is in letter form, but fails to include a description of any reasonable activities

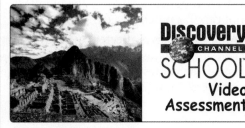

Discovery CHANNEL SCHOOL Video Assessment

Circulation

Show the Video Assessment to review chapter content and as a prompt for the writing assignment. Discussion questions: **What are the two paths of the circulatory system?** *(Pulmonary circulation and systemic circulation)* **How does an athlete's heart differ from the heart of a non-athlete?** *(An athlete's heart is stronger and it pumps more efficiently than that of a non-athlete.)*

Checking Concepts

11. The left ventricle contracts with more force than the right ventricle. The left ventricle needs to contract with enough force to pump blood throughout the entire body, while the right ventricle pumps blood only to the lungs.

12. The cell will pass through branching arteries into a capillary in your leg and then into a vein. A vein will then carry the cell to the right atrium of the heart.

13. Capillaries have thin walls, allowing substances to pass in and out of them easily.

14. Hemoglobin binds to oxygen in the lungs and releases it in the body.

15. Lymph is fluid inside vessels of the lymphatic system and consists of water, dissolved materials such as glucose, and some white blood cells. Lymph returns to the cardiovascular system through veins in the chest.

16. A high-fat, high-cholesterol diet can lead to atherosclerosis, and dietary sodium can increase blood pressure.

Thinking Critically

17. Oxygen-poor blood from the right ventricle could flow to the left ventricle and be pumped to the rest of the body, impairing the delivery of oxygen.

18. Ventricles—B and D; Oxygen-poor blood enters through A

19. Iron is an important component of hemoglobin, which is used to transport oxygen. Without enough iron, the blood cannot carry as much oxygen.

20. Atherosclerosis is affected by behavior. The risk of this disease can be lowered with a diet low in fat, cholesterol, and salt; by regular exercise; and by not smoking.

Review and Assessment

Checking Concepts

11. **Contrast** the forces with which the right and left ventricles contract. How does this relate to each ventricle's function?

12. A red blood cell is moving through an artery in your leg. Describe the path that the blood cell will follow back to your heart. Identify the chamber of the heart to which it will return.

13. How is a capillary's structure adapted to its function?

14. What is the function of hemoglobin?

15. What is lymph? How does lymph return to the cardiovascular system?

16. Give two reasons why food choices are important to cardiovascular health.

Thinking Critically

17. **Predicting** Some babies are born with an opening between the left and right ventricles of the heart. How would this heart defect affect the ability of the cardiovascular system to deliver oxygen to body cells?

18. **Classifying** Which two chambers of the heart shown below are the ventricles? Through which chamber does oxygen-poor blood enter the heart from the body?

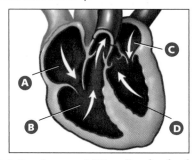

19. **Relating Cause and Effect** People who do not have enough iron in their diets sometimes develop a condition in which their blood cannot carry a normal amount of oxygen. Explain why this is so.

20. **Making Generalizations** Why is atherosclerosis sometimes called a "lifestyle disease"?

Math Practice

21. **Calculating a Rate** The veterinarian listens to your cat's heart and counts 30 beats in 15 seconds. What is your cat's heart rate?

Applying Skills

Use the graph to answer Questions 22–25.

The graph below shows how average blood pressure changes as men and women grow older.

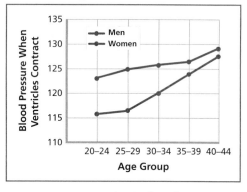

22. **Reading Graphs** What is plotted on each axis?

23. **Interpreting Data** At age 20, who is likely to have higher blood pressure—men or women?

24. **Drawing Conclusions** In general, what happens to blood pressure as people age?

25. **Predicting** Do you think that there is some age at which both men and women have about the same blood pressure? Use the graph lines to explain your prediction.

Lab zone Chapter **Project**

Performance Assessment You should now be ready to present your display. First show it to a small group of classmates to make sure it is clear and accurate. When you present your display, be ready to answer questions.

Lab zone Chapter **Project**   L3

Performance Assessment Allow one class period for students to present their projects. Presentations should include a clear explanation of how the student has chosen to represent the process in his or her display. Encourage other students to ask questions about each model as it is presented.

Reflect and Record Encourage students to identify one aspect of a particular display that helped them understand the concept. Some students may find that they learned more by making their own displays; others may find that they learned more by looking at other displays.

Standardized Test Prep

Choose the letter of the best answer.

1. The most important function of the cardiovascular system is to
   - **A** transport needed materials to body cells and remove wastes.
   - **B** provide structural support for the lungs.
   - **C** generate blood pressure so the arteries and veins do not collapse.
   - **D** produce blood and lymph.

2. The correct sequence for the path of blood through the body is
   - **F** heart—lungs—other body parts.
   - **G** heart—lungs—heart—other body parts.
   - **H** lungs—other body parts—heart.
   - **J** heart—other body parts—lungs—heart.

3. Which of the following is true about blood in the aorta?
   - **A** The blood is going to the lungs.
   - **B** The blood is oxygen-rich.
   - **C** The blood is dark red in color.
   - **D** The blood is going to the heart.

Use the table below and your knowledge of science to answer Questions 4 and 5.

Blood Types		
Blood Type	**Marker Molecules**	**Clumping Proteins**
A	A	anti-B
B	B	anti-A
AB	A and B	none
O	none	anti-A and anti-B

4. A person who has type O blood can safely receive blood from a person with
   - **F** type O blood.
   - **G** type A blood.
   - **H** type AB blood.
   - **J** type B blood.

5. A person who has type O blood can safely donate blood to a person with
   - **A** type AB blood.
   - **B** type O blood.
   - **C** types A, B, AB, or O blood.
   - **D** type A or type B blood.

Constructed Response

6. Explain what blood pressure is and what causes it. How is blood pressure measured and what is the significance of the two numbers in a blood pressure reading? Why can high blood pressure be dangerous?

Math Practice

21. 120 beats per minute (30 × 4)

Applying Skills

22. Age is plotted on the *x*-axis and blood pressure is plotted on the *y*-axis

23. Men

24. Both lines show that, on average, people's blood pressure increases as they age.

25. Sample answer: Yes. The two lines seem to be converging and will probably intersect at some age above 45.

Standardized Test Prep

1. A **2.** G **3.** B **4.** F **5.** C

6. Blood pressure is the force exerted against the walls of the blood vessels by the blood. It is caused by the force with which the ventricles of the heart contract. Blood pressure is measured by briefly cutting off blood flow in an artery (with a sphygmomanometer) and listening for sounds when flow is restored. The first number indicates the pressure when the ventricles contract and pump blood into the arteries. The second number indicates the pressure while the ventricles relax. High blood pressure makes the heart work harder and may damage the walls of blood vessels. Over time, both the heart and the arteries can be harmed.

Chapter at a Glance

 Chapter Project *Get the Message Out*

PRENTICE HALL
TeacherEXPRESS™
Plan • Teach • Assess

Technology

Local Standards

All in One Teaching Resources, Unit 3
- Chapter Project Teacher Notes, pp. 204–205
- Chapter Project Student Overview, pp. 206–207
- Chapter Project Student Worksheets, pp. 208–209
- Chapter Project Scoring Rubric, p. 210

Discovery CHANNEL **SCHOOL**
Video Preview

Section 1

3 periods
1 1/2 blocks

The Respiratory System
17.1.1 Describe the functions of the respiratory system.
17.1.2 Identify the structures that air passes through as it travels to the lungs.
17.1.3 Describe what happens during gas exchange and breathing.

Discovery CHANNEL **SCHOOL**
Video Field Trip

Go Online *active art*

Section 2

1 period
1/2 block

Smoking and Your Health
17.2.1 Identify the harmful chemicals contained in tobacco smoke.
17.2.2 Explain how tobacco smoke affects a person's health over time.

Go Online SCiLINKS NSTA

Section 3

2 periods
1 block

The Excretory System
17.3.1 Identify the structures and functions of the excretory system.
17.3.2 State how the kidneys filter wastes from the blood.
17.3.3 Explain how excretion contributes to homeostasis.

Go Online SCiLINKS NSTA

Review and Assessment

Test Preparation

All in One Teaching Resources, Unit 3
- Key Terms Review, p. 239
- Transparency LS173
- Performance Assessment Teacher Notes, p. 246
- Performance Assessment Scoring Rubric, p. 247
- Performance Assessment Student Worksheet, p. 248
- Chapter Test, pp. 249–252

Go Online PHSchool.com

Discovery CHANNEL **SCHOOL**
Video Assessment

Test Preparation
Blackline Masters

Chapter Activities Planner

Student Edition	Inquiry	Time	Materials	Skills	Resources
Chapter Project, p. 563	Open-Ended	2 to 3 weeks	**All in One Teaching Resources, Unit 3,** p. 204	Inferring, drawing conclusions, applying concepts, communicating	**Lab zone Easy Planner** **All in One Teaching Resources, Unit 3,** Support pp. 204–205
Section 1					
Discover Activity, p. 564	Directed	15 minutes	Round balloon, metric measuring tape	Inferring	**Lab zone Easy Planner**
Try This, p. 568	Directed	20 minutes	Bromthymol blue solution, 2 test tubes, plastic drinking straw, plastic wrap for covering test tubes (optional), safety goggles, water	Predicting	**Lab zone Easy Planner**
Skills Lab, p. 573	Directed	Prep: 30 minutes Class: 30 minutes	Small balloon, large balloon, scissors, transparent plastic bottle with narrow neck	Making models, observing, drawing conclusions	**Lab zone Easy Planner Lab Activity Video** **All in One Teaching Resources, Unit 3,** Skills Lab: *A Breath of Fresh Air,* pp. 220–221
Section 2					
Discover Activity, p. 574	Guided	20 minutes	None	Predicting	**Lab zone Easy Planner**
Skills Activity, p. 576	Guided	5 minutes	None	Calculating	**Lab zone Easy Planner**
Section 3					
Discover Activity, p. 579	Guided	15 minutes	Glucose solution, sand, two small plastic containers, glucose test strip, plastic funnel, filter paper	Observing	**Lab zone Easy Planner**
Skills Activity, . 580	Directed	5 minutes	None	Classifying	**Lab zone Easy Planner**
Skills Lab, pp. 584–585	Directed	Prep: 20 minutes Class: 40 minutes	6 test tubes, test tube rack, 6 plastic droppers, water, glucose solution, protein solution, marking pencil, white paper towels, 6 glucose test strips, Biuret solution, 3 simulated urine samples	Observing, interpreting data, drawing conclusions	**Lab zone Easy Planner Lab Activity Video** **All in One Teaching Resources, Unit 3,** Skills Lab: Clues About Health, pp. 236–238

Section 1 The Respiratory System

🕐 *3 periods, 1 1/2 blocks*

ABILITY LEVELS KEY
L1 Basic to Average
L2 For All Students
L3 Average to Advanced

Objectives

17.1.1 Describe the functions of the respiratory system.
17.1.2 Identify the structures that air passes through as it travel to the lungs.
17.1.3 Describe what happens during gas exchange and breathing.

Local Standards

Key Terms

- respiration • cilia • pharynx • trachea • bronchi • lungs • alveoli
- diaphragm • larynx • vocal cords

Preteach

Build Background Knowledge

Ask students to explain why astronauts wear space suits and carry oxygen with them when they walk outside a spacecraft. Then ask why deep-sea divers take oxygen with them on a dive.

Lab zone **Discover Activity** *How Big Can You Blow Up a Balloon?* **L1**

Targeted Print and Technology Resources

All in One Teaching Resources, Unit 3

L2 Reading Strategy Transparency LS164: Sequencing

🔘 **PresentationEXPRESS™ CD-ROM**

Instruct

Respiratory System Functions Use questions to guide discussion of the functions of the respiratory system.

The Path of Air Use an illustration to discuss the movement of air through the respiratory system.

Gas Exchange Use an illustration to discuss how gas is exchanged in alveoli.

How You Breathe Define diaphragm and discuss its role in breathing.

Lab zone **Skills Lab** *A Breath of Fresh Air* **L2**

Targeted Print and Technology Resources

All in One Teaching Resources, Unit 3

L2 Guided Reading, pp. 213–217
L2 Transparencies LS165, LS166, LS167, LS168
L2 Skills Lab: *A Breath of Fresh Air*, pp. 220–221

DISCOVERY CHANNEL SCHOOL
Video Field Trip

PHSchool.com Web Code: cep-4041

📼 **Lab Activity Video/DVD**
Skills Lab: *A Breath of Fresh Air*

🔘 **Student Edition on Audio CD**

Assess

Section Assessment Questions

🔘 Have students use their flowcharts to answer the questions.

Reteach

List the steps involved in the processes of breathing and gas exchange.

Targeted Print and Technology Resources

All in One Teaching Resources, Unit 3

- Section Summary, p. 212
L1 Review and Reinforce, p. 218
L3 Enrich, p. 219

Section 2 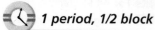 Smoking and Your Health

🕐 *1 period, 1/2 block*

Objectives

17.2.1 Identify the harmful chemicals contained in tobacco smoke.

17.2.2 Explain how tobacco smoke affects a person's health over time.

Key Terms

• tar • carbon monoxide • nicotine • addiction • bronchitis • emphysema

Local Standards

Preteach

Build Background Knowledge

Encourage students to talk about how the image of smoking has changed over the years.

 **Discover Activity** *What Are the Dangers of Smoking?* L1

Targeted Print and Technology Resources

All in One Teaching Resources, Unit 3

L2 Reading Strategy Transparency LS169: Relating Cause and Effect

🔘 **PresentationEXPRESS™ CD-ROM**

Instruct

Chemicals in Tobacco Smoke Make a table to list the three main chemicals found in smoke and their effects on the body.

Health Problems and Smoking Ask leading questions for a discussion on bronchitis, emphysema, lung cancer, and atherosclerosis.

Targeted Print and Technology Resources

All in One Teaching Resources, Unit 3

L2 Guided Reading, pp. 224–226

www.SciLinks.org Web code: scn-0442

🔘 **Student Edition on Audio CD**

Assess

Section Assessment Questions

Have students use their Relating Cause and Effect graphic organizers to answer the questions.

Reteach

Have students identify three parts of the body and the effect of tobacco smoke on each.

Targeted Print and Technology Resources

All in One Teaching Resources, Unit 3

• Section Summary, p. 223

L1 Review and Reinforce, p. 227

L3 Enrich, p. 228

Section 3 **The Excretory System**

⏱ *2 periods, 1 block*

ABILITY LEVELS KEY
L1 Basic to Average
L2 For All Students
L3 Average to Advanced

Objectives

17.3.1 Identify the structures and functions of the excretory system.

17.3.2 State how the kidneys filter wastes from the blood.

17.3.3 Explain how excretion contributes to homeostasis.

Key Terms

• excretion • urea • kidney • urine • ureter • urinary bladder • urethra
• nephron

Local Standards

Preteach

Build Background Knowledge

Relate the removal of family trash to the body's need to remove wastes.

▲ **Lab zone Discover Activity** *How Does Filtering a Liquid Change It?*
L1

Targeted Print and Technology Resources

All in One Teaching Resources, Unit 3

L2 Reading Strategy Transparency LS170: Previewing Visuals

◎ **PresentationEXPRESS™ CD-ROM**

Instruct

The Excretory System Use a diagram to identify the parts of the excretory system.

Filtration of Wastes Use a flowchart to explain the stages of waste removal.

Excretion and Homeostasis Identify roles of organs in maintaining homeostasis.

▲ **Lab zone Skills Lab** *Clues About Health* L2

Targeted Print and Technology Resources

All in One Teaching Resources, Unit 3

L2 Guided Reading, pp. 231–233
L2 Transparencies LS171, LS172
L2 Skills Lab: *Clues About Health*, pp. 236–238

www.SciLinks.org Web Code: scn-0443

◎ **Student Edition on Audio CD**

📼 **Lab Activity Video/DVD**
Skills Lab: *Clues About Health*

Assess

Section Assessment Questions

🔊 Have students use their Previewing Visuals graphic organizers to answer the questions.

Reteach

List each of the structures of the excretory system and their functions.

Targeted Print and Technology Resources

All in One Teaching Resources, Unit 3

• Section Summary, p. 230
L1 Review and Reinforce, p. 234
L3 Enrich, p. 235

Chapter 17 Content Refresher

Section 1 The Respiratory System

Control of Breathing To some extent, people can control their rate of breathing—and whether or not they breathe at all. However, if you hold your breath for a long time, your brain "takes over," and you resume breathing. Much of the control of breathing is involuntary and is directed by breathing centers in the brain. Interestingly, it is the concentration of carbon dioxide (CO_2) in the blood, rather than the concentration of oxygen (O_2), that determines the rate of breathing for the most part. In general, the higher the blood level of carbon dioxide, the more rapidly a person breathes.

Section 2 Smoking and Your Health

Types of Chronic Bronchitis Chronic bronchitis is diagnosed when the individual has a persistent cough with sputum production for at least three months in at least two consecutive years. If there is no obstruction to airflow through the bronchi and smaller airways, the disease is called simple chronic bronchitis. Smokers may start with this type. They cough because their airways are irritated by chemicals in smoke and because there is mucus accumulation caused by damage to cilia.

    Chronic asthmatic bronchitis occurs in people who have hypersensitive airways (and who often have asthma and/or respiratory allergies). This may develop in smokers who are particularly sensitive to ingredients in smoke. It may be even more common in people who have frequent secondary-smoke exposure.

    Finally, some cases of chronic bronchitis represent permanent damage to the airways so they are constantly narrowed and have accumulated mucus. This is the typical long-term smoker's chronic bronchitis, also called obstructive chronic bronchitis. The narrowed airways and mucus significantly limit how much air can reach the lungs and be expired with each breath.

> **Address Misconceptions**
>
> *Some students may think that smoking is less addictive than "hard" drugs, such as heroin and cocaine.* For a strategy for overcoming this misconception, see **Address Misconceptions** in the section *Smoking and Your Health*.

Section 3 The Excretory System

The Formation of Urine The liquid that leaves the blood and enters the capsule in a nephron is called the filtrate. At first, the concentration of small molecules (such as glucose) in the filtrate is basically the same as in blood plasma, the liquid part of blood. However, as the table shows, the concentrations of substances in plasma and urine differ greatly. These differences are the result of the selective reabsorption that occurs as the filtrate travels through the tube of the nephron. Some substances, such as amino acids and glucose, are moved back into capillaries by active transport. Water molecules follow these substances by osmosis. Nitrogenous wastes are not reabsorbed into the blood. Besides urea, nitrogenous wastes include creatinine, ammonia, and uric acid.

Concentrations of Components in Blood Plasma and Urine		
Component	Concentration in Plasma (milligrams/decaliter)	Concentration in Urine (milligrams/decaliter)
Nutrient Molecules		
Glucose	90	0.009
Lipids	600	0.002
Amino acids	4.2	0.188
Nitrogenous Wastes		
Urea	10–20	1,800
Creatinine	1–1.5	150
Ammonia	less than 0.1	60
Uric acid	3	40

Help Students Read

Use Prior Knowledge
Building From the Familiar

Strategy Choose a section such as *The Respiratory System* to use in modeling the strategy. Create a chart with the labels *Heading (subtopic)*, *Prior Knowledge*, and *New Knowledge*.

Example
1. Choose a subtopic heading and record it in the first column.
2. Ask students what they already know about each subtopic.
3. Use students' responses to determine whether they have any misconceptions. If so, begin to address them directly.
4. Have students read the section and correct information recorded in the second column. Direct them to add new information in the third column.

Interactive Textbook
- Complete student edition
- Video and audio
- Simulations and activities
- Section and chapter activities

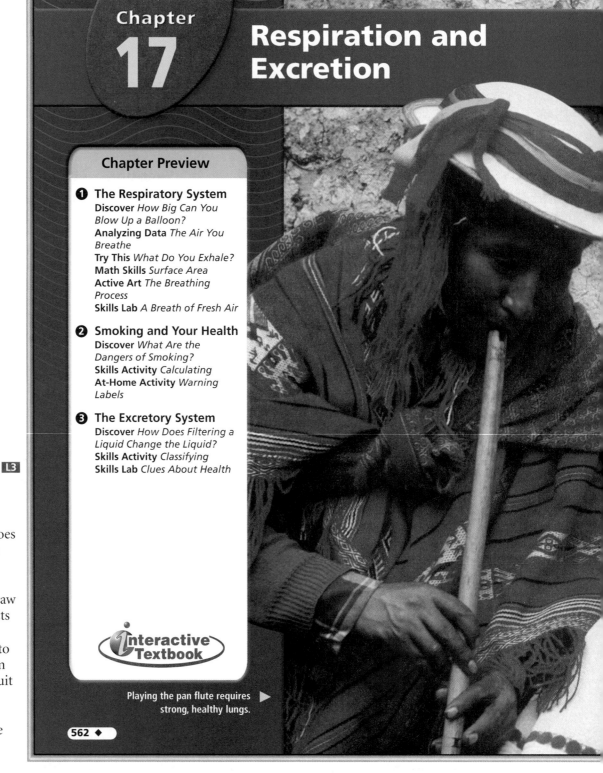

Interactive Textbook

Playing the pan flute requires strong, healthy lungs. ▶

562 ◆

Lab zone Chapter **Project** L3

Objectives
This project will enhance students' knowledge of the damage that smoking does to the body and the effects of smoking on overall health. After this Chapter Project, students will be able to
- pose questions, make inferences, and draw conclusions about the detrimental effects of smoking
- apply the concepts of healthy behavior to designing ads to discourage people from smoking, and to encourage people to quit if they do smoke
- communicate their findings about smoking to people in three different age groups

Skills Focus
Inferring, drawing conclusions, applying concepts, communicating

Project Time Line 2 to 3 weeks

All in One Teaching Resources, Unit 3
- Chapter Project Teacher Notes
- Chapter Project Overview
- Chapter Project Worksheet 1
- Chapter Project Worksheet 2
- Chapter Project Scoring Rubric

Developing a Plan
Students can first talk about advertising, look at ads, and collect information from the chapter about respiratory functions and the detrimental effects of smoking on the body. Then students can address at least two pressures that influence people to smoke as they plan, design, and produce their ads.

Possible Materials
- Fashion, sports, and entertainment magazines will be useful for brainstorming ideas for convincing ads.
- Poster boards or large sheets of paper along with markers, crayons, or colored pencils should be available for making the posters.
- Students who elect to do radio or television commercials will need to write scripts and bring in props and/or costumes.

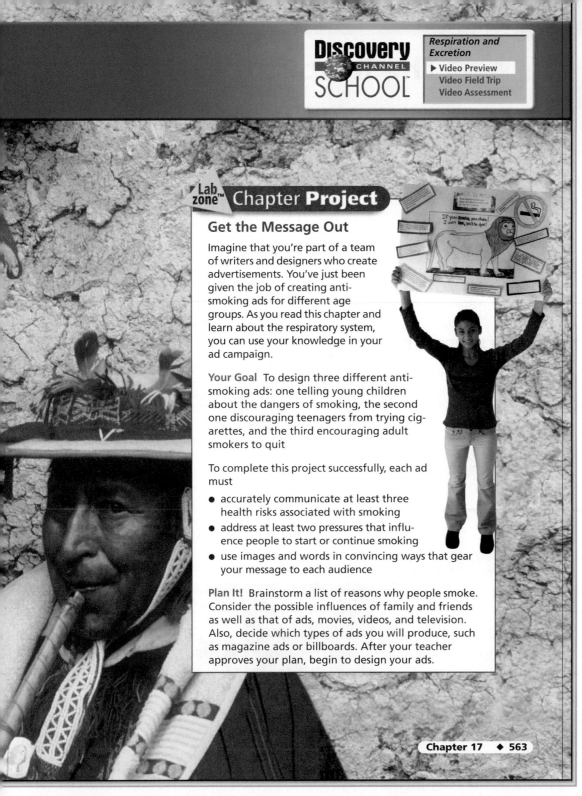

**Chapter Project**

Get the Message Out

Imagine that you're part of a team of writers and designers who create advertisements. You've just been given the job of creating anti-smoking ads for different age groups. As you read this chapter and learn about the respiratory system, you can use your knowledge in your ad campaign.

Your Goal To design three different anti-smoking ads: one telling young children about the dangers of smoking, the second one discouraging teenagers from trying cigarettes, and the third encouraging adult smokers to quit

To complete this project successfully, each ad must

● accurately communicate at least three health risks associated with smoking

● address at least two pressures that influence people to start or continue smoking

● use images and words in convincing ways that gear your message to each audience

Plan It! Brainstorm a list of reasons why people smoke. Consider the possible influences of family and friends as well as that of ads, movies, videos, and television. Also, decide which types of ads you will produce, such as magazine ads or billboards. After your teacher approves your plan, begin to design your ads.

Chapter 17 ◆ 563

Launching the Project

Ask: **Why do people start smoking?** (Sample answers: Peer pressure, curiosity) Ask: **Why do people who smoke keep smoking?** (Sample answer: They might try to stop but find that they can't.) Discuss reasons why people might smoke even though they know that smoking is unhealthy. Students should begin thinking about the detrimental effects of smoking and come up with ways to communicate this information to different age groups. To get students thinking about the influences that sway people of different ages, bring in several ads for different products. Lead a class discussion about the target audience for each ad, and have students explain why the ad would appeal to that audience.

Respiration and Excretion

Show the Video Preview to introduce the Chapter Project and present an overview of the chapter content. Discussion question: **Why is climbing to the summit of Mount Everest such a physical challenge?** (*The air pressure at the summit is one-third that at sea level. The human body isn't equipped to deal with such a low oxygen level.*)

Performance Assessment

The Chapter Project Scoring Rubric will help you evaluate how well students complete the Chapter Project. You may want to share the rubric with your students so that they will know what is expected. Students will be assessed on

● how well they support their decisions in terms of what messages will relate to the concerns of the three age groups

● how accurate the information contained in their ads is

● how thorough and organized their presentations are

● how well they work with other students

Portfolio

Objectives

After this lesson, students will be able to

17.1.1 Describe the functions of the respiratory system.

17.1.2 Identify the structures that air passes through as it travels to the lungs.

17.1.3 Describe what happens during gas exchange and breathing.

Target Reading Skill

Sequencing Explain that organizing information from beginning to end helps students understand a step-by-step process.

Answers
Possible answers:

Path of Air

Air enters the nose.
To the pharynx
To the trachea
To the bronchi
To the lungs
To the alveoli

All in One Teaching Resources, Unit 3

• Transparency LS164

Preteach

Build Background Knowledge   L2

Need for Oxygen

Ask: **Why do astronauts wear space suits and carry oxygen with them when they walk outside a spacecraft?** (*There is not enough oxygen in space to breathe.*) Ask: **Why do deep-sea divers take oxygen with them on a dive?** (*People can't breathe under water. Most students will realize that astronauts and divers need oxygen to survive.*)

The Respiratory System

Reading Preview

Key Concepts

• What are the functions of the respiratory system?

• What structures does air pass through as it travels to the lungs?

• What happens during gas exchange and breathing?

Key Terms

• respiration • cilia • pharynx
• trachea • bronchi • lungs
• alveoli • diaphragm • larynx
• vocal cords

Target Reading Skill

Sequencing As you read, make a flowchart that shows the path of air in the respiratory system. Write each step of the process in a separate box in the order in which it occurs.

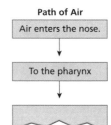

Path of Air

Air enters the nose.

↓

To the pharynx

↓

Lab zone Discover **Activity**

How Big Can You Blow Up a Balloon?

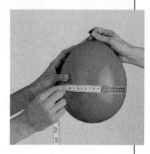

1. Take a normal breath, then blow as much air as possible into a balloon. Twist the end and hold it closed. Have your partner measure around the balloon at its widest point.

2. Let the air out of the balloon. Repeat Step 1 and calculate the average of the two measurements.

3. Compare your results with those of your classmates. The bigger the circumference, the greater the volume of air exhaled.

Think It Over
Inferring What factors might affect the volume of air a person can exhale?

Jerry, the main character in Doris Lessing's story "Through the Tunnel," is on vacation at the seaside. Day after day, he watches some older boys dive into deep water on one side of a huge rock. The boys mysteriously reappear on the other side. Jerry figures out that there must be an underwater tunnel in the rock. He finds the tunnel beneath the water and decides to swim through it. Once inside, though, he is terrified. The walls are slimy, and rocks scrape his body. He can barely see where he is going. But worst of all, Jerry has to hold his breath for far longer than ever before. The author describes Jerry this way: "His head was swelling, his lungs were cracking."

Hold your breath!

564 ◆

Lab zone Discover **Activity**

Skills Focus Inferring   L1

Materials large round balloons, metric measuring tape

Time 15 minutes

Tips Students should blow up the balloon several times and gently stretch it before beginning this activity. Remind students not to share balloons. Students with breathing difficulties may not be able to

blow up the balloons. They can act as measurers or calculators.

Expected Outcome Measurements will vary, depending upon the amount of air exhaled.

Think It Over Students may infer that factors such as smoking, air pollution, breathing difficulties, and colds may affect the volume of air a person can exhale.

Respiratory System Functions

No one can go for very long without breathing. Your body cells need oxygen, and they get that oxygen from the air you breathe. **The respiratory system moves oxygen from the outside environment into the body. It also removes carbon dioxide and water from the body.**

Taking in Oxygen The oxygen your body needs comes from the atmosphere—the mixture of gases that blankets Earth. Your body doesn't use most of the other gases in the air you breathe in. When you exhale, most of the air goes back into the atmosphere.

Oxygen is needed for the energy-releasing chemical reactions that take place inside your cells. Like a fire, which cannot burn without oxygen, your cells cannot "burn" enough fuel to keep you alive without oxygen. The process in which oxygen and glucose undergo a complex series of chemical reactions inside cells is called **respiration.** Respiration, which is also called cellular respiration, is different from breathing. Breathing refers to the movement of air into and out of the lungs. Respiration, on the other hand, refers to the chemical reactions inside cells. As a result of respiration, your cells release the energy that fuels growth and other cell processes.

Removing Carbon Dioxide and Water In addition to the release of energy, respiration produces carbon dioxide and water. Your respiratory system eliminates the carbon dioxide and some of the water through your lungs.

Math — Analyzing Data

The Air You Breathe

The air you breathe in contains several different gases, shown in the circle graph on the left. The air you breathe out contains the same gases, but in the amounts shown in the circle graph on the right.

1. **Reading Graphs** What does each wedge in the graphs represent?
2. **Interpreting Data** Based on the data, which gas is used by the body? Explain.
3. **Drawing Conclusions** Compare the percentage of carbon dioxide in inhaled air with the percentage in exhaled air. How can you account for the difference?

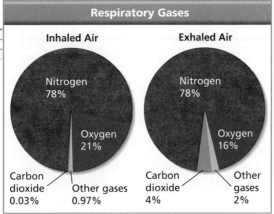

Respiratory Gases

Inhaled Air
Nitrogen 78%
Oxygen 21%
Carbon dioxide 0.03%
Other gases 0.97%

Exhaled Air
Nitrogen 78%
Oxygen 16%
Carbon dioxide 4%
Other gases 2%

4. **Inferring** Explain why the percentage of nitrogen is the same in both inhaled air and exhaled air.

Differentiated Instruction

English Learners/Beginning **L1**
Comprehension: Key Concepts Have students present the concepts in this section in a graphic presentation. For example, they can create flowcharts with pictures to show a sequence of events such as gas exchange or the breathing process. **learning modality: visual**

English Learners/Intermediate **L2**
Comprehension: Key Concepts Have students complete the same activity as Beginning students, but tell them to use words rather than pictures in their flowcharts. **learning modality: verbal**

Instruct

Respiratory System Functions

Teach Key Concepts **L2**
Respiratory System Gases

Focus Ask students what they know about the functions of the respiratory system.

Teach Ask: **What gases are exchanged by the respiratory system?** (*Oxygen and carbon dioxide*)

Apply Have students describe what they think happens in the body when a person holds his or her breath. (*The lungs fill up with carbon dioxide and are unable to provide oxygen to body cells.*) **learning modality: verbal**

All in One Teaching Resources, Unit 3
- Transparency LS165

Math — Analyzing Data

Math Skill Making and interpreting graphs

Focus Point out that circle graphs depict data that are presented as percentages.

Teach Ask: **What respiratory gases are being compared?** (*Inhaled air and exhaled air*) **How are the gases in air identified in each graph?** (*By color and labels*)

Answers
1. Percent of a gas breathed in or out.
2. Oxygen. Less oxygen is breathed out than is breathed in—meaning that some must have been used by the body.
3. There is a higher percentage of carbon dioxide in exhaled air. Carbon dioxide is a waste product of cellular activity.
4. Nitrogen is not used by the body and is not a waste product.

Independent Practice **L2**
All in One Teaching Resources, Unit 3
- Guided Reading and Study Worksheet: *The Respiratory System*

 **Student Edition on Audio CD**

Monitor Progress **L2**

Writing Ask students to write brief paragraphs, explaining the difference between breathing and respiration. Students can save their paragraphs in their portfolios.

The Path of Air

Teach Key Concepts

Tracing Air Through the Body

Focus Explain to students that air that is inhaled must travel through several organs on its way to the lungs.

Teach As you discuss this section, create a sequence map on the board, identifying how each organ processes air on its way to the lungs.

Apply Bring in a gauze mask. Ask: **What is the purpose of this mask?** *(To filter the air)* **When would a person wear a mask like this?** *(When a person is working with materials that might harm the respiratory system.)* **Why is it important that such a mask cover both the nose and the mouth?** *(Possible answer: Both can be used during respiration.)* **learning modality: logical/mathematical**

Use Visuals: Figure 2

The Respiratory System

Focus Have students trace the path that air takes as it enters the body.

Teach Ask: **Why is it important for air to be warmed and moistened when it enters the body?** *(Because the inside of the body is warm and moist; moist warm air helps the body maintain a stable state.)* Have students locate and feel their own tracheas. **learning modality: kinesthetic**

Apply What might happen if the trachea is blocked? *(No air would reach the lungs, and the person could suffocate.)* **learning modality: kinesthetic**

All in One **Teaching Resources, Unit 3**

• Transparency LS166

Help Students Read

Previewing Visuals Have students preview Figure 2. Ask: **Which organs are you familiar with?** *(Sample answer: Lungs, nose, and possibly bronchi)* Invite students to study the labels and descriptions. Tell them that the descriptions in the figure are shortened versions of what they find in the text. Ask them to compare the information in the figure with that in the text.

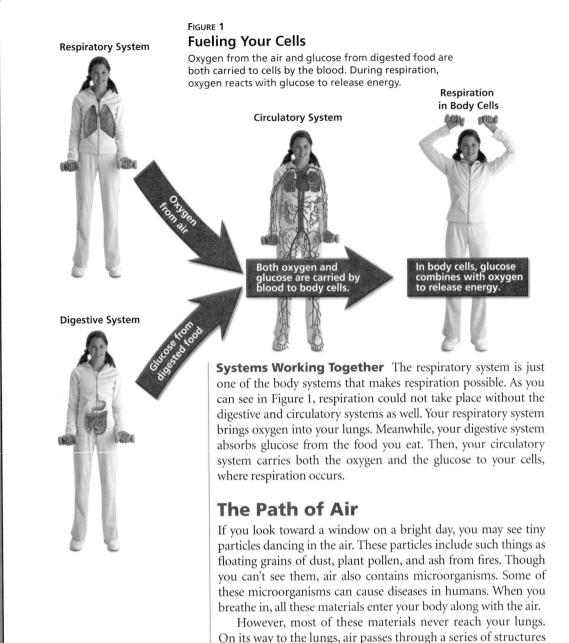

FIGURE 1
Fueling Your Cells
Oxygen from the air and glucose from digested food are both carried to cells by the blood. During respiration, oxygen reacts with glucose to release energy.

Respiratory System

Circulatory System

Respiration in Body Cells

Oxygen from air

Glucose from digested food

Digestive System

Both oxygen and glucose are carried by blood to body cells.

In body cells, glucose combines with oxygen to release energy.

Systems Working Together The respiratory system is just one of the body systems that makes respiration possible. As you can see in Figure 1, respiration could not take place without the digestive and circulatory systems as well. Your respiratory system brings oxygen into your lungs. Meanwhile, your digestive system absorbs glucose from the food you eat. Then, your circulatory system carries both the oxygen and the glucose to your cells, where respiration occurs.

The Path of Air

If you look toward a window on a bright day, you may see tiny particles dancing in the air. These particles include such things as floating grains of dust, plant pollen, and ash from fires. Though you can't see them, air also contains microorganisms. Some of these microorganisms can cause diseases in humans. When you breathe in, all these materials enter your body along with the air.

However, most of these materials never reach your lungs. On its way to the lungs, air passes through a series of structures that filter and trap particles. These organs also warm and moisten the air. **As air travels from the outside environment to the lungs, it passes through the following structures: nose, pharynx, trachea, and bronchi.** It takes air only a few seconds to complete the route from the nose to the lungs.

The Nose Air enters the body through the nose and then moves into spaces called the nasal cavities. Some of the cells lining the nasal cavities produce mucus. This sticky material moistens the air and keeps the lining from drying out. Mucus also traps particles such as dust.

The cells that line the nasal cavities have **cilia** (SIL ee uh), tiny hairlike extensions that can move together in a sweeping motion. The cilia sweep the mucus into the throat, where you swallow it. Stomach acid destroys the mucus, along with everything trapped in it.

Some particles and bacteria can irritate the lining of your nose or throat, causing you to sneeze. The powerful force of a sneeze shoots the particles out of your nose and into the air.

The Pharynx Next, air enters the **pharynx** (FAR ingks), or throat. The pharynx is the only part of the respiratory system that is shared with another system—the digestive system. Both the nose and the mouth connect to the pharynx.

> **Reading Checkpoint** What is the role of cilia?

FIGURE 2
The Respiratory System
On its path from outside the body into the lungs, air passes through several structures that clean, warm, and moisten it. Once in the lungs, the oxygen in the air can enter your bloodstream.
Classifying *Which part of the respiratory system is also part of the digestive system?*

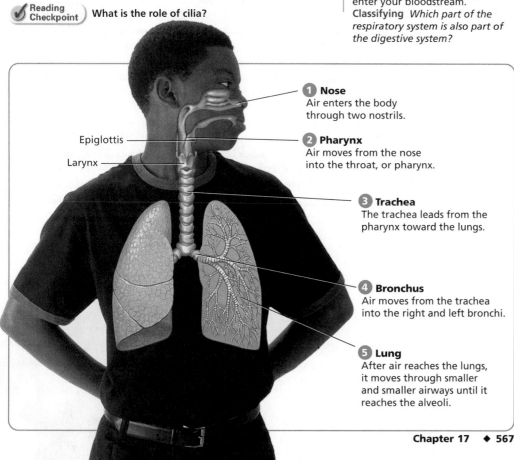

Epiglottis

Larynx

1 Nose
Air enters the body through two nostrils.

2 Pharynx
Air moves from the nose into the throat, or pharynx.

3 Trachea
The trachea leads from the pharynx toward the lungs.

4 Bronchus
Air moves from the trachea into the right and left bronchi.

5 Lung
After air reaches the lungs, it moves through smaller and smaller airways until it reaches the alveoli.

Chapter 17 ◆ 567

Structure of the Trachea

Materials none

Time 5 minutes

Focus Tell students that the trachea is located in front of the tube that takes food to the stomach, the esophagus.

Teach Have students locate the trachea in Figure 2. Then instruct them to gently feel along their necks for their tracheas. Ask students to describe what they feel. (*Students will note that they can feel ridges along the trachea.*) Explain that the ridges they feel are the rings of cartilage in the walls of the trachea.

Apply Ask: **What would happen if the trachea didn't have these rings of cartilage?** (*The trachea would collapse shut.*) **What affect would that have on the body?** (*No air would reach the lungs, and the person would suffocate.*) **learning modality: kinesthetic**

Help Students Read

Summarize Tell students that the information in *The Path of Air* contains a lot of details and that summarizing it will help them pull together the main ideas and avoid getting lost in the details. Allow students to choose whether they would like to present a verbal or written summary.

Gas Exchange

Teach Key Concepts L2

Capillary and Alveoli Characteristics

Focus Explain that the structure of the alveoli and the capillaries that surround them enables the alveoli to function in gas exchange.

Teach Ask: **What structural characteristic do alveoli and capillaries share?** (*Thin walls that allow certain materials to pass through them*) **What carries oxygen and carbon dioxide in the capillaries?** (*Hemoglobin in red blood cells carries oxygen and some carbon dioxide. Plasma carries most of the carbon dioxide.*)

Apply Ask: **What would be the effect on the body if the alveoli were unable to do their job?** (*Body cells would not receive the oxygen they need, and carbon dioxide would not be released from the blood.*) **learning modality: verbal**

Lab zone Try This Activity

What Do You Exhale?
Learn whether carbon dioxide is present in exhaled air.

1. Label two test tubes *A* and *B*.
2. Fill each test tube with 10 mL of water and a few drops of bromthymol blue solution. Bromthymol blue solution turns green or yellow in the presence of carbon dioxide.
3. Using a straw, gently blow air into the liquid in test tube A for a few seconds. **CAUTION:** *Do not suck the solution back through the straw.*
4. Compare the solutions in the test tubes.

Predicting Suppose you had exercised immediately before you blew into the straw. Predict how this would have affected the results.

Lab zone Try This Activity

Skills Focus Predicting L2

Materials bromthymol blue solution, 2 test tubes, plastic drinking straw, plastic wrap for covering test tubes (optional), safety goggles, water

Safety Caution students not to inhale through the straw. Review the safety guidelines in Appendix A.

Time 20 minutes

Expected Outcome The blue solution in test tube A will turn yellow when students blow into it, indicating the presence of carbon dioxide. Students should predict that, had they exercised before the activity, the color change would have occurred more quickly because their bodies would have been generating more carbon dioxide. **learning modality: visual**

The Trachea From the pharynx, air moves into the **trachea** (TRAY kee uh), or windpipe. You can feel your trachea if you gently run your fingers down the center of your neck. The trachea feels like a tube with a series of ridges. The firm ridges are rings of cartilage that strengthen the trachea and keep it open.

The trachea, like the nose, is lined with cilia and mucus. The cilia in the trachea sweep upward, moving mucus toward the pharynx, where it is swallowed. The trachea's cilia and mucus continue the cleaning and moistening of air that began in the nose. If particles irritate the lining of the trachea, you cough. A cough, like a sneeze, sends the particles into the air.

Normally, only air—not food—enters the trachea. If food does enter the trachea, the food can block the opening and prevent air from getting to the lungs. When that happens, a person chokes. Fortunately, food rarely gets into the trachea. The epiglottis, a small flap of tissue that folds over the trachea, seals off the trachea while you swallow.

The Bronchi and Lungs Air moves from the trachea to the **bronchi** (BRAHNG ky) (singular *bronchus*), the passages that direct air into the lungs. The **lungs** are the main organs of the respiratory system. The left bronchus leads into the left lung, and the right bronchus leads into the right lung. Inside the lungs, each bronchus divides into smaller and smaller tubes in a pattern that resembles the branches of a tree.

At the end of the smallest tubes are structures that look like bunches of grapes. The "grapes" are **alveoli** (al VEE uh ly) (singular *alveolus*), tiny sacs of lung tissue specialized for the movement of gases between air and blood. Notice in Figure 3 that each alveolus is surrounded by a network of capillaries. It is here that the blood picks up its cargo of oxygen from the air.

Reading Checkpoint How is food prevented from entering the trachea?

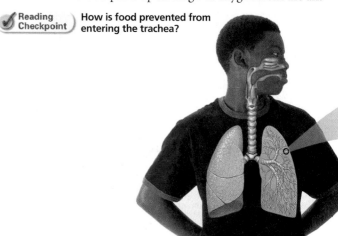

Gas Exchange

Because the walls of both the alveoli and the capillaries are very thin, certain materials can pass through them easily. **After air enters an alveolus, oxygen passes through the wall of the alveolus and then through the capillary wall into the blood. Carbon dioxide and water pass from the blood into the alveoli. This whole process is known as gas exchange.**

How Gas Exchange Occurs Imagine that you are a drop of blood beginning your journey through a capillary that wraps around an alveolus. When you begin that journey, you are carrying a lot of carbon dioxide and little oxygen. As you move through the capillary, oxygen gradually attaches to the hemoglobin in your red blood cells. At the same time, you are getting rid of carbon dioxide. At the end of your journey around the alveolus, you are rich in oxygen and poor in carbon dioxide.

Discovery CHANNEL SCHOOL

Respiration and Excretion

Video Preview
▶ Video Field Trip
Video Assessment

FIGURE 3
Gas Exchange in the Alveoli

Alveoli are hollow air sacs surrounded by capillaries. As blood flows through the capillaries, oxygen moves from the alveoli into the blood. At the same time, carbon dioxide moves from the blood into the alveoli.
Interpreting Diagrams *How is the structure of the alveoli important for gas exchange?*

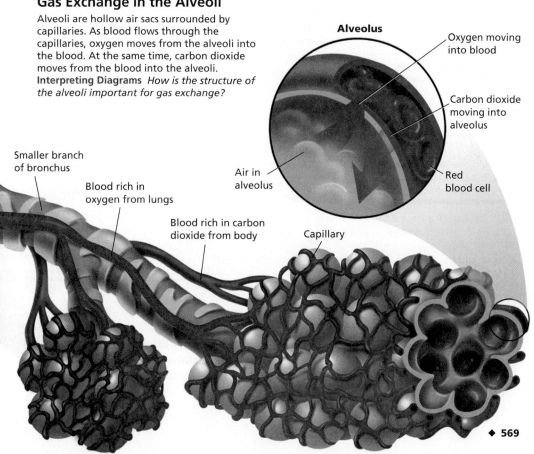

Smaller branch of bronchus

Blood rich in oxygen from lungs

Blood rich in carbon dioxide from body

Capillary

Alveolus

Oxygen moving into blood

Carbon dioxide moving into alveolus

Air in alveolus

Red blood cell

◆ 569

Discovery CHANNEL SCHOOL Video Field Trip

Respiration and Excretion

Show the Video Field Trip to help students understand the effects of lack of oxygen on the body. Discussion questions: **What is altitude sickness?** *(A condition that develops at high altitudes, where the body's cells do not receive enough oxygen; symptoms include headaches and nausea.)* **Why do climbers sometimes suffer from it?** *(The oxygen level decreases as altitude increases; the body needs time to acclimatize.)*

Use Visuals: Figure 3   L2
Gas Exchange in the Alveoli

Focus Explain how the processes in Figure 3 relate to the entire breathing process.

Teach Ask: **How does oxygen get into the alveoli?** *(From the trachea to a bronchus, and then through the smaller branches of the bronchi)* **What do you think happens to the carbon dioxide that the alveoli receive from the blood?** *(It is exhaled when the person breathes out.)*

Apply Ask: **What two body systems are interacting within the lungs?** *(Respiratory and circulatory systems)* **How might the exchange of gases be affected by disease of either body system?** (Sample answer: *The body might not get enough oxygen.*) **learning modality: visual**

All in One Teaching Resources, Unit 3
• Transparency LS167

Monitor Progress _____ L2

Writing Ask students to write explanations of what happens in the alveoli during gas exchange. Students can save their explanations in their portfolios.

Portfolio

Answers
Figure 3 The thin walls and large surface area of alveoli enhance their ability to exchange gases.

✔ **Reading Checkpoint** The epiglottis seals off the trachea during swallowing.

How You Breathe

Focus Remind students that muscles are involved in all movements of the body.

Teach Explain that breathing is considered movement because ribs move to allow the lungs to take in and expel air. Ask: **What muscles are involved in breathing?** *(The rib muscles and diaphragm)* **What occurs as these muscles contract?** *(The chest wall is lifted upward and outward, and the diaphragm moves downward. These actions make the chest cavity larger, allowing for the lungs to expand as air enters.)* Discuss how the opposite occurs when the muscles relax.

Apply Have students place their hands on the lower half of their ribcages and upper abdomen. Ask them to compare the movement of deep and shallow breathing. Ask: **Which is probably used while exercising? Explain.** *(Deep breathing; because more oxygen is taken in)* **learning modality: kinesthetic**

 **Teaching Resources, Unit 3**

• Transparency LS168

Math Skills Whole number operations

Focus Explain that determining surface area of the alveoli without the use of an equation would require a person to open them and spread them out onto a flat surface to measure.

Teach Walk students through the calculations to determine the surface area of a cube 2 cm by 2 cm on a side. For each step in the process, replace the actual measurements with Xs to create formulas. Students can use the formula when determining the surface area of a cube 3 cm by 3 cm on a side.

Answer 54 cm^2

FIGURE 4
Oxygen for Activities
The huge surface area of the alveoli supplies the oxygen these trombone players need to march and play.

Math Skills

Surface Area

Surface area refers to the total area of all of the surfaces of a three-dimensional object. Consider a cube, which has six equal sides. Each side measures 2 cm by 2 cm.

1. To find the surface area of the cube, first calculate the area of one of the six sides:
Area = length × width
= 2 cm × 2 cm = 4 cm^2
Each side has an area of 4 cm^2.

2. Next, add the areas of the six sides together to find the total surface area:
4 cm^2 + 4 cm^2 + 4 cm^2 + 4 cm^2 + 4 cm^2 + 4 cm^2 = 24 cm^2
The surface area of the cube is 24 cm^2.

Practice Problem Calculate the surface area of a cube whose side measures 3 cm.

Surface Area for Gas Exchange Your lungs can absorb a large amount of oxygen because of the large surface area of the alveoli. An adult's lungs contain about 300 million alveoli. If you opened the alveoli and spread them out on a flat surface, you would have a surface area of about 70 square meters.

The huge surface area of the alveoli enables the lungs to absorb a large amount of oxygen. The lungs can, therefore, supply the oxygen that people need—even when they are performing strenuous activities. When you play a wind instrument or a fast-paced game of basketball, you have your alveoli to thank.

Your lungs are not the only organs that provide a large surface area in a relatively small space. Recall from Chapter 2 that the small intestine contains numerous, tiny villi that increase the surface available to absorb food molecules.

Reading Checkpoint What gases are exchanged across the alveoli?

How You Breathe

In an average day, you may breathe more than 20,000 times. The rate at which you breathe depends on your body's need for oxygen. The more oxygen you need, the faster you breathe.

Muscles for Breathing Breathing, like other body movements, is controlled by muscles. Figure 5 shows the structure of the chest, including the muscles that enable you to breathe. Notice that the lungs are surrounded by the ribs, which have muscles attached to them. At the base of the lungs is the **diaphragm** (DY uh fram), a large, dome-shaped muscle that plays an important role in breathing.

Differentiated Instruction

Gifted and Talented L3
Demonstrating Sports coaches, voice teachers, and yoga practitioners, as well as professionals working in the area of stress management promote the benefits of slow, deep breathing from the abdomen. Have students form small groups to research the various systems of breathing techniques and exercises that are promoted in books and articles on exercise, sports competition, voice training, yoga, or stress management. Then have students present the benefits of deep breathing to the class and demonstrate an exercise or technique that they found most helpful. **learning modality: verbal**

The Process of Breathing When you breathe, the actions of your rib muscles and diaphragm expand or contract your chest. As a result, air flows in or out.

Here's what happens when you inhale, or breathe in. The rib muscles contract, lifting the chest wall upward and outward. At the same time, the diaphragm contracts and moves downward. The combined action of these muscles makes the chest cavity larger. The same amount of air now occupies a larger space, causing the pressure of the air inside your lungs to decrease. This change means that the pressure of air inside the chest cavity is lower than the pressure of the atmosphere pushing on the body. Because of this difference in air pressure, air rushes into your chest, in the same way that air is sucked into a vacuum cleaner.

When you exhale, or breathe out, the rib muscles and diaphragm relax. This reduces the size of the chest cavity. This decrease in size squeezes air out of the lungs, the way squeezing a container of ketchup pushes ketchup out of the opening.

 Reading Checkpoint What muscles cause the chest to expand during breathing?

FIGURE 5
The Breathing Process

When you inhale, the diaphragm moves downward and pressure in the lungs decreases, causing air to flow in. When you exhale, the diaphragm moves upward and the pressure in the lungs increases, pushing the air out.
Interpreting Diagrams *How does the movement of the diaphragm affect the size of the chest cavity?*

For: The Breathing Process activity
Visit: PHSchool.com
Web Code: cep-4041

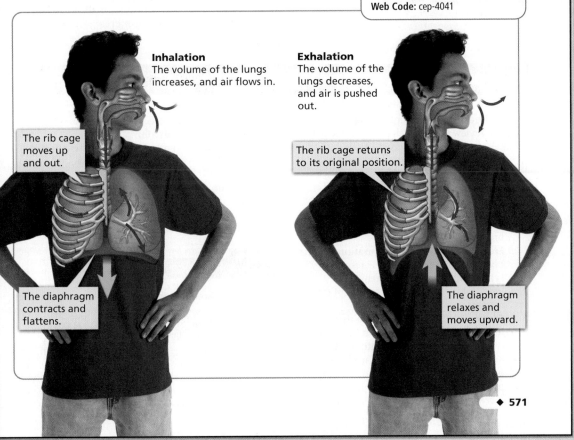

Inhalation
The volume of the lungs increases, and air flows in.

Exhalation
The volume of the lungs decreases, and air is pushed out.

The rib cage moves up and out.

The rib cage returns to its original position.

The diaphragm contracts and flattens.

The diaphragm relaxes and moves upward.

◆ 571

Monitor Progress L2

Answers
Figure 5 When the diaphragm contracts, the chest cavity increases in size. When it relaxes, the chest cavity decreases in size.

 Reading Checkpoint Oxygen and carbon dioxide

 Reading Checkpoint Rib and diaphragm muscles

Answer

Figure 6 The vocal cords stretch across the opening of the larynx.

Assess

Reviewing Key Concepts

1. a. The respiratory system moves oxygen from the outside environment into the body and removes carbon dioxide and water from the body. **b.** Respiration refers to chemical reactions inside cells. Breathing refers to movement of air into and out of the lungs. **c.** Possible answer: Chemical reactions in the cells require oxygen. The body obtains oxygen through the breathing action of the respiratory system. If the respiratory system didn't work, then cells might not get enough oxygen to function properly, and carbon dioxide could build up.

2. a. nose, pharynx, trachea, bronchi, lungs **b.** The oxygen molecule moves through the nostrils, pharynx, trachea, bronchus, smaller and smaller branches of the bronchial tree, and then into the alveolus. **c.** They help the body expel mucus containing dust, pollen, and other particles inhaled.

3. a. oxygen, carbon dioxide, and water **b.** It passes from the blood through the thin capillary wall and the wall of the alveolus into the alveolus. It is then exhaled and released into the environment. **c.** There will be less oxygen passing through the walls of the alveoli and into the bloodstream.

Reteach   L1

As a class, list the steps involved in the processes of breathing and gas exchange.

Performance Assessment   L2

Writing Have students write short stories describing the adventures of an oxygen molecule during respiration. Reports should include the path that the molecule traveled, and what happens to it during the gas exchange. Students can save their stories in their portfolios.

Portfolio

All in One Teaching Resources, Unit 3

- Section Summary: *The Respiratory System*
- Review and Reinforce: *The Respiratory System*
- Enrich: *The Respiratory System*

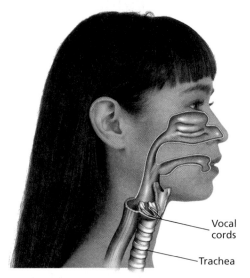

FIGURE 6
The Vocal Cords
Air moving over the vocal cords causes them to vibrate and produce sound.
Interpreting Diagrams *Where are the vocal cords located?*

Vocal cords

Trachea

Relating Breathing and Speaking The air that moves out of your lungs as you breathe also helps you speak. The **larynx** (LAR ingks), or voice box, is located in the top part of the trachea, underneath the epiglottis. Place your fingers on your Adam's apple, which sticks out from the front of your neck. You can feel some of the cartilage that makes up the larynx. Two **vocal cords,** folds of connective tissue that produce your voice, stretch across the opening of the larynx.

If you've ever let air out of a balloon while stretching its neck, you've heard the squeaking sound that the air makes. The neck of the balloon is something like your vocal cords. If you look at Figure 6 you can see that the vocal cords have a slitlike opening between them. When you speak, muscles make the vocal cords contract, narrowing the opening. Air from the lungs rushes through this opening. The movement of the vocal cords makes the air molecules vibrate, or move rapidly back and forth. This vibration creates a sound—your voice.

Section 1 Assessment

Target Reading Skill **Sequencing** With a partner, review your flowchart about the path of air. Add any necessary information.

Reviewing Key Concepts

1. a. Listing What are the functions of the respiratory system?
   b. Comparing and Contrasting Explain the difference between respiration and breathing.
   c. Predicting How might respiration in your body cells be affected if your respiratory system did not work properly?
2. a. Identifying Name the structures of the respiratory system.
   b. Sequencing Describe the path that a molecule of oxygen takes as it moves from the air outside your body into the alveoli.
   c. Relating Cause and Effect In a healthy person, how do coughing and sneezing protect the respiratory system?

3. a. Reviewing What three substances are exchanged in the alveoli?
   b. Explaining What happens to the carbon dioxide in the blood when it flows through the capillaries in the alveoli?
   c. Applying Concepts How would gas exchange be affected at the top of a tall mountain, where air pressure is lower and there is less oxygen than at lower elevations? Explain.

Math Practice

4. Surface Area A cube measures 4 cm × 4 cm on a side. Find its surface area.
5. Surface Area Suppose you cut up the cube into eight smaller cubes, each 2 cm × 2 cm on a side. If the larger cube represents a lung, and the smaller cubes represent alveoli, which would provide a larger surface area for oxygen exchange?

Math Practice

Math Skill Surface area

Answers

4. 4 × 4 = 16; 16 × 6 = 96 square centimeters
5. One cube = 24 square centimeters; thus, eight cubes = 192 square centimeters. The eight smaller cubes would provide more surface area.

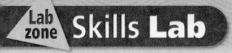

A Breath of Fresh Air

Problem
What causes your body to inhale and exhale air?

Skills Focus
making models, observing, drawing conclusions

Materials
- small balloon
- large balloon
- scissors
- transparent plastic bottle with narrow neck

Procedure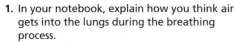

1. In your notebook, explain how you think air gets into the lungs during the breathing process.

2. Cut off and discard the bottom of a small plastic bottle. Trim the cut edge so there are no rough spots.

3. Stretch a small balloon; then blow it up a few times to stretch it further. Insert the round end of the balloon through the mouth of the bottle. Then, with a partner holding the bottle, stretch the neck of the balloon and pull it over the mouth of the bottle.

4. Stretch a large balloon; then blow it up a few times to stretch it further. Cut off and discard the balloon's neck.

5. Have a partner hold the bottle while you stretch the remaining part of the balloon over the bottom opening of the bottle, as shown in the photo.

6. Use one hand to hold the bottle firmly. With the knuckles of your other hand, push upward on the large balloon, causing it to form a dome. Remove your knuckles from the balloon, letting the balloon flatten. Repeat this procedure a few times. Observe what happens to the small balloon. Record your observations in your notebook.

Analyze and Conclude

1. **Making Models** Make a diagram of the completed model in your notebook. Add labels to show which parts of your model represent the chest cavity, diaphragm, lungs, and trachea.

2. **Observing** In this model, what is the position of the "diaphragm" just after you have made the model "exhale"? What do the lungs look like just after you have exhaled?

3. **Drawing Conclusions** In this model, how does the "diaphragm" move? How do these movements of the "diaphragm" affect the "lungs"?

4. **Communicating** Write a paragraph describing how this model shows that pressure changes are responsible for breathing.

More to Explore

How could you improve on this model to show more closely what happens in the chest cavity during the process of breathing? *Obtain your teacher's permission before carrying out your investigation.*

A Breath of Fresh Air

Prepare for Inquiry

Key Concept
A model of the lungs will demonstrate what happens during inhalation and exhalation.

Skills Objectives
After this lab, students will be able to
- make a model of the lungs and diaphragm
- observe how the lungs and diaphragm move in their model
- draw conclusions about how movement of the diaphragm affects the lungs

 Prep Time 30 minutes
Class Time 30 minutes

Alternative Materials
You can use different sizes of bottles and balloons, but make sure the small balloon hangs freely. If a balloon does not make an airtight seal with the bottle, tape the seal.

Safety
You may want to cut the plastic bottles yourself or make the process easier by making the first cut.

All in One Teaching Resources, Unit 3
- Lab Worksheet: *A Breath of Fesh Air*

Guide Inquiry

Invitation
Encourage students to share their responses to Step 1 in the Procedure.

Introduce the Procedure
Have students refer to the photo in the book.

Troubleshooting the Experiment
Be sure students do not pull the large balloon down to model inhalation. To show the relaxed (exhaled) state, the balloon should be dome shaped. The balloon flattens during inhalation.

Expected Outcome
The smaller balloon should deflate when students push up on the larger balloon and inflate when they let go.

Analyze and Conclude
1. Bottle—chest cavity; large balloon—diaphragm; small balloon—lungs; neck of the bottle—trachea

2. The diaphragm rises into the chest cavity. The lungs are deflated.

3. The diaphragm moves down, becoming flat, and then moves upward into its domed shape. When it moves down, the lungs inflate. When it moves upward, the lungs deflate.

4. When the volume inside the plastic bottle increases, it decreases the air pressure inside, and the small balloon inflates. When the volume inside the bottle decreases, it increases the air pressure inside and causes the small balloon to deflate.

Extend Inquiry

More to Explore Students could use many small balloons and straws to show that surface area of the lungs is large because of numerous alveoli; use a flexible plastic bottle to show that the ribs also move during inhalation, increasing the volume of the chest cavity.

Objectives

After this lesson, students will be able to

17.2.1 Identify the harmful chemicals contained in tobacco smoke.

17.2.2 Explain how tobacco smoke affects a person's health over time.

Target Reading Skill 🔁

Relating Cause and Effect Explain that cause is the reason for what happens. The effect is what happens because of the cause. Relating cause and effect helps students relate the reason for what happens to what happens as a result.

Answers

Possible effects:
Damage to protective cilia and risk of cancer due to tar; increase in blood pressure and addiction due to nicotine; risk over time of chronic bronchitis, emphysema, lung cancer, and atherosclerosis.

All in One Teaching Resources, Unit 3

• Transparency LS169

Preteach

Build Background Knowledge L2

Smoking and Popular Culture

Have students discuss their perceptions of smoking and popular culture. Encourage students to talk about how the image of smoking has changed over the years. Students may be aware of laws that restrict the areas where smoking is permitted or of lawsuits that have been brought against cigarette manufacturers.

Reading Preview

Key Concepts

• What harmful chemicals are found in tobacco smoke?
• How can tobacco smoke affect a person's health over time?

Key Terms

• tar • carbon monoxide
• nicotine • addiction
• bronchitis • emphysema

🔁 Target Reading Skill

Relating Cause and Effect As you read, identify the effects of smoking on the body. Write the information in a graphic organizer like the one below.

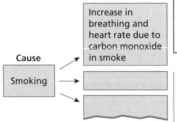

Cause: Smoking

Effects: Increase in breathing and heart rate due to carbon monoxide in smoke

Lab zone Discover Activity

What Are the Dangers of Smoking?

The graph shows the rate of lung cancer deaths in the United States from 1930 to 2000.

1. What was the rate of lung cancer deaths for males in 1930? For females?
2. What was the rate of lung cancer deaths for males in 1990? For females?
3. Did males or females show a faster rate of increase in the number of lung cancer deaths? How can you tell?
4. Cigarette smoking increased until 1965 but then decreased between 1965 and 1990. How does the trend in smoking compare with the rate of lung cancer deaths?

Think It Over

Predicting Do you think that the rate of lung cancer deaths is likely to increase, decrease, or remain the same by 2010? Explain.

Whoosh! Millions of tiny but dangerous aliens are invading the respiratory system. The aliens are pulled into the mouth with an inhaled breath. The cilia trap some aliens, and others get stuck in mucus. But thousands of the invaders get past these defenses and enter the lungs. The aliens then land on the surface of the alveoli!

The "aliens" are not tiny creatures from space. They are the substances found in cigarette smoke. In this section you will learn how tobacco smoke damages the respiratory system.

A heavy smoker may smoke two packs of cigarettes in a day.

Lab zone Discover Activity

Skills Focus Predicting **L1**

Materials none

Time 20 minutes

Expected Outcome 1. For males and females, both about 5 per 100,000
2. Males: about 90; females: almost 40
3. Males; the line rises faster than it does for females. 4. The rate of lung cancer deaths continued to increase until about 1990.

Think It Over The rate may decrease for men, as indicated by the graph. For women, the rate appears to be leveling off.

Chemicals in Tobacco Smoke

With each puff, a smoker inhales more than 4,000 different chemicals. **Some of the most deadly chemicals in tobacco smoke are tar, carbon monoxide, and nicotine.**

Tar The dark, sticky substance that forms when tobacco burns is called **tar.** When someone inhales tobacco smoke, some tar settles on cilia that line the trachea, bronchi, and smaller airways. Tar makes cilia clump together so they can't function to prevent harmful materials from getting into the lungs. Tar also contains chemicals that have been shown to cause cancer.

Carbon Monoxide When substances—including tobacco—are burned, a colorless, odorless gas called **carbon monoxide** is produced. Carbon monoxide is dangerous because its molecules bind to hemoglobin in red blood cells. When carbon monoxide binds to hemoglobin, it takes the place of some of the oxygen that the red blood cells normally carry. The carbon monoxide molecules are something like cars that are parked in spaces reserved for other cars.

When carbon monoxide binds to hemoglobin, red blood cells carry less than their normal load of oxygen throughout the body. To make up for the decrease in oxygen, the breathing rate increases and the heart beats faster. Smokers' blood may contain too little oxygen to meet their bodies' needs.

Nicotine Another dangerous chemical found in tobacco is **nicotine.** Nicotine is a stimulant drug that increases the activities of the nervous system and heart. It makes the heart beat faster and increases blood pressure. Over time, nicotine produces an **addiction,** or physical dependence. Smokers feel an intense craving for a cigarette if they go without one. Addiction to nicotine is one reason why smokers have difficulty quitting.

 Reading Checkpoint How does the tar in cigarettes affect the body?

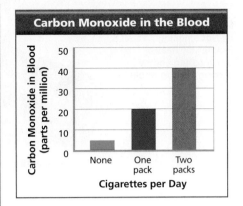

Carbon Monoxide in the Blood

FIGURE 7
Carbon Monoxide in the Blood
The more cigarettes a person smokes, the more carbon monoxide he or she inhales.
Relating Cause and Effect *How does carbon monoxide deprive the body of oxygen?*

SURGEON GENERAL'S WARNING: Cigarette Smoke Contains Carbon Monoxide.

SURGEON GENERAL'S WARNING: Smoking Causes Lung Cancer, Heart Disease, Emphysema, and May Complicate Pregnancy.

SURGEON GENERAL'S WARNING: Smoking By Pregnant Women May Result in Fetal Injury, Premature Birth, and Low Birth Weight.

Chapter 17 ◆ 575

Instruct

Chemicals in Tobacco Smoke

Teach Key Concepts L2
Physical Effects of Smoking

Focus Explain that cigarettes are the most common form of tobacco use, but that cigar and pipe smoke have similar chemicals and effects on the body.

Teach Ask: **What are the three main chemicals found in smoke?** *(Tar, carbon monoxide, nicotine)* Ask: **What are the effects of these chemicals?** *Tar causes cilia to clump so that they can't keep harmful materials out of the lungs. Tar contains chemicals that cause cancer. Carbon monoxide takes the place of oxygen molecules on hemoglobin. This leads to increases in breathing and heart rate to make up for the lack of oxygen. Nicotine speeds up the nervous system and heart and increases blood pressure. Nicotine produces addiction.)*

Apply Discuss the effects of addiction and the misconception that quitting smoking is easy. **learning modality: verbal**

Independent Practice L2
All in One Teaching Resources, Unit 3

• Guided Reading and Study Worksheet: *Smoking and Your Health*

 Student Edition on Audio CD

Monitor Progress _____ L2

Answers
Figure 7 When carbon monoxide binds to hemoglobin, it takes the place of the oxygen that the red blood cells normally carry.

 Reading Checkpoint Tar settles on cilia preventing them from functioning to keep harmful substances out of the lungs.

575

Differentiated Instruction

Special Needs L1
Outlining Help pairs of students work together to create an outline using the headings from the section. Then help them fill in details as they read the section.
learning modality: verbal

Gifted and Talented L3
Building Awareness Tell students that smoking is now forbidden in aircrafts, many workplaces, restaurants, and public buildings. Ask if students can explain why these restrictions have been imposed and whom they were designed to protect. Interested students can research the laws governing smoking in your community.
learning modality: verbal

Health Problems and Smoking

Teach Key Concepts L2
Diseases Associated With Smoking

Focus Emphasize that over time smokers will likely develop one or more diseases of the respiratory or circulatory system.

Teach Ask: **Which diseases are associated with the respiratory system?** *(Bronchitis, emphysema, and lung cancer)* **What is the result of chronic bronchitis and emphysema?** *(Permanent damage to the lungs)* **What makes treatment of lung cancer often ineffective?** *(It is difficult to detect lung cancer early enough.)*

Apply Ask: **Compare the likely quality of life of a smoker and nonsmoker when they are senior citizens.** *(Possible answer: A smoker probably couldn't be as active as a nonsmoker and might be sick more often.)* **learning modality: verbal**

Help Students Read L1

Using Prior Knowledge Refer to the Content Refresher, which provides guidelines for Using Prior Knowledge. Have students make lists in which they address the question: **What are some smoking-related health problems that you already know about?** *(Sample answers: Lung cancer, shortness of breath, frequent coughing)* Invite students to read items from their lists as you record the information on the board. Lead the students in a discussion of other types of problems not mentioned.

◼ Address Misconceptions L2
Addictiveness of Nicotine

Focus Students may have heard statements that nicotine is not an addictive drug like heroin or cocaine, leading them to think that quitting smoking is easier than quitting a so-called "hard" drug.

Teach Inform students that researchers have found that nicotine releases the same chemicals in the brain that heroin, cocaine, and other drugs release. Explain that this research points to a physical basis for nicotine addiction.

Apply Ask: **What are the implications of the research on smoking?** (Sample answer: *A physical addiction to nicotine makes it more difficult to quit smoking; nicotine is a dangerous drug.*) **learning modality: verbal**

FIGURE 8
Staying Healthy by Not Smoking
People stay healthy by exercising and by choosing not to smoke.

Lung of a nonsmoker

Health Problems and Smoking

Tobacco smoke causes health problems in several ways. For example, because the cilia can't sweep away mucus, many smokers have a frequent cough. The mucus buildup also limits the space for airflow, thus decreasing oxygen intake. Because they are not getting enough oxygen, long-term or heavy smokers may be short of breath during even light exercise.

You probably know that smoking damages the respiratory system, but did you know that it strains the circulatory system as well? The respiratory and circulatory systems work together to get oxygen to body cells. If either system is damaged, the other one must work harder. Serious health problems can result from long-term smoking. **Over time, smokers can develop chronic bronchitis, emphysema, lung cancer, and atherosclerosis.** Every year in the United States, more than 400,000 people die from smoking-related illnesses. That's one out of every five deaths. Tobacco smoke is the most important preventable cause of major illness and death.

Chronic Bronchitis Bronchitis (brahng KY tis) is an irritation of the breathing passages in which the small passages become narrower than normal and may be clogged with mucus. People with bronchitis have difficulty breathing. If the irritation continues over a long time, it is called chronic bronchitis. Chronic bronchitis can cause permanent damage to the breathing passages. It is often accompanied by infection with disease-causing microorganisms. Chronic bronchitis is five to ten times more common in heavy smokers than in nonsmokers.

Lab zone Skills **Activity**

Calculating

Heavy smokers may smoke two packs of cigarettes every day. Find out what one pack of cigarettes costs. Then, use that price to calculate how much a person would spend on cigarettes if he or she smoked two packs a day for 30 years.

Lab zone Skills **Activity**

Skills Focus Calculating L2

Materials None

Time 5 minutes

Tips Ask students to provide a range of costs for a pack of cigarettes, based on advertising, or give them an average price to work with.

Expected Outcome Answers will depend on the price of the cigarettes.

Extend Have students figure out some things that the person could do if he or she saved the money spent on cigarettes.

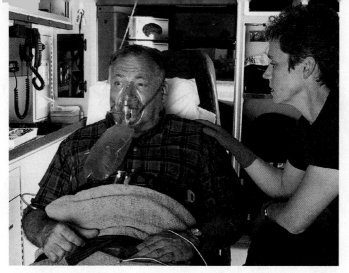

Emphysema The chemicals in tobacco smoke damage lung tissue as well as breathing passages. **Emphysema** (em fuh SEE muh) is a serious disease that destroys lung tissue and causes breathing difficulties. People with emphysema do not get enough oxygen and cannot adequately eliminate carbon dioxide. Therefore, they are always short of breath. Some people with emphysema even have trouble blowing out a match. Unfortunately, the damage caused by emphysema is permanent, even if a person stops smoking.

Lung Cancer About 140,000 Americans die each year from lung cancer caused by smoking. Cigarette smoke contains more than 50 different chemicals that cause cancer, including the chemicals in tar. Cancerous growths, or tumors, take away space in the lungs that are used for gas exchange. Unfortunately, lung cancer is rarely detected early, when treatment would be most effective.

Atherosclerosis The chemicals in tobacco smoke also harm the circulatory system. Some of the chemicals get into the blood and are absorbed by the blood vessels. The chemicals then irritate the walls of the blood vessels. This irritation contributes to the buildup of fatty material on the blood vessel walls that causes atherosclerosis. Atherosclerosis can lead to heart attacks. Compared to nonsmokers, smokers are more than twice as likely to have heart attacks.

 Reading Checkpoint How does emphysema affect a person's lungs?

FIGURE 9
Effects of Smoking on the Lungs
Over time, smoking damages the lungs and leads to serious health problems. **Comparing and Contrasting** *Compare the lungs of a person with emphysema and a person with lung cancer to the lung of a nonsmoker shown in Figure 8.*

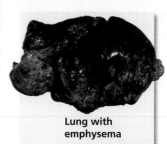
Lung with emphysema

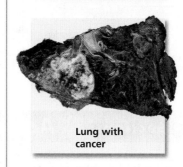
Lung with cancer

Modeling a Health-Checkup Procedure

Materials 2 plastic cups, eraser, water, pencil
Time 5 minutes

Focus Ask: **Have you ever seen a doctor "thumping" on a person's back on television or in a movie or experienced it yourself?** *(Many will have.)* Explain that this is one way a doctor can tell whether the lungs are clear or have liquid in them.

Teach Pairs of students can model this procedure by standing two plastic drinking cups side by side, one filled with water, the other containing an eraser to weigh it down. Have one partner turn with his or her back to the cups while the other sets up the cups and then taps on each one. The student who is not facing the cups can note the differences in sound and try to identify the cup of water.

Apply Ask: **What does liquid in the lungs likely indicate?** *(Illness; chest congestion)* **learning modality: kinesthetic**

Use Visuals: Figure 9 L2
Effects of Smoking on the Lungs
Focus Identify each of the lung samples.

Teach Ask: **How do the lungs of a nonsmoker compare with the diseased lungs in appearance?** *(The healthy lungs are pink and moist; the diseased lungs look dry, blackened or pale, and spotted with growths.)*

Apply Have students infer why the condition of the diseased lungs would likely affect a person's health. *(The diseased lungs would not be able to take in very much air, and they would not be able to exchange gas with the circulatory system.)* **learning modality: visual**

Monitor Progress _____ L2

Oral Presentation Ask students to identify and describe three respiratory system problems that result from cigarette smoking.

Answers
Figure 9 Sample answer: Lungs with emphysema or cancer appear dark, diseased, and as if they have been destroyed. Lungs of nonsmokers appear pink and healthy.

 Reading Checkpoint It destroys lung tissue.

Assess

Reviewing Key Concepts

1. a. tar, carbon monoxide, nicotine
b. Tar affects the respiratory system. It causes cilia to clump together so they can't prevent harmful materials from entering the lungs. Tar also contains chemicals that cause cancer. Carbon monoxide affects the circulatory and respiratory systems. It binds to hemoglobin in red blood cells so that they can't carry enough oxygen, which leads to increased breathing and heart rates. Nicotine affects the nervous system and the heart. It speeds up their activities and increases blood pressure. It also causes addiction. **c.** The nicotine in the products will help satisfy the person's craving for nicotine.
2. a. bronchitis, emphysema, lung cancer, atherosclerosis **b.** Chemicals from smoke get into the blood, are absorbed by blood vessels, and then irritate the walls of the blood vessels. The irritation contributes to the buildup of fatty materials. **c.** The blood could carry more oxygen. The blood vessels would no longer be irritated by the chemicals in the tobacco smoke. Blood pressure might be lower. The person then would be less likely to have atherosclerosis or a heart attack.

Reteach   L1

Have students identify three parts of the body and write one or two sentences about the effect of tobacco smoke on each.

Performance Assessment   L2

Writing Have students write paragraphs in which they convince a friend not to smoke. They can save their paragraphs in their portfolios.

Portfolio

All in One Teaching Resources, Unit 3

- Section Summary: *Smoking and Your Health*
- Review and Reinforce: *Smoking and Your Health*
- Enrich: *Smoking and Your Health*

578

FIGURE 10
Passive Smoking
Billboards like this one increase people's awareness that nonsmokers can also suffer from the effects of tobacco smoke.

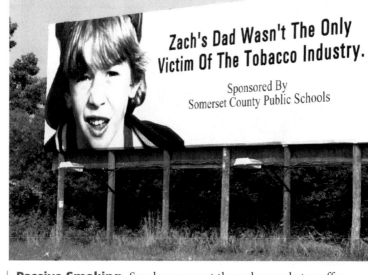

Zach's Dad Wasn't The Only Victim Of The Tobacco Industry.

Sponsored By
Somerset County Public Schools

Passive Smoking Smokers are not the only people to suffer from the effects of tobacco smoke. In passive smoking, people involuntarily inhale the smoke from other people's cigarettes, cigars, or pipes. This smoke contains the same harmful chemicals that smokers inhale. Each year, passive smoking is associated with the development of bronchitis and other respiratory problems, such as asthma, in about 300,000 young children in the United States.

Section 2 Assessment

Target Reading Skill **Relating Cause and Effect** Refer to your graphic organizer about the effects of smoking on the body to help you answer the questions below.

Reviewing Key Concepts

1. a. Listing What are three harmful substances in tobacco smoke?
b. Relating Cause and Effect How does each of the harmful substances directly affect the body?
c. Developing Hypotheses Why might nicotine-containing products, such as chewing gums or skin patches, help a person who is trying to quit smoking?

2. a. Reviewing Identify four health problems that can develop in smokers over time.
b. Describing How does smoking contribute to atherosclerosis?
c. Inferring What effect would it have on the circulatory system if a person quit smoking?

Lab zone **At-Home Activity**

Warning Labels With a family member, make a list of the warning statements found on cigarette labels. What chemicals found in tobacco smoke and health problems do the labels identify? Summarize the information you find to share with the class.

Lab zone **Chapter Project**

Keep Students on Track By now students should have sketched what their ads might look like and written what they might say. Review students' ads to make sure that they indicate a relationship between what students are learning about respiratory function and health problems associated with smoking.

Lab zone **At-Home Activity**

Warning Labels L2 Encourage students to discuss with a family member information that they have learned about chemicals in cigarette smoke and the effects of these chemicals on health. Suggest that students record the information that they gather from the warning labels in a graphic organizer, such as a table, to summarize the information to share with the class.

Reading Preview

Key Concepts
- What are the structures and functions of the excretory system?
- How do the kidneys filter wastes from the blood?
- How does excretion contribute to homeostasis?

Key Terms
- excretion • urea • kidney
- urine • ureter
- urinary bladder • urethra
- nephron

Target Reading Skill
Previewing Visuals Before you read, preview Figure 11. Then, write two questions that you have about the diagram in a graphic organizer like the one below. As you read, answer your questions.

How the Kidneys Filter Wastes

Q.	Where are nephrons located?
A.	
Q.	

How Does Filtering a Liquid Change the Liquid?

1. Your teacher will give you 50 mL of a liquid in a small container. Pour a small amount of sand into the liquid.
2. Use a glucose test strip to determine whether glucose is present in the liquid.
3. Put filter paper in a funnel. Then, put the funnel into the mouth of a second container. Slowly pour the liquid through the funnel into the second container.
4. Look for any solid material on the filter paper. Remove the funnel, and carefully examine the liquid that passed through the filter.
5. Test the liquid again to see whether it contains glucose.

Think It Over

Observing Which substances passed through the filter, and which did not? How might a filtering device be useful in the body?

The human body faces a challenge that is a bit like trying to keep your room clean. Magazines, notebook paper, and CD wrappers tend to pile up in your room. You use all of these things, but sooner or later you must clean your room if you don't want to be buried in trash. Something similar happens in your body. As your cells use nutrients in respiration and other processes, wastes are created. Different organs in the body have roles for the removal of these wastes. The removal process is known as **excretion.**

If wastes were not removed from your body, they would pile up and make you sick. Excretion helps keep the body's internal environment stable and free of harmful materials. **The excretory system is the system in the body that collects wastes produced by cells and removes the wastes from the body.**

Chapter 17 ◆ 579

The Excretory System

Objectives

After this lesson, students will be able to

17.3.1 Identify the structures and functions of the excretory system.

17.3.2 State how the kidneys filter wastes from the blood.

17.3.3 Explain how excretion contributes to homeostasis.

Target Reading Skill 🔄

Previewing Visuals Explain that previewing visuals helps students activate prior knowledge and predict what they are about to read.

Answers

Possible student questions and answers are these: **Where are nephrons located?** *(In the kidneys)* **What three main materials are filtered out of the blood?** *(Urea, water, glucose)* **What happens to these filtered materials?** *(Most of the water and glucose are reabsorbed. Most of the urea is excreted in urine.)*

All in One Teaching Resources, Unit 3
- Transparency LS170

Preteach

Build Background Knowledge L2

Importance of Waste Removal

Have students list some typical items that families discard as trash. Ask: **What would happen if no one ever removed this trash from their apartment?** *(Sample answer: The trash could build up until it overflowed the trash cans, started to fill living areas, and became a health hazard.)* Point out that the body produces "trash" substances that need to be eliminated.

Skills Focus Observing   L1

Materials glucose solution, sand, two small plastic containers, glucose test strip, plastic funnel, filter paper

Time 15 minutes

Tips Prepare the glucose solution, using 5 g of glucose per liter of water. Each plastic container should hold at least 75 mL.

Expected Outcome The glucose solution will pass through the filter, but the sand will not.

Think It Over The glucose and water passed through the filter; the sand did not. A filtering device could remove wastes in the body.

The Excretory System

Teach Key Concepts　L2

Excretory System Function

Focus Remind students that the body produces wastes and removes wastes.

Teach Explain that the kidneys, the major organs of the excretory system, remove wastes from the blood. Ask: **What are examples of wastes that need to be removed?** *(Urea and excess water)* **What parts of the excretory system function to eliminate these wastes from the body?** *(Kidneys, urinary bladder, and urethra)*

Apply Ask: **What might happen if wastes were not eliminated daily?** *(They would build up and keep the body from functioning as it should and eventually cause illness.)*
learning modality: verbal

All in One Teaching Resources, Unit 3

• Transparency LS171

Independent Practice　L2

All in One Teaching Resources, Unit 3

• Guided Reading and Study Worksheet: *The Excretory System*

⊙ **Student Edition on Audio CD**

Filtration of Wastes

Teach Key Concepts　L2

Stages of Waste Removal

Focus Tell students that during the first stage of waste removal blood enters the kidneys.

Teach Direct students' attention to each stage shown in Figure 11. Ask students to identify the artery, nephron, and capillaries and tell how each functions in the stages of urine formation.

Apply Ask: **What might urine analysis tell?** *(It might tell if substances are in the urine that should not be there, such as glucose.)* **learning modality: visual**

All in One Teaching Resources, Unit 3

• Transparency LS172

The Excretory System

Two wastes that your body must eliminate are excess water and urea. **Urea** (yoo REE uh) is a chemical that comes from the breakdown of proteins. **The structures of the excretory system that eliminate urea, water, and other wastes include the kidneys, ureters, urinary bladder, and urethra.**

Your two **kidneys,** which are the major organs of the excretory system, remove urea and other wastes from the blood. The kidneys act like filters. They remove wastes but keep materials that the body needs. The wastes are eliminated in **urine**, a watery fluid that contains urea and other wastes. Urine flows from the kidneys through two narrow tubes called **ureters** (yoo REE turz). The ureters carry urine to the **urinary bladder,** a sacklike muscular organ that stores urine. Urine leaves the body through a small tube called the **urethra** (yoo REE thruh).

 Reading Checkpoint What is the role of the ureters?

Filtration of Wastes

The kidneys are champion filters. Each of your kidneys contains about a million **nephrons,** tiny filtering factories that remove wastes from blood and produce urine. **The nephrons filter wastes in stages. First, both wastes and needed materials, such as glucose, are filtered out of the blood. Then, much of the needed material is returned to the blood, and the wastes are eliminated from the body.** Follow this process in Figure 11.

Filtering Out Wastes During the first stage of waste removal, blood enters the kidneys. Here, the blood flows through smaller and smaller arteries. Eventually it reaches a cluster of capillaries in a nephron. The capillaries are surrounded by a thin-walled, hollow capsule that is connected to a tube. In the capillary cluster, urea, glucose, and some water move out of the blood and into the capsule. Blood cells and most protein molecules do not move into the capsule. Instead, they remain in the capillaries.

Formation of Urine Urine forms from the filtered material in the capsule. This material flows through the long, twisting tube. As the liquid moves through the tube, many of the substances are returned to the blood. Normally, all the glucose, most of the water, and small amounts of other materials pass back into the blood in the capillaries that surround the tube. In contrast, urea and other wastes remain in the tube.

Lab zone Skills **Activity**

Classifying

A number of materials enter the kidney, where they are filtered by the nephrons.

• What materials enter a nephron?

• What materials are returned to the blood?

• What materials leave the body in urine?

580 ◆

Lab zone Skills **Activity**

Skills Focus Classifying

Materials None

Time 5 minutes

Tips Remind students that blood carries many substances, including nutrients, glucose, hormones, wastes, and dissolved gases.

L2 **Expected Outcome** Urea, water, glucose are filtered from the blood into the nephron. Most of the water and glucose and a small amount of the other materials are returned to the blood. Urea and other wastes leave the body in urine.

FIGURE 11
How the Kidneys Filter Wastes

The structures of the excretory system include the kidneys, urinary bladder, and urethra. Each kidney contains about a million tiny filtering units called nephrons. Urine is produced in the nephrons.
Interpreting Diagrams *Where are the kidneys located?*

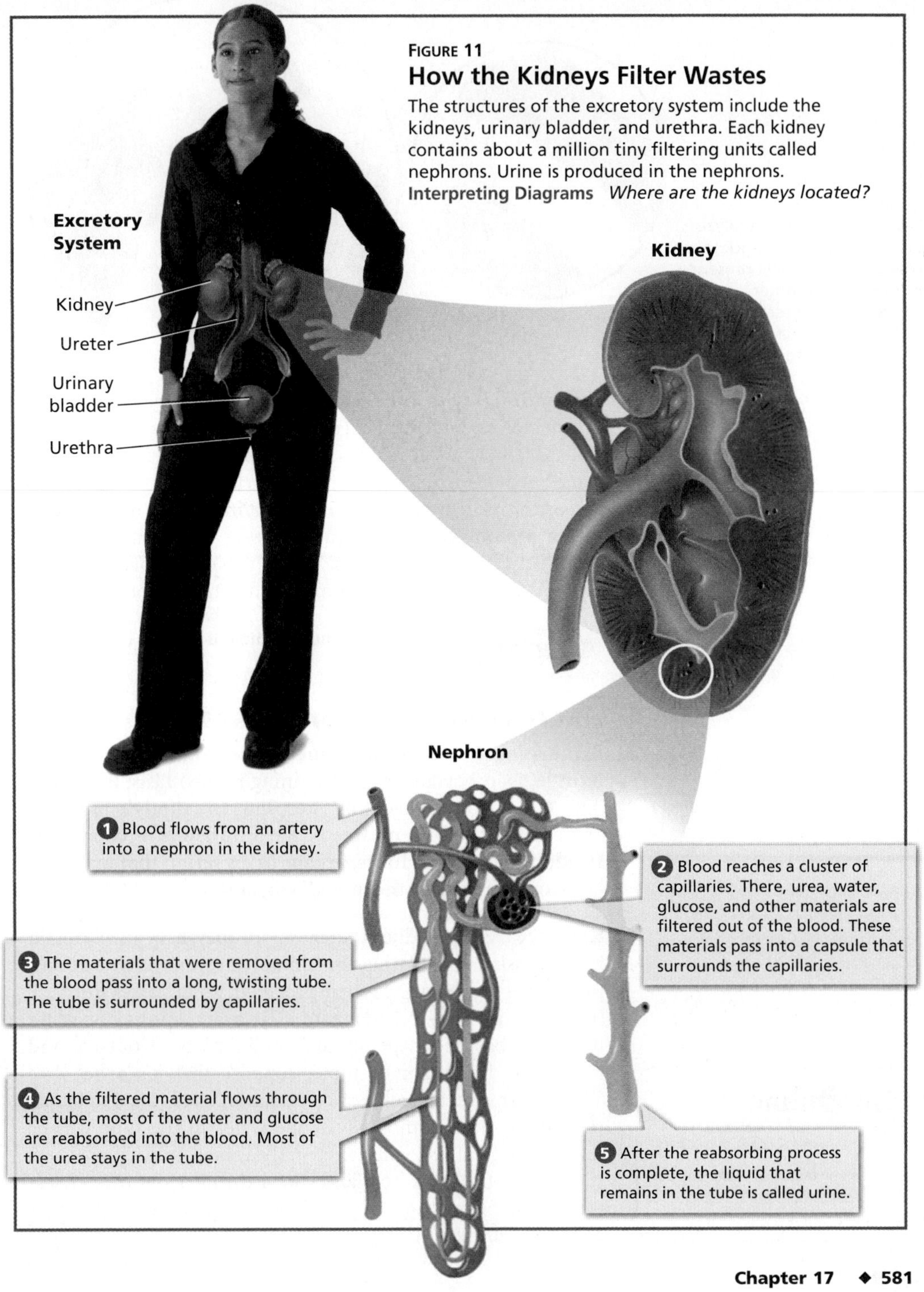

Excretory System

Kidney

Ureter

Urinary bladder

Urethra

Kidney

Nephron

1. Blood flows from an artery into a nephron in the kidney.

2. Blood reaches a cluster of capillaries. There, urea, water, glucose, and other materials are filtered out of the blood. These materials pass into a capsule that surrounds the capillaries.

3. The materials that were removed from the blood pass into a long, twisting tube. The tube is surrounded by capillaries.

4. As the filtered material flows through the tube, most of the water and glucose are reabsorbed into the blood. Most of the urea stays in the tube.

5. After the reabsorbing process is complete, the liquid that remains in the tube is called urine.

Chapter 17 ◆ 581

Lab zone **Teacher Demo** L1

Kidney Function

Materials 30-cm section of cellophane dialysis tubing, 2 large beakers, string, 10 mL of salt-water solution, distilled water, hand-held conductivity tester, ruler

Time 40 minutes

Focus Explain that an important function of the kidneys is to return sodium to the blood during the formation of urine. This activity will demonstrate this process.

Teach Soak the tubing for several hours in a beaker filled with distilled water. Use string to tie one end of the dialysis tubing tightly closed. After the tubing is tied, store it in the container of distilled water. On the day of the activity, prepare a salt solution by mixing a few teaspoons of table salt in 100 mL of water. Fill the tubing three quarters full with the salt solution and then tie the open end of the bag tightly closed with string. Suspend the tubing in a beaker of distilled water by tying it to a ruler placed across the rim. Do not allow the beaker to overflow. Tell students that the bag contains a salt solution, that salt contains sodium, and that the tester indicates the presence of salt in solution. After 20 minutes, test the solution in the beaker with the conductivity tester. (It should light.)

Apply Ask: **How did the salt get into the distilled water, and how does this model the movement of sodium during the formation of urine?** *(The salt in the tubing passes into the water the way sodium in the kidney tubes passes back into the blood in the capillaries that surround the tubes.)* **learning modality: visual**

Differentiated Instruction

Monitor Progress _____ L2

Writing Have students list the functions of the kidneys.

Answers
Figure 11 The kidneys are located above the hips.

 Reading Checkpoint   The ureters carry urine from the kidneys to the urinary bladder.

Excretion and Homeostasis

Teach Key Concepts `L2`
Maintaining Homeostasis

Focus Explain that homeostasis is the process that keeps the body's internal environment stable in spite of changes in the external environment. Homeostasis includes balancing the volume of fluids in the body and eliminating wastes.

Teach Ask: **What organs are involved in eliminating water from the body?** *(Kidneys, lungs, and skin)* **What role does the liver have in maintaining homeostasis?** *(It helps break down wastes so they can be recycled or eliminated.)*

Apply Ask: **Why is more water reabsorbed into the bloodstream by the kidneys during a hot day?** *(Because water is needed to balance the amount of water lost due to perspiration)* **learning modality: logical/mathematical**

Build Inquiry `L1`

Perspiration

Materials plastic sandwich bag for each student, masking tape

Time 10 minutes

Focus Remind students that the sweat glands of the skin also function in excretion of wastes.

Teach Have each student place a plastic bag over one hand and then use masking tape to close the bag at the wrist. After a few minutes, students should observe condensation inside the bag.

Apply Ask: **Does the skin remove wastes from the body all the time or just when you are aware you are perspiring?** *(All the time)* **learning modality: kinesthetic**

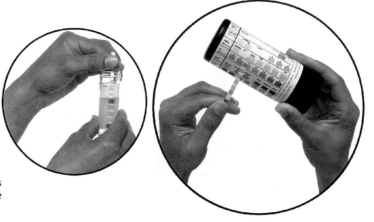

FIGURE 12
Analyzing Urine
Lab technicians can analyze urine by using a dipstick that changes color in the presence of glucose and other substances. The technician dips the dipstick into a urine sample and compares the results to a color chart.
Applying Concepts What are two substances for which urine can be tested?

Analyzing Urine for Signs of Disease When people go to a doctor for a medical checkup, they usually have their urine analyzed. A chemical analysis of urine can be useful in detecting some medical problems. Normally, urine contains almost no glucose or protein. If glucose is present in urine, it may indicate that a person has diabetes, a condition in which body cells cannot absorb enough glucose from the blood. Protein in urine can be a sign that the kidneys are not functioning properly.

 **Reading Checkpoint** What could it mean if there is glucose in the urine?

Excretion and Homeostasis

Eliminating wastes, such as urea, excess water, and carbon dioxide, is important for maintaining homeostasis. **Excretion maintains homeostasis by keeping the body's internal environment stable and free of harmful levels of chemicals. In addition to the kidneys, organs of excretion that maintain homeostasis include the lungs, skin, and liver.**

Kidneys As the kidneys filter blood, they help to maintain homeostasis by regulating the amount of water in your body. Remember that as urine is being formed, water passes from the tube back into the bloodstream. The exact amount of water that is reabsorbed depends on conditions both outside and within the body. For example, suppose that it's a hot day. You've been sweating a lot, and you haven't had much to drink. In that situation, almost all of the water in the tube will be reabsorbed, and you will excrete only a small amount of urine. If, however, the day is cool and you've drunk a lot of water, less water will be reabsorbed. Your body will produce a larger volume of urine.

Lungs and Skin Most of the wastes produced by the body are removed through the kidneys. However, the lungs and skin remove some wastes from the body as well. When you exhale, carbon dioxide and some water are removed from the body by the lungs. Sweat glands in the skin also serve an excretory function because water and urea are excreted in perspiration.

Liver Have you ever torn apart a large pizza box so that it could fit into a wastebasket? If so, then you understand that some wastes need to be broken down before they can be excreted. The liver performs this function. For example, urea, which comes from the breakdown of proteins, is produced by the liver. The liver also converts part of the hemoglobin molecule from old red blood cells into substances such as bile. Because the liver produces a usable material from old red blood cells, you can think of the liver as a recycling facility.

FIGURE 13
Excretion Through the Lungs
Your lungs function as excretory organs. When you exhale on a cold morning, you can see the water in your breath.

 Reading Checkpoint What substances are excreted in perspiration?

Section 3 Assessment

 Target Reading Skill Previewing Visuals Compare your questions and answers about Figure 11 with those of a partner.

Reviewing Key Concepts

1. a. Reviewing What is the role of the excretory system in the body?
   b. Sequencing Name the structures of the excretory system in order of their roles in producing and eliminating urine. Describe the function of each structure.
2. a. Reviewing What are the two main stages of waste removal by the kidneys?
   b. Describing What happens as wastes are filtered in a nephron?
   c. Relating Cause and Effect Why is protein in the urine a sign that something could be wrong with the kidneys?

3. a. Identifying What is the role of excretion in maintaining homeostasis?
   b. Explaining How do the kidneys help maintain homeostasis?
   c. Predicting On a long bus trip, a traveler does not drink any water for several hours. How will the volume of urine she produces that day compare to the volume on a day when she drinks several glasses of water? Explain.

Writing in Science

Explanation Write a paragraph explaining how wastes are filtered in the kidneys. To help you with your writing, first make two lists—one that includes materials removed from the blood in the kidneys and one that includes materials returned to the blood.

Chapter 17 ◆ 583

Clues About Health

Prepare for Inquiry

Key Concept
Urine tests can provide evidence of disease.

Skills Objective
After this lab, students will be able to
- observe color changes as solutions react with the test solutions
- interpret data and draw conclusions about the presence or absence of glucose and protein in the solutions

 Prep Time 20 minutes

Class Time 40 minutes

Advance Planning
Safety

Make up the patients' samples to match the Sample Data Table or according to your own preferences. Prepare a 1% glucose solution by dissolving 10 g of glucose in 990 mL of water. Make a 1% protein solution by dissolving 10 g of albumin or pepsin in 990 mL of water. Add food coloring to make the solutions a pale yellow (like urine), if desired. Use these solutions to make the simulated urine samples. Glucose test strips and Biuret solution can be obtained from biological supply companies.

All in One Teaching Resources, Unit 3
- Lab Worksheet: *Clues About Health*

Guide Inquiry

Invitation
Ask students to list substances that are filtered from the blood and to identify which of those substances should be reabsorbed. (*Sugar is one substance that should be reabsorbed.*) Students should conclude that some substances should not be in the urine of a healthy person.

Introduce the Procedure
Ask: **What is the purpose of testing known solutions?** (*They show how the test materials work.*)

Clues About Health

Problem
How can you test urine for the presence of glucose and protein?

Skills Focus
observing, interpreting data, drawing conclusions

Materials
- 6 test tubes
- test-tube rack
- 6 plastic droppers
- water
- glucose solution
- protein solution
- marking pencil
- white paper towels
- 6 glucose test strips
- Biuret solution
- 3 simulated urine samples

Procedure

PART 1 Testing for Glucose

1. Label six test tubes as follows: *W* for water, *G* for glucose, *P* for protein, and *A*, *B*, and *C* for three patients' "urine samples." Place the test tubes in a test-tube rack.

2. Label six glucose test strips with the same letters: *W*, *G*, *P*, *A*, *B*, and *C*.

3. Copy the data table into your notebook.

4. Fill each test tube about $\frac{3}{4}$ full with the solution that corresponds to its label.

5. Place glucose test strip W on a clean, dry section of a paper towel. Then, use a clean plastic dropper to place 2 drops of the water from test tube W on the test strip. Record the resulting color of the test strip in your data table. If no color change occurs, write "no reaction."

6. Use the procedure in Step 5 to test each of the other five solutions with the correctly labeled glucose test strip. Record the color of each test strip in the data table.

PART 2 Testing for Protein

7. Obtain a dropper bottle containing Biuret solution. Record the original color of the solution in your notebook.

8. Carefully add 30 drops of Biuret solution to test tube W. **CAUTION:** *Biuret solution can harm skin and damage clothing. Handle it with care.* Gently swirl the test tube to mix the two solutions together. Hold the test tube against a white paper towel to help you detect any color change. Observe the color of the final mixture, and record that color in your data table.

9. Repeat Step 8 for each of the other test tubes.

Data Table						
	Test Tube					
Test for	W (water)	G (glucose)	P (protein)	A (Patient A)	B (Patient B)	C (Patient C)
Glucose						
Protein						

Troubleshooting the Experiment
- Food coloring may distort color changes and make them less noticeable.
- Droppers should be labeled and returned to the proper test tube to avoid contamination.

Analyze and Conclude

1. **Observing** What color reaction occurred when you used the glucose test strip on sample W? On sample G?

2. **Interpreting Data** What do the changes in color you observed in Part 1 indicate? Explain.

3. **Observing** What happened when you added Biuret solution to test tube W? To test tube P?

4. **Interpreting Data** What do the changes in color of the Biuret solution you observed in Part II indicate? Explain.

5. **Drawing Conclusions** Which of the three patients' urine samples tested normal? How do you know?

6. **Drawing Conclusions** Which urine sample(s) indicated that diabetes might be present? How do you know?

7. **Drawing Conclusions** Which urine sample(s) indicated that kidney disease might be present? How do you know?

8. **Communicating** Do you think a doctor should draw conclusions about the presence of a disease based on a single urine sample? Write a paragraph in which you discuss this question based on what you know about gathering data in experiments.

More to Explore

Propose a way to determine whether a patient with glucose in the urine could reduce the level through changes in diet.

Expected Outcome

- Glucose test strips will turn green if glucose is present.
- The solution will turn purple-pink when Biuret solution is added if protein is present.
- A 50/50 mix (simulated urine sample) should give positive results for both glucose and protein.

Analyze and Conclude

1. Sample W showed no change in color. Sample G showed a color change to green.

2. It is a positive test result for glucose.

3. The contents of sample W were light blue, the same color as the Biuret solution. The contents of sample G turned purple.

4. It is a positive test result for protein.

5. The normal urine sample (B) is negative in both glucose and protein tests.

6. The urine sample that tests positive for glucose (C) indicates possible diabetes.

7. A urine sample that tests positive for protein (A) indicates possible kidney disease.

8. No. A single test does not provide enough evidence. The person should go for further testing.

Extend Inquiry

More to Explore Students might suggest the patient eat fewer sugary foods. The amount of glucose in the patient's urine can be monitored to determine if diet affects the glucose level.

Sample Data Table						
Test for	W (water)	G (glucose)	P (protein)	A (Patient A)	B (Patient B)	C (Patient C)
Glucose	Yellow	Green	Yellow	Yellow	Yellow	Green
Protein	Lt. Blue	Lt. Blue	Purple	Purple	Lt. Blue	Lt. Blue

Study Guide

nteractive
Textbook

- Complete student edition
- Section and chapter self-assessment
- Assessment reports for teacher

Help Students Read

Developing Vocabulary

Vocabulary Rating Chart Have students construct a chart with five columns: *Term, Can Define or Use It, Have Heard or Seen It, Can Connect to Other Key Terms, Don't Know.* Students should copy the vocabulary words for the chapter under column 1. They should then place a checkmark under one of the other columns for each term.

Paraphrasing Have students define in their own words vocabulary words with which they are still having trouble.

Connecting Concepts

Concept Maps Help students develop one way to show how the information in the chapter is related. The respiratory and excretory systems help to take in needed materials and eliminate wastes from the body. Have students brainstorm to identify the Key Concepts, Key Terms, details, and examples. Then write each one on a sticky note and attach it at random on chart paper or on the board.

Tell students that this concept map will be organized in hierarchical order and to begin at the top with the Key Concepts. Ask students these questions to guide them to categorize the information on the stickies: **What are the structures of the respiratory system? What does it take in and what does it eliminate? What are the structures of the excretory system? What does it eliminate?**

Prompt students by using connecting words or phrases, such as "takes in," "removes," "structures," and "functions," to indicate the basis for the organization of the map. The phrases should form a sentence between or among a set of concepts.

① The Respiratory System

Key Concepts

- The respiratory system moves oxygen from the outside environment into the body. It also removes carbon dioxide and water from the body.
- As air travels from the outside environment to the lungs, it passes through the following structures: nose, pharynx, trachea, and bronchi.
- After air enters an alveolus, oxygen passes through the wall of the alveolus and then through the capillary wall into the blood. Carbon dioxide and water pass from the blood into the alveoli. This whole process is known as gas exchange.
- When you breathe, the actions of your rib muscles and diaphragm expand or contract your chest, causing air to flow in or out.

Key Terms

respiration	lungs
cilia	alveoli
pharynx	diaphragm
trachea	larynx
bronchi	vocal cords

② Smoking and Your Health

Key Concepts

- Some of the most deadly chemicals in tobacco smoke are tar, carbon monoxide, and nicotine.
- Over time, smokers can develop chronic bronchitis, emphysema, lung cancer, and atherosclerosis.

Key Terms

tar	addiction
carbon monoxide	bronchitis
nicotine	emphysema

③ The Excretory System

Key Concepts

- The excretory system is the system in the body that collects wastes produced by cells and removes the wastes from the body.
- The structures of the excretory system that eliminate urea, water, and other wastes include the kidneys, ureters, the urinary bladder, and the urethra.
- The nephrons filter wastes in stages. First, both wastes and needed materials, such as glucose, are filtered from the blood into a nephron. Then, much of the needed material is returned to the blood, and the wastes are eliminated from the body.
- Excretion maintains homeostasis by keeping the body's internal environment stable and free of harmful levels of chemicals. In addition to the kidneys, organs of excretion that maintain homeostasis include the lungs, skin, and liver.

Key Terms

excretion	ureter
urea	urinary bladder
kidney	urethra
urine	nephron

SURGEON GENERAL'S WARNING: Cigarette Smoke Contains Carbon Monoxide.

SURGEON GENERAL'S WARNING: Smoking Causes Lung Cancer, Heart Disease, Emphysema, and May Complicate Pregnancy.

SURGEON GENERAL'S WARNING: Smoking By Pregnant Women May Result in Fetal Injury, Premature Birth, and Low Birth Weight.

All in One Teaching Resources, Unit 3

- Key Terms Review: *Respiration and Excretion*
- Connecting Concepts: *Respiration and Excretion*

Review and Assessment

Go Online
PHSchool.com
For: Self-Assessment
Visit: PHSchool.com
Web Code: cea-4040

Organizing Information

Sequencing Copy the flowchart about excretion onto a separate sheet of paper. Then, fill in the empty spaces and add a title. (For more on Sequencing, see the Skills Handbook.)

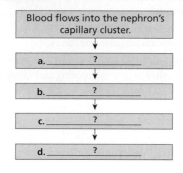

Blood flows into the nephron's capillary cluster.

↓

a. _____ ?

↓

b. _____ ?

↓

c. _____ ?

↓

d. _____ ?

Reviewing Key Terms

Choose the letter of the best answer.

1. The process in which glucose and oxygen react in cells to release energy is called
   a. excretion.
   b. respiration.
   c. bronchitis.
   d. emphysema.

2. The trachea divides into two tubes called
   a. bronchi.
   b. alveoli.
   c. ureters.
   d. vocal cords.

3. Your voice is produced by the
   a. pharynx.   b. larynx.
   c. trachea.   d. alveoli.

4. A colorless, odorless gas produced by burning tobacco is
   a. carbon monoxide.
   b. tar.
   c. nicotine.
   d. urea.

5. The filtration of wastes takes place inside the kidneys in the
   a. ureters.
   b. urethra.
   c. urinary bladder.
   d. nephrons.

If the statement is true, write *true*. If it is false, change the underlined word or words to make the statement true.

6. Dust particles trapped in mucus are swept away by tiny, hairlike <u>alveoli</u>.

7. Clusters of air sacs in the lungs are <u>bronchi</u>.

8. <u>Tar</u> is a chemical in tobacco smoke that makes the heart beat faster.

9. Urine leaves the body through the <u>ureter</u>.

10. Urine is stored in the <u>urethra</u>.

Writing in Science

Informational Brochure Pretend you are a doctor advising high-altitude climbers. Develop an informational brochure that focuses on the effects that high altitude has on the human body. Be sure to include one method climbers can use to become used to the higher altitudes.

Discovery CHANNEL SCHOOL

Respiration and Excretion
Video Preview
Video Field Trip
▶ Video Assessment

Chapter 17 ◆ 587

Go Online
PHSchool.com
For: Self-Assessment
Visit: PHSchool.com
Web Code: cea-4040

Students can take an online practice test that is automatically scored.

All in One Teaching Resources, Unit 3
- Transparency LS173
- Chapter Test
- Performance Assessment Teacher Notes
- Performance Assessment Student Worksheet
- Performance Assessment Scoring Rubric

ExamView® Computer Test Bank CD-ROM

Review and Assessment

Organizing Information

a. Water, urea, glucose, and other materials are removed from the blood and flow into the capsule.
b. From the capsule, the substances flow into a long tube.
c. In the tube, glucose, water, and some other materials are reabsorbed.
d. Urine flows from the kidneys through the ureters to the urinary bladder.

Reviewing Key Terms

1. b   2. a   3. b   4. a   5. d
6. false; cilia
7. false; alveoli
8. false; Nicotine
9. false; urethra
10. false; urinary bladder

Writing in Science

Writing Mode Description

Scoring Rubric

4 Includes accurate, detailed description of effects and method; clearly written

3 Includes accurate description with few details; clearly written

2 Includes minimum description and no details or writing is disorganized

1 Includes inaccurate description

Discovery CHANNEL SCHOOL Video Assessment

Respiration and Excretion

Show the Video Assessment to review chapter content and as a prompt for the writing assignment. Discussion questions: **What is one way climbers can help prepare for climbing at high altitudes?** (*Climbers can train at high altitudes so the body can acclimatize.*) **Describe one way in which the body adjusts to living at higher altitudes.** (*The body begins by breathing deeply to bring in more oxygen; it makes more red blood cells to transport oxygen to the body's tissues more efficiently.*)

Checking Concepts

11. Breathing consists of taking air into the body and removing it from the body. Respiration is the series of chemical reactions in cells in which glucose and oxygen react to release energy.

12. Because there are an enormous number of alveoli, together they have an extremely large surface area.

13. During inhalation, the diaphragm moves downward, and the rib muscles lift the chest wall upward and outward. This increases the volume of the chest cavity and decreases the air pressure in the lungs. Therefore, air rushes into the lungs. During exhalation, the diaphragm moves upward and the rib muscles relax. This makes the chest cavity smaller and increases the air pressure in the lungs, which pushes air out of the lungs.

14. Carbon monoxide binds to hemoglobin, taking the place of oxygen. This deprives the body of oxygen. The body responds by increasing the breathing and heart rates.

15. Kidneys maintain homeostasis by removing wastes from the body; if wastes were not removed, they would poison body cells. In addition, by adjusting the amount of water reabsorbed, kidneys maintain water balance.

Thinking Critically

16. Similar—Both are energy-releasing chemical reactions that require oxygen. Different—Respiration takes place within cells. Burning takes place outside cells and may produce light and flames.

17. The process of inhalation is occurring. When you inhale, the diaphragm moves downward. The air pressure in the lungs decreases, causing air to rush in.

18. If babies inhale smoke from people's cigarettes, this smoke can damage their respiratory systems.

19. Students' judgments will vary. Check for supported arguments. For example: Drugstores are places where people can buy products to make them well. Therefore, drugstores should not carry tobacco products, which can damage health.

20. Proteins could pass into the nephron and end up in urine. Blood cells might also be found in the urine.

Review and Assessment

Checking Concepts

11. Explain the difference between breathing and respiration.

12. Explain how the alveoli provide a large surface area for gas exchange in the lungs.

13. Describe how the diaphragm and rib muscles work together to control inhaling and exhaling.

14. Describe what happens when carbon monoxide enters the body. How does this affect the body?

15. Explain two ways in which the kidneys help to maintain homeostasis in the body.

Thinking Critically

16. Comparing and Contrasting How is respiration similar to the burning of fuel? How is it different?

17. Relating Cause and Effect What process is shown in the diagram below? What role do changes in pressure play in this process?

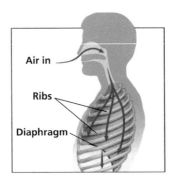

Air in

Ribs

Diaphragm

18. Applying Concepts Explain how babies can develop smoking-related respiratory problems.

19. Making Judgments Do you think that drugstores, which sell medicines, should also sell cigarettes and other tobacco products? Why or why not?

20. Predicting If the walls of the capillary cluster in a nephron were damaged or broken, what substance might you expect to find in urine that is not normally present? Explain.

Math Practice

21. Surface Area Which has a greater surface area, a cube that is 2 cm × 2 cm on a side, or eight cubes that are each 1 cm × 1 cm on a side? Show your work.

Applying Skills

Use your knowledge of the excretory system and the information in the data table below to answer Questions 22–25.

Average Daily Water Loss in Humans (mL)

Source	Normal Weather	Hot Weather	Extended Heavy Exercise
Lungs	350	250	650
Urine	1,400	1,200	500
Sweat	450	1,750	5,350
Digestive waste	200	200	200

22. Interpreting Data Identify the major source of water loss during normal weather and the major source of water loss during hot weather.

23. Drawing Conclusions How do the data for normal weather and hot weather show that the body is maintaining homeostasis?

24. Calculating What is the total amount of water lost on a hot-weather day? What is the total amount of water lost during extended heavy exercise?

25. Inferring Use the data to explain why it is important to drink a lot of water when you are exercising heavily.

Lab zone Chapter Project

Performance Assessment Your three anti-smoking ads should be ready for display. Be prepared to explain why you chose the message you did for each group of viewers. What health risks do each of your ads identify? Why do you think your ads would be effective?

Lab zone Chapter Project   L3

Performance Assessment During their presentations, students should discuss messages and images they chose and why they think their ads will be effective in discouraging people in each age group from smoking. After all presentations have been made, lead a discussion on the effectiveness of advertising.

Reflect and Record Encourage students to reflect on advertising tactics that appealed to them personally. Some students may find they respond to colorful graphics or catchy phrases; others may be interested in statistics or personal stories. Encourage students to identify specific images or attitudes that might influence them to start smoking. Have students develop a plan to combat those influences.

Standardized Test Prep

Choose the letter of the best answer.

1. Which of the following organs functions as both a respiratory organ and an excretory organ?

  A the liver
  B the lungs
  C the skin
  D the kidneys

2. The correct sequence of organs through which air travels when it is breathed into the body is

  F pharynx, nose, trachea, bronchi.
  G nose, trachea, pharynx, bronchi.
  H nose, pharynx, bronchi, trachea.
  J nose, pharynx, trachea, bronchi.

The graph below shows the percentage of total lung function in people who have never smoked and in smokers from ages 25–75. Use the graph to answer Questions 3 and 4.

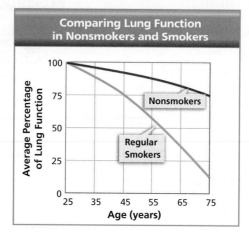

Comparing Lung Function in Nonsmokers and Smokers

3. At approximately what age do the lungs of a smoker have the same capacity as the lungs of a 75-year-old who has never smoked?

  A 25
  B 45
  C 65
  D 75

4. What general conclusion about lung function and smoking could you draw from this graph?

  F Smoking does not affect lung function.
  G People who smoke are more likely to have greater lung function than those who have never smoked.
  H By the age of 50, a smoker will likely have 50 percent lung function.
  J Smoking significantly reduces the lung function of smokers compared to people who have never smoked.

Constructed Response

5. What is respiration? Explain where this process occurs and what body systems are involved in making respiration possible.

Math Practice

21. 2 cm × 2 cm = 4 square centimeters; 4 square centimeters × 6 sides = 24 square centimeters. 1 cm × 1 cm = 1 square centimeter; 1 square centimeter × 6 sides = 6 square centimeters per cube; thus, eight cubes have 48 square centimeters. The eight cubes that are each 1 cm on a side have greater total surface area.

Applying Skills

22. During normal weather, more urine is produced. During hot weather, more sweat is produced.

23. During hot weather, the body reduces urine output to keep from dehydrating and produces sweat to cool the body.

24. 3400 mL on a hot-weather day; 6700 mL during extended heavy exercise

25. The body loses a large amount of water through sweat during heavy exercises, so drinking water helps restore lost water.

Standardized Test Prep

1. B **2.** J **3.** B **4.** J

5. Sample answer: Respiration is the process in which oxygen and glucose undergo chemical reactions that release energy needed by the body. Respiration occurs inside cells. The respiratory, digestive, and circulatory systems make respiration possible.

Chapter at a Glance

PRENTICE HALL

TeacherEXPRESS™
Plan · Teach · Assess

Lab zone Chapter **Project** *Stop the Invasion!*

Technology

Local Standards

All in One Teaching Resources, Unit 3
- Chapter Project Teacher Notes, pp. 262–263
- Chapter Project Student Overview, pp. 264–265
- Chapter Project Student Worksheets, pp. 266–267
- Chapter Project Scoring Rubric, p. 268

Video Preview

Section 1

1 period
1/2 block

Infectious Disease

18.1.1 Explain the relationship between pathogens and infectious disease.

18.1.2 List the kinds of pathogens that cause infectious diseases in humans.

18.1.3 Identify four ways that pathogens can spread.

Go Online
PHSchool.com

Section 2

3 periods
1 1/2 blocks

The Body's Defenses

18.2.1 Explain how the body's first line of defense guards against pathogens.

18.2.2 Describe what happens during the inflammatory response.

18.2.3 State how the immune system responds to pathogens.

18.2.4 Identify how HIV affects the immune system and how it spreads.

Video Field Trip

Go Online
active art

Section 3

1 period
1/2 block

Preventing Infectious Disease

18.3.1 Describe how the body acquires active immunity.

18.3.2 Explain how passive immunity occurs.

Go Online
PLANET DIARY

Section 4

2 periods
1 block

Noninfectious Disease

18.4.1 Identify the cause of allergies.

18.4.2 Explain how diabetes affects the body.

18.4.3 Describe the effects of cancer on the body.

Go Online
SciLINKS™

Review and Assessment

All in One Teaching Resources, Unit 3
- Key Terms Review, p. 303
- Transparency LS179
- Performance Assessment Teacher Notes, p. 310
- Performance Assessment Scoring Rubric, p. 311
- Performance Assessment Student Worksheet, p. 312
- Chapter Test, pp. 313–316

Video Assessment

Go Online
PHSchool.com

Test Preparation

Test Preparation Blackline Masters

Lab zone Chapter Activities Planner

Student Edition	Inquiry	Time	Materials	Skills	Resources
Chapter Project, p. 591	Open-Ended	2 to 3 weeks	**All in One** Teaching Resources, **Unit 3**, p. 262	Posing questions, applying concepts, communicating	**Lab zone Easy Planner** **All in One** Teaching Resources, **Unit 3**, Support pp. 262–263
Section 1					
Discover Activity, p. 592	Guided	10 minutes	None	Calculating	**Lab zone Easy Planner**
Skills Activity, p. 595	Guided	10 minutes	None	Posing questions	**Lab zone Easy Planner**
Section 2					
Discover Activity, p. 597	Guided	10 minutes	Sheets of paper, each cut into two matching jigsaw pieces	Inferring	**Lab zone Easy Planner**
Try This, p. 600	Directed	10 minutes	Modeling clay, large ball, small ball, tape	Making models	**Lab zone Easy Planner**
Skills Lab, pp. 604–605	Directed	Prep: 15 minutes Class: 30 minutes	4 sealable plastic bags, 4 fresh apples, rotting apple, cotton swabs, marking pen, paper towels, toothpick, rubbing alcohol	Observing, interpreting data, controlling variables, making models, drawing conclusions	**Lab zone Easy Planner** **Lab Activity Video** **All in One** Teaching Resources, **Unit 3**, Skills Lab: *The Skin as a Barrier*, pp. 284–285
Section 3					
Discover Activity, p. 606	Open-Ended	15 minutes	Disinfectants and antibacterial products such as creams, mouthwashes, hand soaps, household cleaners, and spray disinfectants	Designing experiments	**Lab zone Easy Planner**
Section 4					
Discover Activity, p. 611	Directed	10 minutes	Plastic drinking straw	Observing	**Lab zone Easy Planner**
Skills Activity, p. 612	Guided	10 minutes	None	Drawing conclusions	**Lab zone Easy Planner**
Skills Lab, pp. 616–617	Directed	30 minutes	Colored pencils, rulers, calculators (optional), protractor, compass	Graphing, interpreting data, drawing conclusions	**Lab zone Easy Planner** **Lab Activity Video** **All in One** Teaching Resources, **Unit 3**, Skills Lab: *Causes of Death, Then and Now*, pp. 300–302

Section 1 **Infectious Disease**

1 period, 1/2 block

Objectives

18.1.1 Explain the relationship between pathogens and infectious disease.

18.1.2 List the kinds of pathogens that cause infectious diseases in humans.

18.1.3 Identify four ways that pathogens can spread.

Key Terms

• pathogen • infectious disease • toxin

Local Standards

Preteach

Build Background Knowledge

Students brainstorm diseases and classify them as infectious or noninfectious.

Lab zone **Discover Activity** *How Does a Disease Spread?* **L1**

Targeted Print and Technology Resources

All in One **Teaching Resources, Unit 3**

L2 Reading Strategy Transparency LS174: Using Prior Knowledge

○ **PresentationEXPRESS™ CD-ROM**

Instruct

Understanding Infectious Disease Discuss how the discovery of pathogens affected the incidence of infectious disease.

Kinds of Pathogens Lead students in a discussion of how bacteria and viruses cause illness.

How Pathogens Are Spread Have students identify ways to prevent the spread of pathogens.

Targeted Print and Technology Resources

All in One **Teaching Resources, Unit 3**

L2 Guided Reading, pp. 271–273

PHSchool.com Web Code: ced-4051

○ **Student Edition on Audio CD**

Assess

Section Assessment Questions

↻ Have students use their completed graphic organizers to answer the questions.

Reteach

Students look at illustrations of pathogens in the section and state what they know about them.

Targeted Print and Technology Resources

All in One **Teaching Resources, Unit 3**

• Section Summary, p. 270

L1 Review and Reinforce, p. 274

L3 Enrich, p. 275

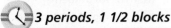
Section 2 The Body's Defenses

🕐 3 periods, 1 1/2 blocks

Objectives

18.2.1 Explain how the body's first line of defense guards against pathogens.

18.2.2 Describe what happens during the inflammatory response.

18.2.3 State how the immune system responds to pathogens.

18.2.4 Identify how HIV affects the immune system and how it spreads.

Key Terms

• inflammatory response • phagocyte • immune response • lymphocyte
• T cell • antigen • B cell • antibody • AIDS • HIV

Local Standards

Preteach

Build Background Knowledge

Students discuss factors that help people to resist infectious disease.

 Discover Activity *Which Pieces Fit Together?* L1

Targeted Print and Technology Resources

 Teaching Resources, Unit 3
• Reading Strategy: Building Vocabulary

💿 **PresentationEXPRESS™ CD-ROM**

Instruct

Barriers That Keep Pathogens Out Lead a discussion on the first lines of defense against pathogens.

The Inflammatory Response Help students identify how the inflammatory response fights pathogens.

The Immune System Ask students to compare and contrast T cells, B cells, and phagocytes.

AIDS Ask students to identify ways that AIDS can and cannot be spread.

 **Skills Lab** *The Skin as a Barrier*

Targeted Print and Technology Resources

Teaching Resources, Unit 3
L2 Guided Reading, pp. 278–281
L2 Transparency LS175
L2 Skills Lab: *The Skin as a Barrier,* pp. 284–285

📼 **Lab Activity Video/DVD**
Skills Lab: *The Skin as a Barrier*

PHSchool.com Web Code: cep-4052

DISCOVERY CHANNEL SCHOOL
Video Field Trip

💿 **Student Edition on Audio CD**

Assess

Section Assessment Questions

🔁 Have students use their definitions to answer the questions.

Reteach

Students describe how T cells and B cells work together.

Targeted Print and Technology Resources

Teaching Resources, Unit 3
• Section Summary, p. 277
L1 Review and Reinforce, p. 282
L3 Enrich, p. 283

Section 3 **Preventing Infectious Disease**

ABILITY LEVELS
L1 Basic to Average
L2 For All Students
L3 Average to Advanced

1 period, 1/2 block

Objectives
18.3.1 Describe how the body acquires active immunity.
18.3.2 Explain how passive immunity occurs.

Local Standards

Key Terms
• immunity • active immunity • vaccination • vaccine • antibiotic
• passive immunity

Preteach

Build Background Knowledge
Students discuss why people are immunized and list diseases for which they think vaccines are available.

 **Discover Activity** *What Substances Can Kill Pathogens?* **L2**

Targeted Print and Technology Resources

 **Teaching Resources, Unit 3**

L2 Reading Strategy Transparency
LS176: Comparing and Contrasting

⊙ **PresentationEXPRESS™ CD-ROM**

Instruct

Active Immunity Have students compare and contrast getting an infection and getting a vaccine.

Passive Immunity Ask students to compare and contrast natural and artificial passive immunity.

Targeted Print and Technology Resources

All in One Teaching Resources, Unit 3

L2 Guided Reading, pp. 288–290
L2 Transparency LS177

PHSchool.com Web Code: ced-4053

⊙ **Student Edition on Audio CD**

Assess

Section Assessment Questions
↻ Have students use their Comparing and Contrasting graphic organizers to answer the questions.

Reteach
Students create a flowchart that shows how the body develops immunity.

Targeted Print and Technology Resources

All in One Teaching Resources, Unit 3

• Section Summary, p. 287
L1 Review and Reinforce, p. 291
L3 Enrich, p. 292

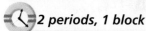
Section 4 Noninfectious Disease

 *2 periods, 1 block*

ABILITY LEVELS
L1 Basic to Average
L2 For All Students
L3 Average to Advanced

Objectives

Local Standards

18.4.1 Identify the cause of allergies.

18.4.2 Explain how diabetes affects the body.

18.4.3 Describe the effects of cancer on the body.

Key Terms

• noninfectious disease • allergy • allergen • histamine • asthma • insulin
• diabetes • tumor • carcinogen

Preteach

Build Background Knowledge

Students brainstorm diseases that are not spread from people, animals, or the environment.

 Discover Activity *What Happens When Airflow Is Restricted?* **L1**

Targeted Print and Technology Resources

 **Teaching Resources, Unit 3**
L2 Reading Strategy Transparency
LS178: Asking Questions

O **PresentationEXPRESS™ CD-ROM**

Instruct

Allergies Lead students in a discussion of the relationship between allergens and the immune response.

Diabetes Have students analyze what causes the symptoms of diabetes.

Cancer Ask students to consider how carcinogens damage cells and how different factors work together to cause cancer.

 Skills Lab *Causes of Death, Then and Now* **L2**

Targeted Print and Technology Resources

All in One Teaching Resources, Unit 3
L2 Guided Reading, pp. 295–297
L2 Skills Lab: *Causes of Death, Then and Now,* pp. 326–328

Lab Activity Video/DVD

Skills Lab: *Causes of Death, Then and Now*
www.SciLinks.org Web Code: scn-0454

O **Student Edition on Audio CD**

Assess

Section Assessment Questions

Have students use their Asking Questions graphic organizers to answer the questions.

Reteach

Students provide facts for the headings and subheadings in the section.

Targeted Print and Technology Resources

All in One Teaching Resources, Unit 3
• Section Summary, p. 294
L1 Review and Reinforce, p. 298
L3 Enrich, p. 299

Go Online

NSTA-PD*L*INKS

For: Professional development support
Visit: www.SciLinks.org/PDLinks
Web Code: scf-0450

Professional Development

Professional Development

Section 1 **Infectious Disease**

Koch's Postulates Robert Koch developed guidelines for determining whether a specific microorganism causes a disease. Today these guidelines are known as Koch's postulates. Koch's postulates are summarized below. The illustration shows how the procedure was used to identify the pathogen that causes Lyme disease, *Borrelia burgdorferi*.

1. If a microorganism is suspected of causing a disease, it should be found in the body of each organism that has the disease.

2. The microorganism must be isolated from the body of an organism with the disease and then grown in the laboratory in a pure culture, i.e., a culture that contains no other types of microorganisms.

3. When microorganisms from the pure culture are placed in the body of a healthy organism, e.g., a laboratory animal, they should cause the same disease that was found in the original host organism.

4. The suspected organism must then be isolated from the second host. It should be the same kind of microorganism as the original pathogen.

Koch's Postulates and Lyme Disease

Pathogen (*Borrelia burgdorferi*) tentatively identified

↓

Pathogen grown in pure culture

↓

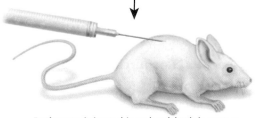

Pathogen injected into healthy lab mouse

↓

Heathly mouse becomes sick with Lyme disease

Section 2 **The Body's Defenses**

T Cells and B Cells The first time the immune system encounters and reacts to an antigen, a primary immune response occurs. Subsequent infections of the body with the same pathogen—and therefore the same antigen—produce a secondary immune response. During a primary response, after activation by a T cell, most B cells produce antibodies. A few B cells, however, are activated to reproduce rather than to produce antibodies. These B cells remain in the circulatory system for a long time, perhaps years, and are called memory B cells. If these memory B cells encounter the same antigen again, a secondary immune response occurs. During the secondary response, the B cells produce antibodies very quickly, so quickly the pathogen may never get well established in the body.

There are helper T cells, killer T cells, and suppressor T cells. Helper T cells account for the vast majority of T cells in the blood. When they are activated by an antigen, they strongly stimulate B cells and killer T cells (killer T cells directly kill microorganisms such as bacteria). Helper T cells also stimulate suppressor T cells. The gradually increasing activity of suppressor T cells shuts off the immune response when it is no longer needed. Some helper T cells become memory T cells and can help trigger a secondary immune response if the pathogen attacks again.

Although human immunodeficiency virus (HIV) can infect all T cells, the virus has a very high affinity for the antigens of helper T cells. Infected helper T cells are much less efficient when activated, and over time, they die. This loss of T-cell function, in addition to infection of other immune-system cells such as macrophages, accounts for the vulnerability of people with AIDS to pathogens that are too weak to cause disease in healthy people. Development of these disorders, called opportunistic infections, is one sign that a person with HIV infection may have developed the disease AIDS.

Section 3 Preventing Infectious Disease

Antibiotics and Antiviral Drugs Antibiotics target specific structures in bacteria, such as the cell wall or cell membranes. Some antibiotics kill bacteria, while others inhibit their growth. Antibiotic resistance occurs when bacteria change in some way that reduces or eliminates the effectiveness of drugs, chemicals, or other agents designed to cure or prevent infections. The bacteria survive and continue to multiply, causing more harm. This is the reason a person should take a full course of antibiotics; bacteria that survive from an incomplete treatment may be resistant to the antibiotic that was used.

Antiviral drugs inhibit the activity of viruses in different ways. For example, drugs used against HIV and HSV (herpes simplex virus) target enzymes needed for the virus to reproduce.

Section 4 Noninfectious Disease

Risk Factors for Cancer In cancer, many factors work together to cause disease. Some cancers do have a genetic link, such as some breast and colon cancers, but scientists think that environment and behavior play a greater role as possible causes of cancer than does genetics.

Over half of all cancers can be attributed to environmental factors. Many of these factors can be avoided— for example, cigarette smoking and excessive exposure to ultraviolet light. Environmental pollution, pesticides, and asbestos account for less than 10 percent of human cancer cases.

However, people who have direct contact with carcinogenic agents in the workplace are at the highest risk for cancer. Occupational exposure to vinyl chloride, for example, is limited by federal law to the lowest feasible level. Workers are required to wear protective clothing and respirators. The risk for the majority of the population is very low. In the past, vinyl chloride has been detected in some foods and beverages that were wrapped in packaging materials containing vinyl chloride. However, this exposure has been eliminated under current FDA regulations.

Address Misconceptions

Many students believe that chemicals cause the majority of cancers and therefore cancer is beyond their control to prevent. However, except for chemicals in tobacco, chemicals represent a small proportion of all causes of cancer. For a strategy for overcoming this misconception, see **Address Misconceptions** in the section *Noninfectious Diseases.*

Dietary factors have received much attention as risks for cancer. Obesity is associated with increased cancer risk. This may be due to the production by excess fat of free radicals, which damage genes. An increase of bile acids in the intestine, which results from a high-fat diet, also can promote colon cancer. Many fruits and vegetables contain antioxidants, which can protect cells from damage caused by free radicals. An interesting fact is that people who eat more fruits and vegetables, in spite of the fact that these foods may be contaminated with trace amounts of pesticides, generally have lower cancer risks than people who eat few fruits and vegetables.

Help Students Read

Anticipation Guide
Stimulating Interest in a Topic

Strategy Engage students actively with a selection by activating prior knowledge, arousing interest, and helping establish purposes for reading.

Example
1. Prior to class, read through the passage and identify major concepts and details.
2. Construct an anticipation guide as follows: Write five to ten short, but thought-provoking, declarative statements about the most important concepts featured in the section. If students are likely to have misconceptions about the topic, include statements that address those misconceptions. The statements could be in either a true-or-false or an agree-or-disagree format. To the left of each statement, put a blank for student responses.
3. Before assigning the section to read, either display the guide on the board or on an overhead, or distribute individual worksheets. Students can respond to the statements individually or as a group.
4. Discuss students' responses, asking students to support their answers using examples from past experience or prior reading.
5. Then have students read the section, evaluating the statements from the anticipation guide as they read.
6. After reading, revisit the guide, encouraging students to compare and contrast their prereading responses with their current one. Have students quote information from the passage to support their decisions.

Chapter 18

Fighting Disease

Chapter Preview

❶ Infectious Disease
Discover *How Does a Disease Spread?*
Skills Activity *Posing Questions*

❷ The Body's Defenses
Discover *Which Pieces Fit Together?*
Try This *Stuck Together*
Active Art *Immune Response*
Skills Lab *The Skin as a Barrier*

❸ Preventing Infectious Disease
Discover *What Substances Can Kill Pathogens?*
Science and History *Fighting Infectious Disease*

❹ Noninfectious Disease
Discover *What Happens When Airflow Is Restricted?*
Skills Activity *Drawing Conclusions*
Analyzing Data *Skin Cancer*
Skills Lab *Causes of Death, Then and Now*
Science and Society *Antibiotic Resistance—An Alarming Trend*

ⓘnteractive Textbook

These rod-shaped bacteria *(Legionella)* ▶
cause Legionnaires' disease.

 Lab zone **Chapter Project** 🄻🅃

Objectives

In this project, students will represent the body's responses to illness as battles in a war. After this Chapter Project, students will be able to

- pose questions about the progression of a disease
- apply concepts in the chapter to the study of a specific disease
- communicate information on how the disease affects the body in the format of a series of news reports

Skills Focus

Posing questions, applying concepts, communicating

Project Time Line 2 to 3 weeks

All in One Teaching Resources, Unit 3

- Chapter Project Teacher Notes
- Chapter Project Overview
- Chapter Project Worksheet 1
- Chapter Project Worksheet 2
- Chapter Project Scoring Rubric

Developing a Plan

Discuss with students how news reports tell stories as they convey information. Explain that students will research a disease of their choice during the first week and begin preparing their news reports during the second. Allow students to discuss options for presenting their projects, such as using recording equipment or visual aids.

Possible Materials

- If the presentations will include pictures or sound effects, provide art materials and equipment, such as markers, poster board, audio or video tape recorders, and slide projectors.
- Encourage students to use computers, if available, to create their reports and slides.
- Provide newspapers, magazines, and transcripts of radio or television news broadcasts for students to examine.

Chapter **Project**

Lab zone™

Stop the Invasion!

When you catch a cold, your body is under attack by cold viruses. Many other diseases are caused by viruses or bacteria that invade your body. In this project, you'll develop a series of informative news reports on how your body defends itself against such invasions.

Your Goal To create a series of imaginary news broadcasts from "battlefield sites" where the body is fighting an infectious disease

To complete this project successfully, you must

• choose a specific disease and represent the sequence of events that occurs when that disease strikes the body

• describe the stages of the disease as if they were battles between two armies

• present your story creatively in at least three reports, using newspaper, radio, or television news-reporting techniques

Plan It! With some classmates, list the techniques reporters use to make stories interesting or to explain complicated information. Also, recall the times you've had a cold, the flu, or another infectious disease. Write down how your body responded, how long you were sick, and any other useful information. Then select a specific disease to research.

Immune System Daily

Inflammatory Response Destroys Pathogens

DISCOVERY CHANNEL **SCHOOL** Video Preview

Fighting Disease

Show the Video Preview to introduce the Chapter Project and overview the chapter content. Discussion Question: **How do people come into contact with pathogens?** *(From contaminated objects, animals, other people, and air)*

• Provide reliable references for classroom use and a list of reliable Internet sites, such as Centers for Disease Control and Prevention.

Possible Shortcuts

You can simplify the project by restricting students to newspaper or radio reports. Students can work in small groups rather than individually to produce one group report.

Launching the Project

Ask students to speculate on what it means to "fight a cold." Ask: **What "weapons" do you use in the fight?** *(Possible answers: Lots of rest, plenty of fluids, cold medicine, tissues)* Allow time for students to read the description of the project in their text. Then encourage discussions on the stages of specific diseases and on any initial questions students may have.

Performance Assessment

The Chapter Project Scoring Rubric will help you evaluate how well students complete the Chapter Project. Share the rubric with your students so that they know what is expected. Students will be assessed on

• the thoroughness of their research, including pathogens, transmission, symptoms, treatments, and recovery stages

• the thoroughness and organization of their presentations, and how well they apply chapter concepts to their research

• the organization of their written or oral analyses

• their group participation, if they worked in groups

Portfolio

Objectives

After completing this lesson, students will be able to

18.1.1 Explain the relationship between pathogens and infectious disease.

18.1.2 List the kinds of pathogens that cause infectious diseases in humans.

18.1.3 Identify four sources of pathogens.

Target Reading Skill

Using Prior Knowledge Explain that using prior knowledge helps students connect what they already know to what they are about to read.

Answers

Possible answers:

What You Know

1. Bacteria and viruses can cause disease.

2. You can catch a cold from another person.

3. Lyme disease is spread by tick bites.

What You Learned

1. Organisms that can cause disease are called pathogens.

2. Some bacteria produce poisons, or toxins.

3. Some pathogens can spread through soil, food, or water.

All in One Teaching Resources, Unit 3

• Transparency LS174

Preteach

Build Background Knowledge L2

Classifying Diseases

Ask students to brainstorm a list of familiar diseases, and then divide the diseases into two groups: those that students think can be spread from person to person and those they think cannot. Revisit the responses once students have studied the section.

Reading Preview

Key Concepts

• What is the relationship between pathogens and infectious disease?

• What kinds of pathogens cause infectious diseases in humans?

• What are four ways that pathogens can spread?

Key Terms

• pathogen
• infectious disease
• toxin

Target Reading Skill

Using Prior Knowledge Before you read, look at the section headings and visuals to see what this section is about. Then write what you know about infectious diseases in a graphic organizer like the one below. As you read, continue to write in what you learn.

What You Know
1. Bacteria and viruses can cause disease.
2.

What You Learned
1.
2.

592 ◆

Lab zone Discover **Activity**

How Does a Disease Spread?

1. On a sheet of paper, write three headings: Round 1, Round 2, and Round 3.

2. Everyone in the class should shake hands with two people. Under Round 1, record the names of the people whose hand you shook.

3. Now shake hands with two different people. Record the name of each person whose hand you shook under Round 2.

4. Repeat Step 3. Under Round 3, record the names of the people whose hand you shook.

Think It Over

Calculating Suppose you had a disease that was spread by shaking hands. Everyone whose hand you shook has caught the disease and so has anyone who later shook hands with those people. Calculate how many people you "infected."

Before the twentieth century, surgery was a risky business. Even if people lived through an operation, they were not out of danger. After the operation, many patients' wounds became infected, and the patients often died. No one knew what caused these infections.

In the 1860s, a British surgeon named Joseph Lister hypothesized that microorganisms caused the infections. Before performing an operation, Lister washed his hands and surgical instruments with carbolic acid, a chemical that kills microorganisms. After the surgery, he covered the patient's wounds with bandages dipped in carbolic acid. Lister's results were dramatic. Before he used his new method, about 45 percent of his surgical patients died from infection. With Lister's new techniques, only 15 percent died.

Lab zone Discover **Activity**

Skills Focus Calculating

Materials None

Time 10 minutes

Tips Create a flowchart on the board that shows how the infection was spread. Ask a volunteer to represent a person with the disease and tell whose hands he or she shook in Round 1. Then calculate how many students that student infected.

L1 **Think It Over** The first student directly infects 6 (2 in each of 3 rounds). The two students infected in Round 1 directly infect a total of 8 (each infects 2 others in each of 2 rounds). The 6 infected in Round 2 directly infect 12 (2 each in Round 3). Therefore, if each student shakes hands with uninfected individuals, one student directly or indirectly infects a total of 26 people.

Understanding Infectious Disease

Like the infections that Lister observed after surgery, many illnesses, such as ear infections and food poisoning, are caused by living things that are too small to see without a microscope. Organisms that cause disease are called **pathogens.**

Diseases that are caused by pathogens are called infectious diseases. An **infectious disease** is a disease that is caused by the presence of a living thing within the body. **When you have an infectious disease, pathogens have gotten inside your body and caused harm.** Pathogens make you sick by damaging individual cells, even though you may feel pain throughout your body. For example, when you have strep throat, pathogens have damaged cells in your throat.

Before Lister's time, people believed that things like evil spirits or swamp air led to sickness. Several scientists in the late 1800s contributed to the understanding of infectious diseases. In the 1860s, the French scientist Louis Pasteur showed that microorganisms cause certain kinds of diseases. Pasteur also showed that killing the microorganisms could prevent the spread of those diseases. In the 1870s and 1880s, the German physician Robert Koch demonstrated that each infectious disease is caused by a specific kind of pathogen. In other words, one kind of pathogen causes pneumonia, another kind causes chickenpox, and still another kind causes rabies.

 Reading Checkpoint What causes infectious disease?

FIGURE 1
Preventing Infections
The illustration on the left shows how Lister used a carbolic steam sprayer to spread a mist of carbolic acid. The photo on the right shows a modern operating room.
Comparing and Contrasting *Identify some ways in which present-day surgery differs from surgery in Lister's time.*

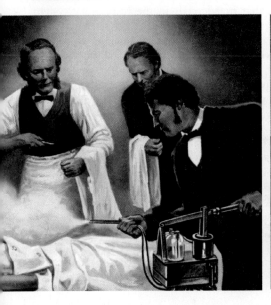

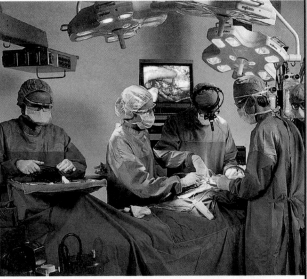

Chapter 18 ◆ **593**

Differentiated Instruction

English Learners/Beginning L1
Vocabulary: Word Analysis Point out that the word *pathogen* comes from the Greek *patho,* meaning "disease," and *gennan,* meaning "origin." Tell students that they can think of pathogens as "disease-causers." Have them state the relationship between pathogens and infectious diseases. **learning modality: verbal**

English Learners/Intermediate L2
Comprehension: Key Concepts Have students make a four-column chart headed by each of the four types of pathogens. Pair English learners with English-proficient students to use references to locate diseases caused by each type. Point out that knowing the pathogen causing an infectious disease helps a physician know how to treat it. **learning modality: visual**

Understanding Infectious Disease

Teach Key Concepts L2
The Discovery of Pathogens

Focus Remind students that the discovery of pathogens was fairly recent.

Teach Explain that in the U.S. in 1900, the three leading causes of death were pneumonia, tuberculosis, and intestinal infections. Today, heart disease and cancers cause half of all deaths. Fewer than 5 percent are caused by pneumonia, influenza, and HIV. Ask: **Why did the number of deaths due to infectious disease change?** *(Identifying pathogens helped people know how to prevent their spread.)*

Apply Ask students to hypothesize how scientists identify the pathogen that causes a specific disease. *(Possible answer: They determine whether the pathogen is present in everyone who has the disease.)* **learning modality: logical/mathematical**

Independent Practice L2
All in One Teaching Resources, Unit 3
• Guided Reading and Study Worksheet: *Infectious Disease*

⊙ **Student Edition on Audio CD**

Monitor Progress L2

Writing Have students summarize the historical events explained in the text.

Answers
Figure 1 The doctors and nurses today wear protective clothing and masks to prevent the transfer of pathogens to the patient.

 Reading Checkpoint Organisms called pathogens

593

Kinds of Pathogens

Teach Key Concepts L2

How Pathogens Cause Illness

Focus Remind students that most microorganisms are harmless.

Teach Ask: **What is one way that bacteria cause illness?** *(They produce toxins that damage cells.)* **How do viruses cause illness?** *(They reproduce inside living cells, damaging or destroying them in the process.)*

Apply Ask: **Why do you think there is no vaccine to prevent the common cold?** *(Because the cold is caused by so many different viruses, one vaccine could not protect against all of them.)* **learning modality: logical/mathematical**

Integrating Environmental Science L3

Tell students that environmental changes can affect the occurrence or increase of some infectious diseases. For example, in the southwestern U.S. in 1993, heavy snows and rainfall resulted in abundant plant growth, which led to a large population of deer mice because they had plenty of food. The mice carried a pathogen called hantavirus that could be transmitted to humans. With ten times more mice than usual, the likelihood increased that humans would come into contact with mice. Though hantavirus infection in humans was not new, the number of people infected was above what was expected. Ask students why a disease that is transmitted by mosquitoes might occur more frequently when rainfall is higher than normal. *(More rain causes more water to accumulate, and mosquitoes breed in water.)* **learning modality: logical/ mathematical**

FIGURE 2
Pathogens
Most infectious diseases are caused by microscopic organisms.

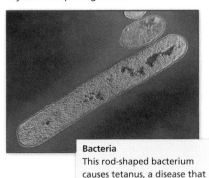

Bacteria
This rod-shaped bacterium causes tetanus, a disease that harms the nervous system.

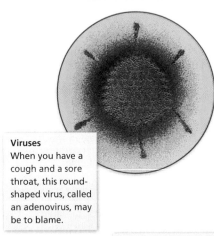

Viruses
When you have a cough and a sore throat, this round-shaped virus, called an adenovirus, may be to blame.

Fungi
This fungus causes ringworm, a disease that makes a round, ring-shaped skin rash.

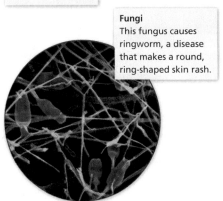

Kinds of Pathogens

You share Earth with many kinds of organisms. Most of these organisms are harmless, but some can make you sick. Some diseases are caused by multicelled animals, such as worms. However, most pathogens can be seen only with a microscope. **The four major groups of human pathogens are bacteria, viruses, fungi, and protists.** Look at Figure 2 to see some examples of pathogens.

Bacteria Bacteria are one-celled microorganisms. They cause a wide variety of diseases, including ear infections, food poisoning, and strep throat.

Some bacterial pathogens damage body cells directly. Strep throat is caused by streptococcus bacteria that invade cells in your throat. Other bacterial pathogens damage cells indirectly by producing a poison, or **toxin.** For example, if the bacteria that cause tetanus get into a wound, they produce a toxin that damages the nervous system. Tetanus is also called lockjaw because the nerve damage can lock the jaw muscles.

Viruses Viruses are tiny particles, much smaller than bacteria. Viruses cannot reproduce unless they are inside living cells. The cells are damaged or destroyed in the process, releasing new viruses to infect other cells. Both colds and flu are caused by viruses that invade cells in the respiratory system. There are more than 200 kinds of cold viruses, each of which can give you a sore throat and runny nose.

Fungi Fungi, which include molds and yeasts, also cause some infectious diseases. Fungi grow best in warm, dark, and moist areas. Two examples of fungal diseases are athlete's foot and ringworm.

Protists Protists are also a cause of disease. Malaria, an infection of the blood that is common in tropical areas, is one disease caused by protists. Other diseases caused by protists are African sleeping sickness and amebic dysentery.

 Reading Checkpoint What is required in order for viruses to reproduce?

How Pathogens Are Spread

Like all living things, pathogens need food and a place to live and reproduce. Unfortunately, your body may be the right place to meet a pathogen's needs. You can become infected by a pathogen in several ways. **Pathogens can spread through contact with either an infected person; soil, food, or water; a contaminated object; or an infected animal.**

Infected People Pathogens often pass from one person to another through direct physical contact, such as kissing and shaking hands. For example, if you kiss someone who has an open cold sore, cold-sore viruses may get into your body.

Diseases are also spread through indirect contact with an infected person. For example, when a person with a cold or the flu sneezes, pathogens shoot into the air. Other people may catch a cold or the flu if they inhale these pathogens.

Soil, Food, and Water Some pathogens occur naturally in the environment. The bacteria that cause botulism, a severe form of food poisoning, live in soil. Botulism bacteria can produce toxins in foods that have been improperly canned.

Some pathogens can contaminate food and water. If people then eat the food or drink the water, they may become sick. Some pathogens that cause severe diarrhea are spread through contaminated food and water. Cholera and dysentery are two deadly diseases that spread through food or water.

Skills Activity

Posing Questions

In 1854, cholera spread throughout London, England. Dr. John Snow analyzed where most of the cholera victims lived, as well as the locations of the water pumps in the area.

1. The map in Figure 3 shows Dr. Snow's findings. Dr. Snow hypothesized that the disease was spread by water that came from one of the pumps. Which pump was probably the source of the contaminated water?

2. Suppose that Dr. Snow just learned that two additional people had died of cholera. What questions would Dr. Snow most likely ask about the additional cholera cases?

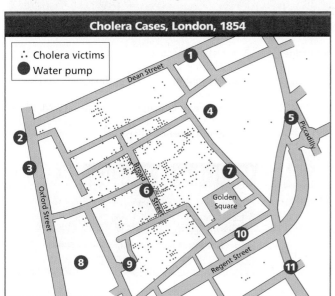

Cholera Cases, London, 1854

∴ Cholera victims
● Water pump

FIGURE 3
Cholera is a deadly disease caused by cholera bacteria. The map shows the location of cholera cases in the 1854 epidemic in London, England.
Inferring How are cholera bacteria spread?

Lab zone Skills Activity

Skills Focus Posing questions

Materials None

Time 10 minutes

Tips Ask students to point out the location of the pumps and of the cholera victims.

Expected Outcome Pump 6 was the source of the contaminated water. Dr. Snow would probably ask where the latest cholera victims lived and from which pumps they obtained water.

Extend Have students write a newspaper story about Dr. Snow's work, including a caption that could accompany the map in Figure 3. **learning modality: visual**

How Pathogens Are Spread

Teach Key Concepts　　　　L2

Sources of Pathogens

Focus Review the different ways that pathogens can be spread.

Teach Tell students that knowing how pathogens are spread can help people take measures to reduce their spread. Ask students to name one way to prevent the spread of pathogens from each source. *(Sample answers: Person to person—cover your mouth when you sneeze; soil, food, and water—cook raw meat thoroughly; contaminated objects—wash hands frequently; animal bites—wear insect and tick repellent)*

Apply Tell students that washing hands is the single most important way to prevent the spread of infectious diseases. Ask students to hypothesize how most infectious diseases are spread. *(Through direct contact with an infected person or objects the person has handled)* **learning modality: logical/ mathematical**

Lab zone Build Inquiry　　　　L2

Applying the Concept of Prevention

Materials references on infectious diseases

Time 30 minutes

Focus Ask students to list infectious diseases they have heard of and would like to know more about.

Teach Have students work in groups to identify the source and prevention measures for the diseases they listed.

Apply Have students create posters that illustrate preventive measures to reduce the risk of infectious diseases. **learning modality: visual**

Monitor Progress _____ L2

Oral Presentation Call on students to name the kinds of pathogens and the ways infectious diseases are spread.

Answers
Figure 3 Cholera bacteria are spread through contaminated water or food.

 Reading Checkpoint They must be inside living cells.

Answers

Figure 4 Avoid walking through areas where ticks may live, or if you do, apply tick repellent. Wear long-sleeved shirts and long pants taped to legs or tucked into shoes.

✓ **Reading Checkpoint** Lyme disease, Rocky Mountain spotted fever

Assess

Reviewing Key Concepts

1. a. An organism that causes disease
b. Pathogens cause disease by getting inside the body and damaging individual cells.
c. Pasteur showed that microorganisms cause certain diseases and that killing microorganisms prevents the spread of diseases. Koch showed that each infectious disease is caused by a specific kind of pathogen.
2. a. Bacteria, viruses, fungi, and protists
b. They can damage cells directly or by producing a toxin. **c.** Bacteria are one-celled microorganisms. They can cause disease by invading and damaging cells directly or by releasing toxins. Viruses are tiny particles that are much smaller than bacteria. They cause disease as they reproduce inside cells. The cells are damaged or destroyed, and the viruses escape to infect new cells.
3. a. Contact with an infected person; soil, food, and water; contaminated objects; an infected animal bite **b.** People can come in contact with pathogens by using objects that have been used by an infected person or animal. **c.** Avoid contact with others, do not share objects you have touched, wash your hands frequently, and cover your mouth and nose when sneezing or coughing. These steps help prevent the cold virus from entering the body of another person.

Reteach

Have students look at the images of pathogens in this section and tell what they know about each one.

All in One **Teaching Resources, Unit 3**
- Section Summary: *Infectious Disease*
- Review and Reinforce: *Infectious Disease*
- Enrich: *Infectious Disease*

FIGURE 4
Deer Ticks and Lyme Disease
The tiny deer tick may carry the bacteria that cause Lyme disease, a serious condition that can damage the joints.
Problem Solving *How might people reduce their risk of catching Lyme disease?*

Contaminated Objects Some pathogens can survive for a time outside a person's body. People can come into contact with pathogens by using objects, such as towels or silverware, that have been handled by an infected person. Colds and flu can be spread in this way. Tetanus bacteria can enter the body if a person steps on a contaminated object.

Infected Animals If an animal that is infected with certain pathogens bites a person, it can pass the pathogens to the person. People can get rabies, a serious disease that affects the nervous system, from the bite of an infected animal, such as a dog or a raccoon. Lyme disease and Rocky Mountain spotted fever are both spread by tick bites. For example, if a deer tick that is carrying Lyme disease bacteria bites a person, the person may get Lyme disease. The protist that causes malaria is transferred by the bites of mosquitoes that live in tropical regions.

✓ **Reading Checkpoint** Name a disease that can be spread by an animal bite.

Section 1 Assessment

🎯 **Target Reading Skill** Using Prior Knowledge Review your graphic organizer and revise it based on what you just learned in the section.

Reviewing Key Concepts

1. a. Defining What is a pathogen?
b. Explaining How do pathogens cause infectious disease?
c. Relating Cause and Effect How did Pasteur and Koch contribute to the understanding of the causes of infectious disease?
2. a. Identifying Name four kinds of pathogens that cause disease in humans.
b. Explaining In what two ways do bacteria cause disease?
c. Comparing and Contrasting Compare and contrast bacteria and viruses—both in terms of their size and how they cause disease.

3. a. Listing What are four ways that pathogens can infect humans?
b. Describing How are pathogens spread by contaminated objects?
c. Applying Concepts If you have a cold, what steps can you take to keep from spreading it to other people? Explain.

Writing in Science

Speech Write a short speech that Joseph Lister might have delivered to other surgeons to convince them to use his surgical techniques. In the speech, Lister should explain why his techniques were so successful.

596 ◆

Lab zone Chapter **Project**

Keep Students on Track Students should have chosen a disease and the method of presentation. Encourage them to make a list of questions that a good news story should answer. They can use the questions when they do their research. Suggest that they highlight interesting facts or stories about the disease.

Writing in Science

Writing Mode Persuasive paragraph
Scoring Rubric
4 Includes a detailed statement of the problem faced by surgeons, Lister's insight into the cause of infections, Lister's methods for combating infection, and the effect of his methods on the survival of patients
3 Includes all major points, but with fewer details
2 Includes limited information
1 Includes partial or inaccurate information

Reading Preview

Key Concepts
- How does the body's first line of defense guard against pathogens?
- What happens during the inflammatory response?
- How does the immune system respond to pathogens?
- How does HIV affect the immune system and how does it spread?

Key Terms
- inflammatory response
- phagocyte • immune response
- lymphocyte • T cell
- antigen • B cell • antibody
- AIDS • HIV

Target Reading Skill
Building Vocabulary After you read this section, reread the paragraphs that contain definitions of Key Terms. Use all the information you have learned to write a definition of each Key Term in your own words.

Lab zone **Discover Activity**

Which Pieces Fit Together?

1. Your teacher will give you a piece of paper with one jagged edge.
2. One student in the class has a piece of paper with a jagged edge that matches yours, like two pieces of a jigsaw puzzle. Find the student whose paper matches yours and fit the two edges together.

Think It Over
Inferring Imagine that one piece of paper in each matching pair is a pathogen. The other is a cell in your body that defends your body against the invading pathogen. How many kinds of invaders can each defender cell recognize?

Your eyes are glued to the video screen. Enemy troops have gotten through an opening in the wall. Your soldiers have held back most of the invaders. However, some enemy soldiers are breaking through the defense lines. You need your backup defenders. They can zap invaders with their more powerful weapons. If your soldiers can fight off the enemy until the backup team arrives, you can save your fortress.

Video games create fantasy wars, but in your body, real battles happen all the time. In your body, the "enemies" are invading pathogens. You are hardly ever aware of these battles. The body's disease-fighting system is so effective that most people get sick only occasionally. By eliminating pathogens that can harm your cells, your body maintains homeostasis.

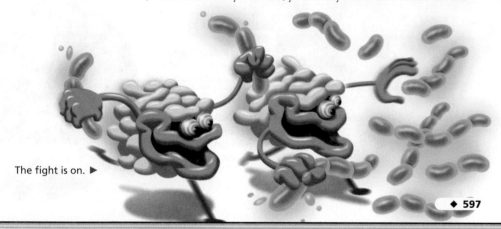

The fight is on. ▶

◆ 597

Objectives
After completing this lesson, students will be able to

18.2.1 Explain how the body's first line of defense guards against pathogens.

18.2.2 Describe what happens during the inflammatory response.

18.2.3 State how the immune system responds to pathogens.

18.2.4 Identify how HIV affects the immune system and how it spreads.

Target Reading Skill

Building Vocabulary Explain that knowing the definitions of Key Terms helps students understand what they read.

As students read each passage that contains a Key Term, remind them to write a sentence in their own words. Encourage students to write one or two descriptive phrases to help them remember the Key Term. Call on students to share their sentences and phrases.

Preteach

Build Background Knowledge   L1

Resisting Infectious Diseases
Ask: **What are some factors that allow people to resist becoming ill with an infectious disease?** *(Possible answers: Getting enough rest, eating healthy foods, avoiding objects contaminated by an infected person, washing hands, getting vaccinated, being immune due to previous illness)*

Lab zone **Discover Activity**

Skills Focus Inferring   L1

Materials sheets of paper, each cut into two matching jigsaw pieces

Time 10 minutes

Tips Prepare matching sets of shapes by cutting sheets of paper in half with a zigzag or wavy pattern. Use a different pattern for each piece of paper. All paper should be the same color.

Expected Outcome Each student should find only one matching piece.

Think It Over Each defender cell recognizes only one type of invader.

Barriers That Keep Pathogens Out

Teach Key Concepts L2
The First Line of Defense

Focus Ask a student to read the passages on the first page of the section. Ask: **How was the wall a first line defense?** *(It kept invaders out.)*

Teach Ask: **How is your skin like the wall?** *(Most pathogens get through the skin only when it is cut.)* Refer students to the inset of cilia in Figure 5. Ask: **How do cilia act as a first line of defense?** *(They trap pathogens.)* **How does your digestive system act as a first line of defense?** *(Chemicals in saliva and acid in the stomach destroy pathogens.)*

Apply Explain that many pathogens enter the body the same way they exit an infected person's body. Ask: **Which defenses would protect you against cold viruses?** *(Mucus and cilia in the breathing passages)* **learning modality: logical/mathematical**

Teacher Demo L1

Bacteria Are Everywhere

Materials disposable petri dish with nutrient agar, sterile cotton ball, tape

Time 10 minutes for setup, 5 minutes each day over several days

Focus Explain that normally harmless bacteria are present on the skin.

Teach Rub your palm with the cotton ball, and then brush the cotton over the agar. Tape the dish closed, and place it upside down in a warm place (not over 37°C.). Each day for several days, allow students to examine the dish with the cover closed. *(The agar should be covered with dots.)* Explain that each dot is a colony that contains millions of bacteria. Ask: **Why can you see the bacteria?** *(Because they multiplied on the agar; and there are now millions.)*

Apply Ask: **Why is hand-washing important even if you are not ill?** *(You can pick up pathogens from the environment.)* **learning modality: visual**

Barriers That Keep Pathogens Out

Your body has three lines of defense against pathogens. The first line consists of barriers that keep most pathogens from getting into the body. You do not wear a sign that says "Pathogens Keep Out," but that doesn't matter. **In the first line of defense, the surfaces of the skin, breathing passages, mouth, and stomach function as barriers to pathogens. These barriers trap and kill most pathogens with which you come into contact.**

Skin When pathogens land on the skin, they are exposed to destructive chemicals in oil and sweat. Even if these chemicals don't kill them, the pathogens may fall off with dead skin cells. If the pathogens manage to stay on the skin, they must get through the tightly packed dead cells that form a barrier on top of living skin cells. Most pathogens get through the skin only when it is cut. Scabs form over cuts so rapidly that the period in which pathogens can enter the body in this way is very short.

Breathing Passages Pathogens can also enter the body when you inhale. The nose, pharynx, trachea, and bronchi, however, contain mucus and cilia. Together, the mucus and cilia trap and remove most of the pathogens that enter the respiratory system. In addition, irritation by pathogens may make you sneeze or cough. Both actions force the pathogens out of your body.

Mouth and Stomach Some pathogens are found in foods, even if the foods are handled safely. The saliva in your mouth contains destructive chemicals, and your stomach produces acid. Most pathogens that you swallow are destroyed by saliva or stomach acid.

> **Reading Checkpoint** How do your breathing passages help keep pathogens out of your body?

FIGURE 5
Barriers to Pathogens
The surfaces of your skin and breathing passages are the first line of defense for keeping pathogens out of your body. *Relating Cause and Effect How can washing your hands help prevent infection?*

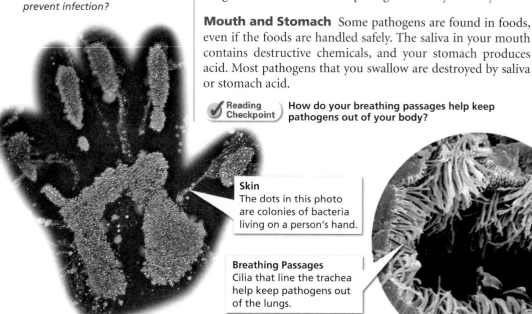

Skin
The dots in this photo are colonies of bacteria living on a person's hand.

Breathing Passages
Cilia that line the trachea help keep pathogens out of the lungs.

598 ◆

Independent Practice L2

All in One Teaching Resources, Unit 3

- Guided Reading and Study Worksheet: *The Body's Defenses*

⊙ **Student Edition on Audio CD**

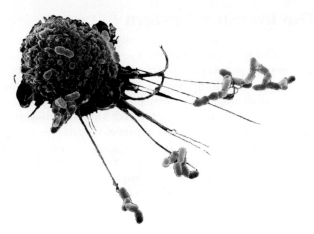

FIGURE 6
Phagocytes Destroy Pathogens
Caught! A phagocyte (shown in red) is a white blood cell that engulfs and destroys bacteria (shown in green). As phagocytes do their job, the body shows visible signs of inflammation, which include redness and swelling.

The Inflammatory Response

In spite of barriers, pathogens sometimes get into your body and begin to damage cells. When body cells are damaged, they release chemicals that trigger the **inflammatory response,** which is the body's second line of defense. **In the inflammatory response, fluid and white blood cells leak from blood vessels into nearby tissues. The white blood cells then fight the pathogens.** Because the inflammatory response is the same regardless of the pathogen, it is called the body's general defense.

White Blood Cells All white blood cells are disease fighters. However, there are different types of white blood cells, each with its own particular function. The type involved in the inflammatory response are the phagocytes. A **phagocyte** (FAG uh syt) is a white blood cell that engulfs pathogens and destroys them by breaking them down.

Inflammation During the inflammatory response, blood vessels widen in the area affected by the pathogens. This enlargement increases blood flow to the area. As a result, more disease-fighting white blood cells are delivered to the area. The enlarged blood vessels, and the fluid that leaks out of them, make the affected area red and swollen. If you touch the swollen area, it will feel slightly warmer than normal.

Fever In some cases, chemicals produced during the inflammatory response cause a fever. Although fever makes you feel bad, it actually helps your body fight the infection. Some pathogens do not grow and reproduce well at higher temperatures.

 Reading Checkpoint What role do white blood cells play in the inflammatory response?

Discovery CHANNEL SCHOOL

Fighting Disease

Video Preview
▶ Video Field Trip
Video Assessment

The Inflammatory Response

Teach Key Concepts   L2
The Second Line of Defense

Focus Refer students to the story at the beginning of this section. Ask them to identify the second line of defense. *(The soldiers trying to hold back the invaders)*

Teach Ask students to look up the origin of the word *phagocyte.* (Phag *means "eat," and* kytos *means "cell.")* Ask: **How does this help you understand what a phagocyte does?** *(Phagocytes take in pathogens the way a person takes in food.)* **What other processes help fight pathogens?** *(Widening blood vessels increase the flow of blood and therefore the number of white cells to the affected area. A fever caused by chemicals produced during the inflammatory response slows down or stops the growth of pathogens.)*

Apply Ask students to imagine waking up and not feeling well. Ask: **Why does taking a body temperature reading help determine whether or not you are sick?** *(A fever can indicate the presence of an infectious disease)* **learning modality: logical/mathematical**

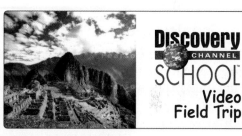
Discovery CHANNEL SCHOOL Video Field Trip

Fighting Disease

Show the Video Field Trip to help students understand the importance of vaccines. Discussion question: **How do vaccines fight flu viruses?** *(Flu vaccines contain unique flu virus proteins that trigger an immune response in the body; vaccines help the body's immune system react quickly enough to destroy the virus before it causes illness.)*

Monitor Progress _____ L2

Writing Have students describe two ways the body defends itself against pathogens.

Answers
Figure 5 It can eliminate or reduce pathogens that you may have picked up.

 Reading Checkpoint They contain mucus and cilia that trap and help remove most of the pathogens that enter the respiratory system.

Reading Checkpoint Phagocytes engulf pathogens and destroy them.

Differentiated Instruction

Special Needs   L1
Modeling Phagocytes Demonstrate the action of phagocytes by grasping a small object completely in your hand. Explain that phagocytes surround a pathogen, and then break it down with chemicals. Provide students with lumps of clay and buttons, and ask them to model the action of phagocytes. *(Students wrap the clay completely around a button.)* **learning modality: kinesthetic**

Less Proficient Readers   L1
Drawing First Lines of Defense Have students sketch an outline of a body, then indicate and label the first lines of defenses. Ask them to write sentences in their own words describing how each line of defense protects against pathogens. **learning modality: visual**

The Immune System

Teach Key Concepts `L2`
T Cells and B Cells

Focus Point out that phagocytes are one kind of white blood cell; lymphocytes are another.

Teach Ask: **What are the two major kinds of lymphocytes?** *(T cells and B cells)* **How are lymphocytes different from phagocytes?** *(Lymphocytes are able to recognize different kinds of pathogens.)* **What is the major function of T cells?** *(To identify pathogens and distinguish one kind from another)* **B cells?** *(To produce antibodies)* **How do T cells recognize pathogens?** *(By the antigens that are found on each pathogen)*

Apply Tell students that some B cells develop into memory cells that circulate through the body indefinitely. If a person is exposed to the same pathogen, the memory cells will become active and trigger rapid production of antibodies. Tell students they will learn more about this in the next section. **learning modality: logical/ mathematical**

All in One Teaching Resources, Unit 3

• Transparency LS175

Use Visuals: Figure 7 `L2`
Functions of T Cells and B Cells

Focus Ask students to identify the parts of the immune system. *(T cells, B cells, antibodies)*

Teach Have student volunteers read aloud each step in Figure 7 and then identify the functions performed by T cells, B cells, and phagocytes. *(T cells identify antigens, activate B cells, and attack damaged cells. B cells produce antibodies. Phagocytes destroy clumps of pathogens.)* Ask: **What happens to the body cells that have been infected by viruses?** *(T cells destroy the body cells along with the viruses.)*

Apply Ask: **Which body cells would T cells attack if you had the mumps, a viral infection that affects salivary glands?** *(Cells in salivary glands)* **learning modality: visual**

Lab zone **Try This Activity**

Stuck Together

In this activity, you will model one way in which an antibody prevents a pathogen from infecting a body cell.

1. Use a large ball to represent a body cell, and a smaller ball to represent a pathogen.
2. Press a lump of modeling clay onto the small ball. Then use the clay to stick the two balls together. This model shows how a pathogen attaches itself to a body cell.
3. Pull the two balls apart, keeping the clay on the small ball (the pathogen).
4. Put strips of tape over the clay, so that the clay is completely covered. The tape represents an antibody.
5. Now try to reattach the small ball to the larger one.

Making Models Use the model to explain how antibodies prevent pathogens from attaching to body cells.

600 ◆

The Immune System

If a pathogen infection is severe enough to cause a fever, it triggers the body's third line of defense—the **immune response.** The immune response is controlled by the immune system, the body's disease-fighting system. **The cells of the immune system can distinguish between different kinds of pathogens. The immune system cells react to each kind of pathogen with a defense targeted specifically at that pathogen.**

The white blood cells that distinguish between different kinds of pathogens are called **lymphocytes** (LIM fuh syts). There are two major kinds of lymphocytes—T lymphocytes and B lymphocytes, which are also called T cells and B cells. In Figure 7, you can see how T cells and B cells work together to destroy flu viruses.

T Cells A major function of **T cells** is to identify pathogens and distinguish one kind of pathogen from another. You have tens of millions of T cells circulating in your blood. Each kind of T cell recognizes a different kind of pathogen. What T cells actually recognize are marker molecules, called antigens, found on each pathogen. **Antigens** are molecules that the immune system recognizes either as part of your body or as coming from outside your body.

You can think of antigens as something like the uniforms that athletes wear. When you watch a track meet, you can look at the runners' uniforms to tell which school each runner comes from. Like athletes from different schools, each different pathogen has its own kind of antigen. Antigens differ from one another because each kind of antigen has a different chemical structure. T cells distinguish one chemical structure from another.

B Cells The lymphocytes called **B cells** produce proteins that help destroy pathogens. These proteins are called **antibodies.** Each kind of B cell produces only one kind of antibody, and each kind of antibody has a different structure. Antigen and antibody molecules fit together like pieces of a puzzle. An antigen on a flu virus will only bind to one kind of antibody—the antibody that acts against that flu virus.

When antibodies bind to the antigens on a pathogen, they mark the pathogen for destruction. Some antibodies make pathogens clump together. Others keep pathogens from attaching to the body cells that they might damage. Still other antibodies make it easier for phagocytes to destroy the pathogens.

 Reading Checkpoint What is the function of an antibody?

Lab zone **Try This Activity**

Skills Focus Making models `L2`

Materials modeling clay, large ball, small ball, tape

Time 10 minutes

Tips Have students reread the last paragraph under B Cells.

Expected Outcome Antibodies prevent the pathogen from attaching to the body's cells.

Extend Have students model how pathogens clump together. *(Students could press bits of clay on the small ball and stick several small balls together.)* **learning modality: kinesthetic**

FIGURE 7

The Immune Response

The immune system includes T cells and B cells. The cells of the immune system work together to combat an infection, such as one caused by flu viruses. **Interpreting Diagrams** *What happens after a T cell recognizes an invading virus?*

Go Online
active art

For: Immune Response activity
Visit: PHSchool.com
Web Code: cep-4052

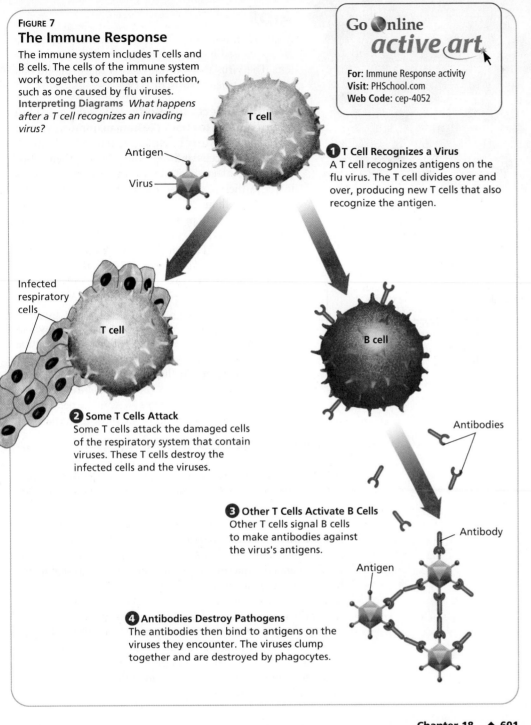

Antigen

Virus

T cell

❶ T Cell Recognizes a Virus
A T cell recognizes antigens on the flu virus. The T cell divides over and over, producing new T cells that also recognize the antigen.

Infected respiratory cells

T cell

B cell

Antibodies

❷ Some T Cells Attack
Some T cells attack the damaged cells of the respiratory system that contain viruses. These T cells destroy the infected cells and the viruses.

❸ Other T Cells Activate B Cells
Other T cells signal B cells to make antibodies against the virus's antigens.

Antibody

Antigen

❹ Antibodies Destroy Pathogens
The antibodies then bind to antigens on the viruses they encounter. The viruses clump together and are destroyed by phagocytes.

Chapter 18 ◆ 601

Differentiated Instruction

Gifted and Talented　**L3**
Describing the Lymphatic System Ask students to identify the organs and tissues that make up the immune system (such as lymph nodes, spleen, and bone marrow) and their functions. Students can present their findings in class. **learning modality: verbal**

Less Proficient Readers　**L1**
Connecting Text and Visuals Read the passages on T cells and B cells aloud as students follow along with you. Stop periodically to help students find supporting visuals in Figure 7. When you have read both passages, ask students to summarize the immune response in their own words. **learning modality: visual**

Lab zone ▸ Build Inquiry　**L2**

Communicating How Immune System Cells Work

Materials tape, paper
Time 30 minutes

Focus Ask students to name Key Terms related to the immune system.

Teach Place students in small groups of four or five, and have them create skits that dramatize the immune response. Group tasks can include research, writing, acting, and narrating. Any one student may take on more than one task. Suggest that students identify their roles by attaching large pieces of paper to their clothing with tape. Roles should include pathogens, T cells, B cells, antigens, antibodies, and phagocytes. Students can present their skits to the class.

Apply Invite students to think of a time when they had a cold or a sore throat. Ask: **At what point in your illness might you have known that your immune system was "winning the fight"?** *(At the point when you started to feel better)* **learning modality: kinesthetic**

Go Online
active art

For: Immune Response activity
Visit: PHSchool.com
Web Code: cep-4052

Students learn how the immune system responds to an infection.

Monitor Progress　L2

Drawing Ask students to draw two or more pathogens with different antigens, label their drawings, and provide a caption that explains how a T cell recognizes a pathogen. Students can place their drawings in their portfolios.

Portfolio

Answers
Figure 7 The T cell divides over and over and produces new T cells that also recognize the antigen.

Reading Checkpoint An antibody recognizes and helps destroy a particular pathogen.

AIDS

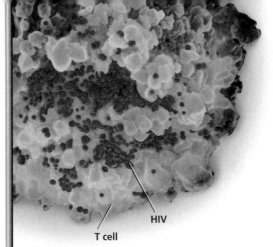

FIGURE 8
Human Immunodeficiency Virus (HIV)
The tiny red particles are HIV viruses emerging from a T cell. The viruses multiply inside the T cell and eventually cause the cell to die.
Relating Cause and Effect
Why does the destruction of T cells interfere with the body's ability to fight disease?

AIDS

Acquired immunodeficiency syndrome, or **AIDS,** is a disease caused by a virus that attacks the immune system. The virus that causes AIDS is called the human immunodeficiency virus, or **HIV.**

How HIV Affects the Body HIV is the only kind of virus known to attack the human immune system directly and destroy T cells. Once it invades the body, HIV enters T cells and reproduces inside them. People can be infected with HIV—that is, have the virus living in their T cells—for years before they become sick. More than 40 million people in the world, including more than 3 million children under 15, are infected with HIV.

Eventually, HIV begins to destroy the T cells it has infected. As the viruses destroy T cells, the body loses its ability to fight disease. Most persons infected with HIV eventually develop the symptoms of AIDS.

Because their immune systems no longer function properly, people with AIDS become sick with diseases not normally found in people with healthy immune systems. Many people survive attack after attack of such diseases. But eventually their immune systems fail, ending in death. At this time, there is no cure for AIDS. However, new drug treatments allow many people with AIDS to survive much longer than those in the past.

How HIV Is Spread Like all other viruses, HIV can only reproduce inside cells. However, the virus can survive for a short time outside the human body in body fluids, such as blood and the fluids produced by the male and female reproductive systems.

HIV can spread from one person to another only if body fluids from an infected person come in contact with those of an uninfected person. Sexual contact is one way in which this can happen. HIV may also pass from an infected woman to her baby during pregnancy or childbirth or through breast milk. In addition, infected blood can spread HIV. For example, if an infected drug user shares a needle, the next person who uses the needle may also become infected. Before 1985, HIV was sometimes transmitted through blood transfusions. Since 1985, however, all donated blood in the United States has been tested for signs of HIV. If blood is identified as infected, it is not used in transfusions.

602 ◆

FIGURE 9
How HIV Is Not Spread
You cannot get HIV, the virus that causes AIDS, by hugging someone infected with the virus.

How HIV Is Not Spread It is important to know the many ways in which HIV is *not* spread. HIV does not live on skin, so you cannot be infected by hugging or shaking hands with an infected person. You can't get infected by using a toilet seat after it has been used by someone with HIV. HIV is also not spread when you bump into someone while playing sports.

 Reading Checkpoint What disease is caused by HIV?

Section 2 Assessment

 Target Reading Skill Building Vocabulary Use your definitions to help you answer the questions below.

Reviewing Key Concepts

1. a. Listing Name four barriers that prevent pathogens from getting into the body.
   b. Explaining Briefly describe how each barrier prevents infections.
   c. Predicting What could happen if you got a cut that did not heal?

2. a. Reviewing What triggers the inflammatory response?
   b. Describing How does the inflammatory response defend against invading pathogens?
   c. Relating Cause and Effect Why is the presence of large numbers of white blood cells in a wound a sign of infection?

3. a. Identifying Identify the cells that are part of the immune system.
   b. Sequencing Outline the steps involved in the immune response.

4. a. Reviewing Where in the body does HIV reproduce?
   b. Summarizing What are three ways that HIV can be passed from one person to another?

Writing in Science

Explanation An antigen and antibody can be compared to a lock and key. Write a paragraph in which you explain how the lock-and-key model is a good way to describe the relationship between an antigen and antibody.

Lab zone Chapter Project

Keep Students on Track At this point, students should have completed their research. Advise them to outline the main ideas they want to communicate before writing their newspaper articles or scripts. Encourage them to make their descriptions sound like real news and to include information about each of the body's lines of defenses.

Writing in Science

Writing Mode Explanation
Scoring Rubric
4 Includes accurate, logical explanation of the analogy; goes beyond requirements to explain the role of antibodies
3 Includes criteria, but does not go beyond requirements
2 Includes only brief explanation
1 Includes inaccurate explanation

Monitor Progress

Answers
Figure 8 T cells recognize pathogens' antigens. When T cells are destroyed, the body loses its ability to mount a response aimed at specific pathogens.

Reading Checkpoint AIDS

Assess

Reviewing Key Concepts

1. a. Skin, breathing passages, mouth, and stomach **b.** The skin forms a barrier against pathogens getting into the body. Breathing passages contain mucus and cilia that trap and remove pathogens. The mouth and stomach contain chemicals (saliva and stomach acids) that destroy some pathogens. **c.** The likelihood that pathogens would get into the body would increase.
2. a. Chemicals that are released when body cells are damaged **b.** Phagocytes engulf pathogens and destroy them. Widening of blood vessels increases the flow of blood and therefore white blood cells to the area where pathogens have entered. Fever slows or stops the growth of pathogens. **c.** Since the function of white blood cells is to fight pathogens, the presence of large numbers of white blood cells in a wound indicates that pathogens may be present.
3. a. T cells and B cells **b.** A T cell recognizes a pathogen; some T cells attack the pathogen; other T cells activate B cells; antibodies then destroy the pathogens.
4. a. T cells **b.** Sexual contact; from an infected woman to her baby during pregnancy, childbirth, or through breast milk; sharing needles that contain infected blood

Reteach
Ask students to close their books. Then describe how T cells and B cells work together as you draw the process on the board.

All in One Teaching Resources, Unit 3
- Section Summary: *The Body's Defenses*
- Review and Reinforce: *The Body's Defenses*
- Enrich: *The Body's Defenses*

The Skin as a Barrier L2

Prepare for Inquiry

Skills Objectives
After this lab students will be able to
- observe differences between apples receiving four different treatments
- make models using apples to demonstrate how skin acts as a barrier
- control variables by modifying the ability of apple skins to act as effective barriers to bacteria
- interpret data and draw conclusions about the effectiveness of apple skins and alcohol in preventing bacterial growth

 Prep Time 15 minutes
Class Time 30 minutes

Advance Planning
Obtain one rotten apple per group to use as a source of bacteria and thick, sturdy toothpicks for piercing apple skins.

Safety
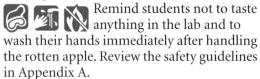 Remind students not to taste anything in the lab and to wash their hands immediately after handling the rotten apple. Review the safety guidelines in Appendix A.

All in One Teaching Resources, Unit 3
- Lab Worksheet: *The Skin as a Barrier*

Guide Inquiry

Invitation
Ask students why they place a bandage on a cut but not on a bruise. (*A cut exposes the body to pathogens, while a bruise is an internal wound protected by the skin.*)

Skills Lab

The Skin as a Barrier

Problem
How does the skin act as a barrier to pathogens?

Skills Focus
observing, making models, controlling variables

Materials
- 4 sealable plastic bags
- 4 fresh apples
- rotting apple
- cotton swabs
- marking pen
- paper towels
- toothpick
- rubbing alcohol

Procedure
1. Read over the entire procedure to see how you will treat each of four fresh apples. Write a prediction in your notebook about the change(s) you expect to see in each apple. Then, copy the data table into your notebook.
2. Label four plastic bags *1, 2, 3,* and *4.*
3. Wash your hands with soap and water. Then, gently wash four fresh apples with water and dry them carefully with paper towels. Place one apple into plastic bag 1, and seal the bag.
4. Insert a toothpick tip into a rotting apple and withdraw it. Lightly draw the tip of the toothpick down the side of the second apple without breaking the skin. Repeat these actions three more times, touching the toothpick to different parts of the apple without breaking the skin. Insert the apple into plastic bag 2, and seal the bag.
5. Insert the toothpick tip into the rotting apple and withdraw it. Use the tip to make a long, thin scratch down the side of the third apple. Be sure to pierce the apple's skin. Repeat these actions three more times, making additional scratches on different parts of the apple. Insert the apple into plastic bag 3, and seal the bag.
6. Repeat Step 5 with the fourth apple. However, before you place the apple into the bag, dip a cotton swab in rubbing alcohol, and swab the scratches. Then, place the apple into plastic bag 4, and seal the bag. **CAUTION:** *Alcohol and its vapors are flammable. Work where there are no sparks, exposed flames, or other heat sources.*

Data Table				
Date	Apple 1 (no contact with decay)	Apple 2 (contact with decay, unbroken skin)	Apple 3 (contact with decay, scratched, untreated)	Apple 4 (contact with decay, scratched, treated with alcohol)

Introducing the Procedure
You may choose to let students practice the technique before they collect data. Watch students' technique of transferring bacteria to ensure proper results.

Troubleshooting the Experiment
- Caution students to take care not to break the apple skins when washing and drying the apples.
- Advise students to dip the toothpick in the rotting apple each time they touch the apple in Step 4, or scratch the apples in Steps 5 and 6.

7. Store the four bags in a warm, dark place. Wash your hands thoroughly with soap and water.

8. Every day for one week, remove the apples from their storage place and observe them without opening the bags. Record your observations, and return the bags to their storage location. At the end of the activity, dispose of the unopened bags as directed by your teacher.

Analyze and Conclude

1. **Observing** How did the appearance of the four apples compare?

2. **Inferring** Explain the differences you observed in Question 1.

3. **Making Models** In this experiment, what condition in the human body is each of the four fresh apples supposed to model?

4. **Controlling Variables** What is the purpose of Apple 1 in this experiment? Explain.

5. **Making Models** What is the role of the rotting apple in this experiment?

6. **Communicating** Write a paragraph in which you explain how this investigation shows why routine cuts and scrapes should be cleaned and bandaged.

Design an Experiment

Using apples as you did in this activity, design an experiment to model how washing hands can prevent the spread of disease. *Obtain your teacher's permission before carrying out your investigation.*

Extend Inquiry

Designing Experiments Sample experiment: Use three washed, freshly cut apples to test for the presence and amount of bacteria. The first apple would serve as a control and would not be handled after being washed. The second would be handled by washed hands. The third would be handled by unwashed hands. All three apples would be sealed in plastic bags for observation.

Expected Outcome

When the skin of the apple is scratched or removed, two different processes take place. First, in a fairly short time, the white of the apple turns brown because oxidation takes place. This is a chemical reaction, which can be slowed by adding an acid such as lemon or orange juice to the apple's surface. Second, bacteria begin the process of decay, a biological process resulting in the darkening and softening of the apple. This process takes longer to become visible than browning does. In this lab, decay—caused by bacteria—serves as the model for disease.

Analyze and Conclude

1. Apples 1 and 2 showed little or no change. Apple 3 showed significant decay. Apple 4 showed less decay than Apple 3.

2. The skins of Apples 1 and 2 prevented bacteria from entering them. The breaks in Apple 3 allowed bacteria to enter. The bacteria on Apple 4 were killed by alcohol.

3. The apple represents the human body. The apple skin represents the human skin. The decay-causing bacteria represent pathogens that can infect humans. Apple 1 shows that unbroken skin prevents bacteria that are normally present from entering the body. Apple 2 shows that unbroken skin prevents a large number of bacteria from entering the body. Apple 3 shows that bacteria can enter through a cut and cause infection. Apple 4 shows that applying a bacteria-killing agent such as alcohol may decrease the numbers of bacteria that get through the skin.

4. Apple 1 is the control. The control shows how the apple changes over time if left unaffected by the other variables in the experiment.

5. The rotting apple is the source of decay-causing bacteria.

6. Paragraphs should include the information that cleaning cuts and scrapes may remove bacteria present at the time of the injury. Bandages keep bacteria from entering a cut that has not healed.

Objectives

After completing this lesson, students will be able to

18.3.1 Describe how the body acquires active immunity.

18.3.2 Explain how passive immunity occurs.

Target Reading Skill

Comparing and Contrasting Explain that comparing and contrasting information shows how ideas, facts, and events are similar and different. The results of the comparison can have importance.

Answers

Sample answers: Active Immunity—The body makes antibodies. Memory cells recognize antigens. Immunity may last for years or a lifetime. Passive Immunity— Antibodies are given; the body does not make antibodies. Immunity lasts only a few months. Immunity can be acquired from the mother during pregnancy. Both active and passive immunity—Both types can prevent diseases. Both may involve an injection.

All in One Teaching Resources, Unit 3

• Transparency LS176

Preteach

Build Background Knowledge   L2

Immunizations

Encourage students to discuss why people get immunizations. Ask them to list diseases for which they think vaccines do and do not exist.

Reading Preview

Key Concepts

• How does the body acquire active immunity?

• How does passive immunity occur?

Key Terms

• immunity • active immunity
• vaccination • vaccine
• antibiotic • passive immunity

Target Reading Skill

Comparing and Contrasting As you read, compare and contrast active immunity and passive immunity in a Venn diagram like the one below. Write the similarities in the space where the circles overlap and the differences on the left and right sides.

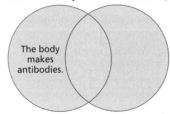

Active Immunity   Passive Immunity

The body makes antibodies.

Lab zone — Discover Activity

What Substances Can Kill Pathogens?

1. Your teacher will give you a variety of products, such as disinfectant cleansers and mouthwashes, that claim to kill pathogens. Read the labels to learn the pathogens that each product is supposed to destroy.

2. Also note the ingredients in each product that act against pathogens. These are labeled "active ingredients."

Think It Over

Designing Experiments How could you determine which of two different cleansers is more effective at killing bacteria? Design an experiment to find out. Do not perform the experiment without obtaining your teacher's approval.

Ask an adult if he or she remembers having the chickenpox. Chances are, the response will be, "Wow, did I itch!" But someone who has had chickenpox can be pretty sure of never getting that disease again. As people recover from some diseases, they develop immunity to the diseases. **Immunity** is the body's ability to destroy pathogens before they can cause disease. There are two basic types of immunity—active and passive.

Active Immunity

Someone who has been sick with chickenpox was invaded by chickenpox viruses. The immune system responded to the virus antigens by producing antibodies. The next time chickenpox viruses invade the body, a healthy immune system will produce antibodies so quickly that the person will not become sick with chickenpox. This reaction is called **active immunity** because the body has produced the antibodies that fight the disease pathogens. **A person acquires active immunity when their own immune system produces antibodies in response to the presence of a pathogen.** Active immunity can result from either getting the disease or being vaccinated.

Lab zone — Discover Activity

Skills Focus Designing experiments   L2

Materials disinfectants and antibacterial products such as creams, mouthwashes, hand soaps, household cleaners, and spray disinfectants

Time 15 minutes

Tips Use clean, empty containers, or seal the tops of containers with tape. Caution students not to taste, smell, or touch any

of the products. Have students list the product name, the pathogens it is supposed to kill, and the active ingredients for each.

Think It Over Possible experiment: Use nutrient agar to grow bacteria from unwashed hands and from hands washed with each soap. Tell students not to perform any experiments without first getting your approval for the procedure.

The Immune Response When someone gets a disease such as chickenpox, active immunity is produced by the immune system as part of the immune response. Remember that during the immune response, T cells and B cells help destroy the pathogens. After the person recovers, some T cells and B cells keep the "memory" of the pathogen's antigen. If that kind of pathogen enters the body again, these memory cells recognize the antigen. The memory cells start the immune response so quickly that the person usually does not get sick. Active immunity often lasts for many years, and sometimes it lasts for life.

Vaccination A second way to gain active immunity is by being vaccinated. **Vaccination** (vac suh NAY shun), or immunization, is the process by which harmless antigens are deliberately introduced into a person's body to produce active immunity. Vaccinations are given by injection, by mouth, or through a nasal spray. Vaccinations can prevent polio, chickenpox, and other diseases.

The substance that is used in a vaccination is called a vaccine. A **vaccine** (vak SEEN) usually consists of pathogens that have been weakened or killed but can still trigger the immune system to go into action. The T cells and B cells still recognize and respond to the antigens of the weakened or dead pathogen. When you receive a vaccination with weakened pathogens, you usually do not get sick. However, your immune system responds by producing memory cells and active immunity to the disease.

FIGURE 10
Vaccination
Follow the steps below to see how vaccinations work. **Classifying** *Why do vaccinations produce active immunity?*

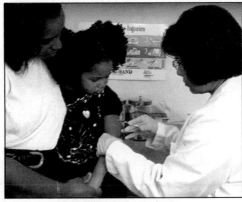

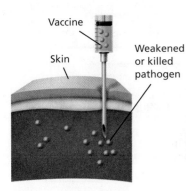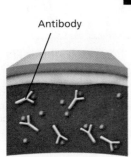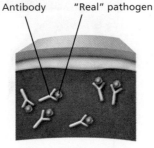

Vaccine
Skin
Weakened or killed pathogen
Antibody
Antibody   "Real" pathogen

1 A person receives an injection with weakened or killed pathogens.

2 The immune system produces antibodies against the disease. It also produces memory cells.

3 If the "real" pathogen invades later, memory cells help to produce antibodies that disable the pathogen.

Chapter 18 ◆ 607

607

Science and History

Focus Tell students that many different factors have contributed to the decrease in infectious diseases over the past two centuries.

Teach Read each caption aloud. Ask students to summarize the different factors shown in this timeline that have decreased infectious disease. *(Vaccines, good hygiene, discovering what pathogens are and how they cause disease, and antibiotics)* Then ask students to identify some of the effects of each discovery. *(Sample answers: Jenner's discovery eventually led to the effective control of smallpox. Fleming's discovery encouraged other scientists to look for other antibiotics.)*

Writing in Science

Writing Skill Research

Scoring Rubric

4 Includes description of the work of that person and why it is important, and is written in the form of a speech; goes beyond requirements in some way, such as stating possible effects of the person's work
3 Includes all criteria, but does not go beyond the requirements
2 Includes only brief description with few details, or is not written as a speech
1 Includes partial or inaccurate information

Help Students Read

Monitor Your Understanding If students have difficulty getting started on their speeches, tell them to think about what they would personally like to know about the person. What interests them? What details would they like to know more about? Explain that speeches educate while entertaining the audience. Encourage them to think about what they would like to hear if they were sitting in the audience.

Go Online
PLANET DIARY
For: More on disease prevention
Visit: PHSchool.com
Web Code: ced-4053

Go Online
PLANET DIARY
For: More on disease prevention
Visit: PHSchool.com
Web Code: ced-4053

When You Do Get Sick You develop immunity to certain diseases either because you have had the diseases or because you have been vaccinated against them. However, no one is immune to all diseases.

Unfortunately, you probably will become sick from time to time. Sometimes, when you become sick, medications can help you get better. If you have a disease that is caused by bacteria, you may be given an antibiotic. An **antibiotic** (an tih by AHT ik) is a chemical that kills bacteria or slows their growth without harming body cells. Unfortunately, there are no medications that are effective against viral illnesses, including the common cold. The best way to deal with most viral diseases is to get plenty of rest.

Science and History

Fighting Infectious Disease

From ancient times, people have practiced methods for preventing disease and caring for sick people. About 200 years ago, people began to learn much more about the causes of infectious diseases and how to protect against them.

1796 Edward Jenner
Edward Jenner, a country doctor in England, successfully vaccinated a child against smallpox, a deadly viral disease. Jenner used material from the sore of a person with cowpox, a mild but similar disorder. Although Jenner's procedure was successful, he did not understand why it worked.

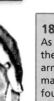

1868 Louis Pasteur
In France, Louis Pasteur showed that microorganisms were the cause of disease in silkworms. Pasteur reasoned that he could control the spread of disease by killing microorganisms. He also proposed that infectious disease in humans are caused by microorganisms.

1854 Florence Nightingale
As an English nurse caring for British soldiers during the Crimean War, Florence Nightingale insisted that army hospitals be kept clean. By doing this, she saved many soldiers' lives. She is considered to be the founder of the modern nursing profession.

| 1800 | 1840 | 1880 |

608 ◆

Background

History of Science Smallpox was recorded as far back as the Roman Empire, when in A.D. 189 there were as many as 2,000 deaths per day throughout the empire. Even after the vaccine became available in the 1800s, epidemics continued to occur.

In 1967, the World Health Organization (WHO) launched a worldwide vaccination campaign against smallpox. By 1975, most nations were free of smallpox.

The world's last known natural case of smallpox occured in 1977. The only deaths reported thereafter occurred when the virus escaped from a laboratory in England.

In 1979, WHO declared the world to be free of the disease. This marks the first time in history that a naturally occuring disease has been completely eradicated from the human population. Stocks of the virus are still stored in the U.S. and Russia.

Although some medicines don't kill pathogens, they may help you feel more comfortable while you get better. Many of these are over-the-counter medications—drugs that can be purchased without a doctor's prescription. Such medications may reduce fever, clear your nose so you can breathe more easily, or stop a cough. Be sure you understand and follow the instructions for all types of medications.

While you recover, be sure to get plenty of rest. Drink plenty of fluids. Unless your stomach is upset, try to eat well-balanced meals. And if you don't start to feel better in a short time, you should see a doctor.

 Reading Checkpoint What is an antibiotic?

Writing in Science

Research and Write Learn more about the work of one of these scientists. Then, imagine that a new hospital is going to be dedicated to that person and that you have been chosen to deliver the dedication speech. Write a speech that praises the person's contributions to fighting disease.

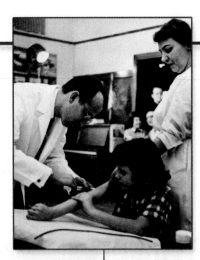

1928 Alexander Fleming
In Britain, Alexander Fleming observed that bacteria growing on laboratory plates were killed when various kinds of fungi grew on the same plate. He discovered that one fungus produced a substance that killed bacteria—penicillin.

1952 Jonas Salk
In 1952, there were more than 57,000 cases of polio, making it one of the most dreaded diseases known at the time. That same year, Jonas Salk, a professor at a medical university in the United States, showed that people injected with killed polio viruses did not get the disease, but produced antibodies against it.

1985 Mathilde Krim
Mathilde Krim, an American biomedical researcher, founded The American Foundation for AIDS Research, or AmFAR. Krim recognized that AIDS was a serious threat to public health and has dedicated her life to supporting AIDS research.

1920   1960   2000

Chapter 18 ◆ 609

Passive Immunity

Teach Key Concepts   L2
Acquiring Passive Immunity

Focus Review the difference between the terms active and passive. (*Active—take action; passive—receive action*)

Teach Ask: **How does a person acquire passive immunity naturally?** (*A baby receives antibodies passed from the mother to the baby during pregnancy.*) **How does a person acquire passive immunity artificially?** (*The person is given antibodies from another source.*)

Apply Ask students to infer why a person who is exposed to rabies, for example, would receive a passive rather than an active vaccine. (*It takes time for the body to produce antibodies after exposure to an antigen.*) **learning modality: logical/mathematical**

Lab zone Build Inquiry   L3

Modeling Active and Passive Immunity

Materials colored marbles, markers, modeling clay, poster board
Time 30 minutes

Focus Review the ways a person can acquire active and passive immunity.

Teach Challenge small groups of students to model the difference between the body's response to pathogens in active immunity and passive immunity. Students can make models or prepare a skit, then present their work to the class.

Apply Ask students to infer where the antibodies that produce passive immunity come from. (*The antibodies were made by another organism.*) **learning modality: kinesthetic**

Monitor Progress   L2

Oral Presentation Call on students to describe ways to treat illnesses and help recover from them.

Answer

 Reading Checkpoint A chemical that kills bacteria or slows their growth without harming body cells

---

Differentiated Instruction

Less Proficient Readers   L1
Distinguishing Similar Words Explain that *antibiotics* can kill several types of bacteria; *antibodies* respond only to the antigens of a particular pathogen. Antibiotics do not work against viruses; antibodies do. Have students list the differences in a two-column chart.
learning modality: verbal

Gifted and Talented   L3
Making a Table Ask students to research vaccines recommended for children from birth to age 18. Have them make a table of the vaccines and the diseases they prevent. (*Example: Hemophilus influenza type b vaccine prevents ear infections and meningitis caused by this type of bacteria.*)
learning modality: visual

609

FIGURE 11
Passive Immunity
This baby has acquired passive immunity from her mother.
Relating Cause and Effect *How do babies acquire passive immunity?*

Passive Immunity

Some diseases, such as rabies, are so uncommon that people rarely receive vaccinations against them. However, if a person is bitten by an animal that might have rabies, the person is usually given injections that contain antibodies to the rabies antigen. The protection that the person acquires this way is an example of passive immunity. **Passive immunity** results when antibodies are given to a person—the person's immune system does not make them. **A person acquires passive immunity when the antibodies that fight the pathogen come from a source other than the person's body.** Unlike active immunity, which is long-lasting, passive immunity usually lasts no more than a few months.

A baby acquires passive immunity to some diseases before birth. This immunity results from antibodies that are passed from the mother's blood into the baby's blood during pregnancy. After birth, these antibodies protect the baby for a few months. By then, the baby's own immune system has begun to function fairly efficiently.

Reading Checkpoint What is one disease for which you can acquire passive immunity?

Section 3 Assessment

Target Reading Skill Comparing and Contrasting Use the information in your Venn diagram about active immunity and passive immunity to help you answer the questions below.

Reviewing Key Concepts

1. a. Defining What is active immunity?
   b. Explaining What are two ways in which active immunity can be acquired?
   c. Applying Concepts After receiving certain vaccinations, some children may develop mild symptoms of the disease. Explain why.
2. a. Reviewing What is passive immunity?
   b. Describing How is passive immunity acquired?
   c. Inferring Why does passive immunity usually not last for very long?

610 ◆

Lab zone At-Home Activity

Vaccination History With a family member, make a list of all the vaccinations you have received. For each, note when you received the vaccination. Then, with your family member, learn about one of the diseases against which you were vaccinated. What kind of pathogen causes the disease? What are the symptoms of the disease? Is the disease still common in the United States?

4 Noninfectious Disease

Reading Preview

Key Concepts
- What causes allergies?
- How does diabetes affect the body?
- What are the effects of cancer on the body?

Key Terms
- noninfectious disease
- allergy • allergen
- histamine • asthma • insulin
- diabetes • tumor • carcinogen

Target Reading Skill

Asking Questions Before you read, preview the red headings. In a graphic organizer like the one below, ask a *what* or *how* question for each heading. As you read, answer your questions.

Noninfectious Disease

Question	Answer
What is an allergy?	An allergy is a disorder in which . . .

Lab zone Discover Activity

What Happens When Airflow Is Restricted?

1. Asthma is a disorder in which breathing passages become narrower than normal. This activity will help you understand how this condition affects breathing. **CAUTION:** *Do not perform this activity if you have a medical condition that affects your breathing.* Begin by breathing normally, first through your nose and then through your mouth. Observe how deeply you breathe.

2. Put one end of a drinking straw in your mouth. Then, gently pinch your nostrils shut so that you cannot breathe through your nose.

3. With your nostrils pinched closed, breathe by inhaling air through the straw. Continue breathing this way for thirty seconds.

Think It Over

Observing Compare your normal breathing pattern to that when breathing through the straw. Which way were you able to take deeper breaths? Did you ever feel short of breath?

Americans are living longer today than ever before. A person who was born in 2000 can expect to live about 77 years. In contrast, a person born in 1950 could expect to live only about 68 years, and a person born in 1900 only about 50 years.

Progress against infectious disease is one reason why life spans have increased. However, as infectious diseases have become less common, noninfectious diseases have grown more common. **Noninfectious diseases** are diseases that are not caused by pathogens in the body. Unlike infectious diseases, noninfectious diseases cannot be transmitted from person to person. One noninfectious disease, cardiovascular disease, is the leading cause of death in the United States. Allergies, diabetes, and cancer are other noninfectious diseases.

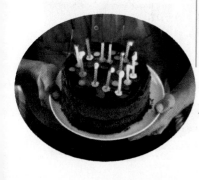

◀ People live longer today than ever before.

Section 4 Noninfectious Disease

Objectives
After completing this lesson, students will be able to

18.4.1 Identify the cause of allergies.

18.4.2 Explain how diabetes affects the body.

18.4.3 Describe the effects of cancer on the body.

Target Reading Skill

Asking Questions Explain that changing a head into a question helps students anticipate the ideas, facts, and events they are going to read about.

Answers

Possible questions and answers: **What is an allergy?** (*An allergy is a disorder in which the body is overly sensitive to a foreign substance.*) **How does diabetes affect the body?** (*A person's body cells do not have enough glucose.*) **What causes cancer?** (*Different factors cause cancer, such as heredity and carcinogens.*)

All in One Teaching Resources, Unit 3
- Transparency LS178

Preteach

Build Background Knowledge L2

Diseases That Are Not Spread
Ask students to brainstorm diseases that cannot be spread from people, animals, or the environment. Record the responses on the board. After studying this section, students can add or eliminate diseases from the list.

Lab zone Discover Activity

Skills Focus Observing

Materials plastic drinking straw

Time 10 minutes

Tips Use narrow straws. Do not allow students with respiratory problems to perform this activity; have them keep time and record observations.

L1

Expected Outcome Students will not be able to breathe as deeply through the straws as through their noses.

Think It Over Students were able to take deeper breaths without the straw. Some students may feel short of breath.

Instruct

Allergies

Teach Key Concepts
The Cause of Allergies

Focus Remind students that the immune system recognizes foreign invaders and makes antibodies to them.

Teach Ask: **What are some invaders that cause an allergic response?** (*Pollen, dust, molds, some foods, some medicines; students may add others.*) **Are allergens responsible for symptoms of allergies?** (*No, the body releases histamine in response to the presence of allergens. Histamine causes the symptoms.*) Tell students that specific antibodies target specific allergens. Ask: **How does this explain allergy symptoms whenever a person is exposed to a particular allergen?** (*The lymphocytes retain memory against allergens, just as they do against pathogens.*)

Apply Ask: **How can avoiding an allergen decrease or eliminate allergic symptoms?** (*If lymphocytes are no longer encountering the allergen, they do not send signals to antibodies to produce histamine.*) **learning modality: logical/mathematical**

Independent Practice

All in One Teaching Resources, Unit 3
- Guided Reading and Study Worksheet: *Noninfectious Disease*

 Student Edition on Audio CD

Modeling Action of Immune Cells

Materials none

Time 20 minutes

Focus Point out that allergens are normally harmless.

Teach Have students diagram what happens when a pathogen invades the body and what happens when an allergen invades the body. Ask students to label their drawings and write captions describing what happens at each stage.

Apply Ask: **Why does your immune system react to these substances if they are not pathogens?** (*Your immune system recognizes them as foreign.*) **learning modality: visual**

612

Allergies

Spring has arrived. Flowers are in bloom, and the songs of birds fill the air. Unfortunately, for some people, sneezing is another sound that fills the air. People who sneeze and cough in the spring may not have colds. Instead, they may be suffering from allergies to plant pollen. An **allergy** is a disorder in which the immune system is overly sensitive to a foreign substance—something not normally found in the body. **An allergy develops in response to various foreign substances that set off a series of reactions in the body.**

Allergens Any substance that causes an allergy is called an **allergen**. In addition to different kinds of pollen, allergens include dust, molds, some foods, and even some medicines. If you are lucky, you have no allergies at all. However, the bodies of many people react to one or more allergens.

Allergens may get into your body when you inhale them, eat them in food, or touch them with your skin. When lymphocytes encounter an allergen, they produce antibodies to that allergen. These antibodies, unlike the ones made during the immune response, signal cells in the body to release a substance called histamine. **Histamine** (HIS tuh meen) is a chemical that is responsible for the symptoms of an allergy, such as sneezing and watery eyes. Drugs that interfere with the action of histamine, called antihistamines, may lessen this reaction. However, if you have an allergy, the best strategy is to try to avoid the substance to which you are allergic.

FIGURE 12
Allergens
Some people have allergic reactions to plant pollen, dust mites, or cats.

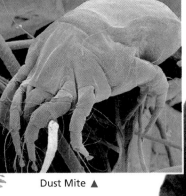

Dust Mite ▲

◄ Pollen

◄ Cat

612 ◆

Asthma Some allergic reactions can create a condition called asthma. **Asthma** (AZ muh) is a disorder in which the respiratory passages narrow significantly. This narrowing causes the person to wheeze and become short of breath. Asthma attacks may be brought on by factors other than allergies, such as stress and exercise.

 Reading Checkpoint What is asthma?

Diabetes

The pancreas is an organ with many different functions. One function is to produce a chemical called insulin. **Insulin** (IN suh lin) enables body cells to take in glucose from the blood and use it for energy. In the condition known as **diabetes** (dy uh BEE tis), either the pancreas fails to produce enough insulin or the body's cells fail to properly use insulin. **As a result, a person with diabetes has high levels of glucose in the blood and may even excrete glucose in the urine. The person's body cells, however, do not have enough glucose.**

Effects of Diabetes If untreated, people with diabetes may lose weight, feel weak, and be hungry all the time. These symptoms occur because body cells are unable to take in the glucose they need. In addition, diabetics may urinate frequently and feel thirsty as the kidneys work to eliminate the excess glucose from the body. The long-term effects of diabetes are serious and can include blindness, kidney failure, and heart disease.

Forms of Diabetes There are two main forms of diabetes. Type I diabetes usually begins in childhood or early adulthood. In Type I diabetes, the pancreas produces little or no insulin. People with this condition must get insulin injections.

Type II diabetes usually develops during adulthood. In this condition, either the pancreas does not make enough insulin, or body cells do not respond normally to insulin. People with Type II diabetes may be able to control their symptoms through proper diet, weight control, and exercise.

 Reading Checkpoint What are two symptoms of diabetes?

For: Links on noninfectious disease
Visit: www.SciLinks.org
Web Code: scn-0454

FIGURE 13
Glucose Testing
Many people with diabetes must test their blood frequently to determine the level of glucose in their blood.
Relating Cause and Effect *What accounts for the high level of glucose in the blood of diabetics?*

For: Links on noninfectious disease
Visit: www.SciLinks.org
Web Code: scn-0454

Download a worksheet that will guide students' review of Internet resources on noninfectious disease.

Diabetes

Teach Key Concepts L2
How Diabetes Affects the Body
Focus Review the function of insulin.

Teach Explain that although a person with diabetes eats, glucose from food does not enter the cells. Ask: **What causes the symptoms of diabetes?** *(The lack of glucose in cells causes weight loss, weakness, and hunger. The excess glucose in the blood causes a person to urinate frequently to eliminate the glucose from the body.)*

Apply Tell students that some people with Type II diabetes stop producing insulin. Ask: **How would their treatment change?** *(They would have to take insulin.)* **learning modality: logical/mathematical**

Monitor Progress L2

Skills Check Have students compare and contrast the two types of diabetes.

Answers
Figure 13 The body does not produce enough insulin or the cells cannot use it, so the body cells do not take in glucose.

 Reading Checkpoint A respiratory disorder characterized by wheezing and shortness of breath

 Reading Checkpoint Any two: Weight loss, weakness, continual hunger, frequent urination, feeling thirsty

---

Differentiated Instruction

Special Needs L1
Organizing Information Students may have difficulty organizing the information in this section. Model a concept map for one disease, showing its causes, symptoms, and treatments. Then, encourage students to create similar concept maps for another disease in this section. **learning modality: visual**

Cancer

Teach Key Concepts L2

How Cancer Develops

Focus Point out that cancer cells are not foreign, but are the body's own cells.

Teach Ask: **What cell part does a carcinogen most likely damage?** *(The nucleus, the cells' control center.)* **How do different factors work together to cause cancer?** *(Inherited traits make some people more likely to develop cancer. Exposure to certain substances in the environment may increase risk.)*

Apply Explain that damaged cells are constantly being destroyed by our immune systems. Ask why people get cancer even though immune systems can destroy cancer cells. *(There may be too many damaged cells or a weakened immune system.)* **learning modality: logical/mathematical**

Address Misconceptions L2

The Causes of Cancer

Focus Many students believe that chemicals cause the majority of cancers, and therefore preventing cancer is beyond their control.

Teach Give students these figures on the causes of cancer in the U. S. to make into a circle graph: Diet 30%, Tobacco 30%, Lack of exercise, Viruses, Alcohol, and Radiation together 15%, Other, 25%.

Apply Ask: **How can the majority of cancer deaths be prevented?** *(Through lifestyle choices)* **learning modality: logical/ mathematical**

Analyzing Data

Math Skill Making and interpreting graphs

Focus Tell students that more than one million people in the U.S. are diagnosed with skin cancer every year.

Teach Ask: **Why is a line graph the best way to show this information?** *(It shows change over time.)*

Answers
1. Estimated number of skin cancer cases
2. 1998—17,300; 2003—24,300
3. 24,300 minus 17,300 equals 7,000
4. 25,800 minus 18,400 equals 7,400
5. If the trend holds, the number of cases will increase over the next five years.

Math ▶ Analyzing Data

Skin Cancer

The graph shows the frequency of skin cancer in the United States from 1998 to 2003.

1. **Reading Graphs** What variable is being plotted on the *y*-axis?

2. **Interpreting Data** How many cases of skin cancer were estimated for women in 1998? In 2003?

3. **Calculating** Using the data from Question 2, calculate the increase in the number of skin cancer cases among women.

4. **Calculating** How did the number of cases differ for men and women in 1999?

5. **Predicting** Will the number of skin cancers change in the next five years? Explain.

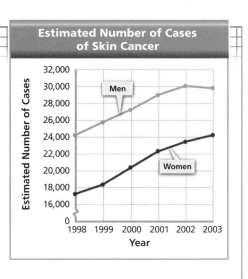

Estimated Number of Cases of Skin Cancer

Cancer

Under normal conditions, the body produces new cells at about the same rate that other cells die. In a condition known as cancer, however, the situation is quite different. **Cancer is a disease in which cells multiply uncontrollably, over and over, destroying healthy tissue in the process.**

How Cancer Develops As cells divide over and over, they often form abnormal tissue masses called **tumors**. Not all tumors are cancerous. Cancerous tumors invade and destroy the healthy tissue around them. Cancer cells can break away from a tumor and invade blood or lymph vessels. The blood or lymph carries the cancer cells to other parts of the body, where they may begin to divide and form new tumors. Unless stopped by treatment, cancer progresses through the body.

Causes of Cancer Different factors may work together in causing cells to become cancerous. One such factor is the characteristics that people inherit from their parents. Because of their inherited characteristics, some people are more likely than others to develop certain kinds of cancer. For example, if you are female, and your mother or grandmother has breast cancer, you have an increased chance of developing breast cancer.

Some substances or factors in the environment, called **carcinogens** (kahr SIN uh junz), can cause cancer. The tar in cigarette smoke is an example of a carcinogen. Ultraviolet light, which is part of sunlight, can also be a carcinogen.

Cancer Treatment Surgery, drugs, and radiation are all used to treat cancer. If cancer is detected before it has spread, doctors may remove the cancerous tumors through surgery. After surgery, radiation or drugs may be used to make sure all the cancer cells have been killed.

Radiation treatment uses high-energy waves to kill cancer cells. When these rays are aimed at tumors, the intense energy damages and kills cancer cells more than it damages normal cells. Drug therapy is the use of chemicals to destroy cancer cells. Many of these chemicals, however, destroy some normal cells as well.

Cancer Prevention As with other diseases, the best way to fight cancer is to prevent it. People can reduce their risk of cancer by avoiding carcinogens, such as those found in tobacco. Even chewing tobacco and snuff contain carcinogens, which can cause mouth cancers. A low-fat diet that includes plenty of fruits and vegetables can help prevent cancers of the digestive system.

People can also increase their chance of surviving cancer by having regular medical checkups. The earlier cancer is detected, the more likely it can be treated successfully.

 Reading Checkpoint What is a carcinogen?

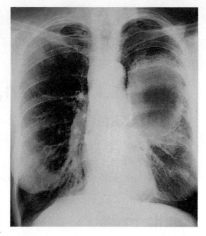

FIGURE 14
Lung Tumor
The large orange mass in the X-ray is a cancerous tumor in the lung.

 Section 4 Assessment

Target Reading Skill Asking Questions Use the answers to the questions you wrote about the headings to help you answer the questions below.

Reviewing Key Concepts

1. a. **Defining** What is an allergy?
   b. **Describing** Describe how the body reacts to the presence of an allergen.
   c. **Inferring** You and your friends go to a movie. When you enter the theater, you start to sneeze and your throat feels scratchy. Explain what you think is happening.
2. a. **Identifying** What is the function of insulin in the body?
   b. **Explaining** How does diabetes affect the level of glucose in the blood and in body cells?

3. a. **Reviewing** What is a cancerous tumor?
   b. **Relating Cause and Effect** Describe how cancerous tumors harm the body.
   c. **Applying Concepts** Why do doctors look for cancerous tumors in the lymphatic system when someone is diagnosed with cancer?

Lab zone At-Home Activity

Family History of Allergies Explain to your family what allergies are and how allergens affect the body. Make a list of any substances to which your family members are allergic. Use this list to determine whether certain allergies occur frequently in your family.

Lab zone Chapter Project

Keep Students on Track Ask students to let you know about props or special lighting they need for their presentations. Set aside enough time for all presentations. Students may end their stories with the complete recovery or death of their patient, or they may announce that the disease is spreading to other people.

Lab zone At-Home Activity

Family History of Allergies You may wish to have students volunteer allergens to which they are allergic as you write the list on the board. Assure students that they can choose not to provide this information. Have students copy the list and take it home. They might discover that what they thought were seasonal colds might be allergies.

Monitor Progress L2
Answer

Reading Checkpoint A substance or factor in the environment that can cause cancer

Assess

Reviewing Key Concepts

1. a. A disorder in which the immune system is overly sensitive to a foreign substance b. When lymphocytes encounter allergens, they produce antibodies that signal the body's cells to release histamine, which causes symptoms such as sneezing. c. You could be allergic to something in the theater.
2. a. Insulin enables body cells to take in glucose from the blood and use it for energy. b. The level of glucose is elevated in the blood, but lowered in body cells.
3. a. An abnormal tissue mass of cancerous cells that divide over and over b. They invade and destroy the healthy tissue around them, and cancer cells may break off and spread to other parts of the body. c. Cancer cells can break away from a tumor and be carried to other parts of the body by the lymphatic system. Finding tumors in the lymphatic system indicates that the cancer has spread.

Reteach L1
List the headings and subheadings in this section on the board. Ask students to provide important facts as you write them under the appropriate heading.

Performance Assessment L2
Oral Presentation Have students choose a noninfectious disease and describe its causes and symptoms.

All in One Teaching Resources, Unit 3
- Section Summary: *Noninfectious Disease*
- Review and Reinforce: *Noninfectious Disease*
- Enrich: *Noninfectious Disease*

Causes of Death, Then and Now L2

Prepare for Inquiry

Key Concept
The leading causes of death have changed over the past hundred years.

Skills Objectives
Students will be able to
- draw graphs that compare the incidence of infectious diseases to that of noninfectious diseases
- interpret data about the leading causes of death
- draw conclusions regarding the change in health threats since 1900

Time 30 minutes

Safety
 Remind students to handle the compass carefully.

Guide Inquiry

Introducing the Procedure
Refer to the Skills Handbook to teach or review how to make bar graphs and circle graphs. Ask: **What do you think is the leading cause of death in the United States today?** (*Students may respond based on news and television reports they have seen.*) **How do you think that compares with the leading cause of death 100 years ago?** (*Students may know that infectious diseases were more prevalent then.*) **How has daily life changed in ways that have improved people's ability to remain healthy?** (*Many changes, including safe drinking water, safer commercial food handling, and improvements in general cleanliness have led to improved health.*)

Troubleshooting the Experiment
- Remind students to round decimals to the nearest whole number in their calculations. However, students should make sure the percentages on their circle graphs add up to 100.
- Some students may need extra help with the math. Encourage students who are comfortable with the math to help others.

Causes of Death, Then and Now

Problem
How do the leading causes of death today compare with those in 1900?

Skills Focus
graphing, interpreting data, drawing conclusions

Materials
- colored pencils
- ruler
- calculator (optional)
- protractor
- compass

Procedure
1. The data table on the next page shows the leading causes of death in the United States in 1900 and today. Examine the data and note that one cause of death—accidents—is not a disease. The other causes are labeled either "I," indicating an infectious disease, or "NI," indicating a noninfectious disease.

PART 1 Comparing Specific Causes of Death

2. Look at the following causes of death in the data table: (a) pneumonia and influenza, (b) heart disease, (c) accidents, and (d) cancer. Construct a bar graph that compares the numbers of deaths from each of those causes in 1900 and today. Label the horizontal axis *"Causes of Death."* Label the vertical axis *"Deaths per 100,000 People."* Draw two bars side by side for each cause of death. Use a key to show which bars refer to 1900 and which refer to today.

PART 2 Comparing Infectious and Noninfectious Causes of Death

3. In this part of the lab, you will make two circle graphs showing three categories: infectious diseases, noninfectious diseases, and "other." You may want to review the information on creating circle graphs on page 262 of the Skills Handbook.

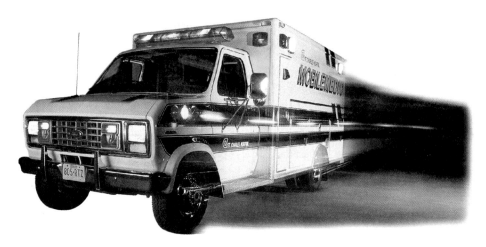

Expected Outcome
- Students should see that the leading causes of death a hundred years ago were pathogens. They should also observe that heart disease has become a more common problem.
- If students do not make appropriate connections, have them try to identify the sources of their error. Some students may not be aware of the causes of pneumonia, tuberculosis, or most kinds of lethal diarrhea.

Ten Leading Causes of Death in the United States, 1900 and Today			
1900		**Today**	
Cause of Death	**Deaths Per 100,000**	**Cause of Death**	**Deaths Per 100,000**
Pneumonia, influenza (I)*	215	Heart disease (NI)	246
Tuberculosis (I)	185	Cancer (NI)	194
Diarrhea (I)	140	Stroke (NI)	57
Heart disease (NI)	130	Lung disease (NI)	43
Stroke (NI)	110	Accidents	34
Kidney disease (NI)	85	Diabetes (NI)	25
Accidents	75	Pneumonia, influenza (I)	22
Cancer (NI)	65	Alzheimer's disease (NI)	19
Senility (NI)	55	Kidney disease (NI)	14
Diphtheria (I)	40	Septicemia (I)	11
Total	**1,100**	**Total**	**665**

* (I) indicates an infectious disease. (NI) indicates a noninfectious disease.

4. Start by grouping the data from 1900 into the three categories—infectious diseases, noninfectious diseases, and other causes. Calculate the total number of deaths for each category. Then find the size of the "pie slice" (the number of degrees) for each category, and construct your circle graph. To find the size of the infectious disease slice for 1900, for example, use the following formula:

$$\frac{\text{Number of deaths from infectious diseases}}{1{,}100 \text{ deaths total}} = \frac{x}{360°}$$

5. Calculate the percentage represented by each category using this formula:

$$\frac{\text{Numbers of degrees in a slice}}{360°} \times 100 = \blacksquare\%$$

6. Repeat Steps 4 and 5 using the data from today to make the second circle graph. What part of the formula in Step 4 do you need to change?

Analyze and Conclude

1. **Observing** What information did you learn from examining the data table in Step 1?

2. **Graphing** According to your bar graph, which cause of death showed the greatest increase between 1900 and today? The greatest decrease?

3. **Interpreting Data** In your circle graphs, which category decreased the most from 1900 to today? Which increased the most?

4. **Drawing Conclusions** Suggest an explanation for the change in the number of deaths due to infectious diseases from 1900 to today.

5. **Communicating** In a paragraph, explain how graphs help you identify patterns and other information in data that you might otherwise overlook.

More to Explore

Write a question related to the data table that you have not yet answered. Then create a graph or work with the data in other ways to answer your question.

Analyze and Conclude

1. Students' answers should reflect that they could determine top causes of death in each year, as well as compare the total number of deaths to deaths attributed to particular causes.

2. Cancer showed the greatest increase. Of the causes of death still listed in the table, pneumonia/influenza showed the greatest decrease.

3. As a cause of death, infectious disease decreased the most. Noninfectious disease increased the most.

4. Sample: Since 1900, infectious diseases have been prevented by many factors including improvements in water treatment and sanitation, immunization, improved diets, medicines, and other disease treatment procedures.

5. Sample: When making graphs, data may be rearranged or reclassified in ways that show new information. For example, when the circle graphs were made, combining the data in new categories showed that infectious diseases have decreased dramatically.

Extend Inquiry

More to Explore Students may find it helpful to work in small groups to list possible questions before they write their question. Sample: Among the ten top causes, how does the percentage of deaths from heart disease today compare with the percentage in 1900? (*Today, about 37% (246 ÷ 665) of these deaths are from heart disease; in 1900 about 12% (130 ÷ 1,100) were from heart disease.*) You might want to have students check each other's work before they share their questions and answers with the class.

Science and Society

Antibiotic Resistance— An Alarming Trend

Key Concept
Antibiotic resistance is an increasing problem resulting from the widespread use of antibiotics.

Build Background Knowledge
Treating Bacterial Diseases
Review with students what they know about the use of antibiotics to treat bacterial diseases. Ask: **What is an antibiotic?** *(A chemical that can kill bacteria without harming the host's cells)* **How do antibiotics work?** *(Some work by weakening the cell walls of the target bacteria.)*

Introduce the Debate
Encourage students to think about how antibiotics have altered everyday life. Before the early 1940s, any significant wound was potentially fatal because of bacterial infection. Today very few individuals die from bacterial infections obtained through cuts. Have students consider the implications of bacteria that are resistant to all known antibiotics. *(Resistant bacteria are difficult to kill.)*

Facilitate the Decision
- Be sure students understand how antibiotic-resistant populations of bacteria can evolve.
- Divide the class into three groups. Have one group research the question of over-prescribing antibiotics and the problems caused when patients do not take all of a prescribed medication. Have the second group research non-medical uses of antibiotics, and have the third group research the search for new antibiotics.
- Each group is to limit the information they want to share with the class to two or three main points, each point being well supported by facts. Have each group select two spokespersons to serve on the panel.

Science and Society

Antibiotic Resistance— An Alarming Trend

Penicillin, the first antibiotic, became available for use in 1943. Soon antibiotics became known as the "wonder drugs." Over the years, they have reduced the occurrence of many bacterial diseases and saved millions of lives. But each time an antibiotic is used, a few resistant bacteria may survive. They pass on their resistance to the next generation of bacteria. As more patients take antibiotics, the number of resistant bacteria increases.

In 1987, penicillin killed more than 99.9 percent of a type of ear infection bacteria. By 2000, about 30 percent of these bacteria were resistant to penicillin. Diseases such as tuberculosis are on the rise due in part to growing antibiotic resistance.

Conjunctivitis Infection of the eyelids

Bacterial Meningitis Infection in the brain and spinal cord

Ear Infection

Strep Throat

Bacterial Pneumonia Inflammation of the lungs

Dental Cavities

Tuberculosis Infection of the lungs

Stomach Ulcer A break in the stomach lining

The Issues

What Can Doctors Do?

Each year, more than 20 billion dollars worth of antibiotics are sold to drugstores and hospitals worldwide. More than half of antibiotic prescriptions are unnecessary. They include those written for colds and other viral illnesses, which antibiotics are ineffective against. If doctors could better identify the cause of an infection, they could avoid prescribing unnecessary antibiotics.

618 ◆

Background

Facts and Figures The problems of antibiotic resistance are often most dramatic in hospitals, where many patients are being treated with antibiotics. Because patients who are already ill are at higher risk because of weakened immune systems, many cases of bacterial infection are acquired in hospitals. One strain of the deadly bacteria *Staphylococcus aureus* was discovered in 1997 to be resistant to the antibiotic vancomycin. Fortunately, this particular strain could be treated with other antibiotics, but many forms of these bacteria have already developed resistance to all drugs except vancomycin.

What Can Patients Do?

If a doctor prescribes a ten-day course of antibiotics, the patient should take all of the prescription to make sure that all the bacteria have been killed. If a patient stops taking the antibiotic, resistant bacteria will survive and reproduce. Then, a second or third antibiotic may be necessary. Patients also need to learn that some illnesses are best treated with rest and not with antibiotics.

Limiting Nonmedical Uses of Antibiotics

About half of the antibiotics used each year are not given to people. Instead, the drugs are fed to food animals, such as cattle and poultry, to prevent illness and increase growth. Reducing this type of use would limit the amount of the drugs in food animals and in the people who eat them. But these actions might increase the risk of disease in animals and lead to higher meat prices.

Finding New Antibiotics

Scientists are trying to identify new antibiotics. By using new and different antibiotics, scientists hope that bacteria will not develop resistance as quickly. Scientists are also researching other ways to fight bacteria.

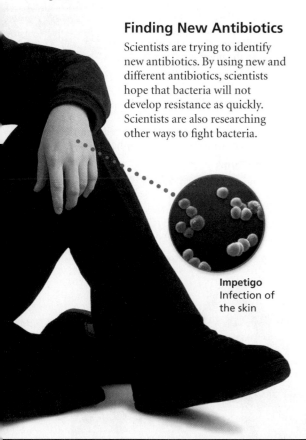

Impetigo
Infection of the skin

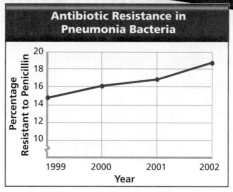

Antibiotic Resistance in Pneumonia Bacteria

The percentage of resistant bacteria has increased steadily over the years.

You Decide

1. Identify the Problem
How can the use of antibiotics make these medicines less effective?

2. Analyze the Options
List all the ways to fight the development of antibiotic resistance in bacteria. Mention any costs or drawbacks.

3. Find a Solution
Make a persuasive poster about one way to deal with antibiotic resistance. Support your viewpoint with sound reasons.

Go Online
PHSchool.com

For: More on bacterial resistance
Visit: PHSchool.com
Web Code: ceh-1020

- On the second day, organize a panel discussion. Allow the spokespersons to present the results of their research (8–10 minutes each), and allow time for the class to ask questions of the panel.
- On the third day, the students make posters to place in selected places within the school. Have students make posters using information collected during the research and panel discussion as well as information from their textbook. Provide students with samples of persuasive or informative posters.

You Decide

1. Each time an antibiotic is used, some bacteria may be resistant and thus survive. With time, the number and kinds of resistant bacteria have increased.

2. To fight the development of antibiotic resistance in bacteria, doctors can avoid prescribing unnecessary antibiotics. When an antibiotic is prescribed, patients should take the full course of the antibiotic. The widespread use of antibiotics in cattle and chickens can be reduced, even though more animals might die of disease and meat prices might rise.

3. Posters should be informative and accurate, supporting a clearly stated viewpoint with logical reasoning.

For: More on bacterial resistance
Visit: PHSchool.com
Web Code: ceh-1020

Students can research this issue online.

Extend

Have the groups prepare a community health bulletin on this issue. Encourage them to list the problems and to identify solutions that individuals can implement to prevent antibiotic resistance.

Differentiated Instruction

Less Proficient Readers   **L1**
Finding the Main Idea Teach students that identifying the main idea of a paragraph is a key step in reading. Tell them that each paragraph is usually about a specific topic. The most important thing that the author says about the topic is called the main idea of the paragraph. Finding the main idea usually involves these three steps: (1) Previewing the paragraph by skimming the sentences to find the main topic. (2) Carefully reading the paragraph to see what supporting details about the topic are included. (3) Identifying the main idea by asking yourself, "What point is the author making by presenting these details?" **learning modality: verbal**

nteractive Textbook

- Complete student edition
- Section and chapter self-assessments
- Assessment reports for teachers

Help Students Read

Building Vocabulary

Word Origins Explain that *carcino* in the word *carcinogenic* refers to cancer, which comes from the Greek word *karkinos,* meaning crab. Hippocrates is thought to be the person who first named this disease. Tumors have a central body, and the tumor extensions are reminiscent of the legs of a crab.

Paraphrasing Divide students into small groups, and assign each group five or six key terms. Ask them to reread the paragraphs in which the Key Terms are introduced. Challenge them to rewrite the paragraphs in their own words. As time permits, have groups read their passages to the class.

Connecting Concepts

Concept Maps Help students develop one way to show how the information in this chapter is related. Diseases can be classified into infectious and noninfectious, and many can be prevented or reduced through immunity and behaviors. Have students brainstorm to identify the Key Concepts, Key Terms, details, and examples, and then write each one on a sticky note and attach it at random on chart paper or on the board.

Tell students that this concept map will be organized in hierarchical order and to begin at the top with the Key Concepts. Ask students these questions to help them categorize the information on the stickies: **How can the risk of infectious diseases be reduced? How does the immune system defend against pathogens? What are some noninfectious diseases, their causes, possible treatments, and ways they can be prevented?** Prompt students by using connecting words or phrases, such as "include," "caused by," "prevention includes," "defenses include," "treatment includes" to

① Infectious Disease

Key Concepts

- When you have an infectious disease, pathogens have gotten inside your body and caused harm.
- The four major groups of human pathogens are bacteria, viruses, fungi, and protists.
- Pathogens can spread through contact with either an infected person; soil, food, or water; a contaminated object; or an infected animal.

Key Terms

pathogen
infectious disease
toxin

② The Body's Defenses

Key Concepts

- In the first line of defense, the surfaces of the skin, breathing passages, mouth, and stomach function as barriers to pathogens. These barriers trap and kill most pathogens with which you come into contact.
- In the inflammatory response, fluid and white blood cells leak from blood vessels into nearby tissues. The white blood cells then fight the pathogens.
- The cells of the immune system can distinguish between different kinds of pathogens. The immune system cells react to each kind of pathogen with a defense targeted specifically at that pathogen.
- HIV is the only kind of virus known to attack the human immune system directly and destroy T cells. HIV can spread from one person to another only if body fluids from an infected person come in contact with those of an uninfected person.

Key Terms

inflammatory response	antigen
phagocyte	B cell
immune response	antibody
lymphocyte	AIDS
T cell	HIV

③ Preventing Infectious Disease

Key Concepts

- A person acquires active immunity when their own immune system produces antibodies in response to the presence of a pathogen.
- A person acquires passive immunity when the antibodies that fight the pathogen come from a source other than the person's body.

Key Terms

immunity	vaccine
active immunity	antibiotic
vaccination	passive immunity

④ Noninfectious Disease

Key Concepts

- An allergy develops in response to various foreign substances that set off a series of reactions in the body.
- A diabetic has high levels of glucose in the blood and excretes glucose in the urine. The person's body cells do not have enough glucose.
- Cancer is a disease in which cells multiply uncontrollably and destroy healthy tissue.

Key Terms

noninfectious disease	insulin
allergy	diabetes
allergen	tumor
histamine	carcinogen
asthma	

indicate the basis for the organization of the map. The phrases should form a sentence between or among a set of concepts.

Answer

Accept logical presentations by students.

All in One Teaching Resources, Unit 3

- Key Terms Review: *Fighting Disease*
- Connecting Concepts: *Fighting Disease*

Review and Assessment

Go Online PHSchool.com

For: Self-Assessment
Visit: PHSchool.com
Web Code: cha-3180

Organizing Information

Sequencing Copy the flowchart showing what happens after strep bacteria begin to multiply in the throat. Then complete it and add a title. (For more on Sequencing, see the Skills Handbook.)

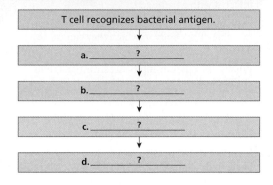

T cell recognizes bacterial antigen.
↓
a. _____ ? _____
↓
b. _____ ? _____
↓
c. _____ ? _____
↓
d. _____ ? _____

Reviewing Key Terms

Choose the letter of the best answer.

1. Some bacteria produce poisons called
   a. histamines.   b. toxins.
   c. phagocytes.   d. pathogens.

2. Antibodies are produced by
   a. phagocytes.   b. B cells.
   c. T cells.   d. pathogens.

3. A chemical that kills bacteria or slows their growth without harming body cells is called a(n)
   a. pathogen.
   b. antibiotic.
   c. allergen.
   d. histamine.

4. High levels of glucose in the blood may be a sign of
   a. an allergy.
   b. AIDS.
   c. cancer.
   d. diabetes.

5. A carcinogen causes
   a. cancer.
   b. AIDS.
   c. an infectious disease.
   d. an allergy.

If the statement is true, write *true.* If it is false, change the underlined word or words to make the statement true.

6. Bacteria, viruses, fungi, and protists are the major human <u>phagocytes</u>.

7. A <u>T cell</u> engulfs pathogens and destroys them.

8. Vaccination produces <u>active immunity.</u>

9. During an allergic reaction, cells in the body release the chemical <u>insulin</u>.

10. A <u>tumor</u> is a mass of abnormal tissue.

Writing in Science

Newspaper Article Suppose you are a reporter who is able to travel inside the human body and document how the body fights a virus. Write an article on the battle between the virus and the human immune system, describing the different ways the body fights pathogens.

DISCOVERY CHANNEL SCHOOL

Fighting Disease

Video Preview
Video Field Trip
▶ Video Assessment

Go Online PHSchool.com

For: Self-Assessment
Visit: PHSchool.com
Web Code: cha-3180

Students can take a practice test online that is automatically scored.

 **Teaching Resources, Unit 3**

- Transparency LS179
- Chapter Test
- Performance Assessment Teacher Notes
- Performance Assessment Student Worksheet
- Performance Assessment Scoring Rubric

ExamView® **Computer Test Bank CD-ROM**

Review and Assessment

Organizing Information
a. Some T cells attack pathogens.
b. Other T cells signal B cells to produce antibodies specific to the antigen.
c. B cells produce antibodies.
d. Antibodies destroy the pathogenic bacteria.

Reviewing Key Terms
1. b 2. b 3. b 4. d 5. a
6. pathogens
7. phagocyte
8. true
9. histamine
10. true

Writing in Science

Writing Mode Explanation
Scoring Rubric
4 Includes accurate, logical reasons; goes beyond requirements to explain reasons
3 Includes criteria but does not go beyond requirements
2 Includes few reasons
1 Includes inaccurate reasons

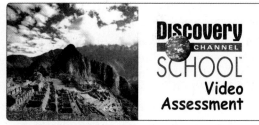

DISCOVERY CHANNEL SCHOOL Video Assessment

Fighting Disease

Show the Video Assessment to review chapter content and as a prompt for the writing assignment. **What is the role of the white blood cells called phagocytes in the body's inflammatory response?** (*Phagocytes destroy pathogens by engulfing them and breaking them down.*) **How do T cells and B cells contribute to the body's immune response?** (*T cells identify a pathogen, then attack the pathogen and activate B cells. The B cells then produce antibodies to that specific pathogen.*)

Checking Concepts

11. A person can become infected with a pathogen through contact with an infected person; soil, food, or water; a contaminated object; or an infected animal.

12. The body has a natural system of barriers to keep pathogens out. The skin, breathing passages, the mouth, and the stomach trap and kill most pathogens.

13. B cells produce antibodies in response to specific antigens on pathogens; antibodies attach to antigens and prevent the pathogens from attacking cells.

14. Active immunity is acquired when a person contracts a disease or receives a vaccination. In both, the person's immune system produces antibodies in response to a pathogen.

15. Diabetes is caused by insufficient insulin or the inability of cells to use insulin. This prevents body cells from properly absorbing and using glucose.

16. Inherited factors and exposure to environmental carcinogens can increase the likelihood of cancer.

Thinking Critically

17. No; colds are not caused by sitting in chilly drafts, but by viruses.

18. Structure A: B cell, produces antibodies; structure B: antibody, recognizes and destroys pathogens; structure C: antigen, structure on pathogen recognized by an antibody

19. The immune system cannot fight HIV because the virus directly attacks T cells and weakens the body's immune response. The body loses its ability to produce antibodies that fight specific diseases.

20. Active immunity is a process in which antibodies are produced by a person's own immune system in response to the presence of a pathogen. In passive immunity, antibodies come from a source other than the person's body. Active immunity can be acquired by vaccination (or by contracting and recovering from a disease); passive immunity can be acquired by an unborn baby from its mother (or by injection of antibodies).

21. Sample answer: To reduce the risk of cancer, people can avoid carcinogens such as those found in tobacco. People can also have regular medical checkups, which would help in detecting cancers earlier.

Review and Assessment

Checking Concepts

11. List four ways in which a person can become infected with a pathogen.

12. Explain why it is difficult for pathogens to get to a part of the body in which they can cause disease.

13. What is the relationship between antigens and antibodies?

14. Describe two ways in which active immunity is acquired. What do they have in common?

15. How does diabetes harm the body?

16. Identify two factors that can make a person likely to develop cancer.

Thinking Critically

17. Applying Concepts Can you catch a cold by sitting in a chilly draft? Explain.

18. Interpreting Diagrams Identify each structure labeled below and its role in the immune response.

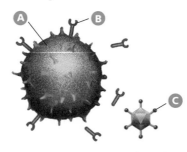

19. Relating Cause and Effect Why is the immune system successful in fighting most pathogens but is unsuccessful in fighting HIV?

20. Comparing and Contrasting Compare and contrast active immunity and passive immunity. Then, describe one way in which a person can acquire each type of immunity.

21. Making Judgments What precautions can people take to decrease their risk of cancer?

Applying Skills

Use the graph to answer Questions 22–25.

A glucose tolerance test can check for diabetes. A doctor gives a patient a sugar drink and measures the blood glucose level over a 2 hour period. The graph below shows the results of this test for two people.

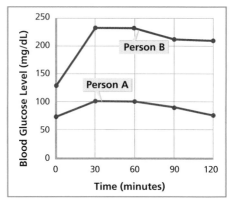

22. Reading Graphs What was each person's glucose level at the start of the test?

23. Interpreting Data Which person's blood glucose level rose more quickly during the first 30 minutes?

24. Interpreting Data Which person's blood glucose level returned to near the starting level after 2 hours? Which person's blood glucose level remained elevated after 2 hours?

25. Drawing Conclusions Which person may have diabetes? Explain your answer.

Lab zone Chapter **Project**

Performance Assessment Before you present your news broadcasts, make sure any sound effects and props support the story. Do your broadcasts help people better understand how the body fights disease?

Lab zone Chapter **Project** L3

Performance Assessment If possible, allow students time to rehearse their presentations before presenting them to the class. You may want to have students perform their news reports for the class, or present written reports or audio or videotapes. Set aside enough time for all students to make their presentations.

Encourage students to describe what parts of the project helped them to understand the body's defenses against disease. For example, some students may have had difficulty using the format of a news report, while others may have found it helpful in asking questions and organizing information.

Standardized Test Prep

Choose the letter of the best answer.

1. All of the following are the body's defenses against pathogens EXCEPT
   A a physical barrier such as the skin.
   B the inflammatory response.
   C the immune response.
   D attack by red blood cells.

Use the data table to answer Questions 2 and 3.

Cancer: New Cases and Survival Rates

Type of Cancer	Estimated New Cases (2003)	Five-Year Survival Rate (1992–1998)
Prostate (males)	221,000	97%
Breast (females)	211,000	86%
Lung	172,000	15%
Colon and rectum	148,000	62%
Bladder	57,000	82%
Melanoma (skin)	54,000	89%

2. The type of cancer with the best five-year survival rate is
   F prostate cancer.
   G bladder cancer.
   H breast cancer.
   J lung cancer.

3. A reasonable inference that can be made from the data is that
   A lung cancer is easy to diagnose and hard to treat.
   B prostate cancer is hard to diagnose and hard to treat.
   C very few females survive for five years after being diagnosed with breast cancer.
   D lung cancer is the most common cancer.

4. Which of the following is paired correctly?
   F diabetes: infectious disease
   G AIDS: noninfectious disease
   H rabies: infectious disease
   J allergy: infectious disease

Constructed Response

5. What is diabetes? What causes diabetes and what effects does it have on the body? How is diabetes usually treated?

Applying Skills

22. Person A: 75mg/dl; Person B: 125mg/dl

23. Person B's blood glucose level rose more quickly.

24. Person A's blood glucose level returned to near the starting level after two hours. Person B's level remained elevated.

25. Person B may have diabetes because the blood glucose level remained high two hours after drinking the sugar drink. The high level indicates that glucose is not being taken up by the cells.

Standardized Test Prep

1. D **2.** F **3.** A **4.** H

5. Diabetes is a noninfectious disease in which the pancreas fails to produce insulin or the body's cells can't use insulin properly. As a result, body cells can't take in the glucose they need. Possible short-term effects include feeling weak, being hungry all the time, and losing weight. The possible long-term effects of diabetes include blindness, kidney failure, and heart disease. Type I diabetes can be treated with insulin injections. Type II diabetes can often be controlled through proper diet, weight control, and exercise.

Chapter **19** The Nervous System

Chapter at a Glance

 Chapter **Project** *Tricks and Illusions*

Technology

PRENTICE HALL
TeacherEXPRESS™
Plan • Teach • Assess

Local Standards

All in One Teaching Resources, Unit 3
- Chapter Project Teacher Notes, pp. 326–327
- Chapter Project Student Overview, pp. 328–329
- Chapter Project Student Worksheets, pp. 330–331
- Chapter Project Scoring Rubric, p. 332

Discovery CHANNEL SCHOOL
Video Preview

 Section 1

2 periods
1 block

How the Nervous System Works
19.1.1 Identify the functions of the nervous system.
19.1.2 Describe the structure of a neuron and the kinds of neurons found in the body.
19.1.3 Explain how nerve impulses travel from one neuron to another.

Go Online
PHSchool.com

 Section 2

1 period
1/2 block

Divisions of the Nervous System
19.2.1 Describe the structures and functions of the central nervous system.
19.2.2 Describe the structures and functions of the peripheral nervous system.
19.2.3 Explain what a reflex is.
19.2.4 Identify two ways in which the nervous system can be injured.

Go Online *active art*

Go Online PHSchool.com

 Section 3

2 periods
1 block

The Senses
19.3.1 Describe how your eyes enable you to see.
19.3.2 Describe how you hear and maintain your sense of balance.
19.3.3 Explain how your senses of smell and taste work together.
19.3.4 Explain how your skin is related to your sense of touch.

Discovery CHANNEL SCHOOL
Video Field Trip

Go Online SC*LINKS* NSTA

 Section 4

2 periods
1 block

Alcohol and Other Drugs
19.4.1 Identify the immediate and long-term effects of drug abuse.
19.4.2 Describe some commonly abused drugs and how each affects the body.
19.4.3 Explain how alcohol abuse harms the body.

Go Online SC*LINKS* NSTA

Review and Assessment

All in One Teaching Resources, Unit 3
- Key Terms Review, p. 368
- Transparency LS190
- Performance Assessment Teacher Notes, p. 375
- Performance Assessment Scoring Rubric, p. 376
- Performance Assessment Student Worksheet, p. 377
- Chapter Test, pp. 378–381

Discovery CHANNEL SCHOOL
Video Assessment

Go Online PHSchool.com

Test Preparation

Test Preparation Blackline Masters

Lab zone Chapter Activities Planner

For more activities
LAB ZONE Easy Planner CD-ROM

Student Edition	Inquiry	Time	Materials	Skills	Resources
Chapter Project, p. 625	Open-Ended	2 weeks	**All in One Teaching Resources, Unit 3,** p. 326	Predicting, observing, designing experiments, creating data tables, making and interpreting graphs, interpreting data, drawing conclusions, communicating	**Lab zone Easy Planner** **All in One Teaching Resources, Unit 3,** Support pp. 326–327
Section 1					
Discover Activity, p. 626	Open-ended	15 minutes	Paper, pencil, penny	Inferring	**Lab zone Easy Planner**
Design Your Own Lab, p. 631	Guided	50 minutes	Meter stick	Developing hypotheses, controlling variables	**Lab zone Easy Planner Lab Activity Video** **All in One Teaching Resources, Unit 3,** Design Your Own Lab: *Ready or Not!*, pp. 340–341
Section 2					
Discover Activity, p. 632	Open-ended	10 minutes	None	Inferring	**Lab zone Easy Planner**
Skills Activity, p. 634	Guided	30 minutes	Tape player, cassette tape of soft music	Controlling variables	**Lab zone Easy Planner**
Try This, p. 637	Directed	15 minutes	Goggles, cotton balls	Interpreting data	**Lab zone Easy Planner**
Section 3					
Discover Activity, p. 642	Open-ended	20 minutes	Opaque paper bags; small objects, such as erasers, pens, paper clips, sponges, cotton balls, marbles, plastic spoons, bottle caps, coins, buttons	Observing	**Lab zone Easy Planner**
Try This, p. 644	Directed	15 minutes	Drinking straw, pipe cleaner	Inferring	**Lab zone Easy Planner**
Skills Activity, p. 649	Guided	15 minutes	Peeled pear, apple, and raw potato	Designing experiments	**Lab zone Easy Planner**
Section 4					
Discover Activity, p. 651	Open-ended	15 minutes	Marbles	Inferring	**Lab zone Easy Planner**
Skills Activity, p. 653	Guided	45 minutes	Paper, drawing materials	Communicating	**Lab zone Easy Planner**
Consumer Lab, pp. 658–659	Guided	Prep: 45 minutes Class: 40 minutes	Blackworms, plastic dropper, adrenaline solution, stereomicroscope, paraffin specimen trough, noncarbonated spring water, beverages with and without caffeine, stopwatch or clock with second hand	Observing, controlling variables, drawing conclusions	**Lab zone Easy Planner Lab Activity Video** **All in One Teaching Resources, Unit 3,** Consumer Lab: *With Caffeine or Without,* pp. 365–367

Section 1 How the Nervous System Works

 2 periods, 1 block

Objectives

19.1.1 Identify the functions of the nervous system.

19.1.2 Describe the structure of a neuron and the kinds of neurons found in the body.

19.1.3 Explain how nerve impulses travel from one neuron to another.

Local Standards

Key Terms

• stimulus • response • neurons • nerve impulse • dendrite • axon • nerve
• sensory neuron • interneuron • motor neuron • synapse

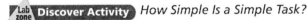

Preteach

Build Background Knowledge

Ask students to state what it means when something makes them nervous. Explain how nervousness relates to the nervous system.

Lab zone Discover Activity *How Simple Is a Simple Task?* **L1**

Targeted Print and Technology Resources

All in One Teaching Resources, Unit 3

L2 Reading Strategy Transparency LS180: Previewing Visuals

PresentationEXPRESS™ CD-ROM

Instruct

Functions of the Nervous System Ask students to identify examples of stimuli and responses and relate them to the nervous system.

The Neuron Have students identify parts of a neuron and classify neurons conducting various messages.

How a Nerve Impulse Travels Ask students to infer what would happen if chemicals could not cross the synapse.

Lab zone Design Your Own Lab *Ready or Not!* **L2**

Targeted Print and Technology Resources

All in One Teaching Resources, Unit 3

L2 Guided Reading, pp. 335–337
L2 Transparencies LS181, LS182
L2 Design Your Own Lab: *Ready or Not!* p. 340–341

Lab Activity Video/DVD
Design Your Own Lab: *Ready or Not!*

PHSchool.com Web Code: ced-4061

Student Edition on Audio CD

Assess

Section Assessment Questions

Have students use their Previewing Visuals graphic organizers to help answer the questions.

Reteach

Have students find facts from the section to support the following: The neurons that make up the nervous system act as a transport system.

Targeted Print and Technology Resources

All in One Teaching Resources, Unit 3

• Section Summary, p. 334
L1 Review and Reinforce, p. 338
L3 Enrich, p. 339

Section 2 Divisions of the Nervous System

 1 period, 1/2 block

ABILITY LEVELS
L1 Basic to Average
L2 For All Students
L3 Average to Advanced

Objectives

19.2.1 Describe the structures and functions of the central nervous system.

19.2.2 Describe the structures and functions of the peripheral nervous system.

19.2.3 Explain what a reflex is.

19.2.4 Identify two ways in which the nervous system can be injured.

Key Terms

- central nervous system • peripheral nervous system • brain • spinal cord
- cerebrum • cerebellum • brain stem • somatic nervous system
- autonomic nervous system • reflex • concussion

Local Standards

Preteach

Build Background Knowledge

Give an example of a reflex action for students to identify and recognize as an automatic response.

 **Discover Activity** *How Does Your Knee React?* L1

Targeted Print and Technology Resources

 **Teaching Resources, Unit 3**
L2 Reading Strategy: Building Vocabulary

◉ **PresentationEXPRESS™ CD-ROM**

Instruct

Central Nervous System Have students trace the path of nerve impulses to the spinal cord and brain.

Brain and Spinal Cord Have students interpret a diagram to identify the main regions of the brain and their functions.

Peripheral Nervous System Ask students to identify the functions of spinal nerves and relate them to the peripheral nervous system.

Reflexes Ask students to sequence the events in a reflex action.

Nervous System Injuries Brainstorm with students ways to prevent nervous system injuries.

Targeted Print and Technology Resources

Teaching Resources, Unit 3
L2 Guided Reading, pp. 344–347
L2 Transparencies LS183, LS184, LS185

PHSchool.com Web Code: cep-4062

PHSchool.com Web Code: ceh-4060

◉ **Student Edition on Audio CD**

Assess

Section Assessment Questions

 Have students use their definitions to help answer the questions.

Reteach

Have students fill in the labels of a diagram to identify the parts of the brain.

Targeted Print and Technology Resources

Teaching Resources, Unit 3
- Section Summary, p. 343
L1 Review and Reinforce, p. 348
L3 Enrich, p. 349

624D

Section 3 The Senses

 *2 periods, 1 block*

Objectives

19.3.1 Describe how your eyes enable you to see.

19.3.2 Describe how you hear and maintain your sense of balance.

19.3.3 Explain how your senses of smell and taste work together.

19.3.4 Explain how your skin is related to your sense of touch.

Key Terms

• cornea • pupil • iris • lens • retina • nearsightedness • farsightedness
• eardrum • cochlea • semicircular canal

Local Standards

Preteach

Build Background Knowledge

Challenge students to brainstorm a list of items or activities in the classroom that they perceive through each sense.

Lab zone Discover Activity *What's in the Bag?* **L1**

Targeted Print and Technology Resources

All in One Teaching Resources, Unit 3

L2 Reading Strategy Transparency
LS186: Outlining

⊙ **PresentationEXPRESS™ CD-ROM**

Instruct

Vision Invite students to compare the eye with a camera.

Hearing and Balance Have students look at a diagram to identify the parts of the ear and how sound waves are perceived and interpreted.

Smell and Taste Ask students to describe how smell and taste work together.

Touch Ask students to identify the different receptors that respond to touch.

Targeted Print and Technology Resources

All in One Teaching Resources, Unit 3

L2 Guided Reading, pp. 352–354
L2 Transparencies LS187, LS188

www.SciLinks.org Web Code: scn-0463

DISCOVERY CHANNEL SCHOOL
Video Field Trip

⊙ **Student Edition on Audio CD**

Assess

Section Assessment Questions

Have students use their outlines to answer the questions.

Reteach

Have students list the senses and identify the types of receptors in each associated sense organ.

Targeted Print and Technology Resources

All in One Teaching Resources, Unit 3

• Section Summary, p. 351
L1 Review and Reinforce, p. 355
L3 Enrich, p. 356

Section 4 Alcohol and Other Drugs

🕐 *2 periods, 1 block*

Objectives

19.4.1 Identify the immediate and long-term effects of drug abuse.

19.4.2 Describe some commonly abused drugs and how each affects the body.

19.4.3 Explain how alcohol abuse harms the body.

Key Terms

• drug • drug abuse • tolerance • addiction • withdrawal • depressant
• stimulant • anabolic steroid • alcoholism

Local Standards

Preteach

Build Background Knowledge

Ask students to infer what happens if you take medicines improperly.

Lab zone Discover Activity *How Can You Best Say No?* L1

Targeted Print and Technology Resources

All in One Teaching Resources, Unit 3

L2 Reading Strategy Transparency
LS189: Relating Cause and Effect

⊙ **PresentationEXPRESS™ CD-ROM**

Instruct

Drug Abuse Ask students to differentiate between tolerance and addiction.

Kinds of Abused Drugs Have students classify commonly abused drugs, and answer questions about the effects of each type.

Alcohol Challenge students to describe the short-term and long-term effects of alcohol abuse.

Lab zone Consumer Lab *With Caffeine or Without?* L2

Targeted Print and Technology Resources

All in One Teaching Resources, Unit 3

L2 Guided Reading, pp. 359–362
L2 Consumer Lab: *With Caffeine or Without?* pp. 365–367

📼 **Lab Activity Video/DVD**
Consumer Lab: *With Caffeine or Without?*

www.SciLinks.org Web Code: scn-0464

⊙ **Student Edition on Audio CD**

Assess

Section Assessment Questions

↩ Have students use their Relating Cause and Effect graphic organizers to answer the questions.

Reteach

Have students review major concepts by making flash cards.

Targeted Print and Technology Resources

All in One Teaching Resources, Unit 3

• Section Summary, p. 358
L1 Review and Reinforce, p. 363
L3 Enrich, p. 364

Go Online

NSTA-PDLINKS

For: Professional Development Support
Visit: www.SciLinks.org/PDLinks
Web Code: scf-0460

Professional Development

Section 1 How the Nervous System Works

What Causes a Nerve Impulse? The start of a nerve impulse is related to the distribution of ions inside and outside a neuron's cell membrane. An ion is a particle with an electrical charge. Some ions, such as a sodium ion (Na^+) and a potassium ion (K^+), have positive charges, while other ions, such as a chloride ion (Cl^-), have negative charges. A neuron's cell membrane is polarized, or electrically charged, because there is a difference in charges between the membrane's surface outside the cell and the surface inside the cell. When a neuron is not transmitting a nerve impulse, or resting, the outside of the cell has a net negative charge, and the inside has a net positive charge. This difference in charge is called the resting potential.

The membrane's polarization is caused by a difference in the distribution of sodium and potassium ions inside and outside the cell, as shown in the illustration. There are more sodium ions outside the cell, and more potassium ions inside the cell. This difference in distribution is maintained by a "pumping" action that moves sodium ions outside the cell and potassium ions inside the cell. The sodium-potassium pump is maintained by active transport.

If a resting neuron receives a stimulus of sufficient strength, sodium ions rush into the cell. The entry of sodium ions temporarily makes the inside of the cell membrane more positive than the outside. This temporary reversal of charges, which is called the action potential, starts a nerve impulse traveling down the axon. After the impulse passes, the resting distribution of potassium and sodium ions on both sides of the cell membrane is restored.

Charges on a Neuron Cell Membrane

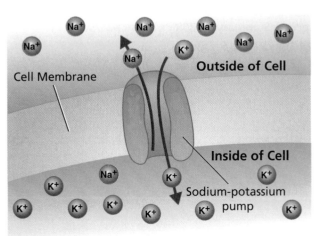

The speed of an impulse down an axon is increased by the action of myelin sheath cells. The myelin sheath cells that surround some axons prevent the axons from opening and exchanging their ions with the outside environment. Gaps between the myelin sheath, known as the nodes of Ranvier, allow for the ion exchange that is necessary for an action potential to take place. An action potential at one node excites an adjacent node. The jumps between nodes allow for faster propagation than continuous propagation along a nerve membrane.

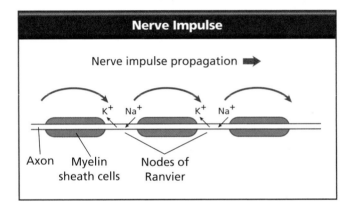

Section 2 Divisions of the Nervous System

Development of the Cerebrum Unlike some organs such as the heart, which form early in pregnancy and are fully functional at birth, the cerebral cortex develops slowly and continues developing both structurally and functionally after birth. The ridge-groove pattern of the cortex becomes visibly apparent at roughly 28–30 weeks gestation, an age at which many premature babies can now survive with modern medical care. In full-term newborns (40 weeks gestation), the volume of the brain (primarily the cerebral cortex) is roughly 25 percent of average adult volume. At the end of the first year of life, however, the brain has grown to roughly 75 percent of adult size. The brain completes development and comes to full adult volume relatively late in life—roughly age 16 to 17 years. This relatively slow development means that good nutrition and nurturing experiences can aid brain development throughout pregnancy and childhood. It also means there is a long window of time during which negative influences ranging from infections to substance exposure can harm brain development.

Professional Development

Section 3 The Senses

Types of Receptors The first stage in the transmission of a nerve impulse from a sense organ to the brain is the stimulation of a cell or group of cells called a sensory receptor. Animals, including humans, have several types of sensory receptors, including electromagnetic receptors, chemoreceptors, mechanoreceptors, thermoreceptors, and pain receptors. Each of these types detects a different type of stimulus.

Electromagnetic receptors are stimulated by electromagnetic energy, that is, waves that form part of the electromagnetic spectrum that includes visible light. Photoreceptors, which detect light, are one type of electromagnetic receptor. The rods and cones in the retina are photoreceptors. Many animals contain sophisticated electromagnetic receptors for detecting infrared radiation, electric currents, and magnetic fields.

Chemoreceptors, as their name indicates, detect chemical stimuli. The human senses of taste and smell are activated by chemoreceptors in the mouth and nose.

Mechanoreceptors are stimulated by forms of mechanical energy, such as motion, pressure, touch, and sound. The sensory receptors in the skin that detect touch and pressure are mechanoreceptors. Hair cells, including those found in the cochlea and semicircular canals of the inner ear, are also mechanoreceptors. The hair cells in both the cochlea and semicircular canals are activated by the movement of fluid.

Changes in heat activate thermoreceptors. The human skin contains thermoreceptors that detect heat and cold. Scientists are not yet sure of the specific nature of the thermoreceptors in the human skin.

In humans, pain receptors, which are also called nociceptors, are especially common in the skin, around the walls of blood vessels, in the joints, and in bones. Different pain receptors in the skin respond to stimuli such as extreme heat or cold, mechanical damage such as cuts, and chemicals that have been released by damaged tissues.

Section 4 Alcohol and Other Drugs

Drug Interactions Taking two or more drugs or taking a drug while consuming a certain food can result in an interaction. Any time another substance interacts with a drug, it alters the effect of the drug. The interaction may make the drug less effective, cause unexpected side effects, or increase the action of the drug. Such alterations can sometimes be harmful. At times, though, a drug interaction can be beneficial, such as when food or milk is taken with a medicine to prevent an upset stomach.

Alcohol is a common drug that has adverse effects on many drugs. For example, when alcohol is consumed while taking an antihistamine to treat symptoms of an allergy, reaction times slow, making certain activities like driving a car very dangerous.

To reduce the risk of drug interaction, you should read the label every time you use a prescription or an over-the-counter drug. Warning statements on labels often alert you to the possibility of a drug interaction with specific substances.

Address Misconceptions

Students may not think of over-the-counter and prescription medicines as drugs. However, medicines are drugs and can be dangerous if not taken correctly. For a strategy to help overcome this misconception, see **Address Misconceptions** in the section *Alcohol and Other Drugs.*

Help Students Read

Identifying Main Ideas
Paragraph and Subheading Organization

Strategy Help students become aware of text organization and help students identify key information. Before you begin, assign students two paragraphs, each with a subhead, within the chapter to read.

Example

1. Main Idea of a Paragraph Review with students the fact that some paragraphs have a topic sentence expressing the paragraph's main idea, while the other sentences provide supporting details.

2. Main Idea of a Subheading Guide students to make the connection that just as a paragraph has a main idea and supporting details, the text under each subheading has a main idea with supporting details carried within the paragraphs.

3. Inferring or Synthesizing a Main Idea State that it may be necessary to infer an unstated main idea by combining information.

Interactive Textbook
- Complete student edition
- Video and audio
- Simulations and activities
- Section and chapter activities

Chapter 19
The Nervous System

Chapter Project

L3

Objectives
In this project, students will observe their own responses to several illusions and choose at least one to investigate. After this Chapter Project, students will be able to

- predict typical responses and observe their own responses and those of others to simple illusions
- design an experiment to monitor responses to an illusion
- create a data table to record responses to a particular illusion
- create graphs or tables to interpret data and draw conclusions
- communicate their results to the class

Skills Focus
Predicting, observing, designing experiments, creating data tables, making and interpreting graphs, interpreting data, drawing conclusions, communicating

Project Time Line 2 weeks

 **Teaching Resources, Unit 3**
- Chapter Project Teacher Notes
- Chapter Project Overview
- Chapter Project Worksheet 1
- Chapter Project Worksheet 2
- Chapter Project Scoring Rubric

Interactive Textbook

Without your nervous system, a sport like windsurfing would be impossible! ▶

624 ◆

Developing a Plan
About one week will be devoted to trying out and selecting illusions. A second week will involve holding the science fair, gathering data, and presenting results. Class time will be needed for trying out the illusions, the science fair, and for presentations.

Possible Materials
Materials will vary, depending on the illusions chosen. Reference books for this project include *You Won't Believe Your Eyes!* by Catherine O'Neil Grace; *Science, Art and Visual Illusions* by Robert Froman; *How to Really Fool Yourself: Illusions for All Your Senses* by Vicki Cobb; *Illusions: A Journey Into Perception* by Patricia Ann Rainey; and *Optricks* by Melinda Wentzell and D.K. Holland.

The Nervous System

▶ Video Preview
Video Field Trip
Video Assessment

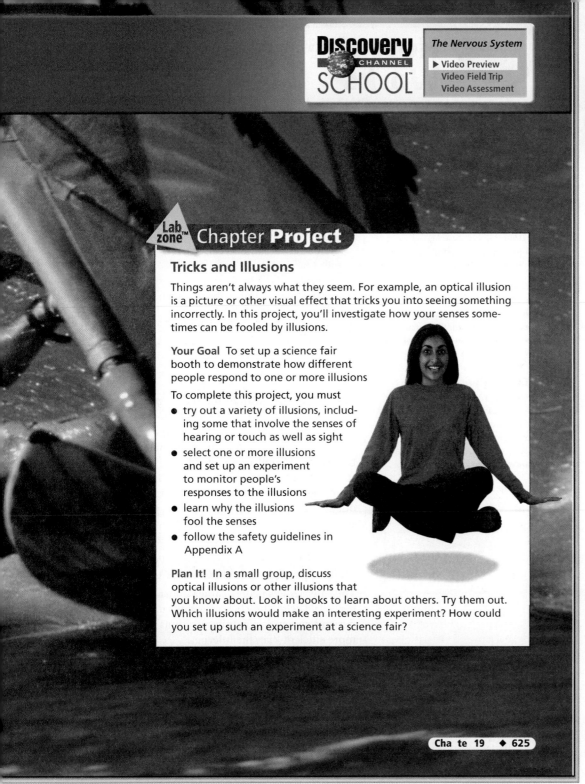

Chapter **Project**

Tricks and Illusions

Things aren't always what they seem. For example, an optical illusion is a picture or other visual effect that tricks you into seeing something incorrectly. In this project, you'll investigate how your senses sometimes can be fooled by illusions.

Your Goal To set up a science fair booth to demonstrate how different people respond to one or more illusions

To complete this project, you must

● try out a variety of illusions, including some that involve the senses of hearing or touch as well as sight

● select one or more illusions and set up an experiment to monitor people's responses to the illusions

● learn why the illusions fool the senses

● follow the safety guidelines in Appendix A

Plan It! In a small group, discuss optical illusions or other illusions that you know about. Look in books to learn about others. Try them out. Which illusions would make an interesting experiment? How could you set up such an experiment at a science fair?

Cha te 19 ◆ 625

Possible Shortcuts

Simplify the project by choosing a variety of illusions and setting them up in stations. Students could test these illusions on each other during one class period and report their findings during another.

The Nervous System

Show the Video Preview to introduce the Chapter Project and overview the chapter content. Discussion question: **Describe one way in which the horseshoe crab eye differs from the human eye.** *(The horseshoe crab eye has a thousand little lenses. The human eye has only one lens.)*

Launching the Project

Have students play the game of "gossip." Ask one student to start the gossip line by reading (only once) in a whisper the following message to a second student: "If a rabbit runs twice around the school, then puts butter in its ear, it will grow green fur." The second student whispers (only once) what was heard to a third, and so on. Every fifth person writes down what he or she heard. At the end of the game and after the written messages are compared, discuss how the mind tries to make sense of information gathered by the senses.

Performance Assessment

The Chapter Project Scoring Rubric will help you evaluate how well students complete the Chapter Project. You may want to share the scoring rubric with your students so they are clear about what will be expected of them. Students will be assessed on

● their research (if appropriate) and selection of an appropriate illusion

● the design of their experiment and data sheets to record responses

● their participation in and gathering of data during the science fair

● their class presentation of their results

Portfolio

625

Objectives

After this lesson, students will be able to

19.1.1 Identify the functions of the nervous system.

19.1.2 Describe the structure of a neuron and the kinds of neurons found in the body.

19.1.3 Explain how nerve impulses travel from one neuron to another.

Target Reading Skill

Previewing Visuals Explain that looking at the visuals before they read helps students activate prior knowledge and predict what they are about to read.

Answers

Sample questions and answers: **What is a sensory neuron?** (*A neuron that picks up stimuli from the internal or external environment and converts each stimulus into a nerve impulse*) **What does an interneuron do?** (*It carries nerve impulses from one neuron to another.*)

All in One Teaching Resources, Unit 3

• Transparency LS180

Preteach

Build Background Knowledge   L2

Reactions to the Environment

Ask: **What does it mean when someone says that something makes them nervous?** (*Students may say it means that a person is anxious or worried about something.*) Explain that anxiety and worry are different ways in which people react to their environment. Point out that the nervous system allows people to react to their environment in various ways.

Section 1
How the Nervous System Works

Reading Preview

Key Concepts
• What are the functions of the nervous system?
• What is the structure of a neuron and what kinds of neurons are found in the body?
• How do nerve impulses travel from one neuron to another?

Key Terms
• stimulus • response
• neuron • nerve impulse
• dendrite • axon • nerve
• sensory neuron • interneuron
• motor neuron • synapse

Target Reading Skill

Previewing Visuals Before you read, preview Figure 3. Then, write two questions that you have about the diagram in a graphic organizer like the one below. As you read, answer your questions.

The Path of a Nerve Impulse

Q.	What is a sensory neuron?
A.	
Q.	

Lab zone Discover Activity

How Simple Is a Simple Task?

1. Trace the outline of a penny in twelve different places on a piece of paper.
2. Number the circles 1 through 12. Write the numbers randomly, in no particular order.
3. Now, pick up the penny again. Put it in each circle, one after another, in numerical order, beginning with 1 and ending with 12.

Think It Over

Inferring Make a list of all the sense organs, muscle movements, and thought processes used in this activity. Compare your list with your classmates' lists. What organ system coordinated all the different processes involved in this task?

The ball whizzes toward the soccer goalie. She lunges for the ball, and in one swift movement blocks it from entering the net. To tend goal, soccer players need excellent coordination and keen vision. In addition, they must remember what they have learned from years of practice.

Whether or not you play soccer, you too need coordination, memory, and the ability to learn. Your nervous system carries out all these functions. The nervous system includes the brain, spinal cord, and nerves that run throughout the body. It also includes sense organs, such as the eyes and ears.

Functions of the Nervous System

The Internet lets people gather information from anywhere in the world with the click of a button. Like the Internet, your nervous system is a communications network. But it is much more efficient than the Internet.

The nervous system receives information about what is happening both inside and outside your body. It also directs the way in which your body responds to this information. In addition, your nervous system helps maintain homeostasis. Without your nervous system, you could not move, think, feel pain, or taste a spicy taco.

Lab zone Discover Activity

Skills Focus Inferring

Materials paper, pencil, penny

Time 15 minutes

Tips Remind students to follow directions carefully as they complete the activity.

Think It Over Sample answer: Sense organs used include eyes and skin. Muscle movements include the muscles of the   L1

arms and hands holding the penny down, moving the penny from place to place, picking up the pencil, and tracing the circle. Thought processes involved include reading and understanding the instructions, choosing where to place the penny, and following the sequence of numbers. The nervous system coordinated all these processes.

Receiving Information Because of your nervous system, you are aware of what is happening in the environment around you. For example, you know that a fly is buzzing around your head, that the wind is blowing, or that a friend is telling a funny joke. Your nervous system also checks conditions inside your body, such as the level of glucose in your blood.

Responding to Information Any change or signal in the environment that can make an organism react is called a **stimulus** (STIM yoo lus) (plural: *stimuli*). A buzzing fly is a stimulus. After your nervous system analyzes the stimulus, it causes a response. A **response** is what your body does in reaction to a stimulus—you swat at the fly.

Some nervous system responses, such as swatting a fly, are voluntary, or under your control. However, many processes necessary for life, such as heart rate, are controlled by involuntary actions of the nervous system.

Maintaining Homeostasis The nervous system helps maintain homeostasis by directing the body to respond appropriately to the information it receives. For example, when you are hungry, your nervous system prompts you to eat. This action maintains homeostasis by supplying your body with the nutrients and energy it needs.

Reading Checkpoint What is a stimulus?

FIGURE 1
The Nervous System at Work
The zooming soccer ball is a stimulus. The goalie responds by lunging toward the ball and blocking the shot.
Interpreting Diagrams *How does the goalie's nervous system help her body maintain homeostasis?*

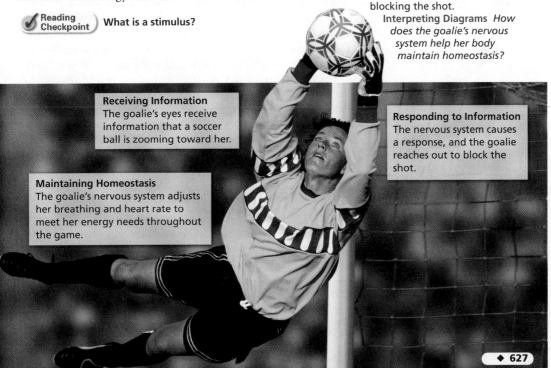

Receiving Information
The goalie's eyes receive information that a soccer ball is zooming toward her.

Responding to Information
The nervous system causes a response, and the goalie reaches out to block the shot.

Maintaining Homeostasis
The goalie's nervous system adjusts her breathing and heart rate to meet her energy needs throughout the game.

◆ 627

Functions of the Nervous System

Teach Key Concepts L2
Receiving and Responding to Information

Focus Ask: **Why do you need to communicate when you play team sports?** (*Sample answers: The coach needs to call plays. Players need to signal to one another.*)

Teach Explain that your body needs a communication system, too. The nervous system receives messages and responds to them. Ask: **If you touched a hot object, what would be the stimulus?** (*Heat from the object*) **The response?** (*Jerking away from the object*) Remind students that homeostasis is the process of maintaining stable internal conditions. Ask: **When you run, how does your breathing change?** (*You breathe faster and deeper.*) Explain that your nervous system causes this change because the muscles are using more oxygen.

Apply Have students identify the stimulus and response in the following situations: **tasting a lemon wedge** (*Sour taste; mouth fills with saliva*); **smelling vinegar** (*Sour smell; nose wrinkles*); **someone throwing a ball toward you** (*Speed and direction of ball; you catch the ball*). **learning modality: logical/mathematical**

Independent Practice L2

All in One Teaching Resources, Unit 3
• Guided Reading and Study Worksheet: *How the Nervous System Works*

⊙ **Student Edition on Audio CD**

Monitor Progress L2

Oral Presentation Call on students to name the three functions of the nervous system and give examples of each.

Answers
Figure 1 It directs her body to respond appropriately to the information it receives, for example, getting hungry and eating after using lots of energy.

Reading Checkpoint A change or signal in the environment that can make an organism react

The Neuron

Teach Key Concepts L2

Types of Neurons

Focus Remind students that the nervous system receives and transmits messages all through the body.

Teach Ask: **What are the parts of a neuron?** *(Nucleus, axon, dendrite)* **What do axons and dendrites do?** *(Axons carry impulses away from the cell body. Dendrites carry impulses toward to the cell body.)* **Where does the message from a sensory neuron end up?** *(In the brain or spinal cord)* **Where does a motor neuron send an impulse?** *(A muscle or gland)*

Apply Have students identify which type of neuron, sensory or motor, would conduct the message in the following situations: **Seeing a picture** *(sensory);* **feeling pain from skinning your knee** *(sensory);* **moving your arm to catch a ball** *(motor).* **learning modality: logical/mathematical**

 **Teaching Resources, Unit 3**

- Transparency LS181

 **Build Inquiry** L1

Classifying Neuron Types

Materials notecards, markers

Time 10 minutes

Focus Review the three types of neurons.

Teach Divide the class into three groups, and assign each group to portray a type of neuron. Challenge students to model how nerve impulses are sent through the body. Explain that students in the sensory neuron group will write descriptions of stimuli and then pass their notes to students representing interneurons. The interneuron group will then pass the notes to students playing motor neurons, who write notes describing responses. (Example: Sensory group writes "You feel a hot stove"; interneuron group passes the note to motor group, who writes "Remove hand from stove.")

Apply After groups have modeled several actions, have a member of each group draw on the board the sequence of one of the actions. Ask the student to include how the message traveled along axons and dendrites. **learning modality: kinesthetic**

FIGURE 2
Structure of a Neuron
A neuron has one axon and many dendrites that extend from the cell body.

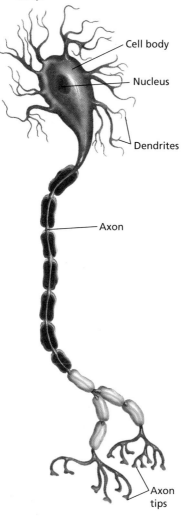

Cell body

Nucleus

Dendrites

Axon

Axon tips

Go Online
PHSchool.com

For: More on nerve impulses
Visit: PHSchool.com
Web Code: ced-4061

628 ◆

The Neuron

Your nervous system includes various organs, tissues, and cells. For example, your brain is an organ, and the nerves running throughout your body are tissues. The cells that carry information through your nervous system are called **neurons** (NOO rahnz), or nerve cells. The message that a neuron carries is called a **nerve impulse.**

The Structure of a Neuron The structure of a neuron enables it to carry nerve impulses. **A neuron has a large cell body that contains the nucleus, threadlike extensions called dendrites, and an axon.** The **dendrites** carry impulses toward the neuron's cell body. The **axon** carries impulses away from the cell body. Nerve impulses begin in a dendrite, move toward the cell body, and then move down the axon. A neuron can have many dendrites, but it has only one axon. An axon, however, can have more than one tip, so the impulse can go to more than one other cell.

Axons and dendrites are sometimes called nerve fibers. Nerve fibers are often arranged in parallel bundles covered with connective tissue, something like a package of uncooked spaghetti wrapped in cellophane. A bundle of nerve fibers is called a **nerve.**

Kinds of Neurons Three kinds of neurons are found in the body—sensory neurons, interneurons, and motor neurons. Figure 3 shows how these three kinds of neurons work together.

A **sensory neuron** picks up stimuli from the internal or external environment and converts each stimulus into a nerve impulse. The impulse travels along the sensory neuron until it reaches an interneuron, usually in the brain or spinal cord. An **interneuron** is a neuron that carries nerve impulses from one neuron to another. Some interneurons pass impulses from sensory neurons to motor neurons. A **motor neuron** sends an impulse to a muscle or gland, and the muscle or gland reacts in response.

 **Reading Checkpoint** What is the function of an axon?

How a Nerve Impulse Travels

Every day of your life, billions of nerve impulses travel through your nervous system. Each of those nerve impulses begins in the dendrites of a neuron. The impulse moves rapidly toward the neuron's cell body and then down the axon until it reaches the axon tip. A nerve impulse travels along the neuron in the form of electrical and chemical signals. Nerve impulses can travel as fast as 120 meters per second!

FIGURE 3

The Path of a Nerve Impulse

When you hear your phone ring, you pick it up to answer it. Many sensory neurons, interneurons, and motor neurons are involved in this action.

Interpreting Diagrams *To where does the impulse pass from the sensory neurons?*

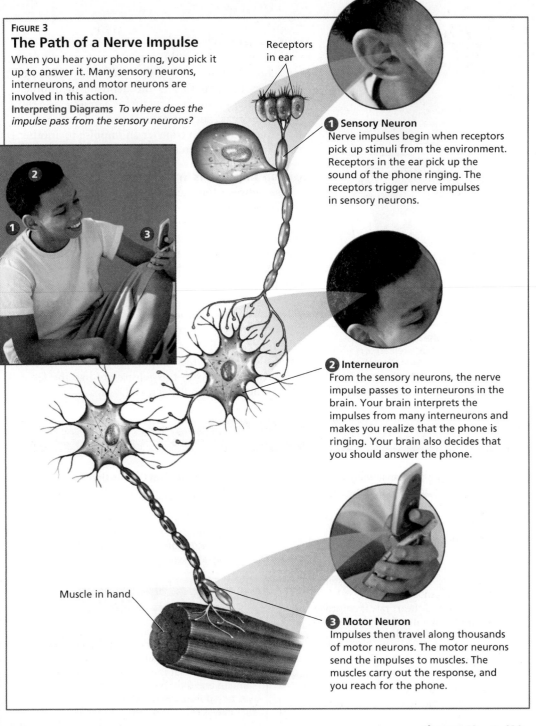

Receptors in ear

1 Sensory Neuron
Nerve impulses begin when receptors pick up stimuli from the environment. Receptors in the ear pick up the sound of the phone ringing. The receptors trigger nerve impulses in sensory neurons.

2 Interneuron
From the sensory neurons, the nerve impulse passes to interneurons in the brain. Your brain interprets the impulses from many interneurons and makes you realize that the phone is ringing. Your brain also decides that you should answer the phone.

Muscle in hand

3 Motor Neuron
Impulses then travel along thousands of motor neurons. The motor neurons send the impulses to muscles. The muscles carry out the response, and you reach for the phone.

Chapter 19 ◆ 629

How a Nerve Impulse Travels

Teach Key Concepts   L2
Transmission Across Synapses

Focus Review the sequence of an impulse within a nerve cell (dendrite to cell body to axon).

Teach Ask: **What carries an impulse across the synapses?** (*Chemicals released from the axons*) **What would happen if the chemical were not available?** (*The nerve impulse would stop.*) **Where can impulses be received?** (*Other dendrites, muscles, or cells in another organ*)

Apply Ask: Why is pain not experienced in an area after an injection to numb the area is given by a doctor? (*The chemicals in the injection may affect neurotransmitters, thereby causing the sensory neurons in the area not to sense pain.*) **learning modality: verbal**

Use Visuals: Figure 3   L1
Tracing the Path of Nerve Impulses

Focus Refer students to Figure 3.

Teach Have students trace the path of the nerve impulse. Ask: **What is the stimulus to which each kind of neuron responds?** (*Sensory neurons respond to the ringing sound of the phone. Interneurons respond to the impulses from the sensory neurons. Motor neurons respond to impulses from interneurons.*)

Apply Have students measure on their bodies the distance the nerve impulse travels from the ear to the brain, and then to the hand. **learning modality: visual**

 **Teaching Resources, Unit 3**
• Transparency LS182

For: More on nerve impulses **Visit:** PHSchool.com **Web Code:** ced-4061	

Students can review nerve impulses in an online interactivity.

Monitor Progress   L2

Answers
Figure 3 To the interneurons

Reading Checkpoint An axon carries a nerve impulse away from the cell body.

Differentiated Instruction

English Learners/Beginning   L1
Comprehension: Key Concepts
Emphasize that a nerve cell is the same as a neuron, but not the same as a nerve or a nerve fiber. As an analogy, show students a piece of cable with the insulation removed as you explain the differences between these structures. **learning modality: visual**

English Learners/Intermediate   L2
Vocabulary: Science Glossary
Encourage students to compile a section glossary that includes all the Key Terms and then write definitions for each term in English and in their native language. **learning modality: verbal**

Reviewing Key Concepts

1. a. Receive information about internal and external events, respond to this information, and maintain homeostasis
b. Sample answer: The stimulus is seeing a ball being thrown toward you. The nervous system sends messages, and the brain analyzes the stimulus. The body responds by making your arm move to catch the ball.
c. You would have to think all the time about keeping your heart beating and adjusting its rate in response to changing events.
2. a. Sensory neurons, interneurons, and motor neurons **b.** A sensory neuron detects a stimulus and sends an impulse that travels to interneurons. Interneurons then send an impulse to motor neurons, which send the nerve impulse to a muscle or gland. **c.** A sensory neuron picks up a stimulus from the internal or external environment, converts it into an impulse, and sends the impulse to the nervous system. A motor neuron sends an impulse to muscles or glands.
3. a. The junction where one neuron can transfer an impulse to another neuron.
b. (1) A nerve impulse reaches the tip of an axon. (2) Chemicals are released into the gap at the synapse. (3) The chemicals carry the nerve impulse across the gap to the next structure.

Reteach   **L1**

Have students find facts from the section to support the following statement: The neurons that make up the nervous system act as a transportation system.

Performance Assessment   **L2**

Oral Presentation Ask pairs of students to choose an everyday action, create posters that illustrate the path of the nerve impulses that action involves, and then present the posters to the class.

All in One **Teaching Resources, Unit 3**

- Section Summary: *How the Nervous System Works*
- Review and Reinforce: *How the Nervous System Works*
- Enrich: *How the Nervous System Works*

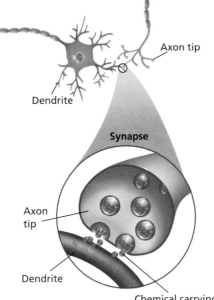

FIGURE 4
The Synapse
When a nerve impulse reaches the tip of an axon, chemicals are released into the gap at the synapse. The chemicals carry the nerve impulse across the gap.

The Synapse What happens when a nerve impulse reaches the axon tip at the end of a neuron? At that point, the impulse can pass to the next structure. Sometimes the structure is the dendrite of another neuron. Other times, the structure is a muscle or a cell in another organ, such as a sweat gland. The junction where one neuron can transfer an impulse to another structure is called a **synapse** (SIN aps).

How an Impulse is Transferred Figure 4 shows a synapse between the axon tip of one neuron and the dendrite of another neuron. Notice that a small gap separates these two structures. **For a nerve impulse to be carried along at a synapse, it must cross the gap between the axon and the next structure. The axon tips release chemicals that carry the impulse across the gap.**

You can think of the gap at a synapse as a river, and an axon as a road that leads up to the riverbank. The nerve impulse is like a car traveling on the road. To get to the other side, the car has to cross the river. The car gets on a ferry boat, which carries it across the river. The chemicals that the axon tips release are like the ferry, carrying the nerve impulse across the gap.

Section 1 Assessment

⟳ Target Reading Skill Previewing Visuals Refer to your questions and answers about Figure 3 to help you answer Question 2 below.

Reviewing Key Concepts

1. a. Listing What are three functions of the nervous system?
   b. Describing Give an example of a stimulus and describe how the nervous system produces a response.
   c. Predicting Your heart rate is controlled by involuntary actions of the nervous system. What would life be like if your heartbeat were under voluntary control?
2. a. Identifying Identify the three kinds of neurons that are found in the nervous system.
   b. Explaining How do the three kinds of neurons interact to carry nerve impulses?

   c. Comparing and Contrasting How do sensory neurons and motor neurons differ?
3. a. Reviewing What is a synapse?
   b. Sequencing Outline the steps by which a nerve impulse reaches and then crosses the gap at a synapse.

Lab zone At-Home **Activity**

Pass the Salt, Please During dinner, ask a family member to pass the salt and pepper to you. Observe what your family member then does. Explain that the words you spoke were a stimulus and that the family member's reaction was a response. Discuss other examples of stimuli and responses with your family.

Lab zone At-Home **Activity**

Pass the Salt, Please **L2** Make sure students define stimulus and response for their families. Students may realize that if they say "Thank you" when the salt and pepper are passed, the passing is a stimulus and the thanks is a response.

Ready or Not!

Problem

Do people's reaction times vary at different times of the day?

Skills Focus

developing hypotheses, controlling variables, drawing conclusions

Material

• meter stick

Procedure

PART 1 Observing a Response to a Stimulus

1. Have your partner hold a meter stick with the zero end about 50 cm above a table.

2. Get ready to catch the meter stick by positioning the top of your thumb and forefinger just at the zero position, as shown in the photograph.

3. Your partner should drop the meter stick without any warning. Using your thumb and forefinger only (no other part of your hand), catch the meter stick as soon as you can. Record the distance in centimeters that the meter stick fell. This distance is a measure of your reaction time.

PART 2 Designing Your Experiment

4. With your partner, discuss how you can use the activity from Part 1 to find out whether people's reaction times vary at different times of day. Consider the questions below. Then, write up your experimental plan.
   • What hypothesis will you test?
   • What variables do you need to control?
   • How many people will you test? How many times will you test each person?

5. Submit your plan for your teacher's review. Make any changes your teacher recommends. Create a data table to record your results. Then, perform your experiment.

Analyze and Conclude

1. **Inferring** In this lab, what is the stimulus? What is the response? Is the response voluntary or involuntary? Explain.

2. **Developing Hypotheses** What hypothesis did you test in Part 2?

3. **Controlling Variables** In Part 2, why was it important to control all variables except the time of day?

4. **Drawing Conclusions** Based on your results in Part 2, do people's reaction times vary at different times of the day? Explain.

5. **Communicating** Write a paragraph to explain why you can use the distance on the meter stick as a measure of reaction time.

More to Explore

Do you think people can do arithmetic problems more quickly and accurately at certain times of the day? Design an experiment to investigate this question. *Obtain your teacher's permission before carrying out your investigation.*

Analyze and Conclude

1. Stimulus—sight of the dropping stick; response—grabbing the stick. The response is voluntary. The person consciously chooses to do it.

2. Some students may hypothesize that time of day has no effect on reaction times. Others may hypothesize that reaction times are fastest at a particular time of day.

3. So that any differences in reaction time can be directly attributed to the time of day

4. Sample answer: Yes, reaction times vary. Research indicates that the reaction times of an individual do vary during the day.

5. Sample answer: If people's thumbs and forefingers are at zero at the time of the drop, the distance the stick drops will be directly proportional to the reaction time because the stick always falls at the same rate.

Ready or Not! L2

Prepare for Inquiry

Key Concept

An individual's behaviors can be affected by various factors such as time of day.

Skills Objectives

Students will be able to
• develop hypotheses about the effect of time of day on reaction times, and control variables as they test those hypotheses
• draw conclusions about the effect of time of day on response time

🕐 **Prep Time** none
Class Time 50 minutes

Safety

Remind students to take care while dropping or catching the meter stick. Review the safety guidelines in Appendix A.

All in One Teaching Resources, Unit 3
• Lab Worksheet: *Ready or Not!*

Guide Inquiry

Invitation

Ask: **What are some situations when a quick reaction time would be advantageous?** *(Sample answers: Applying the brakes to a car to avoid an accident; catching a falling object)*

Introduce the Procedure

Tell students that in Part 1 they should test each person at least five times, and then take the average of all trials.

Troubleshooting the Experiment

Advise students to hold the stick in the same position for every trial.

Extend Inquiry

More to Explore Advise students to use simple arithmetic calculations because they give more consistent results than more complex calculations. Also, discuss why students cannot use the same calculations more than once with each person tested.

Section
2
Divisions of the Nervous System

Objectives

After this lesson, students will be able to

19.2.1 Describe the structures and functions of the central nervous system.
19.2.2 Describe the structures and functions of the peripheral nervous system.
19.2.3 Explain what a reflex is.
19.2.4 Identify two ways in which the nervous system can be injured.

Target Reading Skill

Building Vocabulary Explain that knowing the definitions of key vocabulary terms helps students understand what they need.

Answers

Sample answers:

central nervous system: division of nervous system made up of brain and spinal cord
peripheral nervous system: division of nervous system made up of all nerves outside the central nervous system
brain: part of central nervous system that is located in the skull and that controls most functions in the body

Preteach

Build Background Knowledge L2

Nervous System Responses
Ask: **What happens if you accidentally touch a hot frying pan handle?** *(You quickly move your hand.)* **Is that response automatic or do you have to think about it?** *(Automatic)* Tell students that they will learn how the body controls this and other automatic responses.

Reading Preview

Key Concepts

- What are the structures and functions of the central nervous system?
- What are the structures and functions of the peripheral nervous system?
- What is a reflex?
- What are two ways in which the nervous system can be injured?

Key Terms

- central nervous system
- peripheral nervous system
- brain • spinal cord
- cerebrum • cerebellum
- brain stem
- somatic nervous system
- autonomic nervous system
- reflex • concussion

Target Reading Skill

Building Vocabulary After you read this section, reread the paragraphs that contain definitions of Key Terms. Use all the information you have learned to write a definition of each Key Term in your own words.

Discover **Activity**

How Does Your Knee React?

1. Sit on a table or counter so that your legs dangle freely. Make sure that your partner is not directly in front of your legs.

2. Have your partner use the side of his or her hand to tap one of your knees gently just below the kneecap. Observe what happens to your leg. Note whether you have any control over your reaction.

3. Change places with your partner. Repeat Steps 1 and 2.

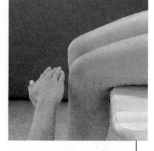

Think It Over
Inferring When might it be an advantage for your body to react very quickly and without your conscious control?

You are standing at a busy street corner, waiting to cross the street. A traffic cop blows his whistle and waves his arms energetically. For the heavy traffic to move smoothly, there needs to be a traffic cop and responsive drivers. The traffic cop coordinates the movements of the drivers, and they maneuver the cars safely through the intersection.

Similarly, your nervous system has two divisions that work together. The **central nervous system** consists of the brain and spinal cord. The **peripheral nervous system** (puh RIF uh rul) includes all the nerves located outside of the central nervous system. The central nervous system is like a traffic cop. The peripheral nervous system is like the drivers and pedestrians.

The traffic cop keeps everybody moving.

Discover **Activity**

Skills Focus Inferring
Materials none
Time 10 minutes

Tips CAUTION: *Make sure students do not engage in horseplay or roughhousing while carrying out the activity. Remind them that serious damage can be done if they strike one another too hard on the kneecap.*

L1 **Expected Outcome** Students' legs will swing forward.

Think It Over It might be an advantage in situations that could cause injury, such as touching a hot stove.

Central Nervous System

You can see the central and peripheral nervous systems in Figure 5. **The central nervous system is the control center of the body. It includes the brain and spinal cord.** All information about what is happening in the world inside or outside your body is brought to the central nervous system. The **brain,** located in the skull, is the part of the central nervous system that controls most functions in the body. The **spinal cord** is the thick column of nervous tissue that links the brain to most of the nerves in the peripheral nervous system.

Most impulses from the peripheral nervous system travel through the spinal cord to get to the brain. Your brain then directs a response. The response usually travels from the brain, through the spinal cord, and then to the peripheral nervous system.

For example, here is what happens when you reach under the sofa to find a lost quarter. Your fingers move over the floor, searching for the quarter. When your fingers finally touch the quarter, the stimulus of the touch triggers nerve impulses in sensory neurons in your fingers. These impulses travel through nerves of the peripheral nervous system to your spinal cord. Then the impulses race up to your brain. Your brain interprets the impulses, telling you that you've found the quarter. Your brain starts nerve impulses that move down the spinal cord. From the spinal cord, the impulses travel through motor neurons in your arm and hand. The impulses in the motor neurons cause your fingers to grasp the quarter.

 Reading Checkpoint What are the parts of the central nervous system?

Go Online
active art

For: Nervous System activity
Visit: PHSchool.com
Web Code: cep-4062

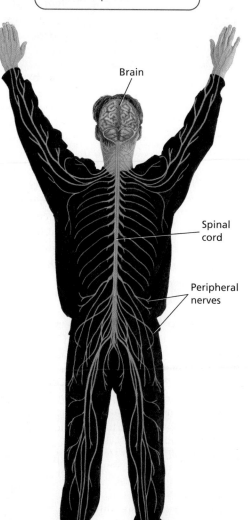

Brain

Spinal cord

Peripheral nerves

FIGURE 5
The Nervous System
The central nervous system consists of the brain and spinal cord. The peripheral nervous system includes all the nerves that branch out from the brain and spinal cord.

Differentiated Instruction

Special Needs   L1
Demonstrating Nerve Pathways
Review the path of a nerve impulse using Figure 3 in the previous section. Then read the last paragraph on this page aloud. Read the paragraph again, but this time, role-play the action by reaching under a desk, for example, to retrieve a real quarter. Trace the pathways the nerve impulses would follow by running your finger along your fingers, arm, upper back, neck, and head. Give students another situation and have them demonstrate the pathway as you did. **learning modality: kinesthetic**

Central Nervous System

Teach Key Concepts   L2
Central Nervous System Function

Focus Remind students that sensory neurons transmit impulses to interneurons in the brain or spinal cord.

Teach Ask: **Why must impulses from sensory neurons be routed to the brain or spinal cord?** *(The brain and spinal cord control the functions of the body. They direct a response to be sent back to the peripheral nervous system.)* Ask students to look at Figure 5 and trace the path of the nerve impulses that begin in the hands of the figure. Ask: **What direction does the nerve impulse move?** *(From the hand to the brain)*

Apply Invite students to think of examples that illustrate an impulse originating from the body, such as hunger, and examples that illustrate an impulse originating from the environment, such as a pesky fly. Then have them describe the pathway the impulses would take in the body. **learning modality: verbal**

All in One Teaching Resources, Unit 3
• Transparency LS183

Independent Practice   L2

All in One Teaching Resources, Unit 3
• Guided Reading and Study Worksheet: *Divisions of the Nervous System*

◉ **Student Edition on Audio CD**

Go Online
active art

For: Nervous system activity
Visit: PHSchool.com
Web Code: cep-4062

Students can interact online with art of the nervous system.

Monitor Progress _____ L2
Answer
 Reading Checkpoint The spinal cord and the brain

The Brain and Spinal Cord

Teach Key Concepts
Functions of the Brain

Focus Remind students that the brain and spinal cord make up the central nervous system.

Teach Explain that the brain has three main regions that receive and process information. Have students locate these regions in Figure 6. Ask students to make lists in which they answer the following questions: **What are the activities controlled by the cerebrum?** *(Sample answers: Learning, creativity, speech, the senses)* **What are the functions of the cerebellum?** *(Coordinating muscle actions and helping you keep your balance)* **Which part of the brain controls involuntary actions?** *(Brain stem)*

Apply Ask: **Which parts of the brain do gymnasts heavily rely on as they perform? Explain your answer.** *(The cerebrum and the cerebellum. The cerebrum directs the action of skeletal muscles. The cerebellum is responsible for the coordination of muscles and helps maintain balance, both of which are important to gymnasts.)* **learning modality: verbal**

Help Students Read
Identifying Main Ideas Read aloud the passage under the subheading "Cerebrum." Have students volunteer their ideas about which sentences express the main concepts. You can also approach this as a written exercise by having students circle sentences on a copy of the chosen paragraph.

The Brain and Spinal Cord

Your brain contains about 100 billion neurons, all of which are interneurons. Each of those neurons may receive messages from up to 10,000 other neurons and may send messages to about 1,000 more! Three layers of connective tissue cover the brain. The space between the middle layer and innermost layer is filled with a watery fluid. The skull, the layers of connective tissue, and the fluid all help protect the brain from injury.

There are three main regions of the brain that receive and process information. These are the cerebrum, the cerebellum, and the brain stem. Find each in Figure 6.

Cerebrum The largest part of the brain is called the cerebrum. The **cerebrum** (suh REE brum) interprets input from the senses, controls movement, and carries out complex mental processes such as learning and remembering. Because of your cerebrum, you can locate your favorite comic strip in the newspaper, read it, and laugh at its funny characters.

The cerebrum is divided into a right and a left half. The right half sends impulses to skeletal muscles on the left side of the body. In contrast, the left half controls the right side of the body. When you reach with your right hand for a pencil, the messages that tell you to do so come from the left half of the cerebrum. In addition, each half of the cerebrum controls slightly different kinds of mental activity. The right half is usually associated with creativity and artistic ability. The left half is usually associated with mathematical skills and logical thinking.

As you can see in Figure 6, certain areas of the cerebrum are associated with smell, touch, taste, hearing, and vision. Other areas control movement, speech, written language, and abstract thought.

Cerebellum and Brain Stem The second largest part of your brain is called the cerebellum. The **cerebellum** (sehr uh BEL um) coordinates the actions of your muscles and helps you keep your balance. When you walk, the impulses that tell your feet to move start in your cerebrum. However, your cerebellum gives you the muscular coordination and sense of balance that keep you from falling down.

The **brain stem,** which lies between the cerebellum and spinal cord, controls your body's involuntary actions—those that occur automatically. For example, neurons in the brain stem regulate your breathing and help control your heartbeat.

 Reading Checkpoint What actions does the brain stem control?

Lab zone Skills Activity

Controlling Variables
Are people better able to memorize a list of words in a quiet room or in a room where soft music is playing?

1. Write a hypothesis that addresses this question.
2. Design an experiment to test your hypothesis. Make sure that all variables are controlled except the one you are testing—music versus quiet.
3. Check your procedure with your teacher. Then perform your experiment.

Did your results support your hypothesis?

Lab zone Skills Activity

Skills Focus Controlling variables **L2**

Materials tape player, cassette tape of soft music

Time 30 minutes

Tips Advise students to test three or four people, first in a quiet room, then with music playing softly. Make sure the person looks at a different list each time you test him or her.

Expected Outcome Sample hypothesis: Soft music increases the rate of learning. Sample experiment: Make up two lists of words with the same number of words, same word lengths, and same degree of familiarity. **learning modality: logical/ mathematical**

FIGURE 6
The Brain

Each of the three main parts of the human brain—the cerebrum, cerebellum, and brain stem—carries out specific functions.
Interpreting Diagrams *What are three functions of the cerebrum?*

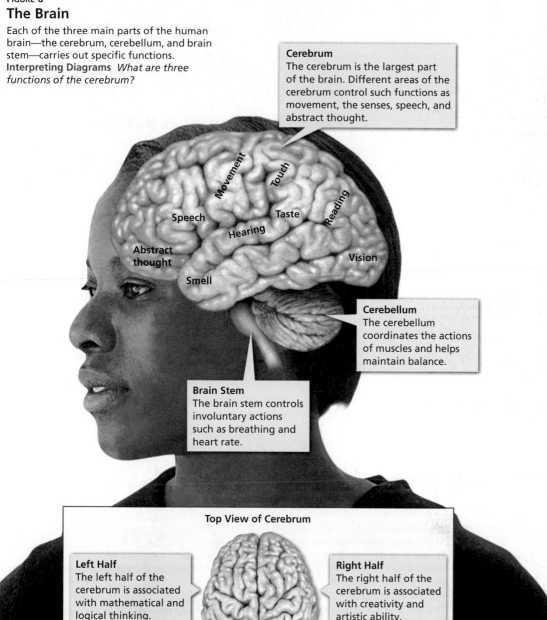

Cerebrum
The cerebrum is the largest part of the brain. Different areas of the cerebrum control such functions as movement, the senses, speech, and abstract thought.

Movement
Touch
Speech
Reading
Taste
Hearing
Abstract thought
Vision
Smell

Cerebellum
The cerebellum coordinates the actions of muscles and helps maintain balance.

Brain Stem
The brain stem controls involuntary actions such as breathing and heart rate.

Top View of Cerebrum

Left Half
The left half of the cerebrum is associated with mathematical and logical thinking.

Right Half
The right half of the cerebrum is associated with creativity and artistic ability.

◆ 635

Focus Refer students to Figure 6.

Teach Direct students to study the relative locations of the cerebrum, the brain stem, and the cerebellum in the illustration. Ask: **How are the structures of the cerebrum and cerebellum different?** *(The cerebrum is larger than the cerebellum, and the cerebrum's surface is creased by deeper folds.)* Point out that folds increase the surface area of the cerebrum, allowing it to be compacted into a small space.

Apply With eyes closed, have students point to their own spinal cord near the base of their skull and to their brain stem, cerebellum, and cerebrum as they visualize the illustration of the brain's regions.
learning modality: visual

 **Teaching Resources, Unit 3**
• Transparency LS184

 Build Inquiry   L2

Making Models of the Brain

Materials modeling clay of different colors
Time 20 minutes

Focus Remind students that different functions are controlled by different parts of the brain.

Teach Invite students to make model brains and label each part with a description of the processes it controls.

Apply Have each student think of an action or process, such as looking up something on the Internet, playing a team sport, or sitting down to a meal. Ask them to write a brief description of how the different parts of the brain work together to help the person accomplish the task. **learning modality: kinesthetic**

Monitor Progress _____ L2

Writing Have students write a job description for each part of the brain.

Answers
Figure 6 The cerebrum interprets input from the senses, controls the movement of skeletal muscles, and carries out complex mental processes.

Reading Checkpoint Involuntary actions

635

Peripheral Nervous System

Teach Key Concepts   L2

How the Peripheral Nervous System Works

Focus Point out to students the spinal nerves and related structures in Figure 7.

Teach Explain that the spinal nerves in the neck and shoulder region of the spinal cord connect with peripheral nerves of the arms and hands, while those on lower portions of the spinal cord connect with peripheral nerves of the legs. Ask: **How do impulses travel on spinal nerves?** (*Impulses travel in two directions—both to and from the spinal cord.*) **How does a spinal nerve's structure help it to function in this way?** (*It contains both sensory and motor neurons.*)

Apply Ask: **What might you assume about a person who is in an accident and cannot feel or move his or her legs afterward?** (*The person damaged a portion of the spinal cord containing spinal nerves that connect with the muscles of legs.*) **learning modality: visual**

Classifying Somatic and Autonomic Functions   L1

Materials none

Time 15 minutes

Focus Brainstorm with the class examples of voluntary and involuntary actions.

Teach Divide the class into small groups. Challenge each group to think of a task a person might do that involves voluntary and involuntary actions and then act out a skit without speaking. An example is eating a meal (students might point to their stomach after they pretend to take a bite to show involuntary action). Have the class classify each action as somatic or autonomic.

Apply Challenge students to think of a situation where all functions of the body are under autonomic control. (*While a person is unconscious or asleep*) **learning modality: kinesthetic**

The Spinal Cord Run your fingers down the center of your back to feel the bones of the vertebral column. The vertebral column surrounds and protects the spinal cord. **The spinal cord is the link between your brain and the peripheral nervous system.** The layers of connective tissue that surround and protect the brain also cover the spinal cord. In addition, like the brain, the spinal cord is further protected by a watery fluid.

Peripheral Nervous System

The second division of the nervous system is the peripheral nervous system. **The peripheral nervous system consists of a network of nerves that branch out from the central nervous system and connect it to the rest of the body. The peripheral nervous system is involved in both involuntary and voluntary actions.**

A total of 43 pairs of nerves make up the peripheral nervous system. Twelve pairs originate in the brain. The other 31 pairs—the spinal nerves—begin in the spinal cord. One nerve in each pair goes to the left side of the body, and the other goes to the right. As you can see in Figure 7, spinal nerves leave the spinal cord through spaces between the vertebrae.

How Spinal Nerves Function A spinal nerve is like a two-lane highway. Impulses travel on a spinal nerve in two directions—both to and from the central nervous system. Each spinal nerve contains axons of both sensory and motor neurons. The sensory neurons carry impulses from the body to the central nervous system. The motor neurons carry impulses in the opposite direction—from the central nervous system to the body.

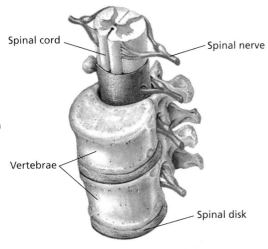

FIGURE 7
The Spinal Nerves
The spinal nerves, which connect to the spinal cord, emerge from spaces between the vertebrae. Each spinal nerve consists of both sensory and motor neurons.

Spinal cord

Spinal nerve

Vertebrae

Spinal disk

636 ◆

Differentiated Instruction

English Learners/Beginning   L1
Vocabulary: Word Analysis Help students remember the meaning of *peripheral* by explaining that *peri-* means "around," and *-phery* comes from the Greek word meaning "to carry." Ask: **How does the peripheral nervous system carry impulses around the body?** (*It connects the rest of the body to the central nervous system.*) **learning modality: verbal**

English Learners/Intermediate   L2
Vocabulary: Word Analysis Explain that *somatic* comes from a Greek word meaning "body." The prefix *auto-* comes from a Greek word meaning "self." (Compare with *automobile* and *autotroph.*) Have students speak or write sentences using *somatic* and *autonomic.* **learning modality: verbal**

FIGURE 8
Somatic and Autonomic Nervous Systems
The somatic nervous system controls voluntary actions. The autonomic nervous system controls involuntary actions. **Classifying** *Which system helps regulate the artist's heartbeat?*

Actions Controlled by the Somatic Nervous System
- Hands shape the clay.
- Foot turns the wheel.
- Mouth smiles.

Actions Controlled by the Autonomic Nervous System
- Heartbeat is regulated.
- Breathing rate is kept steady.
- Body temperature remains constant.

Somatic and Autonomic Systems The nerves of the peripheral nervous system can be divided into two groups, the somatic (soh MAT ik) and autonomic (awt uh NAHM ik) nervous systems. The nerves of the **somatic nervous system** control voluntary actions such as using a fork or tying your shoes. In contrast, nerves of the **autonomic nervous system** control involuntary actions. For example, the autonomic nervous system regulates the contractions of the smooth muscles that adjust the diameter of blood vessels.

 Reading Checkpoint What kinds of actions are controlled by the autonomic nervous system?

Reflexes

Imagine that you are watching an adventure movie. The movie is so thrilling that you don't notice a fly circling above your head. When the fly zooms right in front of your eyes, however, your eyelids immediately blink shut. You didn't decide to close your eyes. The blink, which is a **reflex,** is a response that happened automatically. **A reflex is an automatic response that occurs very rapidly and without conscious control. Reflexes help to protect the body.** If you did the Discover activity for this section, you observed another reflex.

Lab zone Try This Activity

You Blinked!

Can you make yourself *not* blink? To answer this question, try the following activity.

1. Put on safety goggles.
2. Have your partner stand across from you and gently toss ten cotton balls toward your goggles. Your partner should not give you any warning before tossing the cotton balls.
3. Count the number of times you blink and the number of times you are able to keep from blinking.

Interpreting Data Compare the two numbers. Why is blinking considered a reflex?

Lab zone Try This Activity

Skills Focus Interpreting data
Materials goggles, cotton balls
Time 15 minutes

Tips Have partners stand approximately at arm's length from one another. Limit the time for each trial to 1–2 minutes. Suggest that students vary the pattern in which they toss the cotton balls.

L2
Expected Outcome Without warning, most students will automatically blink when a cotton ball is tossed. Students will resist blinking when they concentrate. Blinking is an automatic response to prevent eye injury, but it can be controlled by the brain. **learning modality: kinesthetic**

Reflexes

Teach Key Concepts   **L2**
Reflex Action

Focus Ask: **What are some examples of reflexes?** *(Sample answers: "Jumping" when startled, blinking, jerking a hand away from a hot object)*

Teach Explain that a reflex action by the nervous system allows for a quick response because it does not require interpretation by the brain. Ask: **What happens during most reflexes?** *(Impulses involving most reflex actions travel quickly to the spinal cord, which directs the pathway of the impulse in two different directions. The impulse is sent to motor neurons, which enable a quick response, while the impulse is also sent to the brain—making the person aware of pain or what just happened.)* Clarify that awareness comes after the response has taken place.

Apply Ask: **Why is it important that the brain be notified of events requiring a reflex action?** *(Sample answers: It helps a person recognize possible danger, learn to avoid certain circumstances, or understand why an injury occurred.)* **learning modality: verbal**

Monitor Progress   **L2**
Drawing
Have students illustrate how the impulses for a voluntary action and an involuntary action travel through the nervous system. Students can save their drawings in their portfolios.

Answers
Figure 8 The autonomic nervous system

Reading Checkpoint Involuntary actions such as contractions of smooth muscle, heartbeat, breathing

Use Visuals: Figure 9 ⬜L1

Reflex Action Pathways

Focus Remind students that the brain is not part of the reflex reaction.

Teach Direct students to trace the path of the impulse in the figure from the stimulus to its response.

Apply Ask: **How does it benefit people that the spinal cord is able to send an impulse to motor neurons in response to a stimulus without involving the brain?** (*It allows people to respond more quickly to danger than if the nerve impulses traveled all the way to and from the brain.*) **learning modality: visual**

All in One Teaching Resources, Unit 3 Transparency LS185

Nervous System Injuries

Teach Key Concepts ⬜L1

Protecting Against Nervous System Injuries

Focus Ask: **What protection does your body provide the brain and spinal cord against injuries?** (*Skull and backbone*)

Teach Point out that bones cannot protect the nervous system from all injuries. Ask students to describe what happens during a concussion. (*The soft tissue of the brain bumps into the skull.*) Ask: **What can happen to the spinal cord if it is injured?** (*It can be cut or crushed.*) **What two precautions are suggested for preventing these injuries?** (*Wear a helmet during activities in which you risk bumping your head. Wear a seatbelt when traveling in a car.*)

Apply Have students brainstorm situations in sports and other physical activities in which wearing a helmet is important. (*Possible answers: Football, in-line skating, riding a bike*) **learning modality: verbal**

A Reflex Pathway As you have learned, the contraction of skeletal muscles is usually controlled by the brain. However, in some reflex actions, skeletal muscles contract with the involvement of the spinal cord only—not the brain.

Figure 9 shows the reflex action that occurs when you touch a sharp object. When your finger touches the object, sensory neurons send impulses to the spinal cord. The impulses may then pass to interneurons in the spinal cord. From there the impulses pass directly to motor neurons in your arm and hand. The muscles then contract, and your hand jerks up and away from the sharp object. By removing your hand quickly, this reflex protects you from getting badly cut.

Signaling the Brain At the same time that some nerve impulses make your arm muscles contract, other nerve impulses travel up your spinal cord to your brain. When these impulses reach your brain, your brain interprets them. You then feel a sharp pain in your finger.

It takes longer for the pain impulses to get to the brain and be interpreted than it does for the reflex action to occur. By the time you feel the pain, you have already moved your hand away.

Reading Checkpoint What is an example of a reflex?

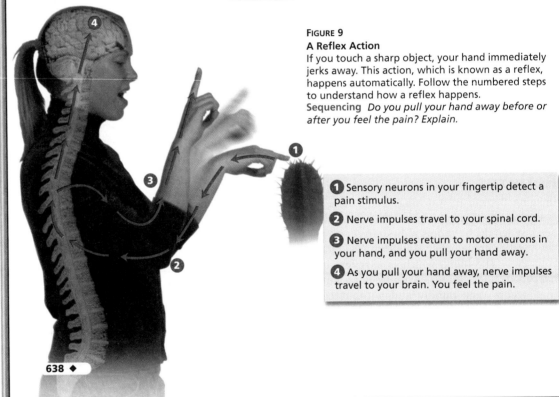

FIGURE 9
A Reflex Action
If you touch a sharp object, your hand immediately jerks away. This action, which is known as a reflex, happens automatically. Follow the numbered steps to understand how a reflex happens.
Sequencing *Do you pull your hand away before or after you feel the pain? Explain.*

1 Sensory neurons in your fingertip detect a pain stimulus.

2 Nerve impulses travel to your spinal cord.

3 Nerve impulses return to motor neurons in your hand, and you pull your hand away.

4 As you pull your hand away, nerve impulses travel to your brain. You feel the pain.

638 ◆

Nervous System Injuries

The nervous system can suffer injuries that interfere with its functioning. **Concussions and spinal cord injuries are two ways in which the central nervous system can be damaged.**

Concussions A **concussion** is a bruiselike injury of the brain. A concussion occurs when the soft tissue of the brain collides against the skull. Concussions can happen when you bump your head in a hard fall, an automobile accident, or a contact sport such as football.

With most concussions, you may have a headache for a short time, but the injured tissue heals by itself. However, with more serious concussions, you may lose consciousness, experience confusion, or feel drowsy after the injury. To decrease your chances of getting a brain injury, wear a helmet during activities in which you risk bumping your head.

Spinal Cord Injuries Spinal cord injuries occur when the spinal cord is cut or crushed. As a result, axons in the injured region are damaged, so impulses cannot pass through them. This type of injury usually results in paralysis, which is the loss of movement in some part of the body. Car crashes are the most common cause of spinal cord injuries.

 Reading Checkpoint What is paralysis?

FIGURE 10
Protecting the Nervous System
You can help protect yourself from a spinal cord injury by wearing a seatbelt when you travel in a car.

Section 2 Assessment

Target Reading Skill Building Vocabulary Use your definitions to help you answer the questions below.

Reviewing Key Concepts

1. a. Listing What two structures are part of the central nervous system?
   b. Describing Describe the functions of the three main regions of the brain.
   c. Relating Cause and Effect What symptoms might indicate that a person's cerebellum has been injured?
2. a. Identifying What are the two groups of nerves into which the peripheral nervous system is divided?
   b. Comparing and Contrasting How do the functions of the two groups of peripheral nerves differ?

3. a. Defining What is a reflex?
   b. Sequencing Trace the pathway of a reflex in the nervous system.
   c. Inferring How do reflexes help protect the body from injury?
4. a. Reviewing What is a concussion?
   b. Applying Concepts How can you reduce your risk of concussion?

Writing in Science

Comparison Paragraph Write a paragraph in which you compare the functions of the left and right halves of the cerebrum. Discuss what kinds of mental activities each half controls as well as which side of the body it controls.

Answers
Figure 9 In a reflex action, you respond before you feel pain. This quick response offers greater protection than would a response controlled by the brain.

Reading Checkpoint Sample answer: Blinking

Reading Checkpoint The loss of movement in some part of the body

Assess

Reviewing Key Concepts

1. a. The brain and the spinal cord
b. Cerebrum: interprets sensory input, controls movement, and carries out complex processes; cerebellum: coordinates muscle action and helps maintain balance; brain stem: controls involuntary, or automatic, actions. **c.** Loss of balance; poor muscle coordination
2. a. The somatic and the autonomic nervous systems **b.** The somatic nervous system controls voluntary actions. The autonomic nervous system controls involuntary actions.
3. a. An automatic response that occurs rapidly and without conscious control
b. Sample answer: When you touch a sharp object, impulses travel on sensory nerves from your finger to your spinal cord. The impulses may pass to interneurons. Nerve impulses then travel to your hand via motor neurons. **c.** Reflexes allow the body to respond quickly to danger, reducing possible damage.
4. a. A bruiselike injury of the brain
b. Wear a helmet during actions in which you risk bumping your head.

Reteach L1
Provide students with copies of a diagram of the parts of the brain without the labels, and have them label each part.

Performance Assessment L2
Skills Check Have students make concept maps that identify the parts of the central nervous system and the peripheral nervous system.

All in One Teaching Resources, Unit 3
• Section Summary: *Divisions of the Nervous System*
• Review and Reinforce: *Divisions of the Nervous System*
• Enrich: *Divisions of the Nervous System*

Lab zone Chapter Project

Keep Students on Track Check that students have chosen one or more illusions by this time. Advise them to write their plans, listing questions they will ask the subjects. Check the plans for safety. Note that illusions do not necessarily affect all people the same way. Have students try out their illusions on a partner to refine their questions before the actual experiment.

Writing in Science

Writing Mode Description
Scoring Rubric
4 Includes all the functions for both sides of the brain and types of activities; goes beyond requirements, such as providing detailed examples
3 Includes all criteria, but does not go beyond requirements
2 Includes only brief description
1 Includes inaccurate description

Science and Society

Should People Be Required to Wear Bicycle Helmets?

Key Concept
Helmets are known to help prevent brain damage from accidents while biking. The question facing communities is whether to require bicyclists to wear helmets.

Build Background Knowledge
Recalling the Effects of Concussions
Help students recall the temporary and sometimes long-term effects of brain injury. Ask: **What is a concussion?** (*A bruiselike injury to the brain*) **What are the effects of a concussion?** (*Headache for a short time; serious concussion may cause you to black out, experience confusion, or feel drowsy.*)

Introduce the Debate
Remind students that wearing a helmet can help decrease the chances of concussion. Also make students aware that many communities have laws that require bicyclists to wear helmets.

Facilitate the Debate
- Divide students into four groups: (1) a group to represent state lawmakers, (2) a group to argue for the passage of a bicycle helmet law, (3) a group to argue against a bicycle helmet law, but for an education program paid for with taxes, and (4) a group to argue against any government regulation or tax-supported education programs.
- Tell the first group to work out rules and an agenda for a committee hearing on a proposed helmet law. Students in each of the other groups can work together to prepare a presentation to the committee during the hearing. Then hold the hearing, using the rules and agenda worked out by the committee members. Encourage students to act the way they think citizens would act in a real public hearing of this kind.

Should People Be Required to Wear Bicycle Helmets?

Bicycling is an enjoyable activity. Unfortunately, many bicyclists are injured while riding. Each year, more than 500,000 people in the United States are treated in hospitals for bicycling injuries. Many of those people suffer head injuries. Head injuries can affect everything your brain does—thinking, remembering, seeing, and being able to move.

Depending on the age group and geographic location, helmet use ranges from less than 10 percent to about 80 percent of bicyclists. What is the best way to get bicyclists to protect themselves from head injury?

The Issues

Should Laws Require the Use of Bicycle Helmets?
Experts estimate that bicycle helmets could reduce the risk of bicycle-related head injuries by as much as 85 percent. Today, about 19 states have passed laws requiring bicycle riders to wear helmets. Most of these statewide laws, however, apply only to children.

Some supporters of helmet laws want to see the laws extended to all riders. They claim that laws are the most effective way to increase helmet use.

Background

Facts and Figures Even if people do wear bicycle helmets, they may not be protected from head injury if they do not wear the helmets properly. Therefore, educational programs that teach people about the advantages of helmets often emphasize how to wear a helmet properly. The front edge of the helmet should be positioned 2 to 3 cm above the rider's eyebrows, and the helmet and the chin strap should be snug, but not uncomfortable. The helmet should be straight and not tilted forward or backward on the head. Communities can also help reduce bicycle head injuries by creating safer environments for bike riders, such as setting aside special lanes on roads or making biking trails through parks.

What Are the Drawbacks of Helmet Laws?

Opponents of helmet laws believe it is up to the individual to decide whether or not to wear a helmet. They say it is not the role of government to stop people from taking risks. They argue that, rather than making people pay fines if they don't wear bicycle helmets, governments should educate people about the benefits of helmets. Car drivers should also be educated about safe driving procedures near bicycles.

Are There Alternatives to Helmet Laws?

Instead of laws requiring people to wear helmets, some communities and organizations have set up educational programs that teach about the advantages of helmets. Effective programs teach about the dangers of head injuries and the protection that helmets provide. Effective education programs, though, can be expensive. They also need to reach a wide audience, including children, teens, and adults.

You Decide

1. Identify the Problem
In your own words, explain the issues concerning laws requiring people to wear bicycle helmets.

2. Analyze the Options
List two different plans for increasing helmet use by bicycle riders. List at least one advantage and one drawback of each plan.

3. Find a Solution
You are a member of the city government hoping to increase helmet use. Write a speech outlining your position for either a helmet law or an alternative plan. Support your position.

For: More on bicycle helmets
Visit: PHSchool.com
Web Code: ceh-4060

You Decide

1. Sample answer: Helmets protect against injury. Passing laws and having education programs can be expensive. People have a right to make their own decisions regarding helmet use.

2. Sample answer: Plan 1. Fine people for not wearing helmets; advantage—may cause more people to wear helmets; drawback—may cause public resentment. Plan 2. Educate people about helmet use; advantage—people will "buy in" on the issue; drawback—people may not wear helmets unless educated, and education is expensive.

3. Sample answer: I propose passage of a helmet law for people of all ages. Many states have laws for children 16 and under, but it is important to protect adults—the parents of the children—too. Helmets are a small price to pay for an 88 percent decrease in bike-related head injuries.

For: More on bicycle helmets
Visit: PHSchool.com
Web Code: ceh-4060

Students can research this issue online.

Extend

Challenge students to find out whether your state or local government has passed a helmet law and, if so, whether it applies only to children or to bicycle riders of all ages. Suggest that students contact a member of a local law enforcement agency to ask what the penalties are for breaking such a law.

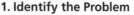

Objectives

After this lesson, students will be able to

19.3.1 Describe how your eyes enable you to see.

19.3.2 Describe how you hear and maintain your sense of balance.

19.3.3 Explain how your senses of smell and taste work together.

19.3.4 Explain how your skin is related to your sense of touch.

Target Reading Skill

Outlining Explain that using an outline format helps students organize information by main topic, subtopic, and details.

Answers
The Senses
I. Vision
 A. How Light Enters Your Eye
 B. How Light Is Focused
 C. How You See an Image
 D. Correcting Nearsightedness
 E. Correcting Farsightedness
II. Hearing and Balance
 A. How Sound Is Produced
 B. The Outer Ear
 C. The Middle Ear
 D. The Inner Ear
 E. The Inner Ear and Balance
III. Smell and Taste
IV. Touch

All in One Teaching Resources, Unit 3

• Transparency LS186

Preteach

Build Background Knowledge   L2

Identifying the Senses

Challenge students to name the senses, and then list them on the board. Have the class brainstorm a list of items or activities in the classroom that they perceive through each sense.

Reading Preview

Key Concepts
• How do your eyes enable you to see?
• How do you hear and maintain your sense of balance?
• How do your senses of smell and taste work together?
• How is your skin related to your sense of touch?

Key Terms
• cornea • pupil • iris • lens
• retina • nearsightedness
• farsightedness • eardrum
• cochlea • semicircular canal

Target Reading Skill

Outlining As you read, make an outline about the senses. Use the red headings for the main ideas and the blue headings for the supporting ideas.

The Senses
I. Vision
A. How light enters your eye
B.
C.

Lab zone Discover Activity

What's in the Bag?

1. Your teacher will give you a paper bag that contains several objects. Your challenge is to use only your sense of touch to identify each object. You will not look inside the bag.

2. Put your hand in the bag and carefully touch each object. Observe the shape of each object. Note whether its surface is rough or smooth. Also note other characteristics, such as its size, what it seems to be made of, and whether it can be bent.

3. After you have finished touching each object, write your observations on a sheet of paper. Then, write your inference about what each object is.

Think It Over
Observing What could you determine about each object without looking at it? What could you not determine?

You waited in line to get on the ride, and now it's about to begin. You grip the wheel as the bumper cars jerk into motion. The next thing you know, you are zipping around crazily and bumping into cars driven by your friends.

You can thrill to the motion of amusement park rides because of your senses. The sense organs pick up information about your environment, change the information into nerve impulses, and send the impulses to your brain. Your brain then interprets the information. Your senses and brain working together enable you to respond to things in your environment, such as the other bumper cars around you.

Enjoy the ride, and thank your senses!

Lab zone Discover Activity

Skills Focus Observing   L1

Materials opaque paper bags; small objects, such as erasers, pens, paper clips, sponges, cotton balls, marbles, plastic spoons, bottle caps, coins, buttons

Time 20 minutes

Tips Include objects of different sizes, shapes, and textures. Be certain to use objects that are not sharp. Encourage

students to take notes about the objects they feel and record what objects they believe are in the bag.

Expected Outcome Students will be able to identify most of the objects using their sense of touch.

Think It Over Students could determine size, shape, texture, and weight. They could not determine color, scent, or taste.

Pupil in Bright Light

Pupil in Dim Light

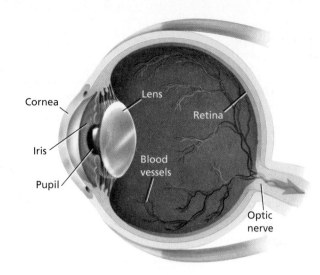

Cornea

Lens

Retina

Iris

Blood vessels

Pupil

Optic nerve

Vision

Your eyes are the sense organs that enable you to see the objects in your environment. They let you see this textbook in front of you, the window across the room, and the world outside the window. **Your eyes respond to the stimulus of light. They convert that stimulus into impulses that your brain interprets, enabling you to see.**

How Light Enters Your Eye When rays of light strike the eye, they pass through the structures shown in Figure 11. First, the light strikes the **cornea** (KAWR nee uh), the clear tissue that covers the front of the eye. The light then passes through a fluid-filled chamber behind the cornea and reaches the pupil. The **pupil** is the opening through which light enters the eye.

You may have noticed that people's pupils change size when they go from a dark room into bright sunshine. In bright light, the pupil becomes smaller. In dim light, the pupil becomes larger. The size of the pupil is adjusted by muscles in the iris. The **iris** is a circular structure that surrounds the pupil and regulates the amount of light entering the eye. The iris also gives the eye its color. If you have brown eyes, it is actually your irises that are brown.

How Light Is Focused Light that passes through the pupil strikes the lens. The **lens** is a flexible structure that focuses light. The lens of your eye functions something like the lens of a camera, which focuses light on photographic film. Because of the way in which the lens of the eye bends the light rays, the image it produces is upside down and reversed. Muscles that attach to the lens adjust its shape, producing an image that is in focus.

FIGURE 11

The Eye

The eye is a complex organ that allows you to sense light. The pupil is the opening through which light enters the eye. In bright light, the pupil becomes smaller. In dim light, the pupil enlarges and allows more light to enter the eye.

Interpreting Diagrams What structure adjusts the size of the pupil?

DISCOVERY
CHANNEL
SCHOOL

The Nervous System

Video Preview
▶ Video Field Trip
Video Assessment

Chapter 19 ◆ 643

Vision

Teach Key Concepts L2
Structure and Function of the Eyes

Focus Refer students to Figure 11.

Teach Explain that the eye functions similarly to a camera lens. Discuss how the lens bends light rays to focus them on film, and the aperture of a camera controls the amount of light. Ask: **Which parts of the eye correspond to the parts of a camera?** *(Lens of eye—camera lens; pupil—aperture; retina—photographic film)* **How is the shape of the lens adjusted?** *(Muscles that attach to the lens)*

Apply Explain that when taking a picture in bright light, a photographer must make the aperture small to limit the amount of light that enters the camera. Ask: **What does the pupil of the eye do in bright light?** *(It becomes smaller.)* **learning modality: visual**

All in One Teaching Resources, Unit 3
• Transparency LS187

Independent Practice L2

All in One Teaching Resources, Unit 3
• Guided Reading and Study Worksheet: *The Senses*

⊙ **Student Edition on Audio CD**

DISCOVERY
CHANNEL
SCHOOL
Video Field Trip

The Nervous System

Show the Video Field Trip to review chapter content and as a prompt for the writing assignment. Discussion question: **How does the iris control the amount of light that enters the eye?** *(The muscles of the iris contract to reduce the amount of light that enters the eye.)*

Monitor Progress _____ L2

Writing Have students list the structures that make up the eye and identify the function of each.

Answer

Figure 11 The iris

Observing the Eye's Pupil

Materials mirror

Time 5 minutes

Focus Remind students that the iris is the colored part of the eye.

Teach Have students observe their own eyes in the mirror and compare the size of their pupils in bright light, dim light, and extremely dim light. Ask: **What happens to your pupils as the light darkens?** *(Pupils widen.)* **What happens to the irises?** *(You can see less of the color when the pupil widens.)*

Apply Ask: **What function is served when the pupil gets wider in dim light?** *(It allows more light to enter the eye so you can see better.)* **learning modality: kinesthetic**

Modeling Lens Function

Materials candle in holder, double-convex lens, white paper, optics bench (optional)

Time 15 minutes

Focus Remind students that receptors in the retina convert light energy into nerve impulses.

Teach In a dark room, place the candle in the holder on a table, and light the candle. **CAUTION:** *Use safety precautions with open flames. Do not allow students to light the candle or get too close to the flame.* Hold a converging or double-convex lens between the candle and a piece of white paper. Adjust the lens so that it reflects an image of the candle onto the paper. Ask: **What happens to the image of the candle?** *(It appears upside down.)* Extinguish the candle.

Apply Ask: **Where in the eye is the upside-down image focused?** *(On the retina)* **learning modality: visual**

FIGURE 12

How You See

Light coming from an object enters your eye and is focused by the lens. The light produces an upside-down image on your retina. Receptors in your retina then send impulses to your cerebrum, which turns the image right-side up. **Comparing and Contrasting** *Which receptors work best in dim light?*

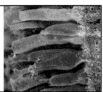

Rods and Cones Receptors in the retina include rods (shown in green) and cones (shown in blue).

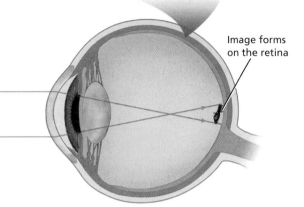

Object

Image forms on the retina

How You See an Image After passing through the lens, the focused light rays pass through a transparent, jellylike fluid. Then the light rays strike the **retina** (RET 'n uh), the layer of receptor cells that lines the back of the eye. The retina contains about 130 million receptor cells that respond to light. There are two types of receptors: rods and cones. Rod cells work best in dim light and enable you to see black, white, and shades of gray. In contrast, cone cells work best in bright light and enable you to see colors. This difference between rods and cones explains why you see colors best in bright light, but you see only shadowy gray images in dim light.

When light strikes the rods and cones, nerve impulses travel to the cerebrum through the optic nerves. One optic nerve comes from the left eye and the other one comes from the right eye. In the cerebrum, two things happen. The brain turns the reversed image right-side up, and it also combines the images from each eye to produce a single image.

Correcting Nearsightedness A lens—whether it is in your eye or in eyeglasses—is a curved, transparent object that bends light rays as they pass through it. If the lens of the eye does not focus light properly on the retina, vision problems result. The lenses in eyeglasses can help correct vision problems.

Try This Activity

Working Together

Discover how your two eyes work together.

1. With your arms fully extended, hold a drinking straw in one hand and a pipe cleaner in the other.
2. With both eyes open, try to insert the pipe cleaner into the straw.
3. Now close your right eye. Try to insert the pipe cleaner into the straw.
4. Repeat Step 3 with your left eye closed.

Inferring How does closing one eye affect your ability to judge distances?

644 ◆

Try This Activity

Skills Focus Inferring

Materials drinking straw, pipe cleaner

Time 15 minutes

Tips Students may find the task easier if the open eye is their dominant eye.

Expected Outcome Closing one eye impairs the ability to judge distances.

Extend Challenge students to design a test that shows how closing one eye reduces the total field of vision. *(Sample test: Cover one eye and identify objects on the edges of the field of vision. Compare with both eyes open.)* **learning modality: kinesthetic**

FIGURE 13

Correcting Vision Problems

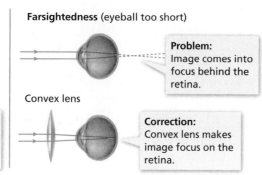

Nearsightedness (eyeball too long)

Concave lens

Problem:
Image comes into focus in front of the retina.

Correction:
Concave lens makes image focus on the retina.

Farsightedness (eyeball too short)

Convex lens

Problem:
Image comes into focus behind the retina.

Correction:
Convex lens makes image focus on the retina.

People with **nearsightedness** can see nearby objects clearly. However, they have trouble seeing objects far away. Nearsightedness results when the eyeball is too long. Because of the extra length that light must travel to reach the retina, distant objects do not focus sharply on the retina. Instead, the lens of the eye makes the image come into focus at a point in front of the retina, as shown in Figure 13.

To correct nearsightedness, eyeglasses with concave lenses are worn. A concave lens is thicker at the edges than it is in the center. When light rays pass through a concave lens, they are bent away from the center of the lens. The concave lenses in glasses make light rays spread out before they reach the lens of the eye. After the rays pass through the lens of the eye, they focus on the retina rather than in front of it.

Correcting Farsightedness People with **farsightedness** can see distant objects clearly. Nearby objects, however, look blurry. The eyeballs of people with farsightedness are too short. Because of this, the lens of the eye bends light from nearby objects so that the image does not focus properly on the retina. If light could pass through the retina, the image would come into sharp focus at a point behind the retina, as shown in Figure 13.

Convex lenses are used to help correct farsightedness. A convex lens is thicker in the middle than at the edges. The convex lens makes the light rays bend toward each other before they reach the eye. Then the lens of the eye bends the rays even more. This bending makes the image focus exactly on the retina.

 Reading Checkpoint What type of lens corrects nearsightedness?

Differentiated Instruction

Special Needs L1
Comparing Lenses Allow students to feel a convex lens and a concave lens. Ask: **Which lens is thicker in the middle and thinner at the edges?** (*The convex lens*) Ask them to describe the shape of a concave lens. (*Thinner in the middle; thicker on the edges*) **learning modality: kinesthetic**

Gifted and Talented L3
Interpreting Visual Acuity Have students find out what it means to have 20/20, 20/60, and 20/10 vision. (*A person with 20/20 vision can see letters at 20 feet, which is normal. A person with 20/60 vision can see letters at 20 feet that a person with normal vision can see at 60 feet. A person with 20/10 vision can see letters at twice the distance of a person with 20/20 vision.*) **learning modality: logical/mathematical**

Use Visuals: Figure 13 L3
Correcting Vision Problems

Focus Ask students to volunteer the kinds of vision problems that glasses or contact lenses they may be wearing are correcting.

Teach Direct students to trace the path of light rays as they move through the nearsighted eye in the figure, then through the concave lens. Ask: **What does the concave lens do to the image? How does this correct the vision?** (*The concave lens bends the light rays outward so they are spread apart when they reach the lens of the eye. Then the lens of the eye can correctly focus the rays.*) Have students repeat the process for the convex lens. (*The convex lens bends the light rays inward so they are closer together when they reach the lens of the eye.*)

Apply Some students may have volunteered astigmatism as the reason for wearing corrective lenses. Explain that astigmatism is distorted vision caused when the curvature of the cornea or the lens is uneven. Light rays entering the eye cannot be focused at a single point on the retina. **learning modality: visual**

Monitor Progress L2

Skills Check Tell students that people who are farsighted sometimes wear reading glasses to bring nearby objects into focus. Ask students what kind of lens is found in reading glasses. (*Convex*)

Answers
Figure 12 Rods

 **Reading Checkpoint** Concave

645

Hearing and Balance

Teach Key Concepts `L2`

How You Hear

Focus Refer students to Figure 14.

Teach Explain that the brain converts sound waves to nerve impulses just as it converts light waves to nerve impulses. Ask: **What causes sound waves?** (*Vibrations*) Direct students to trace the path of a sound wave as it passes from the outer ear to the middle ear. Ask: **What happens when the sound waves reach the eardrum?** (*Sound waves make the eardrum vibrate, which in turn passes the vibrations to the bones of the middle ear.*) Finally, ask students to locate where the auditory nerve connects to the inner ear. Point out the cochlea and ask: **What happens to vibrations in this structure?** (*The vibrations stimulate receptor cells to send impulses to the brain through the auditory nerve.*)

Apply Tell students that a person's recorded voice and speaking voice often sound different to the person. The sound of one's voice when speaking is altered because some of the sound waves pass directly to the inner ear through the bones in the head. **learning modality: visual**

All in One Teaching Resources, Unit 3

• Transparency LS188

Math Analyzing Data

Math Skill Making and interpreting graphs

Focus Explain that a bar graph is used to display sound levels because each bar can represent a different type of sound.

Teach Tell students that the values that fall between the lines of a graph can be approximated by determining the increments between lines and then estimating the percentage of that interval that the value takes up.

Answers
1. decibels, or sound level; type of sound
2. 20 dB; 60 dB; 120 dB
3. 20 dB vs. 60 dB, which is 10,000 times more intense
4. rock concert, jet plane taking off

Hearing and Balance

What wakes you up in the morning? Maybe an alarm clock buzzes, or perhaps your parent calls you. On a summer morning, you might hear birds singing. Whatever wakes you up, there's a good chance that it's a sound of some sort. **Your ears are the sense organs that respond to the stimulus of sound. The ears convert the sound to nerve impulses that your brain interprets.** So when you hear an alarm clock or another morning sound, your brain tells you that it's time to wake up.

How Sound Is Produced Sound is produced by vibrations. The material that is vibrating, or moving rapidly back and forth, may be almost anything—a guitar string, an insect's wings, or a stereo speaker.

The vibrations move outward from the source of the sound, something like ripples moving out from a stone dropped in water. The vibrations cause particles, such as the gas molecules that make up air, to vibrate. In this way, sound is carried. When you hear a friend's voice, for example, sound has traveled from your friend's larynx to your ears. In addition to being able to travel through gases such as those in air, sound waves can also travel through liquids, such as water, and solids, such as wood.

Math Analyzing Data

Sound Intensity

Sound intensity, or loudness, is measured in units called decibels. The threshold of hearing for the human ear is 0 decibels. For every 10-decibel increase, the sound intensity increases ten times. Thus, a 20-decibel sound is ten times more intense than a 10-decibel sound, not twice as intense. A 30-decibel sound is 100 times more intense than a 10-decibel sound. Sound levels for several sound sources are shown in the bar graph.

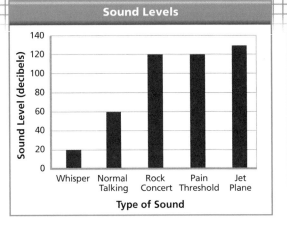

1. **Reading Graphs** What unit of measure is represented on the *y*-axis? What is represented on the *x*-axis?

2. **Interpreting Data** What is the sound intensity in decibels of a whisper? Normal talking? A rock concert?

3. **Calculating** How much more intense is normal talking than a whisper? Explain.

4. **Predicting** Based on the graph, what types of sound could be painful if you were exposed to them?

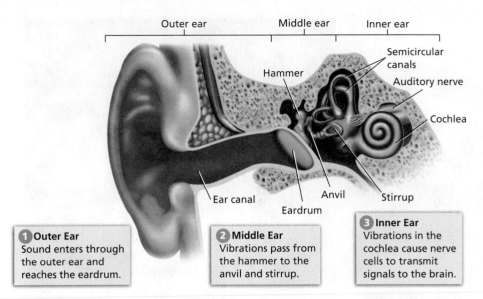

Outer ear | Middle ear | Inner ear

Semicircular canals

Auditory nerve

Hammer

Cochlea

Ear canal

Eardrum

Anvil

Stirrup

1 Outer Ear Sound enters through the outer ear and reaches the eardrum.

2 Middle Ear Vibrations pass from the hammer to the anvil and stirrup.

3 Inner Ear Vibrations in the cochlea cause nerve cells to transmit signals to the brain.

FIGURE 14
The Ear
Sound waves enter the outer ear and make structures in the middle ear vibrate. When the vibrations reach the inner ear, nerve impulses travel to the cerebrum through the auditory nerve. **Predicting** *What would happen if the bones of the middle ear were stuck together and could not move?*

The Outer Ear The ear is structured to receive sound vibrations. The three regions of the ear—the outer ear, middle ear, and inner ear—are shown in Figure 14. The visible part of the outer ear is shaped like a funnel. This funnel-like shape enables the outer ear to gather sound waves. The sound vibrations then travel down the ear canal, which is also part of the outer ear.

The Middle Ear At the end of the ear canal, sound vibrations reach the eardrum. The **eardrum,** which separates the outer ear from the middle ear, is a membrane that vibrates when sound strikes it. Your eardrum vibrates in much the same way that a drum vibrates when it is struck. Vibrations from the eardrum pass to the middle ear, which contains the three smallest bones in the body—the hammer, anvil, and stirrup. These bones are named for their shapes. The vibrating eardrum makes the hammer vibrate. The hammer passes the vibrations to the anvil, and the anvil passes them to the stirrup.

The Inner Ear The stirrup vibrates against a thin membrane that covers the opening of the inner ear. The membrane channels the vibrations into the fluid in the cochlea. The **cochlea** (KAHK le uh) is a snail-shaped tube that is lined with receptor cells that respond to sound. When the fluid in the cochlea vibrates, it stimulates these receptors. Sensory neurons then send nerve impulses to the cerebrum through the auditory nerve. These impulses are interpreted as sounds that you hear.

For: Links on the senses
Visit: www.SciLinks.org
Web Code: scn-0463

Modeling How Motion Affects the Semicircular Canals

Materials clear plastic jar with lid, water

Time 5 minutes

Focus Remind students that fluid in the semicircular canals moves when a person's head moves.

Teach Have pairs of students fill a plastic jar halfway with water and seal it tightly. **CAUTION:** *Do not use glass containers. Make sure the outside of the jar is completely dry.* In an open area, have one partner hold the jar and spin quickly for about 10 seconds. The observing student notes the movement of the liquid. Have students switch roles.

Apply Ask: **How does this model explain what happens inside the semicircular canals?** (*Like the water, the fluid in the semicircular canals is sloshed around when you move your head.*) **learning modality: kinesthetic**

Smell and Taste

Teach Key Concepts

How Smell and Taste Work Together

Focus Ask a student volunteer to hold his or her nose while chewing something such as a jelly bean and describe the taste.

Teach Explain that taste and smell work closely together, and both work by first detecting chemicals in air or in food. Ask: **What effect do the chemicals have in the nose and mouth?** (*The chemicals trigger responses in the receptors in the nose and mouth.*) **Where are nerve impulses interpreted as smells or tastes?** (*In the brain*)

Apply Explain that while about 75–80 percent of what you taste is actually due to smell, taste buds have been important in human survival. Saltiness cannot be smelled, and salt is needed by the body. Likewise, very bitter foods helped our ancestors avoid poisons and seek out sweet foods that contained sugar, which is needed as a source of energy by the body. **learning modality: verbal**

Semicircular canals

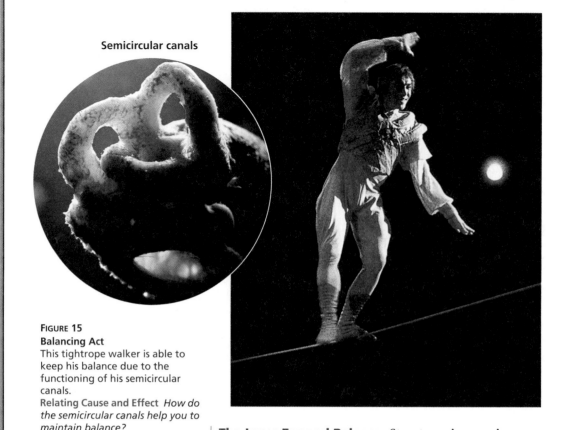

FIGURE 15
Balancing Act
This tightrope walker is able to keep his balance due to the functioning of his semicircular canals.
Relating Cause and Effect *How do the semicircular canals help you to maintain balance?*

The Inner Ear and Balance Structures in your inner ear control your sense of balance. Above the cochlea in your inner ear are the **semicircular canals,** which are the structures in the ear that are responsible for your sense of balance. You can see how these structures got their name if you look at Figure 15. These canals, as well as the two tiny sacs located behind them, are full of fluid. The canals and sacs are also lined with tiny cells that have hairlike extensions.

When your head moves, the fluid in the semicircular canals is set in motion. The moving fluid makes the cells' hairlike extensions bend. This bending produces nerve impulses in sensory neurons. The impulses travel to the cerebellum. The cerebellum then analyzes the impulses to determine the way your head is moving and the position of your body. If the cerebellum senses that you are losing your balance, it sends impulses to muscles that help you restore your balance.

 Reading Checkpoint Where in the ear are the semicircular canals located?

Smell and Taste

You walk into the house and smell the aroma of freshly baked cookies. You bite into one and taste its rich chocolate flavor. When you smelled the cookies, receptors in your nose reacted to chemicals carried by the air from the cookies to your nose. When you took a bite of a cookie, taste buds on your tongue responded to chemicals in the food. These food chemicals were dissolved in saliva, which came in contact with your taste buds.

The senses of smell and taste work closely together. Both depend on chemicals in food or in the air. The chemicals trigger responses in receptors in the nose and mouth. Nerve impulses then travel to the brain, where they are interpreted as smells or tastes.

The nose can distinguish at least 50 basic odors. In contrast, there are only five main taste sensations—sweet, sour, salty, bitter, and a meatlike taste called *umami*. When you eat, however, you experience a much wider variety of tastes. The flavor of food is influenced by both smell and taste. When you have a cold, foods may not taste as good as they usually do. That is because a stuffy nose decreases your ability to smell food.

 Reading Checkpoint What basic tastes can the tongue detect?

Lab zone Skills **Activity**

Designing Experiments

Can people tell one food from another if they can taste the foods but not smell them? Design an experiment to find out. Use these foods: a peeled pear, a peeled apple, and a peeled raw potato. Be sure to control all variables except the one you are testing. Write your hypothesis and a description of your procedure. Obtain your teacher's approval before carrying out your experiment.

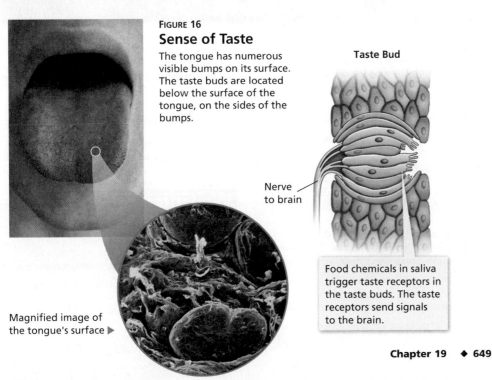

FIGURE 16
Sense of Taste
The tongue has numerous visible bumps on its surface. The taste buds are located below the surface of the tongue, on the sides of the bumps.

Taste Bud

Nerve to brain

Food chemicals in saliva trigger taste receptors in the taste buds. The taste receptors send signals to the brain.

Magnified image of the tongue's surface ▶

Chapter 19 ◆ 649

Touch

Teach Key Concepts — **L1**
How Your Skin Detects Touch

Focus Remind students that the sense of touch allows for enjoying things in the environment, such as stroking a dog's soft fur, or protecting you from injury, such as detecting a very hot drink when you put it to your lips.

Teach Explain that touch is different from the other senses in that receptors that sense touch are not located in a specific place. Ask: **What kinds of receptors are in the skin?** *(Receptors that respond to light pressure, heavy pressure, pain, and temperature change)*

Apply Tell students that the greatest density of touch receptors is found on the fingers, toes, and face. Ask: **What might be the advantage to this?** *(Sample answers: They are more exposed and are more susceptible to injury. Hands perform many tasks and need to be able to distinguish different pressures and react to possible injury.)* **learning modality: verbal**

Address Misconceptions — **L1**
Sensing Touch With Fingers Only

Focus Many students associate the sense of touch with their ability to feel things only with their fingers.

Teach Explain that all of the regions of the skin are sensitive to touch. Remind students that the sense of touch includes pressure, temperature, and pain.

Apply Have students experience receptors in the skin by using the eraser end of a pencil to gently touch the skin on their arms and other exposed areas. **learning modality: verbal**

Monitor Progress — **L2**

Skills Check Have students describe the sequence of events that must occur to keep one's balance.

Answers
Figure 15 Fluid in the canals moves when you move, bending hairlike cells, which send impulses to the cerebellum indicating whether you are losing balance.

 Reading Checkpoint In the inner ear

 Reading Checkpoint Sweet, sour, salty, bitter, and a meatlike taste called *umami*

Lab zone Skills **Activity**

Skills Focus Designing experiments **L3**
Materials peeled pear, apple, and raw potato
Time 15 minutes
Tips Make sure students wash their hands before and after handling the food.

Expected Outcome Sample experiment: Blindfolded students taste and identify small pieces of food, and then repeat the procedure holding their noses closed.

Extend Have students test whether a person can identify the food based on the food's scent without tasting it. **learning modality: kinesthetic**

Reviewing Key Concepts

1. a. Cornea, iris, pupil, lens, fluid-filled chamber, retina **b.** Light from an object is focused as it passes through the lens of the eye; then it travels to the retina where it forms an upside-down image. The light strikes the rods and cones, and nerve impulses travel to the brain. The brain reverses the image from each eye and combines them into a single image.
c. Farsightedness; with a convex lens.
2. a. The outer ear, middle ear, and inner ear **b.** The eardrum, a thin membrane that separates the outer ear from the middle ear, vibrates, which causes fluid in the cochlea to vibrate. The cochlea is in the inner ear. The vibrating fluid in the cochlea stimulates receptor cells that send nerve impulses to the brain. **c.** The semicircular canals help maintain balance, so an infection could interfere with their operation, causing a person to lose balance.
3. a. Taste and smell **b.** Similarity—both depend on chemicals. Nerve impulses from both senses then travel to the brain. Differences—Taste responds to chemicals in saliva, while smell responds to chemicals in air. There are about 50 basic odors, but only 5 basic tastes.
4. a. Receptors that sense light touch, heavy pressure, pain, and temperature change **b.** Temperature and pain receptors sense the heat and pain, and can help trigger reflex actions.

Reteach L1
Have students list the senses and identify the types of receptors in each associated sense organ.

Performance Assessment L2
Writing Have students write a brief explanation of how each of the senses sends information to the brain when students eat a sandwich.

All in One Teaching Resources, Unit 3
- Section Summary: *The Senses*
- Review and Reinforce: *The Senses*
- Enrich: *The Senses*

FIGURE 17
Reading by Touch
People who are blind use their sense of touch to read. To do this, they run their fingers over words written in Braille. Braille uses raised dots to represent letters and numbers. Here, a teacher shows a blind child how to read Braille.

Touch

Unlike vision, hearing, balance, smell, and taste, the sense of touch is not found in one specific place. Instead, the sense of touch is found in all areas of your skin. Your skin is your largest sense organ! **Your skin contains different kinds of touch receptors that respond to a number of stimuli.** Some of these receptors respond to light touch and others to heavy pressure. Still other receptors pick up sensations of pain and temperature change.

The receptors that respond to light touch are in the upper part of the dermis. They tell you when something brushes against your skin. These receptors also let you feel the textures of objects, such as smooth glass and rough sandpaper. Receptors deeper in the dermis pick up the feeling of pressure. Press down hard on the top of your desk, for example, and you will feel pressure in your fingertips.

The dermis also contains receptors that respond to temperature and pain. Pain is unpleasant, but it can be one of the body's most important feelings because it alerts the body to possible danger. Have you ever stepped into a bathtub of very hot water and then immediately pulled your foot out? If so, you can appreciate how pain can trigger an important response in your body.

Section 3 Assessment

Target Reading Skill Outlining Use the information in your outline about the senses to help you answer the questions below.

Reviewing Key Concepts
1. a. Listing What are the parts of the eye?
  b. Sequencing Describe the process by which the eye produces an image. Begin at the point at which light is focused by the lens.
  c. Inferring If nearby objects seem blurry, what type of vision problem might you have? How can it be corrected?
2. a. Identifying What are the three regions of the ear?
  b. Describing Describe the location and function of the eardrum and the cochlea.
  c. Relating Cause and Effect Why may an infection of the inner ear cause you to lose your balance?

3. a. Reviewing What two senses work together to influence the flavor of food?
  b. Comparing and Contrasting How are the senses of taste and smell similar? How are they different?
4. a. Identifying What kinds of touch receptors are found in the skin?
  b. Applying Concepts What happens in the dermis when you accidentally touch a hot stove?

Writing in Science

Cause-and-Effect Paragraph Write a description of how you feel after an amusement park ride. Explain how your feeling is related to the structure and function of the semicircular canals. Be sure to include a topic sentence and three to four supporting points.

Lab zone Chapter Project

Keep Students on Track Check that students have submitted their plans for their experiment. Advise them to prepare all the materials for the fair and have a data table ready to record responses. Explain that people should be tested in such a way that they cannot see or hear one another's responses. An adequate number of individuals should be tested.

Writing in Science

Writing Mode Description
Scoring Rubric
4 Includes complete, accurate description; uses vivid, detailed description
3 Includes all criteria, but account is uninteresting
2 Includes only brief description of the effects on the semicircular canals
1 Includes inaccurate description or lacks supporting points

4 Alcohol and Other Drugs

Reading Preview

Key Concepts
- What are the immediate and long-term effects of drug abuse?
- What are some commonly abused drugs and how does each affect the body?
- How does alcohol abuse harm the body?

Key Terms
- drug • drug abuse
- tolerance • addiction
- withdrawal • depressant
- stimulant • anabolic steroid
- alcoholism

Target Reading Skill
Relating Cause and Effect As you read, identify commonly abused drugs and how they affect the body. Write the information in a graphic organizer like the one below.

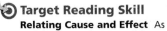

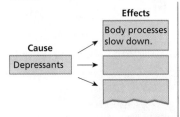

Lab zone Discover **Activity**

How Can You Best Say No?

1. In this activity, you will use marbles to represent drugs. Your teacher will divide the class into groups of three students. In each group, your teacher will appoint two students to try to convince the other person to take the "drugs."

2. Depending on your role, you should think of arguments to get the person to accept the marbles or arguments against accepting them. After everyone has had a chance to think of arguments, begin the discussion.

3. After a while, students in each group should exchange roles.

Think It Over
Inferring What role does peer pressure play in whether or not a person decides to abuse drugs?

Drugs! You probably hear and see that word in a lot of places. Drugstores sell drugs to relieve headaches, soothe upset stomachs, and stop coughs. Radio and television programs and magazine articles explore drug-related problems. Your school probably has a program to educate students about drugs. When people talk about drugs, what do they mean? To a scientist, a **drug** is any chemical taken into the body that causes changes in a person's body or behavior. Many drugs affect the functioning of the central nervous system.

Drug Abuse

The deliberate misuse of drugs for purposes other than medical ones is called **drug abuse.** Even medicines can be abused drugs if they are used in a way for which they were not intended. Many abused drugs, however, such as cocaine and heroin, are illegal under any circumstances. The use of these drugs is against the law because their effects on the body are almost always dangerous.

Chapter 19 ◆ **651**

Lab zone Discover **Activity**

Skills Focus Inferring

Materials Marbles

Time 15 minutes

Tips After the activity, have students try to identify different kinds of arguments, for example, suggesting that drug use enhances popularity or insisting that drugs are harmless.

L1 **Think It Over** If peers encourage someone to do something, such as use drugs, it may be difficult not to agree with them. Therefore, peer pressure can make it hard for people to say no to drugs.

Objectives
After this lesson, students will be able to
19.4.1 Identify the immediate and long-term effects of drug abuse.
19.4.2 Describe some commonly abused drugs and how each affects the body.
19.4.3 Explain how alcohol abuse harms the body.

Target Reading Skill

Relating Cause and Effect Explain that the cause is the reason for what happens. The effect is what happens because of the cause. Relating cause and effect helps students relate the reason for what happens to what happens as a result.

Answer
Possible effects: Body processes slow down; muscle relaxation; drowsiness; slower response time

All in One Teaching Resources, Unit 3
- Transparency LS189

Preteach

Build Background Knowledge **L2**
Proper Use of Medicines
Ask: **If you get sick, is it okay to take someone else's prescription? If a medicine makes you feel better, will taking twice as much make you feel better faster?** (*Sample answers: It is not okay to take someone's prescription because the dose may be wrong for you, or you may be allergic. Taking twice as much could lead to an overdose.*) Encourage students to discuss similar issues. Explain that this section will give them information about the proper way to use medicine and other drugs.

Drug Abuse

Teach Key Concepts   L1
Drug Effects on the Body

Focus Review the meaning of drug abuse.

Teach Explain that abused drugs can start to affect a person shortly after they are taken. A person can be affected mentally or physically. Ask students to read the passage *Effects of Abused Drugs* and then identify the effects of different drugs as you list them on the board. Ask: **What is the difference between tolerance and addiction?** *(Tolerance is needing larger amounts of a drug to have the same effect. Addiction is becoming physically dependent on a drug.)* Ask: **What other consequences can drug abuse have besides effects on your health?** *(A person can go to jail, or be unable to get along with others. The person may do poorly at work or in school.)*

Apply Ask: **What are reasons people consider abusing a drug?** *(Sample answers: To become part of a group, boredom, to see what it is like, to alleviate depression—thinking they will feel better)* **How could you use the information in this section to resist peer pressure to use a drug illegally?** *(Sample answer: You understand that the effects and consequences of drug abuse aren't worth any perceived benefit.)* **learning modality: verbal**

Independent Practice   L2

 **Teaching Resources, Unit 3**

- Guided Reading and Study Worksheet: *Alcohol and Other Drugs*

 **Student Edition on Audio CD**

Go **Online**
SciLINKS NSTA

For: Links on drug addiction
Visit: www.SciLinks.org
Web Code: scn-0464

Download a worksheet that will guide students' review of Internet resources on addiction.

Go **Online**
SciLINKS NSTA

For: Links on drug addiction
Visit: www.SciLinks.org
Web Code: scn-0464

FIGURE 18
Drug Abuse
Drug abuse can have serious consequences. However, there are ways to tell if someone is abusing drugs and ways to help that person. **Interpreting Diagrams** *What are two ways you can help if someone you know is abusing drugs?*

Signs of Drug Abuse
- Sudden changes in mood
- Lying, cheating
- Forgetfulness, withdrawn attitude, aggressiveness
- Poor coordination
- Slurred speech

652 ◆

Effects of Abused Drugs Abused drugs start to affect the body shortly after they are taken. **Most commonly abused drugs, such as marijuana, alcohol, and cocaine, are especially dangerous because of their immediate effects on the brain and other parts of the nervous system. In addition, long-term drug abuse can lead to addiction and other health and social problems.**

Different drugs have different effects. Some drugs cause nausea and a fast, irregular heartbeat. Others can cause sleepiness. Drug abusers may also experience headaches, dizziness, and trembling. Alcohol can cause confusion, poor muscle coordination, and blurred vision. These effects are especially dangerous in situations in which an alert mind is essential, such as driving a car.

Most abused drugs can alter, or change, a person's mood and feelings. Because of this effect, these drugs are often called mood-altering drugs. For example, the mood of a person under the influence of marijuana may change from calm to anxious. Alcohol can sometimes make a person angry and even violent. Mood-altering drugs also affect patterns of thinking and the way in which the brain interprets information from the senses.

Tolerance If a person takes a drug regularly, the body may develop a tolerance to the drug. **Tolerance** is a state in which a drug user needs larger and larger amounts of the drug to produce the same effect on the body. Tolerance can cause people to take a very large amount of a drug, or an overdose. People who take an overdose may become unconscious or even die.

Differentiated Instruction

Gifted and Talented   L3
Communicating Encourage students to use reference books or online sources to learn more about the effects and possible consequences of drug addiction and the challenge addicts face in breaking the habit. Allow them to present their findings to the class. **learning modality: verbal**

Addiction For many commonly abused drugs, repeated use can result in addiction. In **addiction,** the body becomes physically dependent on the drug. If a drug addict misses a few doses of the drug, the body reacts to the lack of the drug. The person may experience headaches, dizziness, fever, vomiting, body aches, and muscle cramps. The person is experiencing **withdrawal,** a period of adjustment that occurs when a person stops taking a drug on which the body is dependent.

Some drugs may also cause a person to become emotionally dependent on them. The person becomes accustomed to the feelings and moods produced by the drug. Therefore, the person has a strong desire to continue using the drug.

Other Effects of Drug Abuse Drugs can also affect a person's health indirectly. Some drug users sometimes share needles. When a person uses a needle to inject a drug, some of the person's blood remains in the needle after it is withdrawn. If the person has HIV or another pathogen in the blood, the next person to use the needle may become infected with the pathogen.

The abuse of drugs also has serious legal and social effects. A person who is caught using or selling an illegal drug may have to pay a fine or go to jail. Drug abuse can also make a person unable to get along with others. Drug abusers often have a hard time doing well in school or holding a job.

 Reading Checkpoint What is withdrawal?

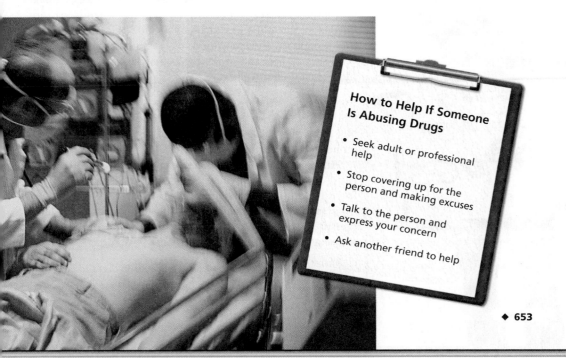

How to Help If Someone Is Abusing Drugs

- Seek adult or professional help
- Stop covering up for the person and making excuses
- Talk to the person and express your concern
- Ask another friend to help

◆ 653

Kinds of Abused Drugs

Teach Key Concepts L2

Commonly Abused Drugs

Focus Tell students that drugs are classified by the kinds of effects that they have on the body.

Teach Introduce the four main categories of commonly abused drugs. Explain the general mode of action of each type. For example, depressants slow activity, whereas stimulants speed up activity. Ask: **How does a depressant affect a person's response time?** *(It slows down response time.)* **How does a stimulant affect heart rate?** *(It increases heart rate.)* **How do hallucinogens affect perception?** *(They can make people see or hear things that aren't there.)* **What chemicals in the body do steroids resemble?** *(Hormones)*

Apply Explain that some prescription medicines are antidepressants. These drugs help people with depression, eating disorders, and other mental disorders. However, like any drug, they also can be dangerous if abused. **learning modality: verbal**

FIGURE 19
Making a Statement About Drug Abuse
Many teens are becoming active in antidrug campaigns.

654 ◆

Kinds of Abused Drugs

There are many kinds of drugs, with a wide range of effects on the body. Some are legitimate medicines that a doctor prescribes to help the body fight disease and injury. However, many kinds of drugs are frequently abused. **Commonly abused drugs include depressants, stimulants, inhalants, hallucinogens, anabolic steroids, and alcohol. Many drugs affect the central nervous system, while others affect the overall chemical balance in the body.** Figure 20 lists and describes the characteristics of some commonly abused drugs.

Depressants Notice in Figure 20 that some drugs are classified as depressants. **Depressants** are drugs that slow down the activity of the central nervous system. When people take depressants, their muscles relax and they may become sleepy. They may take longer than normal to respond to stimuli. For example, depressants may prevent people from reacting quickly to the danger of a car rushing toward them. Alcohol and narcotics, such as heroin, are depressants.

Stimulants In contrast to depressants, **stimulants** speed up body processes. They make the heart beat faster and make the breathing rate increase. Cocaine and nicotine are stimulants, as are amphetamines (am FET uh meenz). Amphetamines are prescription drugs that are sometimes sold illegally.

Inhalants and Hallucinogens Some substances, called inhalants, produce mood-altering effects when they are inhaled, or breathed in. Inhalants include paint thinner, nail polish remover, and some kinds of cleaning fluids. Hallucinogens, such as LSD and mescaline, can make people see or hear things that do not really exist.

Steroids Some athletes try to improve their performance by taking drugs known as steroids. **Anabolic steroids** (an uh BAH lik STEER oydz) are synthetic chemicals that are similar to hormones produced in the body.

Anabolic steroids may increase muscle size and strength. However, steroids can cause mood changes that lead to violence. In addition, steroid abuse can cause serious health problems, such as heart damage, liver damage, and increased blood pressure. Steroid use is especially dangerous for teenagers, whose growing bodies can be permanently damaged.

Reading Checkpoint What kinds of drugs are classified as stimulants?

Differentiated Instruction

Less Proficient Readers L1
Interpreting Tables Refer students to Figure 20. Ask students to identify words that they don't understand, for example, *behavioral changes* or *hypertension*. Explain the terms, and then guide students in

applying the information in the table. Ask: **How might a person act who has been taking barbiturates for a long time?** *(Sleepy, irritable, confused)* **learning modality: verbal**

FIGURE 20
Abused drugs can have many serious effects on the body. **Interpreting Tables** *What are the long-term effects of using inhalants?*

Some Effects of Commonly Abused Drugs				
Drug Type	**Short-Term Effects**	**Long-Term Effects**	**Addiction?**	**Emotional Dependence?**
Marijuana (including hashish)	Unclear thinking, loss of coordination, increased heart rate	Difficulty with concentration and memory; respiratory disease and lung cancer	Probably not	Yes
Nicotine (in cigarettes, cigars, chewing tobacco)	Stimulant; nausea, loss of appetite, headache	Heart and lung disease, difficulty breathing, heavy coughing	Yes, strongly so	Yes
Alcohol	Depressant; decreased alertness, poor reflexes, nausea, emotional depression	Liver and brain damage, inadequate nutrition	Yes	Yes
Inhalants (glue, nail polish remover, paint thinner)	Sleepiness, nausea, headaches, emotional depression	Damage to liver, kidneys, and brain; hallucinations	No	Yes
Cocaine (including crack)	Stimulant; nervousness, disturbed sleep, loss of appetite	Mental illness, damage to lining of nose, irregular heartbeat, heart or breathing failure, liver damage	Yes	Yes, strongly so
Amphetamines	Stimulant; restlessness, rapid speech, dizziness	Restlessness, irritability, irregular heartbeat, liver damage	Possible	Yes
Hallucinogens (LSD, mescaline, PCP)	Hallucinations, anxiety, panic; thoughts and actions not connected to reality	Mental illness; fearfulness; behavioral changes, including violence	No	Yes
Barbiturates (Phenobarbital, Nembutal, Seconal)	Depressant; decreased alertness, slowed thought processes, poor muscle coordination	Sleepiness, irritability, confusion	Yes	Yes
Tranquilizers (Valium, Xanax)	Depressant; blurred vision, sleepiness, unclear speech, headache, skin rash	Blood and liver disease	Yes	Yes
Narcotics (opium, codeine, morphine, heroin)	Depressant; sleepiness, nausea, hallucinations	Convulsion, coma, death	Yes, very rapid development	Yes, strongly so
Anabolic steroids	Mood swings	Heart, liver, and kidney damage; hypertension; overgrowth of skull and facial bones	No	Yes

Chapter 19 ◆ 655

Use Visuals: Figure 20 [L1]

Effects of Drugs

Focus Refer students to Figure 20.

Teach Have students make generalizations about the different categories of drugs and their effects. Ask: **What percent of the types of drugs listed may be physically addictive?** *(about 60 percent)* **What percent of the drugs cause emotional dependency?** *(100 percent)*

Apply Ask: **How is information about the effects of drugs a useful tool in influencing others not to use drugs?** *(The information about the effects of drugs can help people make informed decisions. Recognizing the risks can help people choose not to engage in drug abuse.)* **learning modality: verbal**

Help Students Read [L1]

Compare and Contrast Have students refer to the table in Figure 20 to compare and contrast the drugs nicotine and marijuana. Ask: **Which drug would put a driver of a car at risk?** *(Marijuana)* **What serious diseases can both drugs cause?** *(Heart and lung disease)*

Monitor Progress _____ [L2]

Skills Check Have students use Figure 20 to compare and contrast short- and long-term effects of stimulants, depressants, and hallucinogens.

Answers
Figure 20 Damage to the liver, kidneys, and brain, as well as hallucinations

 Reading Checkpoint — Stimulants include cocaine, nicotine, and amphetamines.

Alcohol

Effects of Alcohol and Alcohol Abuse

Focus Remind students that even though its use is legal and widespread, alcohol is still a drug.

Teach Explain that alcohol affects the brain and other organs of the body, and the more alcohol in the blood, the more serious the effects. Ask: **How does alcohol enter the blood?** *(It is absorbed by the digestive system and enters the blood.)* **What is the immediate effect of alcohol on the brain?** *(Loss of normal judgment)* **What kinds of health problems can result from heavy drinking?** *(Destruction of cells in the brain and liver, addiction, and emotional dependence)*

Apply Explain that all forms of alcohol can be involved in alcohol abuse. For example, a person can develop alcoholism from drinking alcopops (sweetened, pre-mixed malt beverages and hard lemonades that appeal especially to teens). **learning modality: verbal**

Build Inquiry   L2

Resisting Alcohol Use

Materials None

Time 20 minutes

Focus Remind students that some teens drink alcohol because their friends do it.

Teach Have small groups of students role-play scenarios, such as confronting a sibling who is using drugs or alcohol and helping a friend decide not to drink a beer at a party. After students have taken turns in different roles, have them present one scenario for the class.

Apply Put up a large sheet of paper on the wall or bulletin board. As students present their scenarios, list what they say to resist or to persuade others. Encourage the class to add to the list. The list can serve as a model to help students refuse alcohol. **learning modality: verbal**

Alcohol

Alcohol is a drug found in many beverages, including beer, wine, cocktails, and hard liquor. Alcohol is a powerful depressant. In all states, it is illegal for people under the age of 21 to buy or possess alcohol. In spite of this fact, alcohol is the most commonly abused legal drug in people aged 12 to 17.

FIGURE 21
Alcohol's Effects
Alcohol affects every system of the body. It also impacts a person's thought processes, judgment, and reaction time. In the bottom photo, a police officer tests the blood alcohol concentration of a driver suspected of drinking.

How Alcohol Affects the Body Alcohol is absorbed by the digestive system quickly. If a person drinks alcohol on an empty stomach, the alcohol enters the blood and gets to the brain and other organs almost immediately. If alcohol is drunk with a meal, it takes longer to get into the blood.

The chart in Figure 21 describes what alcohol does to the body. The more alcohol in the blood, the more serious the effects. The amount of alcohol in the blood is usually expressed as blood alcohol concentration, or BAC. A BAC value of 0.1 percent means that one tenth of one percent of the fluid in the blood is alcohol. In some states, if car drivers have a BAC of 0.08 percent or more, they are legally drunk. In other states, drivers with a BAC of 0.1 are considered legally drunk.

Alcohol produces serious negative effects, including loss of normal judgment, at a BAC of less than 0.08 percent. This loss of judgment can have serious consequences. People who have been drinking may not realize that they cannot drive a car safely. About every two minutes, a person in the United States is injured in a car crash related to alcohol.

656 ◆

Short-Term Effects of Alcohol	
Body System	**Effect**
Cardiovascular system	First, heartbeat rate and blood pressure increase. Later, they may decrease.
Digestive system	Alcohol is absorbed directly from the stomach and small intestine, which allows it to enter the bloodstream quickly.
Excretory system	The kidneys produce more urine, causing the drinker to excrete more water than usual.
Nervous system	Vision blurs. Speech becomes unclear. Control of behavior is reduced. Judgment becomes poor.
Skin	Blood flow to the skin increases, causing rapid loss of body heat.

Differentiated Instruction

Special Needs   L1
Demonstrating BAC Have students fill a 1 L container with 999 mL of water and then use a dropper to place 1 mL of oil on top of the water. Explain that the water represents blood and the oil represents alcohol, and that these are the relative volumes of blood and alcohol for a BAC value of 0.1 percent. Ask: **What does this demonstration tell you about the effects of small amounts of alcohol?** *(Even a small amount of alcohol in the bloodstream can have a serious impact on the body.)* Remind students that a person with a BAC of 0.1 percent is considered legally drunk in many states. **learning modality: kinesthetic**

Long-Term Alcohol Abuse Many adults drink occasionally and in moderation, without serious safety or health problems. However, heavy drinking, especially over a long period, can result in significant health problems. **Alcohol abuse can cause the destruction of cells in the brain and liver, and can lead to addiction and emotional dependence.** Damage to the brain can cause mental disturbances, such as hallucinations and loss of consciousness. The liver, which breaks down alcohol for elimination from the body, can become so scarred that it does not function properly. In addition, long-term alcohol abuse can increase the risk of getting certain kinds of cancer.

Abuse of alcohol can result in **alcoholism,** a disease in which a person is both physically addicted to and emotionally dependent on alcohol. To give up alcohol, as with any addictive drug, alcoholics must go through withdrawal. To give up drinking, alcoholics need both medical and emotional help. Medical professionals, psychologists, and organizations such as Alcoholics Anonymous can help a person stop drinking.

 Reading Checkpoint What organs are affected by alcohol abuse?

Healthy Liver

Alcohol-damaged Liver

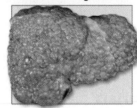

FIGURE 22
Alcohol's Effect on the Liver
Long-term alcohol abuse can cause serious damage to the liver. **Relating Cause and Effect** *What other effects can alcohol abuse have on the body?*

Section 4 Assessment

Target Reading Skill Relating Cause and Effect Refer to your graphic organizer about commonly abused drugs to help you answer Question 2.

Reviewing Key Concepts

1. **a. Defining** In your own words, explain what a drug is. What is drug abuse?
   b. Explaining How can the repeated use of some drugs lead to addiction and emotional dependence?
   c. Applying Concepts What reasons would you give someone to not try drugs in the first place?
2. **a. Listing** Name two commonly abused depressants and two commonly abused stimulants.
   b. Comparing and Contrasting Contrast the effects that depressants and stimulants have on the body.

   c. Inferring Why might a person's risk of a heart attack increase with the use of stimulants?
3. **a. Reviewing** What type of drug is alcohol?
   b. Explaining What immediate effects does alcohol have on the body?
   c. Relating Cause and Effect Based on alcohol's effect on the nervous system, explain why drinking and driving is extremely dangerous.

Lab zone At-Home Activity

Medicine Labels Collect several medicine bottles and read the warning labels. Make a list of the kinds of warnings you find. Discuss these warnings with a family member. Why do you think medicines provide warnings?

Lab zone At-Home Activity

Medicine Labels **L2** Advise students to ask a parent or guardian to assist them in creating the list. For privacy reasons, do not request students to share their findings with the class. Ask them to summarize why medicines provide warnings.

Lab zone Chapter Project

Keep Students on Track Encourage students to work together to plan their presentations and then divide the work. For example, one student or student pair could analyze the results, another describe the tests, and another explain how illusions trick the senses. Encourage students to prepare visual aids, such as circle graphs, to support their findings.

Monitor Progress _____ L2

Answers
Figure 22 Destruction of brain cells, addiction, and emotional dependence

Reading Checkpoint Brain, liver

Assess

Reviewing Key Concepts

1. **a.** A drug is any chemical people take that causes changes in their body or behavior. Drug abuse is an intentional use of drugs for nonmedicinal purposes. **b.** Repeated use of a drug can lead to tolerance, in which larger amounts of a drug are needed for the same effect. The body can then become physically dependent, and the user can become emotionally dependent on the drug's effect. **c.** The perceived advantages are not worth the negative effects.
2. **a.** Depressants: alcohol, heroin; Stimulants: cocaine, nicotine, amphetamines **b.** Depressants slow the activity of the nervous system. They relax the muscles, make people sleepy, and decrease response time to stimuli. Stimulants speed up body processes. They increase the rates of heart beat and breathing. **c.** Stimulants speed up the heart rate, thus increasing the risk of heart attack.
3. **a.** A depressant; it decreases alertness, slows down reflexes, and can cause nausea and emotional depression **b.** It can cause destruction of cells in the brain and liver and can increase a person's risk of getting certain kinds of cancer. It can also lead to addiction and emotional dependence. **c.** Drinking alcohol interferes with a person's ability to drive a car safely because vision becomes blurred, response time is longer, and judgment becomes poor.

Reteach L1

Have students review major concepts by making flash cards—writing a vocabulary term on one side of an index card and its meaning on the other.

Performance Assessment L2

Drawing Have small groups of students choose one type of drug in this section and create an informational poster.

All in One Teaching Resources, Unit 3

- Section Summary: *Alcohol and Other Drugs*
- Review and Reinforce: *Alcohol and Other Drugs*
- Enrich: *Alcohol and Other Drugs*

With Caffeine or Without?

Prepare for Inquiry

Key Concept
Stimulants such as caffeine cause body processes to speed up.

Skills Objectives
Students will be able to
- observe the effects of caffeine
- control variables to test a hypothesis about the effects of caffeine
- draw conclusions about stimulants

Prep Time 45 minutes

Class Time 40 minutes

Advance Planning
Purchase *Lumbriculus* (blackworms) and biological adrenaline (epinephrine) from a biological supply company. Prepare the adrenaline solution (about 0.01%) by dissolving 10 mg epinephrine hydrochloride in 100 mL distilled water. Dilute beverages to reduce the pH level (1 mL beverage to 100 mL water).

To make the paraffin specimen blocks, use a paper clip to make a shallow trough approximately 4 centimeters long in the center of the block. Use the edge of a microscope slide to push a piece of thread into the bottom of the trough.

Safety
 Remind students to treat the blackworms as gently as possible and to handle scissors with care. Caution them not to taste any of the beverages. Make sure they wash their hands after the lab. Review the safety guidelines in Appendix A.

All in One Teaching Resources, Unit 3
- Lab Worksheet: *With Caffeine or Without?*

Lab zone Consumer **Lab**

With Caffeine or Without?

Problem
What body changes does caffeine produce in blackworms *(Lumbriculus)*?

Skills Focus
observing, controlling variables, drawing conclusions

Materials
- blackworms
- plastic dropper
- adrenaline solution
- stereomicroscope
- paraffin specimen trough
- noncarbonated spring water
- beverages with and without caffeine
- stopwatch or clock with second hand

Procedure

PART 1 Observing the Effects of a Known Stimulant

1. Copy the data table into your notebook. Use a dropper to remove one worm and a drop or two of water from the blackworm population provided by your teacher.

2. Place the worm and the water in the trough of the paraffin block. Use the dropper or the corner of a paper towel to remove any excess water that does not fit in the trough. Let the blackworm adjust for a few minutes.

3. Place the paraffin block under the stereomicroscope. Select the smallest amount of light and the lowest possible power to view the blackworm.

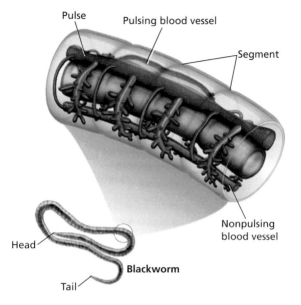

4. Look through the stereomicroscope and locate a segment near the middle of the worm. Count the number of times blood pulses through this segment for 30 seconds. Multiply this number by two to get the pulse in beats per minute. Record the pulse in your data table.

Data Table	
Condition	Pulse Rate
No adrenaline	
With adrenaline	
Beverage without caffeine	
Beverage with caffeine	

Guide Inquiry

Invitation
Have students read through the lab. Ask: **Why is adrenaline used in Part 1 when the experiment is testing the effects of caffeine?** *(It illustrates how a known stimulant will affect the blackworms.)* Ask: **What are the** **advantages and disadvantages of using blackworms as test subjects?** *(Sample answers: The transparent body allow easy observation of changes in pulse rate. Effects of caffeine on blackworms may be different than effects on humans.)*

5. Remove the block from the stereomicroscope. Use the dropper to add 1 drop of adrenaline solution to the trough. (Adrenaline is a substance produced by the human body that acts as a stimulant.) Let the worm sit in the adrenaline solution for 5 minutes.

6. Place the paraffin block under the stereomicroscope. Again locate a segment near the middle of the worm. Count the number of pulses through this segment for 30 seconds. Multiply this number by two to get the pulse in beats per minute. Record the blackworm's pulse with adrenaline.

PART 2 **Testing the Effects of Caffeine**

7. Using the procedures you followed in Part 1, design an experiment that tests the effect of caffeine on the blackworm's pulse. You can use beverages with and without caffeine in your investigation. Be sure to write a hypothesis and control all necessary variables.

8. Submit your experimental plan to your teacher for review. After making any necessary changes, carry out your experiment.

Analyze and Conclude

1. **Observing** In Part 1, what was the blackworm's pulse rate before you added adrenaline? After you added adrenaline?

2. **Interpreting Data** Use the data you collected in Part 1 to explain how you know that adrenaline acts as a stimulant.

3. **Controlling Variables** In the experiment you performed in Part 2, what was your control? Explain.

4. **Drawing Conclusions** Based on your results in Part 2, does caffeine act as a stimulant? Explain your answer.

5. **Communicating** Write a paragraph to explain how you think your body would react to drinks with caffeine and without caffeine. Use the results from this investigation to support your viewpoint.

Design an Experiment

Do you think that "decaffeinated" products will act as a stimulant in blackworms? Design a controlled experiment to find out. *Obtain your teacher's permission before carrying out your investigation.*

Introduce the Procedure
- Demonstrate the proper procedure for applying a blackworm to the paraffin block.
- Use the illustration of *Lumbriculus* to show students where the pulsing blood vessel is located, and demonstrate how to determine the pulse rate.

Troubleshooting the Experiment
- Advise students to determine the pulse rate as soon as they are able to view the blackworm.
- Viewing the lower half of the body close to the tail will more likely show pulsation than near the head.
- Have students use new blackworm samples for Part 2 and for Design an Experiment. Exposing a single blackworm to many different substances in quick succession would stress the organism and lead to erroneous data. In addition, residual amounts of the various test substances could remain on the blackworm as it is exposed to new test substances.

Expected Outcome
- Normal pulse rate for blackworms, depending on the species, varies from 24 to 32 beats per minute.
- Adrenaline and caffeine are stimulants and should cause the pulse rate to increase. Drinks without caffeine should not increase the heart rate.

Extend Inquiry

Design an Experiment Students can design an experiment similar to Part 2 of this lab, substituting a decaffeinated beverage for the beverage with caffeine. Results may vary depending on how completely the caffeine has been removed from the beverage.

Analyze and Conclude
1. Normal pulse rate is 24 to 32 beats per minute. Adrenaline should cause the pulse rate to increase.

2. Students should cite their data to show that the number of pulses increased when adrenaline was added.

3. Sample answer: Measuring the pulse of the same blackworm both before and after the drink was added. This procedure serves as a control because it ensures that any difference in pulse rate is due to the added caffeine.

4. Yes; caffeine caused the pulse rate to increase.

5. Some students may say that drinks without caffeine will have no effect on humans, whereas drinks with caffeine will cause increased pulse rates and related changes. Other students may say that because humans and *Lumbriculus* are so different, the effect of caffeine on humans cannot be predicted based on this evidence. Students should refer to their results as part of their explanation.

interactive **Textbook**

- Complete student edition
- Section and chapter self-assessments
- Assessment reports for teachers

Help Students Read   L1

Building Vocabulary

Vocabulary Knowledge Rating Chart
Have students construct a chart with four columns: *Term, Can Define or Use It, Have Heard or Seen It, Don't Know.* Have students copy the vocabulary terms for this chapter under column 1. They should then place a checkmark under one of the other columns for each term. If students did not check the *Can Define* or *Use It* column, have them reread passages with those terms and work with a partner to review the term.

Words in Context Select Key Terms from the chapter. For each term, have students write a sentence that places the term in a correct context. Provide them with one example before they begin: *Neurons carry nerve impulses through the nervous system.*

Connecting Concepts

Concept Maps Help students develop one way to show how the information in this chapter is related. The nervous system consists of the central nervous system and the peripheral nervous system that work together to receive and respond to sensory information detected by the five senses and, in the process, to maintain homeostasis. Have students brainstorm to identify Key Concepts, Key Terms, details, and examples and then write each one on a sticky note and attach it at random on chart paper or on the board.

Chapter 19 Study Guide

① How the Nervous System Works

Key Concepts

- The nervous system directs how your body responds to information about what is happening inside and outside your body. Your nervous system also helps maintain homeostasis.
- The three kinds of neurons found in the body are sensory neurons, interneurons, and motor neurons.
- For a nerve impulse to be carried along at a synapse, it must cross the gap between an axon and the next structure.

Key Terms

stimulus	axon
response	nerve
neuron	sensory neuron
nerve impulse	interneuron
dendrite	motor neuron
	synapse

② Divisions of the Nervous System

Key Concepts

- The central nervous system is the control center of the body. It includes the brain and spinal cord.
- The peripheral nervous system consists of a network of nerves that branch out from the central nervous system and connect it to the rest of the body.
- A reflex is an automatic response that occurs very rapidly and without conscious control.
- Concussions and spinal cord injuries are two ways the central nervous system can be damaged.

Key Terms

central nervous system	brain stem
peripheral nervous system	somatic nervous system
brain	autonomic nervous system
spinal cord	reflex
cerebrum	concussion
cerebellum	

③ The Senses

Key Concepts

- The eyes convert light into nerve impulses that your brain interprets, enabling you to see.
- The ears convert sound into nerve impulses that your brain interprets, enabling you to hear. Structures in your inner ear control your sense of balance.
- The senses of smell and taste work together.
- The skin contains touch receptors that respond to a number of stimuli.

Key Terms

cornea	nearsightedness
pupil	farsightedness
iris	eardrum
lens	cochlea
retina	semicircular canal

④ Alcohol and Other Drugs

Key Concepts

- Most abused drugs are dangerous because of their immediate effects on the nervous system. Long-term drug abuse can lead to addiction and other health and social problems.
- Commonly abused drugs include depressants, stimulants, inhalants, steroids, and alcohol.
- Alcohol use can destroy cells in the brain and liver, and lead to addiction.

Key Terms

drug
drug abuse
tolerance
addiction
withdrawal
depressant
stimulant
anabolic steroid
alcoholism

Tell students that this concept map will be organized in hierarchical order to begin at the top with the Key Concepts. Ask students these questions to guide them to categorize the information on the sticky notes: **What are the structures and functions of the two divisions of the nervous system? What are the types of neurons and what are their functions? How do people see, hear, smell, taste, and touch?**

Prompt students by using connecting words or phrases, such as "consists of," "travel to," and "controls." The phrases should form a sentence between or among a set of concepts.

Answer Accept logical presentations by students.

All in One Teaching Resources, Unit 3

- Key Terms Review: *The Nervous System*
- Connecting Concepts: *The Nervous System*

Review and Assessment

Go Online
PHSchool.com
For: Self-Assessment
Visit: PHSchool.com
Web Code: cea-4060

Organizing Information

Concept Mapping Copy the concept map about neurons and their functions onto a separate sheet of paper. Then, complete it and add a title. (For more on Concept Mapping, see the Skills Handbook.)

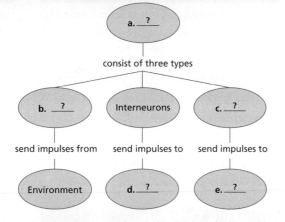

a. ?

consist of three types

b. ?   Interneurons   c. ?

send impulses from   send impulses to   send impulses to

Environment   d. ?   e. ?

Reviewing Key Terms

Choose the letter of the best answer.

1. A change or signal in the environment that makes the nervous system react is called a
   a. stimulus.
   b. response.
   c. nerve impulse.
   d. synapse.

2. The structures that carry messages toward a neuron's cell body are
   a. axons.
   b. dendrites.
   c. nerves.
   d. nerve impulses.

3. Which structure links the brain and the peripheral nervous system?
   a. the cerebrum
   b. the cerebellum
   c. the cochlea
   d. the spinal cord

4. Which structure adjusts the size of the pupil?
   a. the cornea   b. the retina
   c. the lens   d. the iris

5. Physical dependence on a drug is called
   a. withdrawal.   b. response.
   c. addiction.   d. tolerance.

If the statement is true, write *true*. If it is false, change the underlined word or words to make the statement true.

6. A nerve message is also called a <u>synapse</u>.

7. The <u>cerebrum</u> is the part of the brain that controls involuntary actions.

8. In <u>nearsightedness</u>, a person can see distant objects clearly.

9. The <u>cochlea</u> is part of the inner ear.

10. Alcohol is a <u>depressant</u>.

Writing in Science

Descriptive Paragraph Draw a diagram of the human eye, and label the key parts. Then, write a paragraph that describes how each part helps a person "see" an image.

The Nervous System
Video Preview
Video Field Trip
▶ Video Assessment

Review and Assessment

Organizing Information

a. Neurons
b. Sensory neurons
c. Motor neurons
d. Other neurons
e. Muscles and glands

Reviewing Key Terms

1. a   2. b   3. d   4. d   5. c
6. nerve impulse
7. brain stem
8. farsightedness
9. true
10. true

Writing in Science

Writing Skill Description

Scoring Rubric

4 Diagram and paragraph are accurate and complete; uses detailed, precise descriptions
3 Includes all criteria, but description is not detailed
2 Includes only a brief description
1 Includes inaccurate diagram, or description.

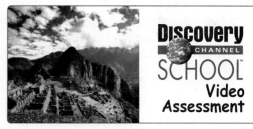

Discovery CHANNEL SCHOOL
Video Assessment

The Nervous System

Show the Video Assessment to review chapter content and as a prompt for the writing assignment. Discussion questions: **What are the functions of rods and cones?** *(Rods enable people to see black, white, and shades of gray. Cones enable people to see colors.)* **Where are images that we see interpreted as objects?** *(In the brain)*

Go Online
PHSchool.com
For: Self-Assessment
Visit: PHSchool.com
Web Code: cea-4060

Students can take a practice test online that is automatically scored.

All in One Teaching Resources, Unit 3
- Transparency LS190
- Chapter Test
- Performance Assessment Teacher Notes
- Performance Assessment Student Worksheet
- Performance Assessment Scoring Rubric

ExamView® Computer Test Bank CD-ROM

Checking Concepts

11. Axons carry impulses away from the cell body. Dendrites carry impulses toward the cell body.

12. The cerebrum interprets input from the senses, controls the movement of muscles of the arms and legs, and helps you remember how to ride and make judgments. The cerebellum coordinates the actions of your arms and legs and helps you keep your balance.

13. The autonomic nervous system controls involuntary actions.

14. Nerve impulses would no longer pass through the region that is cut. Lack of sensitivity and paralysis would result to areas beneath the cut.

15. For nearsightedness, concave lenses bend light away from the center of the lens before they reach the lens of the eye, allowing the light rays to focus on the retina rather than in front of it. For farsightedness, convex lenses bend light rays toward each other before they reach the lens of the eye, allowing the light rays to focus on the retina.

16. The structures are the eardrum, hammer, anvil, stirrup, thin membrane, and fluid in the cochlea.

17. Anabolic steroids increase muscle size and strength, and cause mood changes that can lead to violence.

Thinking Critically

18. When a nerve impulse reaches the tip of an axon, chemicals are released into the gap at the synapse. The chemicals cross the gap and transfer the nerve impulse to another structure.

19. The stroke occurred in the left side of the brain; the left side of the brain has control over the right side of the body.

20. This process is an example of a reflex. It protects the man by making him jerk his foot automatically up, before his foot pushes down further and causes any more damage or pain. The reflex action quickly prevents the man from doing any more harm to himself.

21. Sample answers: I don't want to risk negative health effects, addiction, and social and legal problems. These arguments would be effective because they are based on real consequences as well as personal choice.

Review and Assessment

Checking Concepts

11. Compare the functions of axons and dendrites.

12. How do the cerebrum and cerebellum work together when you ride a bicycle?

13. What is the function of the autonomic nervous system?

14. What is the result if the spinal cord is cut?

15. Describe how lenses in eyeglasses correct nearsightedness and farsightedness.

16. List in order all the structures in your ear that must vibrate before you hear a sound.

17. How do anabolic steroids affect the body?

Thinking Critically

18. Interpreting Diagrams The diagram below shows a synapse. Explain how a nerve impulse crosses the gap.

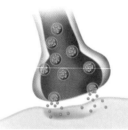

19. Relating Cause and Effect When a person has a stroke, blood flow to part of the brain is reduced, and some brain cells die. Suppose that after a stroke, a woman is unable to move her right arm and right leg. In which side of her brain did the stroke occur? Explain.

20. Applying Concepts As a man walks barefoot along a beach, he steps on a sharp shell. His foot automatically jerks upward, even before he feels pain. What process is this an example of? How does it help protect the man?

21. Making Judgments If someone tried to persuade you to take drugs, what arguments would you use as a way of refusing? Why do you think these arguments would be effective?

Applying Skills

Use the graph to answer Questions 22–25.

A person with normal vision stood at different distances from an eye chart and tried to identify the letters on the chart. The line graph gives the results.

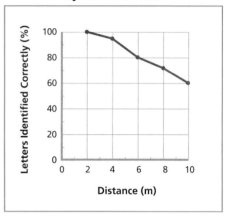

Eye Chart Results

22. Reading Graphs What variable is plotted on the *x*-axis? On the *y*-axis?

23. Interpreting Data As the distance from the eye chart increases, what happens to the percentage of letters identified correctly?

24. Controlling Variables What was the manipulated variable in this experiment? What was the responding variable?

25. Predicting How would you expect the results to differ for a farsighted person? Explain.

Lab zone Chapter **Project**

Performance Assessment Explain to your classmates how you set up your experiment, which illusions you used, which senses were involved in the illusions, and why the illusions worked. Include information on how the nervous system was involved in your illusions.

Lab zone Chapter **Project**

Performance Assessment Allow students to demonstrate the illusions they studied. Conclude the project presentation with a discussion of what students learned about the ways in which their nervous system interprets sensory nerve impulses.

Reflect and Record Ask students to write about what they have learned by doing their experiments. Have them think about what they would do differently if they were performing their experiments again, and write descriptions of their revised procedures.

Standardized Test Prep

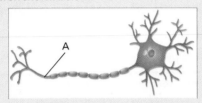
Choose the letter of the best answer.

1. A scientist studying the brain is studying part of the
 A peripheral nervous system.
 B somatic nervous system.
 C autonomic nervous system.
 D central nervous system.

Use the diagram below and your knowledge of science to answer Questions 2 and 3.

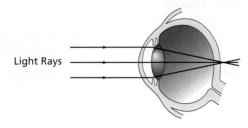

Light Rays

2. To correct the vision of the eye shown above, a lens would have to make the light rays
 F bend toward each other before they reach the eye's lens.
 G spread out before they reach the eye's lens.
 H focus on the eye's lens.
 J focus behind the retina.

3. Which of the following correctly pairs the vision problem in the eye shown above with the proper corrective lens?
 A farsightedness; convex lens
 B farsightedness; concave lens
 C nearsightedness; convex lens
 D nearsightedness; concave lens

4. The brain stem is involved in controlling
 F breathing.
 G the ability to learn.
 H movement of skeletal muscles.
 J balance.

5. You can infer that a person who has lost his or her sense of smell is also likely to have a poor
 A sense of balance.
 B sense of touch.
 C sense of taste.
 D sense of hearing.

Constructed Response

6. Outline the path of the reflex action that takes place when you step on a tack. What is the advantage of the nerve impulse not needing to go through the brain before action is taken?

Applying Skills

22. Distance is plotted on the *x*-axis. Percentage of letters correctly identified is plotted on the *y*-axis.

23. The percent identified correctly decreases.

24. Manipulated variable—distance from the eye chart; responding variable—the percentage of letters identified correctly

25. The graph probably would slope upward from left to right because a farsighted person would score better standing far away than standing close to the chart.

Standardized Test Prep

1. D **2.** F **3.** A **4.** F **5.** C

6. When you step on a tack, sensory neurons in your foot are stimulated. Nerve impulses travel along the sensory neurons to the spinal cord, where they are passed to an interneuron. The impulses are then sent directly to motor neurons, which stimulate a muscle in your leg to contract. Your leg jerks up and away from the sharp tack. Reflex actions save time because they bypass the brain. If the impulses had to travel to the brain before your body responded, you probably would be further hurt by the tack.

Chapter at a Glance

 Chapter Project *A Precious Bundle*

Technology

Local Standards

Teaching Resources, Unit 3
- Chapter Project Teacher Notes, pp. 390–391
- Chapter Project Student Overview, pp. 392–393
- Chapter Project Student Worksheets, pp. 394–395
- Chapter Project Scoring Rubric, p. 396

 **Discovery** CHANNEL SCHOOL Video Preview

 Section 1

2 periods
1 block

The Endocrine System
20.1.1 Describe how the endocrine system controls body processes.
20.1.2 Identify the endocrine glands.
20.1.3 Explain how negative feedback controls hormone levels.

 Go Online active art

 Section 2

2 periods
1 block

The Male and Female Reproductive Systems
20.2.1 Define sexual reproduction.
20.2.2 Describe the structures and functions of the male reproductive system.
20.2.3 Describe the structures and functions of the female reproductive system.
20.2.4 Sequence the events that occur during the menstrual cycle.

 Go Online SCiLINKS NSTA

 Section 3

2 periods
1 block

The Human Life Cycle
20.3.1 List the stages of human development that occur before birth.
20.3.2 Explain how the developing embryo is protected and nourished.
20.3.3 Describe what happens during childbirth.
20.3.4 Identify changes that occur from infancy to adulthood.

 Go Online SCiLINKS NSTA

 Discovery CHANNEL SCHOOL Video Field Trip

Review and Assessment

Teaching Resources, Unit 3
- Key Terms Review, p. 424
- Transparency LS200
- Performance Assessment Teacher Notes, p. 432
- Performance Assessment Scoring Rubric, p. 433
- Performance Assessment Student Worksheet, p. 434
- Chapter Test, pp. 435–438

 Discovery CHANNEL SCHOOL Video Assessment

 Go Online PHSchool.com

Test Preparation
Test Preparation Blackline Masters

Lab zone Chapter Activities Planner

For more activities

LAB ZONE
Easy Planner
CD-ROM

Student Edition	Inquiry	Time	Materials	Skills	Resources
Chapter Project, p. 665	Open-Ended	1 to 2 weeks	**All in One Teaching Resources, Unit 3**, p. 390	Making models, observing, problem solving, making generalizations, communicating	**Lab zone Easy Planner** **All in One Teaching Resources, Unit 3**, Support pp. 390–391
Section 1					
Discover Activity, p. 666	Open-ended	15 minutes	None	Inferring	**Lab zone Easy Planner**
Skills Activity, p. 668	Guided	15 minutes	Construction paper, pipe cleaners, modeling clay, scissors	Making models	**Lab zone Easy Planner**
Technology Lab, pp. 672–673	Guided	Prep: 15 minutes; Class: 40 minutes	2-L plastic bottle, 1-L plastic bottle, duct tape, round balloon, scissors, rubber stopper, string, plastic tray, water	Making models, observing, evaluating the design	**Lab zone Easy Planner Lab Activity Video** **All in One Teaching Resources, Unit 3**, Technology Lab: *Modeling Negative Feedback*, pp. 404–405
Section 2					
Discover Activity, p. 674	Guided	20 minutes	Slides of human egg and sperm cells, microscope	Observing	**Lab zone Easy Planner**
Skills Activity, p. 679	Directed	5 minutes	Calculator (optional)	Calculating	**Lab zone Easy Planner**
Section 3					
Discover Activity, p. 682	Open-ended	15 minutes	None	Observing	**Lab zone Easy Planner**
Try This Activity, p. 685	Guided	15 minutes	Balance, objects of various masses	Making models	**Lab zone Easy Planner**
Try This Activity, p. 689	Guided	15 minutes	Magazine ads directed at teenagers	Drawing conclusions	**Lab zone Easy Planner**
Skills Lab, p. 691	Guided	Prep: 20 minutes; Class: 30 minutes	None	Calculating, predicting	**Lab zone Easy Planner Lab Activity Video** **All in One Teaching Resources, Unit 3**, Skills Lab: *Growing Up,* pp. 422–423

Section 1 The Endocrine System

🕐 *2 periods, 1 block*

Objectives

20.1.1 Describe how the endocrine system controls body processes.

20.1.2 Identify the endocrine glands.

20.1.3 Explain how negative feedback controls hormone levels.

Key Terms

• endocrine gland • hormone • target cell • hypothalamus • pituitary gland
• negative feedback

Local Standards

Preteach

Build Background Knowledge

Elicit a "fight or flight" response from students, and connect it to what they will be studying.

Lab zone Discover Activity *What's the Signal?* L1

Targeted Print and Technology Resources

All in One Teaching Resources, Unit 3

L2   Reading Strategy Transparency
LS191: Relating Cause and Effect

⊙ **PresentationEXPRESS™ CD-ROM**

Instruct

Endocrine Hormones Define the functions of the endocrine system and hormones.

Functions of Endocrine Glands Use a diagram to explain the functions of endocrine glands, and compare and contrast ovaries and testes.

Negative Feedback Use an analogy to describe how the negative feedback loop works.

Lab zone Technology Lab *Modeling Negative Feedback* L3

Targeted Print and Technology Resources

All in One Teaching Resources, Unit 3

L2   Guided Reading, pp. 399–401
L2   Transparencies LS192, LS193
L3   Technology Lab: *Modeling Negative Feedback*, pp. 404–405

📼 **Lab Activity Video/DVD**
Technology Lab: *Modeling Negative Feedback*

PHSchool.com Web Code: cep-4071

⊙ **Student Edition on Audio CD**

Assess

Section Assessment Questions

Have students use their graphic organizers about the effects of pituitary hormones to help answer the questions.

Reteach

Use a diagram to summarize the functions of the endocrine system.

Targeted Print and Technology Resources

All in One Teaching Resources, Unit 3

• Section Summary, p. 398
L1   Review and Reinforce, p. 402
L3   Enrich, p. 403

Section 2 The Male and Female Reproductive Systems

2 periods, 1 block

Objectives

20.2.1 Define sexual reproduction.

20.2.2 Describe the structures and functions of the male reproductive system.

20.2.3 Describe the structures and functions of the female reproductive system.

20.2.4 Sequence the events that occur during the menstrual cycle.

Local Standards

Key Terms

• egg • sperm • fertilization • zygote • testis • testosterone • scrotum • semen
• penis • ovary • estrogen • fallopian tube • uterus • vagina • menstrual cycle
• ovulation • menstruation

Preteach

Build Background Knowledge

Guide students to recall what they already know about the male and female reproductive systems.

 **Discover Activity** *What's the Big Difference?* L2

Targeted Print and Technology Resources

All in One Teaching Resources, Unit 3

L2 Reading Strategy Transparency LS194: Sequencing

⊙ **PresentationEXPRESS™ CD-ROM**

Instruct

Sexual Reproduction Ask questions to help students identify the process of sexual reproduction, and use a diagram to compare and contrast sex cells.

Male Reproductive System Use a diagram to explain the functions of the scrotum and testes.

Female Reproductive System Compare and contrast male and female hormones, and describe the functions of female reproductive organs.

The Menstrual Cycle Use a diagram to identify the events that occur during the menstrual cycle.

Targeted Print and Technology Resources

All in One Teaching Resources, Unit 3

L2 Guided Reading, pp. 408–411
L2 Transparencies LS195, LS196, LS197

www.SciLinks.org Web Code: scn-0472

⊙ **Student Edition on Audio CD**

Assess

Section Assessment Questions

Have students use their cycle diagrams to help answer the questions.

Reteach

Use diagrams to review the structures and functions of the male and female reproductive systems.

Targeted Print and Technology Resources

All in One Teaching Resources, Unit 3

• Section Summary, p. 407
L1 Review and Reinforce, p. 412
L3 Enrich, p. 413

Section 3 The Human Life Cycle

🕐 *2 periods, 1 block*

Objectives

20.3.1 List the stages of human development that occur before birth.
20.3.2 Explain how the developing embryo is protected and nourished.
20.3.3 Describe what happens during childbirth.
20.3.4 Identify changes that occur from infancy to adulthood.

Key Terms

• embryo • fetus • amniotic sac • placenta • umbilical cord • adolescence
• puberty

Local Standards

Preteach

Build Background Knowledge

Show pictures of mammals and have students describe their characteristics as a group.

Lab zone Discover Activity *How Many Ways Does a Child Grow?* **L1**

Targeted Print and Technology Resources

All in One Teaching Resources, Unit 3
L2 Reading Strategy: Building Vocabulary
⊙ **PresentationEXPRESS™ CD-ROM**

Instruct

Development Before Birth Ask questions to help students identify the three stages of development before birth and characteristics of each stage.

Protection and Nourishment Use a diagram to explain how the amniotic sac, placenta, and umbilical cord protect and nourish the developing baby.

Birth Identify the sequence of events that occur in childbirth.

Growth and Development

List major stages during growth and prompt students to identify changes that occur in each one.

Lab zone Skills Lab *Growing Up* **L2**

Targeted Print and Technology Resources

All in One Teaching Resources, Unit 3
L2 Guided Reading, pp. 416–419
L2 Transparencies LS198, LS199
L2 Skills Lab: *Growing Up,* pp. 422–423

📼 **Lab Activity Video/DVD**
Skills Lab: *Growing Up*

www.SciLinks.org Web Code: scn-0473

DISCOVERY
CHANNEL
SCHOOL
Video Field Trip

⊙ **Student Edition on Audio CD**

Assess

Section Assessment Questions

🎯 Have students use their sentences with Key Terms to answer the questions.

Reteach

Draw a timeline on which students identify the stages of growth and development.

Targeted Print and Technology Resources

All in One Teaching Resources, Unit 3
• Section Summary, p. 415
L1 Review and Reinforce, p. 420
L3 Enrich, p. 421

Chapter 20 Content Refresher

Go Online

NSTA-PDLINKS

For: Professional development support
Visit: www.SciLinks.org/PDLinks
Web Code: scf-0470

Professional Development

Section 1 The Endocrine System

Functions of the Adrenal Glands The adrenal glands, located on top of the kidneys, consist of two parts: an outer region called the adrenal cortex and an inner core called the adrenal medulla. The adrenal cortex secretes hormones that affect metabolism, chemicals in the blood, and certain body characteristics. For example, cortisol controls the body's use of fats, proteins, and carbohydrates. Aldosterone affects salt and water balance. The adrenal medulla helps a person cope with physical and emotional stress. For example, adrenaline and noradrenalin increase the rate of glycogen breakdown and glucose release during "fight-or-flight" situations.

Section 2 The Male and Female Reproductive Systems

Hormones of the Menstrual Cycle Each ovary contains about 400,000 follicles, the structures in which eggs develop. During a typical menstrual cycle, one egg is released from a follicle. This process is regulated by hormones, some of which include estrogen, progesterone, follicle-stimulating hormone (FSH), and luteinizing hormone (LH).

At the onset of menstruation, the level of estrogen in the blood is fairly low. The low level of estrogen causes the pituitary gland to release FSH and LH. FSH stimulates follicle growth. The follicle, in turn, releases estrogen, which makes the lining of the uterus thicken. Rapidly increasing levels of estrogen cause a rapid increase in the production of FSH and LH. The LH surge causes the final maturation of the follicle and release of the egg.

After ovulation, LH causes the follicle to develop into a structure called the corpus luteum. Like the follicle, the corpus luteum releases estrogen, but it also releases progesterone. Progesterone increases the blood supply to the uterus's lining. If the egg is fertilized, it implants in the uterus, and the corpus luteum continues to function for a time. If fertilization and implantation do not occur, the corpus luteum breaks down and releases progressively less estrogen and progesterone. Decreasing levels of these hormones cause the breakdown of the lining of the uterus, and menstruation begins.

Section 3 The Human Life Cycle

Early Embryonic Development Successive cell divisions of the zygote (fertilized egg) eventually produce a hollow structure called a blastocyst, which implants in the wall of the uterus. During gastrulation, the next stage of development, the embryo differentiates into three layers. The outermost layer is the ectoderm, the innermost layer is the endoderm, and the middle layer is the mesoderm.

As development proceeds to produce a recognizable embryo, the ectoderm contributes to formation of the skin and nervous system. The mesoderm is the origin of the muscular and skeletal systems, the circulatory system, and other internal organs and structures. The endoderm provides the cells that line the organs of the gastrointestinal system and many of the digestive organs themselves.

Address Misconceptions

Some students think that the physical changes during puberty occur at a steady pace over a relatively brief period of time. However, puberty lasts about four years and can proceed at varying rates. For a strategy to overcome this misconception, see **Address Misconceptions** in the section *The Human Life Cycle.*

Help Students Read

Summarizing
Briefly Restating the Main Ideas

Strategy Help students understand a topic by restating the main ideas. To summarize, students briefly restate the main concepts in a sentence or two.

Example
1. Ask students to read a selected passage. Then, have them review the passage and identify the main ideas. Demonstrate this process by using the headings, Key Concept statements, and Key Terms to determine what the passage is about.
2. Direct students to write summaries of the passage by restating each of the main ideas in one or two sentences using their own words. Remind students to focus on the most important concepts, omitting details and examples.

Interactive Textbook
- Complete student edition
- Video and audio
- Simulations and activities
- Section and chapter reviews

Chapter Preview

❶ The Endocrine System
Discover *What's the Signal?*
Skills Activity *Making Models*
Active Art *Negative Feedback*
Technology Lab *Modeling Negative Feedback*

❷ The Male and Female Reproductive Systems
Discover *What's the Big Difference?*
Skills Activity *Calculating*
Analyzing Data *Changing Hormone Levels*

❸ The Human Life Cycle
Discover *How Many Ways Does a Child Grow?*
Try This *Way to Grow!*
Try This *Teenagers in Ads*
At-Home Activity *Parenting Skills*
Skills Lab *Growing Up*

Interactive Textbook

▶ Identical twins result when a single fertilized egg splits and forms two embryos.

664 ◆

Lab zone Chapter **Project** L3

Objectives
Students will model parenting behavior and consider how the presence of a baby could change their lives. After this Chapter Project, students will be able to
- make a model "baby"
- observe behavior and use their observations to develop a list of tasks involved in caring for an infant
- solve problems in terms of the model
- make generalizations based on their feelings and reactions
- communicate their results

Skills Focus
Making models, observing, problem solving, making generalizations, communicating

Project Time Line 1 to 2 weeks

All in One Teaching Resources, Unit 3
- Chapter Project Teacher Notes
- Chapter Project Overview
- Chapter Project Worksheet 1
- Chapter Project Worksheet 2
- Chapter Project Scoring Rubric

Developing a Plan
Use the first day to explain the project, hand out the materials, and discuss the responsibilities and expectations of the project. Devote three to five days to the modeling phase. Allow students a day or two to reflect on their journal entries. On the last day, discuss as a class the students' experiences and journal entries.

Possible Materials
- Provide each student with a 5-lb bag of flour or a suitable substitute, a plastic bag to cover the bag of flour, and twist ties to secure the plastic bags.
- Encourage students to suggest and use other materials as well, such as blankets and other accessories.

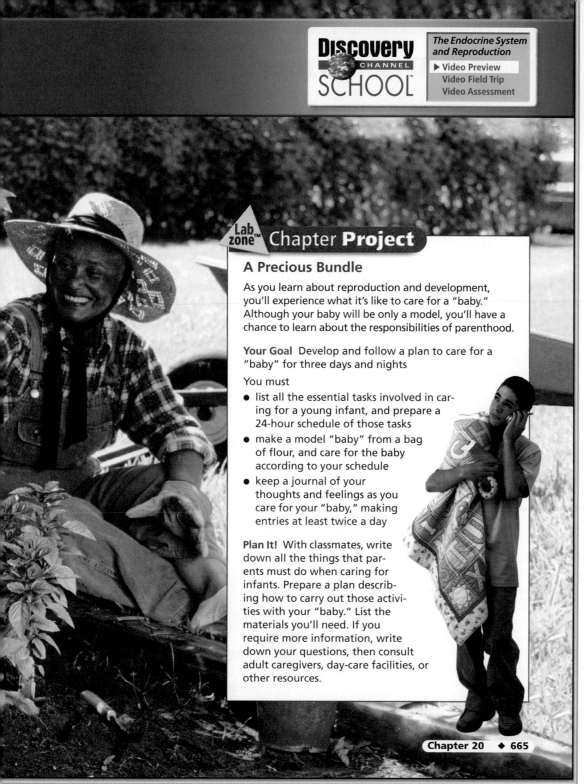

Video Preview

Lab zone™ Chapter **Project**

A Precious Bundle

As you learn about reproduction and development, you'll experience what it's like to care for a "baby." Although your baby will be only a model, you'll have a chance to learn about the responsibilities of parenthood.

Your Goal Develop and follow a plan to care for a "baby" for three days and nights

You must

- list all the essential tasks involved in caring for a young infant, and prepare a 24-hour schedule of those tasks
- make a model "baby" from a bag of flour, and care for the baby according to your schedule
- keep a journal of your thoughts and feelings as you care for your "baby," making entries at least twice a day

Plan It! With classmates, write down all the things that parents must do when caring for infants. Prepare a plan describing how to carry out those activities with your "baby." List the materials you'll need. If you require more information, write down your questions, then consult adult caregivers, day-care facilities, or other resources.

Chapter 20 ◆ 665

The Endocrine System and Reproduction

Show the Video Preview to introduce the Chapter Project and overview the chapter content. Discussion question: **Other than their looks, name two ways that Barbara and Daphne are alike.** *(They colored their hair the same shade, and they were both afraid of blood and heights. Both women even preferred drinking their coffee cold.)*

Performance Assessment

The Chapter Project Scoring Rubric will help you evaluate how well students complete the Chapter Project. You may want to share the scoring rubric with your students so they are clear about what will be expected of them. Students will be assessed on

- how well they prepared their model
- how well they plan their daily tasks and prepare themselves to take care of the model baby
- how thoroughly they complete the task chart
- their willingness to take the role seriously, indicated by the completeness of writing and discussion responses that show evidence of child-care practices and issues
- their communication in class discussions and written work

Launching the Project

Allow time for students to read the description of the project in their text. Then encourage discussion on infant care. Ask: **Why do babies cry?** *(Sample answer: They may be hungry or feel pain.)* Have students brainstorm a list of daily child-care activities covering basic physical needs as well as meeting infants' needs to learn, feel loved, and interact with their environment.

Explain that this process of modeling an event is a scientific way of testing a hypothesis or discovering behaviors. Emphasize that the most accurate and valuable information will come from following the routines as accurately as possible.

Portfolio

Objectives

After this lesson, students will be able to
20.1.1 Describe how the endocrine system controls body processes.
20.1.2 Identify the endocrine glands.
20.1.3 Explain how negative feedback controls hormone levels.

Target Reading Skill 🔄

Relating Cause and Effect Explain that cause is the reason for what happens. The effect is what happens because of the cause. Relating cause and effect helps students relate the reason for what happens to what happens as a result.

Answers

Sample effects: Regulates growth, regulates water balance (by directing the kidneys to regulate the amount of water in the blood), regulates blood pressure

All in One **Teaching Resources, Unit 3**

• Transparency LS191

Preteach

Build Background Knowledge 　　　　L2

Reactions to the Environment
Tell students you are going to give them a "pop" quiz on what they learned in a previous chapter. Ask: **What is the name of the reaction when you feel panic or fear?** *(Students should recall the "fight or flight" response.)* Inform students the same body system that regulates the "fight or flight" response controls their bodies' daily activities and many long-term changes.

Section 1
The Endocrine System

Reading Preview

Key Concepts

• How does the endocrine system control body processes?
• What are the endocrine glands?
• How does negative feedback control hormone levels?

Key Terms

• endocrine gland • hormone
• target cell • hypothalamus
• pituitary gland
• negative feedback

🔄 Target Reading Skill

Relating Cause and Effect As you read, identify the effects of pituitary hormones. Write the information in a graphic organizer like the one below.

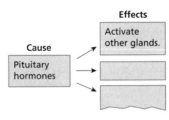

Cause

Pituitary hormones →

Effects

→ Activate other glands.

→

→

🔬 Lab zone　Discover **Activity**

What's the Signal?

1. Stand up and move around the room until your teacher says "Freeze!" Then, stop moving immediately. Stay perfectly still until your teacher says "Start!" Then, begin moving again.
2. Anyone who moves between the "Freeze!" command and the "Start!" command has to leave the game.
3. When only one person is left, that person wins.

Think it Over
Inferring Why is it important for players in this game to respond to signals? What types of signals does the human body use?

Imagine that you are trapped in a damp, dark dungeon. Somewhere near you is a deep pit with water at the bottom. Overhead swings a pendulum with a razor-sharp edge. With each swing, the pendulum lowers closer and closer to your body.

The main character in Edgar Allan Poe's story "The Pit and the Pendulum" finds himself in that very situation. Here is his reaction: "A fearful idea now suddenly drove the blood in torrents upon my heart. . . . I at once started to my feet, trembling convulsively in every fibre. . . . Perspiration burst from every pore, and stood in cold, big beads upon my forehead."

Poe's character is terrified. When people are badly frightened, their bodies react in the ways that the character describes. These physical reactions, such as sweating and rapid heartbeat, are caused mainly by the body's endocrine system.

🔬 Lab zone　Discover **Activity**

Skills Focus Inferring

Materials none

Time 15 minutes

Tips If possible, play this game in a large area such as in a gym or outdoors.

Expected Outcome Players will be eliminated from the game when they do not immediately respond to the "Freeze!" signal.

**　L1**

Think It Over Winning the game depends on responding quickly to the signal; one mistake or delayed response will put a player out of the game. The body uses nerve impulses as signals. Tell students they will learn about another type of signal in this chapter.

Hormones and the Endocrine System

The human body has two systems that regulate its activities, the nervous system and the endocrine system. The nervous system regulates most activities by sending nerve impulses throughout the body. **The endocrine system produces chemicals that control many of the body's daily activities. The endocrine system also regulates long-term changes such as growth and development.**

The endocrine system is made up of glands. A gland is an organ that produces or releases a chemical. Some glands, such as those that produce saliva and sweat, release their chemicals into tiny tubes. The tubes deliver the chemicals to a specific location within the body or to the skin's surface.

Unlike sweat glands, the glands of the endocrine system do not have delivery tubes. **Endocrine glands** (EN duh krin) produce and release their chemical products directly into the bloodstream. The blood then carries those chemicals throughout the body.

Hormones The chemical product of an endocrine gland is called a **hormone.** Hormones turn on, turn off, speed up, or slow down the activities of different organs and tissues. You can think of a hormone as a chemical messenger. Hormones are carried throughout the body by the blood. Therefore, hormones can regulate activities in tissues and organs that are not close to the glands that produce them.

FIGURE 1
Endocrine Control
The endocrine system controls the body's response to an exciting situation such as a roller-coaster ride. Endocrine glands also regulate the changes that occur as a baby grows.
Applying Concepts What are the substances produced by endocrine glands called?

Chapter 20 ◆ 667

Functions of Endocrine Glands

Teach Key Concepts   L2
Glands of the Endocrine System

Focus Ask: **When you hear the word** *hormone,* **what hormones do you think of?** *(Some students may respond that they think of hormones associated with puberty.)*

Teach Refer students to Figure 2, and point out that the body relies on many different types of hormones throughout life. Have different student volunteers read the captions. Ask: **Which two glands control other glands?** *(Hypothalamus and pituitary)* **How does the hypothalamus link the nervous system and the endocrine system?** *(The hypothalamus releases hormones and also sends nerve impulses.)* **How do the hypothalamus and the pituitary gland work together?** *(The hypothalamus sends nerve impulses or hormone signals to the pituitary, which releases certain hormones in response.)* Compare and contrast the endocrine glands of males and females. Ask: **Are all the same glands found in both males and females?** *(No.)* **Which are found only in males?** *(Testes)* **Only in females?** *(Ovaries)*

Apply Have students predict the symptoms of a disorder in various endocrine glands. For example, ask: **What do you think would happen to a person whose pancreas was not functioning properly?** *(The body could not control the amount of glucose in the blood.)* Encourage interested students to use reference books or an electronic resource in the school library to find out whether their predictions are correct. **learning modality: visual**

All in One Teaching Resources, Unit 3
• Transparency LS192

 Lab zone Skills Activity

Making Models
Make a model that shows a hormone and a target cell that the hormone affects. Your model should show how the structures of the hormone and target cell enable the two to fit together. Make your model from materials such as construction paper, pipe cleaners, or modeling clay. When you have finished your model, write an explanation of how it shows the relationship between a hormone and its target cell.

Hormone Production What causes the release of hormones? Often, nerve impulses from the brain make that happen. Suppose, for example, a person sees a deadly, knife-edged pendulum. Nerve impulses travel from the person's eyes to the brain. The brain interprets the information and then sends an impulse to an endocrine gland. That gland, in turn, releases the hormone adrenaline into the bloodstream. Adrenaline immediately makes the heart rate and breathing rate increase.

Hormone Action In contrast to the body's response to a nerve impulse, hormones usually cause a slower, but longer-lasting, response. For example, the brain sends a signal to an endocrine gland to release adrenaline into the bloodstream. When the adrenaline reaches the heart, it makes the heart beat more rapidly. The heart continues to race until the amount of adrenaline in the blood drops to a normal level.

Target Cells When a hormone enters the bloodstream, it affects some organs but not others. Why? The answer lies in the hormone's chemical structure. A hormone interacts only with specific target cells. **Target cells** are cells that recognize the hormone's chemical structure. A hormone and its target cell fit together the way a key fits into a lock. Hormones will travel through the bloodstream until they find the "lock"— or particular cell type—that they fit.

Reading Checkpoint What is a target cell?

Functions of Endocrine Glands

Each endocrine gland releases different hormones and thus controls different processes. **The endocrine glands include the hypothalamus, pituitary, thyroid, parathyroid, adrenal, thymus, and pancreas. They also include the ovaries in females and testes in males.** Figure 2 shows the locations of the endocrine glands and describes some activities they control.

The Hypothalamus The nervous system and the endocrine system work together. The **hypothalamus** (hy poh THAL uh mus), a tiny part of the brain near the middle of your head, is the link between the two systems. Nerve messages controlling sleep, hunger, and other basic body processes come from the hypothalamus. The hypothalamus also produces hormones that control other endocrine glands and organs. The hypothalamus plays a major role in maintaining homeostasis because of the nerve impulses and hormones it produces.

Lab zone Skills Activity

Skills Focus Making models   L1

Materials Construction paper, pipe cleaners, modeling clay, scissors

Time 15 minutes

Tips Many students may work with one material and focus only on making complementary shapes, while some students may work with two materials to further distinguish the hormone from its target cell.

Expected Outcome Results will vary, depending on the shapes students create, but models shouls show "lock-and-key" idea.

Extend Have students use models to explain how a hormone fails to act on cells that are not its target cells. **learning modality: kinesthetic**

FIGURE 2

Glands of the Endocrine System

Each of the endocrine glands has an important regulatory role in the body. Note the location of each gland and the functions of the hormones it produces.

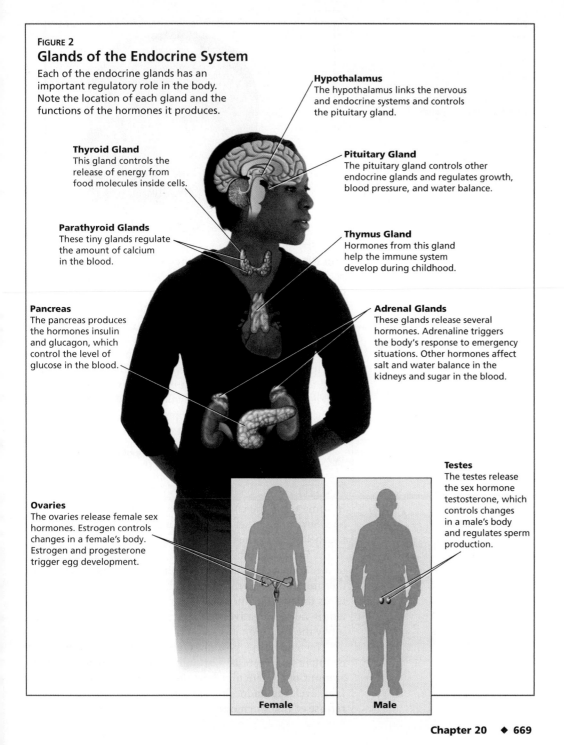

Hypothalamus
The hypothalamus links the nervous and endocrine systems and controls the pituitary gland.

Thyroid Gland
This gland controls the release of energy from food molecules inside cells.

Pituitary Gland
The pituitary gland controls other endocrine glands and regulates growth, blood pressure, and water balance.

Parathyroid Glands
These tiny glands regulate the amount of calcium in the blood.

Thymus Gland
Hormones from this gland help the immune system develop during childhood.

Pancreas
The pancreas produces the hormones insulin and glucagon, which control the level of glucose in the blood.

Adrenal Glands
These glands release several hormones. Adrenaline triggers the body's response to emergency situations. Other hormones affect salt and water balance in the kidneys and sugar in the blood.

Ovaries
The ovaries release female sex hormones. Estrogen controls changes in a female's body. Estrogen and progesterone trigger egg development.

Testes
The testes release the sex hormone testosterone, which controls changes in a male's body and regulates sperm production.

Female

Male

Chapter 20 ◆ 669

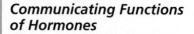

Build Inquiry L2

Communicating Functions of Hormones

Materials poster paper, markers, note cards, up-to-date reference books or information from the Internet (check student sources)

Time 20 minutes

Focus Tell students that in this activity they will learn more about the function of hormones.

Teach Divide students into six groups, and assign each group one of the glands in Figure 3, except testes, ovaries, and hypothalamus. Ask each group to find out what hormones are secreted by the gland and how the hormones affect the body, and then devise a way to show it graphically. For example, the group researching the pancreas might show a person eating carbohydrates and insulin being released as a response. Have groups present their posters to the class and explain the action of each gland.

Apply Have students use the information in the posters to write a paragraph describing how each gland affects their daily lives. For example, the parathyroid glands help them to move around because parathyroid hormone promotes proper muscle function. **learning modality: visual**

Monitor Progress _____ L2

Writing Have students list the glands in the endocrine system and describe one function of each gland.

Answer

✓ **Reading Checkpoint** A cell that recognizes a hormone's chemical structure and is affected by the hormone.

669

Negative Feedback

Teach Key Concepts L2
How Negative Feedback Works

Focus Ask students what *feedback* means in relation to schoolwork. *(Information from the teacher on how a student performed on a task and how he or she could improve)*

Teach Explain that *negative* as used in *negative feedback loop* does not mean bad, wrong, or undesirable; it means that an action stops instead of continuing. Point out that just as the thermostat of a heating system turns on and shuts off the heat to maintain a set temperature, the hypothalamus and pituitary gland work together to control the amount of certain hormones in the blood. Each system is turned off by the condition it produces. Ask: **What conditions turn off a home heating system?** *(Air that has reached the temperature set on the thermostat.)* **What conditions turn off the production of a certain hormone?** *(When blood contains the right level of hormones)* **If the thyroid were a furnace, what would the thermostat be?** *(The hypothalamus, because it senses changes in the level of thyroxine)*

Apply Explain that the hypothalamus senses when a person is losing too much water, for example, through sweating during exercise. It signals the pituitary gland to produce a hormone called antidiuretic hormone (ADH) that causes the kidneys to conserve water. The person becomes thirsty and drinks water. Ask: **How would the negative feedback loop work in this example?** *(The hypothalamus senses when there is enough water in the blood and signals the pituitary gland to stop releasing ADH.)*

Extend The Active Art will show students how a negative feedback loop works.
learning modality: logical/mathematical

All in One Teaching Resources, Unit 3

• Transparency LS193

Go Online
active art

For: Negative Feedback activity
Visit: PHSchool.com
Web Code: cep-4071

Students explore the negative feedback loop.

FIGURE 3
The Pituitary Gland
The pituitary gland is located below the hypothalamus. The pituitary controls several important body functions either directly or indirectly by signaling other endocrine glands.

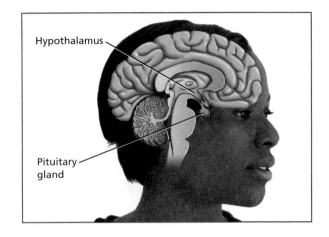

Hypothalamus

Pituitary gland

The Pituitary Gland Just below the hypothalamus is an endocrine gland about the size of a pea. The **pituitary gland** (pih TOO ih tehr ee) communicates with the hypothalamus to control many body activities. In response to nerve impulses or hormone signals from the hypothalamus, the pituitary gland releases its hormones. Some of those hormones act as an "on" switch for other endocrine glands. For example, one pituitary hormone signals the thyroid gland to produce hormones. Other pituitary hormones control body activities directly. Growth hormone regulates growth from infancy to adulthood. Another pituitary hormone directs the kidneys to regulate the amount of water in the blood.

 **Reading Checkpoint** What causes the pituitary gland to release hormones?

Negative Feedback

In some ways, the endocrine system works like a heating system. Suppose you set a thermostat at 20°C. If the temperature falls below 20°C, the thermostat signals the furnace to turn on. When the furnace heats the area to the proper temperature, information about the warm conditions "feeds back" to the thermostat. The thermostat then gives the furnace a signal that turns the furnace off. The type of signal used in a heating system is called **negative feedback** because the system is turned off by the condition it produces.

The endocrine system often uses negative feedback to maintain homeostasis. **Through negative feedback, when the amount of a particular hormone in the blood reaches a certain level, the endocrine system sends signals that stop the release of that hormone.**

670 ◆

Differentiated Instruction

Special Needs L1
Demonstrating the Negative Feedback Loop
Ask two student volunteers to help in this demonstration. The first student holds a small bowl of jellybeans and the second student holds a small empty bowl. The first student places jellybeans in the empty bowl until the second student says "Stop." Have them do the demonstration again as you guide them to identify how their roles are like the feedback loop. *(First student is a gland releasing a hormone. The jellybeans are the hormones traveling to the target cells. The second student is the organ giving a signal—telling the first student to stop—that it has enough of the hormone.)* **learning modality: kinesthetic**

You can see an example of negative feedback in Figure 4. Like a thermostat in a cool room, the endocrine system senses when there's not enough thyroxine in the blood. Thyroxine is a thyroid hormone that controls how much energy is available to cells. When there's not enough energy available, the hypothalamus signals the pituitary gland to release thyroid-stimulating hormone (TSH). That hormone signals the thyroid gland to release thyroxine. When the amount of thyroxine reaches the right level, the endocrine system signals the thyroid gland to stop releasing thyroxine.

 Reading Checkpoint How is thyroxine involved in negative feedback?

FIGURE 4
Negative Feedback
The release of the hormone thyroxine is controlled through negative feedback. When enough thyroxine is present, the system signals the thyroid gland to stop releasing the hormone. **Predicting** *What happens when the amount of thyroxine becomes too low?*

Go Online
active art
For: Negative Feedback activity
Visit: PHSchool.com
Web Code: cep-4071

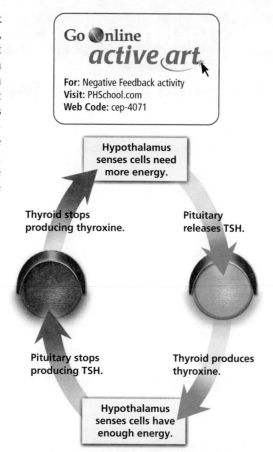

Hypothalamus senses cells need more energy.

Thyroid stops producing thyroxine.

Pituitary releases TSH.

Pituitary stops producing TSH.

Thyroid produces thyroxine.

Hypothalamus senses cells have enough energy.

Section 1 Assessment

Target Reading Skill

Relating Cause and Effect For Question 2, refer to your graphic organizer about the pituitary gland.

Reviewing Key Concepts

1. **a. Identifying** What is the role of the endocrine system?
   b. Explaining How does adrenaline affect the heart?
   c. Predicting What could happen if your body continued to release adrenaline into your bloodstream, and the amount of adrenaline did not return to normal?
2. **a. Listing** List the endocrine glands.
   b. Summarizing How do the hypothalamus and the pituitary gland interact?

   c. Relating Cause and Effect Explain how the hypothalamus indirectly controls growth from infancy to adulthood.
3. **a. Defining** Define negative feedback.
   b. Applying Concepts How does negative feedback help to maintain homeostasis?

Writing in Science

Cause-and-Effect Paragraph Explain how the nervous system and endocrine system work together when adrenaline is released.

Lab zone Chapter Project

Keep Students on Track As you review students' schedules, make sure each student has included all essential child-care tasks. Encourage students to be realistic. Remind them that babies need to eat several times a day and that real babies will often disrupt scheduled events by crying or being ill. Make sure students arrange for alternative child-care when they need to meet other obligations.

Writing in Science

Writing Skill Explanation
Scoring Rubric
4 Includes clear explanation of how conditions may cause the brain to signal the adrenal glands to produce adrenaline
3 Includes all criteria but is sometimes unclear.
2 Includes only brief explanation
1 Includes inaccurate explanation

Monitor Progress L2

Answers

Figure 4 Energy available to cells decreases, so the hypothalamus signals the pituitary gland to release TSH.

Reading Checkpoint Nerve impulses or hormone signals from the hypothalamus

Reading Checkpoint Increased thyroxine levels cause the hypothalamus to signal the pituitary gland to stop producing TSH.

Assess

Reviewing Key Concepts

1. **a.** Produces chemicals that control many body activities and regulate changes such as growth and development **b.** Makes the heart beat more rapidly **c.** Sample answer: Your heart and breathing rates would not return to normal, which could become dangerous.
2. **a.** Hypothalamus, pituitary, thyroid, thymus, parathyroid, adrenal, pancreas, testes (in males), ovaries (in females) **b.** The pituitary gland produces hormones in response to nerve impulses or hormones sent out by the hypothalamus. **c.** The hypothalamus regulates the release of hormones from the pituitary gland, including growth hormones.
3. **a.** The process in which a system is turned off by the condition it produces **b.** When the amount of a hormone in the blood reaches the right level, the endocrine system signals the gland to stop producing that hormone.

Reteach L1

Use Figure 2 to summarize the functions of the endocrine system.

Performance Assessment L2

Writing Have students write short paragraphs describing how the endocrine system helps the body maintain homeostasis.

All in One Teaching Resources, Unit 3
• Section Summary: *The Endocrine System*
• Review and Reinforce: *The Endocrine System*
• Enrich: *The Endocrine System*

Modeling Negative Feedback

L3

Prepare for Inquiry

Key Concept
Negative feedback is a process by which a system is regulated by the condition it produces.

Skills Objectives
After this lab, students will be able to:
- make and observe a model that illustrates negative feedback
- evaluate how the model illustrates negative feedback in the endocrine system

⏱ **Prep Time** 15 minutes
Class Time 40 minutes

All in One **Teaching Resources, Unit 3**
- Lab Worksheet: *Modeling Negative Feedback*

Safety
 Suggest that students wear lab aprons to keep clothing dry in case of water spills.

Advance Planning
Several days before doing the activity, ask students to bring in empty 1-L and 2-L plastic soda bottles. Check the size of stoppers in advance to make sure they fit properly in the inside neck of the larger bottle. Use bottles that can hold at least 1 L of water to provide enough space for the balloon to move freely and act as a value. Cut the bottoms off the 2-L bottles.

Alternative Materials
Other plastic bottles besides soda bottles may be used, (for example, plastic milk bottles) but the two bottles need to have mouths of the same size. If the mouth is large, this will necessitate using larger balloons and stoppers. Corks may be used in place of rubber stoppers.

Guide Inquiry

Invitation
Ask: **How does negative feedback control hormones in the body?** (*When the amount of a particular hormone in the blood reaches a certain level, the endocrine system sends signals that stop the release of the hormone.*)

Modeling Negative Feedback

Problem
How can you model negative feedback?

Skills Focus
observing, making models, evaluating the design

Materials
- duct tape
- round balloon
- scissors
- rubber stopper
- string, 40 cm
- large plastic soda bottle (2 L) with bottom removed
- small plastic soda bottle (1 L)
- plastic tray
- water

Procedure

PART 1 Research and Investigate

1. Figure 1 shows how a flush toilet uses negative feedback to regulate the water level. In your notebook, describe which part of the process involves negative feedback.

FIGURE 1

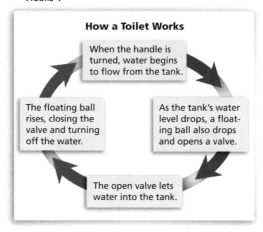

How a Toilet Works

When the handle is turned, water begins to flow from the tank.

As the tank's water level drops, a floating ball also drops and opens a valve.

The open valve lets water into the tank.

The floating ball rises, closing the valve and turning off the water.

FIGURE 2

PART 2 Design and Build

2. As you hold the open end of a balloon, push its closed end through the mouth of a small plastic bottle. Do not push the open end of the balloon into the bottle. Then, slide a straw partway into the bottle so that the air inside the bottle can escape as you blow up the balloon.

3. Partially blow up the balloon inside the bottle as shown in Figure 2. The partially inflated balloon should be about the size of a tennis ball. Remove the straw. Tie the balloon tightly, then push it into the bottle.

4. Place the large plastic bottle mouth to mouth with the small bottle. Tape the two bottles together. Make sure that the seal is waterproof.

Introducing the Procedure
Make sure that students understand the concept of negative feedback before constructing the model.

- In Step 3, students should make sure that the inflated balloon is small enough to fall freely. When the water flows from the reservoir to the bottle below, the balloon needs to float upward freely in order to function as a valve.

- The upper bottle needs to be larger than the lower bottle to ensure that the volume of water it holds is beyond the capacity of the lower bottle.

- The purpose of placing a stopper in the large bottle and filling it in Steps 6 and 7, rather than allowing the water to begin draining into the smaller bottle below as the top one is filled, is to enable students to see that draining stops before the upper bottle is empty.

FIGURE 3

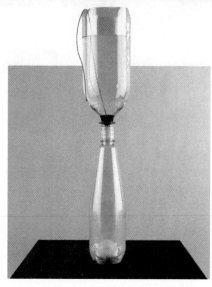

FIGURE 4

5. Tie one end of a piece of string around the top of a rubber stopper as shown in Figure 3.

6. Place the attached bottles on the tray with the smaller bottle on the bottom. Place the stopper loosely into the mouth of the larger bottle as shown in Figure 4.

7. While one partner holds the bottles upright, add water to the large bottle until it is about three fourths full. Then gently pull the string to remove the stopper. Watch what happens. Pay close attention to the following: What does the balloon do as water rises in the small bottle? Does the small bottle completely fill with water? Record your observations.

8. In your notebook, record which part of your device models negative feedback.

PART 3 **Evaluate and Redesign**

9. In the human endocrine system, negative feedback occurs as part of a cycle. With your partner, think of one or more ways that you could modify the model from Part 2 to show a cycle.

Analyze and Conclude

1. **Inferring** Summarize your research from Part 1 by describing an example of negative feedback.

2. **Observing** Describe the events you observed in Step 7.

3. **Making Models** In Step 7, which part of the process involves negative feedback? Explain your answer.

4. **Evaluating the Design** In a short paragraph, summarize the ideas you and your partner thought of in Step 9 to show that negative feedback can be part of a cycle.

Communicating

Suppose you are a TV health reporter preparing a program on human hormones. You need to do a 30-second segment on hormones and negative feedback. Write a script for your presentation. Include references to a model to help viewers understand how negative feedback works in the endocrine system.

Troubleshooting the Experiment

- Be sure the two bottles are securely taped together to prevent water from leaking.
- Students will need to hold the apparatus steady while filling the top bottle with water to prevent the now top-heavy apparatus from tipping over.
- Make sure students hold onto the balloon firmly while blowing it up so the untied balloon does not slip into the bottle.
- Students should not press the stopper tightly into place. A little leakage will not harm the results, but a stopper that won't budge when the string is pulled will interfere.
- If the students fail to make the necessary observations, have them pour the water out through the top bottle, and repeat Steps 6–8.

Expected Outcome

As the water level rises, the balloon will float up and block the mouth of the bottle preventing further water from pouring from the upper bottle to the lower bottle. This will occur even though there is still water in the upper bottle, and there is still space in the lower bottle.

Analyze and Conclude

1. The rising water level in a toilet tank lifts a ball that causes a valve to close, stopping the flow of water into the tank.

2. The balloon began to rise as the water level increased. When the balloon reached the top of the bottle, the flow of water stopped.

3. The water illustrates negative feedback. Rising water causes the water level to stop rising.

4. Sample answer: The setup can be modified by placing a drain valve in the lower bottle to empty it and recycling the water into the reservoir in the top bottle. Then the water can be released back into the lower bottle again.

Extend Inquiry

Communicating

Student scripts should include a brief explanation of the role of hormones in the body and how they are regulated by negative feedback. Models described should be clear representations of the process.

673

Section 2
The Male and Female Reproductive Systems

Objectives

After this, students will be able to

20.2.1 Define sexual reproduction.
20.2.2 Describe the structures and functions of the male reproductive system.
20.2.3 Describe the structures and functions of the female reproductive system.
20.2.4 Sequence the events that occur during the menstrual cycle.

Target Reading Skill

Sequencing Explain that organizing information from beginning to end helps students understand a step-by-step process.

Answers

The Menstrual Cycle
Days 1–4 Menstrual discharge
Days 5–13 Developing egg
Days 14–15 Ovulation
Days 16–22 Egg moves through oviduct
Days 23–28 Egg enters uterus

All in One Teaching Resources, Unit 3

• Transparency LS194

Preteach

Build Background Knowledge L2

Reproductive Systems

Organize students in small discussion groups and have them brainstorm lists of things they think they already know about the male and female reproductive systems. Use these lists as students study the chapter to address any misconceptions they may have.

Reading Preview

Key Concepts

• What is sexual reproduction?
• What are the structures and functions of the male and female reproductive systems?
• What events occur during the menstrual cycle?

Key Terms

• egg • sperm • fertilization
• zygote • testis • testosterone
• scrotum • semen • penis
• ovary • estrogen
• fallopian tube • uterus
• vagina • menstrual cycle
• ovulation • menstruation

Target Reading Skill

Sequencing As you read, make a cycle diagram like the one below that shows the menstrual cycle. Write each event of the process in a separate circle.

The Menstrual Cycle

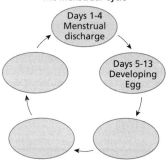

Days 1-4 Menstrual discharge

Days 5-13 Developing Egg

Hormones control growth and development.

674 ◆

Lab zone Discover **Activity**

What's the Big Difference?

1. Your teacher will provide prepared slides of eggs and sperm.
2. Examine each slide under the microscope, first under low power, then under high power. Be sure you view more than one example of each kind of cell.
3. Sketch and label each sample.

Think It Over
Observing What differences did you observe between sperm cells and egg cells? What general statement can you make about eggs and sperm?

Many differences between an adult animal and its young are controlled by the endocrine system. In humans, two endocrine glands—the ovaries and the testes—control many of the changes that occur as a child matures. These glands release hormones that cause the body to develop as a person grows older. They also produce sex cells that are part of sexual reproduction.

Lab zone Discover **Activity**

Skills Focus Observing L2

Materials slides of human egg and sperm cells, microscope

Time 20 minutes

Tips Students may need help focusing the microscope and finding the egg and sperm cells. Encourage them to begin at low power before switching to high power.

Think It Over Sperm cells are much smaller than egg cells and have long tail-like parts. Eggs are round, usually much larger than sperm, and do not have tails. Sperm have tails (flagella) that enable them to move. Eggs contain most of the cytoplasm that will make up the new cells that form from the zygote.

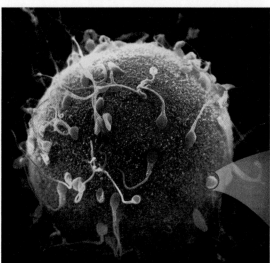

FIGURE 5
Egg and Sperm
An egg is one of the largest cells in the body. A sperm, which is much smaller than an egg, has a head (rounded end) and a tail that allows it to move. In the photograph on the left, sperm are swarming around the large egg. On the right, a sperm, which has been colored blue, has penetrated the egg.
Applying Concepts *What structure results when the sperm fertilizes the egg?*

Sexual Reproduction

You may find it hard to believe that you began life as a single cell. That single cell was produced by the joining of two other cells, an egg and a sperm. An **egg** is the female sex cell. A **sperm** is the male sex cell.

The joining of a sperm and an egg is called **fertilization.** Fertilization is an important part of sexual reproduction, the process by which male and female living things produce new individuals. **Sexual reproduction involves the production of eggs by the female and sperm by the male. The egg and sperm join together during fertilization.** When fertilization occurs, a fertilized egg, or **zygote,** is produced. Every one of the trillions of cells in your body is descended from the single cell that formed during fertilization.

Like other cells in the body, sex cells contain rod-shaped structures called chromosomes. Chromosomes (KROH muh sohmz) carry the information that controls inherited characteristics, such as eye color and blood type. Every cell in the human body that has a nucleus, except the sex cells, contains 46 chromosomes. Each sex cell contains half that number, or 23 chromosomes. During fertilization, the 23 chromosomes in a sperm join the 23 chromosomes in an egg. The result is a zygote with 46 chromosomes. The zygote contains all of the information needed to produce a new human being.

 Reading Checkpoint **What happens to the number of chromosomes when a male sex cell and a female sex cell join?**

Instruct

Sexual Reproduction

Teach Key Concepts · L2
Fertilization

Focus Have students locate a period at the end of a sentence in the text. Explain that everyone began life from a single cell that was about that size.

Teach Explain that trillions of cells result from a single fertilized cell. Ask: **What is that single cell called?** *(A zygote)* **How did it form?** *(Through fertilization, in which an egg from a female and sperm from a male joined)* **What is that process called?** *(Sexual reproduction)* Have students refer to Figure 6 and read the caption. Ask: **How do the two sex cells differ?** *(The egg cell is larger, while the sperm cell has a tail that enables it to move.)* Point out that a human sperm and egg cell each have 23 chromosomes so that when they join, every cell from then on will have 46 chromosomes, except the sex cells.

Apply Ask: **Why do the two sex cells differ in form?** *(The sperm must travel to the egg to allow for fertilization. The egg must have a food supply.)* **learning modality: visual**

Independent Practice · L2

 **Teaching Resources, Unit 3**

• Guided Reading and Study Worksheet: *The Male and Female Reproductive Systems*

⊙ **Student Edition on Audio CD**

Less Proficient Readers · L1
Organizing Information As students read, have them list the differences between the male and female reproductive systems in a table such as the one shown. When they have finished reading the section, ask: **What is the function of ovaries?** *(Produce eggs)* **Why are the testes located outside the body?** *(Sperm need cooler temperatures.)* **learning modality: verbal**

Characteristic	Male	Female
Sex cell	sperm	egg
Organs	testes	ovaries
Hormones	testosterone	estrogen

Monitor Progress · L2

Drawing Ask students to draw a diagram showing how a zygote is formed and how it has 46 chromosomes.

Answers
Figure 5 Zygote

 Reading Checkpoint The number of chromosomes is restored to 46, the number typical of human body cells.

675

Male Reproductive System

Teach Key Concepts

Structures of the Male Reproductive System

Focus Review with students that sperm cells are produced by the male reproductive system.

Teach Refer students to Figure 6. Explain that hundreds of coiled tubes in the testes produce and store sperm cells and produce testosterone. Ask: **What does this hormone do?** *(It controls the development of physical characteristics in men.)* Explain that the scrotum helps the testes maintain a temperature 2–3°C below the usual body temperature. Ask: **Why is the location of the scrotum important?** *(Sperm need slightly cooler conditions to develop normally.)*

Apply Ask: **What might happen if a man has a high fever for a long time?** *(Sperm might not develop properly.)* **learning modality: verbal**

Teaching Resources, Unit 3

• Transparency LS195

Male Reproductive System

The organs of the male reproductive system are shown in Figure 6. **The male reproductive system is specialized to produce sperm and the hormone testosterone. The structures of the male reproductive system include the testes, scrotum, and penis.**

The Testes The oval-shaped **testes** (TES teez) (singular *testis*) are the organs of the male reproductive system in which sperm are produced. The testes consist of clusters of hundreds of tiny coiled tubes and the cells between the tubes. Sperm are formed inside the tubes.

The testes also produce testosterone. **Testosterone** (tes TAHS tuh rohn) is a hormone that controls the development of physical characteristics in mature men. Some of those characteristics include facial hair, deepening of the voice, broadening of the shoulders, and the ability to produce sperm.

Notice in Figure 6 that the testes are located in an external pouch of skin called the **scrotum** (SKROH tum). The external location keeps the testes about 2°C to 3°C below 37°C, which is the usual temperature within the body. That temperature difference is important. Sperm need the slightly cooler conditions to develop normally.

FIGURE 6
The Male Reproductive System

In the male reproductive system, the testes produce sperm and the hormone testosterone.
Interpreting Diagrams *Trace the pathway of sperm in the male reproductive system. What structures does a sperm cell pass through before exiting the body?*

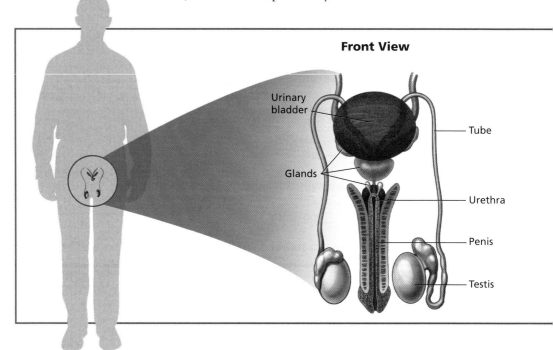

Front View

Urinary bladder

Glands

Tube

Urethra

Penis

Testis

Sperm Production The production of sperm cells begins in males at some point during the teenage years. Each sperm cell is composed of a head that contains chromosomes and a long, whiplike tail. Basically, a sperm cell is a tiny package of chromosomes that can swim.

The Path of Sperm Cells Once sperm cells form in the testes, they travel through other structures in the male reproductive system. During this passage, sperm mix with fluids produced by nearby glands. This mixture of sperm cells and fluids is called **semen** (SEE mun). Semen contains a huge number of sperm—about 5 to 10 million per drop! The fluids in semen provide an environment in which sperm are able to swim. Semen also contains nutrients that the moving sperm use as a source of energy.

Semen leaves the body through an organ called the **penis.** The tube in the penis through which the semen travels is called the urethra. Urine also leaves the body through the urethra. When semen passes through the urethra, however, muscles near the bladder contract. Those muscles prevent urine and semen from mixing.

 Reading Checkpoint What is the pouch of skin in which the testes are located?

Go Online
SciLINKS NSTA

For: Links on the reproductive system
Visit: www.SciLinks.org
Web Code: scn-0472

Go Online
SciLINKS NSTA

For: Links on the reproductive system
Visit: www.SciLinks.org
Web Code: scn-0472

Download a worksheet that will guide students' review of the reproductive system.

Lab zone Build **Inquiry** L1

Comparing and Contrasting the Male and Female Reproductive Systems

Materials reference books or online sources of information
Time 20 minutes

Focus After discussing the female reproductive system on the next two pages, briefly review the structures of both reproductive systems.

Teach Use the text and additional sources to gather information on the similarities and differences between the functions of the ovaries and the testes.

Apply Students can then use the information to develop compare-and-contrast tables. Invite students to share their tables with the class. **learning modality: verbal**

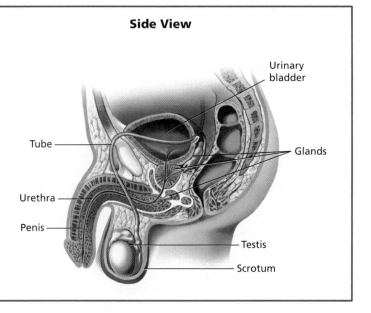

Side View

- Urinary bladder
- Tube
- Glands
- Urethra
- Penis
- Testis
- Scrotum

Monitor Progress L2

Have students draw concept maps describing the production and path of sperm. Students can save the concept maps in their portfolios. **Portfolio**

Answers
Figure 6 From the testis, through the tube and then the urethra in the penis

 Reading Checkpoint Scrotum

Female Reproductive System

Teach Key Concepts   L2

Structures of the Female Reproductive System

Focus Review with students that egg cells are produced by the female reproductive system.

Teach Explain that the ovaries produce the egg cells and that ovaries are the endocrine glands that produce estrogen, the female hormone. Ask: **How is the function of estrogen like the function of testosterone?** *(Estrogen triggers the female characteristics to develop; testosterone plays a similar role in males.)* Explain that other structures of the female reproductive system function to move the egg cell for fertilization, support a fertilized egg, or remove an unfertilized egg from the body. Ask: **What are fallopian tubes?** *(Passageways for eggs as they travel from the ovary to the uterus)* **What is the function of the uterus?** *(To hold a fertilized egg through its development)*

Apply Ask: **How is the function of the female reproductive system different from that of the male?** *(The female system is structured to contain and nourish a developing baby until birth.)* **learning modality: verbal**

All in One Teaching Resources, Unit 3

• Transparency LS196

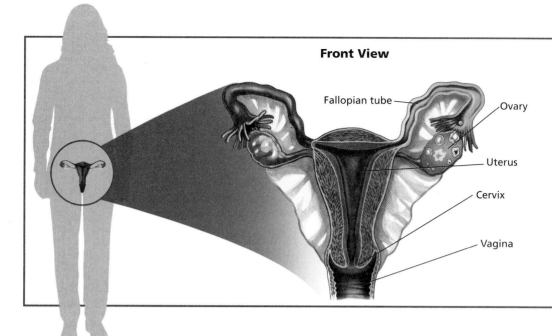

Front View

Fallopian tube

Ovary

Uterus

Cervix

Vagina

FIGURE 7
Female Reproductive System
In the female reproductive system, the two ovaries produce eggs and hormones such as estrogen. **Relating Cause and Effect** *What changes does estrogen produce in a female's body?*

Female Reproductive System

Figure 7 shows the female reproductive system. **The role of the female reproductive system is to produce eggs and, if an egg is fertilized, to nourish a developing baby until birth. The organs of the female reproductive system include the ovaries, fallopian tubes, uterus, and vagina.**

The Ovaries The **ovaries** (OH vuh reez) are the female reproductive structures that produce eggs. The ovaries are located slightly below the waist, one ovary on each side of the body. The name for these organs comes from the Latin word *ova*, meaning "eggs."

Female Hormones Like the testes in males, the ovaries also are endocrine glands that produce hormones. One hormone, **estrogen** (ES truh jun), triggers the development of some adult female characteristics. For example, estrogen causes the hips to widen and the breasts to develop. Estrogen also plays a role in the process by which egg cells develop.

The Path of the Egg Cell Each ovary is located near a fallopian tube. The **fallopian tubes,** also called oviducts, are passageways for eggs as they travel from the ovary to the uterus. Each month, one of the ovaries releases a mature egg, which enters the nearest fallopian tube. Fertilization usually occurs within a fallopian tube.

678 ◆

⌐ Differentiated Instruction ⌐

Less Proficient Readers   L1
Remembering Vocabulary Encourage students to create a list of terms and definitions in this section. They can make flash cards with the terms on one side and the definitions on the other, then work in pairs to quiz each other. Encourage students to refer to the diagrams often to visualize the meaning of the terms.
learning modality: verbal

Gifted and Talented   L3
Interpreting Health Information Ask students to use reliable sources, including their family doctors, to find out what causes painful menstrual cramps. *(Chemicals called prostaglandins)* and how cramps can be treated. Have students share their findings with teen girls in the class.
learning modality: verbal

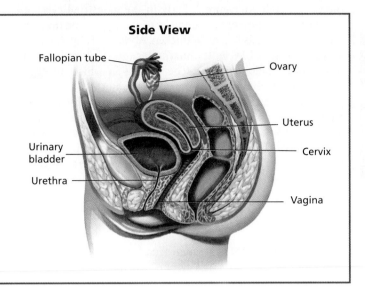

Side View

Fallopian tube

Ovary

Uterus

Cervix

Urinary bladder

Urethra

Vagina

The egg moves through the fallopian tube, which leads to the uterus. The **uterus** (YOO tur us) is a hollow muscular organ about the size of a pear. If an egg has been fertilized, it becomes attached to the wall of the uterus.

An egg that has not been fertilized starts to break down in the uterus. It leaves the uterus through an opening at the base of the uterus, called the cervix. The egg then enters the vagina. The **vagina** (vuh JY nuh) is a muscular passageway leading to the outside of the body. The vagina, or birth canal, is the passageway through which a baby leaves the mother's body.

 Reading Checkpoint What is the role of the fallopian tube?

The Menstrual Cycle

When the female reproductive system becomes mature, usually during the teenage years, there are about 400,000 undeveloped eggs in the ovaries. However, only about 500 of those eggs will actually leave the ovaries and reach the uterus. An egg is released about once a month in a mature woman's body. The monthly cycle of changes that occur in the female reproductive system is called the **menstrual cycle** (MEN stroo ul).

During the menstrual cycle, an egg develops in an ovary. At the same time, the uterus prepares for the arrival of an embryo. In this way, the menstrual cycle prepares the woman's body for pregnancy, which begins after fertilization.

Lab zone Skills **Activity**

Calculating
An egg is about 0.1 mm in diameter. In contrast, the head of a sperm is about 0.005 mm. Calculate how much bigger an egg is than a sperm.

Chapter 20 ◆ 679

679

Address Misconceptions
Confusing Concepts and Terminology

Focus Many students may confuse the term *menstrual cycle* with the term *menstruation.*

Teach Explain that the menstrual cycle includes the maturation of the egg, the thickening of the uterine lining, the release of the egg, and the breakdown of the uterine lining, as well as menstruation. Menstruation describes the process by which the blood and tissue of the lining exit the body.

Apply Ask: **During which part of the menstrual cycle does menstruation take place?** *(During the first four days of the cycle)* Explain that menstruation may last longer for some women and that differences in the length of menstruation are normal.
learning modality: verbal

Math **Analyzing Data**

Math Skills Making and interpreting graphs

Focus Remind students that hormones in addition to estrogen are involved in the menstrual cycle.

Teach Explain that the horizontal axis represents the time period in days of the menstrual cycle. The vertical axis represents the amount of a particular female hormone that is present. Together, the information can be used to show variances in the levels of the hormone during the menstrual cycle.

Answers
1. Level of LH
2. About 12, 12, 12
3. About 56
4. Day 13; ovulation occurs

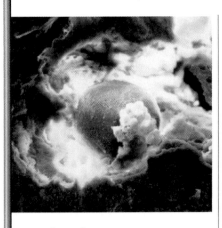

FIGURE 8
Release of an Egg
The ovary releases an egg, shown here in pink. The egg will then travel down the fallopian tube to the uterus. **Applying Concepts** *Through what opening does an unfertilized egg pass when leaving the uterus?*

Stages of the Menstrual Cycle Follow the stages of the menstrual cycle in Figure 9. Early in the menstrual cycle, an egg starts to mature in one of the ovaries. At the same time, the lining of the uterus begins to thicken. About halfway through a typical menstrual cycle, the mature egg is released from the ovary into a fallopian tube. The process in which an egg is released is called **ovulation** (ahv yuh LAY shun).

Once the egg is released, it can be fertilized for the next few days if sperm are present in the fallopian tube. If the egg is not fertilized, it begins to break down. The lining of the uterus also breaks down. The extra blood and tissue of the thickened lining pass out of the body through the vagina in a process called **menstruation** (men stroo AY shun). On average, menstruation lasts about four to six days. At the same time that menstruation takes place, a new egg begins to mature in the ovary, and the cycle continues.

Endocrine Control The menstrual cycle is controlled by hormones of the endocrine system. Hormones also trigger a girl's first menstruation. Many girls begin menstruation sometime between the ages of 10 and 14 years. Some girls start earlier, while others start later. Women continue to menstruate until about the age of 50. At around that age, the production of sex hormones drops. As a result, the ovaries stop releasing mature egg cells.

 Reading Checkpoint How often is an egg released from an ovary?

Math **Analyzing Data**

Changing Hormone Levels
A woman's hormone levels change throughout the menstrual cycle. The graph shows the levels of one female hormone, known as LH, during the menstrual cycle.

1. **Reading Graphs** What does the *y*-axis show?
2. **Interpreting Data** What is the level of LH on day 1? On day 17? On day 21?
3. **Calculating** What is the difference between LH levels on days 9 and 13?
4. **Drawing Conclusions** On what day does LH reach its highest level? What event takes place at about the same time?

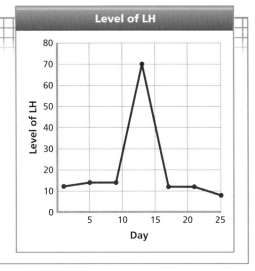

FIGURE 9
The Menstrual Cycle

During the menstrual cycle, the lining of the uterus builds up with extra blood and tissue. About halfway through a typical cycle, ovulation takes place. **Predicting** *What happens if the egg is not fertilized?*

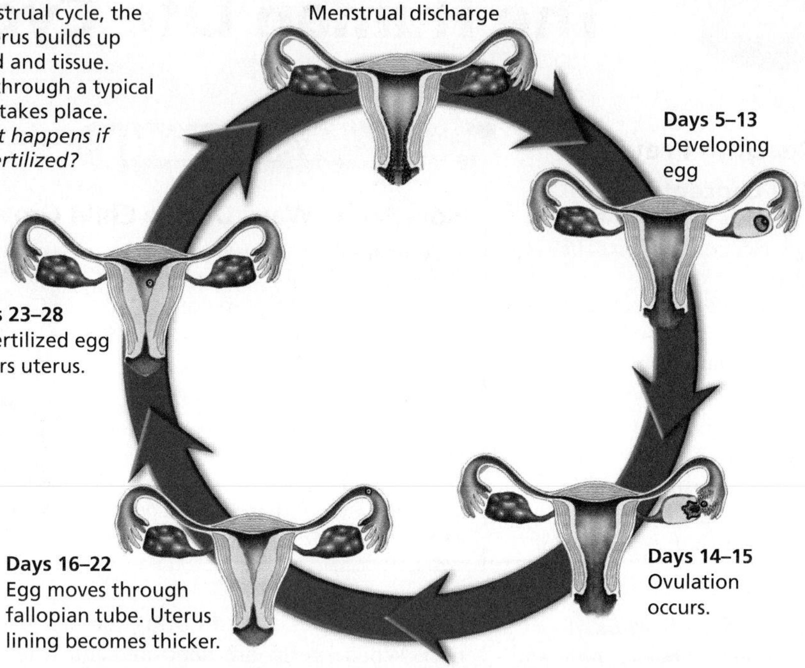

Days 1–4
Menstrual discharge

Days 5–13
Developing egg

Days 14–15
Ovulation occurs.

Days 16–22
Egg moves through fallopian tube. Uterus lining becomes thicker.

Days 23–28
Unfertilized egg enters uterus.

Section 2 Assessment

🎯 **Target Reading Skill** **Sequencing** Refer to your cycle diagram about the menstrual cycle as you answer Question 3.

Reviewing Key Concepts

1. a. Reviewing What is fertilization?
 b. Explaining Explain how fertilization produces a new individual.
 c. Comparing and Contrasting Contrast the number of chromosomes in sex cells and in a zygote. Explain why the zygote has the number of chromosomes that it does.
2. a. Listing List the structures of the male and female reproductive systems.
 b. Describing Describe the functions of the structures you named in Question 2a.

 c. Comparing and Contrasting In what ways are the functions of the ovaries and the testes similar? How do their functions differ?
3. a. Defining What is the menstrual cycle?
 b. Sequencing Events At what point in the menstrual cycle does ovulation occur?

Writing in Science

Explanatory Paragraph Write a paragraph explaining why the ovaries and testes are part of both the endocrine system and the reproductive system.

Chapter 20 ◆ 681

Writing in Science

Writing Skill Exposition
Scoring Rubric
4 Includes detailed explanations of the roles each system plays in reproduction and hormone production
3 Includes correct explanations, but lacks some details
2 Includes incomplete explanations
1 Includes inaccurate explanations

Lab zone Chapter Project

Keep Students on Track Check that students are continuing to care for their "babies." They must perform all tasks and write in their journals each day. You may want to set aside some time for discussions in which students compare child-care experiences and give each other pointers.

Monitor Progress _____ L2
Answers
Figure 8 The vagina
Figure 9 The egg and uterine lining break down and menstruation takes place.

 Reading Checkpoint Once a month

Assess

Reviewing Key Concepts

1. a. The joining of an egg and a sperm **b.** The egg and sperm join together and the resulting fertilized egg contains all the information needed to grow into a new individual. **c.** A sex cell has 23 chromosomes, while a zygote has 46. A zygote results from the joining of an egg and sperm during fertilization.
2. a. Male—testes, scrotum, penis; female—ovaries, fallopian tubes, uterus, vagina **b.** Testes—produce sperm and testosterone; scrotum—external pouch of skin that contains the testes and keeps them cooler than body temperature; penis—organ through which semen leaves the body; ovaries—produce eggs and hormones, such as estrogen; fallopian tubes—passageways eggs travel to the uterus—holds the fertilized egg; vagina—birth canal. **c.** Similar—both produce sex cells and hormones; different—testes produce sperm and testosterone, while ovaries produce eggs and estrogen

3. a. The monthly cycle of changes that occur in the female reproductive system **b.** Days 14 to 15

Reteach L1
Have students name the structures and functions of the male and female reproductive systems using the diagrams in this section.

Performance Assessment L2
Skills Check Have students create flowcharts showing the path of sperm or egg through its respective reproductive system.

All in One Teaching Resources, Unit 3
• Section Summary: *The Male and Female Reproductive Systems*
• Review and Reinforce: *The Male and Female Reproductive Systems*
• Enrich: *The Male and Female Reproductive Systems*

Objectives

After this lesson, students will be able to

20.3.1 List the stages of human development that occur before birth.

20.3.2 Explain how the developing embryo is protected and nourished.

20.3.3 Describe what happens during childbirth.

20.3.4 Identify changes that occur from infancy to adulthood.

Target Reading Skill 🔄

Building Vocabulary Explain that knowing the definitions of Key Terms helps students understand what they read.

Preteach

Build Background Knowledge   L2

Identifying Characteristics

Show students several pictures of a variety of baby mammals, including human beings. Encourage students to brainstorm a list of characteristics that they all have in common. *(Sample answers: Feed on mother's milk, depend on parents for food, are smaller than parents but have similar characteristics)*

The Human Life Cycle

Reading Preview

Key Concepts

- What are the stages of human development that occur before birth?
- How is the developing embryo protected and nourished?
- What happens during childbirth?
- What changes occur from infancy to adulthood?

Key Terms

- embryo • fetus
- amniotic sac • placenta
- umbilical cord • adolescence
- puberty

🔄 Target Reading Skill

Building Vocabulary After you read Section 3, reread the paragraphs that contain definitions of Key Terms. Use all the information you have learned to write sentences using each Key Term.

Lab zone Discover **Activity**

How Many Ways Does a Child Grow?

1. Compare the two photographs. One shows a baby girl. The other shows the same girl at the age of five.
2. List the similarities you see. Also list the differences.
3. Compare your lists with those of your classmates.

Think It Over

Observing Based on your observations, list three physical changes that occur in early childhood.

An egg can be fertilized during the first few days after ovulation. When sperm are deposited into the vagina, the sperm move into and through the uterus and then into the fallopian tubes. If a sperm fertilizes an egg, pregnancy can occur. Then, the amazing process of human development begins.

Development Before Birth

A fertilized egg, or zygote, is no larger than the period at the end of this sentence. Yet after fertilization, the zygote undergoes changes that result in the formation of a new human. **The zygote develops first into an embryo and then into a fetus.** About nine months after fertilization, a baby is born.

> **Four-cell stage**
> 48 hours after fertilization

FIGURE 10
Development of the Fetus
As a fetus grows and develops, it gains mass, increases in length, and develops all its body systems.
Applying Concepts *How large is a zygote?*

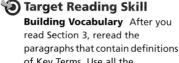
Zygote

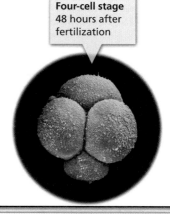

682 ◆

Lab zone Discover **Activity**

Skills Focus Observing

Materials none

Time 15 minutes

Tips Bring in additional photographs showing individuals as babies and as children.

L1 **Think It Over** The child has grown to be taller and heavier than the baby. The proportions of her body have also changed; the child's head is smaller in proportion to the rest of her body, and the child's limbs are longer in proportion to the rest of her body. The child's features have become less rounded.

Zygote and Embryo After an egg and sperm join, the zygote moves down the fallopian tube toward the uterus. During this trip, which takes about four days, the zygote begins to divide. The original cell divides to make two cells. These two cells divide to make four, and so on. Eventually, the growing mass of hundreds of cells forms a hollow ball. The ball attaches to the lining of the uterus. From the two-cell stage through the eighth week of development, the developing human is called an **embryo** (EM bree oh).

Fetus From about the ninth week of development until birth, the developing human is called a **fetus** (FEE tus). Although at first the fetus is only the size of a whole walnut shell, it now looks more like a baby. Many internal organs have developed. The head is about half the body's total size. The fetus's brain is developing rapidly. The fetus also has dark eye patches, fingers, and toes. By the end of the third month, the fetus is about 9 centimeters long and has a mass of about 26 grams.

Between the fourth and sixth months, bones become distinct. A heartbeat can be heard with a stethoscope. A layer of soft hair grows over the skin. The arms and legs develop more completely. The fetus begins to move and kick, a sign that its muscles are growing. At the end of the sixth month, the mass of the fetus is approaching 700 grams. Its body is about 30 centimeters long.

The final three months prepare the fetus to survive outside the mother's body. The brain surface develops grooves and ridges. The lungs become ready to carry out the exchange of oxygen and carbon dioxide. The eyelids can open. The fetus doubles in length. Its mass may reach 3 kilograms or more.

 Reading Checkpoint At what point during development can a heartbeat be detected in a fetus?

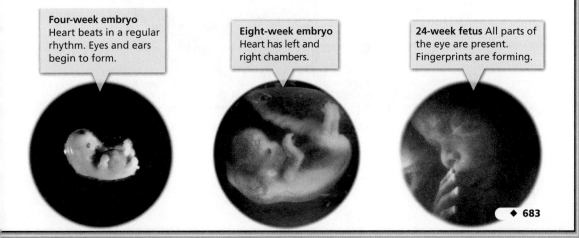

Four-week embryo Heart beats in a regular rhythm. Eyes and ears begin to form.

Eight-week embryo Heart has left and right chambers.

24-week fetus All parts of the eye are present. Fingerprints are forming.

◆ 683

Development Before Birth

Teach Key Concepts   L2
Stages of Prenatal Development

Focus Remind students that an individual begins as a zygote.

Teach Refer students to the diagram in this chapter that shows the fallopian tubes and uterus. Have them trace the path the zygote takes to the uterus. Ask: **What is happening to the zygote during this time?** (*Its cells are dividing and it is becoming larger.*) **What is the second stage of development before birth and how long does it last?** (*The embryo stage begins when the zygote divides to form two cells and continues until the ninth week of development.*) **At the point where the zygote divides to form two cells, what is it called?** (*Embryo*) **What is the third stage of human development before birth?** (*Fetus*)

Apply Explain that prenatal care is important. A pregnant woman should see a health-care professional who can monitor the fetus's development and help the mother-to-be avoid or practice behaviors to promote a healthy baby. **learning modality: verbal**

Independent Practice   L2

All in One Teaching Resources, Unit 3

• Guided Reading and Study Worksheet: *The Human Life Cycle*

 Student Edition on Audio CD

Monitor Progress _____   L2

Oral Presentation Call on students to provide various details of the stages of development of the zygote, embryo, or fetus.

Answers
Figure 10 About the size of a period at the end of a sentence

 Reading Checkpoint Between the fourth and sixth months with a stethoscope

Help Students Read

Sequencing As students read the section *The Human Life Cycle*, tell them to think about what takes place first, next, then, and finally. At the end of the section, ask students to identify the events involved in the human life cycle. On the board, draw a flowchart using boxes to represent each event. Have students fill in each box with an event.

Protection and Nourishment

Teach Key Concepts L1

Structures That Protect and Nourish

Focus Refer students to Figure 11, and ask them to locate the amniotic sac.

Teach Ask: **What is the function of the amniotic sac?** (*To cushion and protect the developing baby*) Explain that the enlargement shows details of the placenta. Ask: **Is the embryo connected directly to a part of the mother's reproductive system?** (*No; it is connected to the placenta.*) Point out that separate blood vessels carry wastes from and nutrients to the developing baby. Ask: **What structure contains these blood vessels?** (*The umbilical cord*)

Apply Ask: **Why is it so important for a pregnant woman to keep herself healthy, for example, eating healthfully?** (*The developing baby relies completely on its mother for all its protection and nourishment.*)
learning modality: visual

All in One Teaching Resources, Unit 3
• Transparency LS198

Protection and Nourishment

Just like you, the embryo and fetus need nourishment and protection to develop properly. Soon after the embryo attaches to the uterus, many changes take place. The hollow ball of cells grows inward. New membranes form. **The membranes and other structures that form during development protect and nourish the developing embryo, and later the fetus.**

Amniotic Sac One membrane surrounds the embryo and develops into a fluid-filled sac called the **amniotic sac** (am NEE aht ik). Locate the amniotic sac in Figure 11. The fluid in the amniotic sac cushions and protects the developing baby.

Placenta Another membrane also forms, which helps to form the placenta. The **placenta** (pluh SEN tuh) is the link between the embryo and the mother. In the placenta, the embryo's blood vessels are located next to the mother's blood vessels. Blood from the two systems does not mix, but many substances are exchanged between the two blood supplies. The embryo receives nutrients, oxygen, and other substances from the mother. It gives off carbon dioxide and other wastes.

FIGURE 11
The Placenta
The placenta provides a connection between the mother and the developing fetus. But the mother's and the fetus's blood vessels remain separate, as you can see in the close-up of the placenta.
Interpreting Diagrams *What structure carries nutrients and oxygen from the placenta to the fetus?*

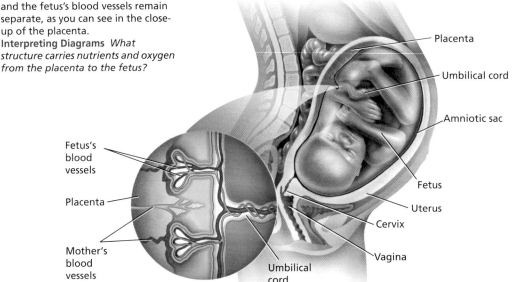

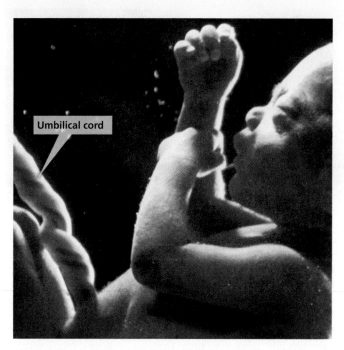

Umbilical cord

FIGURE 12
Eight-Month Fetus
This eight-month fetus is capable of surviving outside the mother. However, the fetus will remain protected within the uterus until birth, at approximately nine months.

Umbilical Cord A ropelike structure called the **umbilical cord** forms between the fetus and the placenta. It contains blood vessels that link the fetus to the mother. However, the two circulatory systems remain separated by a thin barrier.

The barrier that separates the fetus's and mother's blood prevents some diseases from spreading from the mother to the fetus. However, substances such as alcohol, chemicals in tobacco, and many other drugs can pass through the barrier to the fetus. For this reason, pregnant women should not smoke, drink alcohol, or take any drug without a doctor's approval.

 Reading Checkpoint How does a fetus obtain oxygen?

Birth

After about nine months of development inside the uterus, the baby is ready to be born. **The birth of a baby takes place in three stages—labor, delivery, and afterbirth.**

Labor During the first stage of birth, strong muscular contractions of the uterus begin. These contractions are called labor. The contractions cause the cervix to enlarge, eventually allowing the baby to fit through the opening. Labor may last from about 2 hours to more than 20 hours.

Lab zone Try This **Activity**

Way to Grow!

The table lists the average mass of a developing baby at different months of pregnancy.

Month of Pregnancy	Mass (grams)
1	0.02
2	2.0
3	26
4	150
5	460
6	640
7	1,500
8	2,300
9	3,200

1. Use a balance to identify an everyday object with a mass approximately equal to each mass listed in the table. You may need to use different balances to cover the range of masses listed.
2. Arrange the objects in order by month.

Making Models What did you learn by gathering these physical models?

Lab zone Try This **Activity**

Skills Focus Making models [L2]

Materials balance, objects of various masses

Time 15 minutes

Tips Provide balances that can handle the listed range of masses. To save time, shorten the list or have groups of students work together and then combine their findings. Students can combine objects to reach the higher masses.

Expected Outcome The sequence of objects will reflect the increases in mass and range of values shown in the data.

Extend Challenge students to create graphs showing the relative gain in mass of the developing fetus. **learning modality: kinesthetic**

Lab zone Teacher **Demo** [L1]

The Amniotic Sac

Materials raw egg, gallon-size resealable plastic storage bag, water

Time 10 minutes

Focus Review with students the function of the amniotic sac.

Teach Place the egg in the bag, fill the bag with water, and seal it shut. Challenge a student to try to break the egg. (Breaking the egg is difficult; the student might succeed, but only after a great effort.) Ask: **How is the bag like the amniotic sac?** (*It cushions the developing baby from outside injuries.*)

Apply Ask: **Why is it important to protect the developing baby?** (*The mother could fall or be in an automobile accident, or get pushed up against something.*) **learning modality: visual**

Birth

Teach Key Concepts [L2]
The Stages of Birth

Focus Ask: **Why are body organs normally fully developed before birth?** (*The baby must be able to breathe and take in food on its own.*)

Teach Ask: **What causes the baby to be pushed out of the mother's body?** (*The uterus contracts and the cervix enlarges, allowing the baby to fit through the vagina.*) **What happens during delivery?** (*The baby is pushed completely out.*) **What is the afterbirth?** (*The stage in which the placenta and other membranes are pushed out of the uterus*)

Apply Ask: **When is the baby no longer directly dependent on the mother?** (*After delivery; the baby is no longer in the uterus and the umbilical cord is cut. The baby can live on its own with the help of an adult.*) **learning modality: verbal**

Monitor Progress ——— [L2]

Skills Check Have students create flowcharts for the events in the three stages of childbirth.

Answers
Figure 11 The umbilical cord

 Reading Checkpoint From the mother through the placenta

Build Inquiry

L2

Communicating Facts About Twins

Materials up-to-date reference books or Internet resources, index cards

Time 25 minutes

Focus Brainstorm a list of ideas students have about twins, and write them on the board.

Teach Give each student an index card. Ask students to write one question about twins that they would like to know more about. Examples include: **How often are conjoined twins born? Are there any differences between identical twins? Do twins run in families?** Have students work together in small groups to find the answers, then present their findings to the class.

Apply Have students prepare a "Facts About Twins" bulletin board display, or display their findings in a hallway for other students to see. **learning modality: verbal**

For: Links on before birth
Visit: www.SciLinks.org
Web Code: scn-0473

Download a worksheet that will guide students' review of Internet resources on birth.

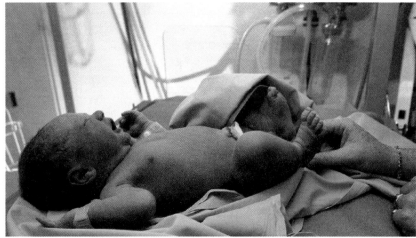

FIGURE 13
Birth
After about nine months of growth and development inside the uterus, a baby is born. You can see where the umbilical cord of this newborn was tied and cut.

For: Links on before birth
Visit: www.SciLinks.org
Web Code: scn-0473

Delivery The second stage of birth is called delivery. During normal delivery, the baby is pushed completely out of the uterus, through the vagina, and out of the mother's body. The head usually comes out first. At this time, the baby is still connected to the placenta by the umbilical cord. Delivery of the baby usually takes less time than labor does—from several minutes to an hour or so.

Shortly after delivery, the umbilical cord is clamped, then cut about 5 centimeters from the baby's abdomen. Within seven to ten days, the remainder of the umbilical cord dries up and falls off, leaving a scar called the navel, or belly button.

Afterbirth About 15 minutes after delivery, the third stage of the birth process begins. Contractions of the uterus push the placenta and other membranes out of the uterus through the vagina. This stage, called afterbirth, is usually completed in less than an hour.

Birth and the Baby The birth process is stressful for both the baby and the mother. The baby is pushed and squeezed as it travels out of the mother's body. Muscle contractions put pressure on the placenta and umbilical cord. This pressure briefly decreases the baby's supply of oxygen.

In response to the changes, the baby's endocrine system releases adrenaline. The baby's heart rate increases. Within a few seconds of delivery, the baby begins breathing with a cry or a cough. This action helps rid the lungs of fluid and fills them with air. The newborn's heart rate then slows to a steady pace. Blood travels to the lungs and picks up oxygen from the air that the baby breathes in. The newborn's cry helps it adjust to the changes in its surroundings.

Multiple Births The delivery of more than one baby from a single pregnancy is called a multiple birth. In the United States, about 1 out of every 30 babies born each year is a twin. Multiple births of more than two babies, such as triplets and quadruplets, occur less frequently than do twin births.

There are two types of twins: identical twins and fraternal twins. Identical twins develop from a single fertilized egg, or zygote. Early in development, the embryo splits into two identical embryos. The two embryos have identical inherited traits and are the same sex. Fraternal twins develop when two eggs are released from the ovary and are fertilized by two different sperm. Fraternal twins are no more alike than any other brothers or sisters. Fraternal twins may or may not be the same sex.

 Reading Checkpoint What are the two types of twins?

FIGURE 14
Twins

Identical twins (left) develop from the same fertilized egg. They share identical characteristics. Fraternal twins (right) develop from two different fertilized eggs. **Applying Concepts** *Why can fraternal twins be different sexes while identical twins cannot?*

Identical Twins

A sperm fertilizes a single egg.

The single egg splits and forms two identical embryos.

Identical twins result.

Fraternal Twins

Two different sperm fertilize two eggs.

Each of the eggs develops into an embryo.

Fraternal twins result.

Chapter 20 ◆ 687

Differentiated Instruction

English Learners/Beginning L1
Vocabulary: Prior Knowledge Students have probably heard descriptions of childbirth from family members, on television, or in the movies. Encourage them to think about the main events that occur during the three stages of childbirth. Have students write key words and phrases in their native language and in English.
learning modality: verbal

English Learners/Intermediate L2
Vocabulary: Science Glossary After students do the Beginning activity, have them write the definitions of each of those terms in their own words in their science glossaries. **learning modality: verbal**

Use Visuals: Figure 14 L1

Focus Tell students that there is a difference between identical and fraternal twins.

Teach Ask: **When identical twins are formed, how many sperm cells and egg cells formed the original egg?** *(One sperm cell and one egg cell)* **How are two embryos formed?** *(The cell splits in two.)* Point out that each of the two cells have the same chromosomes. Ask: **When fraternal twins are formed, how many sperm cells and egg cells form the eggs?** *(Two sperm cells and two egg cells)* Explain that the chromosomes each zygote receives are different.

Apply Tell students that an increasing number of multiple births are the result of treatments for fertility, including in-vitro fertilization and drugs that cause the ovaries to release several mature eggs at once.
learning modality: visual

All in One **Teaching Resources, Unit 3**
• Transparency LS199

Monitor Progress L2

Writing Have students close their books and write a paragraph explaining how identical and fraternal twins form.

Answers
Figure 14 Fraternal twins develop from two different fertilized eggs, so the chances that they are the same sex is the same as for any other brothers or sisters. Identical twins develop from the same fertilized egg, so they must be the same sex.

 Reading Checkpoint Identical and fraternal

687

Growth and Development

Teach Key Concepts L2

Changes in Growth and Development

Focus Tell students that although the most rapid growth in humans occurs before birth, a person continues developing throughout life.

Teach Write the three major stages of growth and development on the board, and list descriptions of the changes that occur in each stage. Ask students to help identify the changes. Ask: **At what stage does a person begin reaching for objects?** (*Infancy*) **How do bones and muscles grow in childhood?** (*They increase in size so the child becomes taller and heavier.*)

Apply Ask students to identify important developmental milestones in each stage of development. (*Sample answers: infancy—walking unassisted; childhood—learning to read; adolescence—the onset of puberty*)
learning modality: verbal

⚑ Address Misconceptions L1

Body Changes and Puberty

Focus Some students think that the physical changes during puberty occur at a steady pace over a relatively brief period of time.

Teach Explain that on average, puberty lasts about four years and can proceed at varying rates. Tell students that it is normal for teens to be concerned about their rate of maturation. Everyone develops at his or her own pace. The age at which puberty begins and the rate at which the changes progress are primarily determined by heredity.

Apply Encourage students to talk with a parent or adult relative of their gender about the relative's personal development and how it affected him or her. However, make sure students know that students' patterns of development may differ from those of family members. **learning modality: verbal**

▲ Infancy   ▲ Early childhood   ▲ Childhood

FIGURE 15
Development
You can see the changes in development from infancy through adolescence.
Applying Concepts *What mental development takes place during childhood?*

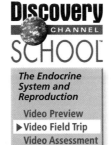

DISCOVERY
CHANNEL
SCHOOL™

The Endocrine System and Reproduction
Video Preview
▶ Video Field Trip
Video Assessment

688 ◆

Growth and Development

What can a newborn baby do? You might say "Not much!" A newborn can perform only simple actions, such as crying, sucking, yawning, and blinking. You can do a lot more, from playing sports to solving math problems. Many changes have taken place in you that allow you to do these things. **The changes that take place between infancy and adulthood include physical changes, such as an increase in size and coordination. They also include mental changes, such as the ability to communicate and solve complex problems.**

Infancy During infancy—the first two years of life—babies undergo many changes and learn to do many things. A baby's shape and size change greatly. When a baby is born, its head makes up about one fourth of its body length. As the infant develops, its head grows more slowly, and its body, legs, and arms begin to catch up. Its nervous and muscular systems become better coordinated. After about 3 months, it can hold its head up and reach for objects. At about 7 months, most infants can move around by crawling. Somewhere between 10 and 16 months, most infants begin to walk by themselves.

You may think that babies display feelings mostly by crying. But young infants can show pleasure by smiling and laughing. Sometime between the ages of one and three years, many children speak their first word. By the end of two years, children can do many things for themselves, such as understand simple directions, feed themselves, and play with toys.

▲ Early adolescence   ▲ Adolescence

Childhood Infancy ends and childhood begins at about two years of age. Throughout childhood, children continue to grow. They become taller and heavier as their bones and muscles increase in size. They become more coordinated as they practice skills such as walking, using a pencil, and playing games.

As they develop, children show a growing curiosity and increasing mental abilities. Language skills improve rapidly. For example, most four-year-olds can carry on conversations. With the help of family members and teachers, children learn to read and to solve problems. Over time, children learn to make friends, care about others, and behave responsibly.

Adolescence The stage of development during which children become adults physically and mentally is called **adolescence** (ad ul ES uns). Adolescents gradually become able to think like adults and take on adult responsibilities. The bodies of adolescents also undergo specific physical changes.

Sometime between the ages of about 9 and 15 years, girls and boys enter puberty. **Puberty** (PYOO bur tee) is the period of sexual development in which the body becomes able to reproduce. In girls, hormones produced by the pituitary gland and the ovaries control the physical changes of puberty. The sex organs develop. Ovulation and menstruation begin. The breasts enlarge, and the hips start to widen. In boys, hormones from the testes and the pituitary gland govern the changes. The sex organs develop, and sperm production begins. The voice deepens. Hair appears on the face and chest.

Lab zone — Try This **Activity**

Teenagers in Ads
In this activity, you will examine an ad taken from a teen magazine.

1. Examine an ad that shows one or more teenagers. Read the words and examine the pictures.
2. Think about how the ad portrays teenagers. How do they look and act? How accurate is this "picture" of teenagers?

Drawing Conclusions How does this ad try to influence people your age? Do you think the ad is effective? Explain your opinion.

Chapter 20   ◆   689

689

Answer

Reading Checkpoint Skin wrinkles, muscle strength decreases, eyes may not focus as well on close objects, hair may lose color, women stop menstruating and ovulating

Assess

Reviewing Key Concepts

1. a. Zygote, embryo, and fetus **b.** The brain surface develops grooves and ridges, lungs become ready to breathe, eyelids can open, fetus doubles in length and increases in mass. **c.** Not all changes that take place during development are complete, so the baby's body may not be able to carry out all its functions well.

2. a. The membranes protect and nourish the fetus **b.** The placenta allows the exchange of materials between the mother and the fetus. **c.** Alcohol and substances in tobacco smoke can pass from the mother to the developing baby through the placenta.

3. a. Labor, delivery, and afterbirth **b.** Uterine contractions cause the cervix to enlarge.

4. a. Physical changes and mental changes; physical—increase in size and coordination; mental—ability to communicate and solve complex problems **b.** During puberty, the body becomes able to reproduce. Girls begin to ovulate and menstruate. Boys begin to produce sperm. Both sexes undergo physical changes. **c.** Sample answer: Yes; puberty results in many physical and emotional changes that prepare a person for adulthood.

Reteach   L1

Draw a timeline on the board. Ask students to name the stages of human growth and development and to provide details of each stage.

Performance Assessment   L2

Skills Check Have students create a concept map showing the physical and mental changes that occur during adolescence.

All in One Teaching Resources, Unit 3

- Section Summary: *The Human Life Cycle*
- Review and Reinforce: *The Human Life Cycle*
- Enrich: *The Human Life Cycle*

FIGURE 16
Adulthood
Young adults often enjoy helping older adults.

Adulthood The mental and emotional growth of adolescence continues after puberty ends. It is difficult to say when adolescence ends and adulthood begins. And adults, like adolescents, continue to learn new things.

After about the age of 30, a process known as aging begins. As people age, the skin becomes wrinkled and muscle strength decreases. The eyes may lose their ability to focus on close objects, and hair may lose its coloring. Aging becomes more noticeable between the ages of 40 and 65. During this period, women stop menstruating and ovulating. Men usually continue to produce sperm throughout their lives. However, as men become older, the number of sperm they produce decreases.

The effects of aging can be slowed if people follow sensible diets and good exercise plans. With the help of such healthy behaviors, more and more adults remain active throughout their lives. In addition, older people have learned a lot from their experiences. Because of this learning, many older people have a great deal of wisdom. Older adults can share their knowledge and experience with younger people.

 Reading Checkpoint What are the physical effects of aging?

Section 3 Assessment

Target Reading Skill Building Vocabulary Use your sentences to help answer the questions.

Reviewing Key Concepts

1. a. Identifying What three steps of development does a fertilized egg go through before birth?
   b. Describing What happens to the fetus during the final three months of development?
   c. Relating Cause and Effect Explain why a baby born before the seventh month of development needs special care to survive.

2. a. Reviewing What is the general function of the membranes that surround a fetus?
   b. Explaining What is the specific function of the placenta?
   c. Relating Cause and Effect Why is it dangerous for a pregnant woman to drink alcohol or to smoke cigarettes?

3. a. Listing What are the three stages of birth?
   b. Summarizing What happens during labor?

4. a. Identifying Identify two general kinds of change that occur between infancy and adulthood. Give an example of each.
   b. Describing Describe what happens during puberty.
   c. Making Judgments Is puberty the most important process that occurs during adolescence? Explain your answer.

Lab zone At-Home **Activity**

Parenting Skills Interview a family member about what is involved in being a parent. Ask the following questions: What skills do parents need? What are some of the rewards of parenthood? What are some of the challenges?

Lab zone Chapter **Project**

Keep Students on Track Students can use their daily journal entries to help them prepare summaries of their experiences. Challenge students to imagine how they would feel after three days of caring for a real baby, and to express how they feel about no longer having to care for their flour "baby."

Lab zone At-Home **Activity**

Parenting Skills L2 Encourage students to work in small groups to discuss and compare their findings. Have each group create a "Tips for Good Parenting" manual. Allow groups to present their manuals and provide copies for their classmates.

Lab zone Skills Lab

Growing Up

Problem

How do the proportions of the human body change during development?

Skills Focus

calculating, predicting

Procedure

1. Examine the diagram below. Notice that the figures are drawn against a graph showing percentages. You can use this diagram to determine how the lengths of major body parts compare to each figure's height. Make a data table in which to record information about each figure's head size and leg length.

2. Look at Figure D. You can use the graph to estimate that the head is about 15 percent of the figure's full height. Record that number in your data table.

3. Examine Figures A through C. Determine the percentage of the total height that the head makes up. Record your results.

4. Next, compare the length of the legs to the total body height for Figures A through D. Record your results. (*Hint*: Figure A shows the legs folded. You will need to estimate the data for that figure.)

Analyze and Conclude

1. **Calculating** How do the percentages for head size and leg length change from infancy to adulthood?

2. **Predicting** If you made a line graph using the data in the diagram, what would be on the horizontal axis? On the vertical axis? What additional information could you gain from this line graph?

3. **Communicating** What can you infer about the rate at which different parts of the body grow? Write a paragraph in which you discuss the answer to this question.

Design an Experiment

Make a prediction about the relationship between the circumference of the head compared with body height. Then, design an experiment to test your prediction, using people for test subjects. *Obtain your teacher's permission before carrying out your investigation.*

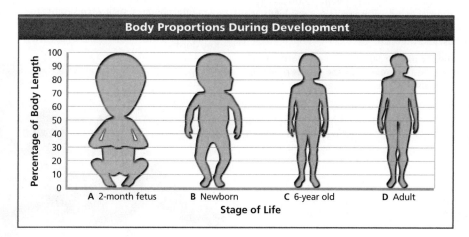

Body Proportions During Development

Percentage of Body Length

A 2-month fetus   B Newborn   C 6-year old   D Adult

Stage of Life

Chapter 20 ◆ 691

Lab zone Skills Lab

Growing Up

Prepare for Inquiry

Skills Objectives

After this lab, students will be able to
- calculate percentages
- predict the information available in a line graph

Prep Time 20 minutes
Class Time 30 minutes

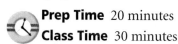 **Teaching Resources, Unit 3**
- Lab Worksheet: *Growing Up*

Guide Inquiry

Invitation

Obtain illustrations from magazines showing people of various ages. Invite students to compare the pictures and describe general differences between people of different ages.

Introducing the Procedure

Have students find the lines on the diagram that represent 50% and 100%. Ask them what height measurements would correspond to those figures for their own height. Make sure students understand the diagram compares the whole height at each stage without comparing the heights directly.

Analyze and Conclude

1. Head: about 45% of body length in newborns, 15% in adults; leg: 35–40% of total body height in newborns, 50% in adults

2. Horizontal: age in years; vertical: body length; you could estimate the values between the ages given in the diagram.

3. Different parts of the body grow at different rates. Students' paragraphs should cite examples from the data to support the inference.

Extend Inquiry

Design an Experiment Sample prediction: The difference between head circumference and overall height will increase with age. Make sure that plans are safe and that students obtain permission from subjects before conducting their investigations.

interactive Textbook

- Complete student edition
- Section and chapter self-assessments
- Assessment reports for teachers

Help Students Read

Building Vocabulary

Vocabulary Knowledge Rating Chart
Have students construct a chart with four columns: *Term, Can Define or Use It, Have Heard or Seen It, Don't Know.* Students should copy the vocabulary terms for this section under column 1. They should then place a checkmark under one of the other columns for each term. If students did not check the *Can Define or Use It* column, have them reread passages with those terms, then work with a partner to review the term.

Words in Context Select Key Terms from the chapter. Have students write a sentence for each term that places the term in a correct context. Provide them with one example before they begin. *Amniotic sac: The amniotic sac cushions and protects the developing baby.*

Connecting Concepts

Concept Maps Help students develop one way to show how the information in this chapter is related. The endocrine system controls daily activities and long-term changes, such as development of the reproductive system, which functions to form new individuals. Have students brainstorm to identify Key Concepts, Key Terms, details, and examples, then write each one on a sticky note and attach it at random on chart paper or on the board.

Tell students that this concept map will be organized in hierarchical order to begin at the top with the Key Concepts. Ask students these questions to guide them to categorize the information on the sticky notes: **How do hormones move through the body? What pathways do egg cells and sperm cells take through the reproductive system? What are the stages of the human life cycle from zygote to adolescence?**

1 The Endocrine System

Key Concepts

- The endocrine system produces chemicals that control many of the body's daily activities as well as growth and development.

- The endocrine glands include the pituitary, hypothalamus, thyroid, parathyroid, adrenal, thymus, and pancreas. They include ovaries in females and testes in males.

- Through negative feedback, when the amount of a particular hormone in the blood reaches a certain level, the endocrine system sends signals that stop the release of that hormone.

Key Terms

endocrine gland	hypothalamus
hormone	pituitary gland
target cell	negative feedback

2 The Male and Female Reproductive Systems

Key Concepts

- Sexual reproduction involves the production of eggs by the female and sperm by the male. The egg and sperm join during fertilization.

- The male reproductive system produces sperm and the hormone testosterone. Its structures include the testes, scrotum, and penis.

- The female reproductive system produces eggs and nourishes a developing baby until birth. Its structures include the ovaries, fallopian tubes, uterus, and vagina.

- During the menstrual cycle, an egg develops in an ovary. At the same time, the uterus prepares for the arrival of a fertilized egg.

Key Terms

egg	ovary
sperm	estrogen
fertilization	fallopian tube
zygote	uterus
testis	vagina
testosterone	menstrual cycle
scrotum	ovulation
semen	menstruation
penis	

3 The Human Life Cycle

Key Concepts

- The zygote develops first into an embryo and then into a fetus.

- The membranes and other structures that form during development protect and nourish the developing embryo and then the fetus.

- The birth of a baby takes place in three stages—labor, delivery, and afterbirth.

- The changes that take place between infancy and adulthood include physical changes, such as an increase in size and coordination, and mental changes, such as the ability to communicate and solve complex problems.

Key Terms

embryo
fetus
amniotic sac
placenta
umbilical cord
adolescence
puberty

Prompt students by using connecting words or phrases, such as "travels to," "produces," and "consists of," to indicate the basis for the organization of the map. The phrases should form a sentence between or among a set of concepts.

Answer
Accept logical presentations by students.

All in One Teaching Resources, Unit 3

- Key Terms Review: *The Endocrine System and Reproduction*
- Connecting Concepts: *The Endocrine System and Reproduction*

Review and Assessment

Organizing Information

Sequencing Copy the flowchart showing the main stages that occur between fertilization and birth onto a sheet of paper. Then, complete it and add a title. (For more on Sequencing, see the Skills Handbook.)

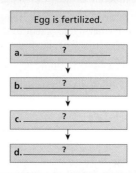

Egg is fertilized.

a. _____ ?

b. _____ ?

c. _____ ?

d. _____ ?

Reviewing Key Terms

Choose the letter of the best answer.

1. The structure that links the nervous system and the endocrine system is the
   a. thyroid gland.
   b. target cell.
   c. umbilical cord.
   d. hypothalamus.

2. The male sex cell is called the
   a. testis.
   b. sperm.
   c. egg.
   d. ovary.

3. The release of an egg from an ovary is known as
   a. ovulation.
   b. fertilization.
   c. menstruation.
   d. negative feedback.

4. The structure that protects and cushions the embryo is called the
   a. umbilical cord.
   b. scrotum.
   c. amniotic sac.
   d. ovary.

5. Sex organs develop rapidly during
   a. fertilization.
   b. ovulation.
   c. puberty.
   d. menstruation.

If the statement is true, write *true*. If it is false, change the underlined word or words to make the statement true.

6. A <u>target cell</u> recognizes a hormone's chemical structure.

7. The joining of a sperm and an egg is called <u>menstruation</u>.

8. A fluid that contains sperm is <u>testosterone</u>.

9. A <u>fallopian tube</u> is the passageway through which an egg travels from the ovary to the uterus.

10. The <u>amniotic sac</u> contains blood vessels that link the fetus to the mother.

Writing in Science

Creative Writing Imagine you just found out that you have an identical twin who was raised in another country. Write a description of what you think your twin would be like. Be sure to include information about what your twin looks like, his or her interests, and unique characteristics of your twin.

Discovery CHANNEL SCHOOL

The Endocrine System and Reproduction

Video Preview
Video Field Trip
► Video Assessment

Chapter 20 ◆ 693

Go Online
PHSchool.com
For: Self-Assessment
Visit: PHSchool.com
Web Code: cea-4070

Students can take a practice test online that is automatically scored.

All in One Teaching Resources, Unit 3
- Transparency LS200
- Chapter Test
- Performance Assessment Teacher Notes
- Performance Assessment Student Worksheet
- Performance Assessment Scoring Rubric

ExamView® Computer Test Bank CD-ROM

Review and Assessment

Organizing Information
a. Zygote is formed.
b. Embryo develops.
c. Fetus develops.
d. Baby is born.

Reviewing Key Terms
1. d **2.** b **3.** a **4.** c **5.** c
6. true
7. fertilization
8. semen
9. true
10. umbilical cord

Writing in Science

Writing Mode Description
Scoring Rubric
4 Includes complete description with personal examples of physical characteristics and personality traits
3 Includes all criteria, but examples are not as personal or detailed
2 Includes only brief description
1 Includes inaccurate description

Discovery CHANNEL SCHOOL Video Assessment

The Endocrine System and Reproduction

Show the Video Assessment to review chapter content and as a prompt for the writing assignment. Discussion questions: **Explain the difference between identical and fraternal twins.** *(Identical twins develop from a single fertilized egg, fraternal twins develop from two different fertilized eggs that develop in the uterus at the same time.)* **What have scientists discovered about the role genetics might play in personality development?** *(Dr. Bouchard's research suggests that the personalities of identical twins are determined more by their genetic inheritance than by the environment in which they were raised.)*

693

Checking Concepts

11. The pituitary gland regulates other endocrine glands, and it regulates some body activities directly, such as growth.

12. The signal to stop secreting thyroxine is sent to the thyroid through negative feedback. After the hypothalamus senses that cells have enough energy, it signals the pituitary to stop producing TSH, which then makes the thyroid stop producing thyroxine.

13. The testes produce sperm cells and testosterone.

14. The egg is released from an ovary and travels through one of the fallopian tubes to the uterus. When the egg is not fertilized, it breaks down in the uterus and leaves the body through the vagina.

15. At the beginning of the cycle, the uterine lining builds up in preparation for a fertilized egg. If the egg is unfertilized, the uterus sheds its lining.

16. A zygote forms when a sperm fertilizes an egg. During the first four days, the zygote rapidly divides to become a hollow ball of cells. After about four days, it reaches the uterus and attaches to the uterine lining.

17. A fetus receives food and oxygen and gets rid of wastes through the placenta, which provides a connection between the developing fetus and the mother. The umbilical cord contains blood vessels that carry oxygen and nutrients from the placenta to the embryo. It also contains blood vessels that carry waste products from the embryo to the placenta.

18. He will begin puberty, which includes the development of the sex organs, the start of sperm production, the growth of facial and chest hair, the deepening of his voice. He will also learn to think like adults and take on adult responsibilities.

Checking Concepts

11. What is the function of the pituitary gland?

12. When enough thyroxine has been released into the blood, what signal is sent to the thyroid gland? How is that signal sent?

13. Identify two functions of the testes.

14. Describe the path of an unfertilized egg, beginning with its release and ending when it leaves the body.

15. What changes occur in the uterus during the menstrual cycle?

16. How does a zygote form? What happens to the zygote about four days after it forms?

17. Describe how a fetus receives food and oxygen and gets rid of wastes.

18. List five changes that a 10-year-old boy should expect to happen during the next five years. Include physical and mental changes.

Thinking Critically

19. Inferring Study the diagram below. Then, suggest how the two hormones, glucagon and insulin, might work together to maintain homeostasis in the body.

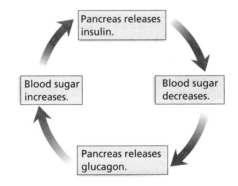

20. Calculating The average menstrual cycle is 28 days in length but can vary from 24 to 32 days. Ovulation usually occurs 14 days before the end of the cycle. How long after the start of a 24-day cycle will ovulation occur? A 32-day cycle?

21. Comparing and Contrasting Contrast the ways in which identical twins and fraternal twins form.

22. Relating Cause and Effect How can playing games help children develop important skills?

Applying Skills

Use the table to answer Questions 23–25.

The data table below shows how the length of a developing baby changes during pregnancy.

Length of Fetus

Week of Pregnancy	Average Length (mm)	Week of Pregnancy	Average Length (mm)
4	4	24	300
8	30	28	350
12	75	32	410
16	180	36	450
20	250	38	500

23. Measuring Use a metric ruler to mark each length on a piece of paper. During which four-week period did the greatest increase in length occur?

24. Graphing Graph the data by plotting time on the *x*-axis and length on the *y*-axis.

25. Interpreting Data At the twelfth week, a developing baby measures about 75 mm. By which week has the fetus grown to four times that length? Six times that length?

Lab zone Chapter **Project**

Performance Assessment Explain what you learned as you cared for your "baby." What did you learn about parenting that you didn't know before? Consider reading passages from your journal to the class.

Lab zone Chapter **Project** L3

Performance Assessment Have a class discussion in which volunteers can read selections from their journals. Refer to the list of tasks the class developed at the beginning of the project. Ask students to describe how they addressed these tasks and to explain how they feel after the project. Encourage students to talk about their experiences and how their attitudes have changed.

Reflect and Record Make sure students know that although they are being evaluated on how well they carried out the procedures, a greater value can be obtained by reflecting honestly on their experiences and using their assessments as a basis for future behaviors.

Standardized Test Prep

Choose the letter of the best answer.

1. You are riding your bike when a small child suddenly darts out in front of you. Which of your endocrine glands is most likely to release a hormone in response to this situation?
   - **A** pituitary gland
   - **B** adrenal glands
   - **C** thyroid gland
   - **D** parathyroid gland

2. On day 10 of a woman's menstrual cycle, the egg is most likely
   - **F** moving through the fallopian tube.
   - **G** in the uterus.
   - **H** in the ovary.
   - **J** leaving the body.

Use the table below and your knowledge of science to answer Questions 3 and 4.

Number of Chromosomes in Body Cells of Various Animals

Organism	Chromosome Number
Roundworm	2
Fruit Fly	8
Cricket	22
Mouse	40
Human	46
Pigeon	80

3. An egg cell produced by a female mouse probably contains
   - **A** 20 chromosomes.
   - **B** 40 chromosomes.
   - **C** 60 chromosomes.
   - **D** 80 chromosomes.

4. How many chromosomes will a pigeon zygote have?
   - **F** 20
   - **G** 40
   - **H** 60
   - **J** 80

5. A woman gives birth to twins that developed from a single fertilized egg that split early in development. Which of the following is a reasonable prediction that you can make about the twins?
   - **A** They will be the same sex.
   - **B** They will be different sexes.
   - **C** They will not look alike.
   - **D** They will have different inherited traits.

Constructed Response

6. What is negative feedback? Choose an example of a hormone, and describe in a general way how negative feedback regulates its release.

Thinking Critically

19. These two hormones work together to maintain homeostasis in the body by regulating the amount of sugar in the blood. When the sugar levels are high, the pancreas produces insulin to lower the blood sugar levels. When the sugar in blood is low, the pancreas produces glucagon to increase the blood sugar levels.

20. Ovulation will occur on the 11th day of a 24-day cycle and on the 19th day of a 32-day cycle.

21. Identical twins form from the same fertilized egg. The developing embryo splits into two identical embryos with the same inherited traits. Fraternal twins form from two different eggs that are fertilized by two different sperm. Fraternal twins are no more alike than any other brothers or sisters.

22. Playing games can help children learn to get along with others and become stronger and more coordinated. Some games also help them develop important mental and social skills.

Applying Skills

23. The greatest increase occurred during weeks 12 through 16.

24. Graphs should show length increasing as time increases. The slope of the line should change until it becomes a fairly straight diagonal line after 20 weeks.

25. The fetus has grown to four times that length by week 24 and six times that length by week 36.

Standardized Test Prep

1. B **2.** H **3.** A **4.** J **5.** A

6. Sample answer: Negative feedback is a type of signal in which a system is turned off by the condition it produces. For example, when the endocrine system senses that body cells do not have enough energy, it signals the thyroid gland to release thyroxine. When the endocrine system senses that the level of thyroxine is correct, it signals the thyroid gland to stop releasing thyroxine. Feedback is negative because the level of a hormone (thyroxine) is a signal that stops the release of that hormone.

Interdisciplinary Exploration

African Rain Forests

The interdisciplinary feature presents the central theme of rain forest diversity from four different curriculum perspectives: science, mathematics, social studies, and language arts. The four explorations are designed to capture students' interest and help them see how the content they are studying in science relates to other school subjects and real-world events. Share with others for a team-teaching experience.

All in One Teaching Resources, Unit 4

- Interdisciplinary Exploration: *Science*
- Interdisciplinary Exploration: *Mathematics*
- Interdisciplinary Exploration: *Social Studies*
- Interdisciplinary Exploration: *Language Arts*

Build Background Knowledge

Where are rain forests located?

Help students recall what they learned in the chapter *Ecosystems and Biomes*. Ask: **Where are Earth's tropical rain forests located?** *(South and Central America, Southeast Asia, Indonesia, and Africa)* **What other type of rain forest is there? Where is it located?** *(Temperate rain forests are found along the northwestern coast of the United States and Canada.)*

Introduce the Exploration

Have students examine the map on this page. Ask: **Where are rain forests in Africa located?** *(At or close to the equator)* **Describe the climate of a tropical rain forest.** *(Warm, humid, and rainy)* **Why do you think many nations in East Africa do not have tropical rain forests?** *(Much of East Africa's climate is not humid and rainy enough to support a rain forest.)*

African Rain Forests

What forest—

- contains a frog that's 30 cm long?
- is home to gorillas, pottos, and pygmy hippos?
- is preserving diversity?

It's an African rain forest. Thousands of plants and animals live here, from colorful orchids to fruit bats to elephants.

The rain forests of Africa grow near the equator. About 70 percent of the rain forests are in central Africa, in the vast basin of the great Congo River. Some parts of the central African rain forest are so dense and hard to reach that explorers have never visited them. East Africa, which is drier, has only scattered areas of rain forest.

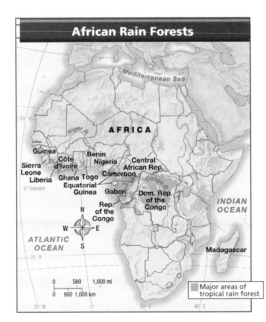

African Rain Forests

Golden Potto
This golden potto eats insects and fruits in the African rain forest.

Rain Forest Layers

The rain forest is really many forests in one—like different levels in an apartment building. Each layer varies in climate and is home to different plants and animals. The four layers are the emergent layer, the canopy, the understory, and the forest floor.

Over time, plants and animals have developed unusual adaptations to life at different layers of the rain forest. Some monkeys living in the canopy have long, muscular legs so they can run and leap through branches. Others have strong teeth and jaws that allow them to crunch fruits, nuts, and seeds. Some monkeys that live mainly on the forest floor have shorter tails but longer front legs.

Emergent Layer 40–70 Meters
This layer is formed by a few taller trees that poke through the canopy. The emergent layer captures the most rain, sunlight, heat, and wind. Colobus monkeys and vast numbers of birds live at this level.

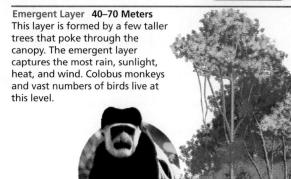

Black and White Colobus Monkey

Canopy 10–40 Meters
The canopy is the dense "roof" of the rainforest. The crowns of trees capture sunlight to use in photosynthesis. Rain and sunlight filter through thick vegetation. Epiphytic orchids grow to the top of the canopy.

Epiphytic Orchid

Paradise Flycatcher

Understory 0–10 Meters
The understory has trees and plants that need little light. Pythons lurk in the vegetation. Some small animals such as squirrels glide from branch to branch.

Forest Floor 0 Meters
The forest floor is dark, humid, and still. Some animals, including frogs and insects, grow to gigantic sizes. Others are little, like the pygmy hippo.

Pygmy Hippo

♦ 697

Science Activity

Design a rain forest animal that is adapted to life at a certain level of the rain forest. Consider how your animal lives, how it travels, and what food it eats. Outline its characteristics and explain how each adaptation helps the animal survive. Draw a sketch of your design.

Background

Facts and Figures Taking up less space than the area of Texas, Madagascar is home to some 200,000 species of plants and animals, making it one of the most biologically diverse countries in the world. Separated from the African continent by plate tectonics, the island has been isolated for more than 100 million years. Most of the species that evolved on the island are found nowhere else on Earth. For example, lemurs, a type of primate, are found only in Madagascar and the neighboring Comoro Islands. People have lived on Madagascar for about 2,000 years, but during that time the island has lost about 80 percent of its rain forests and about 50 percent of its native species. Except for a few patches, the forests that once covered the island's eastern half have been cleared to create farms and housing for Madagascar's 17 million people.

Explore Science Concepts

Use Tables Challenge students to make tables to compare the features of the four layers of the rain forest. The headings for the table could include *Layer, Height, Microclimate Conditions,* and *Sample Organisms.* After students have completed their tables, ask: **Why is biodiversity in rain forests so high?** (*Students may answer that there are many different niches within the rain forest, there is high productivity in the rain forest, and that temperatures and rainfall amounts are stable year round.*)

Research Have students choose an animal or plant that lives in the rain forest, identify which layer it lives in, and describe the adaptations the organism has to help it survive and succeed in the rain forest. Students should create a one-page profile about the animal to display in the classroom.

Extend Ask students to research the impact that deforestation of tropical rain forests has on the plants and animals that inhabit this biome. Suggest they pay particular attention to efforts that are being made throughout the world to conserve rain forests.

Science Activity

Focus Encourage students to refer to their tables about each layer of the rain forest to determine what type of adaptations would be helpful in order to survive. Have students explain the different structures or behaviors the animal would have and what purpose each would serve toward the animal's survival.

Teach Have students work individually or in pairs. Students could create a bulletin board display with an enlarged version of the text's illustration in the center and each student's sketch posted next to the appropriate layer.

Scoring Rubric

4 Includes which layer of forest the animal will live in, a detailed description of structures and behaviors that will allow it to survive, and a sketch of the animal
3 Includes a description of structures and behaviors that will allow the animal to survive and a sketch of the animal
2 Includes a description of structures and behaviors that will allow the animal to survive
1 Includes a sketch of the animal with no details

Explore Mathematics Concepts

Review Ask: **Why must trees in a rain forest grow tall and straight?** *(So they can reach sunlight at the top of the canopy)* **What might happen to older trees to give young trees a better chance of growing?** *(The older trees might fall and open up sunny clearings.)* **What are some products that can be made from African trees?** *(Student answers may include furniture, tools, boats, soaps, and candles.)*

Use Visuals Have students compare the tree heights listed in the table with the figure of forest layers on the previous page. Ask: **Which trees' tops are found in each forest layer?** *(Emergent: kapok, teak; canopy: African oil palm, African yellowwood, ebony, raffia palm; understory: cape fig)*

Math Activity

Review Review how to make and label a bar graph.

Teach Have each student make his or her own graph. The sample graph below presents the trees in alphabetical order. Some students may prefer to sequence the trees from shortest to tallest (or vice versa) on the horizontal axis.

Expected Outcome See below

Height of Rain Forest Trees

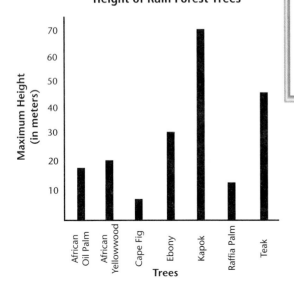

Reaching for Sunlight

Most rain forest trees are evergreens with broad leathery leaves. Some, like the African yellowwood, are conifers. Because the forest is so dense, trees must grow tall and straight to reach sunlight at the top of the canopy.

Along rivers, the floor and understory of the rain forest are a tangle of thick vegetation. But deep in the rain forest the floor is surprisingly bare. The canopy trees prevent sunlight from reaching plants below. Water drips from the leaves of the canopy high overhead. Young trees have the best chance to grow when older trees fall and open up sunny clearings.

West Africa's tropical forests contain many valuable trees. African mahogany and teak are used to make furniture, tools, and boats. Oil from the oil palm is used in soaps, candles, and some foods. Trees, such as ebony, that can tolerate shade grow slowly and develop dark, hard, long-lasting wood.

Rain Forest Tree
Rain forest trees like this kapok tree grow straight up toward the sun.

Trees of the Rain Forest	
Tree	**Maximum Height**
African oil palm	18 m
African yellowwood	20 m
Cape fig	7 m
Ebony	30 m
Kapok	70 m
Raffia palm	12 m
Teak	46 m

Math Activity

The table on this page gives the height of some of the trees in the rain forest. Use the information in the table to make a bar graph. Label the horizontal axis with the tree names. Use the vertical axis to show the heights of the trees.

- Which tree has the greatest maximum height? The least maximum height?

- What is the difference between the maximum heights of the tallest and the shortest trees?

- What is the average maximum height of all the trees shown in the graph?

Bark Cloth
Traditional Mbuti clothing
is made of bark cloth.

Ituri Forest People

The native peoples of the African rain forest live as they have for thousands of years—by hunting and gathering. The forest supplies them with everything they need—food, water, firewood, building materials, and medicines.

One group of rain forest dwellers is the Mbuti people. The Mbuti live in the Ituri forest of the Democratic Republic of the Congo. Many of the Mbuti are quite small. The men hunt game, such as gazelle and antelope. The women gather wild fruits, nuts, and greens. Their traditional Mbuti clothing is made of tree bark and is wrapped around the waist. The bark is beaten to make it soft. Then it's decorated with geometric designs.

Most Mbuti live as nomads, with no settled home. Every few months they set up new hunting grounds. They build temporary dome-shaped huts of branches and leaves. Hunting groups of about 10 to 25 families live together.

Modern Africa has brought changes to the forest people, especially for those who live near the edges of the rain forest. For a few months of the year, some Mbuti work as laborers for farmers who live in villages at the edge of the forest. When their work is finished, the Mbuti return to the Ituri forest. Most forest people prefer not to cultivate their own land. Since the farmers don't hunt, they trade their goods for meat. In exchange for meat, the Mbuti receive goods such as iron tools, cooking pots, clothes, bananas, and other farm produce.

The Mbuti
The Mbuti hunt and fish along the Congo River.

Social Studies Activity

List the goods that forest people and farmers might have to trade. Assume that no modern conveniences, such as tractors and stoves, are available. In writing, explain how goods might be exchanged. Assign a value to the farmers' goods and the Mbuti goods, depending upon each group's needs. How would the trading process change if money were exchanged?

◆ 699

Background

Cultural Diversity Anthropologists use the term Pygmies to refer to human groups in which the average stature of adult males is less than 150 cm. The Mbuti, averaging less than 137 cm, are the shortest Pygmies in Africa.

The Mbuti have traded goods with their farming neighbors for over 2,000 years. Mbuti culture has remained essentially unchanged. Group discussion is the usual means by which any dispute is settled. Some groups hunt with nets and spears, while others use bows and arrows. Special songs honoring the forest are important in Mbuti rites of passage associated with puberty, marriage, and death. Values are reinforced in music, dance, and mime. Family bonds are strong and lasting.

Explore Social Studies Concepts

Use Maps Have students find the Democratic Republic of the Congo (formerly Zaire) on the map on page 696. Point out that the Democratic Republic of the Congo and the Republic of the Congo are two separate nations. Have students do further research to find a more detailed map of the Democratic Republic of the Congo and locate the Ituri forest within the country.

Discuss Ask: **What does it mean to be nomadic?** (*To move from one place to another frequently, with no permanent residence*) Ask: **What things that you have now would you not have as hunter-gatherers? How would you prepare and cook food? Where would you sleep? What would you do if you became ill? How would you spend most of your time?** (*Student answers will vary but should indicate that they understand the idea of a hunter-gatherer society.*)

Social Studies Activity

Focus Have students consider the lifestyle of the Mbuti people. Ask: **What goods would be important to their survival?** (*Tools that aid in hunting and gathering*) **What goods could the Mbuti provide that would be valuable to farmers?** (*Meats and other forest products*)

Teach Have students work in groups of three or four to create a list of goods that each of the groups (the Mbuti and the farmers) might bring to exchange. Have each group share their list with the class and record all of the suggestions on the board.

Extend Have students work in pairs to role-play a trading session between an Mbuti trader and a farmer.

Scoring Rubric

4 Student's list contains realistic goods for exchange, student has set a value of exchange based on the needs of each group, and student has answered the question as to how trade would change if money were exchanged

3 Student's list contains goods for exchange, student has set a value of exchange based on the needs of each group, and student has answered the question as to how trade would change if money were exchanged

2 Student's list contains goods for exchange and student has set a value of exchange based on the needs of each group

1 Student's list contains goods for exchange

Explore Language Arts Concepts

Oral Presentation To enhance student comprehension of Durrell's memoirs, have volunteers take turns reading the selection aloud. Encourage students to read with drama by including appropriate vocal inflections, word emphasis, gestures, and facial expressions. Ask: **Why did Durrell use the word *magical* to describe his experience?** *(He had never seen the rain forest and its wildlife from that viewpoint before.)* Ask students if they have ever ridden in an airplane, been on a mountain, or been in a tall building where they could look down on things they usually only see from ground level. Encourage them to describe their experiences.

Language Arts Activity

Focus Have students work in pairs. To make the task manageable, limit the pamphlet size to four or six pages. Six pages can be created by folding a standard sheet of paper into thirds.

Teach Provide students with a variety of source materials to prompt their ideas. Use materials that are generously illustrated with color photographs of the rain forest and its wildlife. Allow students to photocopy or scan photographs and incorporate them into their pamphlets. If possible, allow students to use software programs to create their pamphlets. Have students share their pamphlets by posting them on a bulletin board.

Scoring Rubric

4 Includes at least four pages of photos, facts, and descriptive, persuasive information that would encourage people to travel to the rain forest

3 Includes at least four pages of photos, facts, and information that would encourage people to travel to the rain forests, does not include descriptive or persuasive phrasing

2 Less than four pages of photos, facts, and information that would encourage people to travel to the rain forest

1 Less than four pages of information with inaccurate facts or no photos

Climbing the Canopy

Much of the rain forest is still a mystery because it's so difficult for scientists to study the canopy. Native forest people sometimes climb these tall trees using strong, thick vines called lianas as support. But rain forest scientists have had to find different methods. Naturalist Gerald Durrell, working in the African rain forest, was lucky enough to find another way to observe the canopy. He describes it here.

Gerald Durrell
British conservationist Gerald Durrell wrote about his adventures with wildlife around the world. In this photo, Durrell holds an anteater.

While the canopy is one of the most richly inhabited regions of the forest it is also the one that causes the naturalist the greatest frustration. There he is, down in the gloom among the giant tree trunks, hearing the noises of animal life high above him and having half-eaten fruit, flowers, or seeds rained on him by legions of animals high in their sunlit domain—all of which he cannot see. Under these circumstances the naturalist develops a very bad temper and a permanent crick in the neck.

However, there was one occasion when I managed to transport myself into the forest canopy, and it was a magical experience. It happened in West Africa when I was camped on the thickly forested lower slopes of a mountain called N'da Ali. Walking through the forest one day I found I was walking along the edge of a great step cut out of the mountain. The cliff face, covered with creepers, dropped away for about 50 yards, so that although I was walking through forest, just next to me and slightly below was the canopy of the forest growing up from the base of the cliff. This cliff was over half a mile in length and provided me with a natural balcony from which I could observe the treetop life simply by lying on the cliff edge, concealed in the low undergrowth.

Over a period of about a week I spent hours up there and a whole pageant of wildlife passed by. The numbers of birds were incredible, ranging from minute glittering sunbirds in rainbow coloring, zooming like helicopters from blossom to blossom as they fed on the nectar, to the flocks of huge black hornbills with their monstrous yellow beaks who flew in such an ungainly manner and made such a noise over their choice of forest fruits.

From early morning to evening when it grew too dark to see, I watched this parade of creatures. Troops of monkeys swept past, followed by attendant flocks of birds who fed eagerly on the insects that the monkeys disturbed during their noisy crashing through the trees. Squirrels chased each other, or hotly pursued lizards, or simply lay spread-eagled on branches high up in the trees, enjoying the sun.

Background

Facts and Figures Gerald Durrell (1925–1995) first developed his love of animals and ambition to be a naturalist during childhood on the island of Corfu, off the west coast of Greece. Long hours spent observing wildlife led Durrell to collect many local animals as pets—to the consternation of his family.

Durrell's first job was as a student keeper at England's Whipsnade Zoo. After joining several collecting expeditions abroad, he began to organize them himself. In the 1950s, he founded the Jersey Wildlife Preservation and Zoological Garden to raise, study, and breed rare and threatened species. Durrell wrote the first of his many books, *The Overloaded Ark,* when he was only 22.

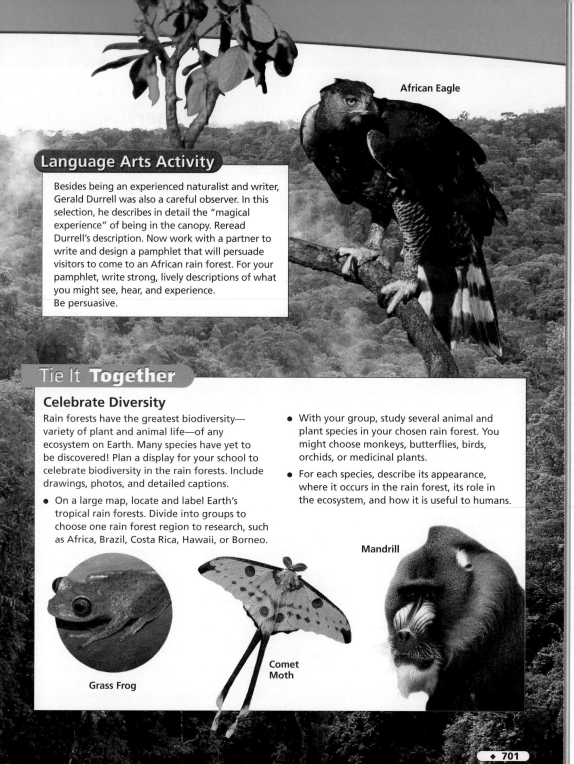

African Eagle

Language Arts Activity

Besides being an experienced naturalist and writer, Gerald Durrell was also a careful observer. In this selection, he describes in detail the "magical experience" of being in the canopy. Reread Durrell's description. Now work with a partner to write and design a pamphlet that will persuade visitors to come to an African rain forest. For your pamphlet, write strong, lively descriptions of what you might see, hear, and experience. Be persuasive.

Tie It **Together**

Celebrate Diversity

Rain forests have the greatest biodiversity—variety of plant and animal life—of any ecosystem on Earth. Many species have yet to be discovered! Plan a display for your school to celebrate biodiversity in the rain forests. Include drawings, photos, and detailed captions.

- On a large map, locate and label Earth's tropical rain forests. Divide into groups to choose one rain forest region to research, such as Africa, Brazil, Costa Rica, Hawaii, or Borneo.

- With your group, study several animal and plant species in your chosen rain forest. You might choose monkeys, butterflies, birds, orchids, or medicinal plants.

- For each species, describe its appearance, where it occurs in the rain forest, its role in the ecosystem, and how it is useful to humans.

Mandrill

Comet Moth

Grass Frog

◆ 701

Tie It Together

Celebrate Diversity

Time 4 class periods (2 for research, 2 for designing and creating the display)

Tips Have students work in groups of three or four.

- Monitor each group's choices of plant and animal species to make sure the group's research will be well-focused and not too wide-ranging.

- Arrange with your school office for a suitable display area, such as the school entryway, a heavily trafficked hallway, the library, or the cafeteria.

Extend After students have displayed their work in their own school, encourage them to ask permission to post the displays in areas accessible to the general public, such as the local library.

Chapter at a Glance

 Chapter Project *What's a Crowd?*

Technology

PRENTICE HALL
TeacherEXPRESS™
Plan • Teach • Assess

Local Standards

All in One Teaching Resources, Unit 4
- Chapter Project Teacher Notes, pp. 38–39
- Chapter Project Student Overview, pp. 40–41
- Chapter Project Student Worksheets, pp. 42–43
- Chapter Project Scoring Rubric, p. 44

DISCOVERY CHANNEL SCHOOL
Video Preview

 Section 1

Living Things and the Environment

21.1.1 Identify the needs that must be met by an organism's surroundings.

21.1.2 Identify biotic and abiotic parts of a habitat.

21.1.3 Describe the levels of organizations within an ecosystem.

2 periods
1 block

Go Online
SCiLINKS™ NSTA

 Section 2

Studying Populations

21.2.1 Describe methods for determining the size of a population.

21.2.2 Explain the causes of changes in population size.

21.2.3 Identify factors that limit population growth.

2 periods
1 block

Go Online
active art

Go Online
PHSchool.com

 Section 3

Interactions Among Living Things

21.3.1 Explain how an organism's adaptations help it survive.

21.3.2 Describe the major kinds of interaction among organisms in an ecosystem.

21.3.3 Identify the three types of symbiotic relationships.

1 period
1/2 block

Go Online
PHSchool.com

DISCOVERY CHANNEL SCHOOL
Video Field Trip

 Section 4

Changes in Communities

21.4.1 Describe the differences between primary and secondary succession.

1 period
1/2 block

Go Online
SCiLINKS™ NSTA

Review and Assessment

All in One Teaching Resources, Unit 4
- Key Terms Review, p. 78
- Transparency LS211
- Performance Assessment Teacher Notes, p. 86
- Performance Assessment Scoring Rubric, p. 87
- Performance Assessment Student Worksheet, p. 88
- Chapter Test, pp. 89–92

Go Online
PHSchool.com

DISCOVERY CHANNEL SCHOOL
Video Assessment

Test Preparation

Test Preparation Blackline Masters

Chapter Activities Planner

Student Edition	Inquiry	Time	Materials	Skills	Resources
Chapter Project, p. 703	Open-Ended	2 to 3 weeks	**All in One Teaching Resources, Unit 4**, p. 38	Developing a hypothesis, identifying and controlling variables, measuring, communicating	**Lab zone Easy Planner** **All in One Teaching Resources, Unit 4**, pp. 38–39
Section 1					
Discover Activity, p. 704	Open-Ended	10 minutes	Old magazines, scissors, paste or glue, sheet of white paper, three pencils of different colors	Inferring	**Lab zone Easy Planner**
Try This, p. 707	Directed	Setup, 15 minutes, follow-up, 5 minutes per day	4 600-mL beakers, masking tape, pen, 2 L spring water, 25 g noniodized salt, stirrers, brine shrimp eggs, 4 paper squares, paper cups, hand lens (optional)	Drawing conclusions	**Lab zone Easy Planner**
Skills Lab, p. 710	Directed	Prep: 30 minutes Class: 30 minutes Follow-up: 5–10 minutes per day	Gravel, soil, moss plants, plastic spoon, charcoal, spray bottle, large rubber band, 2 vascular plants, plastic wrap, pre-cut clear plastic bottle	Making models, observing	**Lab zone Easy Planner** **All in One Teaching Resources, Unit 4**, Skills Lab: *A World in a Bottle*, pp. 53–54
Section 2					
Discover Activity, p. 711	Guided	10 minutes	2 large plastic jars, dried beans, ruler, small beaker, timer	Forming operational definitions	**Lab zone Easy Planner**
Skills Activity, p. 713	Directed	5 minutes	None	Calculating	**Lab zone Easy Planner**
Try This, p. 717	Directed	15 minutes	Masking tape, meter stick, small jigsaw puzzle, watch or clock	Making models	**Lab zone Easy Planner**
Skills Lab, p. 719	Directed	Prep: 20 minutes Class: 40 minutes	Model paper turtle population, calculator, graph paper	Calculating, graphing, predicting	**Lab zone Easy Planner** **All in One Teaching Resources, Unit 4**, Skills Lab: *Counting Turtles*, pp. 61–63
Section 3					
Discover Activity, p. 722	Guided	15 minutes	Sheet of white paper, colored pencils or markers, tape	Predicting	**Lab zone Easy Planner**
Skills Activity, p. 728	Directed	10 minutes	None	Classifying	**Lab zone Easy Planner**
Section 4					
Discover Activity, p. 730	Guided	10 minutes	None	Posing questions	**Lab zone Easy Planner**

Section 1 Living Things and the Environment

ABILITY LEVELS KEY
L1 Basic to Average
L2 For All Students
L3 Average to Advanced

⏱ *2 periods, 1 block*

Objectives
21.1.1 Identify the needs that must be met by an organism's surroundings.
21.1.2 Identify biotic and abiotic parts of a habitat.
21.1.3 Describe the levels of organization within an ecosystem.

Local Standards

Key Terms
• organism • habitat • biotic factor • abiotic factor • photosynthesis • species
• population • community • ecosystem • ecology

Preteach

Build Background Knowledge
Students identify ecosystems they are familiar with.

 **Discover Activity** *What's in the Scene?* **L1**

Targeted Print and Technology Resources

 **Teaching Resources, Unit 4**

L2 Reading Strategy Transparency
LS201: Identifying Main Ideas

⊙ **PresentationEXPRESS™ CD-ROM**

Instruct

Habitats Define *habitat* and examine what needs are met by an organism's habitat.

Biotic Factors Identify a variety of biotic factors in a habitat.

Abiotic Factors Describe abiotic factors that are part of a habitat.

Levels of Organization Use pictures to describe the relationship among populations, communities, and ecosystems.

 Skills Lab *A World in a Bottle* **L3**

Targeted Print and Technology Resources

 **Teaching Resources, Unit 4**

L2 Guided Reading, pp. 47–50
L2 Transparency LS202
L3 Skills Lab: *A World in a Bottle,*
pp. 53–54

📼 **Lab Activity Video/DVD**
Skills Lab: *A World in a Bottle*

www.SciLinks.org Web Code: scn-0511

⊙ **Student Edition on Audio CD**

Assess

Section Assessment Questions
Have students use their Identifying Main Ideas graphic organizers to help answer the questions.

Reteach
Use a graphic organizer to show the relationships among populations, communities, and ecosystems.

Targeted Print and Technology Resources

Teaching Resources, Unit 4
• Section Summary, p. 46
L1 Review and Reinforce, p. 51
L3 Enrich, p. 52

Section 2 Studying Populations

🕐 *2 periods, 1 block*

Objectives

21.2.1 Describe methods for determining the size of a population.
21.2.2 Explain the causes of changes in population size.
21.2.3 Identify factors that limit population growth.

Key Terms

• estimate • birth rate • death rate • immigration • emigration
• population density • limiting factor • carrying capacity

Local Standards

Preteach

Build Background Knowledge

Describe the purpose of tagging individuals in a population study.

 **Discover Activity** *What's the Population of Beans in a Jar?* **L2**

Targeted Print and Technology Resources

 Teaching Resources, Unit 4

L2 Reading Strategy Transparency
LS203: Asking Questions

⊙ **PresentationEXPRESS™ CD-ROM**

Instruct

Determining Population Size Use photographs to help students understand methods for determining population size.

Changes in Population Size Use a graph to show how population size can change.

Limiting Factors Identify limiting factors for populations.

 **Skills Lab** *Counting Turtles* **L2**

Targeted Print and Technology Resources

 Teaching Resources, Unit 4

L2 Guided Reading, pp. 57–58
L2 Transparencies LS204, LS205
L2 Skills Lab: *Counting Turtles*, pp. 61–63

📼 **Lab Activity Video/DVD**
Skills Lab: *Counting Turtles*

PHSchool.com Web Code: cep-5012
PHSchool.com Web Code: ceh-5010

⊙ **Student Edition on Audio CD**

Assess

Section Assessment Questions

Have students use their Answering Questions graphic organizers to answer the questions.

Reteach

Discuss how specific limiting factors can cause populations to decrease.

Targeted Print and Technology Resources

Teaching Resources, Unit 4

• Section Summary, p. 56
L1 Review and Reinforce, p. 59
L3 Enrich, p. 60

Section 3 Interactions Among Living Things

ABILITY LEVELS KEY
L1 Basic to Average
L2 For All Students
L3 Average to Advanced

🕐 *1 period, 1/2 block*

Objectives

21.3.1 Explain how an organism's adaptations help it survive.

21.3.2 Describe the major kinds of interactions among organisms in an ecosystem.

21.3.3 Identify the three types of symbiotic relationships.

Key Terms

• natural selection • adaptations • niche • competition • predation • predator
• prey • symbiosis • mutualism • commensalism • parasitism • parasite • host

Local Standards

Preteach

Build Background Knowledge

Identify how different organisms have adapted to their environment.

Lab zone **Discover Activity** *Can You Hide a Butterfly?*   **L1**

Targeted Print and Technology Resources

All in One Teaching Resources, Unit 4

L2   Reading Strategy Transparency LS206: Using Prior Knowledge

⊙ **PresentationEXPRESS™ CD-ROM**

Instruct

Adapting to the Environment Use an illustration to explore how natural selection has resulted in organisms that are adapted to their environment.

Competition Discuss reasons for competition.

Predation Define *predation* and discuss the effect it has on population size.

Symbiosis Compare and contrast the three types of symbiosis.

Targeted Print and Technology Resources

All in One Teaching Resources, Unit 4

L2   Guided Reading, pp. 66–69
L2   Transparency LS207

PHSchool.com Web Code: ced-5013

Discovery CHANNEL SCHOOL
Video Field Trip

⊙ **Student Edition on Audio CD**

Assess

Section Assessment Questions

🔄 Have students use their Using Prior Knowledge graphic organizers to answer the questions.

Reteach

Review and summarize information about competition, predation, and symbiosis.

Targeted Print and Technology Resources

All in One Teaching Resources, Unit 4

• Section Summary, p. 65
L1   Review and Reinforce, p. 70
L3   Enrich, p. 71

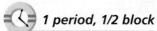

Section 4 Changes in Communities

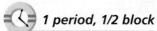 *1 period, 1/2 block*

ABILITY LEVELS KEY
- **L1** Basic to Average
- **L2** For All Students
- **L3** Average to Advanced

Objectives

21.4.1 Describe the differences between primary and secondary succession.

Local Standards

Key Terms

- succession • primary succession • pioneer species • secondary succession

---

Preteach

Build Background Knowledge

Observe over time a vacant lot or unattended garden and describe any changes.

Lab zone Discover Activity *What Happened Here?* **L1**

Targeted Print and Technology Resources

All in One Teaching Resources, Unit 4

L2 Reading Strategy Transparency LS208: Comparing and Contrasting

⊙ **PresentationEXPRESS™ CD-ROM**

Instruct

Primary Succession Use labeled illustrations to describe the process of primary succession.

Secondary Succession Use labeled illustrations to compare and contrast the processes of secondary and primary succession.

Targeted Print and Technology Resources

All in One Teaching Resources, Unit 4

L2 Guided Reading, pp. 74–75
L2 Transparencies LS209, LS210

www.SciLinks.org Web Code: scn-0514

⊙ **Student Edition on Audio CD**

Assess

Section Assessment Questions

Have students use their Comparing and Contrasting graphic organizers to answer the questions.

Reteach

Summarize the processes of primary and secondary succession.

Targeted Print and Technology Resources

All in One Teaching Resources, Unit 4

- Section Summary, p. 73
L1 Review and Reinforce, p. 76
L3 Enrich, p. 77

Section Lesson Plans

Chapter 21 **Content Refresher**

Go Online

NSTA–*PD*LINKS

For: Professional development support
Visit: www.SciLinks.org/PDLinks
Web Code: scf-0110

Professional Development

Section 1 **Living Things and the Environment**

Carbon Dioxide Carbon dioxide is an abiotic factor that all plants and some algae require to carry out photosynthesis. Chlorophyll, the green pigment in plants and some algae, absorbs energy in sunlight. The organism uses this energy to combine carbon dioxide (CO_2) and water (H_2O) in a chemical reaction that produces sugars, including glucose ($C_6H_{12}O_6$). Water and oxygen (O_2) are produced as byproducts of the reaction. The sugars provide energy for sustaining the organism's life processes. Other organisms obtain this energy when they eat plants or algae. The energy is released during cellular respiration when glucose is broken down into carbon dioxide and water.

Biosphere All of Earth's communities are part of a higher level of organization, the biosphere. The levels of organization that make up the biosphere interact with each other. But they also interact in various ways with Earth's other "spheres." These include the atmosphere (the gases that envelop Earth), the hydrosphere (Earth's water), and the lithosphere (Earth's rocky outer covering and soils). While scientists study the relationships among organisms of the biosphere, they also consider the biosphere in relation to the other spheres of the physical environment.

Section 2 **Studying Populations**

Principle of Competitive Exclusion The Gause principle, also known as the principle of competitive exclusion, was named for G. F. Gause, a Soviet biologist. Gause was the first to suggest that species cannot coexist for long in the same niche. Gause developed his ideas by studying two similar species of *Paramecium*. When he grew populations of the two species separately, both grew rapidly and then leveled off at a population size that could be supported by available resources in the growing medium, as shown on the upper graph. However, when Gause grew the two species together, one species survived and the other species died out, as shown on the lower graph. Gause concluded that the surviving species had a competitive advantage in obtaining food and other resources. His work was later confirmed by other studies.

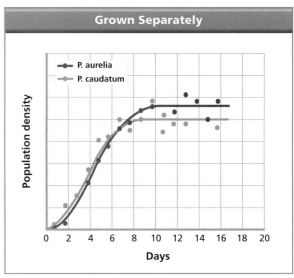

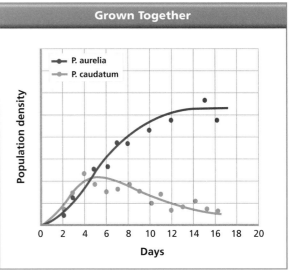

Section 3 **Interactions Among Living Things**

Moose and Wolves on Isle Royale When a population grows beyond the carrying capacity of its habitat, a population crash may occur. One example of such a crash occurred with the moose population on Isle Royale. Moose came to Isle Royale around 1900 by walking across the frozen lake in winter. Over the next 35 years, without predators, the moose population increased to about 3,000. As a result, the food supply became exhausted, and 90 percent of the moose starved. The population increased again until 1948 and then declined sharply once more because of lack of food. Wolves arrived in 1949. The moose and wolf populations have cycled up and down for decades.

Sometimes factors other than carrying capacity cause a population to decrease. In the early 1980s, the Isle Royale wolf population declined sharply. Biologists hypothesize that the extreme genetic uniformity of the population is one reason for the decline. Populations that lack genetic variability often have low reproductive success. For example, in 1994, only two wolf pups were born on the island. Genetic uniformity also makes a population more susceptible to disease. Analysis of the wolves' blood has revealed antibodies to canine parvovirus, indicating that the wolves have been exposed to this lethal disease. More recently, the wolf population has begun to increase slowly.

Address Misconceptions

Students may not understand that adaptation occurs in species, not in individuals. Individuals inherit a set of traits that do not change when factors in the environment change. For a strategy clarifying how a population rather than an individual may become adapted to a changed environment, see **Address Misconceptions** in the section *Interactions Among Living Things.*

Section 4 Changes in Communities

Lichens Lichens are an example of one type of symbiotic relationship—mutualism. In this type of association, both organisms depend on each other and cannot live independently. In the lichen, one organism, the alga, carries out photosynthesis and produces the food that the other organism, the fungus, requires. The fungus absorbs vital nutrients and water for the process. Notice in the cross-section diagram that the fungus provides a top layer (1) that protects the algae directly beneath (2). Fungal filaments (3) lie below the algae. The bottom protective layer (4) and the rootlike structures that anchor the lichen (5) are provided by the fungus.

Cross-Section of a Lichen

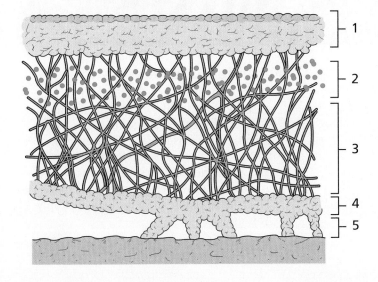

Lichens occur in most habitats, especially those unsuitable for plant growth. They have even been found growing on the shells of tortoises in the Galapagos and on beetles in New Guinea. In arid habitats lichens may have a ball-like shape that enables them to blow about and disperse in the wind.

Lichens are very sensitive to sulfur dioxide, which makes them good indicators of pollution and acid rain. Because they can tolerate and accumulate metals, they can be an indicator of industrial pollutants. Lichens also are used in traditional dyes, in herbal medicines, and as human and animal food. In the arctic, they are the main source of food for caribou and reindeer.

interactive Textbook
- Complete student edition
- Video and audio
- Simulations and activities
- Section and chapter activities

Chapter 21

Populations and Communities

interactive Textbook

A population of Grant's zebras roams on the Masai Mara Reserve in Kenya. ▶

702 ◆

Chapter Project

L3

Objectives
In addition to giving students an opportunity to observe the effect of crowding on plant growth, this project will enhance understanding of the procedure involved in scientific experimentation. After this Chapter Project, students will be able to
- design an experiment to test the effect of crowding on plant growth
- identify and control variables
- measure plant growth, record data, and analyze results
- communicate experimental procedures and results in a written report and graph

Skills Focus
Developing a hypothesis, identifying and controlling variables, measuring, communicating

Project Time Line 2 to 3 weeks

All in One Teaching Resources, Unit 4
- Chapter Project Teacher Notes
- Chapter Project Overview
- Chapter Project Worksheet 1
- Chapter Project Worksheet 2
- Chapter Project Scoring Rubric

Safety
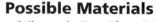
Review the Safety Guidelines in Appendix A.

Developing a Plan
During the first phase of the project, each group should plan an experiment and submit the plan for your review.

Possible Materials
- Wisconsin Fast Plants™ *(Brassica rapa),* a strain of radishlike plants specifically developed for their short life cycle, are preferred for this project. They germinate within 24 hours, develop leaves within one week and flowers in about two weeks, and can be grown easily in a small space. They are available from biological supply houses.

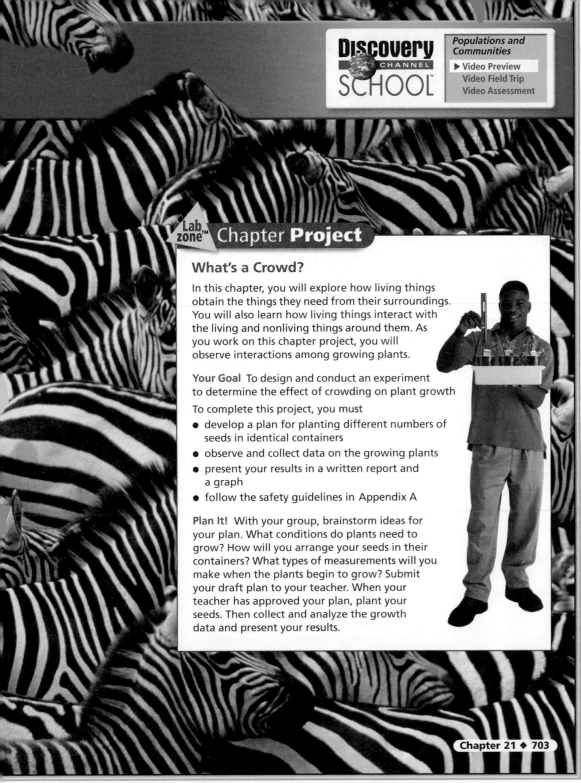

Lab zone™ Chapter **Project**

What's a Crowd?

In this chapter, you will explore how living things obtain the things they need from their surroundings. You will also learn how living things interact with the living and nonliving things around them. As you work on this chapter project, you will observe interactions among growing plants.

Your Goal To design and conduct an experiment to determine the effect of crowding on plant growth

To complete this project, you must

● develop a plan for planting different numbers of seeds in identical containers

● observe and collect data on the growing plants

● present your results in a written report and a graph

● follow the safety guidelines in Appendix A

Plan It! With your group, brainstorm ideas for your plan. What conditions do plants need to grow? How will you arrange your seeds in their containers? What types of measurements will you make when the plants begin to grow? Submit your draft plan to your teacher. When your teacher has approved your plan, plant your seeds. Then collect and analyze the growth data and present your results.

Chapter 21 ◆ 703

Populations and Communities

Show the Video Preview to introduce the Chapter Project and present an overview of the chapter content. Ask: **What are some of the characteristics of the cheetah population?** *(Accept all student responses that show an understanding of the characteristics of a population.)*

- Each group will need several identical planting containers. Possibilities include large margarine tubs or half-gallon milk cartons with one of the sides removed.

- Provide potting soil, trowels or large spoons, watering cans or spray bottles, and rulers.

- Set aside a location where the plant containers will receive direct sunlight or strong indirect sunlight for several hours a day. If sunlight is limited, set up lamps on tables.

Launching the Project

To introduce the project, ask: **What do plants need to grow?** *(Students may mention sunlight, water, a certain temperature, soil, or nutrients in the soil.)* **Do you think that every seed that germinates grows into a mature plant? Why or why not?** *(Most students will realize that many young plants do not mature because their needs are not met.)* Discuss with students how overcrowding of plants might affect growth.

Performance Assessment

The Chapter Scoring Rubric will help you evaluate how well students complete the Chapter Project. You may want to share the rubric with students so that they will know what is expected. Students will be assessed on

- how well they design an experiment to test the effect of crowding on plant growth

- how carefully they identify and control variables, make observations, and record data

- how well they communicate their procedures, results, and conclusion to the class

- how well they participate in their groups

Portfolio

703

Objectives

After this lesson, students will be able to

21.1.1 Identify the needs that must be met by an organism's surroundings.

21.1.2 Identify biotic and abiotic parts of a habitat.

21.1.3 Describe the levels of organization within an ecosystem.

Target Reading Skill 🔄

Identifying Main Ideas Explain that identifying main ideas and details helps students sort the facts from the information into groups. Each group can have a main topic, subtopics, and details.

Answers

Possible answers:

Main Idea: An organism obtains food, water, shelter, and other things it needs from its environment.

Detail: Each organism must live in a specific type of environment, called its habitat.

Detail: Organisms live in different habitats because they have different requirements for survival.

Detail: One area may contain many habitats.

All in One Teaching Resources, Unit 4

• Transparency LS201

Preteach

Build Background Knowledge
L2

Experience with Ecosystems

Ask: **What is an ecosystem?** (*Students may say that it is a particular type of place with different kinds of organisms living in it. Accept all responses without comment at this time.*)
What kinds of ecosystems do you know of?
(*Students may mention a swamp, desert, seashore, forest, and so on.*)

Reading Preview

Key Concepts
• What needs are met by an organism's environment?
• What are the two parts of an organism's habitat with which it interacts?
• What are the levels of organization within an ecosystem?

Key Terms
• organism • habitat
• biotic factor • abiotic factor
• photosynthesis • species
• population • community
• ecosystem • ecology

🔄 Target Reading Skill

Identifying Main Ideas As you read the Habitats section, write the main idea—the biggest or most important idea—in a graphic organizer like the one below. Then write three supporting details that give examples of the main idea.

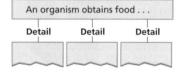

Main Idea

An organism obtains food . . .

Detail   Detail   Detail

Lab zone | Discover **Activity**

What's in the Scene?

1. Choose a magazine picture of a nature scene. Paste the picture onto a sheet of paper, leaving space all around the picture.
2. Locate everything in the picture that is alive. Use a colored pencil to draw a line from each living thing. If you know its name, write it on the line.
3. Using a different colored pencil, label each nonliving thing.

Think It Over
Inferring How do the living things in the picture depend on the nonliving things? Using a third color, draw lines connecting the living things to the nonliving things they need.

As the sun rises on a warm summer morning, the Nebraska town is already bustling with activity. Some residents are hard at work building homes for their families. They are working underground, where it is dark and cool. Other inhabitants are collecting seeds for breakfast. Some of the town's younger residents are at play, chasing each other through the grass.

Suddenly, an adult spots a threatening shadow—an enemy has appeared in the sky! The adult cries out several times, warning the others. Within moments, the town's residents disappear into their underground homes. The town is silent and still, except for a single hawk circling overhead.

Have you guessed what kind of town this is? It is a prairie dog town on the Nebraska plains. As these prairie dogs dug their burrows, searched for food, and hid from the hawk, they interacted with their environment, or surroundings.

Black-Tailed Prairie Dog ▶

Lab zone | Discover **Activity**

Skills Focus Inferring   L1

Materials old magazines, scissors, paste or glue, sheet of white paper, three pencils of different colors

Time 10 minutes

Tips Encourage students to look for pictures with close-enough views to allow them to distinguish various living and nonliving things.

Expected Outcome The specific living things shown will vary. Students should identify water, soil, sunlight, and air among the nonliving things.

Think It Over Students should indicate that living things needs water and air and that plants also need sunlight.

Habitats

A prairie dog is one type of **organism,** or living thing. Different types of organisms must live in different types of environments. **An organism obtains food, water, shelter, and other things it needs to live, grow, and reproduce from its environment.** An environment that provides the things the organism needs to live, grow, and reproduce is called its **habitat.**

One area may contain many habitats. For example, in a forest, mushrooms grow in the damp soil, salamanders live on the forest floor, and woodpeckers build nests in tree trunks.

Organisms live in different habitats because they have different requirements for survival. A prairie dog obtains the food and shelter it needs from its habitat. It could not survive in a tropical rain forest or on the rocky ocean shore. Likewise, the prairie would not meet the needs of a spider monkey or hermit crab.

 Why do different organisms live in different habitats?

Biotic Factors

To meet its needs, a prairie dog must interact with more than just the other prairie dogs around it. **An organism interacts with both the living and nonliving parts of its habitat.** The living parts of a habitat are called **biotic factors** (by AHT ik). Biotic factors in the prairie dogs' habitat include the grass and plants that provide seeds and berries. The hawks, ferrets, badgers, and eagles that hunt the prairie dogs are also biotic factors. In addition, worms, fungi, and bacteria are biotic factors that live in the soil underneath the prairie grass.

 Name a biotic factor in your environment.

FIGURE 1
An Organism in Its Habitat
Like all organisms, this red-tailed hawk obtains food, water, and shelter from its habitat. Prairie dogs are a major source of food for the red-tailed hawk.

Chapter 21 ◆ 705

Abiotic Factors

Help Students Read L1

Word-Part Analysis Explain that knowing the meanings of prefixes and root words can help students figure out and remember the meaning of key concept words. Write the word *biotic* on the board and ask student to identify the root word. *(Bio)* Tell students that *bio* comes from the Greek *bios,* which means "life." Next write the word *abiotic* on the board and point out that *a-* is a prefix meaning "not." Ask students to use the meanings of the prefix and root word to construct a meaning for *abiotic.* *("Not living")*

Teach Key Concepts L2

Identifying Abiotic Factors

Focus Remind students that biotic factors are the living parts of an organism's habitat.

Teach Ask: **What are some nonliving parts of a habitat?** *(Water, sunlight, oxygen, temperature, soil)* Define *abiotic factor.* Discuss how each factor helps an organism survive.

Apply Ask: **Does a squirrel need all the abiotic factors in its habitat to survive?** *(No)* Help students identify those that are essential to the squirrel's survival. *(Water, oxygen, temperature)* Ask students what might happen to a squirrel if its habitat did not provide an essential factor. *(It might die.)* **learning modality: verbal**

Observing Soil Components

Materials soil sample, jar with screw-on lid, water, metric ruler

Time 10 minutes

Focus Discuss with students the different materials that they might find in soil.

Teach Have small groups of students put about 200 mL of soil into a jar, add water to about 3 cm from the top, and screw on the lid tightly. Tell students to shake the jar thoroughly to mix the soil and water and then place the jar on the desk. When the soil has settled, have students observe the layers of separated soil. Remind student to wash their hands after completing the activity.

Apply Challenge students to identify the materials that make up the soil and to tell which are biotic and which are abiotic. **learning modality: kinesthetic**

706

FIGURE 2
Abiotic Factors

The nonliving things in an organism's habitat are abiotic factors. **Applying Concepts** *Name three abiotic factors you interact with each day.*

▲ This orangutan is enjoying a drink of water.

▲ Sunlight enables this plant to make its own food.

▲ This banjo frog burrows in the soil to stay cool.

706 ◆

Abiotic Factors

Abiotic factors (ay by AHT ik) are the nonliving parts of an organism's habitat. They include water, sunlight, oxygen, temperature, and soil.

Water All living things require water to carry out their life processes. Water also makes up a large part of the bodies of most organisms. Your body, for example, is about 65 percent water. Plants and algae need water, along with sunlight and carbon dioxide, to make their own food in a process called **photosynthesis** (foh toh SIN thuh sis). Other living things depend on plants and algae for food.

Sunlight Because sunlight is needed for photosynthesis, it is an important abiotic factor for most living things. In places that do not receive sunlight, such as dark caves, plants and algae cannot grow. Because there are no plants or algae to provide food, few other organisms can live in such places.

Oxygen Most living things require oxygen to carry out their life processes. Oxygen is so important to the functioning of the human body that you can live only a few minutes without it. Organisms that live on land obtain oxygen from air, which is about 20 percent oxygen. Fish and other water organisms obtain oxygen that is dissolved in the water around them.

Temperature The temperatures that are typical of an area determine the types of organisms that can live there. For example, if you took a trip to a warm tropical island, you might see colorful orchid flowers and tiny lizards. These organisms could not survive on the frozen plains of Siberia.

Some animals alter their environments so they can survive very hot or very cold temperatures. Prairie dogs, for example, dig underground dens to find shelter from the hot summer sun and cold winter winds.

Soil Soil is a mixture of rock fragments, nutrients, air, water, and the decaying remains of living things. Soil in different areas consists of varying amounts of these materials. The type of soil in an area influences the kinds of plants that can grow there. Many animals, such as the prairie dogs, use the soil itself as a home. Billions of microscopic organisms such as bacteria also live in the soil.

 Reading Checkpoint How do abiotic factors differ from biotic factors?

FIGURE 3
A Population
All these garter snakes make up a population.

Levels of Organization

Of course, organisms do not live all alone in their habitat. Instead, organisms live together in populations and communities, and with abiotic factors in their ecosystems.

Populations In 1900, travelers saw a prairie dog town in Texas that covered an area twice the size of the city of Dallas. The town contained more than 400 million prairie dogs! These prairie dogs were all members of one species, or single kind, of organism. A **species** (SPEE sheez) is a group of organisms that are physically similar and can mate with each other and produce offspring that can also mate and reproduce.

All the members of one species in a particular area are referred to as a **population.** The 400 million prairie dogs in the Texas town are one example of a population. All the pigeons in New York City make up a population, as do all the bees that live in a hive. In contrast, all the trees in a forest do not make up a population, because they do not all belong to the same species. There may be pines, maples, birches, and many other tree species in the forest.

Communities A particular area usually contains more than one species of organism. The prairie, for instance, includes prairie dogs, hawks, grasses, badgers, and snakes, along with many other organisms. All the different populations that live together in an area make up a **community.**

To be considered a community, the different populations must live close enough together to interact. One way the populations in a community may interact is by using the same resources, such as food and shelter. For example, the tunnels dug by prairie dogs also serve as homes for burrowing owls and black-footed ferrets. The prairie dogs share the grass with other animals. Meanwhile, prairie dogs themselves serve as food for many species.

Lab zone — Try This Activity

With or Without Salt?

In this activity you will explore salt as an abiotic factor.

1. Label four 600-mL beakers A, B, C, and D. Fill each with 500 mL of room-temperature spring water.
2. Set beaker A aside. Add 2.5 grams of noniodized salt to beaker B, 7.5 grams of salt to beaker C, and 15 grams of salt to beaker D. Stir each beaker.
3. Add $\frac{1}{8}$ spoonful of brine shrimp eggs to each beaker.
4. Cover each beaker with a square of paper. Keep them away from direct light or heat. Wash your hands.
5. Observe the beakers daily for three days.

Drawing Conclusions In which beakers did the eggs hatch? What can you conclude about the amount of salt in the shrimps' natural habitat?

Chapter 21 ◆ 707

Levels of Organization

Levels of Organization

Teach Key Concepts [L2]
Identifying Species, Populations, and Communities

Focus Write the names of these organisms on the board: grass, grasshoppers, field mice, red-tailed hawks. Ask: **Where might you find these organisms living together?** (*In a grassland*)

Teach Tell students that the members of each single kind of organism make up a species. Although the members of a species might have some small differences, they are physically similar and can mate with each other and produce young that can also mate with each other. Ask: **Do all members of each species, such as the red-tailed hawk, live in the same grassland?** (*No*) **What do we call the members of a single species living in this grassland?** (*Population*) **What do we call all the species living together in a grassland?** (*Community*)

Apply Ask: **Would white-tailed deer living in a forest in Pennsylvania be members of the same population as white-tailed deer living in Illinois? Why or why not?** (*No, a population is composed of individuals that live in a particular area.*) **learning modality: logical/mathematical**

Use Visuals: Figure 3 [L1]
Identifying Populations

Focus Have students study Figure 3 and read the caption.

Teach Ask: **Why is this group of garter snakes a population?** (*Because all the individuals are the same species and they live in the same area*)

Apply Ask students what other populations they might find living in a community with these snakes. (*Possible answers: plants, including grasses; mice; insects*) **learning modality: verbal**

Lab zone — Try This Activity

Skills Focus Drawing conclusions [L2]

Materials 4 600-mL beakers, masking tape, pen, 2 L spring water, 25 g noniodized salt, stirrers, brine shrimp eggs, 4 paper squares, paper cups, hand lens (optional)

Time setup—15 minutes; follow-up— 5 minutes per day

Tips Allow the water to sit overnight. Put brine shrimp eggs in a paper cup for each group. Add 1/2 teaspoon of dry yeast to each beaker to feed the shrimp. NOTE: Newly hatched brine shrimp are tiny and orange.

Expected Outcome Beaker A, no eggs hatch; beaker B, eggs hatch well; beaker C, less well; beaker D, little or no hatching. **learning modality: kinesthetic**

Monitor Progress [L2]

Skills Check Have students make a chart that lists abiotic factors in the first column. In the second column they should tell why each factor is necessary for life.

Answers
Figure 2 Answers might include: oxygen, water, temperature, sunlight.

 Reading Checkpoint Biotic factors are living; abiotic factors are nonliving.

Use Visuals: Figure 4 **L2**

Diagram Levels of Organization

Focus Review with students the definitions of *population* and *community*.

Teach Have students study Figure 4. Ask: **Which level has the most different kinds of individuals?** *(Ecosystem)* **How many different species are in the population?** *(One)* **What do the organisms in the community have in common?** *(They all live in the same place.)*

Apply Tell students to think of a different ecosystem. Then have each student create a diagram that shows the levels of organization for the chosen ecosystem. **learning modality: visual**

All in One Teaching Resources, Unit 4

• Transparency LS202

Ecosystems The community of organisms that live in a particular area, along with their nonliving surroundings, make up an **ecosystem.** A prairie is just one of the many different ecosystems found on Earth. Other ecosystems in which living things make their homes include mountain streams, deep oceans, and evergreen forests.

Figure 4 shows the levels of organization in a prairie ecosystem. **The smallest level of organization is a single organism, which belongs to a population that includes other members of its species. The population belongs to a community of different species. The community and abiotic factors together form an ecosystem.**

Because the populations in an ecosystem interact with one another, any change affects all the different populations that live there. The study of how living things interact with each other and with their environment is called **ecology.** Ecologists are scientists who study ecology. As part of their work, ecologists study how organisms react to changes in their environment. An ecologist, for example, may look at how a fire affects a prairie ecosystem.

 Reading Checkpoint What is ecology?

Section 1 Assessment

Target Reading Skill Identifying Main Ideas Use your graphic organizer to help you answer Question 1 below.

Reviewing Key Concepts

1. a. Listing What basic needs are provided by an organism's habitat?
  b. Predicting What might happen to an organism if its habitat could not meet one of its needs?
2. a. Defining Define the terms *biotic factors* and *abiotic factors.*
  b. Interpreting Illustrations List all the biotic and abiotic factors in Figure 4.
  c. Making Generalizations Explain why water and sunlight are two abiotic factors that are important to all organisms.

3. a. Sequencing List these terms in order from the smallest level to the largest: *population, organism, ecosystem, community.*
  b. Classifying Would all the different kinds of organisms in a forest be considered a population or a community? Explain.
  c. Relating Cause and Effect How might a change in one population affect other populations in a community?

Writing in Science

Descriptive Paragraph What habitat do you live in? Write a one-paragraph description of your habitat. Describe how you obtain the food, water, and shelter you need from your habitat. How does this habitat meet your needs in ways that another would not?

Differentiated Instruction

English Learners/Beginning **L1**
Vocabulary: Link to Visual Use Figure 4 to explain levels of organization. Have students identify each kind of organism (species) in their home language and in English. Then pronounce aloud the picture labels: Organism, Population, Community and Ecosystem. Ask students how each level differs. **learning modality: visual**

English Learners/Intermediate **L2**
Vocabulary: Link to Visual Repeat the Beginning activity but have students write a sentence to describe what they see in each level. **learning modality: visual**

FIGURE 4
Ecological Organization
The smallest level of organization is the organism. The largest is the entire ecosystem.

Organism: Prairie dog

Population: Prairie dog town

Community: All the living things that interact on the prairie

Ecosystem: All the living and nonliving things that interact on the prairie

◆ 709

Keep Students on Track Make sure students have identified the major variables that affect plant growth: size of the containers, amount of soil in each, density and depth for planting the seeds, amount and frequency of watering, and location in which the containers will be placed. Also review students' data tables to make sure they will be recording all relevant data.

Writing in Science

Writing Mode Description
Scoring Rubric
4 Includes detailed descriptions of what student needs, how the student will get it, and how another habitat would not meet the student's needs
3 Includes incomplete descriptions of all three factors
2 Includes only two of the three factors
1 Includes only one of the factors

Monitor Progress _____ L1
Answer
✓ Reading Checkpoint Ecology is the study of how living things interact with each other and with their environment.

Assess

Reviewing Key Concepts
1. a. A habitat provides food, water, shelter, and other things an organism needs to grow and reproduce. **b.** The organism might die.
2. a. Biotic factors are the living parts of a habitat that an organism interacts with; abiotic factors are the nonliving parts. **b.** Biotic—grass, birds, snake, badger, bison, prairie dogs; abiotic—soil, air, temperature, sunlight **c.** All organisms need water to carry on life processes. Plants and algae need sunlight to make food in photosynthesis. Other organisms depend directly or indirectly on the plants and algae for food.
3. a. Organism, population, community, ecosystem **b.** A community because a community consists of different populations living together **c.** Sample answer: If a population that is a food source for another population decreases, then the second population may decrease due to starvation.

Reteach L1
Write the word *prairie* on the board and draw a very large circle around it. Inside the circle draw smaller squares with these labels: *hawks, grasses, mice, snakes, water, air.* Inside the mice square, draw smaller triangles and label each *mouse.* Have students identify the shape that represent populations, a community, and an ecosystem.

Performance Assessment L2
Writing Ask students to choose an organism and describe its habitat. Tell them to identify the biotic and abiotic factors in the habitat.

All in One Teaching Resources, Unit 4
- Section Summary: *Living Things and the Environment*
- Review and Reinforce: *Living Things and the Environment*
- Enrich: *Living Things and the Environment*

A World in a Bottle [L3]

Prepare for Inquiry

Skills Objectives
After this lab, student will be able to
- make a model of a closed system
- observe the interactions of biotic and abiotic factors in a closed system

Prep Time 30 minutes

Class Time 30 minutes followed by 5–10 minutes per day for observations

Safety
Be sure students wear lab aprons to protect their clothing from soil stains. Students who are allergic to molds should not handle the soil. Remind students to wash their hands after they finish the activity. Review the safety guidelines in Appendix A.

All in One Teaching Resources, Unit 4
- Lab Worksheet: *A World in a Bottle*

Guide Inquiry

Introducing the Procedure
Have students study the picture of the lab setup in their books. Ask: **Why do you think a layer of gravel is included in the setup?** (*The gravel helps prevent the soil from becoming too wet and harming the plants.*)

Troubleshooting the Experiment
- Store-bought potting soil may result in better, more-uniform growth.

Expected Outcome
The plants will grow and thrive as long as not too little and not too much water is provided, and plants receive sunlight. Plants may decline if they become too crowded, or if nutrients in the soil are depleted.

Analyze and Conclude
1. Biotic factors: plants, any microscopic organisms in the soil; abiotic factors: gravel, soil, charcoal, water, air, light

2. Yes, light, an abiotic factor

3. Diagrams should show plants taking in carbon dioxide, water, and sunlight and giving off oxygen gas and water.

A World in a Bottle

Problem
How do organisms survive in a closed ecosystem?

Skills Focus
making models, observing

Materials
- gravel • soil • moss plants • plastic spoon
- charcoal • spray bottle • large rubber band
- 2 vascular plants • plastic wrap
- pre-cut, clear plastic bottle

Procedure
1. In this lab, you will place plants in moist soil in a bottle that then will be sealed. This setup is called a terrarium. Predict whether the plants can survive in this habitat.

2. Spread about 2.5 cm of gravel on the bottom of a pre-cut bottle. Then sprinkle a spoonful or two of charcoal over the gravel.

3. Use the spoon to layer about 8 cm of soil over the gravel and charcoal. After you add the soil, tap it down to pack it.

4. Scoop out two holes in the soil. Remove the vascular plants from their pots. Gently place their roots in the holes. Then pack the loose soil firmly around the plants' stems.

5. Fill the spray bottle with water. Spray the soil until you see water collecting in the gravel.

6. Cover the soil with the moss plants, including the areas around the stems of the vascular plants. Lightly spray the mosses with water.

7. Tightly cover your terrarium with plastic wrap. Secure the cover with a rubber band. Place the terrarium in bright, indirect light.

8. Observe your terrarium daily for two weeks. Record your observations in your notebook. If its sides fog, move the terrarium to an area with a different amount of light. You may need to move it a few times. Note any changes you make in your terrarium's location.

Analyze and Conclude
1. **Making Models** List all of the biotic factors and abiotic factors that are part of your ecosystem model.

2. **Observing** Were any biotic or abiotic factors able to enter the terrarium? If so, which ones?

3. **Inferring** Draw a diagram showing the interactions between the terrarium's biotic and abiotic factors.

4. **Predicting** Suppose a plant-eating insect were added to the terrarium. Predict whether it would be able to survive. Explain your prediction.

5. **Communicating** Write a paragraph that explains how your terrarium models an ecosystem on Earth. How does your model differ from that ecosystem?

Design an Experiment
Plan an experiment that would model a freshwater ecosystem. How would this model be different from the land ecosystem? *Obtain your teacher's approval before carrying out your plan.*

---

4. Sample answer: The insect probably would not survive because it would eat the plants faster than they could grow.

5. Paragraphs should explain that the model shows how biotic and abiotic factors interact within an ecosystem. The model is closed, not as complex, contains fewer organisms than an ecosystem.

Extend Inquiry

Design an Experiment Students should include both plants and animals in their ecosystem. Make sure students let the water stand uncovered for a few days before adding it to the ecosystem to get rid of dissolved chemicals in the water. Water temperature should be maintained around 23°C.

Studying Populations

Reading Preview

Key Concepts
• How do ecologists determine the size of a population?
• What causes populations to change in size?
• What factors limit population growth?

Key Terms
• estimate • birth rate
• death rate • immigration
• emigration
• population density
• limiting factor
• carrying capacity

↻ Target Reading Skill
Asking Questions Before you read, preview the red headings. In a graphic organizer like the one below, ask a question for each heading. As you read, write the answers to your questions.

Studying Populations

Question	Answer
How do you determine population size?	Some methods of determining population size are . . .

FIGURE 5
Studying Populations
These young albatrosses are part of a larger albatross population in the Falkland Islands.

Lab zone ▸ Discover **Activity**

What's the Population of Beans in a Jar?
1. Fill a plastic jar with dried beans. This is your model population.
2. Your goal is to determine the bean population size, but you will not have time to count every bean. You may use any of the following to help you: a ruler, a small beaker, another large jar. Set a timer for two minutes when you are ready to begin.
3. After two minutes, record your answer. Then count the beans. How close was your answer?

Think It Over
Forming Operational Definitions In this activity, you came up with an estimate of the size of the bean population. Write a definition of the term *estimate* based on what you did.

How would you like to be an ecologist today? Your assignment is to study the albatross population on an island. One question you might ask is how the size of the albatross population has changed over time. Is the number of albatrosses on the island more than, less than, or the same as it was 50 years ago? To answer this question, you must first determine the current size of the albatross population.

◆ 711

Lab zone ▸ Discover **Activity**

Skills Focus Forming operational definitions

Materials 2 large plastic jars, dried beans, ruler, small beaker, timer

Time 10 minutes

Expected Outcome Possible methods: (1) Fill the small beaker with beans, count the beans, estimate how many small beakers would fit into the large jar,

multiply the bean count by that number. (2) Put a 1-cm layer of beans in the second large jar, count the beans, measure the height of the jar, multiply the height by the number of beans in one layer.

Think It Over Definitions should focus on the idea of making an informed or educated guess.

Objectives
After this lesson, students will be able to
21.2.1 Describe methods for determining the size of a population.
21.2.2 Explain the causes of changes in population size.
21.2.3 Identify factors that limit population growth.

Target Reading Skill ↻
Asking Questions Explain that changing a head into a question helps students anticipate the ideas, facts, and events they are about to read.

Answers
Possible student question and answers are these: **How do you determine population size?** *(Some methods of determining population size are direct observation, indirect observation, sampling, and mark-and-recapture studies.)* **What causes populations to change in size?** *(Some factors include birth, death, immigration, and emigration.)* **What are limiting factors?** *(These are factors that can limit population growth if they are unfavorable for the organisms in the population. Food and water, space, and weather conditions can be limiting factors.)*

All in One Teaching Resources, Unit 4
• Transparency LS203

Preteach

Build Background Knowledge   L2

Experience with Mark-and-Recapture
Ask: **Have you ever seen scientists in a television documentary capture a wild animal, such as a wolf, bear, or bird, and then tag it with a specific color or mark and release it? What was the purpose of this procedure?** *(Answers might include to count the number of individuals in a population.)* Tell students that this is only one technique that scientists use to find the number of individuals in a population.

Determining Population Size

Teach Key Concepts L2

Estimating

Focus Remind students that a population is all the members of a species living in a particular area.

Teach Ask: **Why might scientists want to determine the number of individuals in a population?** (*Possible answer: To see if a population is increasing or decreasing*) Review the techniques for determining population size by direct and indirect observation, sampling, and mark-and-recapture studies.

Apply Ask students what method they would use to count the number of individuals in the following populations: grizzly bears in a national park, grasshoppers in a field, and herons on a large pond. Have students give reasons for their answers. (*Possible answers: grizzly bears: indirect observation because there are few, they are difficult to capture, and they would be spread over a large area; grasshoppers: sampling because there would be too many to count individually; herons: direct observation because only a few would live in the same pond*) **learning modality: logical/ mathematical**

Independent Practice

All in One Teaching Resources, Unit 4

- Guided Reading and Study Worksheet: *Studying Populations*

○ **Student Edition Audio CD**

FIGURE 6
Determining Population Size
Scientists use a variety of methods to determine the size of a population.

Indirect Observation
One way to determine this cliff swallow population is to count their cone-shaped nests.

Direct Observation
Counting these crabs one by one is an example of direct observation.

712 ◆

Determining Population Size

Some methods of determining the size of a population are direct and indirect observations, sampling, and mark-and-recapture studies.

Direct Observation The most obvious way to determine the size of a population is to count all of its members. For example, you could try to count all the crabs in a tide pool.

Indirect Observation Sometimes it may be easier to observe signs of organisms rather than the organisms themselves. Look at the mud nests built by cliff swallows in Figure 6. Each nest has one entrance hole. By counting the entrance holes, you can determine the number of swallow nests in this area. Suppose that the average number of swallows per nest is four: two parents and two offspring. If there are 120 nests, you can multiply 120 by 4 to determine that there are 480 swallows.

Sampling In many cases, it is not even possible to count signs of every member of a population. The population may be very large or spread over a wide area. In such cases, ecologists usually make an estimate. An **estimate** is an approximation of a number, based on reasonable assumptions.

Differentiated Instruction

Gifted and Talented L3
Researching Population Studies Have students research specific population studies around the world. Ask them to prepare a 10–15 minute oral report for the class that tells what is being studied, where and why the study is taking place, and who is doing the study. Tell them to include a description of the methods that are being used. Encourage students to include pictures, diagrams, and graphs to explain their information. **learning modality: logical/mathematical**

Special Needs L1
Practice Calculations For students who need extra help with the Math Skills activity, provide additional examples so that they can practice the calculations; for example, 144 dandelion plants in a lawn 12 m long and 6 m wide. (*2 plants per m²*) You may want to let students use calculators to solve the problems. Also, invite students to make up problems for the class to solve.

One way to estimate the size of a population is to count the number of organisms in a small area (a sample), and then multiply to find the number in a larger area. To get the most accurate estimate, your sample area should be typical of the larger area. Suppose you count 8 birch trees in 100 square meters of a forest. If the entire forest were 100 times that size, you would multiply your count by 100 to estimate the total population, or 800 birch trees.

Mark-and-Recapture Studies Another estimating method is called "mark and recapture." Here's an example showing how mark and recapture works. First, turtles in a bay are caught in a way that does not harm them. Ecologists count the turtles and mark each turtle's shell with a dot of paint before releasing it. Two weeks later, the researchers return and capture turtles again. They count how many turtles have marks, showing that they have been recaptured, and how many are unmarked. Using a mathematical formula, the ecologists can estimate the total population of turtles in the bay. You can try this technique for yourself in the Skills Lab at the end of this section.

 Reading Checkpoint When might an ecologist use indirect observation to estimate a population?

Lab zone Skills **Activity**

Calculating

An oyster bed is 100 meters long and 50 meters wide. In a 1-square-meter area you count 20 oysters. Estimate the population of oysters in the bed. (*Hint:* Drawing a diagram may help you set up your calculation.)

Mark and Recapture
This researcher is releasing a marked turtle as part of a mark-and-recapture study.

Sampling
To estimate the birch tree population in a forest, count the birches in a small area. Then multiply to find the number in the larger area.

◆ 713

Lab zone Skills **Activity**

Skills Focus Calculating
Materials none
Time 5 minutes
Tips If necessary, review the formula for finding area: length × width = area.

L2

Expected Outcome The total population is 100,000 oysters (100 m × 50 m = 5,000 m² × 20 oysters per m²).

Extend Ask: **Why is your answer only an estimate of the total population?** (*Every square meter may not have exactly 20 oysters.*) **learning modality: logical/ mathematical**

 **Lab zone** Build **Inquiry** **L2**

Estimating a Population

Materials 500 wooden toothpicks
Time 15 minutes

Focus Tell students that in this activity they will estimate the population of toothpicks.

Teach Scatter 500 toothpicks over a rectangular area large enough to provide a 1-square-meter section for each student, or use a floor with 1-ft-square tiles, allowing one tile per student. Tell students the total area but not the number of toothpicks you used. Have each student estimate the number of toothpicks in his or her "sample" and then calculate the total "population" of toothpicks. Write the estimates on the board.

Apply Ask: **Why did the estimates vary?** (*Sampling methods may have varied slightly. Different samples contained different numbers of toothpicks.*) **Which techniques does this activity model?** (*Sampling*) **Do you think this is the best way to determine the population of toothpicks? Why?** (*Accept all answers that show logical thinking. Most students will agree that sampling is the best method for counting the toothpicks because the total number is large, and it would take a lot of time to count individuals.*) **learning modality: kinesthetic**

Monitor Progress _____ **L2**

Oral Presentation Write descriptions of various populations on index cards. Have each student choose a card and tell what method they would use to determine the population size.

Answer

✔ **Reading Checkpoint** Scientists might use indirect observation when a population is small or difficult to find.

Changes in Population Size

Teach Key Concepts L2

Emigration and Immigration

Focus Ask: **What might happen to the size of a particular population over time?** *(It might increase or decrease.)*

Teach Discuss with students the meanings of *immigration* and *emigration*. Ask: **What might cause individuals to immigrate?** *(Possible answers might include an abundant food supply.)* **Why might individuals emigrate?** *(Students might suggest drought, food scarcity, or habitat destruction.)*

Apply Ask: **Why might scientists want to monitor the size of a population?** *(Possible answers: To make sure the population isn't getting too large, which could lead to habitat destruction; to see if a population is at risk of becoming endangered)*

Extend The Active Art shows students how populations change over time. **learning modality: verbal**

All in One Teaching Resources, Unit 4
- Transparency LS204

Math Skill Inequalities

Focus Ask students what the term *inequality* means. *(Not equal in amount, size, value, and so on)*

Teach Direct students' attention to the symbols for "greater than" and "less than." Point out that the smaller value appears on the side of the symbol that forms the point. The larger value is placed on the side with the open end.

Answers

1. $5 > -6$

2. $0.4 < \dfrac{3}{5}$

$\qquad \dfrac{2}{5} < \dfrac{3}{5}$

$\qquad 0.4 < 0.6$

3. $-2 - (-8) > 7 - 1.5$

$\qquad 6 > 5.5$

Math Skills

Inequalities

The population statement is an example of an inequality. An inequality is a mathematical statement that compares two expressions. Two signs that represent inequalities are

$\qquad <$ (is less than)

$\qquad >$ (is greater than)

For example, an inequality comparing the fraction to the decimal 0.75 would be written

$$\frac{1}{2} < 0.75$$

Practice Problems Write an inequality comparing each pair of expressions below.

1. $5 \ \blacksquare \ -6$
2. $0.4 \ \blacksquare \ \dfrac{3}{5}$
3. $-2 - (-8) \ \blacksquare \ 7 - 1.5$

Changes in Population Size

By returning to a location often and using one of the methods described on the previous pages, ecologists can monitor the size of a population over time. **Populations can change in size when new members join the population or when members leave the population.**

Births and Deaths The main way in which new individuals join a population is by being born into it. The **birth rate** of a population is the number of births in a population in a certain amount of time. For example, suppose that a population of 100 cottontail rabbits produces 600 young in a year. The birth rate in this population would be 600 young per year.

The main way that individuals leave a population is by dying. The **death rate** is the number of deaths in a population in a certain amount of time. If 400 rabbits die in a year in the population, the death rate would be 400 rabbits per year.

The Population Statement When the birth rate in a population is greater than the death rate, the population will generally increase. This can be written as a mathematical statement using the "is greater than" sign:

> **If birth rate > death rate, population size increases.**

However, if the death rate in a population is greater than the birth rate, the population size will generally decrease. This can also be written as a mathematical statement:

> **If death rate > birth rate, population size decreases.**

Immigration and Emigration The size of a population also can change when individuals move into or out of the population, just as the population of your town changes when families move into town or move away. **Immigration** (im ih GRAY shun) means moving into a population. **Emigration** (em ih GRAY shun) means leaving a population. For instance, if food is scarce, some members of an antelope herd may wander off in search of better grassland. If they become permanently separated from the original herd, they will no longer be part of that population.

Graphing Changes in Population Changes in a population's size can be displayed on a line graph. Figure 7 shows a graph of the changes in a rabbit population. The vertical axis shows the numbers of rabbits in the population, while the horizontal axis shows time. The graph shows the size of the population over a ten-year period.

Differentiated Instruction

English Learners/Beginning L1
Vocabulary: Word Analysis Write the words *immigration* and *emigration* on the board and circle *migration* in each. Explain that *migration* means "traveling from one place to another." Tell students that the prefix *im-* is similar in meaning to the word *in*, so *immigration* means "in-migration." Then explain that when they see the prefix *e-*, students can think of *exit*, so *emigration* means "out-migration." Demonstrate these meanings by leaving the room and walking back into it, stating the words as you do each act. **learning modality: verbal**

English Learners/Intermediate L2
Vocabulary: Word Analysis Use the procedure for Beginning students, but have students write sentences using the words *immigration* and *emigration*. **learning modality: verbal**

FIGURE 7
This line graph shows how the size of a rabbit population changed over a ten-year period. **Interpreting Graphs** *In what year did the rabbit population reach its highest point? What was the size of the population in that year?*

Go Online
active art

For: Changes in Population activity
Visit: PHSchool.com
Web Code: cep-5012

▼ Young cottontail rabbits in a nest

From Year 0 to Year 4, more rabbits joined the population than left it, so the population increased.

Changes in a Rabbit Population

Number of Rabbits (thousands) / Year of Study

From Year 4 to Year 8, more rabbits left the population than joined it, so the population decreased.

◄ Cottontail rabbit caught by a fox

Differentiated Instruction

Gifted and Talented **L3**
Calculating Growth Rate Tell students that ecologists use the birth and death rates to calculate a population's growth rate, the rate at which the population is changing. The birth rate (*b*) minus the death rate (*d*) equals the growth rate (*g*): $b - d = g$. Have students use this formula to calculate the growth rate of rabbits discussed in the text. *(600 births per year – 400 deaths per year = a growth rate of 200 rabbits per year)* **learning modality: logical/mathematical**

Calculating Growth Rate

Materials none

Time 5 minutes

Focus Review with students the definitions of *birth rate* and *death rate*.

Teach Ask: **Suppose 1,600 snow geese died in the same year that 1,400 were born. What would the growth rate be for that year?** *(Tell students that birth rate – death rate = growth rate:* $b - d = g$. *1,400 – 1,600 = growth rate of –200 geese for that year)* **What does a negative growth rate mean?** *(The population is declining.)*

Apply Ask: **What might account for a death rate that is higher than the birth rate?** *(Possible answers: Disease; not enough food; being eaten by other animals; unfavorable environmental conditions)* **learning modality: logical/mathematical**

Go Online
active art

For: Changes in Population Activity
Visit: PHSchool.com
Web Code: cep-5012

Students investigate the factors influencing changes in population size.

Monitor Progress _____ **L2**

Writing Have each student write a paragraph explaining how birth rate and death rate affect the size of a population. Students can save their paragraphs in their portfolios.

Portfolio

Answer
Figure 7 Fourth year of the study; about 850

Limiting Factors

Teach Key Concepts

L2

Inferring Limiting Factors of Plants

Focus Review with students the biotic and abiotic factors that might be found in an organism's habitat. Help students identify the factors that are essential for all living things, such as food, water, space, and appropriate weather conditions.

Teach Ask: **If all the needs of a population are met, what will most likely happen to the size of the population?** (*It will increase.*) **Can the size of the population continue to increase indefinitely? Why?** (*No, because at some time, one or more of the factors will become insufficient for the size of the population*) Tell students that any factor that causes a population to decrease is a limiting factor.

Apply Ask: **Is food a limiting factor for plants?** (*No*) **Why not?** (*Plants make their own food.*) **What factors do limit the size of plant populations?** (*The amounts of sunlight, carbon dioxide in the air, water, and nutrients in the soil*) **How do these factors limit plant populations?** (*Plants need light, carbon dioxide, and water to conduct photosynthesis, and they need nutrients for their own life processes.*) **learning modality: logical/ mathematical**

All in One Teaching Resources, Unit 4

- Transparency LS205

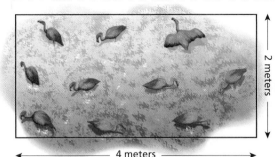 

FIGURE 8
Population Density
In the pond on the top left, there are ten flamingos in 8 square meters. The population density is 1.25 flamingos per square meter. *Calculating What is the population density of the flamingos in the pond on the top right?*

◄ Greater flamingo

Population Density Sometimes an ecologist may need to know more than just the total size of a population. In many situations, it is helpful to know the **population density**—the number of individuals in an area of a specific size. Population density can be written as an equation:

$$\text{Population density} = \frac{\text{Number of individuals}}{\text{Unit area}}$$

For example, suppose you counted 20 monarch butterflies in a garden measuring 10 square meters. The population density would be 20 monarchs per 10 square meters, or 2 monarchs per square meter.

Reading Checkpoint What is meant by the term *population density*?

Limiting Factors

When the living conditions in an area are good, a population will generally grow. But eventually some environmental factor will cause the population to stop growing. A **limiting factor** is an environmental factor that causes a population to decrease. **Some limiting factors for populations are food and water, space, and weather conditions.**

Food and Water Organisms require food and water to survive. Since food and water are often in limited supply, they are often limiting factors. Suppose a giraffe must eat 10 kilograms of leaves each day to survive. The trees in an area can provide 100 kilograms of leaves a day while remaining healthy. Five giraffes could live easily in this area, since they would only require a total of 50 kilograms of food. But 15 giraffes could not all survive—there would not be enough food. No matter how much shelter, water, and other resources there were, the population would not grow much larger than 10 giraffes.

The largest population that an area can support is called its **carrying capacity.** The carrying capacity of this giraffe habitat would be 10 giraffes. A population usually stays near its carrying capacity because of the limiting factors in its habitat.

Space Space is another limiting factor for populations. Gannets are seabirds that are usually seen flying over the ocean. They come to land only to nest on rocky shores. But the nesting shores get very crowded. If a pair does not find room to nest, they will not be able to add any offspring to the gannet population. So nesting space on the shore is a limiting factor for gannets. If there were more nesting space, more gannets would be able to nest, and the population would increase.

Space is also a limiting factor for plants. The amount of space in which a plant grows determines whether the plant can obtain the sunlight, water, and soil nutrients it needs. For example, many pine seedlings sprout each year in a forest. But as the seedlings grow, the roots of those that are too close together run out of space. Branches from other trees may block the sunlight the seedlings need. Some of the seedlings then die, limiting the size of the pine population.

FIGURE 9
Food as a Limiting Factor
These jackals are fighting over the limited food available to them.

FIGURE 10
Space as a Limiting Factor
Could any more sunflower plants grow in this field? If not, the field has reached its carrying capacity for sunflowers.

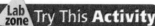

Lab zone Try This **Activity**

Elbow Room

1. Using masking tape, mark off several one-meter squares on the floor of your classroom.

2. Your teacher will set up groups of 2, 4, and 6 students. Each group's task is to put together a small jigsaw puzzle in one of the squares. All the group members must keep their feet within the square.

3. Time how long it takes your group to finish the puzzle.

Making Models How long did it take each group to complete the task? How does this activity show that space can be a limiting factor? What is the carrying capacity of puzzle-solvers in a square meter?

◆ 717

Lab zone Try This **Activity**

Skills Focus Making models
Materials masking tape, meter stick, small jigsaw puzzle, watch or clock
Time 15 minutes
Tips Use very simple puzzles so that puzzle difficulty is not a factor.

L1 **Expected Outcome** Smaller groups will probably finish their puzzles before groups of six. Crowding in groups of six made the task more difficult.

Extend Invite students to suggest other simple models of space as a limiting factor.
learning modality: kinesthetic

Lab zone Build **Inquiry**

L2

Exponential Growth

Materials 2 boxes of small paper clips
Time 15 minutes

Focus Tell students that limiting factors help control population growth.

Teach Give small groups of students boxes of paper clips. Tell students that each paper clip represents an amoeba, a one-celled organism that reproduces by splitting in half. Have students show uncontrolled population growth by laying out the paper clips to show growth through six generations. *(The results: Generation 1—1 amoeba; Generation 2—2 amoebas; Generation 3—4 amoebas; Generation 4—8 amoebas; Generation 5—16 amoebas; Generation 6—32 amoebas)* Then tell students that the food supply for the amoebas has become scarce, and some members of each generation will die. Tell students to remove one "amoeba" and its resulting offspring from Generations 4, 5, and 6. Have students compare the numbers of organisms in the last generation of both models.

Apply Discuss how populations can grow out of control without limiting factors. Tell students that under laboratory conditions, a common bacterium, *E. coli*, can reproduce once every 20 minutes. Explain that without limiting factors, one *E. coli* could multiply to a mass twice that of Earth in 48 hours.
learning modality: kinesthetic

Monitor Progress L2

Writing Have students write a few sentences telling in their own words what a limiting factor is.

Answers
Figure 8 2.5 flamingos/m²

Reading Checkpoint Population density is the number of individuals in a specific area.

Answers

Figure 11 Temperature, amount of rainfall (too much or too little), storms, floods

 Reading Checkpoint Possible answers: A cold snap in late spring, a hurricane, a flood

Assess

Reviewing Key Concepts

1. a. Direct observation, indirect observation, sampling, mark and recapture **b.** Sampling; there would be too many mushrooms over too large an area to count them individually.

2. a. Join—birth, immigration; leave—death, emigration **b.** 500 mice **c.** Some mice may have immigrated into the population.

3. a. Food and water, space, weather **b.** Any of the following: A population cannot grow beyond the number that can be supported by the amount of food and water available; if organisms do not have enough space, some will not be able to reproduce or survive; severe weather conditions can kill members of a population. **c.** Sample answer: A severely cold winter could kill large numbers of pigeons and reduce the population.

Reteach   **L1**

As a class make a two-column chart. In the first column, list the limiting factors for populations. In the second column, tell how the factor can limit populations.

Performance Assessment   **L2**

Oral Presentation Call on students to identify a factor that affects the size of a population. *(Birth/death rates, immigration, emigration, limiting factors)*

All in One Teaching Resources, Unit 4

- Section Summary: *Studying Populations*
- Review and Reinforce: *Studying Populations*
- Enrich: *Studying Populations*

718

FIGURE 11
Weather as a Limiting Factor
A snowstorm can limit the size of an orange crop.
Applying Concepts *What other weather conditions can limit population growth?*

Weather Weather conditions such as temperature and the amount of rainfall can also limit population growth. A cold snap in late spring can kill the young of many species of organisms, including birds and mammals. A hurricane or flood can wash away nests and burrows. Such unusual events can have long-lasting effects on population size.

 Reading Checkpoint What is one weather condition that can limit the growth of a population?

Section 2 Assessment

Target Reading Skill Asking Questions Use the answers to the questions you wrote about the headings to help you answer the questions below.

Reviewing Key Concepts

1. a. **Listing** What are four methods of determining population size?
   b. **Applying Concepts** Which method would you use to determine the number of mushrooms growing on the floor of a large forest? Explain.
2. a. **Identifying** Name two ways organisms join a population and two ways organisms leave a population.
   b. **Calculating** Suppose a population of 100 mice has produced 600 young. If 200 mice have died, how many mice are in the population now? (Assume for this question that no mice have moved into or out of the population for other reasons.)
   c. **Drawing Conclusions** Suppose that you discovered that there were actually 750 mice in the population. How could you account for the difference?

3. a. **Reviewing** Name three limiting factors for populations.
   b. **Describing** Choose one of the limiting factors and describe how it limits population growth.
   c. **Inferring** How might the limiting factor you chose affect the pigeon population in your town?

Math Practice

4. **Inequalities** Complete the following inequality showing the relationship between carrying capacity and population size. Then explain why the inequality is true.

   If population size ▇ carrying capacity, then population size will decrease.

Math Practice

Math Skill Inequalities

Answer

4. If population size > carrying capacity, then population size will decrease. The carrying capacity is the largest population an area can support. If there are more individuals than an area can support, they won't all survive so the population will decrease.

Counting Turtles

Problem
How can the mark-and-recapture method help ecologists monitor the size of a population?

Skills Focus
calculating, graphing, predicting

Materials
• model paper turtle population • calculator
• graph paper

Procedure
1. The data table shows the results from the first three years of a population study to determine the number of snapping turtles in a pond. Copy the table into your notebook.

Data Table

Year	Number Marked	Total Number Captured	Number Recaptured (With Marks)	Estimated Total Population
1	32	28	15	
2	25	21	11	
3	23	19	11	
4	15			

2. Your teacher will give you a box representing the pond. Fifteen of the turtles have been marked, as shown in the data table for Year 4.

3. Capture a member of the population by randomly selecting one turtle. Set it aside.

4. Repeat Step 3 nine times. Record the total number of turtles you captured.

5. Examine each turtle to see whether it has a mark. Count the number of recaptured (marked) turtles. Record this number in your data table.

Analyze and Conclude
1. **Calculating** Use the equation below to estimate the turtle population for each year. The first year is done for you as a sample. If your answer is a decimal, round it to the nearest whole number. Record the population for each year in the last column of the data table.

$$\text{Total population} = \frac{\text{Number marked} \times \text{Total number captured}}{\text{Number recaptured (with marks)}}$$

Sample (Year 1):

$$\frac{32 \times 28}{15} = 59.7 \text{ or } 60 \text{ turtles}$$

2. **Graphing** Graph the estimated total populations for the four years. Mark years on the horizontal axis. Mark population size on the vertical axis.

3. **Interpreting Data** Describe how the turtle population has changed over the four years of the study. Suggest three possible causes for the changes.

4. **Predicting** Use your graph to predict what the turtle population will be in Year 5. Explain your prediction.

5. **Communicating** Write a paragraph that explains why the mark-and-recapture method is a useful tool for ecologists. When is this technique most useful for estimating a population's size?

More to Explore
Suppose that only six turtles had been recaptured in Year 2. How would this change your graph?

Chapter 21 ◆ 719

Analyze and Conclude
1. The estimated totals for Years 1–3 are 60, 48, and 40. Total number captured for Year 4 is 10. If 0 are recaptured, the total population cannot be determined. If 1 is recaptured, the estimated total is 150; if 2, 75; if 3, 50; if 4, 38; if 5, 30; if 6, 25; if 7, 21; if 8, 19; if 9, 17; if 10, 15.

2. Year 4 will vary.

3. The turtle population declined steadily from Year 1 to Year 3. Possible causes include limited food, overcrowding, weather conditions, disease, predation, and use of chemicals in the pond.

4. Most students will probably predict a continuing decline in the population.

5. Sample answer: Mark and recapture is useful because it allows scientists to study a population over time. It is most useful when a population is fairly large, concentrated in one area, and can't be observed directly or indirectly.

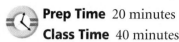

Counting Turtles   L2

Prepare for Inquiry

Skills Objectives
After this lab, students will be able to
• calculate the size of a population
• graph population estimates
• predict the size of a future population

Prep Time 20 minutes
Class Time 40 minutes

Advance Planning
Prepare a model population for each group. Use 30 paper squares to represent turtles. Mark a dot on one side of 15 cards. Spread all 30 cards in a box, marked sides down.

All in One Teaching Resources, Unit 4
• Lab Worksheet: *Counting Turtles*

Guide Inquiry

Invitation
Review with students the mark-and-recapture method for determining population size.

Introducing the Procedure
Tell students that each square represents a turtle and that some of the "turtles" have been marked with a dot on one side.

Troubleshooting the Experiment
• In Step 2, clarify that the 15 marked turtles refer to the bottom box in the second column of the table, "Number Marked."
• Students may assume that more turtles recaptured with marks means a bigger population, and fewer turtles with marks means a smaller population. Point out that the opposite is true because unmarked turtles could be new turtles added (birth, immigration) since the last count.

Expected Outcome
The number of marked turtles recaptured will vary. Therefore, students' estimates of the total population of Year 4 will also vary.

Extend Inquiry

More to Explore
The estimated total population would increase to 88.

Science and Society

Animal Overpopulation: How Can People Help?

Key Concept
Food has become a limiting factor for the rapidly growing populations of white-tailed deer in many parts of the United States. People must decide how to reduce the deer populations.

Build Background Knowledge

Recalling Limiting Factors
Help students recall that several factors can limit populations. Ask: **What are some limiting factors for populations?** *(Food, water, space, weather)* **What would be the effect on a population if the food supply is insufficient to support all the individuals?** *(Some individuals will die of starvation.)*

Introduce the Debate
Direct attention to the large picture of the white-tailed deer. Explain that in many areas of the country these animals have no natural predators and, as a result, their populations have increased rapidly. Point out that, in addition, many of their habitats have been destroyed due to land development. Explain that these conditions have made the food supply for many of these populations inadequate. Ask: **What are some ways that the deer population might be controlled?** *(Accept any reasonable responses at this point.)*

Facilitate the Debate
Have students read the feature and answer the You Decide questions individually as a homework assignment. The next day, organize the class into small groups for discussion. Have students consider these questions: **What are the advantages and disadvantages of each proposed action? Which action do you think is in the best interests of the deer? Of other populations in the area? Which solution would you support if your area had a deer overpopulation problem? Why would you choose that solution?** Organize the class into three groups. Arbitrarily assign each group to argue each proposed action. Alternately call on students from each group to state the group's position or refute an idea from someone in the other group.

White-Tailed Deer
To obtain food, deer are moving into people's yards.

Animal Overpopulation: How Can People Help?

Populations of white-tailed deer are growing rapidly in many parts of the United States. As populations soar, food becomes a limiting factor. Many deer die of starvation. Others grow up small and unhealthy. In search of food, hungry deer move closer to where humans live. There they eat farm crops, garden vegetables, shrubs, and even trees. In addition, increased numbers of deer near roads can cause automobile accidents.

People admire the grace and swiftness of deer. Most people don't want these animals to suffer from starvation or illness. Should people take action to limit growing deer populations?

Wildlife Technician
This wildlife researcher in Virginia studies white-tailed deer populations. Here he prepares to tag a young deer.

The Issues

Should People Take Direct Action?

Many people argue that hunting is the best way to reduce animal populations. Wildlife managers look at the supply of resources in an area and determine its carrying capacity. Then hunters are issued licenses to help reduce the number of deer. Hunting is usually not allowed in cities or suburbs, however.

Some people favor nonhunting approaches to control deer populations. One plan is to trap the deer and relocate them. But this method is expensive and requires finding another location that can accept the deer without upsetting the balance of its own ecosystem.

Scientists are also working to develop chemicals to reduce the birth rate in deer populations. But this plan is effective for only one year at a time.

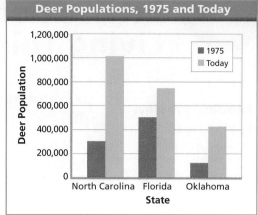

Deer Populations, 1975 and Today

White-Tailed Deer Populations
This graph shows how the deer populations have grown in North Carolina, Florida, and Oklahoma.

Should People Take Indirect Action?

Some suggest bringing in natural predators of deer, such as wolves, mountain lions, and bears, to areas with too many deer. But these animals could also attack cattle, dogs, cats, and even humans. Other communities have built tall fences around areas to keep out the deer. However, this solution is impractical for farmers or ranchers.

Should People Do Nothing?

Some people oppose any kind of action. They support leaving the deer alone and allowing nature to take its course. Animal populations in an area naturally cycle up and down over time. Doing nothing means that some deer will die of starvation or disease. But eventually, the population will be reduced to a size within the carrying capacity of the environment.

You Decide

1. Identify the Problem
In your own words, explain the problem created by the over-population of white-tailed deer.

2. Analyze the Options
List the ways that people can deal with the overpopulation of white-tailed deer. State the positive and negative points of each method.

3. Find a Solution
Suppose you are an ecologist in an area that has twice as many deer as it can support. Propose a way for the community to deal with the problem.

For: More on white-tailed deer overpopulation
Visit: PHSchool.com
Web Code: ceh-5010

Chapter 21 ◆ 721

You Decide

1. Possible response: Overpopulation results in starvation for many animals; others may grow up unhealthy. In search of limited food, the deer may destroy crops and landscape plants in areas where human live, which can affect other organisms dependent on those plants. Increased numbers of deer also can cause more automobile accidents.

2. Direct actions—*hunting*: inexpensive but many people object to this method and it is impractical in suburban areas where deer are most troublesome; *trapping and relocating*: animals are not killed but the method is expensive and requires finding another location to accept the deer, which can upset the existing balance in the new location; *using chemicals to reduce birth rates*: the chemicals are only effective for one year at a time. Indirect action—*bringing in natural enemies*: predators could attack other animals in the area; *building fences*: impractical for large areas. Do nothing—some deer will die but eventually the population will reduce to within the carrying capacity.

3. Encourage students to provide reasons for their plans.

For: More on white-tailed deer overpopulation
Visit: PHSchool.com
Web Code: ceh-5010

Extend

If your community has a problem with animal overpopulation—with deer, gypsy moths, or skunks, for example—suggest that students discuss the issue with family members and, if possible, consult with community and state agencies to find out how people are dealing with the problem.

Background

Facts and Figures Deer overpopulation can also be hazardous to human health, as shown by the increasing occurrence of Lyme disease in the United States. White-tailed deer may carry tiny ticks that may be smaller than the head of a pin. The ticks in turn carry a bacterium, *Borrelia burgdorferi,* which causes Lyme disease. The ticks attach themselves to

people walking through infested areas. The ticks' bite transfers the bacteria to humans.

A reddish rash shaped like a bull's eye usually appears within days of the tick's bite. Other early symptoms of Lyme disease may include fatigue, fever, chills, and headache. Left untreated, the disease can inflame the heart muscle and nerves or cause painful arthritis in the joints.

Antibiotics, if taken soon after symptoms appear, are an effective treatment for Lyme disease. In 1998, the U.S. FDA approved a vaccine for Lyme disease, but it was taken off the market in 2002.

Objectives

After this lesson, students will be able to

21.3.1 Explain how an organism's adaptations help it survive.

21.3.2 Describe the major kinds of interaction among organisms in an ecosystem.

21.3.3 Identify the three types of symbiotic relationships.

Target Reading Skill

Using Prior Knowledge Explain that using prior knowledge helps students connect what they already know to what they are about to read.

Answers

Possible answers:

What You Know

1. Organisms interact in different ways.

What You Learned

1. Organisms are adapted to their environments.

2. Organisms have niches, which are their roles in their habitats.

3. Organisms compete for resources. Some organisms eat others, and this affects the size of populations.

4. Some organisms live together in symbiotic relationships, of which there is mutualism (both benefit), commensalism (one benefits, the other is not helped or harmed), and parasitism (one benefits, the other is harmed).

All in One Teaching Resources, Unit 4

• Transparency LS206

Preteach

Build Background Knowledge L1

Identifying Adaptations

Ask: **What features enable fish to survive in an underwater environment?** *(Students most likely will mention fins and tails for moving through the water, and gills for breathing oxygen dissolved in the water.)* Encourage students to think of other examples of how organisms are adapted to their environments.

Section 3
Interactions Among Living Things

Reading Preview

Key Concepts

• How do an organism's adaptations help it to survive?

• What are the major ways in which organisms in an ecosystem interact?

• What are the three types of symbiotic relationships?

Key Terms

• natural selection
• adaptations • niche
• competition • predation
• predator • prey • symbiosis
• mutualism • commensalism
• parasitism • parasite • host

Target Reading Skill

Using Prior Knowledge Before you read, look at the section headings and visuals to see what this section is about. Then write what you know about how living things interact in a graphic organizer like the one below. As you read, continue to write in what you learn.

What You Know
1. Organisms interact in different ways.
2.

What You Learned
1.
2.

Lab zone Discover Activity

Can You Hide a Butterfly?

1. Trace a butterfly on a piece of paper, using the outline shown here.

2. Look around the classroom and pick a spot where you will place your butterfly. You must place your butterfly out in the open. Color your butterfly so it will blend in with the spot you choose.

3. Tape your butterfly down. Someone will now have one minute to find the butterflies. Will your butterfly be found?

Think It Over

Predicting Over time, do you think the population size of butterflies that blend in with their surroundings would increase or decrease?

Can you imagine living in a cactus like the one in Figure 12? Ouch! You probably wouldn't want to live in a house covered with sharp spines. But many species live in, on, and around saguaro cactuses.

As day breaks, a twittering sound comes from a nest tucked in one of the saguaro's arms. Two young red-tailed hawks are preparing to fly for the first time. Farther down the stem, a tiny elf owl peeks out of its nest in a small hole. This owl is so small it could fit in your palm! A rattlesnake slithers around the base of the saguaro, looking for lunch. Spying a shrew, the snake strikes it with its needle-like fangs. The shrew dies instantly.

Activity around the saguaro continues after sunset. Long-nosed bats come out to feed on the nectar from the saguaro's blossoms. The bats stick their faces into the flowers to feed, dusting their long snouts with white pollen. As they move from plant to plant, they carry the pollen to other saguaros. This enables the cactuses to reproduce.

Lab zone Discover Activity

Skills Focus Predicting L1

Materials Sheet of white paper, colored pencils or markers, tape

Time 15 minutes

Tips Tell students that the butterflies do not have to be colored realistically. Arrange to have another staff member or a student from another class look for the butterflies.

Expected Outcome Butterflies whose colors and patterns closely match their background will be most difficult to see.

Think It Over Butterflies that blend well with their surroundings will escape predators and survive to reproduce, thus increasing the population.

Adapting to the Environment

Each organism in the saguaro community has unique characteristics. These characteristics affect the individual's ability to survive in its environment.

Natural Selection A characteristic that makes an individual better suited to its environment may eventually become common in that species through a process called **natural selection**. Natural selection works like this: Individuals whose unique characteristics are best suited for their environment tend to survive and produce offspring. Offspring that inherit these characteristics also live to reproduce. In this way, natural selection results in **adaptations,** the behaviors and physical characteristics that allow organisms to live successfully in their environments.

Individuals with characteristics that are poorly suited to the environment are less likely to survive and reproduce. Over time, poorly suited characteristics may disappear from the species.

Niche Every organism has a variety of adaptations that are suited to its specific living conditions. The organisms in the saguaro community have adaptations that result in specific roles. The role of an organism in its habitat, or how it makes its living, is called its **niche.** A niche includes the type of food the organism eats, how it obtains this food, and which other organisms use the organism as food. A niche also includes when and how the organism reproduces and the physical conditions it requires to survive.

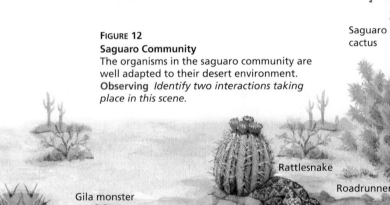

FIGURE 12
Saguaro Community
The organisms in the saguaro community are well adapted to their desert environment.
Observing *Identify two interactions taking place in this scene.*

Red-tailed hawk
Flycatcher
Hawk nest
Purple martin
Woodpecker
Elf owl
Wasps
Saguaro cactus
Gila monster
Rattlesnake
Roadrunner
Scorpion

 ◆ 723

Competition

Teach Key Concepts
Limited Resources

Focus Remind students that in any community, organisms interact.

Teach Tell students that in a community, there is a limited amount of some resources. Ask: **What happens when more than one species requires the same limited resource?** *(Competition)* Refer students to Figure 13, and point out that each bird species feeds in a different part of the tree. Ask: **What advantage is this for the three birds?** *(The three species do not compete with each other for the same food and space.)*

Apply Ask: **For what resources do the tree and the grass in Figure 13 compete?** *(Sunlight, water, minerals, space)* **learning modality: visual**

 **Teaching Resources, Unit 4**
• Transparency LS207

Observing Cricket Competition L3

Materials several male crickets (from a pet store), terrarium, soil, materials to provide hiding places (rocks, leaves, pieces of bark, small branches), paint of different colors

Time 15 minutes for setup

Focus Ask students what they know about crickets.

Teach Tell students that male crickets compete for territories. Have volunteers set up a cricket habitat in a terrarium. Tell them to cover the bottom of the terrarium with soil and then add several items under which the crickets can hide. Before students place the crickets in the terrarium, have them mark each cricket's back with a different color dot of paint for identification. Caution students to handle the crickets carefully and wash their hands afterward. When the crickets are first introduced into the terrarium, they will fight. In time, each will establish its own territory, remain in it most of the time, and defend it against other males. After the activity, you can release the crickets.

Apply Ask: **What is the advantage of having a territory?** *(It reduces competition.)* **learning modality: visual**

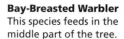
Cape May Warbler
This species feeds at the tips of branches near the top of the tree.

Bay-Breasted Warbler
This species feeds in the middle part of the tree.

Yellow-Rumped Warbler
This species feeds in the lower part of the tree and at the bases of the middle branches.

FIGURE 13
Niche and Competition
Each of these warblers occupies a different niche in its spruce tree habitat. By feeding in different areas of the tree, the birds avoid competing for food.
Comparing and Contrasting *How do the niches of these three warblers differ?*

For: More on population interactions
Visit: PHSchool.com
Web Code: ced-5013

724 ◆

Competition

During a typical day in the saguaro community, a range of interactions takes place among organisms. **There are three major types of interactions among organisms: competition, predation, and symbiosis.**

Different species can share the same habitat and food requirements. For example, the roadrunner and the elf owl both live on the saguaro and eat insects. However, these two species do not occupy exactly the same niche. The roadrunner is active during the day, while the owl is active mostly at night. If two species occupy the same niche, one of the species will eventually die off. The reason for this is **competition,** the struggle between organisms to survive as they attempt to use the same limited resource.

In any ecosystem, there is a limited amount of food, water, and shelter. Organisms that survive have adaptations that enable them to reduce competition. For example, the three species of warblers in Figure 13 live in the same spruce forest habitat. They all eat insects that live in the spruce trees. How do these birds avoid competing for the limited insect supply? Each warbler "specializes" in feeding in a certain part of a spruce tree. This is how the three species coexist.

 **Reading Checkpoint** Why can't two species occupy the same niche?

For: More on population interactions
Visit: PHSchool.com
Web Code: ced-5013

Students can review population interactions in an online activity.

Predation

A tiger shark lurks below the surface of the clear blue water, looking for shadows of albatross chicks floating above. The shark spots a chick and silently swims closer. Suddenly, the shark bursts through the water and seizes the albatross with one snap of its powerful jaw. This interaction between two organisms has an unfortunate ending for the albatross.

An interaction in which one organism kills another for food is called **predation.** The organism that does the killing, in this case the tiger shark, is the **predator.** The organism that is killed, in this case the albatross, is the **prey.**

The Effect of Predation on Population Size Predation can have a major effect on the size of a population. Recall from Section 2 that when the death rate exceeds the birth rate in a population, the size of that population usually decreases. So if there are many predators, the result is often a decrease in the size of the population of their prey. But a decrease in the number of prey results in less food for their predators. Without adequate food, the predator population starts to decline. So, generally, populations of predators and their prey rise and fall in related cycles.

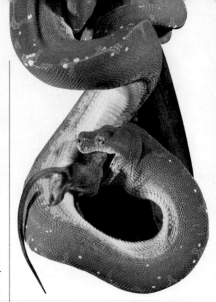

FIGURE 14
Predation
This green tree python and mouse are involved in a predator-prey interaction.

Math — Analyzing Data

Predator-Prey Interactions

On Isle Royale, an island in Lake Superior, the populations of wolves (the predator) and moose (the prey) rise and fall in cycles. Use the graph to answer the questions.

1. **Reading Graphs** What variable is plotted on the *x*-axis? What two variables are plotted on the *y*-axis?

2. **Interpreting Data** How did the moose population change between 1965 and 1972? What happened to the wolf population from 1973 through 1976?

3. **Inferring** How might the change in the moose population have led to the change in the wolf population?

4. **Drawing Conclusions** What is one likely cause of the dip in the moose population between 1974 and 1981?

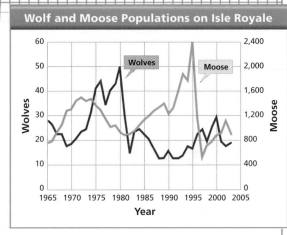

Wolf and Moose Populations on Isle Royale

5. **Predicting** How might a disease in the wolf population one year affect the moose population the next year?

Predation

Teach Key Concepts L2

Predation in a Terrarium

Focus Have students visualize a cricket habitat set up in a terrarium.

Teach Ask: **What would happen if you added a toad to the habitat?** *(It would eat the crickets.)* **What would happen if you then added a snake?** *(It would eat the toad.)* **Which of these animals would be prey?** *(The crickets are prey for the toad, and the toad is prey for the snake.)* **Which would be a predator?** *(The toad is a predator of crickets, and the snake is a predator of toads.)*

Apply Challenge students to identify other feeding relationships in which one organism is both predator and prey. **learning modality: logical/mathematical**

Math — Analyzing Data

Math Skill Making and interpreting graphs

Focus Remind students that without enough prey, a predator population declines.

Teach Direct attention to the graph. Ask: **What does the horizontal axis show?** *(The years from 1965 to 2005)* **The two vertical axes?** *(The populations of wolves and moose)* **What are the wolf and moose populations in 1970?** *(Wolves, 18; moose, 1,300)*

Answers
1. Year; numbers of wolves and moose
2. The moose population increased and then decreased; the wolf population increased.
3. As the moose population increased, more food was available to the wolf population and it increased.
4. The wolf population increased.
5. Disease would cause a decrease in the wolf population, so fewer moose would be eaten and the population could increase.

Monitor Progress _____ L2

Oral Presentation Present students with various predator-prey pairs. Have them identify the predator and prey in each case.

Answers
Figure 13 Each species feeds at a different location on the tree

✓ **Reading Checkpoint** If two species occupy the same niche, they will compete directly against each other and one species will eventually die off.

Observing an Insect-Eating Plant

Materials sundew or Venus's fly-trap, cooked ground beef, tweezers

Time 5 minutes a day for several days

Focus Review with students the definitions of *predator* and *prey*.

Teach Have students take turns feeding the plant small pieces of the ground beef from time to time. (**CAUTION:** *Remind students to wash their hands afterward.*) Ask: **What did you observe after you fed the meat to the plant?** (*The plant's leaf blades snapped closed, trapping the meat.*) **What did you notice when the leaves opened again?** (*The meat was gone.*) Explain that the plant produces enzymes that digest the meat. Explain that carnivorous plants living in the wild capture and digest live insects and other small organisms.

Apply Tell students that many carnivorous plants live in areas with poor soil. Ask: **How does this adaptation enable carnivorous plants to survive in areas of poor soil?** (*The plant can get the nutrients it needs from the digested insects.*) **learning modality: visual**

Discovery
CHANNEL
SCHOOL
Video Field Trip

Populations and Communities

Show the Video Field Trip to help students understand the predator–prey relationship. Discussion question: **What makes the cheetah a successful predator?** (*It can run faster over short distances than any other land animal.*)

FIGURE 15
Predator Adaptations
This greater horseshoe bat has adaptations that allow it to find prey in the dark. The bat produces pulses of sound and locates prey by interpreting the echoes.
Inferring *What other adaptations might contribute to the bat's success as a predator?*

Discovery
CHANNEL
SCHOOL

Populations and Communities

Video Preview
▶ Video Field Trip
Video Assessment

Predator Adaptations Predators have adaptations that help them catch and kill their prey. For example, a cheetah can run very fast for a short time, enabling it to catch its prey. A jellyfish's tentacles contain a poisonous substance that paralyzes tiny water animals. Some plants, too, have adaptations for catching prey. The sundew is covered with sticky bulbs on stalks—when a fly lands on the plant, it remains snared in the sticky goo while the plant digests it.

Some predators have adaptations that enable them to hunt at night. For example, the big eyes of an owl let in as much light as possible to help it see in the dark. Insect-eating bats can hunt without seeing at all. Instead, they locate their prey by producing pulses of sound and listening for the echoes. This precise method enables a bat to catch a flying moth in complete darkness.

Prey Adaptations How do organisms avoid being killed by such effective predators? Organisms have many kinds of adaptations that help them avoid becoming prey. The alertness and speed of an antelope help protect it from its predators. And you're probably not surprised that the smelly spray of a skunk helps keep its predators at a distance. As you can see in Figure 16, other organisms also have some very effective ways to avoid becoming a predator's next meal.

 Reading Checkpoint What are two predator adaptations?

726 ◆

FIGURE 16
Defense Strategies
Organisms display a wide array of adaptations that help them avoid becoming prey.

Mimicry ▶
If you're afraid of snakes, you'd probably be terrified to see this organism staring at you. But this caterpillar only looks like a snake. Its convincing resemblance to a viper tricks would-be predators into staying away.

Protective Covering ▼
Have you ever seen a pine cone with a face? This organism is actually a pangolin, a small African mammal. When threatened, the pangolin protects itself by rolling up into a scaly ball.

False Coloring ▲
If you saw this moth in a dark forest, you might think you were looking into the eyes of a large mammal. The large false eyespots on the moth's wings scare potential predators away.

▼ Warning Coloring
A grasshopper this brightly colored can't hide. So what defense does it have against predators? Like many brightly colored animals, this grasshopper is poisonous. Its bright blue and yellow colors warn predators not to eat it.

Camouflage ▲
Is it a leaf? Actually, it's a walking leaf insect. But if you were a predator, you might be fooled into looking elsewhere for a meal.

Chapter 21 ◆ 727

727

Symbiosis

Teach Key Concepts L2
Identifying Relationships

Focus Have students look at Figure 17 and read the caption. Ask: **Why are these birds sitting on the hippo?** (*To feed and to hitch a ride*)

Teach Tell students that the birds and the hippo have a symbiotic relationship. Ask: **What are three types of symbiosis?** (*Mutualism, commensalism, parasitism*) Explain that this type of symbiotic relationship is mutualism. Ask: **How do the birds benefit?** (*They get food.*) **How does the hippo benefit?** (*The birds eat the ticks that feed on the hippo's blood.*)

Apply Ask: **What type of relationship do the tick and the hippo have?** (*A parasitic relationship*) **Which animal is the parasite?** (*The tick*) **learning modality: visual**

Integrating Health

Students are probably unaware that their own bodies are inhabited by other living things. Tell students that microscopic mites (*Demodex folliculorum*) live at the base of eyelashes, where they feed on tiny bits of dead skin and other detritus. Ask: **What type of symbiotic relationship is this? Explain your answer.** (*Commensalism because the mites benefit and humans are neither harmed nor helped*) **learning modality: verbal**

Classifying

Classify each interaction as an example of mutualism, commensalism, or parasitism. Explain your answers.

- A remora fish attaches itself to the underside of a shark without harming the shark, and eats left-over bits of food from the shark's meals.
- A vampire bat drinks the blood of horses.
- Bacteria living in cows' stomachs help them break down the cellulose in grass.

FIGURE 17
Mutualism
Three yellow-billed oxpeckers get a cruise and a snack aboard an obliging hippopotamus. The oxpeckers eat ticks living on the hippo's skin. Since both the birds and the hippo benefit from this interaction, it is an example of mutualism.

728 ◆

Symbiosis

Many of the interactions in the saguaro community you read about are examples of symbiosis. **Symbiosis** (sim bee OH sis) is a close relationship between two species that benefits at least one of the species. **The three types of symbiotic relationships are mutualism, commensalism, and parasitism.**

Mutualism A relationship in which both species benefit is called **mutualism** (MYOO choo uh liz um). The relationship between the saguaro and the long-eared bats is an example of mutualism. The bats benefit because the cactus flowers provide them with food. The saguaro benefits as its pollen is carried to another plant on the bat's nose.

In some cases of mutualism, two species are so dependent on each other that neither could live without the other. This is true for some species of acacia trees and stinging ants in Central and South America. The stinging ants nest only in the acacia tree, whose thorns discourage the ants' predators. The tree also provides the ants' only food. The ants, in turn, attack other animals that approach the tree and clear competing plants away from the base of the tree. To survive, each species needs the other.

Commensalism A relationship in which one species benefits and the other species is neither helped nor harmed is called **commensalism** (kuh MEN suh liz um). The red-tailed hawks' interaction with the saguaro is an example of commensalism. The hawks benefit by having a place to build their nest, while the cactus is not affected by the hawks.

Commensalism is not very common in nature because two species are usually either helped or harmed a little by any interaction. For example, by creating a small hole for its nest in the cactus stem, the elf owl slightly damages the cactus.

Skills Focus Classifying

Materials none

Time 10 minutes

Expected Outcome Remora/shark—commensalism; the remora benefits. Vampire bat/horses—parasitism; the bat benefits, and the horses are harmed. Bacteria/cows— mutualism; the bacteria receive food and a place to live, and the bacteria help the cows digest their food.

L1 **Extend** Have students classify the relationships between: clown fish and anemones (commensalism—the clown fish receives protection); termites and gut protozoa (mutualism—the protozoa enable the termites to digest wood, and the termites provide shelter and food); dogs and heartworms (parasitism). **learning modality: logical/mathematical**

Parasitism Parasitism (PA ruh sit iz um) involves one organism living on or inside another organism and harming it. The organism that benefits is called a **parasite,** and the organism it lives on or in is called a **host.** The parasite is usually smaller than the host. In a parasitic relationship, the parasite benefits from the interaction while the host is harmed.

Some common parasites are fleas, ticks, and leeches. These parasites have adaptations that enable them to attach to their host and feed on its blood. Other parasites live inside the host's body, such as tapeworms that live inside the digestive systems of dogs, wolves, and some other mammals.

Unlike a predator, a parasite does not usually kill the organism it feeds on. If the host dies, the parasite loses its source of food. An interesting example of this rule is shown by a species of mite that lives in the ears of moths. The mites almost always live in just one of the moth's ears. If they live in both ears, the moth's hearing is so badly affected that it is likely to be quickly caught and eaten by its predator, a bat.

FIGURE 18
Parasitism
Ticks feed on the blood of certain animals. *Classifying Which organism in this interaction is the parasite? Which organism is the host?*

 Reading Checkpoint Why doesn't a parasite usually kill its host?

Section 3 Assessment

Target Reading Skill Using Prior Knowledge Review your graphic organizer and revise it based on what you just learned in the section.

Reviewing Key Concepts

1. **a. Defining** What are adaptations?
   b. Explaining How are a snake's sharp fangs an adaptation that helps it survive in the saguaro community?
   c. Developing Hypotheses Explain how natural selection in snakes might have led to adaptations such as sharp fangs.

2. **a. Reviewing** What are three main ways in which organisms interact?
   b. Classifying Give one example of each type of interaction.

3. **a. Listing** List the three types of symbiotic relationships.
   b. Comparing and Contrasting For each type of symbiotic relationship, explain how the two organisms are affected.

c. Applying Concepts Some of your classroom plants are dying. Others that you planted at the same time and cared for in the same way are growing well. When you look closely at the dying plants, you see tiny mites on them. Which symbiotic relationship is likely occurring between the plants and mites? Explain.

Lab zone At-Home **Activity**

Feeding Frenzy You and your family can observe interactions among organisms at a bird feeder. Fill a clean, dry, 2-liter bottle with birdseed. With paper clips, attach a plastic plate to the neck of the bottle. Then hang your feeder outside where you can see it easily. Observe the feeder at different times of the day. Keep a log of all the organisms you see near it and how they interact.

Lab zone Chapter **Project**

Keep Students on Track All groups should graph the data they collected for plant height. Some groups may wish to create additional graphs for the numbers of leaves and buds.

Lab zone At-Home **Activity**

Feeding Frenzy L2 Organisms seen at the feeder will vary, but most students will see several varieties of birds. Some may also see squirrels and other small animals. Suggest that students use a bird guide to identify the birds they see.

Monitor Progress L2

Skills Check Call on students to name a type of symbiotic relationship and give an example.

Answers
Figure 18 The tick is the parasite; the animal is the host.

✓ **Reading Checkpoint** If a parasite kills its host, the parasite will no longer have a source of food.

Assess

Reviewing Key Concepts

1. **a.** Adaptations are the behaviors and physical characteristics that allow organisms to live successfully in their environments. **b.** The sharp fangs enable the snake to bite into its prey. **c.** Snakes with sharper fangs could capture more prey and thus be able to survive and reproduce. They pass this trait, sharp fangs, on to their offspring.
2. **a.** Competition, predation, and symbiosis **b.** Possible answers: Competition—Two species of birds that eat the same type of insects; predation—a snake eating a mouse; symbiosis—stinging ants nesting in an acacia tree
3. **a.** Mutualism, commensalism, and parasitism **b.** Mutualism—both species benefit; commensalism—one species benefits and the other is neither harmed nor helped; parasitism—one species is helped and the other species is harmed. **c.** Parasitism is most likely. One species is being harmed (the plant).

Reteach L1

Use Figures 13, 14, 17, and 18 to present information about competition, predation, and symbiosis.

Performance Assessment L2

Writing Have each student explain how each type of interaction among species described in this section affects an organism's survival.

All in One Teaching Resources, Unit 4

- Section Summary: *Interactions Among Living Things*
- Review and Reinforce: *Interactions Among Living Things*
- Enrich: *Interactions Among Living Things*

Objective

After completing this lesson, students will be able to

21.4.1 Describe the differences between primary and secondary succession.

Target Reading Skill

Comparing and Contrasting Explain that comparing and contrasting shows how ideas, facts, and events are similar and different. The results of the comparison can have importance.

Answers

Possible answers:

Primary Succession—volcanic eruption; no soil or organisms exist; no

Secondary Succession—fire; soil and organisms exist but have been disturbed; yes

All in One Teaching Resources, Unit 4

• Transparency LS208

Preteach

Build Background Knowledge L2

Changes Over Time

Ask: **Have you ever observed a vacant lot or an untended garden over time? What changes did you see?** (*Answers will depend on students' experiences. They probably will say that first small grassy weeds grew, then larger weeds and some shrubs, and finally small trees.*)

Section 4 — Changes in Communities

Reading Preview

Key Concept

• How do primary and secondary succession differ?

Key Terms

• succession
• primary succession
• pioneer species
• secondary succession

Target Reading Skill

Comparing and Contrasting As you read, compare and contrast primary and secondary succession by completing a table like the one below.

Factors in Succession	Primary Succession	Secondary Succession
Possible cause	Volcanic eruption	
Type of area		
Existing ecosystem?		

Discover Activity

What Happened Here?

1. The two photographs at the bottom of this page show the same area in Yellowstone National Park in Wyoming. The photograph on the left was taken soon after a major fire. The photograph on the right was taken a few years later. Observe the photographs carefully.
2. Make a list of all the differences you notice between the two scenes.

Think It Over

Posing Questions How would you describe what happened during the time between the two photographs? What questions do you have about this process?

In 1988, huge fires raged through the forests of Yellowstone National Park. The fires were so hot that they jumped from tree to tree without burning along the ground. Huge trees burst into flame from the intense heat. It took months for the fires to burn themselves out. All that remained were thousands of blackened tree trunks sticking out of the ground like charred toothpicks.

Could a forest community recover from such disastrous fires? It might seem unlikely. But within just a few months, signs of life had returned. First, tiny green shoots of new grass poked through the sooty ground. Then, small tree seedlings began to grow. The forest was coming back! After 15 years, young forests were flourishing in many areas.

Fires, floods, volcanoes, hurricanes, and other natural disasters can change communities very quickly. But even without disasters, communities change. The series of predictable changes that occur in a community over time is called **succession.**

Changes in a Yellowstone community ▼

730 ◆

Discover Activity

Skills Focus Posing questions

Materials none

Time 10 minutes

Expected Outcome In Photograph A the soil is bare and scorched; trees in the background have been damaged. In Photograph B the soil is covered with small plants and the damaged trees are leafy.

L1 Think It Over Small plants began to grow again; the existing trees recovered. Students' questions will vary. Sample questions: What kinds of plants come back first? Will the area ever look like it did before the fire? How long will that take?

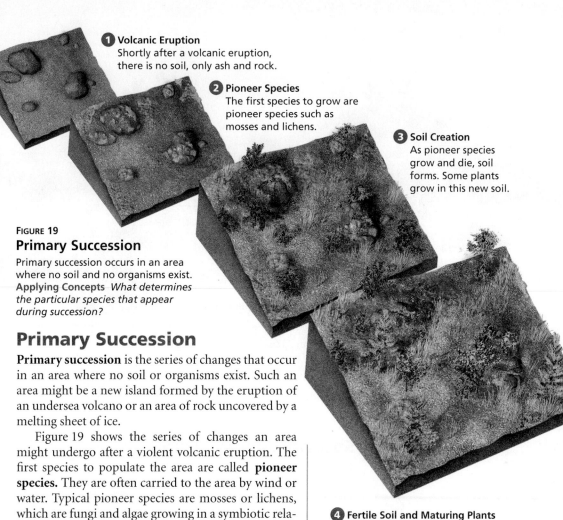

1 Volcanic Eruption
Shortly after a volcanic eruption, there is no soil, only ash and rock.

2 Pioneer Species
The first species to grow are pioneer species such as mosses and lichens.

3 Soil Creation
As pioneer species grow and die, soil forms. Some plants grow in this new soil.

4 Fertile Soil and Maturing Plants
As more plants die, they decompose and make the soil more fertile. New plants grow and existing plants mature in the fertile soil.

FIGURE 19
Primary Succession
Primary succession occurs in an area where no soil and no organisms exist. *Applying Concepts What determines the particular species that appear during succession?*

Primary Succession

Primary succession is the series of changes that occur in an area where no soil or organisms exist. Such an area might be a new island formed by the eruption of an undersea volcano or an area of rock uncovered by a melting sheet of ice.

Figure 19 shows the series of changes an area might undergo after a violent volcanic eruption. The first species to populate the area are called **pioneer species.** They are often carried to the area by wind or water. Typical pioneer species are mosses or lichens, which are fungi and algae growing in a symbiotic relationship. As pioneer species grow, they help break up the rocks. When the organisms die, they provide nutrients that enrich the thin layer of soil that is forming on the rocks.

Over time, plant seeds land in the new soil and begin to grow. The specific plants that grow depend on the climate of the area. For example, in a cool, northern area, early seedlings might include alder and cottonwood trees. Eventually, succession may lead to a community of organisms that does not change unless the ecosystem is disturbed. Reaching this mature community can take centuries.

Reading Checkpoint What are some pioneer species?

Primary Succession

Teach Key Concepts L2
Predicting Changes

Focus Remind students that the events that occur during succession are predictable.

Teach Ask: **Which stage of succession in Figure 19 shows pioneer species?** (*Second stage*) **How might these species arrive at the area?** (*They could be carried by wind or water.*)

Apply Ask: **Why are the changes during succession predictable? How can ecologists tell what will happen in a particular community after a natural disaster?** (*The types of plants that will grow in the area and the types of animals that will live there are determined by climate conditions, which usually are not changed over the long term by a disaster. Certain organisms appear first because they can survive in those conditions. Other species appear later as conditions become suitable for their survival.*) **learning modality: logical/mathematical**

All in One Teaching Resources, Unit 4
• Transparency LS209

Monitor Progress _____ L2

Answers
Figure 19 The first species in an area must be able to survive the barren conditions and are often carried there by wind or water. The particular species that arrive depend on the biome of the area.

 Reading Checkpoint Lichens and mosses

731

Secondary Succession

Teach Key Concepts

Comparing Primary and Secondary Succession

Focus Remind students that primary succession occurs in an area where no soil or organisms exist.

Teach Have students study Figure 20. Ask: **How does secondary succession differ from primary succession?** *(Secondary succession occurs in an area where an ecosystem has been disturbed but soil and some organisms still exist.)* **Which type of succession usually occurs more rapidly?** *(Secondary succession)*

Apply Ask: **What type of succession would occur in an area that has been damaged by floods? Explain your answer.** *(Secondary succession because most likely soil and some organisms will remain after the flood)*
learning modality: logical/mathematical

All in One Teaching Resources, Unit 4

• Transparency LS210

Go Online
SciLINKS NSTA

For: Links on succession
Visit: www.SciLinks.org
Web Code: scn-0514

Download a worksheet that will guide students' review of Internet sources on succession.

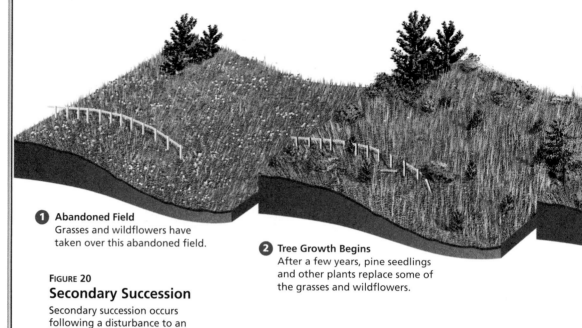

1 Abandoned Field
Grasses and wildflowers have taken over this abandoned field.

2 Tree Growth Begins
After a few years, pine seedlings and other plants replace some of the grasses and wildflowers.

FIGURE 20
Secondary Succession
Secondary succession occurs following a disturbance to an ecosystem, such as clearing a forest for farmland.

Go Online
SciLINKS NSTA

For: Links on succession
Visit: www.SciLinks.org
Web Code: scn-0514

Secondary Succession

The changes following the Yellowstone fire were an example of secondary succession. **Secondary succession** is the series of changes that occur in an area where the ecosystem has been disturbed, but where soil and organisms still exist. Natural disturbances that have this effect include fires, hurricanes, and tornadoes. Human activities, such as farming, logging, or mining, may also disturb an ecosystem. **Unlike primary succession, secondary succession occurs in a place where an ecosystem currently exists.**

Secondary succession usually occurs more rapidly than primary succession. Consider, for example, an abandoned field in the southeastern United States. You can follow the process of succession in such a field in Figure 20. After a century, a hardwood forest is developing. This forest community may remain for a long time.

Reading Checkpoint What are two natural events that can disturb an ecosystem?

732 ◆

Differentiated Instruction

Less Proficient Readers **L1**
Interpreting Diagrams Ask students to compare the first picture in Figures 19 and 20. Help them see that the first picture of Figure 19 shows an area with no soil and no organisms, but in Figure 20 the first picture has plants already living there. Help them relate these differences to the definitions of the terms *primary* and *secondary succession.* **learning modality: visual**

Gifted and Talented **L3**
Researching Succession Encourage students to research examples of succession (a vacant lot, an old farm field). Have them choose a location and find photos of the area, showing how it has changed. Tell students to use the photos to create a timeline that describes the changes in their location over time. **learning modality: logical/mathematical**

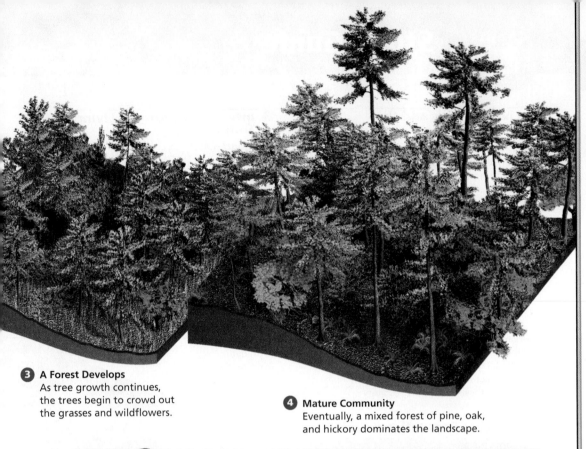

③ A Forest Develops
As tree growth continues, the trees begin to crowd out the grasses and wildflowers.

④ Mature Community
Eventually, a mixed forest of pine, oak, and hickory dominates the landscape.

Section ④ Assessment

Target Reading Skill Comparing and Contrasting Use the information in your table to help you answer Question 1 below.

Reviewing Key Concepts

1. a. Defining What is primary succession? What is secondary succession?
   b. Comparing and Contrasting How do primary succession and secondary succession differ?
   c. Classifying Grass poking through a crack in a sidewalk is an example of succession. Is it primary succession or secondary succession? Explain.

Lab zone **At-Home Activity**

Community Changes Interview a family member or neighbor who has lived in your neighborhood for a long time. Ask the person to describe how the neighborhood has changed over time. Have areas that were formerly grassy been paved or developed? Have any farms, parks, or lots returned to a wild state? Write a summary of your interview. Can you classify any of the changes as examples of succession?

Chapter 21 ◆ **733**

Monitor Progress _____ **L1**

Answer

Reading Checkpoint Possible answers: Fires, hurricanes, tornadoes

Assess

Reviewing Key Concepts

1. a. Primary succession is the series of changes that occur in an area where no soil or organisms exist. Secondary succession is the series of changes that occur after a disturbance in an existing ecosystem.
b. Before primary succession, not even soil is present, so the process is relatively slow. Secondary succession generally occurs more rapidly than primary succession.
c. Secondary succession; before the sidewalk was built, soil was present and an ecosystem had existed there.

Reteach **L1**

Help students use Figures 19 and 20 to present the processes of primary and secondary succession.

All in One Teaching Resources, Unit 4

- Section Summary: *Changes in Communities*
- Review and Reinforce: *Changes in Communities*
- Enrich: *Changes in Communities*

Lab zone **At-Home Activity**

Community Changes **L2** Suggest that students take notes so that they will remember what the person said. Have students present their summaries followed by a class discussion, focusing on any examples of succession they identified.

1 Living Things and the Environment

Key Concepts

- An organism obtains food, water, shelter, and other things it needs to live, grow, and reproduce from its environment.
- An organism interacts with both the living and nonliving parts of its habitat.
- The smallest unit of organization is a single organism, which belongs to a population that includes other members of its species. The population belongs to a community of different species. The community and abiotic factors together form an ecosystem.

Key Terms

organism	species
habitat	population
biotic factor	community
abiotic factor	ecosystem
photosynthesis	ecology

2 Studying Populations

Key Concepts

- Some methods of determining the size of a population are direct and indirect observations, sampling, and mark-and-recapture studies.
- Populations can change in size when new members join the population or when members leave the population.
- Population density can be determined using the following equation:

$$\text{Population density} = \frac{\text{Number of individuals}}{\text{Unit area}}$$

- Some limiting factors for populations are food and water, space, and weather conditions.

Key Terms

estimate	emigration
birth rate	population density
death rate	limiting factor
immigration	carrying capacity

3 Interactions Among Living Things

Key Concepts

- Every organism has a variety of adaptations that are suited to its specific living conditions.
- There are three major types of interactions among organisms: competition, predation, and symbiosis.
- The three types of symbiotic relationships are mutualism, commensalism, and parasitism.

Key Terms

natural selection	symbiosis
adaptations	mutualism
niche	commensalism
competition	parasitism
predation	parasite
predator	host
prey	

4 Changes in Communities

Key Concept

- Unlike primary succession, secondary succession occurs in a place where an ecosystem currently exists.

Key Terms

succession
primary succession
pioneer species
secondary succession

Study Guide

Interactive Textbook

- Comprehension student edition
- Section and chapter self-assessments
- Assessment reports for teachers

Help Students Read   L1

Building Vocabulary

Word-Part Analysis Ask students what words they know that contain the key words *bio* and *photo*. *(Answers may include biology, biography, biohazard; photograph, photocopy.)* Ask them to give a definition of each key word. (*Bio* means "life," and *photo* means "light.")

Vocabulary Knowledge Rating Chart Have students construct a chart with four columns, labeled *Term, Can Define or Use It, Have Heard or Seen It,* and *Don't Know.* They can use the chart to rate their knowledge of each key term.

Connecting Concepts

Concept Map Help students develop one way to show how the information in this chapter is related. Living things interact with the living and nonliving parts of their environment. Have students brainstorm to identify Key Concepts, Key Terms, details, and examples. Then write each item on a self-stick note and attach it at random to chart paper or to the board.

Tell students that this concept map will be organized in hierarchical order and to begin at the top with the Key Concepts. Ask students these questions to guide them to categorize the information on the self-stick notes: **What are some biotic and abiotic factors in the environment? How do organisms interact with them?**

Prompt students by using connecting words or phrases, such as "leads to" and "results in" to indicate the basis for the organization of the map. The phrases should form a sentence between or among a set of concepts.

Answer
Accept logical presentations by students.

All in One Teaching Resources, Unit 4

- Key Terms Review: *Populations and Communities*
- Connecting Concepts: *Populations and Communities*

Review and Assessment

Go Online
PHSchool.com
For: Self-Assessment
Visit: PHSchool.com
Web Code: cea-5010

Organizing Information

Identifying Main Ideas Copy the graphic organizer about determining population size onto a separate sheet of paper. Then complete it and add a title. (For more on Identifying Main Ideas, see the Skills Handbook.)

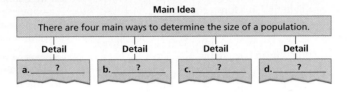

Main Idea

There are four main ways to determine the size of a population.

Detail	Detail	Detail	Detail
a. ___?___	b. ___?___	c. ___?___	d. ___?___

Reviewing Key Terms

Choose the letter of the best answer.

1. A prairie dog, a hawk, and a badger all are members of the same
   a. niche.
   b. community.
   c. species.
   d. population.

2. All of the following are examples of limiting factors for populations *except*
   a. space.
   b. food.
   c. time.
   d. weather.

3. In which type of interaction do both species benefit?
   a. predation
   b. mutualism
   c. commensalism
   d. parasitism

4. Which of these relationships is an example of parasitism?
   a. a bird building a nest on a tree branch
   b. a bat pollinating a saguaro cactus
   c. a flea living on a cat's blood
   d. ants protecting a tree that produces the ants' only food

5. The series of predictable changes that occur in a community over time is called
   a. natural selection.
   b. ecology.
   c. commensalism.
   d. succession.

If the statement is true, write *true*. If it is false, change the underlined word or words to make the statement true.

6. Grass is an example of a biotic factor in a habitat.

7. Immigration is the number of individuals in a specific area.

8. An organism's specific role in its habitat is called its niche.

9. The struggle between organisms for limited resources is called mutualism.

10. A parasite lives on or inside its predator.

Writing in Science

Descriptive Paragraph Use what you have learned about predators and prey to write about an interaction between two organisms. For each organism, describe at least one adaptation that helps it either catch prey or fend off predators.

Discovery CHANNEL SCHOOL

Populations and Communities
Video Preview
Video Field Trip
▶ Video Assessment

Chapter 21 ◆ 735

Review and Assessment

Organizing Information
a. direct observation
b. indirect observation
c. sampling
d. mark-and-recapture studies

Reviewing Key Terms
1. b **2.** c **3.** b **4.** c **5.** d
6. true
7. false; population
8. true
9. false; competition
10. false; host

Writing in Science

Writing Skill Description

Scoring Rubric
4 Includes description of interaction and several adaptations that help predator and prey
3 Includes all criteria
2 Includes incomplete description and one adaptation of each
1 Includes incomplete description and one adaptation of each

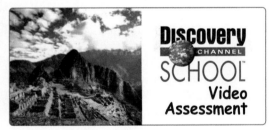

Discovery CHANNEL SCHOOL Video Assessment

Populations and Communities
Show the Video Assessment to review chapter content and as a prompt for the writing assignment. Discussion questions: **What are some dangers cheetahs encounter in the Serengeti?** *(Lions, eagles that prey on cubs)* **What strategies do mother cheetahs use to try to keep their cubs safe?** *(Cubs stay with their mother until about 15 months; mothers distract predators from the cubs.)* **What are two traits of gazelles that help them survive?** *(They are odorless and can turn quickly.)*

Go Online
PHSchool.com
For: Self-Assessment
Visit: PHSchool.com
Web Code: cea-5010

Students can take an online practice test that is automatically scored.

All in One Teaching Resources, Unit 4
• Transparency LS211
• Chapter Test
• Performance Assessment Teacher Notes
• Performance Assessment Student Worksheet
• Performance Assessment Scoring Rubric

ExamView® Computer Test Bank CD-ROM

Checking Concepts

11. Sample answer: Biotic—trees, birds; abiotic—sunlight, soil

12. Plants and algae use the energy of sunlight to combine water and carbon dioxide to make their own food during photosynthesis. All consumers in that ecosystem feed directly or indirectly on plants or algae.

13. Ecologists count the number of organisms in a small area, and then multiply by the number of units in the entire area to estimate the entire population.

14. Limited space may make it impossible for all members of the population to find places to breed or make nests.

15. Any two: Camouflage—The organism blends in with its surroundings, making it difficult for predators to see. Protective covering—the organism's spines, shell, or other outer covering makes it painful or difficult for predators to eat. Warning coloring—An organism that is poisonous has bright colors to warn predators not to eat it. Mimicry—A harmless organism looks like another organism that predators have learned not to eat. False coloring—False "eyes" or other structures can fool predators and scare them away.

Review and Assessment

Checking Concepts

11. Name two biotic and two abiotic factors you might find in a forest ecosystem.

12. Explain how plants and algae use sunlight. How is this process important to other living things in an ecosystem?

13. Describe how ecologists use the technique of sampling to estimate population size.

14. Give an example showing how space can be a limiting factor for a population.

15. What are two adaptations that prey organisms have developed to protect themselves? Describe how each adaptation protects the organism.

Thinking Critically

16. **Making Generalizations** Explain why ecologists usually study a specific population of organisms rather than the entire species.

17. **Problem Solving** In a summer job working for an ecologist, you have been assigned to estimate the population of grasshoppers in a field. Propose a method and explain how you would carry out your plan.

18. **Relating Cause and Effect** Competition for resources in an area is usually more intense within a single species than between two different species. Suggest an explanation for this observation. (*Hint:* Consider how niches help organisms avoid competition.)

19. **Classifying** Lichens and mosses have just begun to grow on the rocky area shown below. Which type of succession is occurring? Explain.

Math Practice

20. **Inequalities** Review the two inequalities about population size. Then revise each inequality to include immigration and emigration in addition to birth rate and death rate.

Applying Skills

Use the data in the table below to answer Questions 21–24.

Ecologists monitoring a deer population collected data during a 30-year study.

Year	0	5	10	15	20	25	30
Population (thousands)	15	30	65	100	40	25	10

21. **Graphing** Make a line graph using the data in the table. Plot years on the horizontal axis and population on the vertical axis.

22. **Interpreting Data** In which year did the deer population reach its highest point? Its lowest point?

23. **Communicating** Write a few sentences describing how the deer population changed during the study.

24. **Developing Hypotheses** In Year 16 of the study, this region experienced a very severe winter. How might this have affected the deer population?

Lab zone Chapter Project

Performance Assessment Review your report and graph to be sure that they clearly state your conclusion about the effects of crowding on plant growth. With your group, decide how you will present your results. Do a practice run-through to make sure all group members feel comfortable with their parts. After your presentation, list some improvements you could have made in your experimental plan.

Lab zone Chapter Project

Performance Assessment Review each group's written report, and let them present their results to the rest of the class in a poster, display, or oral report. As indicated in the Scoring Rubric, base your evaluation of each group's report on both the written report and the class presentation.

Reflect and Record After all groups have made their class presentations, allow time for students to compare their results and discuss the factors that may have accounted for any differences.

Standardized Test Prep

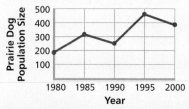
Choose the letter of the best answer.

1. According to the graph above, in what year was the prairie dog population the largest?

A 1980	**B** 1990
C 1995	**D** 2000

2. In general, which of the following is a true statement about population size?

F If birth rate < death rate, population size increases.

G If death rate < birth rate, population size decreases.

H If birth rate > death rate, population size increases.

J If death rate > birth rate, population size increases.

3. A freshwater lake has a muddy bottom, which is home to different types of algae and other organisms. Many species of fish feed on the algae. Which of the following is an *abiotic* factor in this ecosystem?

A the temperature of the water

B the color of the algae

C the number of species of fish

D the amount of food available to the fish

4. Although three different bird species all live in the same trees in an area, competition between the birds rarely occurs. The most likely explanation for this lack of competition is that these birds

F occupy different niches.

G eat the same food.

H have a limited supply of food.

J live in the same part of the trees.

5. During primary succession, a typical pioneer species is

A grass.

B lichen.

C pine trees.

D soil.

Constructed Response

6. Suppose that two species of squirrels living in the same habitat feed on the same type of nut. Describe two possible outcomes of competition between the two squirrel species.

Thinking Critically

16. Studying the entire population of the species usually is not possible because the population is too large or spread out.

17. Answers may include indirect observation (counting egg clusters), sampling (counting the number in a small area and then multiplying by the number of units in the entire area), or mark and capture.

18. Organisms within a species share the same niche. Because individuals within a species are more similar, they will share many of the same advantages and disadvantages in surviving in a certain environment, which intensifies competition for the limited resources. Members of two different species may share some parts of a habitat but do not usually compete for all resources in the same way.

19. Primary succession; there is no soil present and only pioneer organisms are shown.

Math Practice

20. If birth rate > death rate, population size increases. If death rate > birth rate, population size decreases. If immigration > emigration, population size increases. If immigration < emigration, population size decreases.

Applying Skills

21. Check graphs to make sure students have plotted the correct points.

22. Highest: year 15; lowest: year 30

23. Possible answer: Beginning with 15,000 deer at the beginning of the study, the population increased steadily through Year 15. From Year 15 through the end of the study, the deer population declined steadily, reaching the population's lowest point, 10,000 deer, in Year 30.

24. The severe winter may have killed weak or injured deer. Food shortage during this winter also may have weakened deer or caused them to starve.

Standardized Test Prep

1. C **2.** H **3.** A **4.** F **5.** B

6. Students should identify two possible outcomes. Sample: Since two organisms cannot inhabit the same niche for long, one of the following events is likely to occur. (1) If one species is better adapted to the niche, the population of the other species of squirrel might die off. (2) The two species might develop separate niches, such as feeding at different times. (3) One species might emigrate from the area.

Chapter at a Glance

PRENTICE HALL
TeacherEXPRESS™
Plan • Teach • Assess

Lab zone **Chapter Project** *Breaking It Down*

Technology

Local Standards

Discovery CHANNEL **SCHOOL** Video Preview

All in One Teaching Resources, Unit 4
- Chapter Project Teacher Notes, pp. 102–103
- Chapter Project Student Overview, pp. 104–105
- Chapter Project Student Worksheets, pp. 106–107
- Chapter Project Scoring Rubric, p. 108

Section **1**
1 period
1/2 block

Energy Flow in Ecosystems

22.1.1 Name and describe the energy roles that organisms play in an ecosystem.

22.1.2 Explain how energy moves through an ecosystem.

22.1.3 Describe how much energy is available at each level of an energy pyramid.

Go Online
SciLINKS NSTA

Section **2**
1 period
1/2 block

Cycles of Matter

22.2.1 Name and describe the processes involved in the water cycle.

22.2.2 Explain how carbon and oxygen are recycled in ecosystems.

22.2.3 Define and describe the nitrogen cycle.

Go Online
active art

Section **3**
2 periods
1 block

Biogeography

22.3.1 Explain how the movement of the continents has affected the distribution of species.

22.3.2 Name and describe three ways that organism dispersal occurs.

22.3.3 Name and describe factors that can limit the dispersal of a species.

Go Online
active art

Section **4**
3 periods
1 1/2 blocks

Biomes and Aquatic Ecosystems

22.4.1 Name the six major biomes found on Earth.

22.4.2 Name and describe the factors that determine the type of biome found in an area.

22.4.3 Name and describe the two major types of aquatic ecosystems.

Discovery CHANNEL **SCHOOL** Video Field Trip

Go Online
active art

Go Online
SciLINKS NSTA

Review and Assessment

Test Preparation

All in One Teaching Resources, Unit 4
- Key Terms Review, p. 143
- Transparency LS221
- Performance Assessment Teacher Notes, p. 150
- Performance Assessment Scoring Rubric, p. 151
- Performance Assessment Student Worksheet, p. 152
- Chapter Test, pp. 153–156

Discovery CHANNEL **SCHOOL** Video Assessment

Go Online
PHSchool.com

Test Preparation
Blackline Masters

Chapter Activities Planner

Lab zone

For more activities
LAB ZONE Easy Planner CD-ROM

Student Edition	Inquiry	Time	Materials	Skills	Resources
Chapter Project, p. 739	Open-Ended	At least 4 weeks	**All in One Teaching Resources, Unit 4,** See p. 102	Making models, designing experiments, observing, measuring, interpreting data, communicating	**Lab zone Easy Planner** **All in One Teaching Resources, Unit 4,** Support pp. 102–103
Section 1					
Discover Activity, p. 740	Guided	10 minutes	Paper and pencil or pen	Classifying	**Lab zone Easy Planner**
Try This Activity, p. 742	Directed	15 minutes	Long pieces of yarn	Making models	**Lab zone Easy Planner**
Section 2					
Discover Activity, p. 746	Directed	5 minutes	Small mirror	Inferring	**Lab zone Easy Planner**
Skills Activity, p. 747	Open-Ended	5 minutes	None	Developing hypotheses	**Lab zone Easy Planner**
Try This Activity, p. 748	Directed	10 minutes for setup; 15 minutes total of observations over several days	Two plastic cups, bromthymol blue solution, two sprigs of *Elodea*, plastic wrap	Inferring	**Lab zone Easy Planner**
Section 3					
Discover Activity, p. 752	Guided	15 minutes	Shallow pan; corn kernels; possible materials to move corn, such as water, straw, and tape	Predicting	**Lab zone Easy Planner**
Skills Lab, pp. 756–757	Guided	Prep: 30 minutes Class: 30 minutes, then 10 minutes each day for at least one week	Scissors, clear plastic wrap, index card, lamp, tape, empty and clean cardboard milk carton, stapler, about 30 rye grass seeds, 10 impatiens seeds, 5 lima bean seeds, sandy soil or potting soil	Observing, making models	**Lab zone Easy Planner** **Lab Activity Video** **All in One Teaching Resources, Unit 4,** Skills Lab: *Biomes in Miniature,* pp. 129–131
Section 4					
Discover Activity, p. 758	Directed	20 minutes	meter stick, adding-machine paper, scissors, marker, tape	Developing hypotheses	**Lab zone Easy Planner**
Try This Activity, p. 761	Directed	10 minutes	Small potted cactus, hand lens, scissors	Observing	**Lab zone Easy Planner**
Skills Activity, p. 764	Directed	5 minutes	Boreal forest biome map	Inferring	**Lab zone Easy Planner**
Skills Lab, p. 770–771	Guided	Prep: 45 minutes Class: Day 1, set up community: 15 minutes; Days 3, 6, and 9, examine community: 20 minutes daily	Hay solution, pond water, small baby-food jar, wax pencil, plastic dropper, microscope slide, coverslip, microscope	Observing, classifying	**Lab zone Easy Planner** **Lab Activity Video** **All in One Teaching Resources, Unit 4,** Skills Lab: *Change in a Tiny Community,* pp. 141–142

Section 1 **Energy Flow in Ecosystems**

1 period, 1/2 block

Ability Levels Key
L1 Basic to Average
L2 For All Students
L3 Average to Advanced

Objectives

22.1.1 Name and describe the energy roles that organisms play in an ecosystem.

22.1.2 Explain how energy moves through an ecosystem.

22.1.3 Describe how much energy is available at each level of an energy pyramid.

Key Terms

• producer • consumer • herbivore • carnivore • omnivore • scavenger
• decomposer • food chain • food web • energy pyramid

Local Standards

Preteach

Build Background Knowledge

Ask students to recall from previous chapters the definition and characteristics of an ecosystem.

 **Discover Activity** *Where Did Your Dinner Come From?* **L1**

Targeted Print and Technology Resources

 **Teaching Resources, Unit 4**
• Reading Strategy: Building Vocabulary

⊙ **PresentationEXPRESS™ CD-ROM**

Instruct

Energy Roles Discuss familiar habitats and organisms to help students examine the energy roles organisms play in an ecosystem.

Food Chains and Food Webs Use text figures and transparencies to illustrate the ways that energy moves through an ecosystem.

Energy Pyramids Relate the shape of an energy pyramid to how the energy available to organisms changes as it moves up levels of a food web.

Targeted Print and Technology Resources

All in One Teaching Resources, Unit 4
L2 Guided Reading, pp. 111–113
L2 Transparencies LS212, LS213

www.SciLinks.org Web Code: scn-0521

⊙ **Student Edition on Audio CD**

Assess

Section Assessment Questions

Have students use their own definitions of Key Terms to help answer the questions.

Reteach

Review energy roles in an ecosystem and discuss how energy flow is represented by food chains, food webs, and energy pyramids.

Targeted Print and Technology Resources

All in One Teaching Resources, Unit 4
• Section Summary, p. 110
L1 Review and Reinforce, p. 114
L3 Enrich, p. 115

Section 2 Cycles of Matter

 1 period, 1/2 block

Objectives

22.2.1 Name and describe the processes involved in the water cycle.

22.1.2 Explain how carbon and oxygen are recycled in ecosystems.

22.1.3 Define and describe the nitrogen cycle.

Key Terms

• water cycle • evaporation • condensation • precipitation • nitrogen fixation

Local Standards

Preteach

Build Background Knowledge

Prompt students to define the term *cycle* and name familiar examples of cycles.

Lab zone **Discover Activity** *Are You Part of a Cycle?* **L1**

Targeted Print and Technology Resources

All in One Teaching Resources, Unit 4

L2 Reading Strategy Transparency LS214: Sequencing

⊙ **PresentationEXPRESS™ CD-ROM**

Instruct

The Water Cycle Use a diagram of the water cycle to describe its major processes.

The Carbon and Oxygen Cycles Emphasize the link between the recycling of carbon and oxygen in an ecosystem and the roles of producers and consumers.

The Nitrogen Cycle Use text figures and transparencies to illustrate the unique aspects of the nitrogen cycle and the role of decomposers in it.

Targeted Print and Technology Resources

All in One Teaching Resources, Unit 4

L2 Guided Reading, pp. 118–120
L2 Transparencies LS215, LS216, LS217

PHSchool.com Web Code: cfp-4024

⊙ **Student Edition on Audio CD**

Assess

Section Assessment Questions

Have students use their cycle diagram or other sequencing diagrams to help answer the questions.

Reteach

Direct students to review drawings and tables that compare and contrast the cycles that are vital to ecosystem functioning.

Targeted Print and Technology Resources

All in One Teaching Resources, Unit 4

• Section Summary, p. 117
L1 Review and Reinforce, p. 121
L3 Enrich, p. 122

Ability Levels Key
L1 Basic to Average
L2 For All Students
L3 Average to Advanced

Section 3 Biogeography

 *2 periods, 1 block*

Objectives

22.3.1 Explain how the movement of the continents has affected the distribution of species.

22.1.2 Name and describe three ways that organism dispersal occurs.

22.1.3 Name and describe factors that can limit the dispersal of a species.

Key Terms
• biogeography • continental drift • dispersal • exotic species • climate

Local Standards

Preteach

Build Background Knowledge

Encourage students to discuss their own ideas about how and why animals move from one place to another.

Lab zone Discover Activity *How Can You Move a Seed?* **L1**

Targeted Print and Technology Resources

All in One Teaching Resources, Unit 4

L2 Reading Strategy Transparency
LS218: Relating Cause and Effect

PresentationEXPRESS™ CD-ROM

Instruct

Continental Drift Use illustrations of the movement of continents over time to explain how continental drift has affected species distributions.

Means of Dispersal Compare the ways that organisms can be dispersed.

Limits to Dispersal Ask leading questions to discuss factors that limit dispersal of a species.

Lab zone Skills Lab *Biomes in Miniature* **L3**

Targeted Print and Technology Resources

All in One Teaching Resources, Unit 4

L2 Guided Reading, pp. 125–126
L2 Transparency LS219
L3 Skills Lab: *Biomes in Miniature*, pp. 129–131

Lab Activity Video/DVD
Skills Lab: *Biomes in Miniature*

PHSchool.com Web Code: cfp-1015

Student Edition on Audio CD

Assess

Section Assessment Questions

Have students use their graphic organizers identifying causes of dispersal to answer the questions.

Reteach

Direct class discussion on how continental drift has affected species dispersal.

Targeted Print and Technology Resources

All in One Teaching Resources, Unit 4

• Section Summary, p. 124
L1 Review and Reinforce, p. 127
L3 Enrich, p. 128

Section 4 Biomes and Aquatic Ecosystems

Ability Levels Key
L1 Basic to Average
L2 For All Students
L3 Average to Advanced

⏱ *3 periods, 1 1/2 blocks*

Objectives

22.4.1 Name the six major biomes found on Earth.

22.1.2 Name and describe the factors that determine the type of biome found in an area.

22.1.3 Name and describe the two major types of aquatic ecosystems.

Local Standards

Key Terms

• biome • canopy • understory • desert • grassland • savanna • deciduous tree
• coniferous tree • tundra • permafrost • estuary • intertidal zone • neritic zone

---

Preteach

Build Background Knowledge

Encourage students to consider how local climate conditions affect which organisms live in the area.

Lab zone Discover Activity *How Much Rain Is That?* L2

Targeted Print and Technology Resources

All in One Teaching Resources, Unit 4

L2 Reading Strategy Transparency
LS220: Comparing and Contrasting

🔘 **PresentationEXPRESS CD-ROM**

Instruct

Rain Forest Biomes Use a map to compare rain forests.

Desert Biomes Discuss desert biomes in terms of adaptations that organisms there must possess.

Grassland Biomes Explore prairies and savannas.

Deciduous Forest Biomes Discuss the seasonal nature of deciduous forests and how it affects the organisms there.

Boreal Forest Biomes Describe the climate of the boreal forest and the limits placed on the biome's plants and animals.

Tundra Biomes Use a figure to describe the cold tundra biome and the adaptations of its plants and animals.

Mountains and Ice Explain the unique aspects of mountain habitats and ice habitats.

Freshwater Ecosystems Use figures to prompt discussion of freshwater ecosystems.

Marine Ecosystems Compare the components of marine ecosystems.

Lab zone Skills Lab *Change in a Tiny Community* L3

Targeted Print and Technology Resources

All in One Teaching Resources, Unit 4

L2 Guided Reading, pp. 134–138
L3 Skills Lab: *Change in a Tiny Community*, pp. 141–142

📼 **Lab Activity Video/DVD**
Skills Lab: *Change in a Tiny Community*

PHSchool.com Web Code: cep-5024
www.SciLinks.org Web Code: scn-0525

DISCOVERY CHANNEL
SCHOOL
Video Field Trip

🔘 **Student Edition on Audio CD**

Assess

Section Assessment Questions

🔄 Have students use their comparing and contrasting graphic organizers to answer the questions.

Reteach

Use a quiz game to study biomes and ecosystems.

Targeted Print and Technology Resources

All in One Teaching Resources, Unit 4

• Section Summary, p. 133
L1 Review and Reinforce, p. 139
L3 Enrich, p. 140

Section Lesson Plans

Chapter 22 Content Refresher

Section 1 Energy Flow in Ecosystems

Moving Through Energy Pyramids Energy in an ecosystem moves in only one direction, from the bottom (producers) to the top (top-level consumers) of an energy pyramid. Only about 10 percent of the energy in an energy pyramid is transferred from one level to the next. This fact is based on the laws of physics: According to the second law of thermodynamics, no system is 100 percent efficient. Some energy is wasted every time energy is transferred. The law is as true for food webs as it is for machines.

In a food web, energy is wasted not only due to heat but also because not all organisms in one level are eaten by those in the next level. As a result, some energy is not transferred at all. And even those organisms that are consumed might contain parts that cannot be digested—bones, beaks, shells, and so on—which further reduces the total amount of energy that can be transferred.

The narrowing of an energy pyramid from bottom to top illustrates that the amount of available energy in each successively higher level can support fewer organisms. This relationship also is reflected in the biomass present at each level. (Biomass is a measure of the total amount of living material.) Notice in the diagram that, as with energy, biomass in a food web declines by 90 percent from one level to the next. The shape of the energy pyramid and the amount of biomass at each level show why it takes a large number of producers to support one higher-level carnivore.

Biomass Pyramid

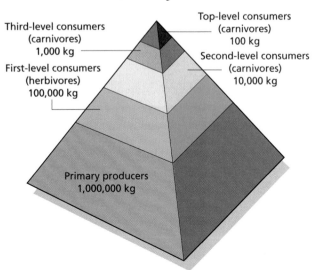

Third-level consumers (carnivores) 1,000 kg

Top-level consumers (carnivores) 100 kg

Second-level consumers (carnivores) 10,000 kg

First-level consumers (herbivores) 100,000 kg

Primary producers 1,000,000 kg

Section 2 Cycles of Matter

Making Nutrients Available Ecosystem cycles are critical to providing organisms, including humans, with the basic building blocks needed for survival. One important building block, nitrogen, is necessary for the formation of amino acids, which combine to form proteins. Some proteins are enzymes, which are catalysts for an organism's chemical reactions. Proteins are also the key components of many body tissues, such as muscle and skin. However, an organism cannot use all forms of nitrogen. In an ecosystem, those organisms that are part of the nitrogen cycle make it possible for nitrogen to be converted into forms other organisms can use.

In most organisms, cell function is impossible without a supply of oxygen. The high concentration of oxygen in Earth's atmosphere today was generated millions of years ago by producers during photosynthesis. That oxygen is now cycled through Earth's atmosphere and living organisms as part of the oxygen cycle.

Most of the material that makes up living things is based primarily on carbon. Only producers can convert carbon dioxide gas from the atmosphere into carbon compounds that other living things can use. The carbon used by organisms is again released as carbon dioxide while living things carry on cellular respiration.

⚑ Address Misconceptions

Some students may think that all ecosystems are dependent on photosynthesis. If true, then there would be no life forms in areas that lack sunlight, which is not the case. For other sources of production in ecosystems, see **Address Misconceptions** in the section, *Cycles of Matter.*

Professional Development

Section 3 Biogeography

Overcoming Dispersal Barriers Continental drift and volcanic eruptions have resulted in land masses separated by large bodies of water. The bodies of water act as barriers to the dispersal of organisms from one land mass to another. As a result, many isolated areas developed their own unique organisms. Today humans can overcome these expanses of water and other natural physical barriers that once prevented the dispersal of species. As they do so, new species can be introduced into an area, and native species that previously did not have to compete for resources now must share them. Often the native species are displaced.

Hawaii represents an example of an isolated location possessing many unique species. As people have accidentally or deliberately introduced new species to Hawaii's unique ecosystem, the balance of the existing ecosystems has been disrupted by the introduced species. Many native species have become threatened, endangered, or extinct. Coupled with the massive loss of native habitat, the introduction of species into Hawaii's ecosystems has caused hundreds of native species to become endangered or extinct.

Section 4 Biomes and Aquatic Ecosystems

Climate and Biomes Although many factors determine the types of organisms that live in a biome, climate is especially important. The two main characteristics that determine the climate of an area—temperature and rainfall—can be summarized in a climate diagram, such as the one here.

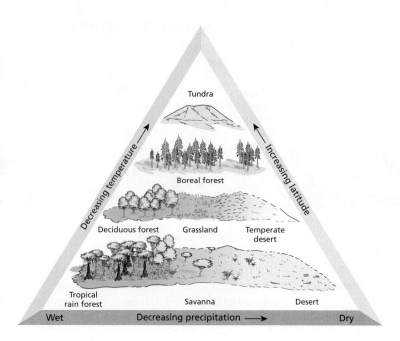

In temperate and tropical regions, the various biomes are distinguished more by amounts of precipitation than by temperature. Temperate rain forests and temperate deserts experience very different amounts of precipitation. Therefore, they vary greatly in their physical conditions and species compositions. In colder regions, tundras and boreal forests have similar levels of yearly precipitation, but their temperatures—and therefore their organisms—differ vastly.

Many different areas of the world share similar climate and soil, another characteristic that determines the types of organisms in a biome. As a result, such areas will share similar types of organisms. For example, deserts can be found in several locations across the globe. Although the specific species that live in each individual desert may be unique to that area, all share certain characteristics that enable them to survive the hot daytime temperatures, dryness, and poor soil.

Help Students Read

Asking Questions
Looking for Answers

Strategy This strategy helps students to anticipate what they will be reading and helps them look for answers in the passage as they read. With practice, students should be able to generate questions that do not simply rephrase the section headings. The headings themselves will give students the hints they need to formulate original questions about what they expect to see in the text.

Example
1. Choose a section within this chapter. A good example is *Biomes and Aquatic Ecosystems*.
2. Draw a two-column chart on the board. Make the heading of the first column of your chart *Questions* and the second heading *Answers*.
3. Have students scan the section. As they encounter headings and subheadings, have them suggest ways to recast them so that they become questions. For example, *Rain Forest Biomes* might become the question, "What is a rain forest?"
4. After you have several questions in the first column of your chart, ask students to read the section. You may ask a volunteer to read aloud or ask the class to read silently.
5. After students have read the section, ask volunteers to supply answers to the questions in the first column. Suggest that students make their own charts as you are writing the answers on the board. Students can use their charts to help answer assessment questions.

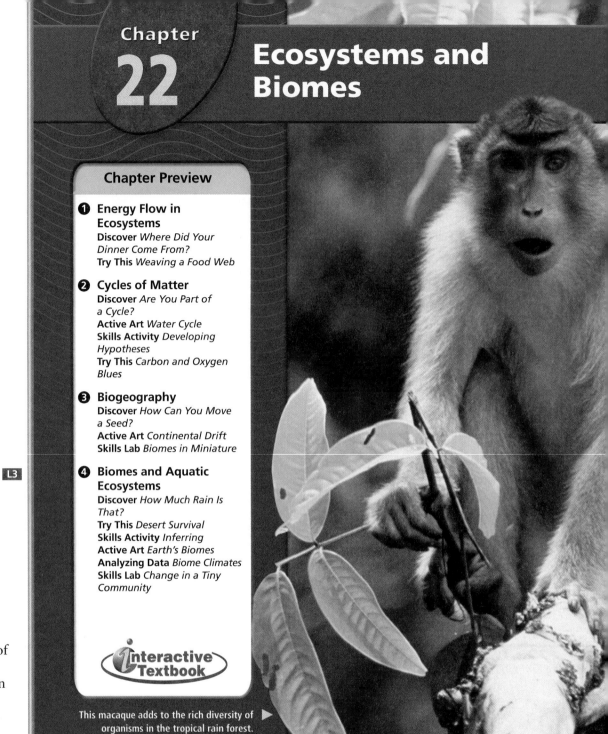

Chapter 22

Ecosystems and Biomes

interactive Textbook

This macaque adds to the rich diversity of ▶
organisms in the tropical rain forest.

738 ◆

Lab zone Chapter **Project** L3

Objectives

This project will give students an opportunity to study the process of decomposition by constructing compost chambers and investigating the effects over time of environmental variables on composting. After this Chapter Project, students will be able to

- make a model compost chamber
- design an experiment to test the effect of one variable on decomposition
- observe, measure, and record changes in composted material
- communicate experimental procedures and results in a report, poster, or other product

Skills Focus

Making models, designing experiments, observing, measuring, interpreting data, communicating

Project Time Line at least 4 weeks

All in One Teaching Resources, Unit 4

- Chapter Project Teacher Notes
- Chapter Project Overview
- Chapter Project Worksheets
- Chapter Project Scoring Rubric

Developing a Plan

Each student or group will first choose a variable to investigate: moisture, oxygen, temperature, or activity of soil organisms. Students will then construct compost chambers, design and launch experiments, observe the decomposition process, record and analyze data, and prepare reports.

Possible Materials

- Each student or group will need materials for the control and test compost chambers. For instructions on building compost chambers, see the Chapter Project Teacher Notes in the All-In-One Teaching Resources.
- Provide chopped leaves as the base material to be composted. Add as desired other organic waste: eggshells, paper, grass

Video
Preview

Ecosystems and Biomes

Show the Video Preview to introduce the Chapter Project and overview the chapter content. Discussion question: **What climatic conditions are common to all deserts?** *(All get very little rain and have extreme temperature shifts.)*

Lab zone™ Chapter **Project**

Breaking It Down

Nothing in an ecosystem is wasted. Even when living things die, organisms such as mushrooms recycle them. This natural process of breakdown is called decomposition. When fallen leaves and other waste products decompose, a fluffy, brown mixture called compost is formed. You can observe decomposition firsthand in this chapter project by building a compost chamber.

Your Goal To design and conduct an experiment to learn more about the process of decomposition

To complete this project, you must

● build two compost chambers
● investigate the effect of one of the following variables on decomposition: moisture, oxygen, temperature, or activity of soil organisms
● analyze your data and present your results
● follow the safety guidelines in Appendix A

Plan It! Your teacher will provide you with a sample of compost material. Observe the wastes in the mixture with a hand lens. Write a hypothesis about which kinds of waste will decay and which will not. Next, decide which variable you will test and plan how you will test it. Once your teacher approves your plan, build your compost chambers and begin your experiment.

Chapter 22 ◆ **739**

Have students read the Chapter Project description. Then show and describe the compost chamber that you made. Explain that each student or group will need to make two such chambers—a control chamber and a test chamber.

If you divide the class into groups, tell students that all group members should help plan the experiment, make observations, analyze results, and develop the report.

Performance Assessment

The Chapter Project Scoring Rubric will help you evaluate how well students complete the Chapter Project. You may want to share the scoring rubric with your students so they are clear about what will be expected of them. Students will be assessed on

● their ability to design an experiment to test the effect of one variable on decomposition
● their completeness and accuracy in doing the experiment, making observations, and recording data
● their ability to draw reasonable conclusions based on experimental results and communicate their procedures, results, and conclusions
● their group participation if they worked in groups

Portfolio

clippings, and orange peels; or inorganic waste: bottle caps or plastic foam pieces.
● Provide garden soil (not commercial potting soil) and earthworms for groups that choose to investigate the effect of soil organisms.
● Set aside protected locations in the classroom to house the compost chambers.

Launching the Project

Construct a compost chamber yourself as a prototype. Fill the chamber with the compost material, but do not add water. Set your chamber aside until the end of the project so students can compare their composted material with the original material.

Section
1
Energy Flow in Ecosystems

Objectives

After completing the lesson, students will be able to

22.1.1 Name and describe energy roles that organisms play in an ecosystem.

22.1.2 Explain how energy moves through an ecosystem.

22.1.3 Describe how much energy is available at each level of an energy pyramid.

Target Reading Skill

Building Vocabulary Explain that knowing the definitions of key concept words helps students understand what they read.

Answers

Sample definitions: **producer** (*An organism that makes its own food*); **consumer** (*An organism that obtains its energy by eating other organisms*); **herbivore** (*Consumer that eats only plants*); **carnivore** (*Consumer that eats only animals*); **omnivore** (*Consumer that eats both plants and animals*); **scavenger** (*Carnivore that feeds on dead organisms*); **decomposer** (*Organism that breaks down dead organisms and returns the raw materials to the ecosystem*); **food chain** (*One possible path that energy can take through an ecosystem*); **food web** (*Diagram of many overlapping food chains*); **energy pyramid** (*Diagram that shows the energy available at each feeding level*)

Preteach

Build Background Knowledge   L2

Recalling Ecosystems

Help students recall what they learned in the previous chapter by asking: **What is an ecosystem?** (*All the living and nonliving things that interact in a particular area*) **What are some things you know about ecosystems?** (*Responses might include information on habitat, biotic and abiotic factors, levels of organization, population size, limiting factors, adaptations, and types of interactions between organisms*)

Reading Preview

Key Concepts

- What energy roles do organisms play in an ecosystem?
- How does energy move through an ecosystem?
- How much energy is available at each level of an energy pyramid?

Key Terms

- producer • consumer
- herbivore • carnivore
- omnivore • scavenger
- decomposer • food chain
- food web • energy pyramid

Target Reading Skill

Building Vocabulary A definition states the meaning of a word or phrase by telling about its most important feature or function. After you read the section, reread the paragraphs that contain definitions of Key Terms. Use all the information you have learned to write a definition of each Key Term in your own words.

Lab zone Discover **Activity**

Where Did Your Dinner Come From?

1. Across the top of a sheet of paper, list the different types of foods you ate for dinner last night.
2. Under each item, write the name of the plant, animal, or other organism that was the source of that food. Some foods have more than one source. For example, macaroni and cheese contains flour (which is made from a plant such as wheat) and cheese (which comes from an animal).

Think It Over

Classifying How many of your food sources were plants? How many were animals?

Do you play an instrument in your school band? If so, you know that each instrument has a role in a piece of music. For instance, the flute may provide the melody while the drum provides the beat.

Just like the instruments in a band, each organism has a role in the movement of energy through its ecosystem. A bluebird's role, for example, is different from that of the giant oak tree where it is perched. But all parts of the ecosystem, like all parts of a band, are necessary for the ecosystem to work.

Energy Roles

An organism's energy role is determined by how it obtains energy and how it interacts with other organisms. **Each of the organisms in an ecosystem fills the energy role of producer, consumer, or decomposer.**

Producers Energy enters most ecosystems as sunlight. Some organisms, such as plants, algae, and some bacteria, capture the energy of sunlight and store it as food energy. These organisms use the sun's energy to turn water and carbon dioxide into food molecules in a process called photosynthesis.

Lab zone Discover **Activity**

Skills Focus Classifying

Materials paper and pen or pencil

Time 10 minutes

Tips Circulate among students as they work to answer questions about the sources or ingredients of some foods.

Expected Outcome As a class, students will undoubtedly cite a wide variety of foods and sources.

L1 **Think It Over** Answers will vary depending on the foods eaten. Except for students whose families are strict vegetarians and eat no animal products of any kind, most students will probably cite both plant and animal sources and possibly fungi, protists, or monerans.

An organism that can make its own food is a **producer.** Producers are the source of all the food in an ecosystem. In a few ecosystems, producers obtain energy from a source other than sunlight. One such ecosystem is found in rocks deep beneath the ground. How is energy brought into this ecosystem? Certain bacteria in this ecosystem produce their own food using the energy in a gas, hydrogen sulfide, that is found in their environment.

Consumers Some members of an ecosystem cannot make their own food. An organism that obtains energy by feeding on other organisms is a **consumer.**

Consumers are classified by what they eat. Consumers that eat only plants are **herbivores.** Familiar herbivores are caterpillars and deer. Consumers that eat only animals are **carnivores.** Lions and spiders are some examples of carnivores. Consumers that eat both plants and animals are **omnivores.** Crows, bears, and most humans are omnivores.

Some carnivores are scavengers. A **scavenger** is a carnivore that feeds on the bodies of dead organisms. Scavengers include catfish and vultures.

Decomposers If an ecosystem had only producers and consumers, the raw materials of life would stay locked up in wastes and the bodies of dead organisms. Luckily, there are organisms in ecosystems that prevent this problem. **Decomposers** break down wastes and dead organisms and return the raw materials to the ecosystem.

You can think of decomposers as nature's recyclers. While obtaining energy for their own needs, decomposers return simple molecules to the environment. These molecules can be used again by other organisms. Mushrooms and bacteria are common decomposers.

 Reading Checkpoint What do herbivores and carnivores have in common?

Consumer—Herbivore

Producer

Consumer—Omnivore

Decomposer

FIGURE 1
Energy Roles
Each organism in an ecosystem fills a specific energy role. Producers, such as oak trees, make their own food. Consumers, such as luna moth larvae and eastern bluebirds, obtain energy by feeding on other organisms. **Classifying** *What role do decomposers play in ecosystems?*

 ◆ 741

Food Chains and Food Webs

Teach Key Concepts
Linking Energy Pathways

Focus Remind students that a food web includes several food chains.

Teach Call on students to identify food chains pictured in Figure 2. Ask: **With only one top consumer, the fox, how many food chains are in the web?** (*At least six*) **What are the producers in this food web?** (*Grasses, trees, other plants*) **What are the first-level consumers?** (*Rabbit, mouse, grasshopper, carpenter ant*) **The second-level consumers?** (*Mouse, garter snake, shrew, fox, woodpecker*) **The third-level consumers?** (*Garter snake, fox*) **How can the mouse be both a first- and second-level consumer?** (*It's an omnivore that eats both plants and insects*) **How do decomposers gain energy?** (*They consume wastes and remains.*)

Apply Challenge each student in a group to draw a food chain from an assigned ecosystem and then as a group to combine the food chains into a food web. **learning modality: visual**

 **Teaching Resources, Unit 4**
• Transparency LS212

Address Misconceptions
Energy for Dark Ecosystems

Focus Tell students that not all ecosystems require light.

Teach Point out that ecosystems surrounding deep-sea hydrothermal vents are too far below the water surface to receive sunlight. Explain that bacteria living near the vents make food by harnessing energy from chemicals in the water.

Apply Ask: **How is this ecosystem similar to the one based on photosynthesis?** (*Like plants, bacteria are producers and provide food for consumers.*) **learning modality: verbal**

Go Online
SC*LINKS* NSTA

For: Links on food chains and food webs
Visit: www.SciLinks.org
Web Code: scn-0521

Download a worksheet that will guide students' review of Internet resources on food chains and food webs.

Go Online
SC*LINKS* NSTA

For: Links on food chains and food webs
Visit: www.SciLinks.org
Web Code: scn-0521

Lab zone Try This Activity

Weaving a Food Web
This activity shows how the organisms in a food web are interconnected.

1. Your teacher will assign you a role in the food web.
2. Hold one end of each of several pieces of yarn in your hand. Give the other ends of your yarn to the other organisms to which your organism is linked.
3. Your teacher will now eliminate an organism. All the organisms connected to the missing organism should drop the yarn that connects them.

Making Models How many organisms were affected by the removal of just one organism? What does this activity show about the importance of each organism in a food web?

Food Chains and Food Webs

As you have read, energy enters most ecosystems as sunlight and is converted into food molecules by producers. This energy is transferred to each organism that eats a producer, and then to other organisms that feed on these consumers. **The movement of energy through an ecosystem can be shown in diagrams called food chains and food webs.**

Food Chains A **food chain** is a series of events in which one organism eats another and obtains energy. You can follow one food chain in Figure 2. The first organism in a food chain is always a producer, such as the tree. The second organism feeds on the producer and is called a first-level consumer. The termite is a first-level consumer. Next, a second-level consumer eats the first-level consumer. The second-level consumer in this example is the woodpecker.

Food Webs A food chain shows only one possible path along which energy can move through an ecosystem. But just as you do not eat the same thing every day, neither do most other organisms. Most producers and consumers are part of many food chains. A more realistic way to show the flow of energy through an ecosystem is a food web. As shown in Figure 2, a **food web** consists of the many overlapping food chains in an ecosystem.

In Figure 2, you can trace the many food chains in a woodland ecosystem. Note that an organism may play more than one role in an ecosystem. For example, an omnivore such as the mouse is a first-level consumer when it eats grass. But when the mouse eats a grasshopper, it is a second-level consumer.

Just as food chains overlap and connect, food webs interconnect as well. While a gull might eat a fish at the ocean, it might also eat a mouse at a landfill. The gull, then, is part of two food webs—an ocean food web and a land food web. All the world's food webs interconnect in what can be thought of as a global food web.

 Reading Checkpoint What energy role is filled by the first organism in a food chain?

Food Chain

Woodpecker

Carpenter ant

Tree

Lab zone Try This Activity

Skills Focus Making models

Materials long pieces of yarn

Time 15 minutes

Tips You can use the food web shown in Figure 2. If you use another food web, be prepared to help students decide which organisms eat and are eaten by other organisms. In Step 3, eliminate either a first- or second-level consumer.

Expected Outcome The number of other organisms affected will depend on the food web you use and the organism you eliminate. In all cases, however, students should recognize that all or most of the food web is affected.

Extend Let students repeat the activity using a different food web. **learning modality: kinesthetic**

FIGURE 2
A Food Web

A food web consists of many interconnected food chains. Trace the path of energy through the producers, consumers, and decomposers. **Interpreting Diagrams** *Which organisms in the food web are acting as herbivores? Which are carnivores?*

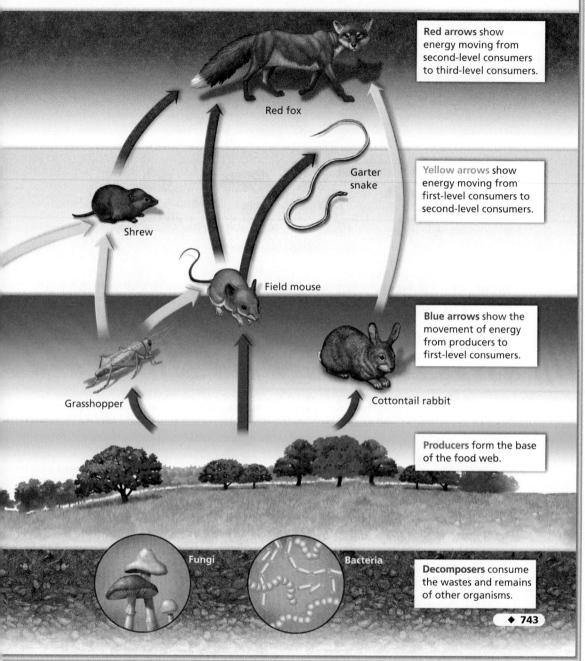

Red fox

Red arrows show energy moving from second-level consumers to third-level consumers.

Garter snake

Shrew

Yellow arrows show energy moving from first-level consumers to second-level consumers.

Field mouse

Grasshopper

Cottontail rabbit

Blue arrows show the movement of energy from producers to first-level consumers.

Producers form the base of the food web.

Fungi

Bacteria

Decomposers consume the wastes and remains of other organisms.

◆ 743

Observing Decomposition

Materials earthworms, terrarium, potting soil, shredded leaves or grass clippings, water

Time 15 minutes for setup

Focus Tell students that earthworms and other small animals in soil help decompose dead material by breaking it down into smaller pieces.

Teach Have students set up a class earthworm farm that they can observe closely. Fill a terrarium about two-thirds full of potting soil, mix in some shredded leaves or grass clippings, moisten the soil, and add the worms. Ask: **What do you think will happen to the food scraps?** *(The worms will break them down.)* Maintain observations throughout the study of this chapter. Students can periodically bury cut-up scraps of fruits and vegetables.

Apply When observations are complete, add the worms and soil to an outdoor garden. Ask: **How did the worms in the farm affect the soil?** *(They composted it.)* **learning modality: visual**

Monitor Progress _____ L2

Oral Presentation Randomly ask students to name a type of consumer and explain how it is classified.

Answers
Figure 2 Herbivores: carpenter ant, grasshopper, field mouse, rabbit; carnivores: woodpecker, field mouse, shrew, garter snake, fox.

 Reading Checkpoint The first organisms in a food chain play the role of producer.

743

Energy Pyramids

Teach Key Concepts L2
Identifying Available Energy

Focus Relate the shape of an energy pyramid to the diminishing amount of energy available, moving from bottom to top.

Teach Draw an empty pyramid on the board; divide it into four horizontal sections, numbered 1–4 from bottom to top. Ask: **Which level will include the producers?** *(Level 1)* **Which level includes the top consumer?** *(Level 4)* **Which levels include consumers?** *(Levels 2, 3, and 4)* **Which level represents the most available energy?** *(Level 1)* **The least available energy?** *(Level 4)* **Which level supports the fewest organisms?** *(Level 4)*

Apply Provide index cards bearing these energy pyramid labels: *Most Energy Available, Least Energy Available, Producers, Consumers, Top Consumer,* and the like. Assign students to attach their labels to a pyramid outline on the board. **learning modality: visual**

All in One **Teaching Resources, Unit 4**

• Transparency LS213

FIGURE 3
Energy Pyramid
This energy pyramid diagram shows the energy available at each level of a food web. Energy is measured in kilocalories, or kcal. *Calculating How many times more energy is available at the producer level than at the second-level consumer level?*

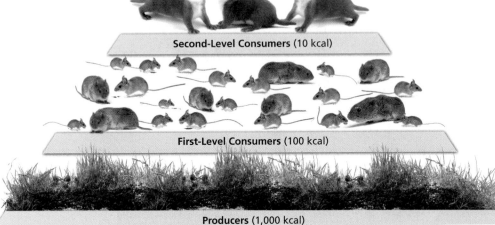

Third-Level Consumers (1 kcal)

Second-Level Consumers (10 kcal)

First-Level Consumers (100 kcal)

Producers (1,000 kcal)

Energy Pyramids

When an organism in an ecosystem eats, it obtains energy. The organism uses some of this energy to move, grow, reproduce, and carry out other life activities. This means that only some of the energy it obtains will be available to the next organism in the food web.

A diagram called an **energy pyramid** shows the amount of energy that moves from one feeding level to another in a food web. You can see an energy pyramid in Figure 3. **The most energy is available at the producer level of the pyramid. As you move up the pyramid, each level has less energy available than the level below.** An energy pyramid gets its name from the shape of the diagram—wider at the base and narrower at the top.

Differentiated Instruction

Special Needs L1
Visualizing Energy Transfers To assist students needing help visualizing energy transfers in an energy pyramid, divide the class into groups of three. Distribute scissors and graph paper. The first student, the "producer," should cut a 10-by-10 block of squares from graph paper. The block represents the total amount of food energy stored in the producer. The "producer" should then cut a row of 10 squares from the block and pass it on to the second student, the "first-level consumer." That student should cut one square from the row and pass it to the third student, the "second-level consumer." Students will see that only a small portion of the original energy stored in the producer reaches the second-level consumer. **learning modality: kinesthetic**

In general, only about 10 percent of the energy at one level of a food web is transferred to the next higher level. The other 90 percent of the energy is used for the organism's life processes or is lost to the environment as heat. Since about 90 percent of the energy is lost at each step, there is not enough energy to support many feeding levels in an ecosystem.

The organisms at higher feeding levels of an energy pyramid do not necessarily require less energy to live than do the organisms at lower levels. Since so much energy is lost at each level, the amount of energy available at the producer level limits the number of consumers that the ecosystem is able to support. As a result, there are usually few organisms at the highest level in a food web.

 Reading Checkpoint Why is the pyramid shape useful for showing the energy available at each of the levels of a food web?

FIGURE 4
Energy Flow
This barn owl will soon use the energy contained in the rat to carry out its own life processes.

Section 1 Assessment

⟳ **Target Reading Skill** **Building Vocabulary** Use your definitions to help answer the questions below.

Reviewing Key Concepts

1. a. **Identifying** Name the three energy roles that organisms fill in an ecosystem.
   b. **Explaining** How do organisms in each of the three energy roles obtain energy?
   c. **Classifying** Identify the energy roles of the following organisms in a pond ecosystem: tadpole, algae, heron.
2. a. **Defining** What is a food chain? What is a food web?
   b. **Comparing and Contrasting** Why is a food web a more realistic way of portraying an ecosystem than is a food chain?
3. a. **Reviewing** What does an energy pyramid show?
   b. **Describing** How does the amount of energy available at one level of an energy pyramid compare to the amount of energy available at the next level up?
   c. **Relating Cause and Effect** Why are there usually few organisms at the top of an energy pyramid?

Lab zone **At-Home Activity**

Energy-Role Walk Take a short walk outdoors with a family member to look for producers, consumers, and decomposers. Create a list of the organisms and their energy roles. For each consumer, try to classify it further according to what it eats and its level. Then explain to your family member how energy flows in ecosystems.

Chapter 22 ◆ **745**

Lab zone **At-Home Activity**

Energy-Role Walk **L2** Before students take the walk with their families, review as a class the different energy roles. Distinguish between the different types of consumers—herbivore, omnivore, carnivore, and scavenger—and discuss the different levels of consumers.

Lab zone **Chapter Project**

Keep Students on Track When students prepare their written plans, instruct them to use this format: a statement of the hypothesis, a list of materials, a step-by-step procedure, and a data table for recording results. Make sure students will keep all variables the same for both chambers except for the variable being tested with the second chamber. Also review students' planned data tables.

Answers
Figure 3 There is 100 times more energy available at the producer level.

✓ **Reading Checkpoint** The shape shows how available energy decreases at higher levels of a food web.

Assess

Reviewing Key Concepts

1. a. Producers, consumers, and decomposers b. Producers use energy, usually sunlight, to make their own food; consumers eat other organisms; decomposers break down organisms' wastes and remains. c. Algae: producers; tadpole and heron: consumers
2. a. A food chain is a series of events by which one organism eats another and obtains energy; a food web consists of many overlapping food chains. b. Because most organisms are part of many overlapping food chains
3. a. The amount of energy that moves from one feeding level to another in a food web
b. The amount of energy available on one level of an energy pyramid is 10 times greater than that available at the next level up.
c. Because so much energy is lost from one level to the next level up, the energy available at the top level can support few organisms.

Reteach **L1**
Review the different energy roles of organisms in an ecosystem, and then discuss how energy flow is represented by food chains, food webs, and energy pyramids.

Performance Assessment
Drawing Have each student draw a food chain of his or her own choice and label each organism to show (1) its energy role, (2) whether each consumer is a herbivore, and (3) the percentage of energy available at each energy level in the food chain.

All in One **Teaching Resources, Unit 4**
• Section Summary: *Energy Flow in Ecosystems*
• Review and Reinforce: *Energy Flow in Ecosystems*
• Enrich: *Energy Flow in Ecosystems*

Objectives

After completing the lesson, students will be able to

22.2.1 Name and describe processes involved in the water cycle.

22.2.2 Explain how carbon and oxygen are recycled in an ecosystem.

22.2.3 Define and describe the nitrogen cycle.

Target Reading Skill

Sequencing Explain that organizing information from beginning to end helps students understand a step-by-step process.

Answers

1. Water evaporates.
2. Clouds form.
3. Precipitation falls.
4. Precipitation runs off or becomes groundwater.

All in One Teaching Resources, Unit 4

• Transparency LS214

Preteach

Build Background Knowledge   L2

Understanding a Cycle

Ask: **What is a cycle?** *(A series of things that repeat over and over again)* **What are some examples of cycles?** *(Seasons of the year, days of the week, life cycles of plants and animals, and so forth)*

Reading Preview

Key Concepts
• What processes are involved in the water cycle?
• How are carbon and oxygen recycled in ecosystems?
• What is the nitrogen cycle?

Key Terms
• water cycle • evaporation
• condensation • precipitation
• nitrogen fixation

Target Reading Skill

Sequencing A sequence is the order in which a series of events occurs. As you read, make a cycle diagram that shows the water cycle. Write each event of the water cycle in a separate oval.

The Water Cycle

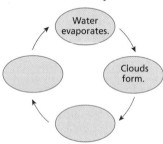

Lab zone Discover **Activity**

Are You Part of a Cycle?

1. Hold a small mirror a few centimeters from your mouth.
2. Exhale onto the mirror.
3. Observe the surface of the mirror.

Think It Over
Inferring What is the substance that forms on the mirror? Where did this substance come from?

A pile of crumpled cars is ready for loading into a giant compactor. The aluminum and copper pieces have already been removed so that they can be recycled, or used again. Now the steel will be reclaimed at a recycling plant. Earth has a limited supply of aluminum, copper, and the iron used in steel. Recycling old cars is one way to ensure a steady supply of these materials.

Like the supply of metal for building cars, the supply of matter in an ecosystem is limited. Matter in an ecosystem includes water, carbon, oxygen, nitrogen, and many other substances. If matter could not be recycled, ecosystems would quickly run out of the raw materials necessary for life. In this section, you will learn about some cycles of matter: the water cycle, the carbon and oxygen cycles, and the nitrogen cycle.

To understand how these substances cycle over and over through an ecosystem, you need to know a few basic terms that describe the structure of matter. Matter is made up of tiny particles called atoms. Two or more atoms that are joined and act as a unit make up a molecule. For example, a water molecule consists of two hydrogen atoms and one oxygen atom.

The Water Cycle

Water is essential for life. To ensure a steady supply, Earth's water must be recycled. The **water cycle** is the continuous process by which water moves from Earth's surface to the atmosphere and back. **The processes of evaporation, condensation, and precipitation make up the water cycle.** As you read about these processes, follow the cycle in Figure 5.

Lab zone Discover **Activity**

Skills Focus Inferring

Materials small mirror

Time 5 minutes

Tips If the weather is very warm and humid when students do this activity, moisture may not condense on the mirror. In this case, you can cool the mirrors in a refrigerator for a short time beforehand.

L1 **Expected Outcome** As water vapor from students' breath cools, tiny droplets of liquid water will condense on the mirrors.

Think It Over The substance is water; it came from water vapor in the students' exhaled breath.

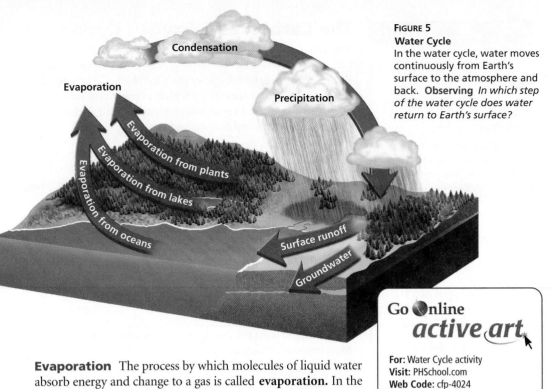

Condensation

Evaporation

Precipitation

Evaporation from plants

Evaporation from lakes

Evaporation from oceans

Surface runoff

Groundwater

FIGURE 5
Water Cycle
In the water cycle, water moves continuously from Earth's surface to the atmosphere and back. **Observing** *In which step of the water cycle does water return to Earth's surface?*

Go Online
active art

For: Water Cycle activity
Visit: PHSchool.com
Web Code: cfp-4024

Evaporation The process by which molecules of liquid water absorb energy and change to a gas is called **evaporation.** In the water cycle, liquid water evaporates from oceans, lakes, and other surfaces and forms water vapor, a gas, in the atmosphere. The energy for evaporation comes from the heat of the sun.

Living things also give off water. For example, plants release water vapor from their leaves. You release liquid water in your wastes and water vapor when you exhale.

Condensation As the water vapor rises higher in the atmosphere, it cools down. The cooled vapor then turns back into tiny drops of liquid water. The process by which a gas changes to a liquid is called **condensation.** The water droplets collect around particles of dust, eventually forming clouds.

Precipitation As more water vapor condenses, the drops of water in the cloud grow larger. Eventually the heavy drops fall back to Earth as **precipitation**—rain, snow, sleet, or hail. Most precipitation falls back into oceans or lakes. The precipitation that falls on land may soak into the soil and become groundwater. Or the precipitation may run off the land, eventually flowing back into a river or ocean.

 Reading Checkpoint What process causes water from the surface of the ocean to enter the atmosphere as water vapor?

Lab zone Skills **Activity**

Developing Hypotheses
You've decided to have cocoa at a friend's house on a cold, rainy day. As your friend boils some water, you notice that the inside of a window near the stove is covered with water droplets. Your friend thinks the window is leaking. Using what you know about the water cycle, can you propose another explanation for the water droplets?

Chapter 22 ◆ 747

Instruct

The Water Cycle

Teach Key Concepts L2

Identifying Water Cycle Processes

Focus Explain that several processes take place in the water cycle.

Teach Direct students to Figure 5. Ask: **What is the function of the water cycle?** *(It moves water from Earth's surface to the atmosphere and back.)* **Which process includes melted snow entering rivers?** *(Surface runoff)*

Apply Ask: **How can you tell by the figure that the water cycle is continuous?** *(All three processes go on at once.)* **learning modality: visual**

All in One Teaching Resources, Unit 4
• Transparency LS215

Go Online
active art

For: Water Cycle activity
Visit: PHSchool.com
Web Code: cfp-4024

Students can examine how water moves through the water cycle.

Independent Practice L2

All in One Teaching Resources, Unit 4
• Guided Reading and Study Worksheet: *Cycles of Matter*

⊙ **Student Edition on Audio CD**

Lab zone Skills **Activity**

Skills Focus Developing hypotheses L1
Materials none
Time 5 minutes
Tips Have students do this activity after they have read the section about the water cycle.
Expected Outcome The water droplets on the cold window condensed from the water vapor that evaporated from the boiling water.
Extend Have students draw and label a simple diagram, similar to Figure 5, which shows the water cycle operating in this example. For precipitation, students could show tiny water droplets joining to form larger drops that trickle down the window. **learning modality: logical/mathematical**

Monitor Progress L2

Drawing Have each student draw and label a simple diagram of the water cycle without referring to Figure 5. Students can save their drawings in their portfolios.

Portfolio

Answers
Figure 5 Precipitation

 Reading Checkpoint Evaporation (a liquid changes into a gas)

The Carbon and Oxygen Cycles

Teach Key Concepts   L2

Describing the Link Between Cycles

Focus Remind students that the carbon and oxygen cycles are linked and that producers and consumers all play a part.

Teach Review the basic processes of photosynthesis. Ask: **What is the role of producers in the carbon and oxygen cycles?** (*Producers take in carbon dioxide during photosynthesis and use it to make carbon-containing food molecules. They release oxygen as a product of photosynthesis.*) **How do consumers fit into the carbon and oxygen cycles?** (*Consumers take in carbon molecules by eating producers; when they break these molecules down, they release carbon. Consumers use oxygen in air to perform life functions.*)

Apply Ask: **How will depriving a closed terrarium of sunlight affect the oxygen and carbon cycles of the plants and small animals inside?** (*Without sunlight, plants can't make food and won't release oxygen; consumers will have no food sources and insufficient oxygen and will not release carbon.*) **learning modality: logical/mathematical**

All in One Teaching Resources, Unit 4

• Transparency LS216

Help Students Read   L1

Asking Questions Refer to the Content Refresher, which provides guidelines for asking questions. Have students make a three-column table. In the first column, have them list the heading and subheadings in this section. In the second column, have them rephrase the headings as questions. Then in the third column have them write the answers to the questions they wrote. When students are finished reading the section, have volunteers read their questions and answers.

Lab zone Try This Activity

Carbon and Oxygen Blues

This activity explores the role of producers in the carbon and oxygen cycles.

1. Your teacher will provide you with two plastic cups containing bromthymol blue solution. Bromthymol blue solution appears blue in the absence of carbon dioxide and appears yellow in the presence of carbon dioxide. Note the color of the solution.

2. Place two sprigs of an *Elodea* plant into one of the cups. Do not put any *Elodea* into the second cup. Cover both cups with plastic wrap. Wash your hands.

3. Place the cups where they will not be disturbed. Observe the two cups over the next few days. Note any color changes.

Inferring What do your observations indicate about the role of producers in the carbon and oxygen cycles?

FIGURE 6
Rising Carbon Dioxide Levels
When forests burn, large amounts of carbon dioxide are released into the air. In addition, there are fewer trees available to absorb carbon dioxide from the air.

748 ◆

The Carbon and Oxygen Cycles

Two other substances necessary for life are carbon and oxygen. Carbon is an essential building block in the bodies of living things. Most organisms use oxygen for their life processes. **In ecosystems, the processes by which carbon and oxygen are recycled are linked. Producers, consumers, and decomposers play roles in recycling carbon and oxygen.**

The Carbon Cycle Producers take in carbon dioxide gas from the air during photosynthesis. They use carbon from the carbon dioxide to make food molecules—carbon-containing molecules such as sugars and starches. When consumers eat producers, they take in the carbon-containing food molecules. When consumers break down these food molecules to obtain energy, they release carbon dioxide and water as waste products. When producers and consumers die, decomposers break down their remains and return carbon compounds to the soil. Some decomposers also release carbon dioxide as a waste product.

The Oxygen Cycle Like carbon, oxygen cycles through ecosystems. Producers release oxygen as a result of photosynthesis. Most organisms take in oxygen from the air and use it to carry out their life processes.

Human Impact Human activities also affect the levels of carbon and oxygen in the atmosphere. When humans burn oil and other fuels, carbon dioxide is released into the atmosphere. When humans clear forests for lumber, fuel, and farmland, carbon dioxide levels also rise. As you know, producers take in carbon dioxide during photosynthesis. When trees are removed from the ecosystem, there are fewer producers to absorb carbon dioxide. There is a greater effect if trees are burned down to clear a forest. If trees are burned down to clear a forest, additional carbon dioxide is released in the burning process.

Reading Checkpoint What role do producers play in the carbon and oxygen cycles?

Lab zone Try This Activity

Skills Focus Inferring   L2

Materials two plastic cups, bromthymol blue solution, two sprigs of *Elodea*, plastic wrap

Time 10 minutes for setup; 15 minutes of observations over several days

Tips Remind students to cover the cups and to keep them in a protected area.

Expected Outcome The solution containing *Elodea* will appear blue because the plant has taken up carbon dioxide; the solution without *Elodea* will appear yellow.

Think It Over Producers remove carbon dioxide from their environment as they make their own food and release oxygen.
learning modality: kinesthetic

FIGURE 7
Carbon and Oxygen Cycles

This scene shows how the carbon and oxygen cycles are linked. Producers, consumers, and decomposers all play a role in recycling these two substances.
Interpreting Diagrams *How do human activities affect the carbon and oxygen cycles?*

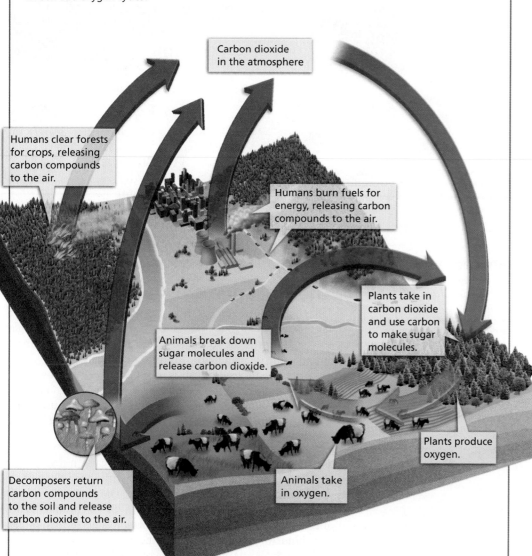

Carbon dioxide in the atmosphere

Humans clear forests for crops, releasing carbon compounds to the air.

Humans burn fuels for energy, releasing carbon compounds to the air.

Plants take in carbon dioxide and use carbon to make sugar molecules.

Animals break down sugar molecules and release carbon dioxide.

Plants produce oxygen.

Decomposers return carbon compounds to the soil and release carbon dioxide to the air.

Animals take in oxygen.

Build Inquiry   L2

Predicting Carbon and Oxygen Cycling

Materials none

Time 10 minutes

Focus Review the differing roles of producers and consumers in recycling carbon and oxygen.

Teach Describe for students a sealed jar containing guppies, plants, algae, and snails. Provide a picture if possible. Ask: **Which organisms in the jar are producers?** (*The plants and algae*) **What do the producers release when they conduct photosynthesis?** (*Oxygen*) **What happens to the oxygen?** (*It is "breathed in" by the guppies and snails.*) **Where do the producers get the carbon dioxide they need?** (*It is released by the guppies and snails.*)

Apply Ask: **Would you predict that this cycle would go on indefinitely? Why or why not?** (*Yes; as long as the producers receive sunlight and the guppies and snails receive food, the carbon and oxygen will continue to cycle between the producers and the consumers.*) **learning modality: logical/mathematical**

Monitor Progress _____ L2

Writing Have each student write a paragraph that describes one way human activities affect the carbon and oxygen cycles.

Answers

Figure 7 Human activities such as burning fuel and clearing forested land cause levels of carbon dioxide to rise.

Reading Checkpoint Producers take in carbon dioxide gas and, through photosynthesis, release oxygen and provide carbon to consumers in the form of food sources.

Differentiated Instruction

English Learners/Beginning Comprehension: Modified Cloze   L1
Distribute a simplified paragraph about carbon and oxygen cycles, leaving some strategic words blank. For example, "In photosynthesis, producers take in _____ from the air and release _____. When consumers eat _____, they take in carbon." Provide students with a list of the correct answers and have them fill in each blank with a word from the list. If necessary, read the paragraph aloud. **learning modality: visual**

English Learners/Intermediate Comprehension: Modified Cloze   L2
Distribute the cloze paragraph designed for Beginning students. Students can work in pairs to collaborate in writing a definition, in English, of the words that they filled in. **learning modality: verbal**

The Nitrogen Cycle

Teach Key Concepts L2

Identifying Nitrogen Cycling

Focus Emphasize that most organisms cannot utilize nitrogen gas until bacteria make nitrogen available.

Teach Refer students to Figure 8. Ask: **By what process do bacteria turn nitrogen into a usable form?** *(Nitrogen fixation)* **What organisms return simple nitrogen compounds to the soil?** *(Decomposers)*

Apply Ask: **How does the nitrogen cycle differ from the carbon and oxygen cycles?** *(Nitrogen becomes available to organisms in the soil rather than in air.)* **learning modality: visual**

 **Teaching Resources, Unit 4**

• Transparency LS217

 Build **Inquiry** L1

Playing Nitrogen Cycle Roles

Materials blue, white index cards; tape

Time 15 minutes

Focus Let students role-play materials and organisms shown in Figure 8.

Teach Assign roles: air, clover plants, sheep, nitrogen-fixing bacteria in nodules on the clover's roots, decomposers in the soil, and bacteria in the soil. Give the "air" students white index cards to represent free nitrogen, and the "nodule bacteria" students blue index cards and tape. Begin the cycle with the air students handing white cards to the nodule bacteria students, who attach, or "fix," each white card to one of their blue cards and then hand the cards to the "clover plants." To show that some plants are eaten by consumers, some clover plants should hand their cards to "sheep." To show that some plants and animals die and decompose, other clover plants should hand their cards to "decomposers," who in turn hand the cards to "soil bacteria."

Apply Ask: **How is the cycle completed?** *(Soil bacteria release nitrogen to the air.)* **learning modality: kinesthetic**

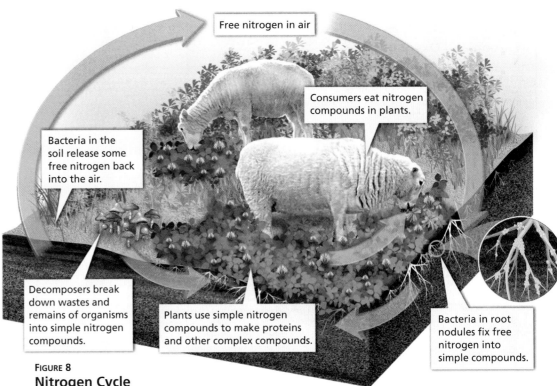

FIGURE 8
Nitrogen Cycle
In the nitrogen cycle, free nitrogen from the air is fixed into compounds. Consumers can then use these nitrogen compounds in carrying out their life processes. *Relating Cause and Effect How does nitrogen get returned to the environment?*

The Nitrogen Cycle

Like carbon, nitrogen is a necessary building block in the matter that makes up living things. **In the nitrogen cycle, nitrogen moves from the air to the soil, into living things, and back into the air.** You can follow this process in Figure 8.

Since the air around you is about 78 percent nitrogen gas, you might think that it would be easy for living things to obtain nitrogen. However, most organisms cannot use nitrogen gas. Nitrogen gas is called "free" nitrogen because it is not combined with other kinds of atoms.

Nitrogen Fixation Most organisms can use nitrogen only once it has been "fixed," or combined with other elements to form nitrogen-containing compounds. The process of changing free nitrogen into a usable form of nitrogen is called **nitrogen fixation.** Most nitrogen fixation is performed by certain kinds of bacteria. Some of these bacteria live in bumps called nodules (NAHJ oolz) on the roots of certain plants. These plants, known as legumes, include clover, beans, peas, alfalfa, and peanuts.

The relationship between the bacteria and the legumes is an example of mutualism. Both the bacteria and the plant benefit from this relationship: The bacteria feed on the plant's sugars, and the plant is supplied with nitrogen in a usable form.

Return of Nitrogen to the Environment

Once nitrogen has been fixed, producers can use it to build proteins and other complex compounds. Decomposers, in turn, break down these complex compounds in animal wastes and the bodies of dead organisms. Decomposition returns simple nitrogen compounds to the soil. Nitrogen can cycle from the soil to producers and then to consumers many times. At some point, however, bacteria break down the nitrogen compounds completely. These bacteria then release free nitrogen back into the air. The cycle continues from there.

 Reading Checkpoint Where do some nitrogen-fixing bacteria live?

FIGURE 9
Growth in Nitrogen-Poor Soil
Pitcher plants can grow in nitrogen-poor soil because they have another way of obtaining nitrogen. Insects become trapped in the plant's tube-shaped leaves. The plant then digests the insects and uses their nitrogen compounds for its functions.

Section 2 Assessment

Target Reading Skill Sequencing Refer to your cycle diagram about the water cycle as you answer Question 1.

Reviewing Key Concepts

1. **a. Defining** Name and define the three major processes that occur during the water cycle.
   b. Making Generalizations Defend this statement: The sun is the driving force behind the water cycle.
2. **a. Reviewing** Which two substances are linked in one recycling process?
   b. Comparing and Contrasting What role do producers play in the carbon and oxygen cycles? What role do consumers play in these cycles?
   c. Developing Hypotheses How might the death of all the producers in a community affect the carbon and oxygen cycles?

3. **a. Reviewing** Why do organisms need nitrogen?
   b. Sequencing Outline the major steps in the nitrogen cycle.
   c. Predicting What might happen in a community if all the nitrogen-fixing bacteria died?

Writing in Science

Comic Strip Choose one of the cycles discussed in this section. Then draw a comic strip with five panels that depicts the important events in the cycle. Remember that the last panel must end with the same event that begins the first panel.

Chapter 22 ◆ 751

Writing in Science

Writing Mode Description

Scoring Rubric

4 Ideas presented are accurate and complete; illustrations are neat and creative

3 Ideas accurate and complete; illustrations inadequate

2 Ideas inaccurate or incomplete; illustrations adequate

1 Ideas incomplete and/or inaccurate; illustrations inadequate

Students can save their comic strips in their portfolios.

Portfolio

751

Section 3 Biogeography

Objectives

After completing the lesson, students will be able to

22.3.1 Explain how the movement of the continents has affected the distribution of species.

22.3.2 Name and describe three ways that dispersal of organisms occurs.

22.3.3 Name and describe factors that can limit the dispersal of a species.

Target Reading Skill

Relating Cause and Effect Explain that cause is the reason why something happens. The effect is what happens because of the cause. Relating cause and effect helps students relate the reason for what happens to what happens as a result.

Answers

Three causes of dispersal: Wind, water, and living things, including humans

All in One Teaching Resources, Unit 4

• Transparency LS218

Preteach

Build Background Knowledge   L2

Identifying Why Organisms Disperse
Ask: **What are some reasons that animals move from one place to another?** (*Seasonal migrations, overpopulation, too much competition in the original area, need for food or water*)

Section 3 Biogeography

Reading Preview

Key Concepts

• How has the movement of the continents affected the distribution of species?

• What are three ways that dispersal of organisms occurs?

• What factors can limit the dispersal of a species?

Key Terms

• biogeography
• continental drift • dispersal
• exotic species • climate

Target Reading Skill

Relating Cause and Effect As you read, identify three causes of dispersal. Write the information in a graphic organizer like the one below.

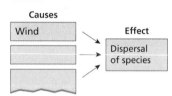

Causes

Wind	→	**Effect**
	→	Dispersal of species
	→	

Lab zone Discover Activity

How Can You Move a Seed?

1. Place a few corn kernels at one end of a shallow pan.
2. Make a list of ways you could move the kernels to the other side of the pan. You may use any of the simple materials your teacher has provided.
3. Now try each method. Record whether each was successful in moving the kernels across the pan.

Think It Over

Predicting How might seeds be moved from place to place?

Imagine how European explorers must have felt when they saw Australia for the first time. Instead of familiar grazing animals such as horses and deer, they saw animals that looked like giant rabbits with long tails. Peering into eucalyptus trees, the explorers saw bearlike koalas. And who could have dreamed up an egg-laying animal with a beaver's tail, a duck's bill, and thick fur? You can see why people who heard the first descriptions of the platypus accused the explorers of lying!

As the explorers had learned, different species live in different parts of the world. The study of where organisms live is called **biogeography.** The word *biogeography* is made up of three Greek word roots: *bio,* meaning "life"; *geo,* meaning "Earth"; and *graphy,* meaning "description of." Together, these root words tell what biogeographers do—they describe where living things are found on Earth.

◄ Koala in a eucalyptus tree in Australia

752 ◆

Lab zone Discover Activity

Skills Focus Predicting   L1

Materials shallow pan; corn kernels; materials to move corn, such as water, straw, and tape

Time 15 minutes

Tips Students may have their own ideas about materials to use in addition to those you have provided.

Expected Outcome Students will find various ways to move the kernels—by pouring water next to them, blowing at them through a straw, picking them up with a piece of tape, and so forth.

Think It Over Based on the results of this activity, students might suggest that seeds are moved by wind, by moving water, and by being caught on an animal's fur or a person's clothing.

FIGURE 10
Continental Drift
The movement of the continents is one factor affecting the distribution of organisms. **Interpreting Maps** *How has Australia's location changed?*

Continental Drift

In addition to studying where species live, biogeographers also try to understand what led to the worldwide distribution of species that exists today. **One factor that has affected how species are distributed is the motion of Earth's continents.** The continents are parts of huge blocks of solid rock, called plates, that make up Earth's surface. Scientists have found that the plates have been moving very slowly for millions of years. As the plates move, the continents move with them in a process called **continental drift.**

Figure 10 shows how much the continents have moved over time. About 225 million years ago, all of today's continents were part of one large landmass now called Pangaea. But after millions of years of slow drifting, they have moved to their present locations.

Continental drift has had a great impact on the distribution of species. Consider Australia, for example. Millions of years ago Australia drifted away from the other landmasses. Organisms from other parts of the world could not reach the isolated island. Kangaroos, koalas, and other unique species developed in this isolation.

 Reading Checkpoint What was Pangaea?

Means of Dispersal

The movement of organisms from one place to another is called **dispersal.** Organisms may be dispersed in several different ways. **Dispersal can be caused by wind, water, or living things, including humans.**

Wind and Water Many animals move into new areas on their own. But plants and small organisms need assistance to move from place to place. Wind can disperse seeds, the spores of fungi, tiny spiders, and other small, light organisms. Similarly, water transports objects that float, such as coconuts and leaves. Small animals may get a free ride to a new home on top of these floating rafts.

225 Million Years Ago

180–200 Million Years Ago

135 Million Years Ago

Earth Today

Go Online
active art
For: Continental Drift activity
Visit: PHSchool.com
Web Code: cfp-1015

Chapter 22 ◆ 753

Differentiated Instruction

Gifted and Talented [L3]
Explaining Continental Drift Ask students to research the geological processes driving continental drift *(plate tectonics)* and relate them to the occurrence of earthquakes and volcanoes. *(Earthquake and volcanic activity is concentrated near plate boundaries.)* Have students report their findings orally. **learning modality: verbal**

Special Needs [L1]
Identifying Dispersal Methods Connect the section's Discover activity to the section's content for students who need extra help by asking: **Which of the dispersal methods did you model when you moved the corn kernels?** *(Most students will have modeled all of the methods of dispersal mentioned in the text.)* **learning modality: logical/mathematical**

Continental Drift

Teach Key Concepts [L2]
Understanding Continents in Motion

Focus Tell students that Figure 10 shows a process that took hundreds of millions of years.

Teach Ask: **Why does Australia have so many unique organisms?** *(Australia drifted from the landmass and its species developed in isolation.)*

Apply Ask: **Have North and South America been connected ever since the breakup of Pangaea?** *(No)* **learning modality: visual**

All in One Teaching Resources, Unit 4
• Transparency LS219

Go Online
active art
For: Continental Drift activity
Visit: PHSchool.com
Web Code: cfp-1015

Students explore the movement of continents from 225 million years ago to today.

Independent Practice [L2]

All in One Teaching Resources, Unit 4
• Guided Reading and Study Worksheet: *Biogeography*

◉ **Student Edition on Audio CD**

Means of Dispersal

Teach Key Concepts [L2]
Describing How Species Disperse

Focus Have students study Figure 11.

Teach Ask: **What are some ways that organisms can be dispersed?** *(By wind and by other living things)*

Apply Ask: **When might seed dispersal not be beneficial?** *(When seeds are carried to an area where you do not want them to grow)*

Monitor Progress _____ [L2]

Answers
Figure 10 Australia moved away from Antarctica less than 135 million years ago.

 Reading Checkpoint A landmass that contained all of today's continents about 225 million years ago

753

Limits to Dispersal

Teach Key Concepts

L2

Exploring Limits to Species Dispersal

Focus Tell students that species can be prevented from dispersing to new areas or from becoming successful there.

Teach Ask: **What are three factors limiting species dispersal?** *(Physical barriers, climate, and competition)* **If the seed of a tropical plant floated to Hawaii, would the species disperse successfully?** Have the class debate for or against this species' success. Ask students to give reasons for their opinions. *(For: seed overcame physical barriers, climate suits a tropical plant; against: existing plants can outcompete new species.)*

Apply Ask: **Which factors that limit dispersal also limit a population's size?** Students can refer to the chapter *Populations and Communities. (Competition and physical barriers)* Students should not equate weather and climate. **learning modality: logical/mathematical**

Relating Continental Drift to Dispersal

Materials world outline map, scissors

Time 15 minutes

Focus Review with students continental drift and species dispersal.

Teach Have students cut out the continents on a copy of a world map and arrange them as in the first map in Figure 10. Then have students move the continents into the positions of the third map, 135 million years ago. Ask: **Where would organisms still be able to move freely from one continent to another?** *(North America and Europe/Asia, Africa and South America, Antarctica and Australia)* Have students move the continents to their present location, in the fourth map. Ask: **What happened to India?** *(It joined Europe/Asia.)*

Apply Ask: **What do you think happened to organisms on the continents that remained separated?** *(They evolved into unique species found nowhere else in the world.)* **learning modality: kinesthetic**

FIGURE 11
Means of Dispersal
Berry seeds can be dispersed by animals, such as cedar waxwings (top left), that eat berries and leave seeds in their wastes. The spores of puffball mushrooms (top center) and the seeds of milkweed plants (top right) are usually dispersed by wind.
Inferring *What are two ways that seeds disperse?*

Other Living Things Organisms may also be dispersed by other living things. For example, a bird may eat berries in one area and deposit the seeds elsewhere in its wastes. And if your dog or cat has ever come home covered with sticky plant burs, you know another way seeds can get around.

Humans are also important to the dispersal of organisms. As people move around the world, they take organisms with them. Sometimes this dispersal is intentional, as when Europeans who explored Central and South America in the 1500s took corn and tomato plants back to Europe. Sometimes it is unintentional, as when insects are carried from one location to another by an airplane passenger. An organism that is carried into a new location by people is referred to as an **exotic species.**

 Reading Checkpoint **What are two ways that an animal can disperse a species?**

Limits to Dispersal

With all these means of dispersal, you might expect to find the same species everywhere in the world. Of course, that's not so. **Three factors that limit dispersal of a species are physical barriers, competition, and climate.**

Physical Barriers Barriers such as water, mountains, and deserts are hard to cross. These features can limit the movement of organisms. For example, once Australia became separated from the other continents, the ocean acted as a barrier to dispersal. Organisms could not easily move to or from Australia.

Competition When an organism enters a new area, it must compete for resources with the species already there. To survive, the organism must find a unique niche. Existing species may outcompete the new species. In this case, competition is a barrier to dispersal. Sometimes, however, new species outcompete the existing species. The existing species may be displaced.

754 ◆

Climate The typical weather pattern in an area over a long period of time is the area's **climate.** Climate differences can limit dispersal. For example, conditions at the top of the mountain shown in Figure 12 are very different from those at the base. The base of the mountain is warm and dry. Low shrubs and cactuses grow there. Higher up, the climate becomes cooler and wetter, and larger trees such as oaks and firs grow. Near the top of the mountain, it is very cold and windy. Only short plants can grow in this area.

Places with similar climates tend to have species that occupy similar niches. For example, most continents have a large area of flat, grassy plains. So these continents have organisms that occupy the niche of "large, grazing mammal." In North America, the large, grazing mammals of the grasslands are bison. In Africa, they are wildebeests and antelopes. And in Australia, they are kangaroos.

 Reading Checkpoint How does the climate at the base of a mountain differ from the climate at the top?

FIGURE 12
Climate Differences and Dispersal
The climate changes dramatically as you move up a tall mountain. Climate determines the distribution of species on different parts of the mountain.

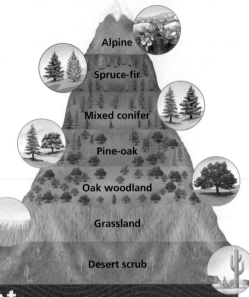

Alpine
Spruce-fir
Mixed conifer
Pine-oak
Oak woodland
Grassland
Desert scrub

Section 3 Assessment

Target Reading Skill

Relating Cause and Effect Refer to your graphic organizer about means of dispersal to help you answer Question 2 below.

Reviewing Key Concepts

1. a. Defining What is continental drift?
  b. Explaining How has continental drift affected the dispersal of organisms?
  c. Relating Cause and Effect How can continental drift explain why unique species are often found on islands?

2. a. Listing What are three ways in which organisms can be dispersed?
  b. Explaining What role do humans play in the dispersal of species?
  c. Predicting Do you think the role of humans in the dispersal of species will increase or decrease in the next 50 years? Defend your answer.

3. a. Identifying What are three factors that can limit the dispersal of a species?
  b. Applying Concepts Suppose that a new species of insect were introduced to your area. How might competition limit its dispersal?

Lab zone At-Home Activity

Sock Walk Take an adult family member on a "sock walk" to learn about seed dispersal. Each person should wear a thick white sock over one shoe. Take a short walk through woods, a field, or a park. Back home, observe how many seeds you collected. Then plant the socks in pans of soil. Place the pans in a sunny spot and water them regularly. How many species did you successfully disperse?

Chapter 22 ◆ 755

Lab zone At Home Activity

Sock Walk **L2** Before students plant their socks, remind them to tend to sprouting plants so that they can grow large enough to be identified as distinct species. Seek regular updates on the various outcomes.

Monitor Progress _____ **L2**

Answers
Figure 11 By other organisms and wind

Reading Checkpoint An animal may eat a plant in one area and deposit its seeds somewhere else, or it may carry an organism with it as it moves.

Reading Checkpoint At the base the climate is warm and dry, but at the top it is cold and windy.

Assess

Reviewing Key Concepts

1. a. The process by which the continents move slowly across Earth's surface **b.** Areas that were isolated long ago developed unique species, but species could disperse across and between continents close to one another. **c.** Islands were not likely to receive many new species through dispersal, so species on islands developed in isolation.
2. a. By wind, water, or living things **b.** Humans intentionally and accidentally disperse species as they travel. **c.** Most likely answer: Humans' role will increase as people travel more freely around the world, including to previously isolated regions.
3. a. Physical barriers, competition, and climate **b.** Accept all well-reasoned responses. Possible answer: Local insect species could outcompete an introduced species.

Reteach **L1**
Ask students to tell three ways that seeds are dispersed and three ways dispersal is limited.

Performance Assessment

Writing Have students suppose that they are hiking through a grassland. Have them write several paragraphs giving specific examples of how they could disperse species.

All in One Teaching Resources, Unit 4

• Section Summary: *Biogeography*
• Review and Reinforce: *Biogeography*
• Enrich: *Biogeography*

755

Biomes in Miniature

Prepare for Inquiry

Key Concept
Differences in soil, light, and precipitation create different biomes.

Skills Objectives
After this lab, students will be able to
- observe and compare the growth of different plants in the model biomes
- make models of given biomes by varying abiotic factors

Prep Time 30 minutes

Class Time 30 minutes, then 5–10 minutes a day for at least one week

Advance Planning
- Ask students to bring in large milk or juice cartons that have been thoroughly washed.
- Obtain sufficient quantities of potting soil and sandy (cactus) soil from a nursery or gardening store.
- Allocate enough table space and lamps for students to expose each model biome to the amount of light required.

Safety
Make sure students wash their hands after they handle the soil and seeds, Review the safety guidelines in Appendix A.

All in One Teaching Resources, Unit 4
- Lab Worksheet: *Biomes in Miniature*

Guide Inquiry

Invitation
Ask students: **Why don't we see [name a non-native plant] growing in our area?** *(Students should describe climate conditions needed by the plant that are not met in your area.)* Review with students the major biomes discussed in the lesson. Tell students that in this activity they will make models of different biomes.

Biomes in Miniature

Problem
What abiotic factors create different biomes around the world?

Skills Focus
observing, making models

Materials
- scissors
- clear plastic wrap
- index card
- lamp
- tape
- empty, clean cardboard milk carton
- stapler
- about 30 rye grass seeds
- 10 impatiens seeds
- 5 lima bean seeds
- sandy soil or potting soil

Procedure

1. Your teacher will assign your group a biome. You will also observe the other groups' model biomes. Based on the chart below, predict how well you think each of the three kinds of seeds will grow in each set of conditions. Record these predictions in your notebook. Then copy the data table on the facing page four times, once for each biome.

2. Staple the spout of the milk carton closed. Completely cut away one of the four sides of the carton. Poke a few holes in the opposite side for drainage, and then place that side down.

3. Fill the carton to 3 centimeters from the top with the type of soil given in the table. Divide the surface of the soil into three sections by making two lines in it with a pencil.

4. In the section near the spout, plant the impatiens seeds. In the middle section, plant the lima bean seeds. In the third section, scatter the rye grass seeds on the surface.

5. Water all the seeds well. Then cover the open part of the carton with plastic wrap.

6. On an index card, write the name of your biome, the names of the three types of seeds in the order you planted them, and the names of your group members. Tape the card to the carton. Put the carton in a warm place where it will not be disturbed.

7. Once the seeds sprout, provide your biome with light and water as specified in the chart. Keep the carton covered with plastic wrap except when you add water.

8. Observe all the model biomes daily for at least one week. Record your observations.

Growing Conditions			
Biome	Soil Type	Hours of Light per Day	Watering Instructions
Forest	Potting soil	1–2 hours of direct light	Let the surface dry; then add water.
Desert	Sandy soil	5–6 hours of direct light	Let the soil dry to a depth of 2.5 cm below the surface.
Grassland	Potting soil	5–6 hours of direct light	Let the surface dry; then add water.
Rain forest	Potting soil	No direct light; indirect light for 5–6 hours	Keep the surface of the soil moist.

Introducing the Procedure
- Invite students to read the entire lab procedure. Then ask: **What is the purpose of this lab?** *(To determine how well three kinds of plants grow in different biomes)*
- Direct students' attention to the Growing Conditions chart and ask: **What variables will you change to create models of four different biomes?** *(Soil type, amount of light, and amount of water)*

Troubleshooting the Experiment
- Observation criteria are not specified in Step 8 and could be determined as a class or by each group. Criteria could include the number of seeds that germinate successfully, plant height, the number and color of leaves, and yellowing (a sign of too much water) or wilting (a sign of not enough water).

Data Table

Name of Biome: _____

Day	Impatiens	Lima Beans	Rye Grass
1			
2			
3			
4			
5			
6			
7			

Analyze and Conclude

1. **Observing** In which model biome did each type of seed grow best? In which model biome did each type of seed grow least well?

2. **Making Models** In this experiment, how did you model the following abiotic factors: sunlight, water, and temperature?

3. **Inferring** How was each type of seed affected by the soil type, amount of light, and availability of water?

4. **Classifying** Why do you think that ecologists who study biomes often focus on identifying the key abiotic factors and typical plants in an area?

5. **Communicating** Write a paragraph explaining how your miniature biomes modeled real-life biomes. Which features of real-life biomes were you able to model well? Which features of real-life biomes were more difficult to model?

Design an Experiment

Write a plan for setting up a model rain forest or desert terrarium. Include typical plants found in that biome. *Obtain your teacher's approval before carrying out your investigation.*

◆ 757

Expected Outcome

Students' data tables will vary depending on the criteria they used for assessing the health of the plants. For general guidelines, see Analyze and Conclude Question 1 answer.

Analyze and Conclude

1. In general, the rye and beans will grow best in the grassland biome, and the impatiens will grow best in the deciduous forest biome. All the seeds will likely grow most poorly in the dry conditions of the desert biome.

2. Sunlight was modeled by controlling how many hours each day a biome received direct and indirect light. Water was modeled by controlling the moisture content of the soil. Temperature was modeled indirectly, as a result of hours of light per day.

3. In general, the seeds will sprout most rapidly when water is plentiful. Every type of plant is adapted to survive in a specific set of soil, light, and water conditions, so each of the three plant types in this lab thrived in only one or two biomes. In nature, the same abiotic factors limit the types of plants that can survive in a specific biome.

4. Abiotic factors limit the types of plants that can grow in a particular biome, which in turn determine the types of animals and other consumers that can survive in that biome.

5. Answers will reflect individual student outcomes. Miniature biomes should model real-life ones by growing the plants predicted by the climate conditions of that biome. Students should discuss successes or challenges with modeling water, sunlight, and soil type.

Extend Inquiry

Design an Experiment Provide field guides and other resources for students to use in selecting typical plants. Discourage students from trying to start plants from seed; instead provide small but mature plants suited to a model rain forest or desert. To simulate the damp conditions found in a rain forest, students will need to cover the rain forest container to prevent evaporation.

Objectives

After completing the lesson, students will be able to

22.4.1 Name the six major biomes found on Earth.

22.4.2 Name and describe the factors that determine the biome found in an area.

22.4.3 Name and describe the two major types of aquatic ecosystems.

Target Reading Skill

Comparing and Contrasting Explain that comparing and contrasting shows how ideas, facts, and events are similar and different.

Answers

Sample: Tropical rain forest: warm all year; wet all year; orangutan. *Tundra:* cold all year; dry all year; mosses.

All in One Teaching Resources, Unit 4

• Transparency LS220

Preteach

Build Background Knowledge   L2

Predicting Effects of Climate

Ask: **What is the climate like in our area?** *(Students should describe local temperature, precipitation, amount of sunlight)* **How do you think our climate affects which organisms live here?** *(Example, students may say that a warm, humid climate supports a great variety of organisms.)*

Ecosystems and Biomes

Show the Video Field Trip to let students experience a desert biome and understand the adaptations and behaviors that help meerkats survive in a desert.

Reading Preview

Key Concepts

• What are the six major biomes found on Earth?
• What factors determine the type of biome found in an area?
• What do freshwater and marine ecosystems include?

Key Terms

• biome • canopy • understory
• desert • grassland • savanna
• deciduous tree
• coniferous tree • tundra
• permafrost • estuary
• intertidal zone • neritic zone

Target Reading Skill

Comparing and Contrasting As you read, compare the biomes by completing a table like this one.

Characteristic	Tropical Rain Forest	Tundra
Temperature	Warm all year	
Precipitation		
Typical Organisms		

Discovery CHANNEL SCHOOL

Ecosystems and Biomes

Video Preview
▶ Video Field Trip
Video Assessment

Lab zone — Discover Activity

How Much Rain Is That?

The table shows the typical amount of precipitation that falls each year in four locations. With your classmates, you will create a full-sized bar graph on a wall to represent these amounts.

Location	Precipitation (cm)
Mojave Desert	15
Illinois Prairie	70
Great Smoky Mountains	180
Costa Rican Rain Forest	350

1. Using a meter stick, measure a strip of adding-machine paper 15 centimeters long. Label this strip "Mojave Desert."
2. Repeat Step 1 for the other locations. Label each strip.
3. Follow your teacher's instructions on hanging your strips.

Think It Over

Developing Hypotheses What effect might the amount of precipitation have on the types of species that live in a location?

Congratulations! You and your classmates have been selected to take part in an around-the-world scientific expedition. On this expedition you will collect data on the climate and typical organisms of each of Earth's biomes. A **biome** is a group of land ecosystems with similar climates and organisms.

The ecologists leading your expedition have agreed to focus on six major biomes. **The six major biomes that most ecologists study are the rain forest, desert, grassland, deciduous forest, boreal forest, and tundra.**

Be sure to pack a variety of clothing for your expedition. You will visit places ranging from steamy tropical jungles to frozen Arctic plains. **It is mostly the climate—temperature and precipitation—in an area that determines its biome.** This is because climate limits the species of plants that can grow in an area. In turn, the species of plants determine the kinds of animals that live there.

Hurry up and pack—it's almost time to go!

Lab zone — Discover Activity

Skills Focus Developing hypotheses

Materials meter stick, adding-machine paper, scissors, marker, tape

Time 20 minutes

Tips CAUTION: Hanging the Costa Rican rain forest strip will require the use of a ladder. Choose three reliable students for this task, one to climb the ladder and two to hold the ladder securely. If you are not

L2 certain that students can do this task safely, have them hang the strips horizontally.

Expected Outcome Students should sequence the strips from least to most rainfall, as indicated in the table.

Think It Over The amount of rainfall affects what plant species can survive in a particular biome, and the plants in turn determine the consumer species found there.

Rain Forest Biomes

The first stop on your expedition is a rain forest. This biome is living up to its name—it's pouring! Fortunately, you remembered to pack a raincoat. After just a short shower, however, the sun reappears. Surprisingly, though, very little sunlight reaches you through the thick leaves above.

Plants are everywhere in the rain forest. Some plants, such as the ferns, flowers, and vines hanging from tree limbs, even grow on other plants! And animals are flying, creeping, and slithering all around you.

Temperate Rain Forests When you hear the term *rain forest,* you probably think of a warm, humid, "jungle" in the tropics. But there is another type of rain forest. The northwestern coast of the United States receives more than 300 centimeters of rain a year. Huge trees grow there, including cedars, redwoods, and Douglas firs. However, it is difficult to classify this region. Many ecologists refer to this ecosystem as a temperate rain forest. The term *temperate* means having moderate temperatures.

Go Online
active art

For: Earth's Biomes activity
Visit: PHSchool.com
Web Code: cep-5024

Rain Forest Biomes
- Tropical rain forest
- Temperate rain forest

FIGURE 13 Temperate Rain Forest
Temperate rain forests receive a great deal of rain and have moderate temperatures. Mule deer are commonly found in the Olympic Rain Forest in Washington State. **Interpreting Maps** *Where is one temperate rain forest located?*

◄ Pileated woodpecker

◆ 759

Go Online
active art

For: Earth's Biomes activity
Visit: PHSchool.com
Web Code: cep-5024

Students compare and contrast rainfall and temperature levels of some biomes.

Instruct

Rain Forest Biomes

Teach Key Concepts L2

Exploring the Rain Forests

Focus Tell students that tropical and temperate rain forests share many traits but differ in location and temperatures.

Teach Display a world map or globe and direct students to the biome map. Ask: **Where are the world's tropical rain forests located?** *(All are located at or near the equator.)* Locate the U. S. Pacific Northwest. Ask: **How do the location and climate of temperate rain forests differ from tropical rain forests?** *(Temperate rain forests are much farther north and much cooler.)*

Apply Ask: **How are temperate and tropical rain forests similar?** *(Both are humid, receive a lot of rain, and have a large variety of plant and animal species.)*
learning modality: visual

Independent Practice L2

All in One Teaching Resources, Unit 4

- Guided Reading and Study Worksheet: *Biomes and Aquatic Ecosystems*

Student Edition on Audio CD

Monitor Progress L2

Answer
Figure 13 Along the U. S. northwestern coast

Differentiated Instruction

Less Proficient Readers L1
Comparing and Contrasting Pair students to assist each other. Assign three headings: *Temperate rain forest, Tropical rain forest, Both,* and a list of words from the section: *firs, rain, trees, equator, warm, cool.* Have students read the text and place the terms under the appropriate headings *(Temperate rain forest: firs, cool; Tropical rain forest: warm, equator; Both: rain, trees).*
learning modality: visual

Gifted and Talented L2
Creating Data Tables Have students use reference sources to compile a table listing average temperatures and precipitation for the six major biomes. **learning modality: logical/mathematical**

759

Identifying Main Ideas Ask students to state the main idea of each paragraph about tropical rain forests. (*Because of the tropical rain forest's warm, humid climate, an astounding number of species grow there; trees in the rain forest form several distinct layers; the abundant plant life in tropical rain forests provides habitats for many animal species.*)

Desert Biomes

Teach Key Concepts L2

Describing Desert Biomes

Focus Ask students who have visited a desert to describe it.

Teach Remind students that climate incorporates both temperature and precipitation. Ask: **What can you say about precipitation and evaporation in the desert?** (*Deserts receive less than 25 centimeters of precipitation each year; evaporation is greater than precipitation.*) **How might desert temperatures vary over a 24-hour day?** (*Deserts are very hot during the day but cool rapidly and can be very cold at night.*) Discuss the desert's hot, dry climate and the necessary adaptations organisms must possess to live under such harsh conditions.

Apply Ask: **How are desert animals adapted to the harsh climate?** (*Some animals burrow for long periods; others are active at night; some plants can store water.*) **learning modality: logical/mathematical**

◀ Orangutan

▲ Bromeliad

FIGURE 14
Tropical Rain Forest
Tropical rain forests are wet, warm biomes that contain an amazing variety of plants and other organisms. In the large photo, a river winds through the lush Indonesian rain forest.

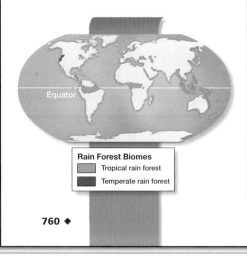

Equator

Rain Forest Biomes
▢ Tropical rain forest
▢ Temperate rain forest

760 ◆

Tropical Rain Forests As you can see on the map, tropical rain forests are found in regions close to the equator. The climate is warm and humid all year long, and there is a lot of rain. Because of these climate conditions, an astounding variety of plants grow in tropical rain forests. In fact, scientists studying a 100-square-meter area of one rain forest identified 300 different kinds of trees!

Trees in the rain forest form several distinct layers. The tall trees form a leafy roof called the **canopy.** A few giant trees poke out above the canopy. Below the canopy, a second layer of shorter trees and vines form an **understory.** Understory plants grow well in the shade formed by the canopy. The forest floor is nearly dark, so only a few plants live there.

The abundant plant life in tropical rain forests provides habitats for many species of animals. Ecologists estimate that millions of species of insects live in tropical rain forests. These insects serve as a source of food for many reptiles, birds, and mammals. Many of these animals are, in turn, food sources for other animals. Although tropical rain forests cover only a small part of the planet, they probably contain more species of plants and animals than all the other biomes combined.

✔ **Reading Checkpoint** What is the climate of the tropical rain forest?

Desert Biomes

The next stop on your expedition is a desert. It couldn't be more different from the tropical rain forest you just left. You step off the bus into the searing summer heat. At midday, it is too hot to walk outside in the desert.

A **desert** is an area that receives less than 25 centimeters of rain per year. The amount of evaporation in a desert is greater than the amount of precipitation. Some of the driest deserts may not receive any precipitation in a year! Deserts often undergo large shifts in temperature during the course of a day. A scorching hot desert like the Namib Desert in Africa cools rapidly each night when the sun goes down. Other deserts, such as the Gobi in central Asia, are cooler, and even experience freezing temperatures in the winter.

Organisms that live in the desert must be adapted to the lack of rain and extreme temperatures. For example, the stem of a saguaro cactus has folds that work like the pleats in an accordion. The stem expands to store water when it is raining. Gila monsters can spend weeks at a time in their cool underground burrows. Many other desert animals are most active at night when the temperatures are cooler.

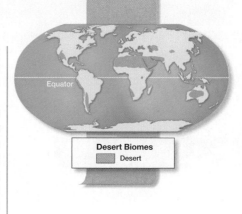

Desert Biomes
☐ Desert

FIGURE 15
Desert
The Mojave Desert in the southwestern United States is a typical hot desert.
Making Generalizations *Describe the climate conditions of a typical desert.*

Gambel's quail

Lab zone Try This **Activity**

Desert Survival

✂ Use a hand lens to carefully observe a small potted cactus. **CAUTION:** *Be careful of the spines.* With a pair of scissors, carefully snip a small piece from the tip of the cactus. Observe the inside of the plant. Note any characteristics that seem different from those of other plants.

Observing How is the inside of the cactus different from the outside? Suggest how the features you observe might be adaptations to its desert habitat.

◆ 761

Grassland Biomes

Teach Key Concepts L2

Exploring Grasslands

Focus Describe grasslands as widely distributed ecosystems that have moderate climates and are dominated by grasses.

Teach Have students locate Kenya on a world map or globe, as well as prairie areas in the midwestern United States. Ask: **What typical features of grassland biomes are visible in Figure 16?** (*Tall grass, large herbivores*) **Why do grasslands have so few trees?** (*They don't get enough rain to support trees.*)

Apply Ask: **How do savannas like that in Figure 16 differ from prairies?** (*Savannas are closer to the equator; they receive more rain.*) **learning modality: visual**

Deciduous Forest Biomes L2

Teach Key Concepts

Identifying Deciduous Forests

Focus Tell students that deciduous forests experience seasonal changes to which organisms are adapted.

Teach Ask: **What are climate patterns in a deciduous forest?** (*Temperatures that vary greatly during the year; sufficient rainfall to support trees*) **How are trees adapted to this seasonal biome?** (*They shed their leaves and grow new ones each year.*) **How are animals adapted?** (*Many birds migrate in winter; some mammals hibernate.*)

Apply Ask: **How does the variety of plant and animal species coexist in a deciduous forest?** (*The different plants create a mix of niches within the forest.*) **learning modality: logical/mathematical**

FIGURE 16
Savanna
Migrating wildebeest make their way across a vast Kenyan savanna. A savanna is one type of grassland biome—an area populated mostly by grasses and other non-woody plants.

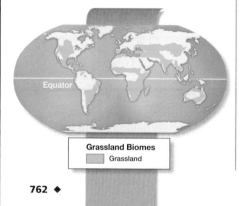

Grassland Biomes
Grassland

762 ◆

Grassland Biomes

The next stop on the expedition is a grassy plain called a prairie. Temperatures here are more comfortable than they were in the desert. The breeze carries the scent of soil warmed by the sun. This rich soil supports grasses as tall as you. Startled by your approach, sparrows dart into hiding places among the waving grass stems.

Although this prairie receives more rain than a desert, it does not get enough rain for trees to grow. Ecologists classify prairies, which are generally found in the middle latitudes, as grasslands. A **grassland** is an area that is populated mostly by grasses and other non-woody plants. Most grasslands receive 25 to 75 centimeters of rain each year. Fires and droughts are common in this biome. Grasslands that are located closer to the equator than prairies are known as savannas. A **savanna** receives as much as 120 centimeters of rain each year. Scattered shrubs and small trees grow on savannas along with grass.

Grasslands are home to many of the largest animals on Earth—herbivores such as elephants, bison, antelopes, zebras, rhinoceroses, giraffes, and kangaroos. Grazing by these large herbivores helps to maintain the grasslands. They keep young trees and bushes from sprouting and competing with the grass for water and sunlight.

 Reading Checkpoint What type of grassland usually receives more rainfall, a prairie or a savanna?

Deciduous Forest Biomes

Your trip to the next biome takes you to another forest. It is now late summer. Cool mornings here give way to warm days. Several members of the expedition are busy recording the numerous plant species. Others are looking through their binoculars, trying to identify the songbirds. You step carefully to avoid a small salamander.

You are now visiting a deciduous forest biome. Many of the trees in this forest are **deciduous trees** (dee SIJ oo us), trees that shed their leaves and grow new ones each year. Oaks and maples are examples of deciduous trees. Deciduous forests receive enough rain to support the growth of trees and other plants, at least 50 centimeters per year. Temperatures in the deciduous forest vary greatly during the year. The growing season usually lasts five to six months.

The variety of plants in a deciduous forest creates many different habitats. Different species of birds live in different parts of the forest, eating the insects and fruits in their specific areas. Mammals such as chipmunks and skunks live in deciduous forests. In a North American deciduous forest you might also see wood thrushes, white-tailed deer, and black bears.

If you were to return to this biome in the winter, you would not see much wildlife. Many of the bird species migrate to warmer areas. Some of the mammals hibernate, or enter a state of greatly reduced body activity similar to sleep. Animals that hibernate rely on fat stored in their bodies during the winter months.

Reading Checkpoint What are deciduous trees?

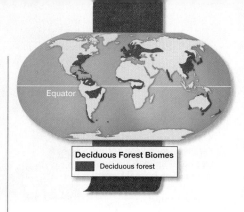

Deciduous Forest Biomes
■ Deciduous forest

FIGURE 17
Deciduous Forest
This forest is a beautiful example of a deciduous forest in autumn. Most of the trees in a deciduous forest have leaves that change color and drop each autumn.
Comparing and Contrasting *How do deciduous forests differ from rain forests?*

▼ Southern flying squirrel

▼ Red fox

◆ 763

Boreal Forest Biomes

Teach Key Concepts [L2]

Exploring a Cold Climate

Focus Tell students that boreal forests are found in northern locations and have cold climates.

Teach Ask: **Why is water availability a challenge in boreal forests?** (*Temperatures are low enough that water is frozen much of the year.*) **How do plants adapt to lack of water?** (*Coniferous trees have thick, waxy needles that prevent water loss.*)

Apply Describe a boreal forest food chain. (*Producers—seeds and bark of coniferous trees; first-level consumers—red squirrel, insects, birds, snowshoe hare, moose, beaver; second-level consumers—wolf, bear, lynx, great horned owl*) **learning modality: logical/mathematical**

Inferring Forest Climates

Materials globe, flashlight, masking tape

Time 10–15 minutes

Focus Allow students to visualize locations of deciduous forests and infer information on climate.

Teach Have pairs of students mark the locations of deciduous and boreal forests on a globe with strips of masking tape labeled *D* and *B*. With the room darkened, have one student shine a flashlight at the globe's equator as the other student slowly turns the globe on its axis. Ask: **Which of the two biomes gets stronger (more direct) light?** (*The deciduous forest*) **What do you think this has to do with the climate differences between the deciduous forest and the boreal forest?** (*"Stronger" sunlight during the year makes the deciduous forests warmer than the boreal forests.*)

Apply Ask: **Which do you think gets stronger sunlight, the tropical rain forest or the temperate rain forest?** (*Tropical rain forest*) **learning modality: kinesthetic**

FIGURE 18
Boreal Forest
This boreal forest in Alaska's Denali National Park is home to coniferous trees and animals such as moose. The boreal forest is often called the "spruce-moose" forest.

Boreal Forest Biomes

Now the expedition heads north into a colder climate. The expedition leaders claim they can identify the next biome, a boreal forest, by its smell. When you arrive, you catch a whiff of the spruce and fir trees that blanket the hillsides. Feeling the chilly early fall air, you pull a jacket and hat out of your bag.

Boreal Forest Plants Most of the trees in the boreal forest are **coniferous trees** (koh NIF ur us), trees that produce their seeds in cones and have leaves shaped like needles. The boreal forest is sometimes referred to by its Russian name, the *taiga* (TY guh). Winters in these forests are very cold. The snow can reach heights well over your head! Even so, the summers are rainy and warm enough to melt all the snow.

Tree species in the boreal forest are well-adapted to the cold climate. Since water is frozen for much of the year, trees in the boreal forest must have adaptations that prevent water loss. Fir, spruce, hemlock, and other coniferous trees all have thick, waxy needles that prevent water from evaporating.

Boreal Forest Animals Many of the animals of the boreal forest eat the seeds produced by the coniferous trees. These animals include red squirrels, insects, and birds such as finches and chickadees. Some herbivores, such as snowshoe hares, moose, and beavers, eat tree bark and new shoots. The variety of herbivores in the boreal forest supports many large predators, including wolves, bears, great horned owls, and lynxes.

Reading Checkpoint How are needles an advantage to trees in the boreal forest?

Skills Activity

Inferring

Observe the map that shows the locations of boreal forests. Where are most boreal forests located? Why are there no boreal forests in the Southern Hemisphere?

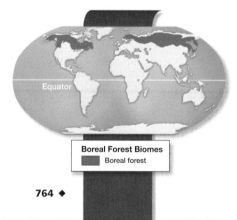

Boreal Forest Biomes
■ Boreal forest

764 ◆

Skills Activity

Skills Focus Inferring [L2]

Materials boreal forest biome map

Time 5 minutes

Tips Begin the activity by pointing out on a globe the equator and the Southern and Northern Hemispheres.

Expected Outcome Boreal forests grow in climates that are too cold for deciduous forests. Such climates typically occur in a band at latitudes far from the equator. There are no such areas in the Southern Hemisphere because that hemisphere does not have large continental land areas at the appropriate latitudes.

Extend Ask: **What type of habitat exists at the southernmost part of the Southern Hemisphere?** (*Ice, in Antarctica*) **learning modality: logical/mathematical**

Tundra Biomes

As you arrive at your next stop, the driving wind gives you an immediate feel for this biome. The **tundra** is an extremely cold and dry biome. Expecting deep snow, many are surprised to learn that the tundra may receive no more precipitation than a desert.

Most of the soil in the tundra is frozen all year. This frozen soil is called **permafrost.** During the short summer, the top layer of soil thaws, but the underlying soil remains frozen. Because rainwater cannot soak into the permafrost, there are many shallow ponds and marshy areas on the tundra in the summer.

Tundra Plants Plants of the tundra include mosses, grasses, shrubs, and dwarf forms of a few trees, such as willows. Most of the plant growth takes place during the long days of the short summer season. North of the Arctic Circle, the sun does not set during midsummer.

Tundra Animals In summer, the animals you might remember most are insects. Insect-eating birds take advantage of the plentiful food and long days by eating as much as they can. But when winter approaches, these birds migrate south. Mammals of the tundra include caribou, foxes, wolves, and Arctic hares. The mammals that remain on the tundra during the winter grow thick fur coats. What can these animals find to eat on the tundra in winter? The caribou scrape snow away to find lichens. Wolves follow the caribou and look for weak members of the herd to prey upon.

Reading Checkpoint What is permafrost?

Tundra Biomes
☐ Tundra

FIGURE 19
Tundra
Although it is frozen and seemingly barren in winter, the tundra in Alaska explodes with color in autumn.
Relating Cause and Effect *Why are there no tall trees on the tundra?*

Musk ox ▲

◆ 765

Math Skill Interpreting graphs

Focus Point out that a line graph is a good way to show change over time.

Teach Remind students that each point represents a monthly average temperature for that location. Ask: **What can such a graph show about a location's temperature pattern?** *(Whether it's high or low, steady or fluctuating)*

Answers

1. Month is plotted on the horizontal axis, temperature on the vertical axis.
2. A: steady; B: fluctuating
3. A: tropical rain forest; B: desert
4. Answers should reflect whether local climate is hot or cold, seasonal or stable, and whether it is wet or dry.

Mountains and Ice

Teach Key Concepts   L2

Identifying High-Altitude Habitats

Focus Explain that mountains and ice do not fit into one biome classification.

Teach Ask: **Is the habitat the same at the bottom of a mountain as at the top?** *(No, the habitats change with altitude.)* **Can you name countries or continents that are covered with ice?** *(Antarctica; most of Greenland)*

Apply Ask: **Can ice sheets support organisms?** *(Yes)* **Name examples.** *(Polar bears, emperor penguins, leopard seals)*
learning modality: logical/mathematical

Lab zone Build **Inquiry**   L2

Drawing Mountain Habitats

Materials paper and pencils

Time 10 minutes

Focus Have students illustrate mountain habitats representing different biomes.

Teach Have small groups of students draw and label a side-view diagram of a mountain with these names: grassland, deciduous forest, boreal forest, and tundra. Ask: **Why does the climate vary at different locations?** *(Climate becomes colder from the base of a mountain to its top.)* Students can add temperature information to their diagrams to see this pattern.

Apply Ask: **Does the mountaintop receive much rain?** *(No, it is a tundra, which is dry)* **learning modality: visual**

766

Biome Climates

An ecologist collected climate data from two locations. The graph shows the monthly average temperatures in the two locations. The total yearly precipitation in Location A is 250 cm. In Location B, the total yearly precipitation is 14 cm.

1. **Reading Graphs** What variable is plotted on the horizontal axis? On the vertical axis?

2. **Interpreting Data** Look over the graph. How would you describe the temperature over the course of a year in Location A? In Location B?

3. **Drawing Conclusions** Given the precipitation and temperature data for these locations, in which biome would you expect each to be located? Explain your answers.

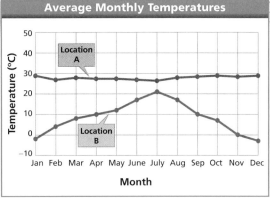

Average Monthly Temperatures

4. **Predicting** What would you expect a temperature graph for your biome to look like? Draw a temperature graph for the biome in which you live.

Mountains and Ice

Some areas of land are not part of any major biome. These areas include mountain ranges and land that is covered with thick sheets of ice.

You read in Section 3 that the climate of a mountain changes from its base to its summit. If you were to hike all the way up a tall mountain, you would pass through a series of biomes. At the base, you might find grasslands. As you climbed, you might pass through deciduous forest and then boreal forest. As you neared the top, your surroundings would resemble the treeless tundra.

Other places are covered year-round with thick ice sheets. Most of the island of Greenland and the continent of Antarctica fall into this category. Organisms that are adapted to life on ice include emperor penguins, polar bears, and leopard seals.

Reading Checkpoint   What are two landmasses that are covered year-round with ice?

FIGURE 20
Mountains
Pikas, such as this one, live in rocky mountain habitats. They spend much of their time in the summer gathering and storing plants for food. This behavior helps pikas survive through the long harsh winter.

766 ◆

Differentiated Instruction

Gifted and Talented   L3
Identifying Biome Composition Have students use biome maps and a world atlas or globe to locate biomes for a given continent. Provide each student or group an outline map of that continent. If possible, assign a different continent to each student or group. Students should refer to the map resources to sketch the locations of the various biomes found on their continent. *(Example: North America has temperate deciduous forest in the East, rain forest in the U. S. Northwest, desert in the U. S. Southwest and northwestern Mexico, grassland through much of the center of the continent, and boreal forest and tundra in Canada and Alaska).* Students should illustrate their maps as clearly and colorfully as possible and present them to the class. **learning modality: visual**

Freshwater Ecosystems

On this part of the expedition, you will explore Earth's waters. Most of Earth's surface is covered with water, but only a tiny fraction is fresh water. **Freshwater ecosystems include streams, rivers, ponds, and lakes.** These ecosystems provide habitats for an amazing variety of organisms, from microscopic algae to huge bears.

Streams and Rivers Your first stop is a mountain stream. Where the stream begins, the cold, clear water flows rapidly. Animals that live here are adapted to the strong current. For example, insects and other small animals have hooks or suckers that help them cling to rocks. Trout have streamlined bodies that allow them to swim despite the rushing water. Few plants or algae can grow in this fast-moving water. Instead, first-level consumers rely on leaves and seeds that fall into the stream.

As the stream flows along, other streams join it. The current slows, and the water becomes cloudy with soil. The slower-moving water is warmer and contains less oxygen. This larger stream might now be called a river. Different organisms are adapted to life in a river. Plants take root among the pebbles on the river bottom. These producers provide food for young insects and homes for frogs and their tadpoles. These consumers, in turn, provide food for many larger consumers.

Ponds and Lakes Your next stop is a pond. Ponds and lakes are bodies of standing, or still, fresh water. Lakes are generally larger and deeper than ponds. Ponds are often shallow enough that sunlight can reach the bottom even in the center of the pond, allowing plants to grow there. In large ponds and most lakes, however, algae floating at the surface are the major producers.

Many animals are adapted for life in the still water. Along the shore of the pond, you observe dragonflies, turtles, snails, and frogs. Sunfish live in the open water, feeding on insects and algae from the surface. Scavengers such as catfish live near the pond bottom. Bacteria and other decomposers also feed on the remains of other organisms.

FIGURE 21
A Pond Ecosystem
Ponds and lakes are freshwater ecosystems characterized by still water. Pickerelweed and herons are typical pond organisms.
Interpreting Photographs How is the heron well-suited to its aquatic environment?

◄ Tricolored heron

♦ 767

Freshwater Ecosystems

Teach Key Concepts L2

Classifying Freshwater Habitats

Focus Tell students that freshwater ecosystems are classified as lakes and ponds or rivers and streams, but these ecosystems include a variety of habitats.

Teach Have students describe the ecosystems in streams and rivers, and ponds and lakes. Ask: **Which habitats would you find in a lake ecosystem?** (*Shoreline, shallow water near shore, deep water away from shore, bottom of the lake, and water surface*) Remind students that organisms must be adapted to their habitat. Ask: **What adaptations does a fish have that allow it to live in lake water?** (*Gills for breathing oxygen in water; fins, a tail, and a streamlined body shape for swimming; scales for insulation and protection*)

Apply Ask: **What adaptations do animals have that live in fast-moving mountain streams?** (*Hooks or suckers to cling to rocks; streamlined body shapes*) **learning modality: verbal**

Differentiated Instruction

Less Proficient Readers L1
Identifying Main Ideas and Details
Students who need additional review of freshwater ecosystems can create their own game. Group students, have them reread this page, and ask them to prepare two sketches, one of a pond or lake and one of a river or stream. Either provide cards with terms from this text passage, or allow groups to prepare the cards. Students should take turns picking a card and placing it on the appropriate drawing, the pond or lake or the river or stream. (*Terms for pond/lake: standing water, algae as producers, turtles, dragonflies, snails, frogs, catfish, sunfish; terms for river/lake: cold, clear, strong current, trout, hooks and suckers, streamlined bodies, few plants or algae*) **learning modality: kinesthetic**

Monitor Progress L2

Oral Presentation Call on various students to each choose one freshwater biome, identify one specific habitat in that biome, and name at least three organisms found in that habitat.

Answers
Figure 21 It has long legs for wading and a sharp beak and flexible neck for preying upon fish.

✔ **Reading Checkpoint** Antartica and most of Greenland

Marine Ecosystems

Teach Key Concepts

Comparing Marine Habitats

Focus Remind students that a major difference between freshwater and marine ecosystems is that marine ecosystems are based on salt water.

Teach Use Figure 22 to describe the differences and similarities between marine habitats in location, water depth, amount of salt in water, organisms, and sunlight. Ask: **How are an estuary and the intertidal zone different?** (*Different organisms live in them; the water in the intertidal zone is saltier than the water in an estuary; the estuary has few waves.*) **How are an estuary and the intertidal zone alike?** (*In both, the land is sometimes covered with water and at other times exposed to the air and sunlight.*)

Apply Ask: **Do you think estuaries are affected by ocean tides?** (*Yes; mudflats there are exposed during low tide and covered during high tide.*) **learning modality: verbal**

Inferring Coral Structure

Materials coral

Time 10 minutes

Focus Ask students if a coral is a plant or animal. (*Animal*)

Teach Provide samples of different types of coral for students to examine. Visually impaired students can closely examine the coral by feeling it. Emphasize that these pieces of coral are not the coral animals, which are soft, but the structures they produced and left behind when they died. Ask: **Where do you think the coral animals lived?** (*Inside the tiny holes*)

Apply Ask: **How do you think this hard structure helps coral animals survive?** (*It provides protection for the animals' soft bodies and also anchors them to the ocean floor.*)

learning modality: visual

FIGURE 22
Marine Ecosystems

The ocean is home to a number of different ecosystems. Factors such as water temperature and the amount of sunlight determine what types of organisms can live in each zone.

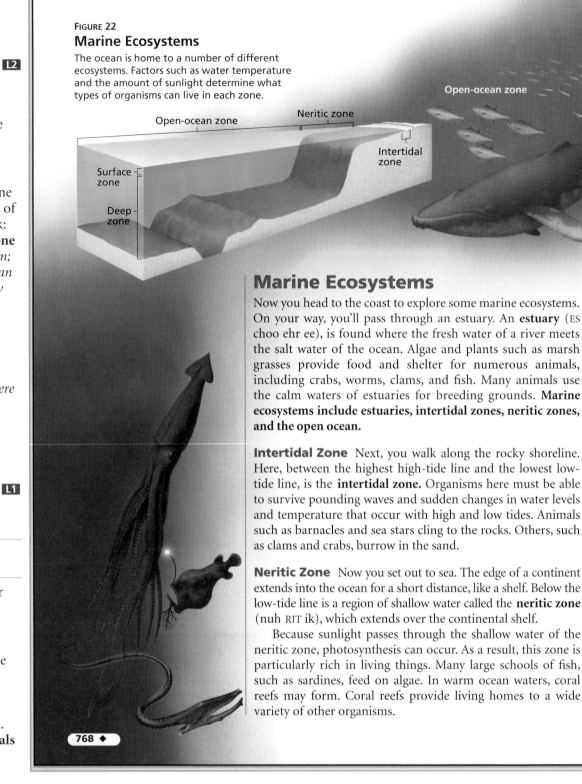

Marine Ecosystems

Now you head to the coast to explore some marine ecosystems. On your way, you'll pass through an estuary. An **estuary** (ES choo ehr ee), is found where the fresh water of a river meets the salt water of the ocean. Algae and plants such as marsh grasses provide food and shelter for numerous animals, including crabs, worms, clams, and fish. Many animals use the calm waters of estuaries for breeding grounds. **Marine ecosystems include estuaries, intertidal zones, neritic zones, and the open ocean.**

Intertidal Zone Next, you walk along the rocky shoreline. Here, between the highest high-tide line and the lowest low-tide line, is the **intertidal zone.** Organisms here must be able to survive pounding waves and sudden changes in water levels and temperature that occur with high and low tides. Animals such as barnacles and sea stars cling to the rocks. Others, such as clams and crabs, burrow in the sand.

Neritic Zone Now you set out to sea. The edge of a continent extends into the ocean for a short distance, like a shelf. Below the low-tide line is a region of shallow water called the **neritic zone** (nuh RIT ik), which extends over the continental shelf.

Because sunlight passes through the shallow water of the neritic zone, photosynthesis can occur. As a result, this zone is particularly rich in living things. Many large schools of fish, such as sardines, feed on algae. In warm ocean waters, coral reefs may form. Coral reefs provide living homes to a wide variety of other organisms.

768 ◆

Neritic zone

Intertidal zone

Go Online
SciLINKS NSTA

For: Links on aquatic ecosystems
Visit: www.SciLinks.org
Web Code: scn-0525

Download a worksheet that will guide students' review of Internet resources on aquatic ecosystems.

The Open Ocean Out in the open ocean, light penetrates only a few hundred meters deep. Algae carry out photosynthesis in this region of the open ocean, known as the surface zone. Many marine animals depend on the algae for food.

The deep zone is located below the surface zone. The deep zone is almost totally dark. Most animals in this zone feed on the remains of organisms that sink down from the surface zone. The deepest parts of the deep zone are home to bizarre-looking animals, such as giant squid whose eyes glow in the dark.

Go Online
SciLINKS NSTA

For: Links on aquatic ecosystems
Visit: www.SciLinks.org
Web Code: scn-0525

Section 4 Assessment

Target Reading Skill Comparing and Contrasting Use the information in your table about biomes to help you answer Question 1.

Reviewing Key Concepts

1. a. **Listing** What are the six major biomes?
   b. **Comparing and Contrasting** How are the three forest biomes alike? How are they different?
   c. **Inferring** A plain is dry, bitterly cold, and contains a few, short plants scattered about. What biome might this describe?
2. a. **Reviewing** What two factors are most important in determining an area's biome?
   b. **Relating Cause and Effect** If deserts and tundras receive similar amounts of rainfall, why are these two biomes so different?

c. **Applying Concepts** Why would hiking up a tall mountain be a good way to observe how climate determines an area's biome?
3. a. **Reviewing** What are some freshwater ecosystems? What are some marine ecosystems?
   b. **Explaining** Why is sunlight an important abiotic factor in all aquatic ecosystems?

Writing in Science

Firsthand Account Choose one of the biomes and write a journal entry detailing the observations you made during your expedition. Describe sights, sounds, and smells you experienced as well as specific details about the organisms you observed.

Assess

Reviewing Key Concepts

1. a. Rain forest, desert, grassland, deciduous forest, boreal forest, and tundra
b. All have tall trees and many habitats for organisms. Students should cite differences in location (latitude), temperature, amount of sunlight, amount of precipitation, and specific types of plants and other organisms.
c. The tundra biome
2. a. Temperature and precipitation
b. They are found at very different latitudes, with tundra much farther north. **c.** Because climate differences determined by altitude cause conditions to change from the base to the summit of a mountain
3. a. Freshwater and marine ecosystems
b. Whether or not an aquatic ecosystem receives sunlight determines if it can support producers.

Reteach L1

Review the tables that students have made to compare and contrast the six biomes.

All in One Teaching Resources, Unit 4

• Section Summary: *Biomes and Aquatic Ecosystems*
• Review and Reinforce: *Biomes and Aquatic Ecosystems*
• Enrich: *Biomes and Aquatic Ecosystems*

Writing in Science

Writing Mode Description
Scoring Rubric
4 Includes sensory descriptions (sights, sounds, and smells), specific details about organisms, and a surprising fact; descriptions are vivid and well supported
3 Includes all descriptive components (sensory descriptions, organisms, surprising fact), but descriptions lack detail or clarity

2 Missing one descriptive component
1 Missing two descriptive components
Students can save their accounts in their portfolios.

Portfolio

Change in a Tiny Community

Prepare for Inquiry

Key Concept
The types of organisms that predominate in a community change over time.

Skills Objectives
After this lab, students will be able to
- observe a microscopic pond community
- classify the organisms present in the community

Prep Time 45 minutes

Class Time Day 1, set up community: 15 minutes; Days 3, 6, and 9, examine community: 20 minutes daily

Advance Planning
- The day before students begin the lab, prepare a hay solution by adding a small amount of hay for each liter of hot water. Let the hay soak overnight, and then use a strainer to remove it from the solution.
- Collect a sample of pond water.
- Collect enough clean baby-food jars to provide one for each student or group.
- Collect field guides and other sources showing microscopic organisms found in ponds

Safety
Make sure students handle the slide and coverslip carefully and wash their hands each time they handle the jar and solution. Review the safety guidelines in Appendix A. Follow the guidelines for the recommended safe disposal of bacteria cultures.

All in One Teaching Resources, Unit 4

Lab Worksheet: *Change in a Tiny Community*

Change in a Tiny Community

Problem
How does a pond community change over time?

Skills Focus
observing, classifying

Materials
- hay solution
- pond water
- small baby-food jar
- wax pencil
- plastic dropper
- microscope slide
- coverslip
- microscope

Procedure

1. Use a wax pencil to label a small jar with your name.

2. Fill the jar about three-fourths full with hay solution. Add pond water until the jar is nearly full. Examine the mixture, and record your observations in your notebook.

3. Place the jar in a safe location out of direct sunlight where it will remain undisturbed. Always wash your hands thoroughly with soap after handling the jar or its contents.

4. After two days, examine the contents of the jar, and record your observations.

5. Use a plastic dropper to collect a few drops from the surface of the solution in the jar. Make a slide following the procedures in the box at the right. **CAUTION:** *Slides and coverslips are fragile, and their edges are sharp. Handle them carefully.*

6. Examine the slide under a microscope, using both low and high power and following the procedures in the box at the right. Draw each type of organism you observe. Estimate the number of each type in your sample. The illustration below shows some of the organisms you might see.

7. Repeat Steps 5 and 6 with a drop of solution taken from the side of the jar beneath the surface.

8. Repeat Steps 5 and 6 with a drop of solution taken from the bottom of the jar. When you are finished, follow your teacher's directions about cleaning up.

9. After 3 days, repeat Steps 5 through 8.

10. After 3 more days, repeat Steps 5 through 8 again. Then follow your teacher's directions for returning the solution.

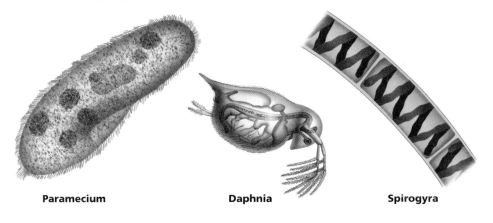

Paramecium　　　**Daphnia**　　　**Spirogyra**

Guide Inquiry

Invitation
Focus students' attention on the illustrations of microorganisms and ask: **Have you ever seen organisms like these before? Where?** *(Answers will depend on students' prior experience. If they have not observed living microorganisms, they may have at least seen photographs or drawings.)* Tell students that in this activity they will observe microscopic pond organisms.

Introducing the Procedure
- Review all procedures related to the correct and safe handling of slides, coverslips, and microscopes. If students have not prepared slides or used a microscope before, demonstrate these procedures.
- Introduce or review the guidelines for making scientific drawings: the drawings should be as realistic and accurate as possible, labeled appropriately, and drawn to scale.

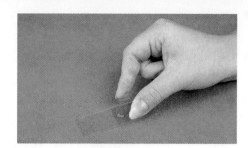
Analyze and Conclude

1. **Classifying** Identify as many of the organisms you observed as possible. Use the diagrams on the facing page and any other resources your teacher provides.

2. **Observing** How did the community change over the period of time that you made your observations?

3. **Inferring** What biotic and abiotic factors may have influenced the changes in this community? Explain.

4. **Developing Hypotheses** Where did the organisms you observed in the jar come from?

5. **Communicating** Based on what you have observed in this lab, write a paragraph that explains why ecosystems change gradually over time. Be sure to discuss the important factors that lead to changes in ecosystems.

Design an Experiment

Write a hypothesis about what would happen if you changed one biotic or abiotic factor in this activity. Design a plan to test your hypothesis. *Obtain your teacher's permission before carrying out your investigation.*

Analyze and Conclude

1. Initially, students can usually expect to see a variety of microorganisms, including the three pictured. Later, they may see tiny aquatic animals.

2. The solution may have become cloudy. Small protists appeared, followed by larger protists, such as green algae, paramecia, and amoebas. Water fleas and rotifers were visible later.

3. Abiotic factors include amount of light, water temperature, and available space. Biotic factors include predation of some organisms by other organisms. As smaller organisms multiplied, they provided food for larger organisms, which then increased in numbers.

4. The organisms were already in the hay solution or pond water, are offspring of those original organisms, or developed from fertilized eggs in the hay solution or pond water.

5. Student answers might explain that adequate nutrients and abiotic conditions must first be present to support producers, then enough producers must multiply and produce enough food to support consumers, and so on. Students may also refer to succession.

Extend Inquiry

Design an Experiment Possible changes in abiotic factors include keeping the jar in a slightly warmer or cooler place or exposing it to more or less light. Changes in biotic factors include varying the amounts of hay solution and pond water (the sources of organisms) or adding a specific population of producers or consumers to the community.

Expected Outcome

In general, large populations of smaller organisms such as bacteria and tiny protists will be present early in the exercise, whereas populations of larger protists and tiny animals will increase toward the end of the exercise.

Study Guide

Interactive Textbook

- Complete student edition
- Section and chapter self-assessments
- Assessment reports for teachers

Help Students Read

Building Vocabulary

Word Forms Before students read, have them write their own definitions of *drift* and *web*, using the dictionary for help. Then have students predict how the definitions relate to the terms *continental drift* and *food web*. After students study the section, have them discuss any differences between their predictions and the definitions in the text.

Paraphrasing Write sentences that feature key terms. Have students rewrite the sentences by paraphrasing the key terms. Example: The zoo animals are *herbivores*, *carnivores*, and *omnivores*; paraphrased: *The zoo animals are plant eaters, meat eaters, and animals that eat both plants and meat.*

Connecting Concepts

Concept Maps Help students develop one way to show how the information in this chapter is related. Earth's ecosystems, which are based on energy moving through food webs and food chains, and on the cycling of matter, cover a range of land and aquatic habitats. Have students brainstorm to identify the key concepts, key terms, details, and examples from this chapter, then write each one on a sticky note and attach it at random on chart paper or on the board. Tell students that this concept map will be organized in hierarchical order and to begin at the top with the key concepts. Ask students these questions to guide them to categorize the information on the stickies: **How does energy move through ecosystems? How is matter cycled? What are the various biomes and aquatic ecosystems?** Prompt students by using connecting words or phrases, such as "is affected by" and "moves up through" to indicate the basis for the organization of the

① Energy Flow in Ecosystems

Key Concepts

- Each organism in an ecosystem fills the energy role of producer, consumer, or decomposer.
- The movement of energy through an ecosystem can be shown in diagrams called food chains and food webs.
- The most energy is available at the producer level of the energy pyramid. As you move up the pyramid, each level has less energy available than the level below.

Key Terms

producer
consumer
herbivore
carnivore
omnivore
scavenger
decomposer
food chain
food web
energy pyramid

② Cycles of Matter

Key Concepts

- The processes of evaporation, condensation, and precipitation make up the water cycle.
- In ecosystems, the processes by which carbon and oxygen are recycled are linked. Producers, consumers, and decomposers play roles in recycling carbon and oxygen.
- In the nitrogen cycle, nitrogen moves from the air to the soil, into living things, and back into the air.

Key Terms

water cycle
evaporation
condensation
precipitation
nitrogen fixation

③ Biogeography

Key Concepts

- One factor that has affected how species are distributed is the motion of Earth's continents.
- Dispersal can be caused by wind, water, or living things, including humans.
- Three factors that limit dispersal of a species are physical barriers, competition, and climate.

Key Terms

biogeography   exotic species
continental drift   climate
dispersal

④ Biomes and Aquatic Ecosystems

Key Concepts

- The six major biomes that most ecologists study are the rain forest, desert, grassland, deciduous forest, boreal forest, and tundra.
- It is mostly the climate—temperature and precipitation—in an area that determines its biome.
- Freshwater ecosystems include streams, rivers, ponds, and lakes.
- Marine ecosystems include estuaries, intertidal zones, neritic zones, and the open ocean.

Key Terms

biome   coniferous tree
canopy   tundra
understory   permafrost
desert   estuary
grassland   intertidal zone
savanna   neritic zone
deciduous tree

map. The phrases should form a sentence between or among a set of concepts.

Answer
Accept logical presentations by students.

All in One Teaching Resources, Unit 4

- Key Terms Review: *Ecosystems and Biomes*
- Connecting Concepts: *Ecosystems and Biomes*

Review and Assessment

Organizing Information

Sequencing Copy the cycle diagram about the nitrogen cycle onto a separate sheet of paper. Then complete it. (For more on Sequencing, see the Skills Handbook.)

Nitrogen Cycle

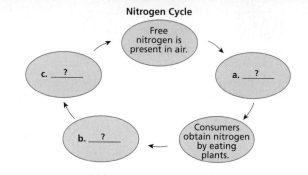

Free nitrogen is present in air.

a. _____?_____

Consumers obtain nitrogen by eating plants.

b. _____?_____

c. _____?_____

Reviewing Key Terms

Choose the letter of the best answer.

1. Which of the following organisms are typical decomposers?
   a. grasses and ferns
   b. mushrooms and bacteria
   c. mice and deer
   d. lions and snakes

2. A diagram that shows how much energy is available at each feeding level in an ecosystem is a(n)
   a. food chain.   b. food web.
   c. water cycle.   d. energy pyramid.

3. When drops of water in a cloud become heavy enough, they fall to Earth as
   a. condensation.   b. evaporation.
   c. permafrost.   d. precipitation.

4. Organisms may be dispersed in all the following ways *except* by
   a. wind.
   b. water.
   c. temperature.
   d. other organisms.

5. Much of Canada is covered in fir and spruce forests. The winter is cold and long. What is this biome?
   a. tundra
   b. boreal forest
   c. deciduous forest
   d. grassland

If the statement is true, write *true*. If it is false, change the underlined word or words to make the statement true.

6. An organism that eats the remains of dead organisms is called a(n) <u>herbivore</u>.

7. The study of where organisms live is called <u>continental drift</u>.

8. <u>Precipitation</u> and temperature are the two major abiotic factors that determine what types of plants can grow in an area.

Writing in Science

Encyclopedia Entry Write a half-page encyclopedia entry about life in the desert. Describe at least two plants and animals that live in the desert. Focus on the adaptations that allow these organisms to thrive in the harsh environment.

Discovery CHANNEL SCHOOL

Ecosystems and Biomes
Video Preview
Video Field Trip
▶ Video Assessment

Chapter 22   ◆ 773

Review and Assessment

Organizing Information
a. Bacteria in root nodules fix free nitrogen into compounds.
b. Decomposers break down wastes and remains of organisms.
c. Bacteria release some free nitrogen back into the air.

Reviewing Key Terms
1. b **2.** d **3.** d **4.** c **5.** b
6. false, scavenger
7. false, biogeography
8. true

Writing in Science

Writing Skill Description
Scoring Rubric
4 Includes detailed information about adaptations of more than two plants and animals
3 Includes all criteria
2 Includes brief descriptions or omits some criteria
1 Includes inaccurate information and omits some criteria

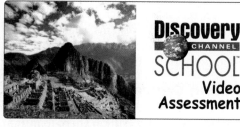

Discovery CHANNEL SCHOOL Video Assessment

Ecosystems and Biomes

Show the Video Assessment to review chapter content and as a prompt for the writing assignment. Discussion question: **What are the typical precipitation and temperature conditions in a dessert?** (*Less than 25 cm of rainfall a year; often major shifts in temperature, from hot days to cool nights*) Urge students to explain how desert organisms survive the harsh conditions.

Go Online
PHSchool.com
For: Self-Assessment
Visit: PHSchool.com
Web Code: cha-4220

Students can take a practice test online that is automatically scored.

All in One Teaching Resources, Unit 4
• Transparency LS221
• Chapter Test
• Performance Assessment Teacher Notes
• Performance Assessment Student Worksheet
• Performance Assessment Scoring Rubric
  ExamView® Computer Test Bank CD-ROM

Checking Concepts

9. Producers capture the energy of sunlight to make their own food. Consumers obtain energy by eating other organisms. Decomposers obtain energy by breaking down wastes and dead organisms.

10. A food chain is a single path of events in which one organism eats another. A food web is a combination of interconnected and overlapping food chains.

11. The sun or sunlight, because it provides energy for photosynthesis, which allows producers to make their food, and producers support consumers.

12. Nitrogen-fixing bacteria convert free nitrogen in the atmosphere into nitrogen-containing molecules that other organisms can use.

13. Competition can be a barrier to dispersal when an existing species outcompetes a new one. Competition can also further dispersal when a new species outcompetes an existing one.

14. The abundant plant life provides a wide variety of habitats for organisms and an abundant supply of food.

15. Grasslands, including savannas, because the grasses and nonwoody plants grow in abundance, protected by large herbivores that keep bushes and trees from becoming abundant

16. Algae are the producers in many freshwater ecosystems, such as ponds and lakes, and marine ecosystems, such as estuaries and the open ocean; algae are less common in rapidly moving water.

Thinking Critically

17. Climate; polar bears' thick, insulating fur would make it difficult for them to live in a warmer environment; the white fur would make them stand out against land that was not covered with ice and snow.

18. The temperate rain forest and tropical rain forest both receive a great deal of rain. As a result, both have very lush vegetation and plentiful animal habitats. Temperatures vary by season in the temperate rain forest, warm in summer and cool in winter, while in the tropical rain forest, temperatures are warm all year.

19. Killing off the algae would have a major impact on the food web, because algae are the major producers in the open ocean, and many marine animals depend on the algae for food.

20. Producers: plants; consumers: fish, snails

Checking Concepts

9. Name and describe each of the three energy roles organisms can play in an ecosystem.

10. How are food chains and food webs different?

11. What is the source of energy for most ecosystems? Explain.

12. Describe the role of nitrogen-fixing bacteria in the nitrogen cycle.

13. Explain how competition can affect the dispersal of species.

14. Why is the tropical rain forest able to support so many species?

15. In which biome would you find large herbivores such as elephants and zebras? Explain.

16. Describe the role of algae in freshwater and marine ecosystems.

Thinking Critically

17. Inferring Polar bears are very well adapted to life around the Arctic Ocean. Their white fur camouflages them in the snow. They can withstand freezing temperatures for a long time. They can swim and hunt in very cold water. Is the distribution of polar bears limited by physical barriers, competition, or climate? Explain your answer.

18. Comparing and Contrasting How are the temperate rain forest and the tropical rain forest similar? How are they different?

19. Predicting A chemical spill has just killed off all the algae in a part of the surface zone in the open ocean. How will this accident affect the food webs in that part of the surface zone?

20. Classifying Which organisms in the illustration are producers? Consumers?

774 ◆

Applying Skills

Use the diagram of a food web below to answer Questions 21–24.

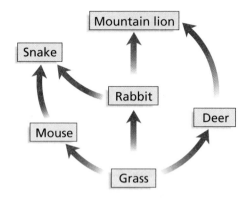

21. Interpreting Diagrams Which organism in this food web fills the role of producer?

22. Classifying Specify whether each consumer in this food web is a first-level, second-level, or third-level consumer.

23. Inferring Which level of the food web contains the greatest amount of available energy?

24. Predicting If a disease were to kill most of the rabbits in this area, predict how the snakes, deer, and mountain lions would be affected.

Lab zone Chapter **Project**

Performance Assessment Create a report, poster, or other product that clearly presents your data and conclusions from your decomposition experiment. In your notebook, compare your results to your predictions about the different waste materials in the compost mixture. Were you surprised by any of your results? Based on what you have learned from your project and those of your classmates, make a list of the ideal conditions for decomposition.

Lab zone Chapter **Project**   L3

Performance Assessment Review students' written reports, posters, and other products. You may wish to have each student or group present its report to the rest of the class. Alternatively, you could have half the class present a "poster session" to the other half and then reverse roles.

Allow time for all students to compare their results so they can compile a list of "ideal" conditions. In general, compost will form most quickly when the compost is kept moist (molds grow better), well aerated (many decomposers are aerobic), and warm (metabolic activity is higher) and when soil organisms are added.

Standardized Test Prep

Test-Taking Tip

Interpreting a Diagram

When answering questions about diagrams, examine the diagram carefully, including labels. Ask yourself what the diagram is about and what it shows you. Make sure that you understand the meaning of any arrows. For example, the arrows in the diagram below indicate the direction of energy flow from producers to consumers in a food chain.

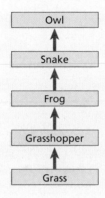

Sample Question

In the food chain shown in the diagram, which of the following organisms obtains its energy directly from the frog?

A the grass   **B** the grasshopper
C the snake   **D** the owl

Answer

The correct answer is **C**. By looking at the arrows in the diagram, you can see that the energy flows in this food chain directly from the frog to the snake.

Choose the letter of the best answer.

1. You are in an area in Maryland where the fresh water of the Chesapeake Bay meets the Atlantic Ocean. What type of habitat are you in?

A a neritic zone   **B** an intertidal zone
C an estuary   **D** the tundra

2. Which pair of terms could apply to the same organism?

F carnivore and producer
G decomposer and consumer
H scavenger and herbivore
J carnivore and consumer

3. You and your classmates have just set up a terrarium in a jar using gravel, moist soil, leafy plants, and mosses. The day after the jar was sealed, you noticed water droplets on the inside of the jar. What process caused the water droplets to form?

A evaporation   **B** condensation
C precipitation   **D** surface runoff

Use the energy pyramid diagram below and your knowledge of science to answer Questions 4 and 5.

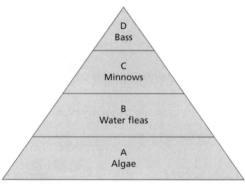

4. Which organisms are the producers in this ecosystem?

F algae   **G** minnows
H water fleas   **J** bass

5. At which level of this energy pyramid is the LEAST energy available?

A level A   **B** level B
C level C   **D** level D

Constructed Response

6. Explain how the processes by which carbon and oxygen cycle through the atmosphere are interrelated.

Applying Skills

21. Grass

22. Mouse, rabbit, and deer: first-level consumers; snake and mountain lion: second-level consumers

23. The producers (grass)

24. Sample: The snake and mountain lion populations would decrease because there would be fewer prey organisms for them to eat. The deer populations would probably decrease at first as hungry lions preyed on deer. Later, as the lion populations decreased, the deer population would increase. Also, the deer would have less competition for grass.

Standardized Test Prep

1. C **2.** J **3.** B **4.** F **5.** D
6. Both are part of the processes of photosynthesis and respiration. Carbon from carbon dioxide is used during photosynthesis, which produces oxygen. The oxygen is used during respiration, which produces carbon dioxide.

Chapter at a Glance

PRENTICE HALL
Teacher EXPRESS™
Plan • Teach • Assess

 Chapter Project *Variety Show*

All in One **Teaching Resources, Unit 4**
- Chapter Project Teacher Notes, pp. 166–167
- Chapter Project Student Overview, pp. 168–169
- Chapter Project Student Worksheets, pp. 170–171
- Chapter Project Scoring Rubric, p. 172

Technology

Video Preview

Local Standards

 Section 1
Environmental Issues

2 periods
1 block

23.1.1 Identify the general categories of environmental issues.

23.1.2 Describe how decision makers balance opposing needs and concerns.

 Section 2
Forests and Fisheries

2 periods
1 block

23.2.1 Describe how forests can be managed as renewable resources.

23.2.2 Describe how fisheries can be managed for a sustainable yield.

 Section 3
Biodiversity

2 periods
1 block

23.3.1 Explain the value of biodiversity.

23.3.2 Identify the factors that affect biodiversity.

23.3.3 Name some human activities that threaten biodiversity.

23.3.4 List some ways to protect biodiversity.

Video Field Trip

Review and Assessment

All in One **Teaching Resources, Unit 4**
- Key Terms Review, p. 199
- Transparency LS225
- Performance Assessment Teacher Notes, p. 206
- Performance Assessment Scoring Rubric, p. 207
- Performance Assessment Student Worksheet, p. 208
- Chapter Test, pp. 209–212

Video Assessment

Test Preparation

Test Preparation Blackline Masters

776A

Lab zone **Chapter Activities Planner**

For more activities

LAB ZONE Easy Planner CD-ROM

Student Edition	Inquiry	Time	Materials	Skills	Resources
Chapter Project, p. 777	Open-Ended	2 to 3 weeks	See Chapter Project in **All in One Teaching Resources, Unit 4,** p. 166	Observing, comparing and contrasting, classifying, inferring, creating data tables, communicating	**Lab zone Easy Planner** **All in One Teaching Resources, Unit 4,** pp. 166–167
Section 1					
Discover Activity, p. 778	Guided	15 minutes	None	Forming operational definitions	**Lab zone Easy Planner**
Skills Lab, p. 783	Directed	Prep: 15 minutes Class: 15 minutes on Day 1, 40 minutes on Day 2, 10 minutes on Day 3	Newspaper, microscope, water, eggbeater, square pan, screen, plastic wrap, mixing bowl, heavy book, microscope slide	Observing, predicting	**Lab zone Easy Planner Lab Activity Video** **All in One Teaching Resources, Unit 4,** Skills Lab: *Recycling Paper*, pp. 180–182
Section 2					
Discover Activity, p. 784	Guided	15 minutes	Graph paper, ruler, pencil	Inferring	**Lab zone Easy Planner**
Skills Activity, p. 787	Guided	5 minutes	Calculator	Calculating	**Lab zone Easy Planner**
Skills Lab, p. 789	Guided	Prep: 15 minutes Class: 40 minutes	Tree cookie, metric ruler, hand lens, colored pencils, calculator (optional)	Observing, inferring, interpreting data	**Lab zone Easy Planner Lab Activity Video** **All in One Teaching Resources, Unit 4,** Skills Lab: *Tree Cookie Tales*, pp. 190–191
Section 3					
Discover Activity, p. 792	Directed	20 minutes	Two labeled cups containing different seed mixtures, paper plate	Inferring	**Lab zone Easy Planner**
Try This Activity, p. 796	Guided	20 minutes	None	Inferring	**Lab zone Easy Planner**

Section 1 **Environmental Issues**

2 periods, 1 block

ABILITY LEVELS
L1 Basic to Average
L2 For All Students
L3 Average to Advanced

Objectives
23.1.1 Identify the general categories of environmental issues.

23.1.2 Describe how decision makers balance opposing needs and concerns.

Local Standards

Key Terms
- natural resource • renewable resource • nonrenewable resource • pollution
- environmental science

Preteach

Targeted Print and Technology Resources

Build Background Knowledge

Ask questions to help students understand the term *issue*.

 **Discover Activity** *How Do You Decide?* **L2**

 **Teaching Resources, Unit 4**

L2 Reading Strategy Transparency
LS222: Identifying Main Ideas

○ **PresentationEXPRESS™ CD-ROM**

Instruct

Targeted Print and Technology Resources

Types of Environmental Issues Define and give examples of three types of environmental issues.

Making Environmental Decisions Ask leading questions for a discussion on the process of balancing needs by considering costs and benefits.

 **Skills Lab** *Recycling Paper* **L2**

Teaching Resources, Unit 4

L2 Guided Reading, pp. 175–177
L2 Skills Lab: *Recycling Paper,* pp. 180–182

■ **Lab Activity Video/DVD**
Skills Lab: *Recycling Paper*

www.SciLinks.org Web Code: scn-0531

○ **Student Edition on Audio CD**

Assess

Targeted Print and Technology Resources

Section Assessment Questions

Have students use their completed Identifying Main Ideas graphic organizers to help them answer questions.

Reteach

Brainstorm a list of the costs and benefits of damming a river and building a hydroelectric plant.

Teaching Resources, Unit 4

- Section Summary, p. 174
L1 Review and Reinforce, p. 178
L3 Enrich, p. 179

Section 2 Forests and Fisheries

2 periods, 1 block

ABILITY LEVELS
L1 Basic to Average
L2 For All Students
L3 Average to Advanced

Objectives

23.2.1 Describe how forests can be managed as renewable resources.

23.2.2 Describe how fisheries can be managed for a sustainable yield.

Local Standards

Key Terms

• clear-cutting • selective cutting • sustainable yield • fishery • aquaculture

---

Preteach

Build Background Knowledge

Help students identify classroom items made from trees.

 **Discover Activity** *What Happened to the Tuna?* L2

Targeted Print and Technology Resources

 **Teaching Resources, Unit 4**

L2 Reading Strategy Transparency LS223: Using Prior Knowledge

🔘 **PresentationEXPRESS™ CD-ROM**

Instruct

Forest Resources Use photographs to help students classify products made from forest plants.

Managing Forests Use diagrams to determine which method of harvesting trees is the least disruptive.

Fisheries Study limits, changed methods, aquaculture, and new resources as ways to manage fisheries.

 Skills Lab *Tree Cookie Tales* L2

Targeted Print and Technology Resources

Teaching Resources, Unit 4

L2 Guided Reading, pp. 185–187
L2 Transparency LS224
L2 Skills Lab: *Tree Cookie Tales,* pp. 190–191

📼 **Lab Activity Video/DVD**
Skills Lab: *Tree Cookie Tales*

PHSchool.com Web Code: cep-5032

PHSchool.com Web Code: ceh-1040

🔘 **Student Edition on Audio CD**

Assess

Section Assessment Questions

 Have students use their Using Prior Knowledge graphic organizers as they answer the questions.

Reteach

Compare and contrast overfishing and clear-cutting.

Targeted Print and Technology Resources

Teaching Resources, Unit 4

• Section Summary, p. 184
L1 Review and Reinforce, p. 188
L3 Enrich, p. 189

Section 3 **Biodiversity**

 *2 periods, 1 block*

Local Standards

Objectives

23.3.1 Explain the value of biodiversity.
23.3.2 Identify the factors that affect biodiversity.
23.3.3 Name some human activities that threaten biodiversity.
23.3.4 List some ways to protect biodiversity.

Key Terms

- biodiversity • keystone species • extinction • endangered species
- threatened species • habitat destruction • habitat fragmentation • poaching
- captive breeding

Preteach

Build Background Knowledge

List the variety of organisms that live in the area and help students infer that there is a great diversity of species around them.

 **Discover Activity** *How Much Variety Is There?*   **L1**

Targeted Print and Technology Resources

All in One Teaching Resources, Unit 4

L2   Reading Strategy: Building Vocabulary

⊙ **PresentationEXPRESS™ CD-ROM**

Instruct

The Value of Biodiversity Describe the economic and ecological values of biodiversity.

Factors Affecting Biodiversity Brainstorm a list of factors affecting biodiversity.

Gene Pool Diversity Discuss the usefulness of gene pool diversity to the survival of a species.

Extinction of Species Use photographs to show that some species, once prevalent on Earth, are no longer present or are endangered.

Causes of Extinction Describe agents causing extinction.

Protecting Biodiversity Define *captive breeding*, and discuss other methods that help protect biodiversity.

Targeted Print and Technology Resources

All in One Teaching Resources, Unit 4

L2   Guided Reading, pp. 194–196

PHSchool.com Web Code: ced-5033

DISCOVERY CHANNEL SCHOOL
Video Field Trip

⊙ **Student Edition on Audio CD**

Assess

Section Assessment Questions

↻ Have students use their completed sentences to answer the questions.

Reteach

List ways in which humans threaten biodiversity and ways to preserve biodiversity.

Targeted Print and Technology Resources

All in One Teaching Resources, Unit 4

- Section Summary, p. 193
L1   Review and Reinforce, p. 197
L3   Enrich, p. 198

Chapter 23 **Content Refresher**

Section 1 **Environmental Issues**

Oil in the Arctic The debate over oil exploration in the Arctic National Wildlife Refuge is one example of an environmental issue. Visitors to this vast preserve in northeastern Alaska can see wildlife ranging from polar bears to arctic foxes. Opponents of oil exploration worry that it would damage the fragile ecosystem. Proponents argue that the United States needs to produce more oil domestically.

Section 2 **Forests and Fisheries**

Deforestation Deforestation can have a profound effect on climate. During transpiration, a tree returns to the air about 97 percent of the water that the roots absorb. This water returns to Earth through the water cycle. Deforestation can reduce rainfall in a region and increase the frequency of droughts.

Deforested tropical rain forests may also contribute to an increase of global temperatures. For example, as felled trees are burned, they add carbon dioxide to the atmosphere, which increases the amount of heat the atmosphere retains. Fewer trees result in less absorption of carbon dioxide from the atmosphere.

Managed forestry is one approach to harvesting needed wood while avoiding deforestation. Today the most visible tenet of managed forestry is selective cutting. Several organizations, including the U.S. Forest Service, work to improve yield through their studies of tree physiology, entomology, and genetics.

Section 3 **Biodiversity**

Pollution by DDT Pesticides such as DDT can threaten biodiversity by endangering animal species. At one time, DDT was applied worldwide for crop protection, mosquito abatement, and other kinds of insect control. DDT was amazingly successful, able to kill off vast numbers of insects quickly and offer protection for many months. But it also created problems.

Alarmed biologists found significant amounts of DDT everywhere: on land and in water worldwide. In her 1962 book *Silent Spring*, Rachel Carson told about the damaging effects of DDT on bird eggs. The shells were so weak that a nesting bird easily crushed them, killing the embryos. Particularly vulnerable were the fish-eating birds such as the brown pelican.

DDT readily passes through food chains, with increasing concentrations at each level. This mechanism is called biological magnification. One study determined that DDT concentrations had increased more than 400 times from producer to top carnivore in the local food chain—from plankton, algae, and plants to fish-eating birds. DDT remained in the body fat of animals. Scientists learned that humans were also accumulating DDT in their fatty tissue, some of it appearing in mother's milk—and, consequently, in the fatty tissue of babies.

Alarm spread throughout the scientific community and into the public sector. The pesticide itself was finally banned from general use in the United States in the late 1970s.

> 🚩 **Address Misconceptions**
>
> *Students may think that all extinct animals lived long ago and became extinct under mysterious circumstances.* In the past few centuries, the number of species becoming extinct has increased dramatically. For more on this misconception, see **Address Misconceptions** in the section *Biodiversity*.

Help Students Read

Identifying Main Ideas

Strategy To see how text develops and supports concepts, students must be able to identify main ideas. Assign students the text following the head Types of Environmental Issues.

Example

1. Main Idea of a Subsection Ask students to identify the main idea in the text they have just read. Help them see that the main idea is expressed by the boldface sentence, "Environmental issues fall into three general categories: resource use, population growth, and pollution."

2. Supporting the Main Idea Ask a volunteer to read aloud the blue subheads under the head Types of Environmental Issues. Relate these three subheads to the main-idea sentence. Help students see how each blue subhead develops one aspect of the main idea.

Interactive Textbook
- Complete student edition
- Video and audio
- Simulations and activities
- Section and chapter activities

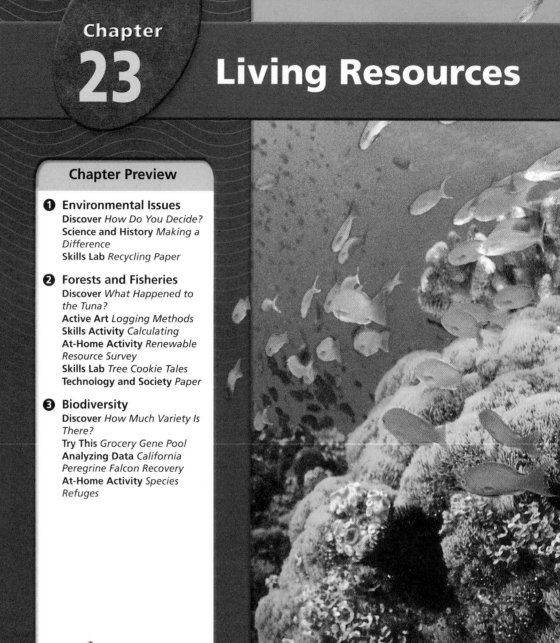

Chapter 23

Living Resources

Chapter Preview

❶ Environmental Issues
Discover *How Do You Decide?*
Science and History *Making a Difference*
Skills Lab *Recycling Paper*

❷ Forests and Fisheries
Discover *What Happened to the Tuna?*
Active Art *Logging Methods*
Skills Activity *Calculating*
At-Home Activity *Renewable Resource Survey*
Skills Lab *Tree Cookie Tales*
Technology and Society *Paper*

❸ Biodiversity
Discover *How Much Variety Is There?*
Try This *Grocery Gene Pool*
Analyzing Data *California Peregrine Falcon Recovery*
At-Home Activity *Species Refuges*

Interactive Textbook

Coral reefs are the most diverse ecosystems in the ocean. ▶

776 ◆

Lab zone Chapter **Project**   L3

Objectives

As this project progresses, students have a chance to apply methods and skills used by field biologists and environmental scientists. Students also develop an appreciation for the rich diversity of living things found in a small plot of land. After this Chapter Project, students will be able to

- observe, compare and contrast, and classify organisms
- infer relationships among organisms and between organisms and the abiotic factors in their environment
- create a data table for recording observations
- communicate observations and conclusions to others

Skills Focus

Observing, comparing and contrasting, classifying, inferring, creating data tables, communicating

Project Time Line 2 to 3 weeks

All in One Teaching Resources, Unit 4
- Chapter Project Teacher Notes
- Chapter Project Overview
- Chapter Project Worksheet 1
- Chapter Project Worksheet 2
- Chapter Project Scoring Rubric

Developing a Plan

Each small group of students should choose a location and secure teacher approval. Students proceed by staking the plot and preparing a notebook for recording observations. Advise students to make regular observations and record data carefully. At the conclusion of the observation period, students should prepare a presentation for the class that may include materials such as photographs, drawings, videos, or computer displays.

Possible Materials

- To mark the plot, each group will need a meter stick or metric tape measure, four small stakes, a hammer, sturdy string, and a directional compass.
- To observe plots, each group will need a thermometer, hand lenses, rulers, and trowels.
- Students will need a variety of field guides in order to identify and classify any unfamiliar organisms. A field guide to animal tracks will be helpful as well.

Living Resources

- ▶ Video Preview
- Video Field Trip
- Video Assessment

Lab zone™ Chapter **Project**

Variety Show

In this chapter's project, you will become an ecologist as you study the diversity of life in a small plot of land. Keep in mind that the area you will study has just a tiny sample of the huge variety of organisms that live on Earth.

Your Goal To observe the diversity of organisms in a plot of land

To complete this project, you must

- stake out a 1.5 meter-by-1.5 meter plot of ground
- keep a record of your observations of the abiotic conditions
- identify the species of organisms you observe
- follow the safety guidelines in Appendix A

Plan It! Look for a location for your plot. With your teacher's approval, stake out a square plot measuring 1.5 meters on each side. Prepare a notebook in which to record your observations, including the date, time, air temperature, and other weather conditions. Also include places for drawings or photographs of the organisms in your plot.

- Students will need art supplies to prepare their presentations. Cameras and videocassette recorders would be helpful, if available.

Living Resources

Show the Video Preview to introduce the Chapter Project and overview the chapter. Discussion questions: **What is overfishing?** *(Overfishing is killing more fish than can be replaced, thereby reducing the fish population in an area.)* **What is one negative effect of overfishing?** *(Few fish are left to reproduce.)*

Launching the Project

To introduce the project, draw a 1.5-by-1.5-meter square on the chalkboard. Ask: **How many different kinds of organisms do you think you can find in a plot of land this size?** *(Sample answer: Dozens; accept all responses at this time, and encourage creative thinking.)* Encourage discussion of the different kinds of living things students think they might find. Students could identify types of source materials they could use for their research. Answer any initial questions that students may have.

Performance Assessment

The Chapter Project Scoring Rubric will help you evaluate how well students complete the Chapter Project. You may want to share the scoring rubric with your students so they are clear about what will be expected of them. Students will be assessed on

- the completeness and accuracy of their observations and data
- their ability to use previous knowledge as well as reference sources to identify and classify organisms
- how well they communicate their findings to the rest of the class
- the extent of their participation in groups

Advance Preparation

Before introducing the project, survey the grounds around your school so that you can guide students to areas where they are likely to find a good variety of organisms. If the school grounds are not appropriate, locate a nearby field, park, vacant lot, or other natural area to which you can take the class during school hours. Obtain permission to use the land, if necessary.

Environmental Issues

Objectives

After this lesson, students will be able to
23.1.1 Identify the general categories of environmental issues.
23.1.2 Describe how decision makers balance different needs and concerns.

Target Reading Skill

Identifying Main Ideas Explain that identifying main ideas and details helps students sort the facts from the information into groups. Each group can have a main topic, subtopics, and details.

Answers

Three types of environmental issues are resource use, population growth, and pollution.

All in One Teaching Resources, Unit 4
• Transparency LS222

Preteach

Build Background Knowledge ▪L2

Defining Issues

Ask: **What is an issue?** *(Students' responses should suggest a problem or question on which people have different viewpoints.)* **What are some examples of issues that you have heard about?** *(Possible responses: Should a run-down historic building in town be restored or demolished? Should owners of beachfront property be allowed to restrict public access to beaches?)*

Environmental Issues

Reading Preview

Key Concepts
• What are the general categories of environmental issues?
• How do decision makers balance different needs and concerns?

Key Terms
• natural resource
• renewable resource
• nonrenewable resource
• pollution
• environmental science

Target Reading Skill
Identifying Main Ideas As you read the Types of Environmental Issues section, write the main idea in a graphic organizer like the one below. Then write three supporting details that give examples of the main idea.

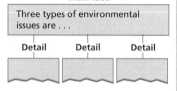

Main Idea

Three types of environmental issues are . . .

Detail | Detail | Detail

Lab zone Discover **Activity**

How Do You Decide?

1. On a sheet of paper, list the three environmental issues you think are most important today.
2. Next to each issue, write the reason it is important.
3. Join with three other classmates and share your lists. Decide which issue on your lists is the most important.

Think It Over
Forming Operational Definitions Based on your group's discussion, how would you define *environmental issue?*

Here's a riddle for you: What is bigger than the United States and Mexico combined; is covered with more than two kilometers of ice; is a unique habitat for many animals; and is a source of oil, coal, and iron? The answer is Antarctica.

People have different ideas about the best way to make use of Antarctica. Some people want access to the minerals. Some want to build hotels, parks, and ski resorts. Others want to protect the ecosystems. What should be done? Who should decide the continent's future?

Types of Environmental Issues

The debate about Antarctica's future is just one environmental issue that people face today. **Environmental issues fall into three general categories: resource use, population growth, and pollution.** Because these three types of issues are interconnected, they are very difficult to study and solve.

1000 B.C.
About 50 million

A.D. 1
About 285 million

Lab zone Discover **Activity**

Skills Focus Forming operational definitions

Materials none

Time 15 minutes

Tips Encourage students to think of specific, *debatable* questions such as "Should people be rewarded for buying smaller, fuel-efficient cars?" "Should

▪L2 companies be given tax credits for using less product packaging?" and "Should recycling be required?"

Expected Outcome Possible answers include pollution or declining resources.

Think It Over Definitions should allow for different viewpoints. Encourage students to apply their operational definitions to all of the environmental issues they listed. Have students explore any issues that do not lend themselves to the operational definition.

Resource Use Anything in the environment that is used by people is called a **natural resource.** Some natural resources are renewable. **Renewable resources** are either always available or are naturally replaced in a relatively short time. Renewable resources include sunlight, wind, fresh water, and trees. Some people think that renewable resources can never be used up. This is not always true. If people cut down trees faster than they can grow back, the supply of trees could run out.

Natural resources that are not replaced in a useful time frame are called **nonrenewable resources.** As nonrenewable resources such as coal or oil are used, the supply decreases.

Population Growth Figure 1 shows how the human population has changed in the last 3,000 years. The population grew very slowly until about A.D. 1650. Then, improvements in medicine, agriculture, and waste disposal resulted in people living longer. The human population has been growing faster and faster ever since. But scientists do not expect it to grow as rapidly in the future.

When a population grows, the demand for resources also grows. Has your town ever experienced a water shortage? If so, you might have noticed that people have been asked to restrict their water use. The water supplies in many areas were designed to serve fewer people than they now do, so shortages sometimes occur during unusually warm or dry weather.

Pollution The contamination of Earth's land, water, or air is called **pollution.** Pollution can be caused by a variety of factors, including chemicals, wastes, noise, heat, and light. Pollution can destroy wildlife and cause human health problems.

Pollution can be related to both resource use and population growth. For example, as more people need to be fed, more fertilizers and other chemicals may be used to produce food. These chemicals can run off the land and pollute bodies of water.

Reading Checkpoint What are three factors that can cause pollution?

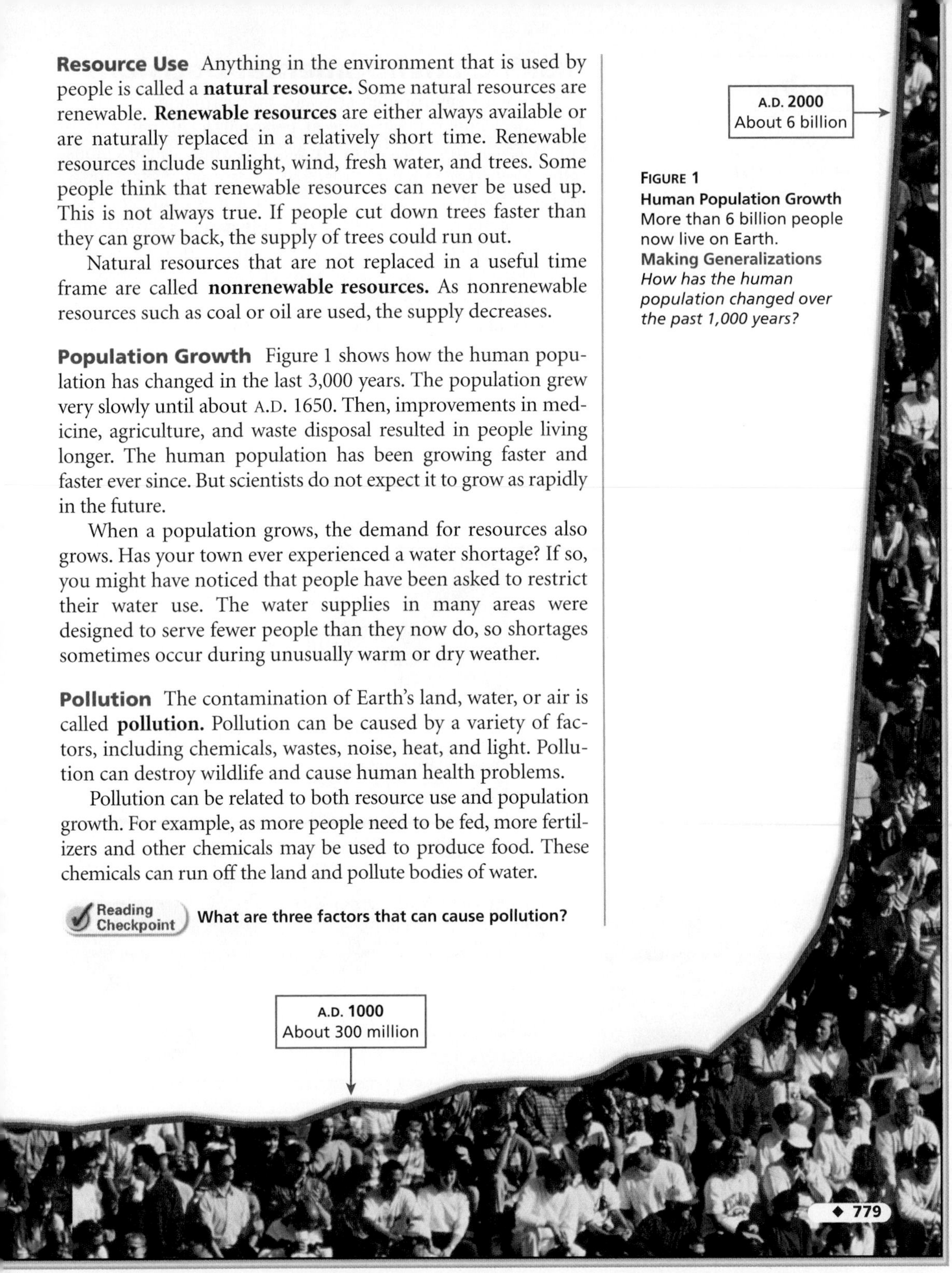

A.D. **2000**
About 6 billion

FIGURE 1
Human Population Growth
More than 6 billion people now live on Earth.
Making Generalizations
How has the human population changed over the past 1,000 years?

A.D. **1000**
About 300 million

 ◆ 779

Graphing

Materials graph paper, ruler, pencil, world map

Time 25 minutes

Focus Point out to students that Figure 1 shows population growth for the entire world. However, actual growth rates and population sizes vary among different regions and countries of the world.

Teach Give students the current populations of several countries listed below and have them construct bar graphs. Have students use their graphs to answer the following questions: **Which country has the largest population?** *(China)* **Which country has the next-largest population?** *(India)* **How many times larger than Japan's population is the U. S. population?** *(About twice as large)*

Apply Have students compare the United States' and Japan's land areas on a world map. Ask: **Which country has a greater population density? Explain.** *(Japan; if necessary, help students recall the term population density.)* **learning modality: logical/mathematical**

2002 Population of Selected Countries	
Brazil	179,914,212
China	1,279,160,885
Great Britain	59,912,431
India	1,034,172,547
Indonesia	231,326,092
Japan	127,065,841
Mexico	102,479,927
Nigeria	130,499,978
Russia	144,978,573
United States	287,675,526

For: Links on the environment
Visit: www.SciLinks.org
Web Code: scn-0531

Students can review environmental issues in an online activity.

For: Links on the environment
Visit: www.SciLinks.org
Web Code: scn-0531

Making Environmental Decisions

Dealing with environmental issues means making decisions. These decisions can be made at personal, local, national, or global levels. Your decision to walk to your friend's house rather than ride in a car is made at a personal level. A town's decision about how to dispose of its trash is made at a local level. A decision about whether the United States should allow oil drilling in a wildlife refuge is a decision made on a national level. Decisions about how to protect Earth's atmosphere are made on a global level.

Every decision has some impact on the environment. Your personal decisions of what to eat or how to travel have a small impact. But when the personal decisions of millions of people are combined, they have a huge impact on the environment.

Science and History

Making a Difference

Can one individual change the way people think? The leaders featured in this timeline have influenced the way that many people think about environmental issues.

1890 John Muir
The actions of John Muir, a nature writer from California, lead to the establishment of Yosemite National Park.

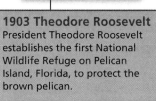

1903 Theodore Roosevelt
President Theodore Roosevelt establishes the first National Wildlife Refuge on Pelican Island, Florida, to protect the brown pelican.

1905 Gifford Pinchot
Forestry scientist Gifford Pinchot is appointed the first director of the United States Forest Service. His goal is to manage forests scientifically to meet current and future lumber needs.

1880	1900	1920

780 ◆

Differentiated Instruction

Gifted and Talented
Research Report Invite pairs of students to research one of the following environmental activists.
- **Jacques Cousteau** introduced millions to ocean life and the importance of preserving it.
- **Dian Fossey** urged the preservation of the endangered mountain gorilla of east-central Africa.
- **Jane Goodall** increased our knowledge of the ecology of wild chimpanzees.
- **Chico Mendes** established reserves where rubber could be harvested without causing damage to the Brazilian rain forests.

Tell students to present their information in the form of an interview in which one student plays the role of the activist and the other student is the interviewer. **learning modality: verbal**

Balancing Different Needs Lawmakers work with environmental scientists and other groups to make environmental decisions. **Environmental science** is the study of natural processes in the environment and how humans can affect them. But the data provided by scientists are only part of the process. Environmental decision making requires a balance between the needs of the environment and the needs of people. **To help balance the different opinions on an environmental issue, decision makers weigh the costs and benefits of a proposal.**

Types of Costs and Benefits Many costs and benefits are economic, but not all. Others can be ecological, recreational, or scenic. For example, suppose a state is deciding whether to allow logging in a park. Removing trees is an ecological cost because it changes the ecosystem. In addition, popular recreational or scenic areas may be lost. But providing jobs and a supply of wood has economic benefits.

1962 Rachel Carson
Biologist Rachel Carson writes *Silent Spring,* which describes the harmful effects of pesticides on the environment. The book raises awareness of how human activities can affect the environment.

1969 Marjory Stoneman Douglas
At the age of 79, journalist Marjory Stoneman Douglas founds Friends of the Everglades. This grassroots organization is dedicated to preserving the unique Florida ecosystem. She continued to work for the Everglades until her death in 1998.

1949 Aldo Leopold
A Sand County Almanac is published shortly after the death of its author, Aldo Leopold. This classic book links wildlife management to the science of ecology.

1977 Wangari Maathai
Biologist Wangari Maathai founds the Green Belt Movement. This organization encourages restoring forests in Kenya and in other African nations.

1940	1960	1980

Chapter 23 ◆ 781

Answer

 Costs—expense, possible ecological damage; *benefits*—new supplies of needed materials, jobs

Assess

Reviewing Key Concepts

1. a. resource use, population growth, and pollution **b.** As the population grows, the demand for natural resources grows.
c. Possible answer: Growing demands for housing might increase demands for lumber, which might increase the demand for trees. Increased demand for trees might result in greater harvesting of trees and, therefore, a smaller supply.
2. a. Weighing costs and benefits allows decision makers to balance the differing opinions on an environmental issue.
b. economic cost: building roads, drilling apparatus, and housing; non-economic cost: disturbance of wildlife habitats; benefit: a new supply of oil **c.** Sample answer: I would vote not to drill for oil in Antarctica. The cost to the environment would be significantly greater than the economic benefits brought by a new source of oil.

Reteach L1

As a class, list the costs and benefits of damming a river to build a hydroelectric plant.

Performance Assessment L2

Have each student choose one action related to an environmental issue. Then have the student create a table with the costs of the action listed in one column and the benefits of the action listed in a second column.

All in One Teaching Resources, Unit 4

- Section Summary: *Environmental Issues*
- Review and Reinforce: *Environmental Issues*
- Enrich: *Environmental Issues*

FIGURE 2
Identifying Costs and Benefits
Drilling for oil in Antarctica could provide a new source of energy. But an oil spill could harm the area's penguins and other wildlife.

Weighing Costs and Benefits Once you have identified the potential costs and benefits of a decision, you must analyze them. For example, it is important to consider a decision's short-term and long-term costs and benefits. A plan's short-term costs might be outweighed by its long-term benefits.

Consider the costs and benefits of drilling for oil in Antarctica. There would be many costs. It would be very expensive to set up a drilling operation in such a cold and distant place. Transporting the oil would also be difficult and costly. An oil spill in the seas around Antarctica could harm the fish, penguins, and seals there.

On the other hand, there would be benefits to drilling for oil in Antarctica. Oil drilling would provide a new supply of oil for heat, electricity, and transportation. If the worldwide supply of oil were larger, the price might drop, making oil available to more people. The plan would also create many new jobs. Would the benefits of drilling for oil in Antarctica outweigh the costs? This is the kind of question lawmakers must ask before they make environmental decisions.

✓ **Reading Checkpoint** What are two types of costs and benefits?

Section 1 Assessment

🔄 **Target Reading Skill Identifying Main Ideas** Use your graphic organizer about types of environmental issues to help you answer Question 1 below.

Reviewing Key Concepts

1. a. Identifying What are the three main types of environmental issues?
   b. Explaining Why is population growth an environmental issue?
   c. Relating Cause and Effect How might a growing population affect the supply of a renewable resource such as trees? Explain your answer.
2. a. Reviewing Why is weighing costs and benefits useful for decision makers?

b. Classifying Name one economic cost and one noneconomic cost of drilling for oil in Antarctica. List one benefit of drilling in Antarctica.
c. Making Judgments Suppose you were a world leader faced with the question of drilling in Antarctica. What decision would you make? Give reasons for your decision.

Writing in Science

Persuasive Letter Write a letter to the editor expressing your viewpoint on whether people should be allowed to use powerboats on a lake in your town. Your letter should clearly show how you weighed the costs and benefits to arrive at your viewpoint.

Lab zone Chapter Project

Keep Students on Track Make sure students leave enough space between plots that they can move around. Encourage students to note any animals behaviors they see, such as feeding, fighting, or cooperating in some way.

Writing in Science

Writing Mode Persuasion
Scoring Rubric
4 Includes description of the issue, economic and noneconomic costs and benefits, explanation of how costs and benefits were weighed
3 Includes three of the four criteria and a brief explanation
2 Includes one or two of the criteria and some accurate details
1 Includes only descriptive details

Portfolio

Recycling Paper

Problem
Is paper a renewable resource?

Skills Focus
observing, predicting

Materials
- newspaper
- microscope
- water
- eggbeater
- square pan
- screen
- plastic wrap
- mixing bowl
- heavy book
- microscope slide

Procedure 🧤 🥼 🔥

1. Tear off a small piece of newspaper. Place it on a microscope slide and examine it under a microscope. Record your observations.

2. Tear a sheet of newspaper into pieces about the size of postage stamps. Place the pieces in the mixing bowl. Add enough water to cover the newspaper. Cover the bowl and let the mixture stand overnight.

3. The next day, add more water to cover the paper if necessary. Use the eggbeater to mix the wet paper until it is smooth. This thick liquid is called paper pulp.

4. Place the screen in the bottom of the pan. Pour the pulp onto the screen, spreading it out evenly. Then lift the screen above the pan, allowing most of the water to drip into the pan.

5. Place the screen and pulp on several layers of newspaper to absorb the rest of the water. Lay a sheet of plastic wrap over the pulp. Place a heavy book on top of the plastic wrap to press more water out of the pulp.

6. After 30 minutes, remove the book. Carefully turn over the screen, plastic wrap, and pulp. Remove the screen and plastic wrap. Let the pulp sit on the newspaper for one or two more days to dry. Replace the newspaper layers if necessary.

7. When the pulp is dry, observe it closely. Record your observations.

Analyze and Conclude

1. **Observing** What kind of structures did you observe when you examined torn newspaper under a microscope?

2. **Inferring** What are these structures made of? Where do they come from?

3. **Predicting** What do you think happens to the structures you observed when paper is recycled? How do you think this affects the number of times paper can be recycled?

4. **Communicating** Based on what you learned in this lab, do you think paper should be classified as a renewable or nonrenewable resource? Defend your answer with evidence and sound reasoning.

Design an Experiment

Using procedures like those in this lab, design an experiment to recycle three different types of paper, such as shiny magazine paper, paper towels, and cardboard. *Obtain your teacher's permission before carrying out your investigation.* How do the resulting papers differ?

Recycling Paper L2

Prepare for Inquiry

Key Concept
Paper is a renewable resource because it can be recycled.

Skills Objectives
After this lab, students will be able to
- observe and compare dry newspaper and recycled paper made from newspaper pulp
- predict how the structure of paper changes when it is recycled

🕐 **Prep Time** 15 minutes

🕐 **Class Time** 15 minutes on Day 1, 40 minutes on Day 2, 10 minutes on Day 3

Advance Planning
Gather an ample supply of old newspapers.

Safety
🧤 🥼 🔥 Students should handle the microscope slide carefully to avoid breakage. Review the safety guidelines in Appendix A.

All in One Teaching Resources, Unit 4
- Lab Worksheet: *Recycling Paper*

Guide Inquiry

Invitation
Ask: **What process do you think you can use to recycle newspapers?** (*Student answers should reflect an understanding of the procedure, including the making of paper pulp and drying the paper.*)

Introducing the Procedure
Emphasize to students that they will do the lab on three different days: Steps 1–2 on Day 1, Steps 3–6 on Day 2, and Step 7 on Day 3.

Troubleshooting the Experiment
- *Day 1:* In Step 1, ask: **What do you see in the paper?** (*Fibers*)
- *Day 2:* Have students reread Steps 3–6. Remind them to replace the newspaper under the screen each day if it is still wet.
- *Day 3:* Make certain the pulp is completely dry before students handle it.

Expected Outcome
The dried pulp will be rough, stiff, and grayish—like cardboard egg cartons. Cellulose fibers will be visible.

Analyze and Conclude

1. Fibers

2. The fibers are made of plant material. They come from the plants used to make the paper.

3. When the paper is soaked and mashed, the fibers are broken. When the pulp is flattened and dried, the fibers intertwine. Each time the fibers are broken, the result is a weaker paper, which limits the number of times it can be recycled.

4. Paper is a renewable resource. It can be recycled.

Extend Inquiry

Design an Experiment Students' plans should be similar to the lab procedure. Have students share their results.

Objectives

After this lesson, students will be able to

23.2.1 Describe how forests can be managed as renewable resources.

23.2.2 Describe how fisheries can be managed for a sustainable yield.

Target Reading Skill 🔄

Using Prior Knowledge Explain that using prior knowledge helps connect what you know to what you read.

Answers

Possible answers:

What You Know

1. Forests provide people with lumber and paper.

2. Commercial fishing boats harvest large amounts of fish.

What You Learned

1. Forests can be renewable resources.

2. Fisheries can be harmed by overfishing.

All in One Teaching Resources, Unit 4

• Transparency LS223

Preteach

Build Background Knowledge   L1

Identifying Forest Products

Invite students to look around. Ask: **What things are made from trees?** *(Examples: textbooks, wood furniture, pencils)*

Instruct

Forest Resources

Teach Key Concepts   L2

Importance of Forests

Focus Remind students that forests are valuable resources.

Teach Ask: **What are some products that come from forests?** *(Possible answers: Nuts, lumber, rubber, fruits, pulp for paper)*

Apply Ask: **Why else are forests valuable?** *(Plants produce oxygen, absorb pollutants, help prevent flooding, and control soil erosion.)* **learning modality: verbal**

784

Reading Preview

Key Concepts

• How can forests be managed as renewable resources?

• How can fisheries be managed for a sustainable yield?

Key Terms

• clear-cutting
• selective cutting
• sustainable yield
• fishery
• aquaculture

🔄 Target Reading Skill

Using Prior Knowledge Before you read, write what you know about forests and fish resources in a graphic organizer like the one below. As you read, write what you learn.

What You Know
1. Forests provide people with lumber and paper.
2.

What You Learned
1.
2.

Lab zone Discover **Activity**

What Happened to the Tuna?

1. Use the data in the table to make a line graph. Label the axes of the graph and add a title. (To review graphing, see the Skills Handbook.)

2. Mark the high and low points on the graph.

Think It Over

Inferring Describe the changes in the tuna population during this period. Can you suggest a reason for these changes?

Year	Western Atlantic Bluefin Tuna Population
1970	218,000
1975	370,000
1980	67,000
1985	58,000
1990	46,000
1995	63,000
2000	67,000

At first glance, an oak tree and a bluefin tuna may not seem to have much in common. One is a plant and the other is an animal. One lives on land and the other lives in the ocean. However, oak trees and tuna are both living resources. People use oak trees to make furniture, lumber, and cork. Tuna are a source of food for people.

Every day you use many different products that are made from living organisms. In this section, you will read about two major types of living resources: forests and fisheries.

Forest Resources

Forests contain many valuable resources. Many products are made from the fruits, seeds, and other parts of forest plants. Some of these products, such as maple syrup, rubber, and nuts, come from living trees. Other products, such as lumber and wood pulp for making paper, require cutting trees down. Coniferous trees, including pine and spruce, are used for construction and for making paper. Hardwoods, such as oak, cherry, and maple, are used for furniture because of their strength and beauty.

Trees and other plants produce oxygen that organisms need to survive. They also absorb carbon dioxide and many pollutants from the air. Trees help prevent flooding and control soil erosion. Their roots absorb rainwater and hold the soil in place.

Lab zone Discover **Activity**

Skills Focus Inferring

Materials graph paper, ruler, pencil

Time 15 minutes

Tips In Step 1, advise students to use *Population (in thousands)* as the vertical axis and *Year* as the horizontal axis.

Expected Outcome Students' graphs should reflect data in the table.

L2 Think It Over The tuna population increased from 1970 to 1975, and then declined steadily from 1975 to 1980. From 1980 until today the population has remained about the same. The decline may have been due to overfishing of tuna. The stabilization may have resulted from limits on tuna fishing.

Managing Forests

There are about 300 million hectares of forests in the United States. That's nearly a third of the nation's area! Many forests are located on public land. Others are owned by individuals or by private timber and paper companies. Forest industries in the United States provide jobs for more than 1 million people.

Because new trees can be planted to replace trees that are cut down, forests can be renewable resources. The United States Forest Service and environmental organizations work with forestry companies to conserve forest resources. They try to develop logging methods that maintain forests as renewable resources.

Logging Methods There are two major methods of logging: clear-cutting and selective cutting. **Clear-cutting** is the process of cutting down all the trees in an area at once. Cutting down only some trees in a forest and leaving a mix of tree sizes and species behind is called **selective cutting**.

Go Online
active art

For: Logging Methods activity
Visit: PHSchool.com
Web Code: cep-5032

FIGURE 3
Logging Methods
Clear-cutting involves cutting down all the trees in an area at once.
Interpreting Diagrams
What is selective cutting?

Old-Growth Forest

Clear-Cutting

Selective Cutting

Replanted Growth

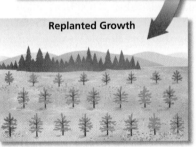

Diverse Growth

◆ 785

Managing Forests

Teach Key Concepts L2
Logging Methods

Focus Direct students' attention to Figure 3.

Teach Ask: **How can you describe the old-growth forest after clear-cutting?** (*No trees are left in the area that was clear-cut.*) **How can you describe the forest after selective cutting?** (*There is a mix of trees remaining.*)

Apply Ask: **Which final stage—replanted growth or diverse growth—is more like the original old-growth forest?** (*Diverse growth*)

Extend Ask: **Do you think you can replace an old-growth forest? Explain.** (*Students probably will recognize that they could replant trees, but not the original forest; the forest ecosystem will have been permanently altered even if selective cutting is used.*) **learning modality: visual**

 **Teaching Resources, Unit 4**

• Transparency LS224

Independent Practice L1

 **Teaching Resources, Unit 4**

• Guided Reading and Study Worksheet: *Forests and Fisheries*

◉ **Student Edition on Audio CD**

Go Online
active art

For: Logging Methods Activity
Visit: PHSchool.com
Web Code: cep-5032

Students can compare two methods of logging: clear-cutting and selective cutting.

Monitor Progress _____ L2

Skills Check Have pairs of students construct a table comparing the advantages and disadvantages of clear-cutting and selective cutting.

Answer

Figure 3 Selective cutting is the practice of cutting down only some of the trees in a forest and leaving a mix of tree sizes and species behind.

Shelterwood Cutting

Materials 20 green, brown, red, and yellow plastic chips per group

Time 10 minutes

Focus Tell students that shelterwood cutting removes all the mature trees in an area at specified time intervals.

Teach Explain that shelterwood cutting occurs in three stages. At stage one, all unwanted trees are removed. Then remaining trees are allowed to grow and seedlings establish themselves. During stage two, many mature trees are removed and the forest is again left alone to grow. At stage three, the remaining mature trees are cut down. By this time, the seedlings have grown into young trees and more new seedlings are growing.

Apply Challenge small groups of students to develop a model of shelterwood cutting. *(Sample model: Use green plastic chips to represent mature trees and brown chips to represent unwanted trees. First stage: Remove all brown chips, leave green chips, add red chips (seedlings). Second stage: Remove some green chips, replace red chips with yellow chips (young trees), and add more red chips (seedlings). Third stage: Remove remaining green chips, replace yellow chips with green chips, replace red chips with yellow chips, and add more red chips.)* Ask: **How does the model illustrate that shelterwood cutting provides a sustainable yield?** *(The forest constantly replenishes itself.)* **learning modality: kinesthetic**

FIGURE 4
Sustainable Forestry
Sustainable forestry practices include the planting of young trees after mature trees have been harvested.

Each logging method has advantages and disadvantages. Clear-cutting is usually quicker and cheaper than selective cutting. It may also be safer for the loggers. In selective cutting, the loggers must move the heavy equipment and logs around the remaining trees in the forest. But selective cutting is usually less damaging to the forest environment than clear-cutting. When an area of forest is clear-cut, the ecosystem changes. After clear-cutting, the soil is exposed to wind and rain. Without the protection of the tree roots, the soil is more easily blown or washed away. Soil washed into streams may harm the fish and other organisms that live there.

Sustainable Forestry Forests can be managed to provide a sustainable yield. A **sustainable yield** is an amount of a renewable resource such as trees that can be harvested regularly without reducing the future supply. Sustainable forestry works sort of like a book swap: as long as you donate a book each time you borrow one, the total supply of books will not be affected. Planting a tree to replace one that was cut down is like donating a book to replace a borrowed one.

In sustainable forestry, after trees are harvested, young trees are planted. Trees must be planted frequently enough to keep a constant supply. Different species grow at different rates. Forests containing faster-growing trees, such as pines, can be harvested and replanted every 20 to 30 years. On the other hand, some forests containing hardwood trees, such as hickory, oak, and cherry, may be harvested only every 40 to 100 years. One sustainable approach is to log small patches of forest. This way, different sections of forest can be harvested every year.

Certified Wood The Forest Stewardship Council is an international organization dedicated to sustainable forest management. This organization oversees certification of forests that are well managed and provide good working conditions for workers. Once a forest is certified, its wood may carry a "well-managed" label. This label allows businesses and individuals to select wood from forests that are managed for sustainable yields.

 What is a sustainable yield?

Fisheries

An area with a large population of valuable ocean organisms is called a **fishery.** Some major fisheries include the Grand Banks off Newfoundland, Georges Bank off New England, and Monterey Canyon off California. Fisheries like these are valuable renewable resources.

Until recently, fisheries seemed like an unlimited resource. The waters held such huge schools of fish. And fish reproduce in incredible numbers. A single codfish can lay as many as 9 million eggs in a single year! But people have discovered that this resource has limits. After many years of big catches, the number of sardines off the California coast suddenly declined. The same thing happened to the huge schools of cod off the New England coast. What caused these changes?

The fish were caught faster than they could breed, so the population decreased. This situation is known as overfishing. Scientists estimate that 70 percent of the world's major fisheries have been overfished. But if fish populations recover, a sustainable yield can again be harvested. **Managing fisheries for a sustainable yield includes strategies such as setting fishing limits, changing fishing methods, developing aquaculture techniques, and finding new resources.**

Fishing Limits Laws can ban the fishing of certain species. Laws may also limit the number or size of fish that can be caught or require that fish be within a certain range of sizes. These laws ensure that young fish survive long enough to reproduce and that all of the largest adult fish aren't caught. If a fishery has been severely overfished, however, the government may ban fishing completely until the populations recover.

FIGURE 5
Fisheries
Even though fisheries are renewable resources, they must be managed for sustainable yields, or the supply of fish may run out.

♦ 787

Answers

Figure 6 Aquaculture provides a much-needed food source. Artificial ponds and bays built for aquaculture often replace natural habitats, and maintaining the farms can cause pollution and spread diseases into natural populations.

> **Reading Checkpoint** Aquaculture is the practice of raising fish and other water-dwelling organisms for food.

Assess

Reviewing Key Concepts

1. a. Because new trees can be replanted to replace cut-down trees, forests are considered renewable resources. **b.** During clear-cutting, the entire tree growth in an area is removed. During selective cutting, trees of a particular species and/or size are removed while other trees remain. **c.** Possible answer: Without tree roots to hold water and soil in place, large amounts of soil were washed into the stream during the rainstorm. The soil in the water has made it more difficult for fish and other aquatic organisms to live.

2. a. Fishing limits can be imposed; fishing methods can be changed; aquaculture can replace catching of wild fish; new resources can be found. **b.** Laws may limit the species, number, and size of fish that can be caught. Fishing methods can be regulated. Laws allow the fish population to reproduce and maintain its size. **c.** If all the largest fish in a region are caught, the average size of the fish may become smaller over time.

Reteach L1

Have students use Figure 3 to explain how overfishing and clear-cutting are similar and how they are different.

Performance Assessment L2

Call on students at random to name a way to conserve forests or fisheries. Evaluate students' understanding of managing resources for sustainable yield.

All in One Teaching Resources, Unit 4

- Section Summary: *Forests and Fisheries*
- Review and Reinforce: *Forests and Fisheries*
- Enrich: *Forests and Fisheries*

FIGURE 6
Aquaculture
Aquaculture is helping to meet the demand for fish. This fish farm in Hawaii raises tilapia.
Applying Concepts *What costs and benefits does aquaculture involve?*

Fishing Methods Today many fishing crews use nets with a larger mesh size that allow small, young fish to escape. In addition, many other fishing practices are regulated by laws. Some fishing methods have been outlawed. These methods include poisoning fish with cyanide and stunning them by exploding dynamite underwater. These techniques harm all the fish in an area rather than targeting certain fish.

Aquaculture The practice of raising fish and other water-dwelling organisms for food is called **aquaculture.** The fish may be raised in artificial ponds or bays. Salmon, catfish, and shrimp are farmed in this way in the United States.

However, aquaculture is not a perfect solution. The artificial ponds and bays often replace natural habitats such as salt marshes. Maintaining the farms can cause pollution and spread diseases into wild fish populations.

New Resources Today about 9,000 different fish species are harvested for food. More than half the animal protein eaten by people throughout the world comes from fish. One way to help feed a growing human population is to fish for new species. Scientists and chefs are working together to introduce people to deep-water species such as monkfish and tile fish, as well as easy-to-farm freshwater fish such as tilapia.

> **Reading Checkpoint** What is aquaculture?

Section 2 Assessment

Target Reading Skills Using Prior Knowledge Review your graphic organizer and revise it based on what you just learned in the section.

Reviewing Key Concepts

1. a. Reviewing Why are forests considered renewable resources?
b. Comparing and Contrasting How does the clear-cutting logging method differ from selective cutting?
c. Developing Hypotheses You are walking in a clear-cut section of forest a few days after a heavy rainstorm. A nearby stream is very muddy and has many dead fish. What might have happened?

2. a. Listing What are four ways fisheries can be managed for a sustainable yield?

b. Explaining What are two kinds of laws that regulate fishing? How can they help ensure the health of a fishery?
c. Predicting What might happen to a fish population over time if all the largest fish in the population were caught? Explain.

Lab zone At-Home **Activity**

Renewable Resource Survey With a family member, conduct a "Forest and Fishery" survey of your home. Make a list of all the things that are made from either forest or fishery products. Then ask other family members to predict how many items are on the list. Are they surprised by the answer?

Lab zone Chapter **Project**

Keep Students on Track Remind students that they need to make notes about abiotic factors as well as notes on organisms. Encourage students to draw or sketch the organisms they observe in detail so that they will be able to identify them using field guides. Students should be beginning to plan how they will present their findings.

Lab zone At-Home **Activity**

Renewable Resource Survey L1
Encourage students to look beyond the most obvious products, such as wood and paper from forests, and salt and seafood from the ocean. Tell them to check labels closely to see if they can find the names of other items. Examples include nuts, spices, tree bark for mulch, and seaweeds.

Skills Lab

Tree Cookie Tales

Problem

What can tree cookies reveal about the past? A tree cookie is a slice of a tree trunk that contains clues about the tree's age, past weather conditions, and fires that occurred during its life.

Skills Focus

observing, inferring, interpreting data

Materials

- tree cookie
- metric ruler
- hand lens
- colored pencils
- calculator (optional)

Procedure

1. Your teacher will give you a "tree cookie." Use a hand lens to examine your tree cookie. Draw a simple diagram of your tree cookie. Label the bark, tree rings, and center, or pith.

2. Notice the light-colored and dark-colored rings. The light ring results from fast springtime growth. The dark ring, where the cells are smaller, results from slower summertime growth. Each pair of light and dark rings represents one year's growth, so the pair is called an annual ring. Observe and count the annual rings.

3. Compare the spring and summer portions of the annual rings. Identify the thinnest and thickest rings.

4. Measure the distance from the center to the outermost edge of the last summer growth ring. This is the radius of your tree cookie. Record your measurement.

5. Measure the distance from the center to the outermost edge of the tenth summer growth ring. Record your measurement.

6. Examine your tree cookie for any other evidence of its history, such as damaged bark or burn marks. Record your observations.

Pith

Summer ring

Spring ring

Bark

Analyze and Conclude

1. **Inferring** How old was your tree? How do you know?

2. **Calculating** What percent of the tree's growth took place during the first ten years of its life? (*Hint:* Divide the distance from the center to the tenth growth ring by the radius. Then multiply by 100. This gives you the percent of growth that occurred during the tree's first ten years.)

3. **Observing** How did the spring rings compare to the summer rings for the same year? Suggest a reason.

4. **Interpreting Data** Why might the annual rings be narrower for some years than for others?

5. **Communicating** Using evidence from your tree cookie, write a paragraph that summarizes the history of the tree. Be sure to include as much detail as possible in your summary.

Design an Experiment

Suppose you had cookies from two other trees of the same species that grew near your tree. Write a plan for verifying the interpretations you made in this lab. *Obtain your teacher's permission before carrying out your investigation.*

---

2. The largest proportion of tree growth usually occurs during a tree's early years.

3. Observations may vary. Spring rings are usually wider because trees undergo a burst of new growth in the spring when it is usually wetter. This is followed by slower growth in summer, when it is usually drier.

4. Growth rings reflect weather conditions. Generally, rings are wider during warmer years and when rainfall is plentiful.

5. In addition to the tree's age and weather-related growth patterns, students may note holes made by insects or birds, blackening due to fire or lightning, a hollow pith due to disease, or cracks and gashes from tools.

Extend Inquiry

Design an Experiment Students' plans should be similar to the lab procedure. Have students share their results.

Skills Lab

Tree Cookie Tales L2

Prepare for Inquiry

Skills Objectives

After this lab, students will be able to

- observe growth rings in a tree cookie
- infer a tree's age from the growth rings
- use their growth ring data to interpret why rings might be narrower some years than others

Prep Time 15 minutes

Class Time 40 minutes

All in One Teaching Resources, Unit 4

- Lab Worksheet: *Tree Cookie Tales*

Advance Planning

Purchase or prepare a tree cookie for each student group. Inexpensive classroom sets of tree cookies are available from biological supply houses. Tree cookies should come from trees that were more than 10 years old. You can make tree cookies by sawing a tree trunk into cross sections 1.5–2.5 cm thick. To preserve homemade tree cookies, spray or paint all surfaces with clear polyurethane or other clear sealant.

Guide Inquiry

Invitation

Point out the picture of the tree cookie and have students read its labels. Ask: **What can you learn from observing a tree cookie?** *(Sample answer: The age of the tree when it was cut down)*

Introducing the Procedure

Before students begin, clarify that a single year's growth is shown by a pair of rings—a light ring for spring and a dark ring for summer.

Troubleshooting the Experiment

When students have counted the number of annual rings, do a spot check to ensure that students have recognized that an annual ring is made up of a pair of rings, one light and one dark.

Expected Outcome

Results will vary depending on the particular tree cookie used.

Analyze and Conclude

1. Ages will vary. The tree's age is equal to the number of annual rings.

Technology and Society

Paper

Key Concept
Evaluate the benefits of using electronic paper versus traditional paper.

Build Background Knowledge
Have students look around the classroom and name all the products they can that are made of paper. Point out that educating students at all levels has been made possible for centuries through printed books. Ask a student volunteer to read the steps in making paper. Have the class identify the resources that are used to make paper. (*Trees, energy in the form of heat, chemicals, and water*) Remind students that even though paper can be recycled, it still remains the single largest component of waste in solid landfills. Explain that paper can be recycled only so many times.

Introduce the Debate
Have a student volunteer read the paragraphs *The Benefits of Paper* and *Paper and the Environment*. Ask: **What are some advantages and disadvantages of using paper?** (*The advantages are that many everyday items are made of paper, paper is inexpensive, and many people are employed in the paper industry. Disadvantages are that resources are used, making paper creates wastes—including dioxins—and paper creates a lot of garbage in landfills.*) **What is the chief advantage of e-paper?** (*It does not have the same environmental costs as paper.*)

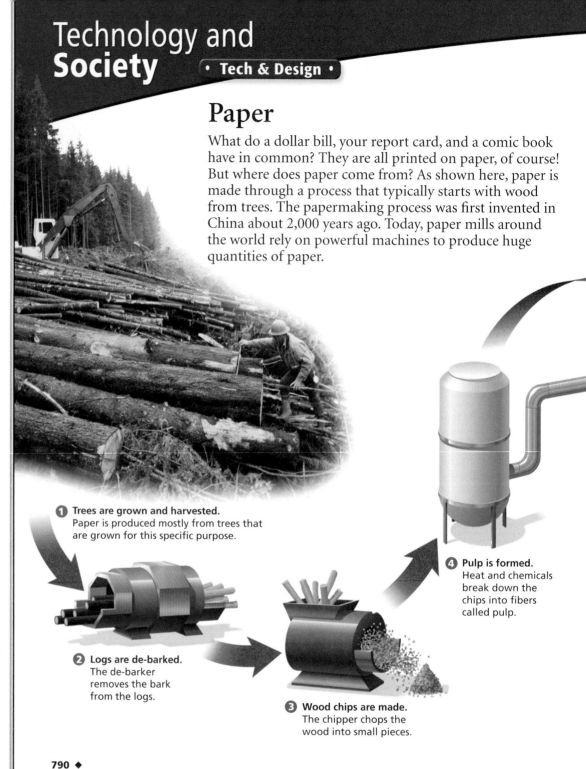

Paper

What do a dollar bill, your report card, and a comic book have in common? They are all printed on paper, of course! But where does paper come from? As shown here, paper is made through a process that typically starts with wood from trees. The papermaking process was first invented in China about 2,000 years ago. Today, paper mills around the world rely on powerful machines to produce huge quantities of paper.

1 Trees are grown and harvested.
Paper is produced mostly from trees that are grown for this specific purpose.

2 Logs are de-barked.
The de-barker removes the bark from the logs.

3 Wood chips are made.
The chipper chops the wood into small pieces.

4 Pulp is formed.
Heat and chemicals break down the chips into fibers called pulp.

790 ◆

Background

History of Science The first recorded effort to make paper was in A.D. 105 by a man in China named Ts'ai Lun. He mashed rags, bamboo, and mulberry wood into a liquid pulp, filtered the pulp on a screen, lifted out a sheet, and let it dry. Over the past 2,000 years, the basic process of making paper has not changed, though the techniques have changed, for example, using different chemicals in the pulping process. E-paper is a major departure from traditional paper. E-paper contains a layer of black and white ink and a layer of tiny electronic circuits. When different voltages are applied to the paper, different patterns of the white and black inks form to produce words and images.

The Benefits of Paper

Paper benefits society in so many ways. Many everyday items are made out of paper—tissues, paper cups, and cardboard packaging. Perhaps most important, paper is used as a portable, inexpensive way to print words and images. Throughout time, paper has allowed people to express their thoughts, record history, and share knowledge. In addition, the paper industry employs many people, and generates income for the economy.

Paper and the Environment

Paper has negative impacts on the environment. Each step in the papermaking process requires energy and produces wastes. Some of these wastes, such as dioxins, are toxic. Dioxins form when water is used to flush chemicals from the paper. Paper products also make up a lot of the garbage in landfills. Because of the environmental costs, engineers are working to create a new type of "paper" called electronic paper, or e-paper. Someday soon, you might use flexible, ultra-thin, digital screens instead of paper.

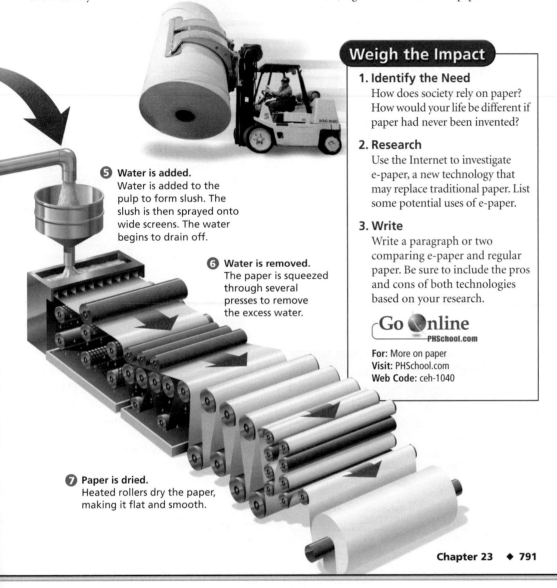

5 **Water is added.**
Water is added to the pulp to form slush. The slush is then sprayed onto wide screens. The water begins to drain off.

6 **Water is removed.**
The paper is squeezed through several presses to remove the excess water.

7 **Paper is dried.**
Heated rollers dry the paper, making it flat and smooth.

Weigh the Impact

1. Identify the Need
How does society rely on paper? How would your life be different if paper had never been invented?

2. Research
Use the Internet to investigate e-paper, a new technology that may replace traditional paper. List some potential uses of e-paper.

3. Write
Write a paragraph or two comparing e-paper and regular paper. Be sure to include the pros and cons of both technologies based on your research.

For: More on paper
Visit: PHSchool.com
Web Code: ceh-1040

Facilitate the Debate

- Divide the class into small groups, and have each group member represent a different viewpoint on whether e-paper should replace traditional paper. Students might represent a person who works for the paper industry, a person whose business relies on paper (such as a bookstore), an ecologist or conservationist, and a citizen. Provide time for the groups to discuss the pros and cons of the widespread use of e-paper.

- After the group discussions, bring the class together to share some of the points discussed in the groups.

Weigh the Impact

1. Society relies on paper for printed words and images, and for everyday items, such as paper cups and cardboard packaging. Possible answer: My life would be different because I would not have had books, magazines, or newspapers to read, and writing would be limited.

2. Possible uses of e-paper include electronic billboards, downloading entire texts of books, downloading daily news instead of getting a paper newspaper, and downloading e-mails from the Internet.

3. Paragraphs should include the factors mentioned in the feature as well as others learned through research. Most students will recognize that e-paper is designed to replace only paper with text and images, not all uses of traditional paper.

Go Online PHSchool.com

For: More on paper
Visit: PHSchool.com
Web Code: ceh-1040

Students can research this issue online.

Extend

Encourage students to research the following on newspapers: 1) the amount of landfill space they take up; 2) the number of trees used to print them; and 3) the amount of energy used to produce them. Explain that these numbers represent resources saved if e-paper is used instead of newspapers.

Objectives

After this lesson, students will be able to

23.3.1 Explain the value of biodiversity.

23.3.2 Identify the factors that affect biodiversity.

23.3.3 Name some human activities that threaten biodiversity.

23.3.4 List some ways to protect biodiversity.

Target Reading Skill

Building Vocabulary Explain that knowing the definitions of key-concept words helps students understand what they read.

Answers

As students read each passage that contains a Key Term, remind them to write a sentence in their own words. Encourage students to write one or two descriptive phrases to help them remember the Key Term. Invite students to share their sentences and phrases.

Preteach

Build Background Knowledge

L1

Millions of Different Species

Ask: **What organisms thrive in our area?** (*Encourage students to consider a wide variety of organism types, including insects, worms, mosses, algae, and bacteria, as well as mammals, birds, fish, reptiles, and amphibians.*) After students have finished naming organisms, ask: **Would you say that there is a great deal of diversity among the species living here?** (*Answers may vary, but in most cases, students will say that there is.*)

Reading Preview

Key Concepts
- In what ways is biodiversity valuable?
- What factors affect an area's biodiversity?
- Which human activities threaten biodiversity?
- How can biodiversity be protected?

Key Terms
- biodiversity • keystone species
- extinction
- endangered species
- threatened species
- habitat destruction
- habitat fragmentation
- poaching • captive breeding

Target Reading Skill

Building Vocabulary After you read this section, reread the paragraphs that contain definitions of Key Terms. Use all the information you have learned to write a meaningful sentence using each Key Term.

Lab zone Discover Activity

How Much Variety Is There?

1. You will be given two cups of seeds and two paper plates. The seeds in cup A represent the trees in a section of tropical rain forest. The seeds in cup B represent the trees in a section of deciduous forest.
2. Pour the seeds from cup A onto a plate. Sort the seeds by type. Count the different types of seeds. This number represents the number of different kinds of trees in that forest.
3. Repeat Step 2 with the seeds in cup B.
4. Share your results with your class. Use the class results to calculate the average number of different kinds of trees in each type of forest.

Think It Over

Inferring How do the variety of trees in the two forests differ? Can you suggest any advantages of having a wide variety of species?

No one knows exactly how many species live on Earth. As you can see in Figure 7, more than 1.5 million species have been identified so far. The number of different species in an area is called its **biodiversity.** It is difficult to estimate the total biodiversity on Earth because many areas of the planet have not been thoroughly studied. Some experts think that the deep oceans alone could contain 10 million new species! Protecting biodiversity is a major environmental issue today.

Diversity of Species

Bacteria
4,000

Insects
950,000

Fungi
72,000

Protists
80,000

Plants
270,000

Other animals
255,000

792 ◆

The Value of Biodiversity

Preserving biodiversity is important. One reason is that wild organisms and ecosystems are a source of beauty and recreation. **In addition, biodiversity has both economic value and ecological value within an ecosystem.**

FIGURE 7
Organisms of many kinds are part of Earth's biodiversity.

Lab zone Discover Activity

Skills Focus Inferring

Materials 2 labeled cups containing different seed mixtures, paper plate

Time 20 minutes

Tips Use a mixture of at least ten types of seeds for Cup A and four or five types for Cup B. Advise students to record their observations in a table with headings "Number of Seeds in Rain Forest,

L1 Sample A" and "Number of Seeds in Deciduous Forest, Sample B."

Expected Outcome The average number of seed types will be greater for the tropical rain forest sample.

Think It Over The wider variety of tree species in a tropical rain forest supports a wider variety of other organisms that depend on the trees for habitat and food.

FIGURE 8
Economic Value of
Biodiversity
These women are breast
cancer survivors. Some of
them probably received
taxol as a treatment. Taxol
was discovered in the Pacific
yew tree by scientists
investigating why the tree
was unusually resistant to
diseases and insects.

Economic Value Many plants, animals, and other organisms have economic value. They provide food and raw materials for medicines, clothing, and other products. For example, taxol, a cancer-fighting chemical, was first discovered in the Pacific yew tree. A country's ecosystems can also be economically valuable. Wildlife tours in rain forests, savannas, mountains ranges, and other locations are common. This ecosystem tourism, or ecotourism, is an important source of jobs for such nations as Brazil, Costa Rica, and Kenya.

Ecological Value All the species in an ecosystem are connected to one another. Species may depend on each other for food and shelter. A change that affects one species will surely affect all the others.

Some species play a particularly important role in their ecosystems. A **keystone species** is a species that influences the survival of many other species in an ecosystem. For example, the sea otter eating a sea urchin in Figure 9 belongs to a keystone species. In the 1800s, hunters on the Pacific coast killed most of the sea otters for fur. The sea urchins, now able to reproduce without control, ate up all the kelp. When sea otters were reintroduced, the kelp population recovered. The ecosystem's balance was restored.

 Reading Checkpoint What is a keystone species?

FIGURE 9
Ecological Value of Biodiversity
The sea otters in the Pacific Ocean near Washington are members of a keystone species. If the population of a keystone species drops too far, the entire ecosystem can be disrupted.
Relating Cause and Effect How do sea otters help keep their ecosystem in balance?

Instruct

The Value of Biodiversity

Teach Key Concepts L2
Economic Value of Biodiversity

Focus Have students describe the different organisms living in some of their favorite areas. Ask: **Would you enjoy this area as much if it didn't have as many different species?**

Teach Tell students that biodiversity is a source of beauty and economic value of any area. Ask: **How can entire ecosystems, such as rain forests, savannas, and mountain ranges, be used to generate sources of money?** *(They can be used for ecotourism, which creates jobs and brings in money from people who visit the sites.)*

Extend Ask: **What might happen if the biodiversity of some of these ecosystems is disrupted?** *(Possible answers: Other species might die out; the area might not be as attractive to tourists.)* **How might this effect the economy of the area?** *(Fewer people might visit the sites, resulting in loss of jobs and revenue.)* **learning modality: logical/ mathematical**

Independent Practice L2

All in One Teaching Resources, Unit 4

• Guided Reading and Study Worksheet: *Biodiversity*

◉ **Student Edition on Audio CD**

Monitor Progress _____ L2

Oral Presentation Have each student present reasons why biodiversity is important to plant and animal species.

Answers
Figure 9 Sea otters prey on and help control the population of sea urchins. If the number of sea otters decreases dramatically, the number of sea urchins increases. The sea urchins are then in a position to eat all the kelp in an area.

Reading Checkpoint A species that influences the survival of many other species in the same ecosystem

Factors Affecting Biodiversity

Teach Key Concepts   **L2**
Identifying Factors

Focus Remind students that climate is the typical weather pattern—precipitation and temperature—of an area over a long period.

Teach Ask: **Which area is more likely to have greater biodiversity—a tropical rain forest or an area closer to Earth's poles?** *(A rain forest)* **Why?** *(Plants there can grow year-round, making food available all year to other organisms.)* **Why does a coral reef have such a diverse ecosystem?** *(A coral reef supports many different niches.)*

Apply Ask: **What might happen to the biodiversity of an area if its climate becomes colder?** *(Its biodiversity might decrease.)* **learning modality: verbal**

Help Students Read   **L1**
Relate Text and Visuals After students have read about factors affecting biodiversity, call their attention to the circle graphs accompanying Figure 10. Ask: **How much of Earth's land area is made up of rain forests?** *(7 percent)* **What percentage of Earth's species are found there?** *(50 percent)* **What explanation can you give to explain how such a small percentage of Earth's land can be home to such a large percentage of species?** *(Rain forests have a climate that allows plants to grow all year and provide many different habitats.)* **learning modality: logical/mathematical**

FIGURE 10
Land and Ocean Ecosystems
Three factors that affect the biodiversity of an ecosystem are area, climate, and niche diversity. **Making Generalizations** *Which factor is most likely responsible for the biodiversity of coral reefs? Of tropical rain forests?*

Earth's Land Ecosystems

Tropical rain forests 7%

Although tropical rain forests make up only 7% of Earth's land area, they are home to more than 50% of the world's species.

Earth's Ocean Ecosystems

Coral reefs 1%

Although coral reefs make up less than 1% of Earth's oceans, they are home to about 20% of the world's saltwater fish species.

794 ◆

Factors Affecting Biodiversity

Biodiversity varies from place to place on Earth. **Factors that affect biodiversity in an ecosystem include area, climate, and diversity of niches.**

Area Within an ecosystem, a large area will contain more species than a small area. For example, suppose you were counting tree species in a forest. You would find far more tree species in a 100-square-meter area than in a 10-square-meter area.

Climate In general, the number of species increases from the poles toward the equator. The tropical rain forests of Latin America, southeast Asia, and central Africa are the most diverse ecosystems in the world. These forests cover only about 7 percent of Earth's land surface but contain more than half of the world's species.

The reason for the great biodiversity in the tropics is not fully understood. Many scientists hypothesize that it has to do with climate. For example, tropical rain forests have fairly constant temperatures and large amounts of rainfall throughout the year. Many plants in these regions grow year-round. This continuous growing season means that food is always available for other organisms.

Differentiated Instruction

Less Proficient Readers   **L1**
Words in Context For students who need more help, review the meanings of the terms *area* (length times width), *climate* (the typical weather pattern in an area over a long period), and *niche* (an organism's unique role in an ecosystem). Students may wish to add these terms, and their definitions, to their own Science Glossaries.

Niche Diversity Coral reefs make up less than 1 percent of the oceans' area. But reefs are home to 20 percent of the world's saltwater fish species. Coral reefs are the second most diverse ecosystems in the world. Found only in shallow, warm waters, coral reefs are often called the rain forests of the sea. A reef supports many different niches for organisms that live under, on, and among the coral. This enables more species to live in the reef than in a more uniform habitat, such as a flat sandbar.

Gene Pool Diversity

Just as the diversity of species is important within an ecosystem, diversity is also important within a species. The organisms in a healthy population have a diversity of traits. Traits such as color, size, and ability to fight disease are determined by genes. Genes are the structures in an organism's cells that carry its hereditary information.

Organisms receive a combination of genes from their parents. Genes determine an organism's characteristics, from its size and appearance to its ability to fight disease.

The organisms in one species share many genes. But each organism also has some genes that differ from those of other individuals. These individual differences make up the total gene "pool" of that species.

Species that lack a diverse gene pool are less able to adapt to changes in the environment. For example, some food crops have little diversity. A fungus once wiped out much of the corn crop in the United States. Fortunately, some wild varieties of corn have genes that make them resistant to the fungus. Scientists were able to use some of those wild varieties to breed corn that could fight off the fungus. A species with a diverse gene pool is better able to survive such challenges.

Reading Checkpoint What do an organism's genes determine?

FIGURE 11
Genetic Diversity
Diverse genes give these potatoes their rainbow of colors. Having a diverse gene pool helps a species fight disease and adapt to changes in its environment.

◆ 795

Lab zone Try This **Activity**

Grocery Gene Pool
With a parent or other adult, visit a supermarket or produce market in your area. Choose one type of fruit or vegetable, such as apples or potatoes. Make a list of all the different varieties of that fruit or vegetable the store sells. Note any differences in appearance between the varieties.

Inferring Judging from the appearance of the different varieties, do you think your fruit or vegetable has a diverse gene pool? Explain.

Lab zone Try This **Activity**

Skills Focus Inferring
Materials none
Time 20 minutes
Tips Each variety of fruit or vegetable will be labeled. Suggest that students take notes as they note differences in appearance.

L1

Expected Outcome Generally, students will infer that the chosen produce has a diverse gene pool.

Extend Suggest students ask the produce manager why the store offers so many varieties. **learning modality: visual**

Gene Pool Diversity

Teach Key Concept **L2**
Diversity and Survival of Species

Focus Ask students how dogs of the same breed might vary. (*Possible answers: Color, coarseness of fur, size*) Tell students that these are only some of the ways a species can vary.

Teach Tell students that genes determine some of an organism's characteristics. Ask: **What is the gene pool of a species?** (*The individual differences resulting from differences in genes between individuals in a species*)

Apply Ask: **How does having a diverse gene pool enable a species to survive changes in the environment?** (*It is likely to have members with characteristics needed in the changing environment.*) **learning modality: logical/mathematical**

Lab zone Build **Inquiry**

L2

Comparing Biodiversity

Materials photographs of ecosystems
Time 15 minutes

Focus Review with students factors that affect biodiversity: area, climate, niche diversity.

Teach Give each pair of students a picture of a different type of ecosystem. Have them analyze the pictures to determine the number and types of organisms shown. Then have students describe the abiotic factors in the ecosystem.

Apply Have students compare the ecosystems to determine which have the greatest biodiversity. Help students identify factors that most likely contribute to the diversity. **learning modality: logical/mathematical**

Monitor Progress **L2**

Writing Have students write a paragraph explaining why gene pool diversity is so important to species' survival.

Answers
Figure 10 Coral reefs—niche diversity; tropical rain forests—climate

Reading Checkpoint Characteristics, such as size, appearance, and ability to fight disease

Extinction of Species

Teach Key Concepts [L2]

Endangered Species

Focus Remind students that not all species of organisms that once lived are still living.

Teach Ask: **What is extinction?** (*The disappearance of all members of a species*) **How do threatened species differ from endangered species?** (*Endangered species are in danger of becoming extinct in the near future. Threatened species could become endangered in the near future.*)

Apply Ask: **What similar problem has caused the populations of California tiger salamanders and grizzly bears to decrease?** (*Destruction of natural habitat*) **learning modality: visual**

Help Students Read [L1]

Use Prior Knowledge Before students read "Extinction of Species," have them work in groups to brainstorm what they know about extinct species, including examples of extinct organisms and causes of extinction. After reading, have groups review their lists and determine how accurate their knowledge of extinction was.

Extinction of Species

The disappearance of all members of a species from Earth is called **extinction.** Extinction is a natural process. But in the last few centuries, the number of species becoming extinct has increased dramatically.

Once the size of a population drops below a certain level, the species may not be able to recover. For example, in the 1800s, there were millions of passenger pigeons in the United States. People hunted the birds, killing many hundreds of thousands. This was only part of the total population. But the remaining birds could not reproduce enough to sustain the population. Only after 1914, when the species became extinct, did people realize that the species could not survive without its enormous numbers.

FIGURE 12
Endangered Species
A broad range of species and habitats are represented on the endangered list in the United States.

◀ **Tennessee Purple Coneflower**
These daisy-like plants grow only in cedar forests in central Tennessee. Conservation organizations and landowners are working together to protect these plants.

California Tiger Salamander ▲
Towns have replaced much of this salamander's habitat. The salamanders that remain are in danger of being run over by cars or washed down storm drains.

◀ **Grizzly Bear**
This omnivore needs a large area to obtain enough food. Shrinking wilderness areas have limited its numbers.

796 ◆

Species in danger of becoming extinct in the near future are called **endangered species.** Species that could become endangered in the near future are called **threatened species.** Threatened and endangered species are found on every continent and in every ocean.

Some endangered or threatened species are well-known animals, such as the tiger or China's giant panda. Others are little known, such as hutias, rodents that live on only a few Caribbean islands. Ensuring that these species survive is one way to protect Earth's biodiversity.

 Reading Checkpoint How has the number of species becoming extinct changed in the last few centuries?

Go Online
PLANET DIARY

For: More on biodiversity
Visit: PHSchool.com
Web Code: ced-5033

Go Online
PLANET DIARY

For: More on biodiversity
Visit: PHSchool.com
Web Code: ced-5033

Students can review biodiversity in an online activity.

▲ **Schaus Swallowtail Butterfly**
Threatened by habitat loss and pesticide pollution in the Florida Keys, this butterfly was nearly wiped out by Hurricane Andrew in 1992.

Whooping Crane ▶
Threatened by habitat destruction and disease, about half of the remaining whooping cranes are in zoos. The species is recovering well since its lowest point in the 1940s.

◀ **Piping Plover**
The population of this tiny coastal bird is recovering as a result of increased protection of its sand-dune nesting sites.

Steller's Sea Lion ▶
Overfishing has led to a decline in this mammal's sources of food. Other factors may also be threatening this species.

◆ 797

Address Misconceptions   L2

Newly Extinct Species

Focus Students usually consider extinction as an event that occurred only in the distant past. Explain to students that many species have become extinct in relatively recent times.

Teach Provide students with a list of species that have become extinct within the past 300 years. Examples include the quagga, dodo, moa, Tasmanian wolf (thylacine), dusky seaside sparrow, Santa Barbara song sparrow, Great auk, Hawaii oo, passenger pigeon, Abington tortoise, blue pike, Tecopa pupfish, and Sampson's pearly mussel. Invite pairs of students to research one of these species. Suggest that students find a description of the species and its habitat and the factors that researchers believe caused the extinction.

Apply Have students create an Extinction Timeline that contains information about all the species students have researched.

Differentiated Instruction

English Learners/Beginning L1
Comprehension: Ask Questions Help students understand the difference between endangered and threatened species. Ask: **What does it mean to be "in danger"? What do you do when you are threatened?** Help students relate the answers to the questions to the meaning of the terms. **learning modality: verbal**

English Learners/Intermediate L2
Comprehension: Ask Questions Have students read the sentences containing the phrases *endangered species* and *threatened species.* Ask whether students can describe the difference between the two, and help them clarify the meanings. **learning modality: verbal**

Monitor Progress   L2

Skills Check Have students explain how endangered species differ from threatened species.

Answer

Reading Checkpoint It increased in the last few centuries.

Living Resources

Show the Video Field Trip to let students experience the world of commercial fishers and understand how aquaculture is helping preserve the world's fish supply. Discussion question: **What is the difference between a fishery and a fish farm?** (*Fisheries are areas of ocean that are home to populations of valuable ocean organisms. A fish farm is a small regulated area in which managers control the environment.*)

Causes of Extinction

Teach Key Concepts L2
Human Causes of Extinction

Focus Tell students that extinction can result from natural causes and human causes.

Teach Ask: **How does habitat fragmentation contribute to extinction?** (*It can expose trees to wind damage; animals may not be able to find enough resources in a small area.*) **What is the illegal removal or killing of wildlife called?** (*Poaching*) **How does pollution contribute to species extinction?** (*Pollution can weaken individuals, kill them, or cause birth defects.*)

Apply Ask: **How does bringing exotic species into an area threaten biodiversity?** (*Some exotic species compete with native species for resources.*) **learning modality: logical/mathematical**

FIGURE 13
Poaching
These scarlet macaws at a zoo in Costa Rica were rescued from poachers who were exporting macaws illegally as pets. Zoo employees will help restore the birds to full health so they can be released back into their habitats.
Inferring *Why are there laws against removing endangered species from their habitats?*

798 ◆

Causes of Extinction

A natural event, such as an earthquake or a volcanic eruption, can damage an ecosystem, wiping out populations or even species. **Human activities can also threaten biodiversity. These activities include habitat destruction, poaching, pollution, and the introduction of exotic species.**

Habitat Destruction The major cause of extinction is **habitat destruction,** the loss of a natural habitat. This can occur when forests are cleared to build towns or create grazing land. Plowing grasslands or filling in wetlands greatly changes those ecosystems. Some species may not be able to survive such changes to their habitats.

Breaking larger habitats into smaller, isolated pieces, or fragments, is called **habitat fragmentation.** For example, building a road through a forest disrupts habitats. This makes trees more vulnerable to wind damage. Plants may be less likely to disperse their seeds successfully. Habitat fragmentation is also very harmful to large mammals. These animals usually need large areas of land to find enough food to survive. They may not be able to obtain enough resources in a small area. They may also be injured trying to cross to another area.

Poaching The illegal killing or removal of wildlife from their habitats is called **poaching.** Many endangered animals are hunted for their skin, fur, teeth, horns, or claws. Hunters sell the animals they kill. The animal parts are then used for making medicines, jewelry, coats, belts, and shoes.

People illegally remove organisms from their habitats to sell them as exotic pets. Tropical fish, tortoises, and parrots are very popular pets, making them valuable to poachers. Endangered plants are sometimes illegally dug up and sold as houseplants or medicines.

California Peregrine Falcon Recovery

The peregrine falcon, the world's fastest bird of prey, was nearly extinct in the United States in 1970. The pesticide DDT was weakening peregrine eggshells, so the eggs rarely hatched. In 1972, the United States banned DDT. Use the graph to answer questions about the peregrine population in California.

1. **Reading Graphs** What variable is plotted on the *x*-axis? What variable is plotted on the *y*-axis?

2. **Interpreting Data** How did California's peregrine population change from 1976 to 1998?

3. **Inferring** Why do you think the peregrine population grew fairly slowly at first?

Peregrine Population in California

4. **Predicting** What might this graph have looked like if DDT had not been banned?

Pollution Some species are endangered because of pollution. Substances that cause pollution, called pollutants, may reach animals through the water they drink or air they breathe. Pollutants may also settle in the soil. From there, they are absorbed by plants and build up in other organisms through the food chain. Pollutants may kill or weaken organisms or cause birth defects.

Exotic Species Introducing exotic species into an ecosystem can threaten biodiversity. When European sailors began visiting Hawaii hundreds of years ago, rats from their ships escaped onto the islands. Without any predators in Hawaii, the rats multiplied quickly. They ate the eggs of the nene goose. To protect the geese, people brought the rat-eating mongoose from India to help control the rat population. Unfortunately, the mongooses preferred eating eggs to rats. With both the rats and the mongoose eating its eggs, the nene goose is now endangered.

 What is poaching?

FIGURE 14
Kudzu
Kudzu is an exotic species that was introduced to the United States from Japan in 1876. It can grow up to 30 centimeters a day, so its vines can quickly strangle native trees and shrubs. It can also take over abandoned structures, such as this house in Georgia.

Chapter 23 ◆ 799

Math Skill Making and interpreting graphs

Focus Tell students that the recovery of the peregrine falcon population is represented by a line graph, the most useful graph for showing change over an interval of time.

Teach Remind students what the axes represent and how the grid is structured. Ask: **What information do you have at any point along the graph?** (*The number of breeding pairs of birds in a particular year*) **How can you determine how many breeding pairs existed in 1990?** (*Follow the grid line for 1990 until it reaches the graph, then follow the grid line to the left. Read the number on the vertical axis: just over 100.*) **About how many breeding pairs existed in 1975?** (*About 10*)

Answers
1. Time interval in years is on the *x*-axis. Number of breeding pairs of peregrine falcons is on the *y*-axis.
2. The population grew steadily, except for a brief drop around 1980, until 1994, when the number of breeding pairs remained the same for the four following years.
3. There were only a few breeding pairs at first, so they could produce only a few young. These, in turn, had to grow up before they had a chance to breed. As more pairs grew to breeding age, more and more young could be produced.
4. The graph probably would have sloped downward from left to right, possibly reaching zero breeding pairs.

Monitor Progress _____ L2

Skills Check Call on students to identify and briefly explain the four causes of extinction presented in the text.

Answers
Figure 13 Removing an individual of an endangered species from its habitat subjects the individual to stress and risks, which may limit the individual's ability to thrive, thereby weakening the already endangered species.

 The illegal killing or removal of wildlife from its habitat

799

Protecting Biodiversity

Teach Key Concepts
L2

Evaluating Approaches

Focus Remind students that biodiversity has both ecological and economic value within an ecosystem.

Teach Encourage students to share what they know about captive breeding programs in zoos and wildlife preserves. Then ask: **What are the advantages and disadvantages of this approach for protecting biodiversity?** (*Sometimes it is the only way to save a species. Captive breeding can be expensive.*) **What is one disadvantage of using laws and treaties to protect species?** (*Laws and treaties that have such a wide scope are sometimes difficult to enforce. The CITES treaty, for example, protects more than 800 species.*) **Why is setting aside wildlife habitats as parks an effective way to preserve biodiversity?** (*Protecting entire ecosystems ensures that many habitats are preserved, which contributes to diversity.*)

Apply How does setting aside large ecosystems as wildlife habitats protect species that live only in a small area of the ecosystem? (*Protecting whole ecosystems saves not only endangered species but also the species they depend on and those that depend on them.*) **learning modality: verbal**

Help Students Read
L1

Identifying Main Ideas

Refer to the Content Refresher, which provides guidelines for identifying main idea. Have students read the main topic sentence in bold type under the heading Protecting Biodiversity. Ask: **Given this topic sentence, what are the main ideas that you should look for in the selection?** (*How captive breeding, laws and treaties, and habitat preservation protect biodiversity*) After students read the selection, have students work in groups to create index cards with a brief explanation of how each factor protects biodiversity.

FIGURE 15
Captive Breeding
Captive breeding programs use a scientific approach to protect endangered species. California condor chicks raised in captivity need to learn what adult condors look like. Here, a scientist uses a puppet to feed and groom a chick. **Predicting** *What sort of problems could animals raised by humans come upon when they are released into the wild?*

FIGURE 16
A Protected Species
Laws against selling products made from endangered species have helped protect animals such as these ocelots. These small cats were once hunted nearly to extinction for their fur.

800 ◆

Protecting Biodiversity

Some people who work to preserve biodiversity focus on protecting individual endangered species. Others try to protect entire ecosystems, such as the Great Barrier Reef in Australia. **Three successful approaches to protecting biodiversity are captive breeding, laws and treaties, and habitat preservation.**

Captive Breeding Captive breeding is the mating of animals in zoos or wildlife preserves. Scientists care for the young, and then release them into the wild when they are grown.

Captive breeding was the only hope for the California condor, the largest bird in North America. Condors became endangered due to habitat destruction, poaching, and pollution. By 1984, there were only 15 California condors. Scientists captured all the condors and brought them to zoos to breed. Today, there are more than 200 California condors. Though successful, this program has cost more than $20 million. You can see the drawback of captive breeding.

Laws and Treaties Laws can help protect individual species. In the United States, the Endangered Species Act prohibits trade in products made from threatened or endangered species. This law also requires the development of plans to save endangered species. American alligators and green sea turtles have begun to recover as a result of this law.

The most important international treaty protecting wildlife is the Convention on International Trade in Endangered Species. This treaty lists more than 800 threatened and endangered species that cannot be traded for profit. Treaties like this are difficult to enforce. Even so, this treaty has helped to protect many endangered species, including African elephants.

Habitat Preservation The most effective way to preserve biodiversity is to protect whole ecosystems. Protecting whole ecosystems saves not only endangered species, but also the species they depend upon and those that depend upon them.

Beginning in 1872 with Yellowstone National Park, the world's first national park, many countries have set aside wildlife habitats as parks and refuges. In addition, private organizations have purchased millions of hectares of endangered habitats throughout the world. Today, there are about 7,000 nature parks, preserves, and refuges in the world.

To be most effective, reserves must have the characteristics of diverse ecosystems. For example, they must be large enough to support the populations that live there. The reserves must contain a variety of niches. And of course, it is still necessary to keep the air, land, and water clean, control poaching, and remove exotic species.

 Reading Checkpoint What is the most effective way to preserve biodiversity?

FIGURE 17
Habitat Preservation
Preserving whole habitats is an effective way to protect biodiversity. Habitat preservation is the aim of national parks such as Yellowstone.

Section 3 Assessment

Target Reading Skill Building Vocabulary Use your sentences to help answer the questions.

Reviewing Key Concepts

1. **a. Listing** What are two ways in which biodiversity is valuable?
   b. Problem Solving What economic reasons could you give people in the rain forest for preserving the ecosystem?
2. **a. Identifying** What are three factors that affect the biodiversity in an ecosystem?
   b. Explaining How does each of these factors affect biodiversity?
   c. Developing Hypotheses Would you expect to find great biodiversity in the tundra biome? Why or why not?
3. **a. Listing** Name four human activities that can threaten biodiversity.
   b. Applying Concepts Black bears are roaming through a new housing development in search of food, even though the housing development is still surrounded by forest. How can you account for the bears' behavior?

4. **a. Reviewing** What are three approaches to protecting biodiversity?
   b. Relating Cause and Effect For each approach to protecting biodiversity, list at least one factor that might limit its success.
   c. Making Judgments List some ways in which those limitations might be dealt with.

Lab zone At-Home Activity

Species Refuges Obtain a map of your community or state. With a family member, identify any city, state, or national parks, reserves, or refuges in your area. Choose one location and find out whether there are endangered or threatened species living there. Then prepare a five-minute presentation for your class on what you learned.

Chapter 23 ◆ 801

Lab zone Chapter Project

Keep Students on Track As students observe their plots, encourage them to draw the organisms in detail so that they can identify them later using field guides. Remind students to make notes about abiotic factors as well. Check each group's notebook occasionally to make sure students are recording data.

Lab zone At-Home Activity

Species Refuges L1 Students can contact their state's EPA, local Audubon Society, or parks department. Remind students that refuges near bodies of water may be used primarily by migrating species. Students' presentations should describe the habitats of endangered or threatened species in the area.

Monitor Progress _____ L2

Skills Check Ask individual students to describe one way to protect biodiversity.

Answers
Figure 15 They may be unable to find food and feed themselves, they might be too trustful of humans, and they might not recognize their natural predators.

Reading Checkpoint Preserving entire ecosystems

Assess

Reviewing Key Concepts

1. **a.** Biodiversity has both economic and ecological value. **b.** Using the rain forest for ecotourism brings in money. Certain organisms may provide food or medicines for humans.
2. **a.** area, climate, niche diversity **b.** Greater area, greater niche diversity, and year-round growing seasons and abundant rainfall all yield greater biodiversity. **c.** No; the tundra growing season is too short to be able to provide a year-round food source for organisms.
3. **a.** Habitat destruction, poaching, pollution, and introduction of exotic species **b.** Habitat fragmentation
4. **a.** Captive breeding, laws and treaties, habitat preservation **b.** Captive breeding is expensive. Laws and treaties are difficult to enforce. Preserved habitats must have characteristics of diverse ecosystems **c.** Sample answer: Make certain exotic species are not accidentally introduced by visitors, campers, and boaters, limit travel by automobile to reduce pollution, and minimize the number of roads.

Reteach L1

As a class, list ways in which humans threaten biodiversity and ways humans preserve biodiversity.

All in One Teaching Resources, Unit 4
- Section Summary: *Biodiversity*
- Review and Reinforce: *Biodiversity*
- Enrich: *Biodiversity*

Interactive Textbook

- Complete student edition
- Section and chapter self-assessments
- Assessment reports for teachers

Help Students Read

Building Vocabulary

Word-Part Analysis List on the board the following word parts and meanings: *bio,* meaning "life"; *aqua,* meaning "water"; and *non,* meaning "not." Have students identify these word parts in the vocabulary terms. Discuss the terms' meanings with students.

Vocabulary Knowledge Rating Chart

Have students construct a chart with four columns: *Term, Can Define or Use It, Have Heard or Seen It,* and *Don't Know.* Have students copy the Key Terms for this chapter under the first column and then rate their knowledge of each.

Connecting Concepts

Concept Maps Help students develop one way to show how the information in this chapter is related. When making environmental decisions, the issues—the impact of resource use, population growth, and pollution—are debated to help balance the needs of the environment and the needs of people. Have students brainstorm to identify the Key Concepts, Key Terms, details, and examples. Then write each one on a sticky note and attach it at random on chart paper or on the board.

Tell students that this concept map will be organized in hierarchical order and to begin at the top with the Key Concepts. Ask students these questions to guide them to categorize the information on the stickies: **How can environmental decisions affect resources? How can environmental decisions affect biodiversity? What must be considered when making environmental decisions?**

① Environmental Issues

Key Concepts

- Environmental issues fall into three general categories: resource use, population growth, and pollution.
- To help balance the different opinions on an environmental issue, decision makers weigh the costs and benefits of a proposal.

Key Terms

natural resource
renewable resource
nonrenewable resource
pollution
environmental science

② Forests and Fisheries

Key Concepts

- Because new trees can be planted to replace trees that are cut down, forests can be renewable resources.
- Managing fisheries for a sustainable yield includes setting fishing limits, changing fishing methods, developing aquaculture techniques, and finding new resources.

Key Terms

clear-cutting
selective cutting
sustainable yield
fishery
aquaculture

③ Biodiversity

Key Concepts

- Biodiversity has both economic value and ecological value within an ecosystem.
- Factors that affect biodiversity in an ecosystem include area, climate, and diversity of niches.
- Human activities can threaten biodiversity. These activities include habitat destruction, poaching, pollution, and the introduction of exotic species.
- Three successful approaches to protecting biodiversity are captive breeding, laws and treaties, and habitat preservation.

Key Terms

biodiversity
keystone species
extinction
endangered species
threatened species
habitat destruction
habitat fragmentation
poaching
captive breeding

Prompt students by using connecting words or phrases such as "affected by" or "managed by" to indicate the basis for the organization of the map. The phrases should form a sentence between or among a set of concepts.

Answers

Accept logical presentations by students.

All in One Teaching Resources, Unit 4

- Key Terms Review: *Living Resources*
- Connecting Concepts: *Living Resources*

Review and Assessment

Go Online
PHSchool.com
For: Self-Assessment
Visit: PHSchool.com
Web Code: cha-4230

Organizing Information

Concept Mapping Copy the concept map about biodiversity onto a separate sheet of paper. Then complete it and add a title. (For more on Concept Mapping, see the Skills Handbook.)

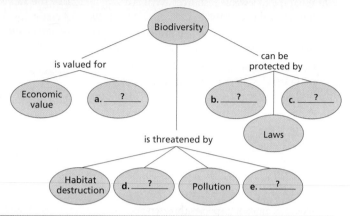

Reviewing Key Terms

Choose the letter of the best answer.

1. The contamination of Earth's air, land, or water is called
   a. extinction.
   b. aquaculture.
   c. pollution.
   d. habitat destruction.

2. The practice of raising fish for food is called
   a. aquaculture.
   b. overfishing.
   c. poaching.
   d. captive breeding.

3. The most diverse ecosystems in the world are
   a. coral reefs.
   b. deserts.
   c. grasslands.
   d. tropical rain forests.

4. If all members of a species disappear from Earth, that species is
   a. extinct.
   b. endangered.
   c. renewable.
   d. threatened.

5. Species that are in danger of becoming extinct in the near future are called
   a. exotic species.
   b. endangered species.
   c. keystone species.
   d. threatened species.

6. The most effective way to preserve biodiversity is through
   a. habitat fragmentation.
   b. habitat destruction.
   c. habitat preservation.
   d. captive breeding.

Writing in Science

Dialogue The salmon population in an area of the ocean has declined significantly. Fishers depend on catching salmon to make a living. Write a dialogue in which an environmental scientist and a fisher try to find a solution to the problem.

Discovery CHANNEL SCHOOL

Living Resources
Video Preview
Video Field Trip
▶ Video Assessment

Chapter 23 ◆ 803

Go Online
PHSchool.com
For: Self-Assessment
Visit: PHSchool.com
Web Code: cha-4230

Students can take a practice online test that is automatically scored.

All in One Teaching Resources, Unit 4
• Transparency LS225
• Chapter Test
• Performance Assessment Teacher Notes
• Performance Assessment Student Worksheet
• Performance Assessment Scoring Rubric

⊚ *ExamView®* **Computer Test Bank CD-ROM**

Review and Assessment

Organizing Information
a. Ecological value
b. Captive Breeding
c. Habitat preservation
d. Poaching
e. Exotic species

Reviewing Key Terms
1. c **2.** a **3.** d **4.** a **5.** b **6.** c

Writing in Science

Writing Mode Persuasion

Scoring Rubric

4 Includes opinions and detailed reasons for both sides of the issue
3 Includes all criteria
2 Includes brief details or omits some criteria
1 Includes inaccurate information and omits some criteria

Discovery CHANNEL SCHOOL Video Assessment

Living Resources

Show the Video Assessment to review chapter content and as a prompt for the writing assignment. Discussion questions: **Why is it important for fishers to throw back the younger, smaller fish and crabs that they catch?** *(The smaller fish and crabs will mature and reproduce.)* **What is aquaculture? Describe one advantage and one disadvantage of aquaculture.** *(A type of fish farming in which managers control the environment, and supply food and protection from predators; aquaculture allows for less fish to be taken from the ocean, but disease can spread easily in the close quarters and runoff can pollute natural waterways and spread disease.)*

Checking Concepts

7. A renewable resource is either always available or is naturally replaced in a relatively short time. A nonrenewable resource is not replaced in a useful time frame.

8. By considering the viewpoints of many different people and weighing the costs and benefits of different solutions

9. For a sustainable yield in a sustainable forest, after trees are harvested, young trees are planted. In fisheries, yields can be sustained by using strategies such as setting limits, changing fishing methods, developing aquaculture, and finding new resources.

10. Any one: Set limits on the amount or size of fish that can be caught; use nets with larger mesh size; outlaw fishing methods that kill all the fish in an area rather than selected species; aquaculture; harvest different species

11. Species with gene pool diversity are better able to adapt to changes in the environment.

12. Species lose the places where they feed, breed, and nest. If they cannot find a substitute niche, they must move to a new location to survive. If they cannot relocate, they will not survive.

13. When an exotic species is introduced into an ecosystem, there may be no natural predators to keep the new species from multiplying. The new species may then threaten one or more local species.

Thinking Critically

14. As the number of humans increase, they use more resources, which can reduce resource availability and contribute to pollution, such as air pollution that is produced when fossil fuels are burned.

15. Clear-cutting is shown. Clear-cutting is usually quicker and cheaper, but it changes the ecosystem. It exposes soil to wind and rain, which can result in erosion. Selective cutting is usually less damaging to the environment.

16. An exotic species may prey on native species or compete with them for limited resources. If the exotic species has no natural predators in its new habitat, it may outcompete the native species.

17. Sample answer: The species might have been the source of a medicine or had another use that is unknown today. The species might have been important to the survival of another species.

Review and Assessment

Checking Concepts

7. What is a renewable resource? What is a nonrenewable resource?

8. Describe how environmental decisions are made.

9. How does the idea of a sustainable yield pertain to forestry? How does it apply to fisheries?

10. Describe one way that overfishing can be prevented.

11. Why is gene pool diversity important to survival of a species?

12. Explain how habitat destruction affects species.

13. How can an exotic species threaten an ecosystem?

Thinking Critically

14. Relating Cause and Effect Explain how human population growth affects resource use and pollution.

15. Comparing and Contrasting Which logging method is shown below? Compare the effects of this method with those of selective cutting.

16. Making Generalizations Describe how an exotic species can threaten other species in an ecosystem.

17. Predicting How could the extinction of a species today affect your life in 20 years?

18. Making Judgments Should keystone species get special legal protection? Explain.

Applying Skills

Use the table to answer Questions 19–23.

A study was done to identify the reasons why mammal and bird species become endangered or threatened. The data are shown in the table below.

Reason	Mammals	Birds
Poaching	31%	20%
Habitat loss	32%	60%
Exotic species	17%	12%
Other causes	20%	8%

19. Graphing Make a bar graph comparing the reasons why mammals and birds become endangered or threatened. Show reasons on the horizontal axis and percentages of animal groups on the vertical axis.

20. Interpreting Data What is the major reason that mammals become endangered or threatened? What is the main threat to birds?

21. Predicting Would stricter laws against poaching be likely to benefit mammal species or bird species more? Explain.

22. Making Judgments If you were on a committee formed to protect bird species in your state, what action would you recommend? Support your recommendation using the data in the table.

23. Developing Hypotheses Suggest two explanations for the differences between the data for mammals and birds.

Lab zone Chapter Project

Performance Assessment In your presentation, clearly describe the biodiversity you observed in your plot. You can use drawings, video, photos, or a computer for your presentation. Be sure to include the data you collected on abiotic factors as well.

18. Answers may vary. Examples: Some students may say that since keystone species influence the survival of other species, they should get special legal protection. Other students may say that particular species may be important and need legal protection even though they are not keystone species.

Lab zone Chapter Project L3

Performance Assessment Before groups give their presentations to the entire class, meet with each group briefly to review students' plans. Suggest any questions that may not have occurred to them.

Let each group reconvene to discuss their answers to these questions. Then encourage all groups to share their ideas in a class discussion.

Standardized Test Prep

Choose the letter of the best answer.

1. A disease kills most members of a plant species
in an ecosystem. Several animal species feed on
that plant species. After a time, the populations
of those animal species decline. Which of the
following inferences is valid?
  A The ecosystem will soon recover.
  B The plant species will become extinct.
  C The plant species is a keystone species in
that ecosystem.
  D Several animal species in the ecosystem will
eventually become extinct.

2. In some areas, foresters plant one tree for every
tree they cut. This activity is an example of
  F a nonsustainable approach to a
nonrenewable natural resource.
  G a sustainable approach to a nonrenewable
natural resource.
  H a nonsustainable approach to a renewable
natural resource.
  J a sustainable approach to a renewable
natural resource.

*The graph below shows how the population of
one kind of fish, haddock, changed in Georges
Bank between 1980 and 2000. Use the graph
below to answer Questions 3 and 4.*

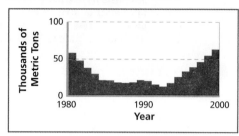

3. Which of the following statements is a valid
interpretation of the graphed data?
  A Overfishing of haddock began in 1990 and
stopped in 2000.
  B By 2000, the haddock population had
recovered.
  C The haddock population from 1980 to 1990
demonstrates the idea of sustainable use.
  D The haddock population is decreasing and
will probably continue to decrease.

4. Which of the following probably accounts for
the trend shown between 1992 and 2000?
  F laws regulating haddock fishing
  G overfishing
  H niche diversity
  J habitat fragmentation

5. An environmental impact statement describes
the possible effects that a project might have on
the environment. Which of the following
would be included in an environmental impact
statement on drilling for oil in Antarctica?
  A the costs of setting up a drilling operation
  B the estimated amount of oil produced by the
drilling operation
  C the effect of oil spills on organisms living in
Antarctica
  D the effect of increased oil production on the
economy

Constructed Response

6. Explain how people benefit when biodiversity
is maintained and worldwide ecosystems
contain a wide variety of organisms.

Applying Skills

19.

Threats to Mammals and Birds

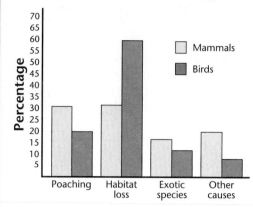

20. Habitat loss is the major cause for both
birds and mammals. Poaching is almost as
significant as habitat loss for mammals.

21. According to the data, stricter laws
against poaching would benefit mammals
more, since poaching is a more important
threat to mammals.

22. Sample answer: Areas where birds tend
to nest and breed, such as wetlands, are
particularly threatened by habitat
destruction and should be protected.

23. Habitat loss is a much more important
cause of extinction for birds than for
mammals because most birds rely on trees,
and forests are being cut down rapidly.
Poaching may be a more important threat to
mammals than birds because most birds are
harder to catch than most mammals.

Standardized Test Prep

1. C **2.** J **3.** B **4.** F **5.** C
6. Sample answer: People benefit both
economically and ecologically when
biodiversity is maintained. Biodiversity
enables a supply of diverse foods and raw
materials for clothing, medicine, and other
products. Ecotourism is an important source
of jobs and money in many nations.

Think Like a Scientist

The Skills Handbook is designed as a reference for students to use whenever they need to review inquiry, reading, or math skills. You can use the activities in this part of the Skills Handbook to teach or reinforce inquiry skills.

Observing

Focus Remind students that an observation is what they can see, hear, smell, taste, or feel.

Teach Invite students to make observations of the classroom. List these observations on the board. Challenge students to identify the senses they used to make each observation. Then, ask: **Which senses will you use to make observations from the photograph on this page?** (*Sight is the only sense that can be used to make observations from the photograph.*)

Activity

Some observations that students might make include that the boy is skateboarding, wearing a white helmet, and flying in the air. Make sure that students' observations are confined to only things that they can actually see in the photograph.

Inferring

Focus Choose one or two of the classroom observations listed on the board, and challenge students to interpret them. Guide students by asking why something appears as it does.

Teach Encourage students to describe their thought processes in making their inferences. Point out where they used their knowledge and experience to interpret the observations. Then invite students to suggest other possible interpretations for the observations. Ask: **How can you find out whether an inference is correct?** (*By further investigation*)

Activity

One possible inference is that the boy just skated off a ramp at a skate park. Invite students to share their experiences that helped them make the inference.

Predicting

Focus Discuss the weather forecast for the next day. Point out that this prediction is an inference about what will happen in the

future based on observations and experience.

Teach Help students differentiate between a prediction and an inference. You might organize the similarities and differences in a Venn diagram on the board. Both are interpretations of observations using experience and knowledge, and both can be incorrect. Inferences describe current or past events. Predictions describe future events.

SKILLS
Handbook

Think Like a Scientist

Scientists have a particular way of looking at the world, or scientific habits of mind. Whenever you ask a question and explore possible answers, you use many of the same skills that scientists do. Some of these skills are described on this page.

Observing

When you use one or more of your five senses to gather information about the world, you are **observing.** Hearing a dog bark, counting twelve green seeds, and smelling smoke are all observations. To increase the power of their senses, scientists sometimes use microscopes, telescopes, or other instruments that help them make more detailed observations.

An observation must be an accurate report of what your senses detect. It is important to keep careful records of your observations in science class by writing or drawing in a notebook. The information collected through observations is called evidence, or data.

Inferring

When you interpret an observation, you are **inferring,** or making an inference. For example, if you hear your dog barking, you may infer that someone is at your front door. To make this inference, you combine the evidence— the barking dog—and your experience or knowledge—you know that your dog barks when strangers approach—to reach a logical conclusion.

Notice that an inference is not a fact; it is only one of many possible interpretations for an observation. For example, your dog may be barking because it wants to go for a walk. An inference may turn out to be incorrect even if it is based on accurate observations and logical reasoning. The only way to find out if an inference is correct is to investigate further.

Predicting

When you listen to the weather forecast, you hear many predictions about the next day's weather—what the temperature will be, whether it will rain, and how windy it will be. Weather forecasters use observations and knowledge of weather patterns to predict the weather. The skill of **predicting** involves making an inference about a future event based on current evidence or past experience.

Because a prediction is an inference, it may prove to be false. In science class, you can test some of your predictions by doing experiments. For example, suppose you predict that larger paper airplanes can fly farther than smaller airplanes. How could you test your prediction?

Activity

Use the photograph to answer the questions below.

Observing Look closely at the photograph. List at least three observations.

Inferring Use your observations to make an inference about what has happened. What experience or knowledge did you use to make the inference?

Predicting Predict what will happen next. On what evidence or experience do you base your prediction?

Activity

Students might predict that the boy will land and skate to the other side. Others might predict that the boy will fall. Students should also describe the evidence or experience on which they based their predictions.

Classifying

Could you imagine searching for a book in the library if the books were shelved in no particular order? Your trip to the library would be an all-day event! Luckily, librarians group together books on similar topics or by the same author. Grouping together items that are alike in some way is called **classifying.** You can classify items in many ways: by size, by shape, by use, and by other important characteristics.

Like librarians, scientists use the skill of classifying to organize information and objects. When things are sorted into groups, the relationships among them become easier to understand.

Activity

Classify the objects in the photograph into two groups based on any characteristic you choose. Then use another characteristic to classify the objects into three groups.

Activity

This student is using a model to demonstrate what causes day and night on Earth. What do the flashlight and the tennis ball in the model represent?

Making Models

Have you ever drawn a picture to help someone understand what you were saying? Such a drawing is one type of model. A model is a picture, diagram, computer image, or other representation of a complex object or process. **Making models** helps people understand things that they cannot observe directly.

Scientists often use models to represent things that are either very large or very small, such as the planets in the solar system, or the parts of a cell. Such models are physical models—drawings or three-dimensional structures that look like the real thing. Other models are mental models—mathematical equations or words that describe how something works.

Communicating

Whenever you talk on the phone, write a report, or listen to your teacher at school, you are communicating. **Communicating** is the process of sharing ideas and information with other people. Communicating effectively requires many skills, including writing, reading, speaking, listening, and making models.

Scientists communicate to share results, information, and opinions. Scientists often communicate about their work in journals, over the telephone, in letters, and on the Internet.

They also attend scientific meetings where they share their ideas with one another in person.

Activity

On a sheet of paper, write out clear, detailed directions for tying your shoe. Then exchange directions with a partner. Follow your partner's directions exactly. How successful were you at tying your shoe? How could your partner have communicated more clearly?

Skills Handbook ◆ 807

Classifying

Focus Encourage students to think of common things that are classified.

Teach Ask: **What things at home are classified?** (*Clothing might be classified in order to place it in the appropriate dresser drawer; glasses, plates, and silverware are grouped in different parts of the kitchen; screws, nuts, bolts, washers, and nails might be separated into small containers.*) **What are some things that scientists classify?** (*Scientists classify many things they study, including organisms, geological features and processes, and kinds of machines.*)

Activity

Some characteristics students might use include color, pattern of color, use of balls, and size. Students' criteria for classification should clearly divide the balls into two, and then three, distinct groups.

Making Models

Focus Ask: **What are some models you have used to study science?** (*Students might have used human anatomical models, solar system models, maps, or stream tables.*) **How have these models helped you?** (*Models can help you learn about things that are difficult to study because they are very large, very small, or highly complex.*)

Teach Be sure students understand that a model does not have to be three-dimensional. For example, a map is a model, as is a mathematical equation. Have students look at the photograph of the student modeling the causes of day and night on Earth. Ask: **What quality of each item makes this a good model?** (*The flashlight gives off light, and the ball is round and can be rotated by the student.*)

Activity

The flashlight represents the sun and the ball represents Earth.

Communicating

Focus Have students identify the methods of communication they have used today.

Teach Ask: **How is the way you communicate with a friend similar to and different from the way scientists communicate about their work to other scientists?** (*Both may communicate using various methods, but scientists must be very detailed and precise, whereas communication between friends may be less detailed and precise.*) Encourage students to communicate like a scientist as they carry out the activity.

Activity

Students' answers will vary but should identify a step-by-step process for tying a shoe. Help students identify communication errors such as leaving out a step, putting steps in the wrong order, or disregarding the person's handedness.

Making Measurements

Students can refer to this part of the Skills Handbook whenever they need to review how to make measurements with SI units. You can use the activities here to teach or reinforce SI units.

Measuring in SI

Focus Review SI units with students. Begin by providing metric rulers, graduated cylinders, balances, and Celsius thermometers. Use these tools to reinforce that the meter is the unit of length, the liter is the unit of volume, the gram is the unit of mass, and the degree Celsius is the unit of temperature.

Teach Ask: **If you want to measure the length and the width of the classroom, which SI unit would you use?** (*Meter*) **Which unit would you use to measure the amount of mass in your textbook?** (*Gram*) **Which would you use to measure how much water a drinking glass holds?** (*Liter*) **When would you use the Celsius scale?** (*To measure the temperature of something*) Then use the measuring equipment to review SI prefixes. For example, ask: **What are the smallest units on the metric ruler?** (*Millimeters*) **How many millimeters are there in one centimeter?** (*10 millimeters*) **How many in 10 centimeters?** (*100 millimeters*) **How many centimeters are there in one meter?** (*100 centimeters*) **What does 1,000 meters equal?** (*One kilometer*)

Activity

Length The length of the shell is 7.8 centimeters, or 78 millimeters. If students need more practice measuring length, have them use meter sticks and metric rulers to measure various objects in the classroom.

Activity

Liquid Volume The volume of water in the graduated cylinder is 62 milliliters. If students need more practice, have them use a graduated cylinder to measure different volumes of water.

808

Making Measurements

By measuring, scientists can express their observations more precisely and communicate more information about what they observe.

Measuring in SI

The standard system of measurement used by scientists around the world is known as the International System of Units, which is abbreviated as SI (**Système International d'Unités,** in French). SI units are easy to use because they are based on multiples of 10. Each unit is ten times larger than the next smallest unit and one tenth the size of the next largest unit. The table lists the prefixes used to name the most common SI units.

Common SI Prefixes		
Prefix	**Symbol**	**Meaning**
kilo-	k	1,000
hecto-	h	100
deka-	da	10
deci-	d	0.1 (one tenth)
centi-	c	0.01 (one hundredth)
milli-	m	0.001 (one thousandth)

Length To measure length, or the distance between two points, the unit of measure is the **meter (m).** The distance from the floor to a door-knob is approximately one meter. Long distances, such as the distance between two cities, are measured in kilometers (km). Small lengths are measured in centimeters (cm) or millimeters (mm). Scientists use metric rulers and meter sticks to measure length.

Common Conversions	
1 km	= 1,000 m
1 m	= 100 cm
1 m	= 1,000 mm
1 cm	= 10 mm

Activity

The larger lines on the metric ruler in the picture show centimeter divisions, while the smaller, unnumbered lines show millimeter divisions. How many centimeters long is the shell? How many millimeters long is it?

808 ◆

Liquid Volume To measure the volume of a liquid, or the amount of space it takes up, you will use a unit of measure known as the **liter (L).** One liter is the approximate volume of a medium-size carton of milk. Smaller volumes are measured in milliliters (mL). Scientists use graduated cylinders to measure liquid volume.

Activity

The graduated cylinder in the picture is marked in milliliter divisions. Notice that the water in the cylinder has a curved surface. This curved surface is called the *meniscus*. To measure the volume, you must read the level at the lowest point of the meniscus. What is the volume of water in this graduated cylinder?

Common Conversion
1 L = 1,000 mL

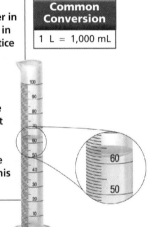

Mass To measure mass, or the amount of matter in an object, you will use a unit of measure known as the **gram (g).** One gram is approximately the mass of a paper clip. Larger masses are measured in kilograms (kg). Scientists use a balance to find the mass of an object.

Common Conversion

1 kg = 1,000 g

Activity

The mass of the potato in the picture is measured in kilograms. What is the mass of the potato? Suppose a recipe for potato salad called for one kilogram of potatoes. About how many potatoes would you need?

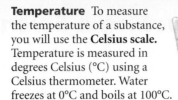

0.25 KG

Temperature To measure the temperature of a substance, you will use the **Celsius scale.** Temperature is measured in degrees Celsius (°C) using a Celsius thermometer. Water freezes at 0°C and boils at 100°C.

Time The unit scientists use to measure time is the **second (s).**

Activity

What is the temperature of the liquid in degrees Celsius?

Converting SI Units

To use the SI system, you must know how to convert between units. Converting from one unit to another involves the skill of **calculating,** or using mathematical operations. Converting between SI units is similar to converting between dollars and dimes because both systems are based on multiples of ten.

Suppose you want to convert a length of 80 centimeters to meters. Follow these steps to convert between units.

1. Begin by writing down the measurement you want to convert—in this example, 80 centimeters.

2. Write a conversion factor that represents the relationship between the two units you are converting. In this example, the relationship is 1 meter = 100 centimeters. Write this conversion factor as a fraction, making sure to place the units you are converting from (centimeters, in this example) in the denominator.

3. Multiply the measurement you want to convert by the fraction. When you do this, the units in the first measurement will cancel out with the units in the denominator. Your answer will be in the units you are converting to (meters, in this example).

Example

80 centimeters = ■ meters

$$80 \text{ centimeters} \times \frac{1 \text{ meter}}{100 \text{ centimeters}} = \frac{80 \text{ meters}}{100}$$

$$= 0.8 \text{ meters}$$

Activity

Convert between the following units.
1. 600 millimeters = ■ meters
2. 0.35 liters = ■ milliliters
3. 1,050 grams = ■ kilograms

Activity

Mass The mass of the potato is 0.25 kilograms. You would need 4 potatoes to make one kilogram. If students need more practice, give them various objects, such as coins, paper clips, and books, to measure mass.

Activity

Temperature The temperature of the liquid is 35°C. Students who need more practice can measure the temperatures of various water samples.

Converting SI Units

Focus Review the steps for converting SI units, and work through the example with students.

Teach Ask: **How many millimeters are in 80 centimeters?** *(With the relationship 10 millimeters = 1 centimeter, students should follow the steps to calculate that 80 centimeters is equal to 800 millimeters.)* Have students do the conversion problems in the activity.

Activity

1. *600 millimeters = 0.6 meters*
2. *0.35 liters = 350 milliliters*
3. *1,050 grams = 1.05 kilograms*

If students need more practice converting SI units, have them make up conversion problems to trade with partners.

809

Conducting a Scientific Investigation

Students can refer to this part of the Skills Handbook whenever they need to review the steps of a scientific investigation. You can use the activities here to teach or reinforce these steps.

Posing Questions

Focus Ask: **What do you do when you want to learn about something?** (*Answers might include asking questions about it or looking for information in books or on the Internet.*) Explain that scientists go through the same process to learn about something.

Teach Tell students that the questions scientists ask may have no answers or many different answers. To answer their questions, scientists often conduct experiments. Ask: **Why is a scientific question important to a scientific investigation?** (*It helps the scientist decide if an experiment is necessary; the answer might already be known. It also helps focus the idea so that the scientist can form a hypothesis.*) **What is the scientific question in the activity on the next page?** (*Is a ball's bounce affected by the height from which it is dropped?*)

Developing a Hypothesis

Focus Emphasize that a hypothesis is one possible explanation for a set of observations. It is *not* a guess. It is often based on an inference.

Teach Ask: **On what information do scientists base their hypotheses?** (*Their observations and previous knowledge or experience*) Point out that a hypothesis does not always turn out to be correct. Ask: **When a hypothesis turns out to be incorrect, do you think the scientist wasted his or her time? Explain.** (*No. The scientist learned from the investigation and will develop another hypothesis that could prove to be correct.*)

Designing an Experiment

Focus Have a volunteer read the Experimental Procedure in the box. Invite students to identify the manipulated variable (*amount of salt*), the variables kept constant (*amount and temperature of water, location of containers*), the control (*Container 3*), and the responding variable (*time required for the water to freeze*).

Conducting a Scientific Investigation

In some ways, scientists are like detectives, piecing together clues to learn about a process or event. One way that scientists gather clues is by carrying out experiments. An experiment tests an idea in a careful, orderly manner. Although experiments do not all follow the same steps in the same order, many follow a pattern similar to the one described here.

Posing Questions

Experiments begin by asking a scientific question. A scientific question is one that can be answered by gathering evidence. For example, the question "Which freezes faster—fresh water or salt water?" is a scientific question because you can carry out an investigation and gather information to answer the question.

Developing a Hypothesis

The next step is to form a hypothesis. A **hypothesis** is a possible explanation for a set of observations or answer to a scientific question. In science, a hypothesis must be something that can be tested. A hypothesis can be worded as an *If . . . then . . .* statement. For example, a hypothesis might be *"If I add salt to fresh water, then the water will take longer to freeze."* A hypothesis worded this way serves as a rough outline of the experiment you should perform.

810 ♦

Teach Ask: **How might the experiment be affected if Container 1 had only 100 milliliters of water?** (*It wouldn't be an accurate comparison with the containers that have more water.*) Also make sure that students understand the importance of the control. Then, ask: **What operational definition is used in this experiment?** (*"Frozen" means the time at which a wooden stick can no longer move in a container.*)

Designing an Experiment

Next you need to plan a way to test your hypothesis. Your plan should be written out as a step-by-step procedure and should describe the observations or measurements you will make.

Two important steps involved in designing an experiment are controlling variables and forming operational definitions.

Controlling Variables In a well-designed experiment, you need to keep all variables the same except for one. A **variable** is any factor that can change in an experiment. The factor that you change is called the **manipulated variable**. In this experiment, the manipulated variable is the amount of salt added to the water. Other factors, such as the amount of water or the starting temperature, are kept constant.

The factor that changes as a result of the manipulated variable is called the **responding variable**. The responding variable is what you measure or observe to obtain your results. In this experiment, the responding variable is how long the water takes to freeze.

An experiment in which all factors except one are kept constant is called a **controlled experiment.** Most controlled experiments include a test called the control. In this experiment, Container 3 is the control. Because no salt is added to Container 3, you can compare the results from the other containers to it. Any difference in results must be due to the addition of salt alone.

Forming Operational Definitions Another important aspect of a well-designed experiment is having clear operational definitions. An **operational definition** is a statement that describes how a particular variable is to be measured or how a term is to be defined. For example, in this experiment, how will you determine if the water has frozen? You might decide to insert a stick in each container at the start of the experiment. Your operational definition of "frozen" would be the time at which the stick can no longer move.

Experimental Procedure

1. Fill 3 containers with 300 milliliters of cold tap water.

2. Add 10 grams of salt to Container 1; stir. Add 20 grams of salt to Container 2; stir. Add no salt to Container 3.

3. Place the 3 containers in a freezer.

4. Check the containers every 15 minutes. Record your observations.

Interpreting Data

The observations and measurements you make in an experiment are called **data.** At the end of an experiment, you need to analyze the data to look for any patterns or trends. Patterns often become clear if you organize your data in a data table or graph. Then think through what the data reveal. Do they support your hypothesis? Do they point out a flaw in your experiment? Do you need to collect more data?

Drawing Conclusions

A **conclusion** is a statement that sums up what you have learned from an experiment. When you draw a conclusion, you need to decide whether the data you collected support your hypothesis or not. You may need to repeat an experiment several times before you can draw any conclusions from it. Conclusions often lead you to pose new questions and plan new experiments to answer them.

Activity

Is a ball's bounce affected by the height from which it is dropped? Using the steps just described, plan a controlled experiment to investigate this problem.

Skills Handbook ◆ 811

Interpreting Data

Focus Ask: **What kind of data would you collect from the experiment with freezing salt water?** (*Time and state of the water*)

Teach Ask: **What if you forgot to record some data during an investigation?** (*You wouldn't be able to draw valid conclusions because some data are missing.*) Then, ask: **Why are data tables and graphs a good way to organize data?** (*They make it easier to record data accurately, as well as compare and analyze data.*) **What kind of data table and graph might you use for this experiment?** (*A table would have columns for each container with a row for each time interval in which the state of water is recorded. A bar graph would show the time elapsed until water froze for each container.*)

Drawing Conclusions

Focus Help students understand that a conclusion is not necessarily the end of a scientific investigation. A conclusion about one experiment may lead right into another experiment.

Teach Point out that in scientific investigations, a conclusion is a summary and explanation of the results of an experiment. For the Experimental Procedure described on this page, tell students to suppose that they obtained the following results: Container 1 froze in 45 minutes, Container 2 in 80 minutes, and Container 3 in 25 minutes. Ask: **What conclusions can you draw from this experiment?** (*Students might conclude that water takes longer to freeze as more salt is added to it. The hypothesis is supported, and the question of which freezes faster is answered—fresh water.*)

Activity

You might wish to have students work in pairs to plan the controlled experiment. Students should develop a hypothesis, such as, "If I increase the height from which a ball is dropped, then the height of its bounce will increase." They can test the hypothesis by dropping a ball from varying heights (the manipulated variable). All trials should be done with the same kind of ball and on the same surface (constants). For each trial, they should measure the height of the bounce (responding variable). After students have designed the experiment, provide rubber balls, and invite them to carry out the experiment so they can collect and interpret data and draw conclusions.

Technology Design Skills

Students can refer to this part of the Skills Handbook whenever they need to review the process of designing new technologies. You can use the activities here to teach or reinforce the steps in this process.

Identify a Need

Focus Solicit from students any situations in which they have thought that a tool, machine, or other object would be really helpful to them or others. Explain that this is the first step in the design of new products.

Teach Point out that identifying specific needs is very important to the design process. Ask: **If it was specified that the toy boat be wind-powered, how might that affect the design?** (*The boat would likely be designed with sails.*)

Research the Problem

Focus Explain that research focuses the problem so that the design is more specific.

Teach Ask: **What might happen if you didn't research the problem before designing the solution?** (*Answers include developing a design that has already been found to fail, using materials that aren't the best, or designing a solution that already exists.*) **What would you research before designing your toy boat?** (*Students might research designs and materials.*)

Design a Solution

Focus Emphasize the importance of a design team. Ask: **Why are brainstorming sessions important in product design?** (*A group will propose more new ideas than one person.*)

Teach Divide the class into teams to design the toy boat. Instruct them to brainstorm design ideas. Then, ask: **Why do you think engineers evaluate constraints after brainstorming?** (*Evaluating constraints while brainstorming often stops the flow of new ideas.*) **What design constraints do you have for your toy boat?** (*Materials must be readily available and teacher-approved. The boat must be 15 centimeters or less in length and must travel 2 meters in a straight line carrying a load of 20 pennies.*)

Technology Design Skills

Engineers are people who use scientific and technological knowledge to solve practical problems. To design new products, engineers usually follow the process described here, even though they may not follow these steps in the exact order. As you read the steps, think about how you might apply them in technology labs.

Identify a Need

Before engineers begin designing a new product, they must first identify the need they are trying to meet. For example, suppose you are a member of a design team in a company that makes toys. Your team has identified a need: a toy boat that is inexpensive and easy to assemble.

Research the Problem

Engineers often begin by gathering information that will help them with their new design. This research may include finding articles in books, magazines, or on the Internet. It may also include talking to other engineers who have solved similar problems. Engineers often perform experiments related to the product they want to design.

For your toy boat, you could look at toys that are similar to the one you want to design. You might do research on the Internet. You could also test some materials to see whether they will work well in a toy boat.

Drawing for a boat design ▼

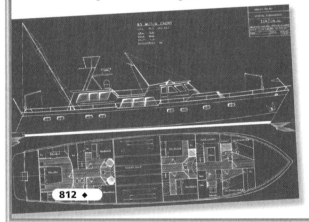

812 ◆

Design a Solution

Research gives engineers information that helps them design a product. When engineers design new products, they usually work in teams.

Generating Ideas Often design teams hold brainstorming meetings in which any team member can contribute ideas. **Brainstorming** is a creative process in which one team member's suggestions often spark ideas in other group members. Brainstorming can lead to new approaches to solving a design problem.

Evaluating Constraints During brainstorming, a design team will often come up with several possible designs. The team must then evaluate each one.

As part of their evaluation, engineers consider constraints. **Constraints** are factors that limit or restrict a product design. Physical characteristics, such as the properties of materials used to make your toy boat, are constraints. Money and time are also constraints. If the materials in a product cost a lot, or if the product takes a long time to make, the design may be impractical.

Making Trade-offs Design teams usually need to make trade-offs. In a **trade-off**, engineers give up one benefit of a proposed design in order to obtain another. In designing your toy boat, you will have to make trade-offs. For example, suppose one material is sturdy but not fully waterproof. Another material is more waterproof, but breakable. You may decide to give up the benefit of sturdiness in order to obtain the benefit of waterproofing.

Build and Evaluate a Prototype

Once the team has chosen a design plan, the engineers build a prototype of the product. A **prototype** is a working model used to test a design. Engineers evaluate the prototype to see whether it works well, is easy to operate, is safe to use, and holds up to repeated use.

Think of your toy boat. What would the prototype be like? Of what materials would it be made? How would you test it?

Troubleshoot and Redesign

Few prototypes work perfectly, which is why they need to be tested. Once a design team has tested a prototype, the members analyze the results and identify any problems. The team then tries to **troubleshoot,** or fix the design problems. For example, if your toy boat leaks or wobbles, the boat should be redesigned to eliminate those problems.

Communicate the Solution

A team needs to communicate the final design to the people who will manufacture and use the product. To do this, teams may use sketches, detailed drawings, computer simulations, and word descriptions.

Activity

You can use the technology design process to design and build a toy boat.

Research and Investigate

1. Visit the library or go online to research toy boats.

2. Investigate how a toy boat can be powered, including wind, rubber bands, or baking soda and vinegar.

3. Brainstorm materials, shapes, and steering for your boat.

Design and Build

4. Based on your research, design a toy boat that
   - is made of readily available materials
   - is no larger than 15 cm long and 10 cm wide
   - includes a power system, a rudder, and an area for cargo
   - travels 2 meters in a straight line carrying a load of 20 pennies

5. Sketch your design and write a step-by-step plan for building your boat. After your teacher approves your plan, build your boat.

Evaluate and Redesign

6. Test your boat, evaluate the results, and troubleshoot any problems.

7. Based on your evaluation, redesign your toy boat so it performs better.

Skills Handbook ◆ 813

Build and Evaluate a Prototype

Focus Explain that building a prototype enables engineers to test design ideas.

Teach Relate building and testing a prototype to conducting an experiment. Explain that engineers set up controlled experiments to test the prototype. Ask: **Why do you think engineers set up controlled experiments?** *(From the data, they can determine which component of the design is working and which is failing.)* **How would you test your prototype of the toy boat?** *(Answers will vary depending on the toy boat's propulsion system.)*

Troubleshoot and Redesign

Focus Make sure students know what it means to troubleshoot. If necessary, give an example. One example is a stapler that isn't working. In that case, you would check to see if it is out of staples or if the staples are jammed. Then you would fix the problem and try stapling again. If it still didn't work, you might check the position of staples and try again.

Teach Explain that engineers often are not surprised if the prototype doesn't work. Ask: **Why isn't it a failure if the prototype doesn't work?** *(Engineers learn from the problems and make changes to address the problems. This process makes the design better.)* Emphasize that prototypes are completely tested before the product is made in the factory.

Communicate the Solution

Focus Inquire whether students have ever read the instruction manual that comes with a new toy or electronic device.

Teach Emphasize the importance of good communication in the design process. Ask: **What might happen if engineers did not communicate their design ideas clearly?** *(The product might not be manufactured correctly or used properly.)*

Activity

The design possibilities are endless. Students might use small plastic containers, wood, foil, or plastic drinking cups for the boat. Materials may also include toothpicks, straws, or small wooden dowels. Brainstorm with students the different ways in which a toy boat can be propelled. The boats may be any shape, but must be no longer than 15 centimeters.

As student groups follow the steps in the design process, have them record their sources, brainstorming ideas, and prototype design in a logbook. Also give them time to troubleshoot and redesign their boats. When students turn in their boats, they should include assembly directions with a diagram, as well as instructions for use.

Creating Data Tables and Graphs

Students can refer to this part of the Skills Handbook whenever they need to review the skills required to create data tables and graphs. You can use the activities provided here to teach or reinforce these skills.

Data Tables

Focus Emphasize the importance of organizing data. Ask: **What might happen if you didn't use a data table for an experiment?** (*Possible answers include that data might not be collected or they might be forgotten.*)

Teach Have students create a data table to show how much time they spend on different activities during one week. Suggest that students first list the main activities they do every week. Then they should determine the amount of time they spend on each activity each day. Remind students to give the data table a title. A sample data table is shown below.

Bar Graphs

Focus Have students compare and contrast the data table and the bar graph on this page. Ask: **Why would you make a bar graph if the data are already organized in a table?** (*The bar graph organizes the data in a visual way that makes them easier to interpret.*)

Teach Students can use the data from the data table they created to make a bar graph that shows the amount of time they spend on different activities during a week. The vertical axis should be divided into units of time, such as hours. Remind students to label both axes and give their graph a title. A sample bar graph is shown below.

SKILLS Handbook

Creating Data Tables and Graphs

How can you make sense of the data in a science experiment? The first step is to organize the data to help you understand them. Data tables and graphs are helpful tools for organizing data.

Data Tables

You have gathered your materials and set up your experiment. But before you start, you need to plan a way to record what happens during the experiment. By creating a data table, you can record your observations and measurements in an orderly way.

Suppose, for example, that a scientist conducted an experiment to find out how many Calories people of different body masses burn while doing various activities. The data table shows the results.

Notice in this data table that the manipulated variable (body mass) is the heading of one column. The responding variable (for

Calories Burned in 30 Minutes

Body Mass	Experiment 1: Bicycling	Experiment 2: Playing Basketball	Experiment 3: Watching Television
30 kg	60 Calories	120 Calories	21 Calories
40 kg	77 Calories	164 Calories	27 Calories
50 kg	95 Calories	206 Calories	33 Calories
60 kg	114 Calories	248 Calories	38 Calories

Experiment 1, the number of Calories burned while bicycling) is the heading of the next column. Additional columns were added for related experiments.

Bar Graphs

To compare how many Calories a person burns doing various activities, you could create a bar graph. A bar graph is used to display data in a number of separate, or distinct, categories. In this example, bicycling, playing basketball, and watching television are the three categories.

To create a bar graph, follow these steps.

1. On graph paper, draw a horizontal, or *x*-, axis and a vertical, or *y*-, axis.

2. Write the names of the categories to be graphed along the horizontal axis. Include an overall label for the axis as well.

3. Label the vertical axis with the name of the responding variable. Include units of measurement. Then create a scale along the axis by marking off equally spaced numbers that cover the range of the data collected.

4. For each category, draw a solid bar using the scale on the vertical axis to determine the height. Make all the bars the same width.

5. Add a title that describes the graph.

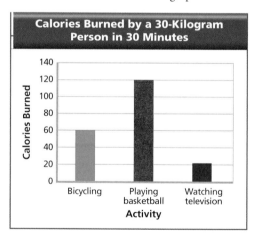

Time Spent on Different Activities in a Week

	Going to Classes	Eating Meals	Playing Soccer	Watching Television
Monday	6	2	2	0.5
Tuesday	6	1.5	1.5	1.5
Wednesday	6	2	1	2
Thursday	6	2	2	1.5
Friday	6	2	2	0.5
Saturday	0	2.5	2.5	1
Sunday	0	3	1	2

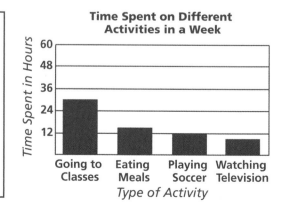

Line Graphs

To see whether a relationship exists between body mass and the number of Calories burned while bicycling, you could create a line graph. A line graph is used to display data that show how one variable (the responding variable) changes in response to another variable (the manipulated variable). You can use a line graph when your manipulated variable is *continuous,* that is, when there are other points between the ones that you tested. In this example, body mass is a continuous variable because there are other body masses between 30 and 40 kilograms (for example, 31 kilograms). Time is another example of a continuous variable.

Line graphs are powerful tools because they allow you to estimate values for conditions that you did not test in the experiment. For example, you can use the line graph to estimate that a 35-kilogram person would burn 68 Calories while bicycling.

To create a line graph, follow these steps.

1. On graph paper, draw a horizontal, or *x*-, axis and a vertical, or *y*-, axis.

2. Label the horizontal axis with the name of the manipulated variable. Label the vertical axis with the name of the responding variable. Include units of measurement.

3. Create a scale on each axis by marking off equally spaced numbers that cover the range of the data collected.

4. Plot a point on the graph for each piece of data. In the line graph above, the dotted lines show how to plot the first data point (30 kilograms and 60 Calories). Follow an imaginary vertical line extending up from the horizontal axis at the 30-kilogram mark. Then follow an imaginary horizontal line extending across from the vertical axis at the 60-Calorie mark. Plot the point where the two lines intersect.

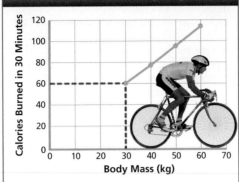

Effect of Body Mass on Calories Burned While Bicycling

5. Connect the plotted points with a solid line. (In some cases, it may be more appropriate to draw a line that shows the general trend of the plotted points. In those cases, some of the points may fall above or below the line. Also, not all graphs are linear. It may be more appropriate to draw a curve to connect the points.)

6. Add a title that identifies the variables or relationship in the graph.

Activity

Create line graphs to display the data from Experiment 2 and Experiment 3 in the data table.

Activity

You read in the newspaper that a total of 4 centimeters of rain fell in your area in June, 2.5 centimeters fell in July, and 1.5 centimeters fell in August. What type of graph would you use to display these data? Use graph paper to create the graph.

Skills Handbook ♦ 815

Line Graphs

Focus Ask: **Would a bar graph show the relationship between body mass and the number of Calories burned in 30 minutes?** (*No. Bar graphs can only show data in distinct categories.*) Explain that line graphs are used to show how one variable changes in response to another variable.

Teach Walk students through the steps involved in creating a line graph using the example illustrated on the page. For example, ask: **What is the label on the horizontal axis? On the vertical axis?** (*Body Mass (kg); Calories Burned in 30 Minutes*) **What scale is used on each axis?** (*10 kg on the x-axis and 20 Calories on the y-axis*) **What does the second data point represent?** (*77 Calories burned for a body mass of 40 kg*) **What trend or pattern does the graph show?** (*The number of Calories burned in 30 minutes of cycling increases with body mass.*)

Activity

Students should make a different graph for each experiment. Each graph should have a different *x*-axis scale that is appropriate for the data. See sample graphs below.

Activity

Students should conclude that a bar graph would be best for displaying the data.

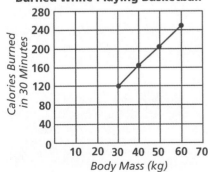

Effect of Body Mass on Calories Burned While Playing Basketball

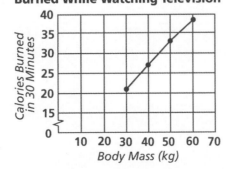

Effect of Body Mass on Calories Burned While Watching Television

Circle Graphs

Focus Emphasize that a circle graph must include 100 percent of the categories for the topic being graphed. For example, ask: **Could the data in the bar graph titled "Calories Burned by a 30-kilogram Person in Various Activities" (on the previous page) be shown in a circle graph? Why or why not?** *(No. It does not include all the possible ways a 30-kilogram person can burn Calories.)*

Teach Walk students through the steps for making a circle graph. If necessary, help them with the compass and the protractor. Use the protractor to illustrate that a circle has 360 degrees. Make sure students understand the mathematical calculations involved in making a circle graph.

Activity

You might have students work in pairs to complete the activity. Students' circle graphs should look like the graph below.

Ways Students Get to School

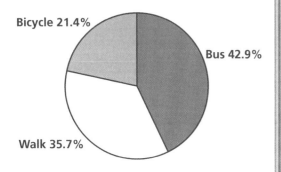

Circle Graphs

Like bar graphs, circle graphs can be used to display data in a number of separate categories. Unlike bar graphs, however, circle graphs can only be used when you have data for *all* the categories that make up a given topic. A circle graph is sometimes called a pie chart. The pie represents the entire topic, while the slices represent the individual categories. The size of a slice indicates what percentage of the whole a particular category makes up.

The data table below shows the results of a survey in which 24 teenagers were asked to identify their favorite sport. The data were then used to create the circle graph at the right.

Favorite Sports	
Sport	Students
Soccer	8
Basketball	6
Bicycling	6
Swimming	4

To create a circle graph, follow these steps.

1. Use a compass to draw a circle. Mark the center with a point. Then draw a line from the center point to the top of the circle.

2. Determine the size of each "slice" by setting up a proportion where x equals the number of degrees in a slice. (*Note:* A circle contains 360 degrees.) For example, to find the number of degrees in the "soccer" slice, set up the following proportion:

$$\frac{\text{Students who prefer soccer}}{\text{Total number of students}} = \frac{x}{\text{Total number of degrees in a circle}}$$

$$\frac{8}{24} = \frac{x}{360}$$

Cross-multiply and solve for x.

$$24x = 8 \times 360$$
$$x = 120$$

The "soccer" slice should contain 120 degrees.

Sports That Teens Prefer

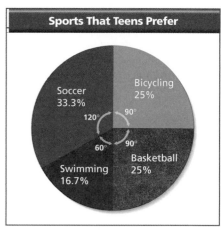

3. Use a protractor to measure the angle of the first slice, using the line you drew to the top of the circle as the 0° line. Draw a line from the center of the circle to the edge for the angle you measured.

4. Continue around the circle by measuring the size of each slice with the protractor. Start measuring from the edge of the previous slice so the wedges do not overlap. When you are done, the entire circle should be filled in.

5. Determine the percentage of the whole circle that each slice represents. To do this, divide the number of degrees in a slice by the total number of degrees in a circle (360), and multiply by 100%. For the "soccer" slice, you can find the percentage as follows:

$$\frac{120}{360} \times 100\% = 33.3\%$$

6. Use a different color for each slice. Label each slice with the category and with the percentage of the whole it represents.

7. Add a title to the circle graph.

Activity

In a class of 28 students, 12 students take the bus to school, 10 students walk, and 6 students ride their bicycles. Create a circle graph to display these data.

Math Review

Scientists use math to organize, analyze, and present data.
This appendix will help you review some basic math skills.

Mean, Median, and Mode

The **mean** is the average, or the sum of the data divided by the number of data items. The middle number in a set of ordered data is called the **median.** The **mode** is the number that appears most often in a set of data.

Example

A scientist counted the number of distinct songs sung by seven different male birds and collected the data shown below.

Male Bird Songs							
Bird	A	B	C	D	E	F	G
Number of Songs	36	29	40	35	28	36	27

To determine the mean number of songs, add the total number of songs and divide by the number of data items—in this case, the number of male birds.

$$\text{Mean} = \frac{231}{7} = 33 \text{ songs}$$

To find the median number of songs, arrange the data in numerical order and find the number in the middle of the series.

27 28 29 35 36 36 40

The number in the middle is 35, so the median number of songs is 35.

The mode is the value that appears most frequently. In the data, 36 appears twice, while each other item appears only once. Therefore, 36 songs is the mode.

Practice

Find out how many minutes it takes each student in your class to get to school. Then find the mean, median, and mode for the data.

Probability

Probability is the chance that an event will occur. Probability can be expressed as a ratio, a fraction, or a percentage. For example, when you flip a coin, the probability that the coin will land heads up is 1 in 2, or $\frac{1}{2}$, or 50 percent.

The probability that an event will happen can be expressed in the following formula.

$$P(\text{event}) = \frac{\text{Number of times the event can occur}}{\text{Total number of possible events}}$$

Example

A paper bag contains 25 blue marbles, 5 green marbles, 5 orange marbles, and 15 yellow marbles. If you close your eyes and pick a marble from the bag, what is the probability that it will be yellow?

$$P(\text{yellow marbles}) = \frac{15 \text{ yellow marbles}}{50 \text{ marbles total}}$$

$$P = \frac{15}{50}, \text{ or } \frac{3}{10}, \text{ or } 30\%$$

Practice

Each side of a cube has a letter on it. Two sides have *A*, three sides have *B*, and one side has *C*. If you roll the cube, what is the probability that *A* will land on top?

Math Review

Students can refer to this part of the Skills Handbook whenever they need to review some basic math skills. You can use the activities provided here to teach or reinforce these skills.

Mean, Median, and Mode

Focus Remind students that data from an experiment might consist of hundreds or thousands of numbers. Unless analyzed, the numbers likely will not be helpful.

Teach Work through the process of determining mean, median, and mode using the example in the book. Make sure students realize that these three numbers do not always equal each other. Point out that taken together, these three numbers give more information about the data than just one of the numbers alone.

Practice

Answers will vary based on class data. The mean should equal the total number of minutes divided by the number of students. The median should equal the number in the middle after arranging the data in numerical order. The mode should equal the number of minutes that is given most frequently.

Probability

Focus Show students a coin and ask: **What is the chance that I will get tails when I flip the coin?** *(Some students might know that there is a 1 in 2, or 50 percent, chance of getting tails.)*

Teach Set up a bag of marbles like the one in the example. Allow students to practice determining the probabilities of picking marbles of different colors. Then, encourage them to actually pick marbles and compare their actual results with those results predicted by probability.

Practice

$P(A) = 2 \text{ sides with } \frac{A}{6} \text{ sides total}$
$P = \frac{2}{6}, \text{ or } \frac{1}{3}, \text{ or } 33\%$

Area

Focus Ask: **Who knows what area is?** *(Area is equal to the number of square units needed to cover a certain shape or object.)* On the board, write the formulas for the area of a rectangle and a circle.

Teach Give students various objects of different shapes. Have them measure each object and determine its area based on the measurements. Point out that the units of the answer are squared because they are multiplied together. If students are interested, you might also explain that π is equal to the ratio of the circumference of a circle to its diameter. For circles of all sizes, π is approximately equal to the number 3.14, or $\frac{22}{7}$.

Practice

The area of the circle is equal to $21 \text{ m} \times 21 \text{ m} \times \frac{22}{7}$, or $1{,}386 \text{ m}^2$.

Circumference

Focus Draw a circle on the board. Then trace the outline with your finger and explain that this is the circumference of the circle, or the distance around it.

Teach Show students that the radius is equal to the distance from the center of the circle to any point on it. Point out that the diameter of a circle is equal to two times the radius. Give students paper circles of various sizes, and have them calculate the circumference of each.

Practice

The circumference is equal to $2 \times 28 \text{ m} \times \frac{22}{7}$, or 176 m.

Volume

Focus Fill a beaker with 100 milliliters of water. Ask: **What is the volume of water?** *(100 milliliters)* Explain that volume is the amount of space that something takes up. Then point out that one milliliter is equal to one cubic centimeter (cm^3).

Teach Write on the board the formulas for calculating the volumes of a rectangle and a cylinder. Point out that volume is equal to the area of an object multiplied by its height. Then measure the beaker to show students the relationship between liquid volume (100 milliliters) and the number of cubic units it contains (100 cubic centimeters).

Area

The **area** of a surface is the number of square units that cover it. The front cover of your textbook has an area of about 600 cm^2.

Area of a Rectangle and a Square To find the area of a rectangle, multiply its length times its width. The formula for the area of a rectangle is

$$A = \ell \times w, \text{ or } A = \ell w$$

Since all four sides of a square have the same length, the area of a square is the length of one side multiplied by itself, or squared.

$$A = s \times s, \text{ or } A = s^2$$

> **Example**
>
> A scientist is studying the plants in a field that measures 75 m $\times$ 45 m. What is the area of the field?
>
> $$A = \ell \times w$$
> $$A = 75 \text{ m} \times 45 \text{ m}$$
> $$A = 3{,}375 \text{ m}^2$$

Area of a Circle The formula for the area of a circle is

$$A = \pi \times r \times r, \text{ or } A = \pi r^2$$

The length of the radius is represented by r, and the value of π is approximately $\frac{22}{7}$.

> **Example**
>
> Find the area of a circle with a radius of 14 cm.
>
> $$A = \pi r^2$$
> $$A = 14 \times 14 \times \frac{22}{7}$$
> $$A = 616 \text{ cm}^2$$

> **Practice**
>
> Find the area of a circle that has a radius of 21 m.

Circumference

The distance around a circle is called the circumference. The formula for finding the circumference of a circle is

$$C = 2 \times \pi \times r, \text{ or } C = 2\pi r$$

> **Example**
>
> The radius of a circle is 35 cm. What is its circumference?
>
> $$C = 2\pi r$$
> $$C = 2 \times 35 \times \frac{22}{7}$$
> $$C = 220 \text{ cm}$$

> **Practice**
>
> What is the circumference of a circle with a radius of 28 m?

Volume

The volume of an object is the number of cubic units it contains. The volume of a wastebasket, for example, might be about 26,000 cm^3.

Volume of a Rectangular Object To find the volume of a rectangular object, multiply the object's length times its width times its height.

$$V = \ell \times w \times h, \text{ or } V = \ell w h$$

> **Example**
>
> Find the volume of a box with length 24 cm, width 12 cm, and height 9 cm.
>
> $$V = \ell w h$$
> $$V = 24 \text{ cm} \times 12 \text{ cm} \times 9 \text{ cm}$$
> $$V = 2{,}592 \text{ cm}^3$$

> **Practice**
>
> What is the volume of a rectangular object with length 17 cm, width 11 cm, and height 6 cm?

Practice

The volume of the rectangular object is equal to $17 \text{ cm} \times 11 \text{ cm} \times 6 \text{ cm}$, or $1{,}122 \text{ cm}^3$.

Math Skills

Fractions

A **fraction** is a way to express a part of a whole. In the fraction $\frac{4}{7}$, 4 is the numerator and 7 is the denominator.

Adding and Subtracting Fractions To add or subtract two or more fractions that have a common denominator, first add or subtract the numerators. Then write the sum or difference over the common denominator.

To find the sum or difference of fractions with different denominators, first find the least common multiple of the denominators. This is known as the least common denominator. Then convert each fraction to equivalent fractions with the least common denominator. Add or subtract the numerators. Then write the sum or difference over the common denominator.

Example

$$\frac{5}{6} - \frac{3}{4} = \frac{10}{12} - \frac{9}{12} = \frac{10-9}{12} = \frac{1}{12}$$

Multiplying Fractions To multiply two fractions, first multiply the two numerators, then multiply the two denominators.

Example

$$\frac{5}{6} \times \frac{2}{3} = \frac{5 \times 2}{6 \times 3} = \frac{10}{18} = \frac{5}{9}$$

Dividing Fractions Dividing by a fraction is the same as multiplying by its reciprocal. Reciprocals are numbers whose numerators and denominators have been switched. To divide one fraction by another, first invert the fraction you are dividing by—in other words, turn it upside down. Then multiply the two fractions.

Example

$$\frac{2}{5} \div \frac{7}{8} = \frac{2}{5} \times \frac{8}{7} = \frac{2 \times 8}{5 \times 7} = \frac{16}{35}$$

Practice

Solve the following: $\frac{3}{7} \div \frac{4}{5}$.

Decimals

Fractions whose denominators are 10, 100, or some other power of 10 are often expressed as decimals. For example, the fraction $\frac{9}{10}$ can be expressed as the decimal 0.9, and the fraction $\frac{7}{100}$ can be written as 0.07.

Adding and Subtracting With Decimals To add or subtract decimals, line up the decimal points before you carry out the operation.

Example

$$\begin{array}{r} 27.4 \\ + 6.19 \\ \hline 33.59 \end{array} \qquad \begin{array}{r} 278.635 \\ - 191.4 \\ \hline 87.235 \end{array}$$

Multiplying With Decimals When you multiply two numbers with decimals, the number of decimal places in the product is equal to the total number of decimal places in each number being multiplied.

Example

$$\begin{array}{r} 46.2 \text{ (one decimal place)} \\ \times 2.37 \text{ (two decimal places)} \\ \hline 109.494 \text{ (three decimal places)} \end{array}$$

Dividing With Decimals To divide a decimal by a whole number, put the decimal point in the quotient above the decimal point in the dividend.

Example

$$15.5 \div 5$$
$$\begin{array}{r} 3.1 \\ 5\overline{)15.5} \end{array}$$

To divide a decimal by a decimal, you need to rewrite the divisor as a whole number. Do this by multiplying both the divisor and dividend by the same multiple of 10.

Example

$$1.68 \div 4.2 = 16.8 \div 42$$
$$\begin{array}{r} 0.4 \\ 42\overline{)16.8} \end{array}$$

Practice

Multiply 6.21 by 8.5.

Fractions

Focus Draw a circle on the board, and divide it into eight equal sections. Shade in one of the sections, and explain that one out of eight, or one eighth, of the sections is shaded. Also use the circle to show that four eighths is the same as one half.

Teach Write the fraction $\frac{3}{4}$ on the board. Ask: **What is the numerator?** *(Three)* **What is the denominator?** *(Four)* Emphasize that when adding and subtracting fractions, the denominators of the two fractions must be the same. If necessary, review how to find the least common denominator. Remind students that when multiplying and dividing, the denominators do not have to be the same.

Practice

$$\frac{3}{7} \div \frac{4}{5} = \frac{3}{7} \times \frac{5}{4} = \frac{15}{28}$$

Decimals

Focus Write the number *129.835* on the board. Ask: **What number is in the ones position?** *(9)* **The tenths position?** *(8)* **The hundredths position?** *(3)* Make sure students know that 0.8 is equal to $\frac{8}{10}$ and 0.03 is equal to $\frac{3}{100}$.

Teach Use the examples in the book to review addition, subtraction, multiplication, and division with decimals. Make up a worksheet of similar problems to give students additional practice. Also show students how a fraction is converted to a decimal by dividing the numerator by the denominator. For example, $\frac{1}{2}$ is equal to 0.5.

Practice

$6.21 \times 8.5 = 52.785$

Ratio and Proportion

Focus Differentiate a ratio from a fraction. Remind students that a fraction tells how many parts of the whole. In contrast, a ratio compares two different numbers. For example, $\frac{12}{22}$, or $\frac{6}{11}$, of a class are girls. But the ratio of boys to girls in the class is 10 to 12, or $\frac{5}{6}$.

Teach Use the example in the book to explain how to use a proportion to find an unknown quantity. Provide students with additional practice problems, if needed.

Practice

$6 \times 49 = 7x$
$294 = 7x$
$294 \div 7 = x$
$x = 42$

Percentage

Focus On the board, write $50\% = \frac{50}{100}$. Explain that a percentage is a ratio that compares a number to 100.

Teach Point out that when calculating percentages, you are usually using numbers other than 100. In this case, you set up a proportion. Go over the example in the book. Emphasize that the number representing the total goes on the bottom of the ratio, as does the 100%.

Practice

Students should set up the proportion

$\frac{42 \text{ marbles}}{300 \text{ marbles}} = \frac{x\%}{100\%}$

$42 \times 100 = 300x$

$4200 = 300x$

$4200 \div 300 = 14\%$

Ratio and Proportion

A **ratio** compares two numbers by division. For example, suppose a scientist counts 800 wolves and 1,200 moose on an island. The ratio of wolves to moose can be written as a fraction, $\frac{800}{1,200}$, which can be reduced to $\frac{2}{3}$. The same ratio can also be expressed as 2 to 3 or 2 : 3.

A **proportion** is a mathematical sentence saying that two ratios are equivalent. For example, a proportion could state that $\frac{800 \text{ wolves}}{1,200 \text{ moose}} = \frac{2 \text{ wolves}}{3 \text{ moose}}$. You can sometimes set up a proportion to determine or estimate an unknown quantity. For example, suppose a scientist counts 25 beetles in an area of 10 square meters. The scientist wants to estimate the number of beetles in 100 square meters.

Example

1. Express the relationship between beetles and area as a ratio: $\frac{25}{10}$, simplified to $\frac{5}{2}$.
2. Set up a proportion, with x representing the number of beetles. The proportion can be stated as $\frac{5}{2} = \frac{x}{100}$.
3. Begin by cross-multiplying. In other words, multiply each fraction's numerator by the other fraction's denominator.

   $5 \times 100 = 2 \times x$, or $500 = 2x$
4. To find the value of x, divide both sides by 2. The result is 250, or 250 beetles in 100 square meters.

Practice

Find the value of x in the following proportion: $\frac{6}{7} = \frac{x}{49}$.

Percentage

A **percentage** is a ratio that compares a number to 100. For example, there are 37 granite rocks in a collection that consists of 100 rocks. The ratio $\frac{37}{100}$ can be written as 37%. Granite rocks make up 37% of the rock collection.

You can calculate percentages of numbers other than 100 by setting up a proportion.

Example

Rain falls on 9 days out of 30 in June. What percentage of the days in June were rainy?

$\frac{9 \text{ days}}{30 \text{ days}} = \frac{d\%}{100\%}$

To find the value of d, begin by cross-multiplying, as for any proportion:

$9 \times 100 = 30 \times d$ $d = \frac{900}{30}$ $d = 30$

Practice

There are 300 marbles in a jar, and 42 of those marbles are blue. What percentage of the marbles are blue?

Significant Figures

The **precision** of a measurement depends on the instrument you use to take the measurement. For example, if the smallest unit on the ruler is millimeters, then the most precise measurement you can make will be in millimeters.

The sum or difference of measurements can only be as precise as the least precise measurement being added or subtracted. Round your answer so that it has the same number of digits after the decimal as the least precise measurement. Round up if the last digit is 5 or more, and round down if the last digit is 4 or less.

Example

Subtract a temperature of 5.2°C from the temperature 75.46°C.

75.46 − 5.2 = 70.26

5.2 has the fewest digits after the decimal, so it is the least precise measurement. Since the last digit of the answer is 6, round up to 3. The most precise difference between the measurements is 70.3°C.

Practice

Add 26.4 m to 8.37 m. Round your answer according to the precision of the measurements.

Significant figures are the number of nonzero digits in a measurement. Zeroes between nonzero digits are also significant. For example, the measurements 12,500 L, 0.125 cm, and 2.05 kg all have three significant figures. When you multiply and divide measurements, the one with the fewest significant figures determines the number of significant figures in your answer.

Example

Multiply 110 g by 5.75 g.

110 × 5.75 = 632.5

Because 110 has only two significant figures, round the answer to 630 g.

Scientific Notation

A **factor** is a number that divides into another number with no remainder. In the example, the number 3 is used as a factor four times.

An **exponent** tells how many times a number is used as a factor. For example, $3 \times 3 \times 3 \times 3$ can be written as 3^4. The exponent 4 indicates that the number 3 is used as a factor four times. Another way of expressing this is to say that 81 is equal to 3 to the fourth power.

Example

$$3^4 = 3 \times 3 \times 3 \times 3 = 81$$

Scientific notation uses exponents and powers of ten to write very large or very small numbers in shorter form. When you write a number in scientific notation, you write the number as two factors. The first factor is any number between 1 and 10. The second factor is a power of 10, such as 10^3 or 10^6.

Example

The average distance between the planet Mercury and the sun is 58,000,000 km. To write the first factor in scientific notation, insert a decimal point in the original number so that you have a number between 1 and 10. In the case of 58,000,000, the number is 5.8.

To determine the power of 10, count the number of places that the decimal point moved. In this case, it moved 7 places.

58,000,000 km = 5.8 × 10^7 km

Practice

Express 6,590,000 in scientific notation.

Significant Figures

Focus Measure the length of a paper clip using two different rulers. Use one ruler that is less precise than the other. Compare the two measurements. Ask: **Which measurement is more precise?** (*The ruler with the smallest units will give the more precise measurement.*)

Teach Give students the opportunity to take measurements of an object using tools with different precision. Encourage students to add and subtract their measurements, making sure that they round the answers to reflect the precision of the instruments. Go over the example for significant digits. Check for understanding by asking: **How many significant digits are in the number 324,000?** (*Three*) **In the number 5,901?** (*Four*) **In the number 0.706?** (*Three*) If students need additional practice, create a worksheet with problems in multiplying and dividing numbers with various significant digits.

Practice

26.4 m + 8.37 m = 34.77 m
This answer should be rounded to 34.8 m because the least precise measurement has only one digit after the decimal. This number is rounded up to 8 because the last digit is more than 5.

Scientific Notation

Focus Write a very large number on the board, such as 100 million, using all the zeros. Then, write the number using scientific notation. Ask: **Why do you think scientists prefer to write very large numbers using scientific notation?** (*Possible answers include that it is easier to do calculations, convert units, and make comparisons with other numbers.*)

Teach Go over the examples, and ask: **In the second example, which numbers are the factors?** (*5.8 and 10^7*) **Which number is the exponent?** (*7*) Explain that very small numbers have a negative exponent because the decimal point is moved to the right to produce the first factor. For example, 0.00000628 is equal to 6.28×10^{-6}.

Practice

6,590,000 = 6.59×10^6

Reading Comprehension Skills

Students can refer to this part of the Skills Handbook whenever they need to review a reading skill. You can use the activities provided here to teach or reinforce these skills.

All in One Teaching Resources

• Target Reading Skills Handbook

Using Prior Knowledge

Focus Explain to students that using prior knowledge helps connect what they already know to what they are about to read.

Teach Point out that prior knowledge might not be accurate because memories have faded or perspectives have changed. Encourage students to ask questions to resolve discrepancies between their prior knowledge and what they have learned.

Asking Questions

Focus Demonstrate to students how to change a text heading into a question to help them anticipate the concepts, facts, and events they will read about.

Teach Encourage students to use this reading skill for the next section they read. Instruct them to turn the text headings into questions. Also challenge students to write at least four *what, how, why, who, when,* or *where* questions. Then, have students evaluate the skill. Ask: **Did asking questions about the text help you focus on the reading and remember what you read?** (*Answers will vary, but encourage honesty.*) If this reading skill didn't help, challenge them to assess why not.

Previewing Visuals

Focus Explain to students that looking at the visuals before reading will help them activate prior knowledge and predict what they are about to read.

Teach Assign a section for students to preview the visuals. First, instruct them to write a sentence describing what the section will be about. Then, encourage them to write one or two questions for each visual to give purpose to their reading. Also have them list any prior knowledge about the subject.

Reading Comprehension Skills

Each section in your textbook introduces a Target Reading Skill. You will improve your reading comprehension by using the Target Reading Skills described below.

Using Prior Knowledge

Your prior knowledge is what you already know before you begin to read about a topic. Building on what you already know gives you a head start on learning new information. Before you begin a new assignment, think about what you know. You might look at the headings and the visuals to spark your memory. You can list what you know. Then, as you read, consider questions like these.

• How does what you learn relate to what you know?

• How did something you already know help you learn something new?

• Did your original ideas agree with what you have just learned?

....

Asking Questions

Asking yourself questions is an excellent way to focus on and remember new information in your textbook. For example, you can turn the text headings into questions. Then your questions can guide you to identify the important information as you read. Look at these examples:

> **Heading:** Using Seismographic Data
> **Question:** How are seismographic data used?
> **Heading:** Kinds of Faults
> **Question:** What are the kinds of faults?

You do not have to limit your questions to text headings. Ask questions about anything that you need to clarify or that will help you understand the content. *What* and *how* are probably the most common question words, but you may also ask *why, who, when,* or *where* questions.

Previewing Visuals

Visuals are photographs, graphs, tables, diagrams, and illustrations. Visuals contain important information. Before you read, look at visuals and their labels and captions. This preview will help you prepare for what you will be reading.

Often you will be asked what you want to learn about a visual. For example, after you look at the normal fault diagram below, you might ask: What is the movement along a normal fault? Questions about visuals give you a purpose for reading—to answer your questions.

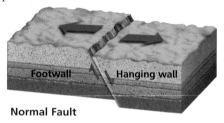

Footwall   **Hanging wall**

Normal Fault

....

Outlining

An outline shows the relationship between main ideas and supporting ideas. An outline has a formal structure. You write the main ideas, called topics, next to Roman numerals. The supporting ideas, called subtopics, are written under the main ideas and labeled A, B, C, and so on. An outline looks like this:

Technology and Society
I. Technology through history
II. The impact of technology on society
A.
B.

Outlining

Focus Explain that using an outline format helps organize information by main topic, subtopic, and details.

Teach Choose a section in the book, and demonstrate how to make an outline for it. Make sure students understand the structure of the outline by asking: **Is this a topic or a subtopic? Where does this information go in the outline? Would I write this heading next to a Roman numeral or a capital letter?** (*Answers depend on the section being outlined.*) Also show them how to indent and add details to the outline using numerals and lowercase letters.

Identifying Main Ideas

When you are reading science material, it is important to try to understand the ideas and concepts that are in a passage. Each paragraph has a lot of information and detail. Good readers try to identify the most important—or biggest—idea in every paragraph or section. That's the main idea. The other information in the paragraph supports or further explains the main idea.

Sometimes main ideas are stated directly. In this book, some main ideas are identified for you as key concepts. These are printed in bold-face type. However, you must identify other main ideas yourself. In order to do this, you must identify all the ideas within a paragraph or section. Then ask yourself which idea is big enough to include all the other ideas.

Comparing and Contrasting

When you compare and contrast, you examine the similarities and differences between things. You can compare and contrast in a Venn diagram or in a table.

Venn Diagram A Venn diagram consists of two overlapping circles. In the space where the circles overlap, you write the characteristics that the two items have in common. In one of the circles outside the area of overlap, you write the differing features or characteristics of one of the items. In the other circle outside the area of overlap, you write the differing characteristics of the other item.

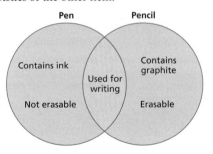

Table In a compare/contrast table, you list the characteristics or features to be compared across the top of the table. Then list the items to be compared in the left column. Complete the table by filling in information about each characteristic or feature.

Blood Vessel	Function	Structure of Wall
Artery	Carries blood away from heart	
Capillary		
Vein		

Identifying Supporting Evidence

A hypothesis is a possible explanation for observations made by scientists or an answer to a scientific question. Scientists must carry out investigations and gather evidence that either supports or disproves the hypothesis.

Identifying the supporting evidence for a hypothesis or theory can help you understand the hypothesis or theory. Evidence consists of facts—information whose accuracy can be confirmed by testing or observation.

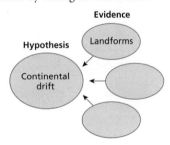

Skills Handbook ◆ 823

Identifying Main Ideas

Focus Explain that identifying main ideas and details helps sort the facts from the information into groups. Each group can have a main topic, subtopics, and details.

Teach Tell students that paragraphs are often written so that the main idea is in the first or second sentence, or in the last sentence. Assign students a page in the book. Instruct them to write the main idea for each paragraph on that page. If students have difficulty finding the main idea, suggest that they list all of the ideas given in the paragraph, and then choose the idea that is big enough to include all the others.

Comparing and Contrasting

Focus Explain that comparing and contrasting information shows how concepts, facts, and events are similar or different. The results of the comparison can have importance.

Teach Point out that Venn diagrams work best when comparing two things. To compare more than two things, students should use a compare/contrast table. Have students make a Venn diagram or compare/contrast table using two or more different sports or other activities, such as playing musical instruments. Emphasize that students should select characteristics that highlight the similarities and differences in the activities.

Identifying Supporting Evidence

Focus Explain to students that identifying the supporting evidence will help them to understand the relationship between the facts and the hypothesis.

Teach Remind students that a hypothesis is neither right nor wrong, but it is either supported or not supported by the evidence from testing or observation. If evidence is found that does not support a hypothesis, the hypothesis can be changed to accommodate the new evidence, or it can be dropped.

Sequencing

Focus Tell students that organizing information from beginning to end will help them understand a step-by-step process.

Teach Encourage students to create a flowchart to show the things they did this morning to get ready for school. Remind students that a flowchart should show the correct order in which events occur. (*A typical flowchart might include: got up ➤ took a shower ➤ got dressed ➤ ate breakfast ➤ brushed teeth ➤ gathered books and homework ➤ put on jacket.*)

Then explain that a cycle diagram shows a sequence of events that is continuous. Point out the cycle diagram that shows how the weather changes with the seasons of the year. Ask: **Why is a cycle diagram used instead of a flowchart to show the sequence of the seasons?** (*A cycle diagram shows that the sequence is continuous, not just a series of events.*) Challenge students to make a sequence diagram for a section of the text. Have them explain why they chose either a cycle diagram or a flowchart. Remind them to include at least four steps in the sequence.

Relating Cause and Effect

Focus Explain to students that cause is the reason for what happens. The effect is what happens in response to the cause. Relating cause and effect helps students relate the reason for what happens to what happens as a result.

Teach Emphasize that not all events that occur together have a cause-and-effect relationship. For example, tell students that you went to the grocery store and your car stalled. Ask: **Is there a cause-and-effect relationship in this situation? Explain.** (*No. Going to the grocery store could not cause a car to stall. There must be another cause to make the car stall.*)

Sequencing

A sequence is the order in which a series of events occurs. A flowchart or a cycle diagram can help you visualize a sequence.

Flowchart To make a flowchart, write a brief description of each step or event in a box. Place the boxes in order, with the first event at the top of the page. Then draw an arrow to connect each step or event to the next.

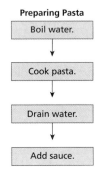

Preparing Pasta

Boil water.
↓
Cook pasta.
↓
Drain water.
↓
Add sauce.

Cycle Diagram A cycle diagram shows a sequence that is continuous, or cyclical. A continuous sequence does not have an end because when the final event is over, the first event begins again. To create a cycle diagram, write the starting event in a box placed at the top of a page in the center. Then, moving in a clockwise direction, write each event in a box in its proper sequence. Draw arrows that connect each event to the one that occurs next.

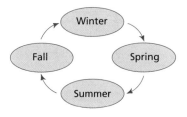

Seasons of the Year

Winter · Spring · Summer · Fall

Relating Cause and Effect

Science involves many cause-and-effect relationships. A cause makes something happen. An effect is what happens. When you recognize that one event causes another, you are relating cause and effect.

Words like *cause, because, effect, affect,* and *result* often signal a cause or an effect. Sometimes an effect can have more than one cause, or a cause can produce several effects.

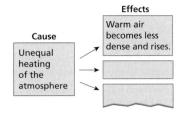

Cause — Unequal heating of the atmosphere

Effects — Warm air becomes less dense and rises.

Concept Mapping

Concept maps are useful tools for organizing information on any topic. A concept map begins with a main idea or core concept and shows how the idea can be subdivided into related subconcepts or smaller ideas.

You construct a concept map by placing concepts (usually nouns) in ovals and connecting them with linking words (usually verbs). The biggest concept or idea is placed in an oval at the top of the map. Related concepts are arranged in ovals below the big idea. The linking words connect the ovals.

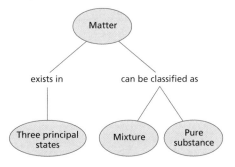

Matter — exists in — Three principal states; can be classified as — Mixture, Pure substance

Concept Mapping

Focus Elicit from students how a map shows the relationship of one geographic area to another. Connect this idea to how a concept map shows the relationship between terms and concepts.

Teach Challenge students to make a concept map with at least three levels of concepts to organize information about types of transportation. All students should start with the phrase *Types of transportation* at the top of the concept map. After that point, their concepts may vary. (*For example, some students might place* private transportation *and* public transportation *at the next level, while other students might choose* human-powered *and* gas-powered.*) Make sure students connect the concepts with linking words.

Building Vocabulary

Knowing the meaning of these prefixes, suffixes, and roots will help you understand the meaning of words you do not recognize.

Word Origins Many science words come to English from other languages, such as Greek and Latin. By learning the meaning of a few common Greek and Latin roots, you can determine the meaning of unfamiliar science words.

Prefixes A prefix is a word part that is added at the beginning of a root or base word to change its meaning.

Suffixes A suffix is a word part that is added at the end of a root word to change the meaning.

Greek and Latin Roots		
Greek Roots	**Meaning**	**Example**
ast-	star	astronaut
geo-	Earth	geology
metron-	measure	kilometer
opt-	eye	optician
photo-	light	photograph
scop-	see	microscope
therm-	heat	thermostat
Latin Roots	**Meaning**	**Example**
aqua-	water	aquarium
aud-	hear	auditorium
duc-, duct-	lead	conduct
flect-	bend	reflect
fract-, frag-	break	fracture
ject-	throw	reject
luc-	light	lucid
spec-	see	inspect

Prefixes and Suffixes		
Prefix	**Meaning**	**Example**
com-, con-	with	communicate, concert
de-	from; down	decay
di-	two	divide
ex-, exo-	out	exhaust
in-, im-	in, into; not	inject, impossible
re-	again; back	reflect, recall
trans-	across	transfer
Suffix	**Meaning**	**Example**
-al	relating to	natural
-er, -or	one who	teacher, doctor
-ist	one who practices	scientist
-ity	state of	equality
-ology	study of	biology
-tion, -sion	state or quality of	reaction, tension

Suffixes

Focus Explain to students that learning the meanings of common suffixes and recognizing them in words are two effective strategies for learning word meanings and building vocabulary.

Teach Remind students that a suffix is added to the end of a word to change its meaning. In addition, students can use suffixes to discover the part of speech of an unfamiliar word. On the chalkboard, draw a four-column chart.

Label the columns Noun, Verb, Adjective, and Adverb. Choose a Key Term that has a familiar base word, such as *tension*. Ask: **What are the noun, verb, adjective, and adverb forms of this word?** (*Students should give all possible answers, which may include only two forms of the word.*) Ask: **What endings signal that the word is a noun, adjective, or adverb?** (*Students should list the suffixes.*) Challenge students to learn the meanings of suffixes and to use them to decode new words.

Building Vocabulary

Reading in a content area presents challenges different from those encountered when reading fiction. Science texts often have more new vocabulary and more unfamiliar concepts that place greater emphasis on inferential reasoning. Students who can apply vocabulary strategies will be more successful in reading and understanding a science textbook. Challenge students to use Greek and Latin word origins and the meanings of prefixes and suffixes to learn the Key Terms in each section.

Word Origins

Focus Explain that word origins describe the older, foreign words that many modern English words have come from. Many science words come from Greek and Latin.

Teach Tell students that most dictionaries give the word origin just before the definition. Choose a section that has a Key Term with a Greek or Latin word origin. Encourage students to learn the meaning of the root word. Ask: **How does knowing the word origin help you remember the meaning of the Key Term?** (*Answers will vary, but the meaning of the Latin or Greek root should provide a clue to the definition of the Key Term.*) Ask: **What other words do you know that come from the same word origin?** (*Students may mention other words related to the Key Term.*) Challenge students to use word origins to figure out the meanings of unfamiliar words as they read. Students should confirm their definitions as necessary by checking a dictionary.

Prefixes

Focus Tell students that learning the meaning of common prefixes can help them determine the meaning of words they don't recognize. They will also increase their vocabulary.

Teach Remind students that a prefix is a word part that is added at the beginning of a root word to change its meaning. List some of the familiar prefixes and meanings, such as *de-* and *re-*, on the chalkboard. Ask: **What words do you know that use these same prefixes?** (*Students should list at least two words for each prefix.*) Ask: **How does the prefix affect the meaning of the root word?** (*Students should explain how it changes the meaning.*) Challenge students to learn the meaning of common prefixes and to use the skill to increase their vocabulary.

- Complete student edition
- Video and audio
- Simulations and activities
- Section and chapter activities

Laboratory Safety

Laboratory safety is an essential element of a successful science class. Students need to understand exactly what is safe and unsafe behavior and what the rationale is behind each safety rule.

All in One Teaching Resources

- Laboratory Safety Teacher Notes
- Science Safety Rules
- Science Safety Symbols
- Laboratory Safety Contract

General Precautions

- Post safety rules in the classroom, and review them regularly with students before beginning every science activity.
- Familiarize yourself with the safety procedures for each activity before introducing it to your students.
- For open-ended activities like Chapter Projects, have students submit their procedures or design plans in writing and check them for safety considerations.
- Always act as an exemplary role model by displaying safe behavior.
- Know how to use safety equipment, such as fire extinguishers and fire blankets, and always have it accessible.
- Have students practice leaving the classroom quickly and orderly to prepare them for emergencies.
- Explain to students how to use the intercom or other available means of communication to get help during an emergency.
- Never leave students unattended while they are engaged in science activities.
- Provide enough space for students to safely carry out science activities.
- Instruct students to report all accidents and injuries to you immediately.

Safety Symbols

These symbols warn of possible dangers in the laboratory and remind you to work carefully.

 Safety Goggles Wear safety goggles to protect your eyes in any activity involving chemicals, flames or heating, or glassware.

 Lab Apron Wear a laboratory apron to protect your skin and clothing from damage.

 Breakage Handle breakable materials, such as glassware, with care. Do not touch broken glassware.

 Heat-Resistant Gloves Use an oven mitt or other hand protection when handling hot materials such as hot plates or hot glassware.

 Plastic Gloves Wear disposable plastic gloves when working with organisms and harmful chemicals. Keep your hands away from your face, and dispose of the gloves according to your teacher's instructions.

 Heating Use a clamp or tongs to pick up hot glassware. Do not touch hot objects with your bare hands.

 Flames Before you work with flames, tie back loose hair and clothing. Follow instructions from your teacher about lighting and extinguishing flames.

 No Flames When using flammable materials, make sure there are no flames, sparks, or other exposed heat sources present.

 Corrosive Chemical Avoid getting acid or other corrosive chemicals on your skin or clothing or in your eyes. Do not inhale the vapors. Wash your hands after the activity.

 Poison Do not let any poisonous chemical come into contact with your skin, and do not inhale its vapors. Wash your hands when you are finished with the activity.

826 ◆

 Fumes Work in a ventilated area when harmful vapors may be involved. Avoid inhaling vapors directly. Only test an odor when directed to do so by your teacher, and use a wafting motion to direct the vapor toward your nose.

 Sharp Object Scissors, scalpels, knives, needles, pins, and tacks can cut your skin. Always direct a sharp edge or point away from yourself and others.

 Animal Safety Treat live or preserved animals or animal parts with care to avoid harming the animals or yourself. Wash your hands when you are finished with the activity.

 Plant Safety Handle plants only as directed by your teacher. If you are allergic to certain plants, tell your teacher; do not do an activity involving those plants. Avoid touching harmful plants such as poison ivy. Wash your hands when you are finished with the activity.

 Electric Shock To avoid electric shock, never use electrical equipment around water, or when the equipment is wet or your hands are wet. Be sure cords are untangled and cannot trip anyone. Unplug equipment not in use.

 Physical Safety When an experiment involves physical activity, avoid injuring yourself or others. Alert your teacher if there is any reason you should not participate.

 Disposal Dispose of chemicals and other laboratory materials safely. Follow the instructions from your teacher.

 Hand Washing Wash your hands thoroughly when finished with the activity. Use soap and warm water. Rinse well.

General Safety Awareness When this symbol appears, follow the instructions provided. When you are asked to develop your own procedure in a lab, have your teacher approve your plan before you go further.

End-of-Experiment Rules

- Always have students use warm water and soap for washing their hands.

Heating and Fire Safety

- No flammable substances should be in use around hot plates, light bulbs, or open flames.
- Test tubes should be heated only in water baths.

- Students should be permitted to strike matches to light candles or burners *only* with strict supervision. When possible, you should light the flames, especially when working with younger students.
- Be sure to have proper ventilation when fumes are produced during a procedure.
- All electrical equipment used in the lab should have GFI (Ground Fault Interrupter) switches.

Science Safety Rules

General Precautions
Follow all instructions. Never perform activities without the approval and supervision of your teacher. Do not engage in horseplay. Never eat or drink in the laboratory. Keep work areas clean and uncluttered.

Dress Code
Wear safety goggles whenever you work with chemicals, glassware, heat sources such as burners, or any substance that might get into your eyes. If you wear contact lenses, notify your teacher.

Wear a lab apron or coat whenever you work with corrosive chemicals or substances that can stain. Wear disposable plastic gloves when working with organisms and harmful chemicals. Tie back long hair. Remove or tie back any article of clothing or jewelry that can hang down and touch chemicals, flames, or equipment. Roll up long sleeves. Never wear open shoes or sandals.

First Aid
Report all accidents, injuries, or fires to your teacher, no matter how minor. Be aware of the location of the first-aid kit, emergency equipment such as the fire extinguisher and fire blanket, and the nearest telephone. Know whom to contact in an emergency.

Heating and Fire Safety
Keep all combustible materials away from flames. When heating a substance in a test tube, make sure that the mouth of the tube is not pointed at you or anyone else. Never heat a liquid in a closed container. Use an oven mitt to pick up a container that has been heated.

Using Chemicals Safely
Never put your face near the mouth of a container that holds chemicals. Never touch, taste, or smell a chemical unless your teacher tells you to.

Use only those chemicals needed in the activity. Keep all containers closed when chemicals are not being used. Pour all chemicals over the sink or a container, not over your work surface. Dispose of excess chemicals as instructed by your teacher.

Be extra careful when working with acids or bases. When mixing an acid and water, always pour the water into the container first and then add the acid to the water. Never pour water into an acid. Wash chemical spills and splashes immediately with plenty of water.

Using Glassware Safely
If glassware is broken or chipped, notify your teacher immediately. Never handle broken or chipped glass with your bare hands.

Never force glass tubing or thermometers into a rubber stopper or rubber tubing. Have your teacher insert the glass tubing or thermometer if required for an activity.

Using Sharp Instruments
Handle sharp instruments with extreme care. Never cut material toward you; cut away from you.

Animal and Plant Safety
Never perform experiments that cause pain, discomfort, or harm to animals. Only handle animals if absolutely necessary. If you know that you are allergic to certain plants, molds, or animals, tell your teacher before doing an activity in which these are used. Wash your hands thoroughly after any activity involving animals, animal parts, plants, plant parts, or soil.

During field work, wear long pants, long sleeves, socks, and closed shoes. Avoid poisonous plants and fungi as well as plants with thorns.

End-of-Experiment Rules
Unplug all electrical equipment. Clean up your work area. Dispose of waste materials as instructed by your teacher. Wash your hands after every experiment.

Handling Organisms Safely
- In an activity where students are directed to taste something, be sure to store the material in clean, *nonscience* containers. Distribute the material to students in *new* plastic or paper dispensables, which should be discarded after the tasting. Tasting or eating should never be done in a lab classroom.
- When growing bacterial cultures, use only disposable petri dishes. After streaking, the dishes should be sealed and not opened again by students. After the lab, students should return the unopened dishes to you.
- Two methods are recommended for the safe disposal of bacterial cultures. *First method:* Autoclave the petri dishes and discard them without opening. *Second method:* If no autoclave is available, carefully open the dishes (never have a student do this), pour full-strength bleach into the dishes, and let them stand for a day. Then pour the bleach from the petri dishes down a drain, and flush the drain with lots of water. Tape the petri dishes back together, and place them in a sealed plastic bag. Wrap the plastic bag with a brown paper bag or newspaper, and tape securely. Throw the sealed package in the trash. Thoroughly disinfect the work area with bleach.
- To grow mold, use a new, sealable plastic bag that is two to three times larger than the material to be placed inside. Seal the bag and tape it shut. After the bag is sealed, students should not open it. To dispose of the bag and mold culture, make a small cut near an edge of the bag, and cook the bag in a microwave oven on a high setting for at least one minute. Discard the bag according to local ordinance, usually in the trash.
- Students should wear disposable nitrile, latex, or food-handling gloves when handling live animals or nonliving specimens.

Using Glassware Safely
- Use plastic containers, graduated cylinders, and beakers whenever possible. If using glass, students should wear safety goggles.
- Use only nonmercury thermometers with anti-roll protectors.

Using Chemicals Safely
- When students use both chemicals and microscopes in one activity, microscopes should be in a separate part of the room from the chemicals so that when students remove their goggles to use the microscopes, their eyes are not at risk.

The microscope is an essential tool in the study of life science. It allows you to see things that are too small to be seen with the unaided eye.

You will probably use a compound microscope like the one you see here. The compound microscope has more than one lens that magnifies the object you view.

Typically, a compound microscope has one lens in the eyepiece, the part you look through. The eyepiece lens usually magnifies 10 ×. Any object you view through this lens would appear 10 times larger than it is.

The compound microscope may contain one or two other lenses called objective lenses. If there are two objective lenses, they are called the low-power and high-power objective lenses. The low-power objective lens usually magnifies 10 ×. The high-power objective lens usually magnifies 40 ×.

To calculate the total magnification with which you are viewing an object, multiply the magnification of the eyepiece lens by the magnification of the objective lens you are using. For example, the eyepiece's magnification of 10 × multiplied by the low-power objective's magnification of 10 × equals a total magnification of 100 ×.

Use the photo of the compound microscope to become familiar with the parts of the microscope and their functions.

The Parts of a Compound Microscope

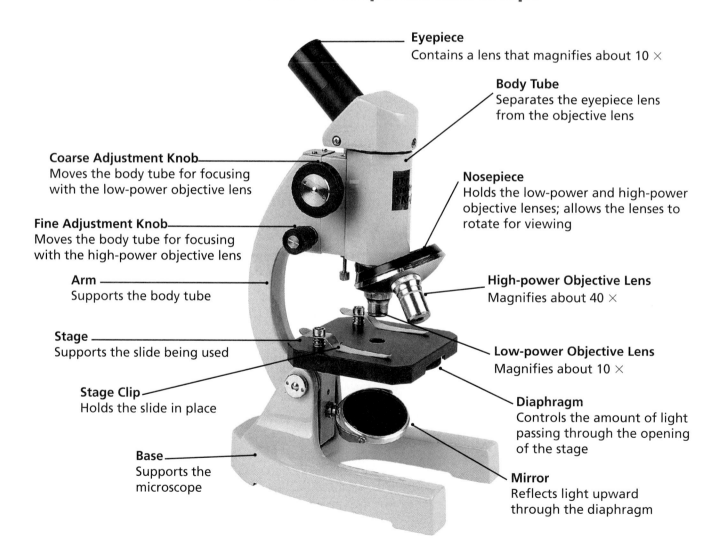

Eyepiece
Contains a lens that magnifies about 10 ×

Body Tube
Separates the eyepiece lens from the objective lens

Coarse Adjustment Knob
Moves the body tube for focusing with the low-power objective lens

Nosepiece
Holds the low-power and high-power objective lenses; allows the lenses to rotate for viewing

Fine Adjustment Knob
Moves the body tube for focusing with the high-power objective lens

Arm
Supports the body tube

High-power Objective Lens
Magnifies about 40 ×

Stage
Supports the slide being used

Low-power Objective Lens
Magnifies about 10 ×

Stage Clip
Holds the slide in place

Diaphragm
Controls the amount of light passing through the opening of the stage

Base
Supports the microscope

Mirror
Reflects light upward through the diaphragm

Using the Microscope

Use the following procedures when you are working with a microscope.

1. To carry the microscope, grasp the microscope's arm with one hand. Place your other hand under the base.
2. Place the microscope on a table with the arm toward you.
3. Turn the coarse adjustment knob to raise the body tube.
4. Revolve the nosepiece until the low-power objective lens clicks into place.
5. Adjust the diaphragm. While looking through the eyepiece, also adjust the mirror until you see a bright white circle of light. **CAUTION:** *Never use direct sunlight as a light source.*
6. Place a slide on the stage. Center the specimen over the opening on the stage. Use the stage clips to hold the slide in place. **CAUTION:** *Glass slides are fragile.*
7. Look at the stage from the side. Carefully turn the coarse adjustment knob to lower the body tube until the low-power objective almost touches the slide.
8. Looking through the eyepiece, very slowly turn the coarse adjustment knob until the specimen comes into focus.
9. To switch to the high-power objective lens, look at the microscope from the side. Carefully revolve the nosepiece until the high-power objective lens clicks into place. Make sure the lens does not hit the slide.
10. Looking through the eyepiece, turn the fine adjustment knob until the specimen comes into focus.

Making a Wet-Mount Slide

Use the following procedures to make a wet-mount slide of a specimen.

1. Obtain a clean microscope slide and a coverslip. **CAUTION:** *Glass slides and coverslips are fragile.*
2. Place the specimen on the slide. The specimen must be thin enough for light to pass through it.
3. Using a plastic dropper, place a drop of water on the specimen.
4. Gently place one edge of the coverslip against the slide so that it touches the edge of the water drop at a 45° angle. Slowly lower the coverslip over the specimen. If air bubbles are trapped beneath the coverslip, tap the coverslip gently with the eraser end of a pencil.
5. Remove any excess water at the edge of the coverslip with a paper towel.

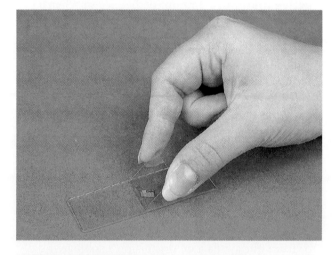

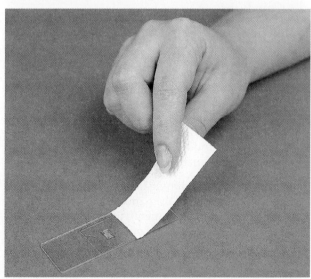

English and Spanish Glossary

A

abdomen The hind section of an arthropod's body that contains its reproductive organs and part of its digestive tract. (p. 340)
abdomen Sección posterior del cuerpo de un artrópodo que contiene sus órganos reproductores y parte de su aparato digestivo.

abiotic factor A nonliving part of an organism's habitat. (p. 706)
factor abiótico La parte no viva del hábitat de un organismo.

absorption The process by which nutrients pass from the digestive system into the blood. (p. 517)
absorción Proceso por el cual las moléculas de los nutrientes pasan a través de la pared del sistema digestivo a la sangre.

active immunity Immunity that occurs when a person's own immune system produces antibodies in response to the presence of a pathogen. (p. 606)
inmunidad activa Inmunidad que ocurre cuando el sistema inmunológico de una persona produce anticuerpos en respuesta a la presencia de un patógeno.

active transport The movement of materials through a cell membrane using energy. (p. 84)
transporte activo Movimiento de materiales a través de la membrana celular que usa energía.

adaptation A behavior or physical characteristic that allows an organism to survive or reproduce in its environment. (pp. 175, 296, 723)
adaptación Comportamiento o característica física que ayuda a un organismo a sobrevivir o a reproducirse en su medio ambiente.

addiction A physical dependence on a substance. (pp. 575, 653)
adicción Dependencia física de una sustancia.

adolescence The stage of development between childhood and adulthood when children become adults physically and mentally. (p. 689)
adolescencia Etapa del desarrollo entre la niñez y la adultez cuando los niños empiezan a ser adultos física y mentalmente.

aggression A threatening behavior that one animal uses to gain control over another. (p. 446)
agresión Comportamiento amenazante que usa un animal para ganar el control sobre otro.

AIDS (acquired immunodeficiency syndrome) A disease caused by a virus that attacks the immune system. (p. 602)

SIDA (Síndrome de inmunodeficiencia adquirida) Enfermedad causada por un virus que ataca el sistema inmunológico.

alcoholism A disease in which a person is both physically addicted to and emotionally dependent on alcohol. (p. 657)
alcoholismo Enfermedad en la que una persona es adicta físicamente y dependiente emocionalmente del alcohol.

algae Plantlike protists. (p. 231)
algas Protistas con características vegetales.

alleles The different forms of a gene. (p. 113)
alelos Diferentes formas de un gen.

allergen A substance that causes an allergy. (p. 612)
alergeno Sustancia que causa la alergia.

allergy A disorder in which the immune system is overly sensitive to a foreign substance. (p. 612)
alergia Trastorno fisiológico en el cual el sistema inmunológico es extremadamente sensible a las sustancias externas.

alveoli Tiny sacs of lung tissue specialized for the movement of gases between air and blood. (p. 568)
alveolos Sacos diminutos de tejido pulmonar especializados en el intercambio de gases entre el aire y la sangre.

amino acid A small molecule that is linked chemically to other amino acids to form proteins.
amino ácido Pequeña molécula que se une químicamente a otros aminoácidos para formar proteínas. (pp. 77, 507)

amniotic egg An egg with a shell and internal membranes that keep the embryo moist (p. 389)
huevo amniótico Huevo con cáscara y membranas internas que mantiene al embrión húmedo.

amniotic sac A fluid-filled sac that cushions and protects a developing embryo and fetus in the uterus. (p. 684)
saco amniótico Saco lleno de líquido que amortigua y protege al embrión y al feto en desarrollo en el útero.

amphibian An ectothermic vertebrate that spends its early life in water and its adult life on land.
anfibio Vertebrado ectotérmico que pasa la primera etapa de su vida en el agua y la madurez en la tierra. (p. 382)

anabolic steroids Synthetic chemicals that are similar to hormones produced in the body. (p. 654)
esteroides anabólicos Sustancias químicas sintéticas que son semejantes a las hormonas producidas por el cuerpo.

angiosperm A flowering plant that produces seeds enclosed in a protective structure. (p. 276)
angiosperma Planta con flores que produce semillas encerradas en una estructura protectora.

annual A flowering plant that completes its life cycle in one growing season. (p. 287)
anual Planta con flores que completa su ciclo de vida en una sola temporada de crecimiento.

antenna An appendage on the head of an arthropod that contains sense organs. (p. 337)
antena Apéndice en la cabeza de un animal que contiene órganos sensoriales.

antibiotic A chemical that kills bacteria or slows their growth without harming body cells. (p. 608)
antibiótico Sustancia química que mata las bacterias o frena su crecimiento sin dañar las células del cuerpo humano.

antibody A protein produced by a B cell of the immune system that destroys pathogens. (p. 600)
anticuerpo Proteína producida por una célula B del sistema inmunológico que destruye un tipo específico de patógeno.

antigen A molecule that the immune system recognizes either as part of the body or as coming from outside the body. (p. 600)
antígeno Molécula en una célula que puede reconocer el sistema inmunológico como parte del cuerpo o como un agente extraño.

anus A muscular opening at the end of the rectum through which waste material is eliminated from the body. (pp. 318, 527)
ano Abertura muscular al final del recto a través de la cual se elimina el material de desecho digestivo del cuerpo.

aorta The largest artery in the body. (p. 539)
aorta La arteria más grande del cuerpo.

aquaculture The practice of raising fish and other water-dwelling organisms for food. (p. 788)
acuicultura Técnica del cultivo de peces y otros organismos acuáticos para consumo humano.

arachnid An arthropod with two body sections, four pairs of legs, and no antennae. (p. 340)
arácnido Artrópodo con dos secciones corporales, cuatro pares de patas y sin antenas.

artery A blood vessel that carries blood away from the heart. (p. 538)
arteria Vaso sanguíneo que transporta la sangre que sale del corazón.

arthropod An invertebrate that has an external skeleton, a segmented body, and jointed appendages.
artrópodo Invertebrado que tiene esqueleto externo, cuerpo segmentado y apéndices anexos. (p. 335)

asexual reproduction A reproductive process that involves only one parent and produces offspring that are identical to the parent. (pp. 220, 297)
reproducción asexual Proceso de reproducción que implica a sólo un progenitor y produce descendencia que es idéntica al progenitor.

asthma A disorder in which the respiratory passages narrow significantly. (p. 613)
asma Trastorno fisiológico por el cual las vías respiratorias se estrechan considerablemente.

atherosclerosis A condition in which an artery wall thickens from a buildup of fatty materials. (p. 553)
arteriosclerosis Condición en la que la pared de una arteria se hace más gruesa debido a la acumulación de materiales grasos.

atrium Each of the two upper chambers of the heart that receives blood that comes into the heart.
aurícula Cada una de las dos cámaras superiores del corazón que reciben la sangre que entra en el corazón. (pp. 384, 537)

autonomic nervous system The group of nerves in the peripheral nervous system that controls involuntary actions. (p. 637)
sistema nervioso autónomo Grupo de nervios en el sistema nervioso periférico que controla las acciones involuntarias.

autotroph An organism that makes its own food.
autótrofo Organismo que produce su propio alimento. (pp. 38, 87)

auxin A plant hormone that speeds up the rate of growth of plant cells. (p. 285)
auxina Hormona vegetal que acelera el crecimiento de las células de la planta.

axon A threadlike extension of a neuron that carries nerve impulses away from the cell body. (p. 628)
axón Extensión con forma de hilo de una neurona que lleva los impulsos nerviosos del cuerpo de la célula.

English and Spanish Glossary

B cell A lymphocyte that produces proteins that help destroy pathogens. (p. 600)
célula B Linfocito que produce proteínas que ayudan a destruir un tipo específico de patógeno.

bacteria Single-celled organisms that lack a nucleus; prokaryotes. (p. 218)
bacteria Organismo unicelular que no tiene núcleo.

bacteriophage A virus that infects bacteria. (p. 211)
bacteriófago Virus que infecta bacterias.

behavior All the actions an animal performs. (p. 437)
comportamiento Todas las acciones que realiza un animal.

biennial A flowering plant that completes its life cycle in two years. (p. 287)
bienal Planta con flores que completa su ciclo de vida en dos años.

bilateral symmetry Body plan with two halves that are mirror images. (p. 301)
simetría bilateral La cualidad de ser divisible en mitades que son imágenes reflejas.

bile A substance produced by the liver that breaks up fat particles. (p. 525)
bilis Sustancia producida por el hígado que descompone las partículas de grasa.

binary fission A form of asexual reproduction in which one cell divides to form two identical cells.
fisión binaria Forma de reproducción asexual en la que una célula se divide para formar dos células idénticas. (p. 220)

binomial nomenclature The system for naming organisms in which each organism is given a unique, two-part scientific name. (p. 44)
nomenclatura binaria Sistema para nombrar organismos, en el cual a cada organismo se le da un nombre científico único de dos partes.

biodiversity The number of different species in an area. (p. 792)
biodiversidad Número de diferentes especies en un área determinada.

biogeography The study of where organisms live.
biogeografía Estudio del lugar donde viven los organismos. (p. 752)

biological control A natural predator or disease used to combat a pest insect. (p. 355)
control biológico Depredador o enfermedad natural liberada en un área para combatir una plaga de insectos.

biome A group of land ecosystems with similar climates and organisms. (p. 758)
bioma Grupo de eco-sistemas terrestres con climas y organismos similares.

biotic factor A living part of an organism's habitat.
factor biótico La parte viva del hábitat de un organismo. (p. 705)

bird An endothermic vertebrate that has feathers and a four-chambered heart, and lays eggs. (p. 407)
ave Vertebrado endotérmico que tiene plumas, un corazón de 4 cámaras y pone huevos.

birth rate The number of births in a population in a certain amount of time. (p. 714)
tasa de natalidad Número de nacimientos en una población en un período determinado.

bivalve A mollusk that has two shells held together by hinges and strong muscles. (p. 331)
bivalvo Molusco que tiene dos conchas unidas por charnelas y fuertes músculos.

blood pressure The pressure that is exerted by the blood against the walls of blood vessels. (p. 542)
presión arterial Presión que ejerce la sangre contra las paredes de los vasos sanguíneos.

brain The part of the central nervous system that is located in the skull and controls most functions in the body. (p. 633)
encéfalo Parte del sistema nervioso central que está ubicado en el cráneo y controla la mayoría de las funciones del cuerpo.

brain stem The part of the brain that lies between the cerebellum and spinal cord, and controls the body's involuntary actions. (p. 634)
tronco encefálico Parte del encéfalo que se encuentra entre el cerebelo y la médula espinal, y controla las acciones involuntarias del cuerpo.

branching tree A diagram that shows how scientists think different groups of organisms are related.
árbol ramificado Diagrama que muestra cómo piensan los científicos que se relacionan diferentes grupos de organismos. (p. 186)

bronchi The passages that direct air into the lungs.
bronquios Conductos que dirigen el aire hacia los pulmones. (p. 568)

bronchitis An irritation of the breathing passages in which the small passages become narrower than normal and may be clogged with mucus. (p. 576)
bronquitis Irritación de los conductos respiratorios en la que los conductos pequeños se hacen más estrechos de lo normal y se pueden obstruir con mucosidad.

budding A form of asexual reproduction of yeast in which a new cell grows out of the body of a parent.
gemación Forma de reproducción asexual de las levaduras, en la que una nueva célula crece del cuerpo de su progenitor. (p. 238)

calorie The amount of energy needed to raise the temperature of one gram of water by one degree Celsius. (p. 503)
caloría Cantidad de energía que se necesita para elevar la temperatura de un gramo de agua un grado Celsius.

cambium A layer of cells in a plant that produces new phloem and xylem cells. (p. 268)
cámbium Una capa de células de una planta que produce nuevas células de floema y xilema.

cancer A disease in which some body cells divide uncontrollably. (p. 493)
cáncer Enfermedad en la que algunas células del cuerpo se dividen descontroladamente.

canopy A leafy roof formed by tall trees. (p. 760)
bóveda arbórea Cubierta densa formada por las cimas hojeadas de los árboles altos.

capillary A tiny blood vessel where substances are exchanged between the blood and the body cells.
capilar Vaso sanguíneo minúsculo donde se intercambian las sustancias de la sangre y las células del cuerpo. (p. 538)

captive breeding The mating of animals in zoos or wildlife preserves. (p. 800)
reproducción en cautiverio Apareamiento de animales en zoológicos y reservas naturales.

carbohydrate An energy-rich organic compound made of the elements carbon, hydrogen, and oxygen. (pp. 76, 504)
carbohidrato Compuesto orgánico altamente energético hecho de elementos de carbono, hidrógeno y oxígeno.

carbon monoxide A colorless, odorless gas produced when substances—including tobacco—are burned. (p. 575)

monóxido de carbono Gas incoloro e inodoro producido cuando se queman algunas sustancias, incluido el tabaco.

carcinogen A substance or a factor in the environment that can cause cancer. (p. 614)
carcinógeno Sustancia o factor en el ambiente que puede causar cáncer.

cardiac muscle Muscle tissue found only in the heart. (p. 485)
músculo cardiaco Tejido muscular que sólo se encuentra en el corazón.

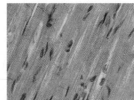

cardiovascular system The body system that consists of the heart, blood vessels, and blood; circulatory system. (p. 534)
sistema cardiovascular Sistema corporal que está formado por el corazón, los vasos sanguíneos y la sangre; tambien llamado sistema circulatoria.

carnivore A consumer that eats only animals. (pp. 330, 741)
carnívoro Consumidor que come sólo animales.

carrier A person who has one recessive allele for a trait, but does not have the trait. (p. 149)
portador Persona que tiene un alelo recesivo para un determinado rasgo, pero que no tiene el rasgo.

carrying capacity The largest population that an area can support. (p. 717)
capacidad de carga La mayor población que puede sustentar un área.

cartilage A connective tissue that is more flexible than bone and that protects the ends of bones and keeps them from rubbing together. (pp. 377, 477)
cartílago Tejido conectivo que es más flexible que el hueso y que protege los extremos de los huesos y evita que se rocen.

cast A type of fossil that forms when a mold becomes filled in with minerals that then harden. (p. 190)
vaciado Tipo de fósil que se forma cuando un molde se llena con minerales que luego se endurecen.

cell The basic unit of structure and function in living things. (pp. 34, 51, 295, 469)
célula Unidad básica de estructura y función de los seres vivos.

cell cycle The regular sequence of growth and division that cells undergo. (p. 96)
ciclo celular Secuencia regular de crecimiento y división de las células.

cell membrane The outside cell boundary that controls which substances can enter or leave the cell.
membrana celular Estructura celular que controla qué sustancias pueden entrar y salir de la célula. (pp. 61, 469)

cell theory A widely accepted explanation of the relationship between cells and living things. (p. 54)
teoría celular Explicación ampliamente aceptada sobre la relación entre las células y los seres vivos.

cell wall A rigid layer of nonliving material that surrounds the cells of plants and some other organisms. (p. 61)
pared celular Capa rígida de material no vivo que rodea las células vegetales y de algunos organismos.

central nervous system The division of the nervous system consisting of the brain and spinal cord.
sistema nervioso central División del sistema nervioso formado por el encéfalo y la médula espinal. (p. 632)

cephalopod An ocean-dwelling mollusk whose foot is adapted as tentacles that surround its mouth.
cefalópodo Molusco que vive en el océano, cuyas extremidades se adaptaron a la forma de tentáculos alrededor de su boca. (p. 332)

cerebellum The part of the brain that coordinates muscle action and helps maintain balance. (p. 634)
cerebelo Parte del encéfalo que coordina las acciones de los músculos y ayuda a mantener el equilibrio.

cerebrum The part of the brain that interprets input from the senses, controls movement, and carries out complex mental processes. (p. 634)
cerebro Parte del encéfalo que interpreta los estímulos de los sentidos, controla el movimiento y realiza procesos mentales complejos.

chlorophyll A green pigment found in the chloroplasts of plants, algae, and some bacteria. (p. 88)
clorofila Pigmento verde que se encuentra en los cloroplastos de las plantas, algas y algunas bacterias.

chloroplast A structure in the cells of plants and some other organisms that captures energy from sunlight and uses it to produce food. (p. 66)
cloroplasto Estructura en las células vegetales y algunos otros organismos que captan la energía de la luz solar y la usan para producir alimento.

chordate The phylum whose members have a notochord, a nerve cord, and slits in their throat area at some point in their lives. (p. 368)
cordado Fílum cuyos miembros poseen un notocordio, un cordón nervioso y aberturas en el área de la garganta en alguna etapa de su vida.

chromosome A doubled rod of condensed chromatin (p. 97)
cromosoma Doble bastón de cromatina condensada; contiene ADN que transporta información genética.

cilia The hairlike projections on the outside of cells that move in a wavelike manner. (pp. 229, 567)
cilios Finas proyecciones en el exterior de las células, que se mueven de manera ondulante.

circadian rhythm A behavior cycle that occurs over a period of approximately one day. (p. 450)
ritmo circadiano Ciclo de comportamiento que ocurre en un período de aproximadamente un día.

classification The process of grouping things based on their similarities. (pp. 10, 43)
clasificación Proceso de agrupar cosas según sus semejanzas.

clear-cutting The process of cutting down all the trees in an area at once. (p. 785)
tala total Proceso de cortar simultáneamente todos los árboles de un área.

climate The typical weather pattern in an area over a long period of time. (p. 755)
clima Patrón típico del tiempo en un área durante un largo período.

clone An organism that is genetically identical to the organism from which it was produced. (p. 159)
clon Organismo que es genéticamente idéntico al organismo del que proviene.

closed circulatory system A circulatory system in which blood moves only within a connected network of tubes called blood vessels. (p. 319)
sistema circulatorio cerrado Sistema circulatorio en el cual la sangre se mueve sólo dentro de una red conectada de conductos llamados vasos sanguíneos.

cnidarian An invertebrate animal that uses stinging cells to capture food and defend itself. (p. 307)
cnidario Animal invertebrado que usa células punzantes para capturar alimento y defenderse.

cochlea A snail-shaped tube in the inner ear that is lined with receptor cells that respond to sound.
cóclea Tubo en forma de caracol en el oído interno que está recubierto de células receptoras que responden al sonido. (p. 647)

codominance A condition in which neither of two alleles of a gene is dominant or recessive. (p. 123)
codominancia Condición en la que ninguno de los dos alelos de un gen es dominante ni recesivo.

colony A group of individual organisms living or growing together. (p. 310)
colonia Grupo de mucho animales individuales.

commensalism A relationship between two species in which one species benefits and the other is neither helped nor harmed. (p. 728)
comensalismo Relación entre dos especies donde una se beneficia y la otra no obtiene ni beneficio ni perjuicio.

communicating The process of sharing ideas with others through writing and speaking. (p. 17)
comunicar Proceso de compartir ideas con otras personas a través de la escritura o el lenguage hablado.

community All the different populations that live together in an area. (p. 707)
comunidad Todas las diferentes poblaciones que viven juntas en un área.

compact bone Hard, dense bone tissue that is beneath the outer membrane of a bone. (p. 478)
hueso compacto Tejido de hueso denso y duro que se encuentra debajo de la membrana externa de un hueso.

competition The struggle between organisms to survive as they attempt to use the same limited resource. (p. 724)
competencia Lucha entre organismos por los recursos limitados en un hábitat.

complete metamorphosis A type of metamorphosis characterized by four dramatically different stages. (p. 346)
metamorfosis completa Tipo de metamorfosis caracterizado por cuatro etapas muy diferentes.

compound Two or more elements that are chemically combined. (p. 75)
compuesto Dos o más elementos que se combinan químicamente.

concussion A bruiselike injury of the brain that occurs when the soft tissue of the brain collides against the skull. (p. 639)
contusión Magulladura en el encéfalo que ocurre cuando el tejido suave del encéfalo choca contra el cráneo.

condensation The process by which a gas changes to a liquid. (p. 747)
condensación Proceso por el cual un gas se convierte en líquido.

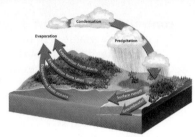

conditioning The process of learning to connect a stimulus with a good or bad outcome. (p. 440)
condicionamiento Proceso de aprendizaje que relaciona un estímulo con un suceso bueno o malo.

cone The reproductive structure of a gymnosperm.
cono Estructura reproductora de una gimnosperma. (p. 274)

coniferous tree A tree that produces its seeds in cones and that has needle-shaped leaves. (p. 764)
árbol conífero Árbol que produce sus semillas en conos y sus hojas tienen forma de aguja.

conjugation The process in which a unicellular organism transfers some of its genetic material to another unicellular organism. (p. 220)
conjugación Proceso por el cual un organismo unicelular transfiere parte de su material genético a otro organismo unicelular.

connective tissue A body tissue that provides support for the body and connects all of its parts.
tejido conectivo Tejido que da soporte al cuerpo y conecta todas sus partes. (p. 470)

consumer An organism that obtains energy by feeding on other organisms. (pp. 350, 741)
consumidor Organismo que obtiene energía alimentándose de otros organismos.

continental drift The very slow motion of the continents. (p. 753)
deriva continental Movimiento muy lento de los continentes.

contour feather A large feather that helps give shape to a bird's body. (p. 407)
pluma remera Pluma grande que ayuda a dar forma al cuerpo del ave.

contractile vacuole The cell structure that collects extra water from the cytoplasm and then expels it from the cell. (p. 228)
vacuola contráctil Estructura celular que recoge el agua sobrante del citoplasma y luego la expulsa de la célula.

controlled experiment An experiment in which only one variable is manipulated at a time. (p. 16)
experimento controlado Experimento en el cual sólo una variable es manipulada a la vez.

coral reef A diverse environment named for the coral animals that make up its stony structure.
arrecife de coral Medio ambiente diverso nombrado así por los animales coralinos que forman la estructura rocosa. (p. 310)

cornea The clear tissue that covers the front of the eye. (p. 643)
córnea Tejido transparente que cubre el frente del ojo.

coronary artery An artery that supplies blood to the heart itself. (p. 540)
arteria coronaria Arteria que lleva sangre al corazón en sí.

cotyledon A seed leaf. (p. 264)
cotiledón Hoja de una semilla.

courtship behavior The behavior that animals of the same species engage in to prepare for mating.
comportamiento de cortejo Comportamiento en el que participan los animales de la misma especie en preparación para el apareamiento. (p. 447)

critical night length The number of hours of darkness that determines whether or not a plant will flower. (p. 286)
longitud nocturna crítica El número de horas de oscuridad que determina si florece una planta o no.

crop A bird's internal storage pouch that allows it to store food inside its body after swallowing it.
buche Depósito de almacenamiento interno del ave que permite guardar el alimento dentro del ave después de tragarlo. (p. 409)

crustacean An arthropod that has two or three body sections, five or more pairs of legs, and two pairs of antennae. (p. 338)
crustáceo Artrópodo que tiene dos o tres secciones corporales, cinco o más pares de patas y dos pares de antenas.

cuticle The waxy, waterproof layer that covers the leaves and stems of most plants. (p. 252)
cutícula Capa cerosa e impermeable que cubre las hojas y los tallos de la mayoría de las plantas.

cytokinesis The final stage of the cell cycle, in which the cell's cytoplasm divides, distributing the organelles into each of the two new cells. (p. 100)
citocinesis Fase final del ciclo celular en la cual se divide el citoplasma de la célula y se distribuyen los organelos en cada una de las dos nuevas células.

cytoplasm The material within a cell apart from the nucleus. (pp. 63, 469)
citoplasma Material que hay en una célula, pero fuera del núcleo.

 D

data Facts, figures, and other evidence gathered through observations. (p. 16)
dato Hecho, cifra u otra evidencia reunida por medio de las observaciones.

day-neutral plant A plant with a flowering cycle that is not sensitive to periods of light and dark.
planta de día neutro Planta cuyo ciclo de floración no es sensible a la duración de los períodos de luz y oscuridad. (p. 286)

death rate The number of deaths in a population in a certain amount of time. (p. 714)
tasa de mortalidad Número de muertes en una población en un período determinado.

deciduous tree A tree that sheds its leaves and grows new ones each year. (p. 763)
árbol caducifolio Árbol cuyas hojas caen y vuelven a crecer anualmente.

decomposer An organism that breaks down chemicals from wastes and dead organisms, and returns important materials to the soil and water. (pp. 224, 350, 741)
descomponedor Organismo que separa sustancias químicas de los organismos muertos y devuelve materiales importantes al suelo y al agua.

dendrite A threadlike extension of a neuron that carries nerve impulses toward the cell body.
dendrita Extensión en forma de hilo de una neurona que lleva los impulsos nerviosos hacia el cuerpo de las células. (p. 628)

depressant A drug that slows down the activity of the central nervous system. (p. 654)
sustancia depresora Droga que disminuye la velocidad de la actividad del sistema nervioso central.

dermis The inner layer of the skin. (p. 491)
dermis Capa más interna de la piel.

desert An area that receives less than 25 centimeters of precipitation per year. (p. 761)
desierto Área que recibe menos de 25 centímetros de precipitación al año.

development The process of change that occurs during an organism's life to produce a more complex organism. (p. 35)
desarrollo Proceso de cambio que ocurre durante la vida de un organismo, mediante el cual se desarrolla un organismo más complejo.

diabetes A condition in which either the pancreas fails to produce enough insulin or the body's cells can't use it properly. (p. 613)
diabetes Condición en la que el páncreas no puede producir suficiente insulina o las células del cuerpo no la pueden usar adecuadamente.

diaphragm A large muscle located at the bottom of a mammal's rib cage that functions in breathing.
diafragma Músculo grande ubicado en la parte inferior de la caja torácica de un mamífero, que participa en la respiración. (pp. 422, 570)

dicot An angiosperm that has two seed leaves.
dicotiledónea Angiosperma cuyas semillas tienen dos cotiledones. (p. 280)

Dietary Reference Intakes (DRIs) Guidelines for the amounts of nutrients needed daily. (p. 514)
Dietéticas ingestas de referencia Pautas que muestran la cantidad de nutrientes que se necesitan diariamente.

diffusion The process by which molecules move from an area of higher concentration to an area of lower concentration. (pp. 81, 541)
difusión Proceso por el cual las moléculas se mueven de un área de mayor concentración a otra de menor concentración.

digestion The process by which the body breaks down food into small nutrient molecules. (p. 517)
digestión Proceso por el cual el cuerpo descompone la comida en pequeñas moléculas de nutrientes.

dispersal The movement of organisms from one place to another. (p. 753)
dispersión Movimiento de los organismos de un lugar a otro.

DNA Deoxyribonucleic acid; the genetic material that carries information about an organism and is passed from parent to offspring. (p. 78)

ADN Ácido desoxirribonucleico; material genético que lleva información sobre un organismo y que se pasa de padres a hijos.

dominant allele An allele whose trait always shows up in the organism when the allele is present.
alelo dominante Alelo cuyo rasgo siempre se manifiesta en el organismo, cuando el alelo está presente. (p. 113)

dormancy A period when an organism's growth or activity stops. (p. 286)
dormición Período durante el cual se suspende el crecimiento o la actividad de un organismo.

down feather A short, fluffy feather that traps heat and keeps a bird warm. (p. 407)
plumones Plumas cortas y mullidas que atrapan el calor y mantienen al ave abrigada.

drug Any chemical taken into the body that causes changes in a person's body or behavior. (p. 651)
droga Cualquier sustancia química que se incorpora al cuerpo, que causa cambios en el cuerpo o comportamiento de una persona.

drug abuse The deliberate misuse of drugs for purposes other than medical. (p. 651)
abuso de drogas Uso indebido deliberado de drogas para fines no médicos.

E

eardrum The membrane that separates the outer ear from the middle ear, and that vibrates when sound waves strike it. (p. 647)
tímpano Membrana que separa el oído externo del oído medio, y que vibra cuando le llegan ondas sonoras.

echinoderm A radially symmetrical invertebrate that lives on the ocean floor and has an internal skeleton and a water vascular system. (p. 358)
equinodermo Invertebrado con simetría radial que vive en el suelo oceánico y tienen un esqueleto interno.

ecology The study of how organisms interact with their environment. (pp. 350, 708)
ecología El estudio de cómo interactúan los organismos con su medio ambiente.

English and Spanish Glossary

ecosystem The community of organisms that live in a particular area, along with their nonliving surroundings. (p. 708)
ecosistema Comunidad de organismos que viven en un área determinada, junto con su medio ambiente no vivo.

ectotherm An animal whose body does not produce much internal heat. (p. 370)
ectotermo Animal cuyo cuerpo no produce mucho calor interno.

egg A female sex cell. (p. 675)
óvulo Célula sexual femenina.

element Any substance that cannot be broken down into simpler substances. (p. 74)
elemento Cualquier sustancia que no puede descomponerse en sustancias más pequeñas.

embryo A young organism that develops from a zygote (p. 264); a developing human during the first eight weeks after fertilization. (p. 683)
embrión Organismo joven que se desarrolla a partir de un cigoto; humano en desarrollo durante las primeras ocho semanas después de ocurrir la fecundación.

emigration Leaving a population. (p. 714)
emigración Abandono de una población.

emphysema A serious disease that destroys lung tissue and causes breathing difficulties. (p. 577)
enfisema Enfermedad grave que destruye el tejido pulmonar y causa dificultades respiratorias.

endangered species A species in danger of becoming extinct in the near future. (p. 797)
especie en peligro de extinción Especie que corre el riesgo de desaparecer en el futuro próximo.

endocrine gland A structure of the endocrine system that produces and releases its chemical products directly into the bloodstream. (p. 667)
glándula endocrina Estructura del sistema endocrino que produce y libera sus productos químicos directamente a la corriente sanguínea.

endoplasmic reticulum A cell structure that forms passageways in which proteins and other materials are carried through the cell. (p. 63)
retículo endoplasmático Estructura celular que forma un laberinto de pasajes por los que se transportan las proteínas y otros materiales de una parte de la célula a otra.

endoskeleton An internal skeleton. (p. 358)
endoesqueleto Esqueleto interno.

endospore A small, rounded, thick-walled, resting cell that forms inside a bacterial cell. (p. 221)
endospora Célula pequeña y redonda de paredes gruesas que se encuentra en reposo, que se forma dentro de una célula bacteriana.

endotherm An animal whose body controls and regulates its temperature by controlling the internal heat it produces. (p. 371)
endotermo Animal cuyo cuerpo controla y regula su temperatura controlando el calor interno que produce.

energy pyramid A diagram that shows the amount of energy that moves from one feeding level to another in a food web. (p. 744)
pirámide de la energía Diagrama que muestra la cantidad de energía que pasa de un nivel de alimentación a otro en una red alimentaria.

engineer A person who is trained to use both technological and scientific knowledge to solve practical problems. (p. 21)
ingeniero Persona capacitada para usar conocimientos tecnológicos y científicos para resolver problemas prácticos.

environmental science The study of the natural processes that occur in the environment and how humans can affect them. (p. 781)
ciencias del medio ambiente Estudio de los procesos naturales que ocurren en el medio ambiente y cómo los seres humanos pueden afectarlos.

enzyme A protein that speeds up chemical reactions in a living thing. (p. 77, 519)
enzima Proteína que acelera las reacciones químicas en un ser vivo.

epidermis The outer layer of the skin. (p. 490)
epidermis Capa más externa de la piel.

epiglottis A flap of tissue that seals off the windpipe and prevents food from entering. (p. 519)
epiglotis Extensión de tejido que sella la entrada de la tráquea impidiendo la entrada del alimento.

epithelial tissue A body tissue that covers the surfaces of the body, inside and out. (p. 470)
tejido epitelial Tejido corporal que cubre la superficie del cuerpo, por dentro y por fuera.

esophagus A muscular tube that connects the mouth to the stomach. (p. 519)
esófago Tubo muscular que conecta la boca con el estómago.

estimate An approximation of a number, based on reasonable assumptions. (p. 712)
estimación Cálculo aproximado de un número, basándose en supuestos razonables.

estrogen A hormone produced by the ovaries that controls the development of eggs and adult female characteristics. (p. 678)
estrógeno Hormona producida por los ovarios que controla el desarrollo de los óvulos y de las características femeninas adultas.

estuary A habitat in which the fresh water of a river meets the salt water of the ocean. (p. 768)
estuario Hábitat en el cual el agua dulce de un río se encuentra con el agua salada del mar.

eukaryote An organism whose cells contain nuclei.
eucariota Organismo cuyas células contienen núcleo. (p. 48)

evaporation The process by which molecules of a liquid absorb energy and change to a gas. (p. 747)
evaporación Proceso por el cual las moléculas de un líquido absorben energía y pasan al estado gaseoso.

evolution The gradual change in a species over time.
evolución Cambio gradual de una especie a través del tiempo. (p. 176)

excretion The process by which wastes are removed from the body. (p. 579)
excreción Proceso por el cual se eliminan los desechos del cuerpo.

exoskeleton A waxy, waterproof outer shell or outer skeleton that protects the animal and helps prevent evaporation of water. (p. 336)
exoesqueleto Concha externa cerosa e impermeable o esqueleto externo que protege al animal y ayuda a evitar la evaporación del agua.

exotic species Species that are carried to a new location by people. (p. 754)
especies exóticas Especies que lleva la gente a un nuevo lugar.

extinction The disappearance of all members of a species from Earth. (pp. 193, 796)
extinción Desaparición de la Tierra de todos los miembros de una especie.

fallopian tube A passageway for eggs from an ovary to the uterus. (p. 678)
trompa de falopio Pasaje por el que pasan los óvulos desde un ovario al útero.

farsightedness The condition in which a person can see distant objects clearly. (p. 645)
hipermetropía Condición en la que una persona puede ver claramente los objetos distantes.

fat Energy-containing nutrients that are composed of carbon, oxygen, and hydrogen. (p. 505)
grasas Nutrientes que contienen energía y están compuestos de carbono, oxígeno e hidrógeno.

fermentation The process by which cells break down molecules to release energy without using oxygen. (p. 93)
fermentación Proceso por el cual las células descomponen las moléculas para liberar energía sin usar oxígeno.

fertilization The joining of a sperm and an egg.
fecundación Unión de un espermatozoide y un óvulo. (pp. 111, 297, 675)

fetus A developing human from the ninth week of development until birth. (p. 683)
feto Humano en desarrollo desde la novena semana de desarrollo hasta el nacimiento.

fish An ectothermic vertebrate that lives in the water and has fins. (p. 375)
pez Vertebrado ectotérmico que vive en el agua y tiene branquias.

fishery An area with a large population of valuable ocean organisms. (p. 787)
pesquería Área con una gran población de organismos marinos.

flagellum A long, whiplike structure that helps a cell to move. (p. 218)
flagelo Estructura larga con forma de látigo que ayuda a la célula para moverse.

flower The reproductive structure of an angiosperm. (p. 276)
flor Estructura reproductora de una angiosperma.

follicle Structure in the dermis of the skin from which a strand of hair grows. (p. 491)
folículo Estructura en la dermis de la piel de donde crece un pelo.

food chain A series of events in which one organism eats another and obtains energy. (pp. 350, 742)
cadena alimentaria Serie de sucesos en los que un organismo se come a otro y obtiene energía.

food web The pattern of overlapping food chains in an ecosystem. (p. 742)
red alimentaria Patrón de cadenas alimentarias sobrepuestas en un ecosistema.

fossil The preserved remains or traces of an organism that lived in the past. (p. 173, 396)
fósil Restos o huellas preservados de un organismo que vivió en el pasado.

fossil record The millions of fossils that scientists have collected. (p. 192)
registro fósil Los millones de fósiles que han descubierto los científicos.

free-living organism An organism that does not live in or on other organisms. (p. 316)
organismo autónomo Organismo que no vive dentro o sobre otro organismo.

frond The leaf of a fern plant. (p. 259)
fronda Hoja de un helecho.

fruit The ripened ovary and other structures of an angiosperm that enclose one or more seeds. (p. 278)
fruto Ovario maduro y otras estructuras que encierran una o más semillas de una angiosperma.

fruiting body The reproductive structure of a fungus that contains many hyphae and produces spores. (p. 238)
órgano fructífero Estructura reproductora de un hongo que contiene muchas hifas y produce esporas.

fungus A eukaryotic organism that has cell walls, uses spores to reproduce, and is a heterotroph that feeds by absorbing its food. (p. 236)
hongo Organismo eucariótico que posee paredes celulares, usa esporas para reproducirse y es un heterótrofo que se alimenta absorbiendo su comida.

gallbladder The organ that stores bile after it is produced by the liver. (p. 525)
vesícula Órgano que almacena la bilis después de ser producida por el hígado.

gametophyte The stage in the life cycle of a plant in which the plant produces gametes, or sex cells.
gametofito Etapa en el ciclo de vida de una planta en la cual la planta produce gametos, es decir, células sexuales. (p. 254)

gastropod A mollusk with a single shell or no shell.
gasterópodo Molusco con una única concha o sin concha. (p. 330)

gene The set of information that controls a trait; a segment of DNA on a chromosone that codes for a specific trait. (p. 113)
gen Conjunto de información que controla un rasgo; un segmento de ADN en un cromosoma el cual codifica un rasgo determinado.

gene therapy The insertion of working copies of a gene into the cells of a person with a genetic disorder in an attempt to correct the disorder. (p. 161)
terapia génica Inserción de copias activas de un gen en las células de una persona con un trastorno genético para intentar corregir dicho trastornó.

genetic disorder An abnormal condition that a person inherits through genes or chromosomes.
trastorno genético Condición anormal que hereda una persona a través de genes o cromosomas. (p. 152)

genetic engineering The transfer of a gene from the DNA of one organism into another organism, in order to produce an organism with desired traits. (p. 160)
ingeniería genética Transferencia de un gen desde el ADN de un organismo a otro, para producir un organismo con los rasgos deseados.

genetics The scientific study of heredity. (p. 110)
genética Ciencia que estudia la herencia.

genome All of the DNA in one cell of an organism.
genoma Todo el ADN de una célula de un organismo. (p. 162)

genotype An organism's genetic makeup, or allele combinations. (p. 122)
genotipo Composición genética de un organismo, es decir, las combinaciones de los alelos.

genus A classification grouping that consists of a number of similar, closely related species. (p. 44)
género Clasificación por grupo formada por un número de especies similares y muy relacionadas.

germination The sprouting of the embryo from a seed that occurs where the embryo resumes growth. (p. 266)
germinación La brotadura del embrión de una semilla; se occura cuando el embrión resuma su crecimiento.

gestation period The length of time between fertilization and birth of a mammal. (p. 424)
período de gestación Tiempo entre la fecundación y el nacimiento del mamífero.

gill An organ that removes oxygen from water. (p. 329)
branquia Órgano que extrae el oxígeno del agua.

gizzard A muscular, thick-walled part of a bird's stomach that squeezes and grinds partially digested food. (p. 409)
molleja Parte muscular, de paredes gruesas del estómago del ave que exprime y muele parcialmente el alimento digerido.

glucose A sugar that is the major source of energy for the body's cells. (p. 504)
glucosa Azúcar que es la principal fuente de energía de las células del cuerpo.

Golgi body A structure in a cell that receives proteins and other newly formed materials from the endoplasmic reticulum, packages them, and distributes them to other parts of the cell. (p. 66)
aparato de Golgi Estructura en la célula que recibe del retículo endoplasmático las proteínas y otros materiales recientemente formados, los empaqueta y los distribuye a otras partes de la célula.

gradual metamorphosis A type of metamorphosis in which an egg hatches into a nymph that resembles an adult, and which has no distinctly different larval stage. (p. 346)
metamorfosis gradual Tipo de metamorfosis en la que un huevo incubado pasa a la etapa de ninfa con aspecto de adulto, y no tiene una etapa de larva diferenciada.

gradualism The theory that evolution occurs slowly but steadily. (p. 197)
gradualismo Teoría que enuncia que la evolución ocurre lenta pero continuamente.

grassland An area populated by grasses and other nonwoody plants. Most grasslands get 25 to 75 centimeters of rain each year. (p. 762)
pradera Área poblada de pastos y de otras plantas no leñosas. La mayoría de las praderas recibe de 25 a 75 centímetros de lluvia al ãno.

gymnosperm A plant that produces seeds that are not enclosed by a protective fruit. (p. 272)
gimnosperma Planta cuyas semillas no están encerradas en una fruta protectora.

H

habitat The specific environment that provides the things an organism needs to live, grow, and reproduce. (pp. 386, 705)

hábitat Medio ambiente específico que proporciona las cosas que un organismo necesita para vivir, crecer y reproducirse.

habitat destruction The loss of a natural habitat.
destrucción del hábitat Pérdida de un hábitat natural. (p. 798)

habitat fragmentation The breaking of a habitat into smaller, isolated pieces. (p. 798)
fragmentación del hábitat Desintegración de un hábitat en porciones aisladas más pequeñas.

half-life The time it takes for half of the atoms in a radioactive element to decay. (p. 192)
vida media Tiempo que demoran en desintegrarse la mitad de los átomos de un elemento radiactivo.

heart A hollow, muscular organ that pumps blood throughout the body. (p. 536)
corazón Órgano muscular hueco que bombea sangre a todo el cuerpo.

heart attack A condition in which blood flow to part of the heart muscle is blocked, causing heart cells to die. (p. 553)
infarto cardiaco Condición en la que se obstruye el flujo de sangre a una parte del músculo cardiaco, lo que causa la muerte de las células cardiacas.

hemoglobin An iron-containing protein that binds chemically to oxygen molecules. (p. 546)
hemoglobina Proteína que contiene hierro, y que se enlaza químicamente a las moléculas de oxígeno.

herbivore A consumer that eats only plants. (pp. 330, 741)
herbívoro Consumidor que come sólo plantas.

heredity The passing of traits from parents to offspring. (p. 110)
herencia Transmisión de rasgos de padres a hijos.

heterotroph An organism that cannot make its own food. (pp. 38, 87)
heterótrofo Organismo que no puede producir su propio alimento.

heterozygous Having two different alleles for a trait. (p. 122)
heterocigoto Tener dos alelos diferentes para el mismo rasgo.

hibernation A state of greatly reduced body activity that occurs during the winter. (p. 450)
hibernación Estado de gran disminución de la actividad corporal que ocurre durante el invierno.

histamine A chemical that is responsible for the symptoms of an allergy. (p. 612)
histamina Sustancia química responsable de los síntomas de una alergia.

HIV (human immunodeficiency virus) The virus that causes AIDS. (p. 602)
VIH (Virus de la inmunodeficiencia humana) Virus que causa el SIDA.

homeostasis The maintenance of stable internal conditions in an organism. (pp. 40, 472)
homeostasis Mantenimiento de condiciones internas estables.

homologous structures Body parts that are structurally similar in related species and that provide evidence for a common ancestor. (p. 184)
estructuras homólogas Partes del cuerpo que son estructuralmente similares entre las especies relacionadas; proveen evidencia de que las estructuras se heredaron de un antepasado común.

homozygous Having two identical alleles for a trait.
homocigoto Tener dos alelos idénticos para el mismo rasgo. (p. 122)

hormone A chemical in an organism that produces a specific effect such as growth or development.
hormona Sustancia química que afecta el crecimiento y el desarrollo. (pp. 285, 667)

host The organism that a parasite or virus lives in or on. (pp. 210, 316, 729)
huésped Organismo dentro o fuera del cual vive un parásito.

hybrid An organism that has two different alleles for a trait; an organism that is heterozygous for a particular trait. (p. 114)
híbrido Organismo que tiene dos alelos diferentes para un rasgo; un organismo que es heterocigoto para un rasgo en particular.

hybridization A selective breeding method in which two genetically different individuals are crossed. (p. 158)
hibridación Método de cruce selectivo en el cual se cruzan dos individuos genéticamente diferentes.

hypertension A disorder in which a person's blood pressure is consistently higher than normal; also called high blood pressure. (p. 554)
hipertensión Trastorno en el que la presión arterial de una persona es constantemente más alta de lo normal; tambien se llama presión alta.

hyphae The branching, threadlike tubes that make up the bodies of multicellular fungi. (p. 237)
hifas Delgados tubos ramificados que constituyen el cuerpo de los hongos multicelulares.

hypothalamus A part of the brain that links the nervous system and the endocrine system. (p. 668)
hipotálamo Parte del encéfalo que une el sistema nervioso con el sistema endocrino.

hypothesis A possible explanation for a set of observations or answer to a scientific question; must be testable. (p. 15)
hipótesis Explicación posible a un conjunto de observaciones o respuesta a una pregunta científica; debe ser verificable.

immigration Moving into a population. (p. 714)
inmigración Ingreso a una población.

immune response Part of the body's defense against pathogens, in which cells of the immune system react to each kind of pathogen with a defense targeted specifically at that pathogen. (p. 600)
reacción inmunológica Parte de la defensa del cuerpo contra los patógenos en la que las células del sistema inmunológico reaccionan a cada tipo de patógeno con una defensa específica.

immunity The body's ability to destroy pathogens before they can cause disease. (p. 606)
inmunidad Capacidad del cuerpo para destruir los patógenos antes de que causen enfermedades.

imprinting A process in which newly hatched birds or newborn mammals learn to follow the first moving object they see. (p. 439)
impronta Proceso por el cual las aves o mamíferos recién nacidos aprenden a seguir al primero objeto que ven.

inbreeding A selective breeding method in which two individuals with identical or similar sets of alleles are crossed. (p. 158)
endogamia Método de cruce selectivo en el que se cruzan dos individuos con pares de alelos idénticos o semejantes.

infectious disease A disease caused by the presence of a living thing in the body. (p. 593)
enfermedad infecciosa Enfermedad causada por la presencia de un ser vivo en el cuerpo.

inferring The process of making an inference, an interpretation based on observations and prior knowledge. (p. 8)
inferir Proceso de realizar una inferencia; una interpretación basada en observaciones y conocimiento previo.

inflammatory response Part of the body's defense against pathogens, in which fluid and white blood cells leak from blood vessels into tissues, and white blood cells destroy pathogens. (p. 599)
reacción inflamatoria Parte de la defensa del cuerpo contra los patógenos en la cual los fluidos y los glóbulos blancos salen de los vasos sanguíneos hacia los tejidos y destruyen los patógenos descomponiéndolos.

insect An arthropod with three body sections, six legs, one pair of antennae, and usually one or two pairs of wings. (p. 344)
insecto Artrópodo con tres secciones corporales, seis patas, un par de antenas y normalmente uno o dos pares de alas.

insight learning The process of learning how to solve a problem or do something new by applying what is already known. (p. 442)
aprendizaje por discernimiento Proceso de aprender cómo resolver un problema o hacer algo nuevo aplicando lo que ya se sabe.

instinct An inborn behavior pattern that an animal performs correctly the first time. (p. 438)
instinto Patrón innato de conducta que un animal ejecuta correctamente desde la primera vez.

insulin A chemical produced in the pancreas that enables the body's cells to take in glucose from the blood and use it for energy. (p. 613)
insulina Sustancia química que se produce en el páncreas, que permite que las células del cuerpo absorban glucosa de la sangre y la usen como energía.

interneuron A neuron that carries nerve impulses from one neuron to another. (p. 628)
interneurona Neurona que lleva los impulsos nerviosos de una neurona a otra.

interphase The stage of the cell cycle that takes place before cell division occurs. (p. 96)
interfase Fase del ciclo celular que ocurre antes de la división.

intertidal zone The area between the highest high-tide line and lowest low-tide line. (p. 768)
zona intermareal Área entre la línea más alta de la marea alta y la línea más baja de la marea baja.

invertebrate An animal that does not have a backbone. (p. 299)
invertebrado Animal que no posee columna vertebral.

involuntary muscle A muscle that is not under conscious control. (p. 482)
músculos involuntarios Músculo que no se puede controlar conscientemente.

iris The circular structure that surrounds the pupil and regulates the amount of light entering the eye.
iris Estructura circular que rodea la pupila y regula la cantidad de luz que entra en el ojo. (p. 643)

J

joint A place in the body where two bones come together. (p. 476)
articulación Lugar en el cuerpo en donde se unen dos huesos.

K

karyotype A picture of all the chromosomes in a cell arranged in pairs. (p. 154)
cariotipo Imagen de todos los cromosomas de una célula, organizados en parejas.

keystone species A species that influences the survival of many others in an ecosystem. (p. 793)
especie clave Especie que influye en la supervivencia de muchas otras en un ecosistema.

kidney A major organ of the excretory system that removes urea and other wastes from the blood.
riñón Órgano principal del sistema excretor que elimina la urea y otros materiales de desecho de la sangre. (pp. 388, 580)

L

large intestine The last section of the digestive system, where water is absorbed into the blood and the remaining material is eliminated from the body. (p. 527)
intestino grueso Última sección del sistema digestivo, donde se absorbe el agua hacia el torrente sanguíneo y los materiales restantes son eliminados del cuerpo.

larva The immature form of an animal that looks very different from the adult. (p. 305)
larva Forma inmadura de un animal que se ve muy diferente al adulto.

larynx The voice box (p. 572)
laringe Dos pliegues de tejido que forman la caja sonora humana.

learning The process that leads to changes in behavior based on practice or experience. (p. 438)
aprendizaje Proceso que conduce a cambios en el comportamiento basados en la práctica o la experiencia.

lens The flexible structure that focuses light that has entered the eye. (p. 643)
cristalino Estructura flexible que enfoca la luz que entra en el ojo.

lichen The combination of a fungus and either an alga or an autotrophic bacterium that live together in a mutualistic relationship. (p. 241)
liquen Combinación de un hongo y una alga o bien una bacteria autótrofa, que viven juntos en una relación de mutualismo.

life science The study of living things. (p. 12)
ciencias de la vida Estudio de los seres vivos.

lift The difference in pressure between the upper and lower surfaces of a bird's wings that produces an upward force that causes the bird to rise. (p. 417)
fuerza de elevación Diferencia de presión entre la superficie superior e inferior de las alas de un ave, que produce una fuerza ascendente que permite que el ave se eleve.

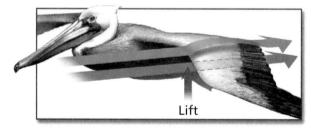

Lift

ligament Strong connective tissue that holds bones together in movable joints. (p. 477)
ligamentos Tejido conectivo resistente que une los huesos en las articulaciones móviles.

limiting factor An environmental factor that prevents a population from increasing. (p. 716)
factor limitante Factor ambiental que impide el crecimiento de una población.

lipid Energy-rich organic compound, such as a fat, oil, or wax, that is made of carbon, hydrogen, and oxygen. (p. 76)
lípido Compuesto orgánico rico en energía, como grasa, aceite y cera, formado por carbono, hidrógeno y oxígeno.

liver The body's largest organ; it produces bile, breaks down medicines, and helps eliminate nitrogen from the body. (p. 525)
hígado Órgano más grande del cuerpo; produce bilis, descompone las medicinas y elimina el nitrógeno del cuerpo.

long-day plant A plant that flowers when the nights are shorter than the plant's critical night length.
planta de día largo Una planta que florece cuando las noches son más cortas que la longitud nocturna critica de la planta. (p. 286)

lung An organ found in air-breathing vertebrates that exchanges oxygen and carbon dioxide with the blood. (pp. 384, 568)
pulmón Órgano que se encuentra en los vertebrados que respiran aire, con el que intercambian oxígeno y dióxido de carbono con la sangre.

lymph The fluid that the lymphatic system collects and returns to the bloodstream. (p. 551)
linfa Fluido que el sistema linfático recoge y devuelve al torrente sanguíneo.

lymph node A small knob of tissue in the lymphatic system that filters lymph, trapping bacteria and other microorganisms that cause disease. (p. 551)
ganglio linfático Pequeña prominencia de tejido en el sistema linfático que filtra la linfa, atrapando las bacterias y otros microorganismos que causan enfermedades.

lymphatic system A network of veinlike vessels that returns the fluid that leaks out of blood vessels to the bloodstream. (p. 550)
sistema linfático Red de vasos semejantes a venas que devuelve al torrente sanguíneo el fluido que sale de los vasos sanguíneos.

lymphocyte White blood cell that distinguishes between each kind of pathogen. (p. 600)
linfocito Glóbulo blanco que reacciona a cada tipo de patógeno con una defensa específica.

lysosome A small, round cell structure containing chemicals that break down large food particles into smaller ones. (p. 66)
lisosoma Pequeña estructura celular redonda que contiene sustancias químicas que descomponen las partículas de alimento grandes en otras más simples.

M

making models The process of creating representations of complex objects or processes. (p. 11)
hacer modelos Proceso de crear representaciones de objetos o procesos complejos.

mammal An endothermic vertebrate with a four-chambered heart, skin covered with fur or hair, and young fed with milk from the mother's body. (p. 420)
mamífero Vertebrado endotérmico con un corazón de cuatro cámaras y piel cubierta de pelaje o pelo, que alimenta a sus crías con leche materna.

mammary gland An organ in female mammals that produces milk for the mammal's young. (p. 421)
glándula mamaria Órgano en los mamíferos hembra que produce leche para alimentar a las crías.

manipulated variable The one factor that a scientist changes during an experiment; also called independent variable. (p. 16)
variable manipulada Único factor que un científico cambia durante un experimento; también llamada variable independiente.

marrow The soft connective tissue that fills the internal spaces in bone. (p. 478)
médula ósea Tejido conectivo suave que rellena los espacios internos de un hueso.

marsupial A mammal whose young are born alive at an early stage of development, and which usually continue to develop in a pouch on their mother's body. (p. 424)
marsupial Mamífero cuyas crías nacen vivas en una etapa muy temprana del desarrollo, y que normalmente sigue su desarrollo en una bolsa en el cuerpo de la madre.

medusa The cnidarian body plan having a bowl shape and adapted for a free-swimming life.
medusa Cnidario cuyo cuerpo se caracteriza por tener forma de cuenco, y que está adaptado para nadar libremente en el agua. (p. 307)

meiosis The process that occurs in the formation of sex cells (sperm and egg) by which the number of chromosomes is reduced by half. (p. 128)
meiosis Proceso que ocurre en la formación de las células sexuales (espermatozoide y óvulo) por el cual el número de cromosomas se reduce a la mitad.

melanin A pigment that gives skin its color. (p. 491)
melanina Pigmento que da color a la piel.

menstrual cycle The cycle of changes that occurs in the female reproductive system, during which an egg develops and the uterus prepares for the arrival of a fertilized egg. (p. 679)
ciclo menstrual Ciclo de cambios que ocurre en el sistema reproductor femenino, durante el cual se desarrolla un óvulo, y el útero se prepara para la llegada del óvulo fecundado.

menstruation The process in which the thickened lining of the uterus breaks down, and blood and tissue then pass out of the female body. (p. 680)
menstruación Proceso en el cual el grueso recubrimiento del útero se descompone la sangre y el tejido salen del cuerpo femenino.

messenger RNA RNA that copies the coded message from DNA in the nucleus and carries the message into the cytoplasm. (p. 133)
ARN mensajero ARN que copia el mensaje codificado del ADN en el núcleo y lo lleva al citoplasma.

metamorphosis A process in which an animal's body undergoes dramatic changes in form during its life cycle. (p. 339)
metamorfosis Proceso por el cual el cuerpo de un animal cambia de manera drástica durante su ciclo de vida.

microscope An instrument that makes small objects look larger. (p. 51)
microscopio Instrumento que hace que los objetos pequeños se vean más grandes.

migration The regular, periodic journey of an animal from one place to another and back again for feeding or reproduction. (p. 450)
migración Viaje regular y periódico de un animal de un lugar a otro y de regreso al mismo lugar con el propósito de alimentarse o reproducirse.

minerals Nutrients that are needed by the body in small amounts and are not made by living things.
minerales Nutrientes que el cuerpo necesita en pequeñas cantidades y que no producen los seres vivos. (p. 510)

mitochondria Rod-shaped cell structures that convert energy in food molecules to energy the cell can use to carry out its functions. (p. 63)
mitocondria Estructura celular con forma de bastón que transforma la energía de las moléculas de alimentos en energía que la célula puede usar para llevar a cabo sus funciones.

mitosis The stage of the cell cycle during which the cell's nucleus divides into two new nuclei and one copy of the DNA is distributed into each daughter cell. (p. 97)
mitosis Fase del ciclo celular durante la cual el núcleo de la célula se divide en dos nuevos nucleolos y se distribuye una copia del ADN a cada célula hija.

mold A type of fossil formed when a shell or other hard part of an organism dissolves, leaving an empty space in the shape of the part. (p. 190)
molde Tipo de fósil que se forma cuando el caparazón, concha u otra parte dura de un organismo enterrado se disuelve y deja un área hueca con la forma de esa parte.

mollusk An invertebrate with a soft, unsegmented body; most are protected by a hard outer shell.
molusco Invertebrado con cuerpo blando y sin segmentos; la mayoría están protegidos por una concha exterior dura. (p. 329)

molting The process of shedding an outgrown exoskeleton. (p. 336)
muda Proceso de cambio de un exoesqueleto a otro.

monocot An angiosperm with one seed leaf. (p. 280)
monocotiledónea Angiosperma cuyas semillas tienen un solo cotiledón.

monotreme A mammal that lays eggs. (p. 424)
monotrema Mamífero que pone huevos.

motor neuron A neuron that sends an impulse to a muscle or gland, causing the muscle or gland to react.
neurona motora Neurona que envía un impulso a un músculo o glándula, haciendo que el músculo o la glándula reaccione. (p. 628)

mucus A thick, slippery substance produced by the body. (p. 519)
mucosidad Sustancia espesa y lubricante que produce el cuerpo.

multicellular Consisting of many cells. (p. 34)
multicelular Que se compone de muchas células.

multiple alleles Three or more forms of a gene that code for a single trait. (p. 146)
alelo múltiple Tres o más formas de un gen que codifican un solo rasgo.

muscle tissue A body tissue that contracts or shortens, making body parts move. (p. 470)
tejido muscular Tejido corporal que se contrae o acorta, permitiendo así que se muevan las partes del cuerpo.

mutation A change in a gene or chromosome. (p. 136)
mutación Cambio en un gen o cromosoma.

mutualism A close relationship between organisms of two species in which both organisms benefit.
mutualismo Relación entre dos especies de la cual ambas se benefician. (pp. 230, 728)

natural resource Anything in the environment that is used by people. (p. 779)
recurso natural Cualquier cosa del medio ambiente que usa la gente.

natural selection A process by which individuals that are better adapted to their environment are more likely to survive and reproduce than others of the same species. (pp. 177, 723)
selección natural Proceso por el cual los individuos que se adaptan mejor a sus ambientes tienen más posibilidades de sobrevivir y reproducirse que otros miembros de la misma especie.

nearsightedness The condition in which a person can see nearby objects clearly. (p. 645)
miopía Condición en la que una persona puede ver claramente los objetos cercanos.

negative feedback A process in which a system is turned off by the condition it produces. (p. 670)
reacción negativa Proceso en el cual un sistema se apaga por la condición que produce.

nephron Small filtering structure found in the kidneys that removes wastes from blood and produces urine.
nefrón Estructura diminuta de filtración que hay en los riñones, que elimina los desechos de la sangre y que produce la orina. (p. 580)

neritic zone The region of shallow ocean water over the continental shelf. (p. 768)
zona nerítica Región donde el agua del océano es poco profunda sobre la placa continental.

nerve A bundle of nerve fibers. (p. 628)
nervio Conjunto de fibras nerviosas.

nerve impulse The message carried by a neuron.
impulso nervioso Mensaje que lleva una neurona. (p. 628)

nervous tissue A body tissue that carries electrical messages back and forth between the brain and every other part of the body. (p. 470)
tejido nervioso Tejido corporal que lleva mensajes eléctricos entre el encéfalo y todas las demás partes del cuerpo y viceversa.

neuron A cell that carries information through the nervous system. (p. 628)
neurona Célula que lleva información a través del sistema nervioso.

niche The role of an organism in its habitat, or how it makes its living. (p. 723)
nicho Función de un organismo en su hábitat, o cómo sobrevive.

nicotine A stimulant drug in tobacco that increases the activities of the nervous system, heart, and other organs. (p. 575)
nicotina Sustancia química en el tabaco que acelera la actividad del sistema nervioso, corazón y otros órganos.

nitrogen fixation The process of changing free nitrogen gas into a usable form. (p. 750)
fijación del nitrógeno Proceso de conversión del gas nitrógeno libre en una forma aprovechable.

noninfectious disease A disease that is not caused by a pathogen. (p. 611)
enfermedad no infecciosa Enfermedad que no es causada por un patógeno.

nonrenewable resource A natural resource that is not replaced in a useful time frame. (p. 779)
recurso no renovable Recurso natural que no se restaura una vez usado, en un período relativamente corto.

nonvascular plant A low-growing plant that lacks true vascular tissue. (p. 253)
planta no vascular Planta de crecimiento lento que carece de tejido vascular verdadero.

notochord A flexible rod that supports a chordate's back. (p. 368)
notocordio Bastoncillo flexible que sostiene el lomo de los cordados.

nucleic acid Very large organic molecule made of carbon, oxygen, hydrogen, nitrogen, and phosphorus, that contains the instructions cells need to carry out all the functions of life. (p. 78)
ácido nucléico Molécula orgánica muy grande compuesta de carbono, oxígeno, hidrógeno, nitrógeno y fósforo, que contiene las instrucciones que las células necesitan para realizar todas las funciones vitales.

nucleus The control center of a eukaryotic cell that directs the cell's activities and contains the information that determines the cell's form and function. (pp. 47, 469)
núcleo Centro de control de la célula eucariota que dirige las actividades de la célula y que contiene información que determina la forma y función de la célula.

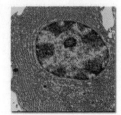

nutrients Substances in food that provide the raw materials and energy the body needs to carry out all its essential processes. (p. 502)
nutrientes Sustancias en los alimentos que proveen la materia prima y la energía que necesita el cuerpo para realizar los procesos elementales.

nymph A stage of gradual metamorphosis that usually resembles the adult insect. (p. 346)
ninfa Etapa de la metamorfosis gradual en la que normalmente el insecto se parece a un insecto adulto.

O

observing The process of using one or more of your senses to gather information. (p. 7)
observar Proceso de usar uno o más de los cinco sentidos para reunir información.

omnivore A consumer that eats both plants and animals. (pp. 331, 741)
omnívoro Consumidor que come tanto plantas como animales.

open circulatory system A circulatory system in which the heart pumps blood into open spaces in the body, and blood is not confined to blood vessels. (p. 329)
sistema circulatorio abierto Sistema circulatorio en el que el corazón bombea la sangre en espacios abiertos del cuerpo y la sangre no se mantiene en vasos sanguíneos.

operational definition A statement that describes how to measure a particular variable or how to define a particular term. (p. 16)
definición operativa Enunciado que describe cómo medir una variable determinada o cómo definir un término determinado.

organ A structure in the body that is composed of different kinds of tissue. (pp. 295, 470)
órgano Estructura del cuerpo compuesta de diferentes tipos de tejidos.

organ system A group of organs that work together to perform a major function in the body. (p. 470)
sistema de órganos Grupo de órganos que trabajan juntos para realizar una función importante del cuerpo.

organelle A tiny cell structure that carries out a specific function within the cell. (p. 60)
organelo Diminuta estructura celular que realiza una función específica dentro de la célula.

organism A living thing. (pp. 34, 705)
organismo Ser vivo.

osmosis The diffusion of water molecules through a selectively permeable membrane. (p. 82)
ósmosis Difusión de las moléculas de agua a través de una membrana con permeabilidad selectiva.

osteoporosis A condition in which the body's bones become weak and break easily. (p. 481)
osteoporosis Condición en la cual los huesos del cuerpo se debilitan y se rompen fácilmente.

ovary A flower structure that encloses and protects ovules and seeds as they develop; Organ of the female reproductive system in which eggs and estrogen are produced. (pp. 277, 678)
ovario Estructura de la flor que encierra y protege a los óvulos y a las semillas durante su desarrollo; órgano del sistema reproductor femenino en el cual se producen los óvulos y el estrógeno.

ovulation The process in which a mature egg is released from the ovary into a fallopian tube.
ovulación Proceso en el cual el óvulo maduro sale del ovario y va a la trompa de falopio. (p. 680)

ovule A structure that contains an egg cell. (p. 274)
óvulo Estructura que contiene una célula reproductora femenina.

 P

pacemaker A group of cells located in the right atrium that sends out signals that make the heart muscle contract and that regulates heartbeat rate.
marcapasos Grupo de células ubicado en la aurícula derecha que envía señales para que el músculo cardiaco se contraiga, y que regula el ritmo cardiaco. (p. 537)

paleontologist A scientist who studies extinct organisms, examines fossil structure, and makes comparisons to present-day organisms. (p. 398)
paleontólogo Científico que estudia los organismos extintos, examina las estructuras de los fósiles y los compara con los organismos de la actualidad.

pancreas A triangular organ that lies between the stomach and the small intestine. (p. 526)
páncreas Órgano triangular ubicado entre el estómago y la primera parte del al intestino delgado.

parasite The organism that benefits by living on or in a host in a parasitism interaction. (pp. 210, 316)
parásito Organismo que se beneficia de vivir en la superficie o en el interior de un húesped en una interacción de parasitismo.

parasitism A relationship in which one organism lives on or in a host and harms it. (p. 729)
parasitismo Relación en la cual un organismo vive en la superficie o en el interior de un huésped y lo perjudica.

passive immunity Immunity in which antibodies are given to a person rather than produced within the person's own body. (p. 610)
inmunidad pasiva Inmunidad en la que los anticuerpos vienen de otro organismo y no del cuerpo de la propia persona.

passive transport The movement of materials through a cell membrane without using the cell's energy. (p. 84)
transporte pasivo Movimiento de materiales a través de la membrana celular sin el uso de energía.

pasteurization A process of heating food to a temperature that is high enough to kill most harmful bacteria without changing the taste of the food.
pasteurización Proceso de calentamiento del alimento a una temperatura suficientemente alta como para matar la mayoría de las bacterias dañinas sin cambiar el sabor de la comida. (p. 223)

pathogen An organism that causes disease. (p. 593)
patógeno Organismo que causa enfermedades.

pedigree A chart or "family tree" that tracks which members of a family have a particular trait.
genealogía Tabla o "árbol genealógico" que muestra qué miembros de una familia tienen un rasgo en particular. (p. 153)

penis The organ through which both semen and urine leave the male body. (p. 677)
pene Órgano a través del cual salen del cuerpo masculino tanto el semen como la orina.

Percent Daily Value A value that shows how the nutritional content of one serving of food fits into the diet of a person who consumes 2,000 Calories per day. (p. 513)
Porcentaje de valor diario Valor que muestra cómo el contenido nutricional de una porción de alimento se corresponde con la dieta de una persona que consume 2,000 Calorías al día.

perennial A flowering plant that lives for more than two years. (p. 287)
perenne Planta con flores que vive más de dos años.

peripheral nervous system The division of the nervous system consisting of all of the nerves located outside the central nervous system. (p. 632)
sistema nervioso periférico Parte del sistema nervioso formada por todos los nervios ubicados fuera del sistema central nervioso.

peristalsis Involuntary waves of muscle contraction that keep food moving along in one direction through the digestive system. (p. 519)
peristaltismo Ondulaciones involuntarias de contracción muscular que empujan el alimento en una dirección a través del sistema digestivo.

permafrost Soil that is frozen all year. (p. 765)
permagélido Suelo que está congelado todo el año.

pesticide A chemical designed to kill a pest animal.
pesticida Sustancia química diseñada para matar una plaga animal. (p. 355)

petal A colorful, leaflike structure of some flowers.
pétalo Estructura de color brillante, en forma de hoja que tienen algunas flores. (p. 276)

petrified fossil A fossil formed when minerals replace all or part of an organism. (p. 190)
fósil petrificado Fósil que se forma cuando los minerales reemplazan todo el organismo o parte de él.

phagocyte A white blood cell that destroys pathogens by engulfing them and breaking them down.
fagocito Glóbulo blanco que destruye los patógenos envolviéndolos y descomponiéndolos. (p. 599)

pharynx The throat. (p. 567)
faringe Garganta.

phenotype An organism's physical appearance, or visible traits. (p. 122)
fenotipo Apariencia física de un organismo, es decir, los rasgos visibles.

pheromone A chemical released by one animal that affects the behavior of another animal of the same species. (p. 445)
feromona Sustancia química liberada por un animal que afecta el comportamiento de otro animal de la misma especie.

phloem The vascular tissue through which food moves in some plants. (p. 263)
floema Tejido vascular por el que circula el alimento en algunas plantas.

photoperiodism A plant's response to seasonal changes in length of night and day. (p. 286)
fotoperiodicidad Respuesta de una planta a los cambios de día y noche por las estaciones.

photosynthesis The process in which some organisms use water along with sunlight and carbon dioxide to make their own food. (pp. 87, 706)
fotosíntesis Proceso por el cual los organismos usan el agua junto con la luz solar y el dióxido de carbono para producir su alimento.

phylum One of the major groups into which biologists classify members of a kingdom. (p. 298)
fílum Uno de alrededor de 35 grupos principales en los que los biólogos clasifican los miembros del reino animal.

pigment A colored chemical that absorbs light.
pigmento Compuesto químico de color que absorbe luz. (p. 88)

pioneer species The first species to populate an area. (p. 731)
especies pioneras Primeras especies en poblar una región.

pistil The female reproductive part of a flower. (p. 277)
pistilo Parte reproductora femenina de una flor.

pituitary gland An endocrine gland that controls many body activities. (p. 670)
glándula pituitaria Glándula endocrina que controla muchas actividades corporales.

placenta A membrane that becomes the link between the developing embryo or fetus and the mother. (pp. 425, 684)
placenta Membrana que se convierte en la unión entre el embrión o feto en desarrollo y la madre.

placental mammal A mammal that develops inside its mother's body until its body systems can function independently. (p. 425)
mamífero placentario Mamífero que se desarrolla dentro del cuerpo de la madre hasta que sus sistemas corporales pueden funcionar por sí solos.

plasma The liquid part of blood. (p. 545)
plasma Parte líquida de la sangre.

platelet A cell fragment that plays an important part in forming blood clots. (p. 548)
plaqueta Fragmento de célula que juega un papel muy importante en la formación de coágulos sanguíneos.

poaching Illegal killing or removal of wildlife from their habitats. (p. 798)
caza ilegal Matanza o eliminación de la fauna silvestre de su hábitat.

pollen Tiny particles (male gametophytes) produced by seed plants that contain the cells that later become sperm cells. (p. 263)
polen Partículas diminutas (gametofitos masculinos) producidas por las plantas de semillas que contienen las células que posteriormente se convierten en células reproductoras masculinas.

pollination The transfer of pollen from male reproductive structures to female reproductive structures in plants. (p. 274)
polinización Transferencia de polen de las estructuras reproductoras masculinas a las estructuras reproductoras femeninas de las plantas.

pollinator An animal that carries pollen from one plant to another of the same species, enabling plants to reproduce. (p. 354)
polinizador Animal que lleva polen de una planta a otra de la misma especie, permitiendo que las plantas se reproduzcan.

pollution Contamination of Earth's land, water, or air. (p. 779)
contaminación Polución del suelo, agua y aire de la Tierra.

polyp The cnidarian body plan is characterized by a vaselike shape and that usually adapted for a life attached to an underwater surface. (p. 307)
pólipo Cnidario cuyo cuerpo se caracteriza por tener forma cilíndrica, y que generalmente está adaptado para vivir adherido a una superficie submarina.

population All the members of one species in a particular area. (p. 707)
población Todos los miembros de una especie en un área particular.

population density The number of individuals in an area of a specific size. (p. 716)
densidad de población Número de individuos en un área de un tamaño específico.

pore An opening through which sweat reaches the surface of the skin. (p. 491)
poro Abertura a través de la cual el sudor sale a la superficie de la piel.

precipitation Rain, snow, sleet, or hail. (p. 747)
precipitación Lluvia, nieve, aguanieve o granizo.

predation An interaction in which one organism kills another for food. (p. 725)
depredación Interacción en la cual un organismo mata y se come a otro.

predator The organism that does the killing in a predation interaction. (p. 725)
depredador Organismo que mata en la depredación.

predicting The process of forecasting what will happen based on past experience or evidence. (p. 9)
predecir Proceso de pronosticar lo que va a suceder en el futuro, basado en la experiencia pasada o en evidencia.

prey An organism that is killed and eaten by another organism. (p. 725)
presa Organismo que otro organismo mata y come.

primary succession The series of changes that occur in an area where no soil or organisms exist. (p. 731)
sucesión primaria Serie de cambios que ocurren en un área en donde no existe suelo ni organismos.

probability A number that describes how likely it is that an event will occur. (p. 118)
probabilidad Número que describe la posibilidad de que ocurra un suceso.

producer An organism that can make its own food.
productor Organismo que puede elaborar su propio alimento. (pp. 350, 741)

prokaryote An organism whose cells lack a nucleus and some other cell structures. (p. 47)
procariota Organismo cuyas células carecen de núcleo y otras estructuras celulares.

protein Large organic molecule made of carbon, hydrogen, oxygen, nitrogen, and sometimes sulfur.
proteína Molécula orgánica grande compuesta de carbono, hidrógeno, oxígeno, nitrógeno y, a veces, azufre. (pp. 77, 507)

protist A eukaryotic organism that cannot be classified as an animal, plant, or fungus. (p. 227)
protista Organismo eucariótico que no se puede clasificar como animal, planta ni hongo.

protozoan An animal-like protist. (p. 227)
protozoario Protista con características animales.

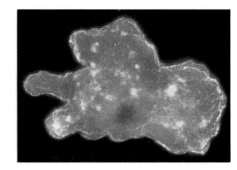

pseudopod A "false foot" or temporary bulge of cytoplasm used for feeding and movement in some protozoans. (p. 228)
seudópodo "Falso pie" o abultamiento temporal del citoplasma, que algunos protozoarios usan para alimentarse o desplazarse.

puberty The period of sexual development in which the body becomes able to reproduce. (p. 689)
pubertad Período de desarrollo sexual durante la adolescencia en el que el cuerpo se vuelve capaz de reproducir.

pulse The alternating expansion and relaxation of an artery wall as blood travels through an artery.
pulso Expansión y relajación alternada de una pared arterial a medida que la sangre viaja por la arteria. (p. 540)

punctuated equilibria The theory that species evolve during short periods of rapid change.
equilibrio puntuado Teoría que enuncia que las especies evolucionan durante períodos breves de cambios rápidos. (p. 197)

Punnett square A chart that shows all the possible combinations of alleles that can result from a genetic cross. (p. 120)
cuadrado de Punnett Tabla que muestra todas las combinaciones posibles de los alelos que pueden resultar de una cruza genética.

pupa The third stage of complete metamorphosis, in which an insect changes from a larva to an adult.
pupa Tercera etapa de la metamorfosis completa, en la cual un insecto cambia de larva a adulto. (p. 346)

pupil The opening through which light enters the eye. (p. 643)
pupila Abertura por la que entra la luz al ojo.

purebred The offspring of many generations that have the same traits. (p. 111)
cepa pura raza pura Descendiente de muchas generaciones que tienen los mismos rasgos.

qualitative observation An observation that deals with characteristics that cannot be expressed in numbers. (p. 7)
observación cualitativa Observación que se centra en las características que no se pueden expresar con números.

quantitative observation An observation that deals with a number or amount. (p. 7)
observación cuantitativa Observación que se centra en un número o cantidad.

radial symmetry The quality of having many lines of symmetry that all pass through a central point.
simetría radial Cualidad de tener muchos ejes de simetría que pasan por un punto central. (p. 301)

radioactive dating A technique used to determine the actual age of a fossil on the basis of the amount of a radioactive element it contains. (p. 192)
datación radiactiva Técnica que se usa para determinar la edad real de un fósil basándose en la cantidad de elementos radiactivos que contiene.

radioactive element An unstable element that breaks down into a different element. (p. 192)
elemento radiactivo Elemento inestable que se descompone en un elemento diferente.

radula A flexible ribbon of tiny teeth in mollusks. (p. 330)
rádula Hilera flexible de minúsculos dientes en los moluscos.

receiver A device that receives radio waves and converts them into a sound or light signal. (p. 455)
receptor Aparato que recibe las ondas de radio y las convierte en señales de sonido o de luz.

recessive allele An allele that is masked when a dominant allele is present. (p. 113)
alelo recesivo Alelo que queda oculto cuando está presente un alelo dominante.

rectum The end of the large intestine where waste material is compressed into a solid form before being eliminated. (p. 527)
recto Final del intestino grueso, donde el material de desecho se comprime a una forma sólida antes de ser eliminado.

red blood cell A cell in the blood that takes up oxygen in the lungs and delivers it to cells elsewhere in the body. (p. 546)
glóbulo rojo Célula de la sangre que capta el oxígeno en los pulmones y lo lleva a las células de todo el cuerpo.

reflex An automatic response that occurs rapidly and without conscious control. (p. 637)
reflejo Respuesta automática que ocurre muy rápidamente y sin control consciente.

relative dating A technique used to determine which of two fossils is older. (p. 191)
datación relativa Técnica que se usa para determinar cuál de dos fósiles es más antiguo.

renewable resource A resource that is either always available or is naturally replaced in a relatively short time. (p. 779)
recurso renovable Recurso que está siempre disponible o que es restituido de manera natural en un período relativamente corto.

replication The process by which a cell makes a copy of the DNA in its nucleus. (p. 96)
replicación Proceso por el cual una célula copia el ADN de su núcleo.

reptile An ectothermic vertebrate that lays eggs and has lungs and scaly skin. (p. 388)
reptil Vertebrado ectotérmico que pone huevos, y que tiene pulmones y piel con escamas.

respiration The process by which cells break down simple food molecules to release the energy they contain. (pp. 91, 565)
respiración Proceso por el cual las células descomponen moléculas simples de alimento para liberar la energía que contienen.

responding variable The factor that changes as a result of changes to the manipulated, or independent, variable in an experiment; also called dependent variable. (p. 16)
variable respuesta Factor que cambia como resultado del cambio de la variable manipulada, o independiente, en un experimento; también llamada variable dependiente.

response An action or change in behavior that occurs in reaction to a stimulus. (pp. 35, 437, 627)
respuesta Acción o cambio en el comportamiento que ocurre como resultado de un estímulo.

retina The layer of receptor cells at the back of the eye on which an image is focused. (p. 644)
retina Capa de células receptoras en la parte posterior del ojo donde se enfoca una imagen.

rhizoid A thin, rootlike structure that anchors a moss and absorbs water and nutrients. (p. 257)
rizoide Estructura fina parecida a una raíz que sujeta un musgo al suelo, y que absorbe el agua y los nutrientes.

ribosome A small grain-like structure in the cytoplasm of a cell where proteins are made. (p. 63)
ribosoma Estructura pequeña parecida a un grano en el citoplasma de una célula donde se fabrican las proteínas.

RNA Ribonucleic acid; a nucleic acid that plays an important role in the production of proteins. (p. 78)
ARN Ácido ribonucleico; ácido nucleico que juega un papel importante en la producción de proteínas.

root cap A structure that covers the tip of a root, protecting the root from injury. (p. 267)
cofia Estructura que cubre la punta de una raíz y la protege contra daños.

saliva The fluid released when the mouth waters that plays an important role in both mechanical and chemical digestion. (p. 518)
saliva Líquido liberado por la boca que juega un papel muy importante en la digestión química y mecánica.

satellite An instrument that orbits a celestial body, such as Earth. (p. 456)
satélite Instrumento que orbita un cuerpo celeste, como la Tierra.

savanna A grassland close to the equator that receives as much as 120 centimeters of rain per year. (p. 762)
sabana Tierra de pastos próxima al ecuador que recibe hasta 120 centímetros de lluvia al año.

scavenger A carnivore that feeds on the bodies of dead organisms. (pp. 316, 741)
carroñero Carnívoro que se alimenta del cuerpo de animales muertos.

science A way of learning about the natural world and the knowledge gained through the process.
ciencia Estudio del mundo natural a través de observaciones y del razonamiento lógico. (p. 6)

scientific inquiry The diverse ways in which scientists study the natural world and propose explanations based on evidence they gather. (p. 14)
investigación científica Diversidad de métodos con los que los científicos estudian el mundo natural y proponen explicaciones del mismo basadas en la evidencia que reúnen.

scientific theory A well-tested concept that explains a wide range of observations. (p. 176)
teoría científica Concepto comprobado que explica una amplia gama de observaciones.

scrotum An external pouch of skin in which the testes are located. (p. 676)
escroto Bolsa externa de piel en donde se ubican los testículos.

secondary succession The series of changes that occur in an area where the ecosystem has been disturbed, but where soil and organisms still exist.
sucesión secundaria Serie de cambios que ocurren en un área después de la perturbación de un ecosistema, pero donde todavía hay suelo y organismos. (p. 732)

sedimentary rock Rock formed of hardened layers of sediments. (p. 396)
roca sedimentaria Roca formada por las capas endurecidas de sedimentos.

seed The plant structure that contains a young plant inside a protective covering. (p. 263)
semilla Estructura de una planta que contiene una plántula dentro de una cubierta protectora.

selective breeding The process of selecting a few organisms with desired traits to serve as parents of the next generation. (p. 158)
cruce selectivo Proceso de selección de algunos organismos con los rasgos deseados para que sirvan de como progenitores de la siguiente generación.

selective cutting The process of cutting down only some trees in an area. (p. 785)
tala selectiva Proceso de cortar sólo algunos árboles de un área.

selectively permeable A property of cell membranes that allows some substances to pass through, while others cannot. (p. 80)
permeabilidad selectiva Propiedad de las membranas celulares que permite que algunas sustancias pasen y otras no.

semen A mixture of sperm and fluids. (p. 677)
semen Mezcla de células de espermatozoides y fluidos.

semicircular canals Structures in the inner ear that are responsible for the sense of balance. (p. 648)
canales semicirculares Estructuras en el oído interno responsables del sentido del equilibrio.

sensory neuron A neuron that picks up stimuli from the internal or external environment and converts each stimulus into a nerve impulse.
neurona sensorial Proceso de selección de algunos organismos con los rasgos deseados para servir como progenitores de la siguiente generación. (p. 628)

sepal A leaflike structure that encloses the bud of a flower. (p. 276)
sépalo Estructura, parecida a una hoja, que encierra el botón de una flor.

sex chromosomes A pair of chromosomes carrying genes that determine whether a person is male or female. (p. 147)
cromosomas sexuales Par de cromosomas portadores de genes que determinan si una persona es macho o hembra.

sex-linked gene A gene that is carried on the X or Y chromosome. (p. 148)
gen ligado al sexo Gen portador del cromosoma X o Y.

sexual reproduction A reproductive process that involves two parents that combine their genetic material to produce a new organism, which differs from both parents. (pp. 220, 297)
reproducción sexual Proceso de reproducción que implica a dos progenitores que combinan su material genético para producir un nuevo organismo diferente a los dos progenitores.

short-day plant A plant that flowers when the nights are longer than the plant's critical night length.
planta de día corto Una planta que florece cuando las noches son más largas que la longitud nocturna critica de la planta. (p. 286)

skeletal muscle A muscle that is attached to the bones of the skeleton and provides the force that moves the bones. (p. 484)
músculos esqueléticos Músculo que está unido a los huesos del esqueleto y que proporciona la fuerza para que los huesos se muevan.

skeleton The inner framework made of all the bones of the body. (p. 474)
esqueleto Estructura formada por todos los huesos del cuerpo.

small intestine The part of the digestive system in which most chemical digestion takes place. (p. 524)
intestino delgado Parte del sistema digestivo en la cual se produce la mayoría de la digestión química.

smooth muscle Involuntary muscle found inside many internal organs of the body. (p. 484)
músculos lisos Músculo involuntario que se encuentra dentro de muchos órganos internos del cuerpo.

society A group of closely related animals of the same species that work together in a highly organized way. (p. 449)
sociedad Grupo de animales de la misma especie estrechamente relacionados que lo realizan juntos de una manera altamente organizada.

somatic nervous system The group of nerves in the peripheral nervous system that controls voluntary actions. (p. 637)
sistema nervioso somático Grupo de nervios en el sistema nervioso periférico que controla las acciones voluntarias.

species A group of organisms that are physically similar and can mate with each other and produce offspring that can also mate and reproduce. (pp. 44, 173, 707)
especie Grupo de organismos que son físicamente semejantes, se pueden cruzar y producen crías que también se pueden cruzar y reproducir.

sperm A male sex cell. (p. 675)
espermatozoide Célula sexual masculina.

spinal cord The thick column of nerve tissue that links the brain to most of the nerves in the peripheral nervous system. (p. 633)
médula espinal Columna gruesa de tejido nervioso que une el encéfalo con la mayoría de los nervios en el sistema nervioso periférico.

spongy bone Layer of bone tissue having many small spaces and found just inside the layer of compact bone. (p. 478)
hueso esponjoso Capa de tejido de un hueso que tiene muchos espacios pequeños y se encuentra justo dentro de la capa del hueso compacto.

spontaneous generation The mistaken idea that living things arise from nonliving sources. (p. 36)
generación espontánea Idea equivocada de que los seres vivos surgen de fuentes inertes.

spore A tiny cell that is able to grow into a new organism. (p. 234)
espora Célula diminuta que, al crecer, puede convertirse en un nuevo organismo.

sporophyte The stage in the life cycle of a plant in which the plant produces spores. (p. 254)
esporofito Etapa en el ciclo de vida de una planta en la que la planta produce esporas.

stamen A male reproductive part of a flower.
estambre Parte reproductora masculina de una flor. (p. 276)

stimulant A drug that speeds up body processes.
estimulante Droga que acelera los procesos del cuerpo. (p. 654)

stimulus A change in an organism's surroundings that causes the organism to react. (pp. 35, 437)
estímulo Cambio en el entorno de un organismo que le hace reaccionar.

stomach A J-shaped, muscular pouch located in the abdomen. (p. 520)
estómago Bolsa muscular con forma de J localizada en el abdomen.

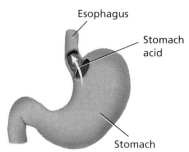

Esophagus

Stomach acid

Stomach

stomata Small openings on a leaf through which oxygen and carbon dioxide can move. (p. 89)
estomas Pequeños orificios en la superficie inferior de la hoja a través de los cuales se intercambia oxígeno y dióxido de carbono.

stress The reaction of a person's body to potentially threatening, challenging, or disturbing events. (p. 473)
estrés Reacción del cuerpo de un individuo a amenazas, retos o sucesos molestos potenciales.

striated muscle A muscle that appears banded; also called skeletal muscle. (p. 484)
músculo estriado Músculo con forma de franjas; también se llama músculo esquelético.

succession The series of predictable changes that occur in a community over time. (p. 730)
sucesión Serie de cambios predecibles que ocurren en una comunidad a través del tiempo.

sustainable yield An amount of a renewable resource that can be harvested regularly without reducing the future supply. (p. 786)
rendimiento sostenible Cantidad de un recurso renovable que puede ser recolectado constantemente sin reducir el abastecimiento futuro.

swim bladder An internal, gas-filled organ that helps a bony fish stabilize its body at different water depths.
vejiga natatoria Órgano interno lleno de gas que ayuda a un pez con esqueleto a estabilizar su cuerpo a diferentes profundidades. (p. 379)

symbiosis A close relationship between two organisms of different species that benefits at least one of the organisms. (pp. 230, 728)
simbiosis Relación estrecha entre especies de la que se beneficia al menos una de ellas.

synapse The junction where one neuron can transfer an impulse to the next structure. (p. 630)
sinapsis Unión donde una neurona puede transferir un impulso a la siguiente estructura.

T cell A lymphocyte that identifies pathogens and distinguishes one pathogen from another. (p. 600)
célula T Linfocito que identifica los patógenos y distingue un patógeno de otro.

tadpole The larval form of a frog or a toad. (p. 383)
renacuajo Estado de larva de una rana o un sapo.

tar A dark, sticky substance that forms when tobacco burns. (p. 575)
alquitrán Sustancia oscura y pegajosa producida cuando se quema tabaco.

target cell A cell in the body that recognizes a hormone's chemical structure. (p. 668)
célula destinataria Célula del cuerpo que reconoce la estructura química de una hormona.

taxonomy The scientific study of how living things are classified. (p. 43)
taxonomía Estudio científico de cómo se clasifican los seres vivos.

technology How people modify the world around them to meet their needs or to solve practical problems. (p. 20)
tecnología Cómo la gente modifica el mundo que la rodea para satisfacer sus necesidades o para solucionar problemas prácticos.

tendon Strong connective tissue that attaches muscle to bone. (p. 484)
tendón Tejido conectivo resistente que une un músculo a un hueso.

territory An area that is occupied and defended by an animal or group of animals. (p. 447)
territorio Área que ocupa y defiende un animal o grupo de animales.

testis Organ of the male reproductive system in which sperm and testosterone are produced.
testículo Órgano del sistema reproductor masculino en el cual se producen los espermatozoides y la testosterona. (p. 676)

testosterone A hormone produced by the testes that controls the development of physical characteristics in mature men. (p. 676)
testosterona Hormona producida por los testículos que controla el desarrollo de las características físicas del hombre maduro.

thorax An arthropod's midsection, to which its wings and legs are attached. (p. 344)
tórax Sección media de un insecto, a la que están unidas las alas y las patas.

threatened species A species that could become endangered in the near future. (p. 797)
especie amenazada Especie que puede llegar a estar en peligro de extinción en el futuro próximo.

tissue A group of similar cells that perform the same function. (pp. 295, 470)
tejido Grupo de células semejantes que realizan la misma función.

tolerance A state in which a drug user needs larger amounts of the drug to produce the same effect on the body. (p. 652)
tolerancia Estado en el que un consumidor de drogas necesita mayores cantidades de la droga para que produzca el mismo efecto en el cuerpo.

toxin A poison produced by bacterial pathogens that damages cells. (p. 594)
toxina Veneno producido por patógenos bacterianos y que daña las células.

trachea The windpipe; a passage through which air moves in the respiratory systems (p. 568)
tráquea Conducto a través del cual se mueve el aire en el sistema respiratorio.

trait A characteristic that an organism can pass on to its offspring through its genes. (p. 110)
rasgo Característica que un organismo puede transmitir a su descendencia a través de sus genes.

transfer RNA RNA in the cytoplasm that carries an amino acid to the ribosome and adds it to the growing protein chain. (p. 133)
ARN de transferencia ARN en el citoplasma que lleva un aminoácido al ribosoma y lo suma a la cadena proteínica que se está formando.

transmitter A device that sends out signals in the form of radio waves. (p. 455)
transmisor Aparato que envía señales en forma de ondas de radio.

transpiration The process by which water is lost through a plant's leaves. (p. 271)
transpiración Proceso por el cual las hojas de una planta eliminan agua.

trial-and-error learning A form of conditioning in which an animal learns to perform a behavior more and more skillfully. (p. 441)
aprendizaje por ensayo y error Forma de condicionamiento en el cual un animal aprende a ejecutar un comportamiento más y más habilmente.

tropism The growth response of a plant toward or away from a stimulus. (p. 284)
tropismo Respuesta de una planta a un estímulo, que consiste en crecer hacia el estímulo o en la dirección opuesta.

tube feet Extensions of an echinoderm's water vascular system that stick out from the body and function in movement and obtaining food. (p. 359)
pies ambulacrales Extensiones del sistema vascular de agua de un equinodermo que sobresalen del cuerpo y sirven para la locomoción y la obtención de alimento.

tumor An abnormal tissue mass that results from the rapid division of cells. (p. 614)
tumor Masa de tejido anormal que resulta de la rápida división de las células cancerosas.

tundra An extremely cold, dry biome. (p. 765)
tundra Bioma extremadamente frío y seco.

umbilical cord A ropelike structure that forms between the embryo or fetus and the placenta.
cordón umbilical Estructura con forma de cuerda que se forma entre el embrión o feto y la placenta. (p. 685)

understory A layer of shorter plants that grow in the shade of a forest canopy. (p. 760)
sotobosque Estrato de plantas de baja estatura que crecen a la sombra de la bóveda arborea.

unicellular Made of a single cell. (p. 34)
unicelular Compuesto por una sola célula.

urea A chemical that comes from the breakdown of proteins. (p. 580)
urea Sustancia química que viene de la descomposición de proteínas.

ureter A narrow tube that carries urine from one of the kidneys to the urinary bladder. (p. 580)
ureter Conducto estrecho que lleva la orina desde cada uno de los riñones a la vejiga urinaria.

urethra A small tube through which urine flows from the body. (p. 580)
uretra Pequeño conducto a través del cual fluye la orina desde el cuerpo.

urinary bladder A sacklike muscular organ that stores urine until it is eliminated from the body.
vejiga urinaria Órgano muscular con forma de saco que almacena la orina hasta que es eliminada del cuerpo. (p. 580)

urine A watery fluid produced by the kidneys that contains urea and other wastes. (pp. 388, 580)
orina Fluido acuoso producido por los riñones que contiene urea y otros materiales de desecho.

uterus The hollow muscular organ of the female reproductive system in which a fertilized egg develops. (p. 679)
utero Organo muscular hueco del sistema reproductor femenino en el que se desarrolla el bebé.

vaccination The process by which harmless antigens are deliberately introduced into a person's body to produce active immunity; also called immunization. (p. 607)
vacunación Proceso por el cual antígenos inocuos se introducen deliberadamente en el cuerpo de una persona para producir inmunidad activa; también se llama inmunización.

vaccine A substance used in a vaccination that consists of weakened or killed pathogens that can trigger the immune system into action. (pp. 215, 607)
vacuna Sustancia usada en una vacunación que está formada por patógenos que han sido debilitados o muertos pero que todavía pueden activar el sistema inmunológico.

vacuole A sac inside a cell that acts as a storage area.
vacuola Saco dentro de la célula que actúa como área de almacenamiento. (p. 66)

vagina A muscular passageway leading to the outside of the body; also called the birth canal. (p. 679)
vagina Pasaje muscular que lleva hacia afuera del cuerpo; también llamado canal de nacimiento.

valve A flap of tissue in the heart or a vein that prevents blood from flowing backward. (p. 537)
válvula Tapa de tejido en el corazón o en una vena que impide que la sangre fluya hacia atrás.

variable A factor in an experiment that can change.
variable Factor que puede cambiar en un experimento. (p. 16)

variation Any difference between individuals of the same species. (p. 177)
variación Cualquier diferencia entre individuos de la misma especie.

vascular plant A plant that has true vascular tissue.
planta vascular Planta que tiene tejido vascular verdadero. (p. 253)

vascular tissue The internal transporting tissue in some plants that is made up of tubelike structures.
tejido vascular Tejido de transporte interno en algunas plantas que está formado por estructuras parecidas a tubos. (p. 252)

vein A blood vessel that carries blood back to the heart. (p. 538)
vena Vaso sanguíneo que devuelve la sangre al corazón.

ventricle A lower chamber of the heart that pumps blood out to the lungs and body. (pp. 384, 537)
ventrículo Cámara inferior del corazón que bombea la sangre hacia los pulmones y el cuerpo.

vertebrae The small bones that make up the backbone. (pp. 369, 475)
vértebras Los huesecillos que forman la columna vertebral de un animal.

vertebrate An animal that has a backbone. (p. 299)
vertebrado Animal que posee columna vertebral.

villi Tiny finger-shaped structures that cover the inner surface of the small intestine and provide a large surface area through which digested food is absorbed. (p. 526)
vellosidades Pequeñas estructuras con forma de dedo que cubren la superficie interna del intestino delgado y proporcionan una amplia superficie a través de la cual se absorbe el alimento digerido.

virus A tiny, nonliving particle that invades and then reproduces inside a living cell. (p. 210)
virus Partícula diminuta no viva que invade una célula viva y luego se reproduce dentro de ella.

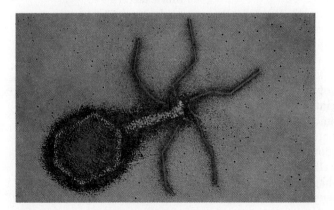

vitamins Molecules that act as helpers in a variety of chemical reactions within the body. (p. 508)
vitaminas Moléculas que actúan como ayudantes en gran variedad de reacciones químicas que se producen en el cuerpo.

vocal cords Folds of connective tissue that stretch across the opening of the larynx and produce a person's voice. (p. 572)
cuerdas vocales Pliegues de tejido conectivo que se extienden a lo largo de la abertura de la laringe y producen la voz de la persona.

voluntary muscle A muscle that is under conscious control. (p. 483)
músculos voluntarios Músculo que se puede controlar conscientemente.

water cycle The continuous process by which water moves from Earth's surface to the atmosphere and back. (p. 746)
ciclo del agua Proceso continuo mediante el cual el agua pasa de la superficie de la Tierra a la atmósfera y viceversa.

water vascular system A system of fluid-filled tubes in an echinoderm's body. (p. 359)
sistema vascular de agua Sistema de vasos llenos de líquidos en el cuerpo de un equinodermo.

white blood cell A blood cell that fights disease.
glóbulo blanco Célula de la sangre que protege contra las enfermedades. (p. 547)

withdrawal A period of adjustment that occurs when a drug-dependent person stops taking the drug. (p. 653)
síndrome de abstinencia Período de ajuste que ocurre cuando una persona adicta a las drogas deja de consumirlas.

xylem The vascular tissue through which water and nutrients move in some plants. (p. 263)
xilema Tejido vascular por el que circulan agua y nutrientes en algunas plantas.

zygote A fertilized egg, produced by the joining of a sperm and an egg. (pp. 252, 675)
cigoto Óvulo fecundado, producido por la unión de un espermatozoide y un óvulo.

Index

Page numbers for key terms are printed in **boldface** type.
Page numbers for illustrations, maps, and charts are printed in *italics*.

Index

Index

Page numbers for key terms are printed in **boldface** type.
Page numbers for illustrations, maps, and charts are printed in *italics*.

Index

Page numbers for key terms are printed in **boldface** type.
Page numbers for illustrations, maps, and charts are printed in *italics*.

Index

Page numbers for key terms are printed in **boldface** type.
Page numbers for illustrations, maps, and charts are printed in *italics*.

Index

Index

Page numbers for key terms are printed in **boldface** type.
Page numbers for illustrations, maps, and charts are printed in *italics*.

Acknowledgments

Acknowledgment for page 206: Excerpt from *James Herriot's Dog Stories.* Copyright © 1986 by James Herriot. Published by St. Martin's Press.

Acknowledgment for page 700: Excerpt from *The Amateur Naturalist* by Gerald Durrell, copyright © 1982 by Gerald Durrell. Used by permission of Alfred A. Knopf, a division of Random House, Inc.

Staff Credits

Diane Alimena, Scott Andrews, Jennifer Angel, Carolyn Belanger, Barbara A. Bertell, Peggy Bliss, James Brady, Anne M. Bray, Sarah M. Carroll, Kerry Cashman, Jonathan Cheney, Joshua D. Clapper, Lisa J. Clark, Patricia M. Dambry, Frederick Fellows, Jonathan Fisher, Patti Fromkin, Paul Gagnon, Robert Graham, Kerri Hoar, Anne Jones, Kelly Kelliher, Toby Klang, Dotti Marshall, Constance J. McCarty, Carolyn McGuire, Ranida Touranont McKneally, Richard McMahon, Natania Mlawer, Dorothy Preston, Maureen Raymond, Rashid Ross, Siri Schwartzman, Melissa, Shustyk, Laurel Smith, Kara Stokes, Jennifer A. Teece, Amanda M. Watters, Merce Wilczek, Amy Winchester, Char Lyn Yeakley **Additional Credits** Louise Gachet, Terence Hegarty, Kevin Keane, Greg Lam, Marcy Rose

Illustration

Articulate Graphics: 645; **Michelle Barbera:** 177, 178, 179; **Sally Bensusen:** 344, 346, 347; **Morgan Cain & Associates;** 36, 37, 75, 128, 129, 381, 429, 601, 636; **Patrice Rossi Calkin:** 317, 440, 476, 477; **David Corrente:** 121t; **Warren Cutler:** 383; **John Edwards & Associates:** 54, 63, 64, 65, 66, 81, 93, 121b, 186, 193, 211, 232, 264, 305, 308, 309, 315, 330, 331, 337, 369, 389, 407, 408t, 409, 414, 417, 455, 478, 479, 484, 485, 490, 491, 517, 518, 519, 521, 525, 535, 536, 537, 539, 540, 541, 546, 547, 560, 628, 629, 630, 635, 662, 676, 677, 678, 679, 684, 768, 769; **Foerster Interactive Arts:** 295, 307, 581, 755; **Tom Gagliano:** 663l; **Andrea Golden:** 321, 339; **Phil Guzy:** 567, 568, 571, 572, 643, 644, 647, 649, 669, 670, 687; **Biruta Hansen:** 722, 723; **Robert Hynes:** 709; **Kevin Jones Associates:** 190, 191, 269, 716, 731, 732, 733, 747, 749, 750; **Steve McEntee:** 83, 84, 101, 102, 133, 134, 135, 136; **Richard McMahon:** 59, 88, 89, 607; **Richard McMahon with J/B Woolsey Associates:** 194, 195; **Fran Milner:** 338, 379, 526, 569; **Karen Minot:** 47, 78, 87, 111, 112, 246, 286, 290, 329, 785; **Paul Mirocha:** 461; **Matthew Pippin:** 398; **Sandra Sevigny:** 475; **Walter Stuart:** 304, 359, 449; **Sam Ward:** 597; **J/B Woolsey Associates:** 117, 123, 129b, 160, 319, 710; **J/B Woolsey Associates (Mark Desman):** 368, 372, 373, 460; **XNR Productions:** 172, 173, 451, 454. **All charts and graphs by Matt Mayerchak.** Content Refreshers developed by Tighe Publishing Services.

Photography

Cover image top- Underwater life at Cayman Island in the Caribbean- Jeff Hunter/Getty Images; **bottom** - Queen angelfish - Ian and Karen Stewart/Bruce Coleman, Inc. **xxii t,1,2 all, 3 all,** Pittsburgh Steelers/Mike Fabus; **xxii b,** Doug Pensinger/Getty Images, Inc.

Chapter 1 Pages 4-5, Barrett and MacKay: **5 inset,** Jon Chomitz; **7b,** Manoh Shah/Getty Images, Inc.; **7t,** Michael Nichols/National Geographic Society; **8,** K. & K. Ammann/Bruce Coleman, Inc.; **9,** Wild Chimpanzees.org; **10b,** Dorling Kindersley Media Library; **10t,** Wild Chimpanzees.org; **11l,** Irven De Vore/Anthrophoto file; **11r,** Adrian Warren/Lastrefuge.co.uk; **12b,** Tony Freeman/PhotoEdit; **12m,** ARS; **12t,** Tim Thompson/Stone/Getty Images, Inc.; **13l,** Dan Lamont/Corbis; **13r** Jeff Greenberg/PhotoEdit; **14b,** M.T. Frazier/Photo Researchers, Inc.; **14t,** Houghton Mifflin Company; **15, 16, 17 all,** Richard Haynes; **18,** Getty Images, Inc.; **19b,** Brad Mangin/Corbis; **19tl,** PhotoDisc, Inc./Getty Images, Inc.; **19tm,** Tony Freeman/PhotoEdit; **19tr,** Mark Antman/The Image Works; **20l,** Sean Cayton/The Image Works; **20r,** Getty Images, Inc.; **21l,** Clayton J. Price/CORBIS; **21m,** Phototake; **21r,** Photo Researchers; **22,** Getty Images, Inc.; **23b,** Richard Haynes; **23t,** Russ Lappa; **24, 25, 28b,** Richard Haynes; **28t,** Manoh Shah/Getty Images, Inc.; **30,** Renee Stockdale/Animals Animals.

Chapter 2 Pages 32-33, Roland Birke/Peter Arnold, Inc.; **33 inset,** Richard Haynes; **34,** Russ Lappa; **35l,** Michael & Patricia Fogden/CORBIS; **35r,** Biodisc/Visuals Unlimited; **36,** Breck Kent/Animals Animals; **37,** Superstock; **38-39,** Stephen J. Krasemann/DRK Photo; **38 inset,** Tom Brakefield/DRK Photo; **39 inset l,** Kennan Ward/Corbis; **39 inset r,** W. Perry Conway/Corbis; **40,** Michael Newman/PhotoEdit; **41, 42t,** Russ Lappa; **42b,** Inga Spence/The Picture Cube, Inc.; **43,** Biophoto Associates/Photo Researchers, Inc.; **44l,** Gerard Lacz/Animals Animals; **44m,** Gavriel Jecan/Art Wolfe, Inc.; **44r,** Ron Kimball Studios; **45,** Lynn Stone/Animals Animals; **46,** Thomas Kitchin/Tom Stack & Associates, Inc.; **48-49,** Daniel J. Krasemann/DRK Photo; **48 inset l,** Carolina Biological/Visuals Unlimited; **48 inset r,** W. Wayne Lockwood, M.D./Corbis; **49 inset l,** Photodisc/Getty Images, Inc.; **49 inset r,** E.R. Degginger/Animals Animals; **50t,** Richard Haynes; **50b,** McDonald Wildlife Photo, Inc./DRK Photo; **51t,** Photo Researcher, Inc.; **51b,** Richard Haynes; **52l,** FSU Research Foundation; **52m,** The Granger Collection; **52r, 53l,** Bettmann/Corbis; **53m,** Pascal Goetgheluck/SPL/Photo Researchers; **53r,** Lawrence Migdale/Stock Boston; **54,** John Locke/Dembinsky Photo Associates; **55,** Getty Images, Inc.; **56t,** Photo Researchers, Inc.; **56bl,** Sinclair Stammers/SPL/Photo Researchers, Inc.; **56br,** SPL/Photo Researchers, Inc.; **57,** CRNI/SPL/Photo Researchers, Inc.; **58,** Richard Haynes; **60t,** Runk/Schoenberger/Grant Heilman Photography, Inc.; **60b,** Corbis; **61l,** Runk/Schoenberger/Grant Heilman Photography; **61r,** Mike Abbey/Visuals Unlimited; **62,** Alfred Paskieka/SPL/Photo Researchers, Inc.; **63t,** Bill Longcore/Photo Researchers, Inc.; **63b,** SPL/Photo Researchers, Inc.; **66,** Photo Researchers, Inc.; **67t,** David Scott/CRNI/Phototake; **67b** Motta & S. Correr/SPL/Photo Researchers, Inc.; **68,** W. Wayne Lockwood, M.D./Corbis; **70,** Runk Schoenberger/Grant Heilman Photography.

Chapter 3 Pages 72-73, Michael J. Doolittle/The Image Works; **73 inset, 74t,** Russ Lappa; **74b,** Jeffrey A. Scovil; **75,** Digital Vision/Getty Images, Inc.; **76t,** Japack Company/Corbis; **76m,** Andrew Syred/Science Photo Library/Photo Researchers, Inc.; **76bl,** Getty Images, Inc.; **76br,** Vittoriano Rastelli/Corbis; **77,** Scheidermeyer/OSF/Animals Animals; **78,** CNRI/Science Photo Library; **79,** Richard Haynes; **80-81b,** Damilo P. Donadomi/Bruce Coleman, Inc.; **85,** M. Abbey/Visuals Unlimited; **86-87,** Todd Gustafson/Panoramic Images; **86t,** Russ Lappa; **87 inset,** Stephen J. Krasemann/Photo Researchers, Inc.; **88,** Biophoto Associates/Photo Researchers, Inc.; **89,** Dr. Jeremy Burgess/SPL/Photo Researchers, Inc.; **90,** Superstock; **94,** Richard Hutchins/PhotoEdit; **95t,** David Scharf/Peter Arnold, Inc.; **95b,** AP/Wide World Photos; **96-97t,** Royalty-Free/Corbis; **97b,** Biophoto Associates/Science Source/Photo Researchers, Inc.; **98 all, 99 all,** M. Abbey/Photo Researchers, Inc.; **100,** Visuals Unlimited; **103,** Runk/Schoenberger/Grant Heilman Photography; **104,** Royalty-Free/Corbis.

Chapter 4 Pages 108-109, Ron Kimball Studios; **109 inset,** Richard Haynes; **110t,** Getty Images, Inc.; **110bl,** Hulton Archive/Getty Images, Inc.; **110-111,** Jerry Howard/Positive Images; **113,** Dorling Kindersley; **114 both,** Meinrad Faltner/Corbis Stock Market; **115,** Villanova University; **116 tl,** Michael Newman/PhotoEdit; **116t,** David Young-Wolf/PhotoEdit; **116bl,** Mary Kate Denny/Photoedit; **116bml,** Nicolas Russell/Getty Images, Inc.; **116bmr,** David Young Wolf/PhotoEdit; **116br,** Corbis; **118t,** U.S. Mint/Omni-Photo Communications, Inc.; **118b,** David Young-Wolff/Photo Edit; **119,** Jim Cummins/Getty Images, Inc.; **124, 125t,** Dorling Kindersley; **125b,** Richard Haynes; **126,** Dennis Kunkel/PhotoTake, **127l,** Michael Abbey/Photo Researchers, Inc.; **127r** E.R. Degginger/Color-Pic, Inc.; **131,** Adrian Warren/Last Refuge Ltd.; **137,** Dorling Kindersley; **138,** Adrian Warren/Last Refuge Ltd.

Chapter 5 Pages 142-143, Royalty-Free/Corbis; **143 inset, 144t,** Richard Haynes; **144b,** Michael Newman/PhotoEdit; **145t,** Everett Collection; **145 all,** David Young-Wolf/PhotoEdit; **145m,** David Urbina/PhotoEdit; **145bl,** Michael Newman/PhotoEdit; **146,** Camille Tokerud/Stone/Getty Images, Inc.; **147 both,** Biophoto Associates/Photo Researchers, Inc.; **148l,** Corbis; **148r,** Michael Douma, Institute for Dynamic Educational Advancement; **150,** Amy Etra/PhotoEdit; **151t,** CNRI/Science Photo Library/Photo Researchers, Inc.; **151b,** Jonathan Nourok/PhotoEdit; **152 both,** Stanley Flegler/Visuals Unlimited; **153,** Craig Farraway; **155 both,** National Hemophilia Foundation; **156,** White Packert/Getty Images, Inc.; **157,** South West News Service; **158t,** Paul McCormick/Getty Images, Inc.; **158m,** Grant Heilman; **158bl,** Foodpix; **158bm,** Photo Researchers, Inc.; **158br,** Foodpix; **159,** The Image Works; **161l,** Animals Animals/Earth Scenes; **161r,** 5-D and Segrest Farms/AP/Wide World Photos; **162,** Photo Researchers, Inc.; **163,** David Parker/Photo Researchers, Inc.; **164t,** Nathan Benn/Corbis; **164b,** Getty Images, Inc.; **165,** Andrew Brooks/CORBIS; **166t,**The Image Works; **166b,** Craig Farraway.

Chapter 6 Pages 170-171, Tui De RoyMinden Pictures; **171 inset,** Richard Haynes; **172t,** Portrait by George Richmond/Down House, Downe/Bridgeman Art Library; **172 frame,** Dorling Kindersley; **172b,** Christopher Ralling; **173t, 173b,** Tui De Roy/Minden Pictures; **174t,** Photo Researchers, Inc.; **174b,** Jeremy Woodhouse/Masterfile; **175,** Dr. Jeremy Burgess/SPL/Photo Researchers, Inc.; **176t, 176b,** Barbara D. Livingston; **176b,** AP/Wide World Photos; **176 horseshoe,** Dorling Kindersley; **181, 182t,** Richard Haynes; **182b,** Dorling Kindersley; **183,** Michael K. Richardson; **184l,** G. Alamany & E. Vicouns/Corbis; **184m,** Photo Researchers, Inc.; **184r,** Robert Pearcy; **185l,** Gary Milburn/Tom Stack & Associates, Inc.; **185r,** Betty K. Bruce/Animals Animals/Earth Scenes; **187l, 187r,** Pat & Tom Leeson/Photo Researchers, Inc.; **189t,** James L. Amos/Photo Researchers, Inc.; **189b,** AP/Wide World Photos; **191,** Peter Pavlovsky/Fossils.de; **196 all,** Douglas Henderson; **197,** Breck P. Kent; **198,** Photo Researchers, Inc.; **202 t,** Bridgeman Art Library; **202b,** Myrleen Ferguson Cate/PhotoEdit; **203,** Ron Kimball; **204tl, 204bl, 204tr, 204 mr,** Corel Corp.; **204br,** Jack Daniels/Getty Images, Inc.; **205tl,** Corel Corp.; **205bl,** C. Jeanne White/Photo Researchers, Inc.; **205tr,** Dorling Kindersley; **205mr, 205br,** Corel Corp.; **206l,** G. K. & Vikki Hart/Getty Images, Inc.; **206r,** AP/ Wide World Photos; **207,** Corbis.

Chapter 7 Pages 208-209, Dennis Kunkel/Phototake; **209 inset,** Richard Haynes; **211,** Lee D. Simon/Science Source/Photo Researchers, Inc.; **212-213,** Peter Minister/Dorling Kindersley; **214,** Institut Pasteur/CNRI/Phototake; **215,** Esbin-Anderson/Omni-Photo; **216t,** Custom Medical Stock; **216b,** Dr. Linda Stannard, UCT/Science Photo Library/Photo Researchers, Inc.; **217,** Richard Haynes; **218,** USDA/Visuals Unlimited; **219l, 219m,** Dennis Kunkel/Phototake; **219r,** Photo courtesy of Agriculture and Agri-Food Canada; **220l,** Dr. K.S. Kim/Peter Arnold, Inc.; **220r,** Dr. Dennis Kunkel/Phototake; **221,** Alfred Pasieka/Peter Arnold, Inc.; **222l,** StockFood/Raben; **222r,** Richard Haynes; **223l,** DK Images; **223m,** J. C. Carton/Bruce Coleman; **223r,** Neil Marsh/DK Images; **224t,** John Riley/Getty Images; **224b,** Ben Osborne; **224 inset,** Michael Abbey/Photo Researchers, Inc.; **225,** David Young-Wolff/PhotoEdit; **226 t,** Science VU/Visuals Unlimited; **226b,** Jan Hinsch/Science Photo Library/Photo Researchers, Inc.; **227t,** O.S.F./Animals

Animals/Earth Scenes; **227m,** A. Le Toquin/Photo Researchers, Inc.; **227b,** Gregory G. Dimijian/Photo Researchers, Inc.; **228,** Astrid & Hanns-Frieder Michler/Photo Researchers, Inc.; **229,** Eric Grave/Photo Researchers, Inc.; **230t,** Layne Kennedy/CORBIS; **230b,** Oliver Meckes/Photo Researchers, Inc.; **230 inset,** Jerome Paulin / Visuals Unlimited; **231,** David M. Phillips/Visuals Unlimited; **232,** Sinclair Stammers Oxford Scientific Films/Animals Animals/Earth Scenes; **233,** Runk/Schoenberger/Grant Heilman Photography; **234l, 234r,** David M. Dennis/Tom Stack & Associates, Inc.; **235t,** Dwight R. Kuhn; **235b,** G.R. Roberts/Omni-Photo; **236,** Michael Fogden/Animals Animals/Earth Scenes; **237,** Fred Unverhau/Animals Animals/Earth Scenes; **238,** David Scharf/Peter Arnold, Inc.; **239l,** Michael Fogden/Animals Animals/Earth Scenes; **239l inset,** Scott Camazine l; **239tr,** Carolina Biological/Visuals Unlimited; **239br,** Runk /Schoenberger/Grant Heilman Photography, Inc.; **239r inset,** E.R. Degginger/Photo Researchers, Inc.; **240,** Photo courtesy of David Read; **241,** Rod Planck/Tom Stack & Associates, Inc.; **241 inset,** V. Ahmadjian / Visuals Unlimited; **242, 243,** Richard Haynes; **244l,** Geoff Brightling/Dorling Kindersley; **244r,** Michael Fogden/Animals Animals/Earth Scenes.

Chapter 8 Pages 248-249, Barrett and MacKay; **249 inset, 250,** Richard Haynes; **251,** Michael J. Doolittle/The Image Works; **252,** Ludovic Maisant/Corbis; **254tl,** Runk/Schoenberger/Grant Heilman Photography, Inc.; **254tr,** Peter Chadwick/DK Images; **254b,** Frans Lanting/Minden Pictures; **256l,** J. Lotter Gurling/Tom Stack & Associates, Inc.; **256r,** Runk/Schoenberger/Grant Heilman Photography, Inc.; **260l,** Gerald Moore; **260r,** Runk/Schoenberger/Grant Heilman Photography, Inc.; **261,** Richard Haynes; **262,** Russ Lappa; **263l, 263r,** Phil Schermeister/Corbis; **265bl,** D. Cavagnaro/Visuals Unlimited; **265br,** Frans Lanting/Minden Pictures; **265tl,** John Pontier/Animals Animals/Earth Scenes; **265tm,** Heather Angel/Natural Visions; **265tr,** Color-Pic/Animals Animals/Earth Scenes; **266,** Color-Pic/Earth Scenes; **266l inset, 266r** inset, Runk/Schoenberger/ Grant Heilman Photography, Inc.; **267,** Color-Pic/Earth Scenes; **267l inset,** Max Stuart/Alamy; **267r inset, 268l,** Runk/Schoenberger/Grant Heilman Photography, Inc.; **268r,** Richard Shiell/Animals Animals/Earth Scenes; **269,** Darrell Gulin/Getty Images, Inc.; **271t, 271b,** Dr. Jeremy Burgess/Photo Researchers, Inc.; **272,** Richard Haynes; **273l,** Michael Fogden/Animals Animals/Earth Scenes; **273tm,** Jim Strawser/Grant Heilman Photography, Inc.; **273bm,** Ken Brate/Photo Researchers, Inc.; **273r,** Breck Kent/Animals Animals/Earth Scenes; **275t,** Grant Heilman/Grant Heilman Photography, Inc.; **275t inset,** Breck P. Kent/Animals Animals/Earth Scenes; **275b,** Patti Murray/Animals Animals/Earth Scenes; **275b inset,** Breck P. Kent; **276,** Frans Lanting/Minden Pictures; **278l,** Perennou et Nuridsany / Photo Researchers, Inc.; **278ml,** Russ Lappa; **278mr,** Philip Dowell /Dorling Kindersley; **278r,** Jules Selmes and Debi Treloar/Dorling Kindersley; **279t,** Nancy Rotenberg/Animals Animals/Earth Scenes; **279b,** Dwight Kuhn; **281,** Michael Keller/Corbis; **282,** Richard Haynes; **284,** David Sieren /Visuals Unlimited; **285t,** John Colwell/Grant Heilman Photography; **285m,** Heather Angel/Natural Visions; **285b, 287t,** E.R. Degginger; **287m,** Mark E. Gibson/Corbis; **287b,** Larry Lefever/Grant Heilman Photography, Inc.

Chapter 9 Pages 292-293, Deep Sea Photos; **293 inset, 294t,** Richard Haynes; **294bl, 294br,** Heather Angel/Natural Visions; **295,** Neil Flether/Oxford University Museum; **296t,** Frank Greenaway /Dorling Kindersley Media Library; **296b,** Frank Oberle/Getty Images; **297,** Michael Quinton/Minden Pictures; **299,** Wolfgang Bayer/Bruce Coleman, Inc.; **300,** Tom and Pat Leeson; **301tl,** Norbert Wu/Minden Pictures; **301tm,** Andrew J. Martinez/Photo Researchers, Inc.; **301tr,** James Watt/Visuals Unlimited; **301b,** Stuart Westmorland/Corbis; **302,** Tom Brakefield/Corbis; **303,** Michael DeFreitas/Bruce Coleman, Inc.; **307l,** Dale Sanders/Masterfile; **307r,** G. S. Grant/Photo Researchers, Inc.; **308t,** © Jeff Rotman/www.jeffrotman.com; **308b all,** Dorling Kindersley; **310 inset,** Linda Pitkin/Getty Images; **310-311,** Tim McKenna/Corbis; **311r,** David B. Fleetham/Tom Stack & Associates, Inc.; **312t,** Richard Cummins/CORBIS; **312-313,** Jeff Hunter/Getty Images; **314t,** Richard Haynes; **314b,** Dr. Alan L. Yen; **316,** Hans Strand/Getty Images; **316 inset,** David M. Dennis/Tom Stack & Associates, Inc.; **318,** Sinclair Stammers/Photo Researchers, Inc.; **320,** David Young-Wolff/PhotoEdit; **322t,** Dorling Kindersley; **322b,** Andrew J. Martinez/Photo Researchers, Inc.

Chapter 10 Pages 326-327, Barrett and MacKay; **327 inset,** Richard Haynes; **328t,** Corel Corp.; **328b,** Richard Nowitz; **330l,** Digital Vision/Getty Images; **330r,** Brandon Cole / Visuals Unlimited; **332l,** Douglas Faulkner/Photo Researchers, Inc.; **332tr,** Ken Lucas/Visuals Unlimited; **332br,** Norbert Wu/Minden Pictures; **333l, 333r,** Dave Fleetham/Tom Stack & Associates; **334,** William Leonard/DRK Photo; **335t,** Richard Haynes; **335b,** R.J.Erwin/Photo Researchers, Inc.; **336t,** John Gerlach/Tom Stack & Associates, Inc.; **336b,** Robert A. Lubeck/Animals Animals; **339,** Dr. P. Wilson/FLAP/Bruce Coleman, Inc.; **340t,** Geoff Dann/Dorling Kindersley; **340b,** Meckes/Ottawa/Eye of Science/Photo Researchers, Inc.; **341t,** Tim Flach/Getty Images, Inc.; **341b,** Robert Calentine/Visuals Unlimited; **342l,** Marty Cordano/DRK Photo; **342r,** Simon D. Pollard/Photo Researchers, Inc.; **343t,** Robert Calentine/Visuals Unlimited; **343b,** Valerie Hodgson/Visuals Unlimited; **345l,** Dorling Kindersley Media Library; **345m,** Gregory G. Dimijian/Photo Researchers, Inc.; **345r,** Andrew Syred/SPL/Photo Researchers, Inc.; **348,** Robert A. Lubeck/Animals Animals; **349, 350t,** Richard Haynes; **350-351,** James P. Rowan/DRK Photo; **351l,** Bob Jensen/Bruce Coleman, Inc.; **351m,** Michael Edergerr/DRK Photo; **351r,** J. Fennell/Bruce Coleman, Inc.; **352l,** Bettmann/Corbis; **352r,** Aberdeen University Library, Scotland/Bridgeman Art Library; **353l,** Robert Frerck/Odyssey Productions; **353m,** Sergio Piumatti; **353r,** Darwin Dale / Photo Researchers, Inc.; **354t,** John Trager/Visuals Unlimited; **354b,** Geoff du Feu /Getty Images; **355,** Anthony Bannister; Gallo Images/CORBIS; **356-357 background,** AGStockUSA, Inc./Alamy; **356-357,** Norm Thomas/PHoto Researchers, Inc.; **357t,** Frank Whitney/Getty Images; **358,** Richard Haynes; **360-361t,** Kerrick James; **360 inset l,** Neil G. McDaniel/Photo Researchers, Inc.; **360 inset r,** Brian Parker/Tom Stack & Associates, Inc.; **361l,** ©Brandon D. Cole/CORBIS; **361r,** Ed Bravendam/Minden Pictures.

Chapter 11 Pages 366-367, Norbert Wu/Minden Pictures; **367 inset,** Richard Haynes; **368,** Russ Lappa; **369,** Tom Flach/Getty Images, Inc.; **370,** Dave King/Dorling Kindersley Media Library; **371l,** Michael Fogden/DRK Photo; **371r,** Frans Lanting/Minden Pictures; **374b,** Brian Parker/Tom Stack & Associates; **374t,** Gerard Lacz/Animals Animals; **375,** NHPA/LUTRA; **376b,** Mark Stouffer Enterprises/Animals Animals/Earth Scenes; **376tl,** John D. Cunningham/Visuals Unlimited; **376tr,** Michael Patrick O'Neil/Photo Researchers, Inc.; **377b,** Animals Animals/Earth Scenes; **377 inset,** Herve Berthoule Jacana/Photo Researchers, Inc.; **377t,** Bruce Coleman, Inc.; **378b,** Amos Nachoum /Corbis; **378t,** Frank Burek/Animals Animals; **380br,** DRK Photo; **380l,** Norbert Wu; **380m,** Stuart Westmorland/Getty Images, Inc.; **380tr,** Norbert Wu; **382,** Michael Fogden/Photo Researchers, Inc.; **384,** Gerry Ellis/Minden Pictures; **385l,** Carmela Leszczynski/ Animals Animals/Earth Scenes; **385r,** Visuals Unlimited; **386,** Michael Fogden/OSF/Animals Animals; **387b,** Joe McDonald/Tom Stack & Associates, Inc.; **387t,** Richard Haynes; **388,** Thomas Wiewandt www.wildhorizons.com; **389,** Jay Ireland & Georgienne Bradley/ Bradleyireland.com; **390,** Dorling Kindersley; **391b,** Art Wolfe/Getty Images; **391t,** Kim Taylor & Jane Burton/DK Images; **392l,** M.C. Chamberlain/DRK Photo; **392r,** Gerald & Buff Corsi/Tom Stack & Associates; **393,** T.A. Wiewandt/DRK Photo; **395b,** Tom Bean/DRK Photo; **395t,** Richard Haynes; **396l,** Typ 605.77.700 F, Department of Printing and Graphic Arts, Houghton Library, Harvard College Library; **396m,** Natural History Museum, London; **396r,** Ernst Mayr Library of the Museum of Comparative Zoology, Harvard University. ©President and Fellows of Harvard; **397l,** Andy Crawford/DK Images; **397r,** Louis Psihoyos/Matrix; **400,** Stuart Westmorland/Getty Images, Inc.

Chapter 12 Pages 404-405, Barrett and MacKay; **405 inset,** Richard Haynes; **406b,** John Downes/DK Images; **406t,** Richard Haynes; **407,** Russell & Martha Hansen; **409,** Geoff Higgings/PhotoLibrary.com; **410b,** Jerome Wexler/Photo Researchers, Inc.; **410m,** Nancy Sheehan/PhotoEdit; **410t,** Stephen J. Krasemann/DRK Photo; **411l,** Kim Taylor/DK Images; **411r,** Richard Wagner; **412br,** Gary Griffen/Animals Animals; **412l,** Dave Watts/Tom Stack & Associates, Inc.; **412tr,** NHPA/Manfred Danegger; **413l,** D. Allen/Animals Animals; **413m,** Stephen J. Krasemann/DRK Photo; **413r,** Wayne Lankinen/DRK Photo; **415,** Richard Haynes; **416b,** Darrell Gulin/DRK photo; **416t,** Richard Haynes; **417,** Thomas Mangelsen/Minden Pictures; **418,** Frans Lanting/Minden Pictures; **419l,** Michio Hoshino/Minden Pictures; **419r,** Arthur Morris / Visuals Unlimited; **420b,** Eric Valli/Minden Pictures; **420t,** Richard Haynes; **421br,** Dave King/DK Images; **421mr,** Philip Dowell/Dorling Kindersley; **421tl,** Hilary Pooley/Animals Animals; **421tr,** Phillip Dowell/DK Images; **422l,** Daryl Balfour/Getty Images, Inc.; **422r,** Art Wolfe; **423b, 423t,** Frans Lanting/Minden Pictures; **424b,** Dave Watts/Tom Stack & Associates, Inc.; **424t,** Tom McHugh/Photo Researchers; **425,** Joe McDonald/Visuals Unlimited; **426bl,** Dave Welling; **426br,** Johnny Johnson/DRK Photo; **426ml,** Chuck Davis/Getty Images, Inc.; **426tl,** Stephen J. Krasemann/DRK PHOTO; **426tr,** Roger Aitkenhead/Animals Animals; **427bl,** M.P. Kahl/DRK Photo; **427br,** Renee Lynn/Getty Images, Inc.; **427ml,** Charlie Heidecker/Visuals Unlimited; **427tl,** Dwight Kuhn; **427tr,** Art Wolfe/Getty Images, Inc.; **428,** Johnny Johnson/DRK Photo; **430l,** Dave Watts/Tom Stack & Associates, Inc.; **430r,** Joe McDonald/Visuals Unlimited.

Chapter 13 Pages 434-435, M. Philip Kahl Jr./Photo Researchers, Inc.; **435 inset,** Getty Images, Inc.; **436b,** Michael Fogden/DRK Photo; **436t,** Jerome Wexler/Photo Researchers, Inc.; **437l, 437r,** Heather Angel/Natural Visions; **438,** Lawrence Stepanowicz/Alamy; **439,** Nina Leen/Time Life Pictures/Getty Images, Inc.; **441,** Steve Solum/Bruce Coleman Inc.; **442,** Bernd Heinrich; **444,** Richard Haynes; **445,** Natural Visions; **446b,** John Cancalosi/DRK Photo; **446t,** Art Wolfe; **447,** OSF/David Boag/Animals Animals; **448,** David E. Myers/Getty Images, Inc.; **450,** Kim Taylor/Bruce Coleman; **451,** M.A. Chappell/Animals Animals; **452,** Doug Wechsler; **453,** Richard Haynes; **454-455,** Douglas Faulkner/Corbis; **455t,** Arthur Morris/Visuals Unlimited; **456,** Natalie Fobes/CORBIS; **457,** Michio Hoshino/Minden Pictures; **458l,** Steve Solum/Bruce Coleman Inc.; **458r,** Natural Visions; **460,** David Hosking/Getty Images, Inc.; **462-463, 463r, 464,** Norbert Wu; **465b,** Dale Stokes/Norbert Wu; **465t,** Norbert Wu.

Chapter 14 Pages 466-467, Matthew Stockman/Getty Images , Inc.; **467 inset, 468, 469l,** Richard Haynes; **469r,** K.G. Murti/Visuals Unlimited; **470b,** Biophoto Associates/Science Source/Photo Researchers, Inc.; **470bm,** James Hayden, RBP/Phototake; **470t,** John D. Cunningham/Visuals Unlimited; **470tm,** Fred Hossler/Visuals Unlimited; **471 all,** Richard Haynes; **472l,** Jon Feingersh/Corbis; **472r,** Myrleen Ferguson Cate/PhotoEdit; **473,** Mike Powell/Getty Images, Inc.; **474,** Russ Lappa; **475l,** Dorling Kindersley; **475r,** Richard Haynes; **476l,** David Young-Wolff/PhotoEdit; **476r,** Rudi Von Briel/PhotoEdit; **477l,** Journal-Courier/Steve Warmowski/The Image Works; **477r,** Peter Hvizdak/The Image Works; **478-479,** Andrew Syred/Science Photo Library/Photo Researchers, Inc.; **479br,** David Madison Sports Images, Inc 2003; **479l,** Prof. P. Motta/Dept. of Anatomy/University, "La Sapienza", Rome/Science Photo Library/Photo Researchers, Inc.; **479tr,** Prof. P. Motta/Dept. of Anatomy/University, "La Sapienza", Rome/Science Photo Library/Photo Researchers, Inc.; **480l,** David Young-Wolff/PhotoEdit; **480r,** Marc Romanelli/Getty Images, Inc.; **481l,** INNERSPACE IMAGING/Photo Researchers, Inc.; **481r,** ZEPHYR/Photo Researchers,